SYMBIOSIS

THE PEARSON CUSTOM LIBRARY FOR THE BIOLOGICAL SCIENCES

MICROBIOLOGY

Jodi Enos-Berlage
Biology 243
Luther College

Pearson Learning Solutions

New York Boston San Francisco
London Toronto Sydney Tokyo Singapore Madrid
Mexico City Munich Paris Cape Town Hong Kong Montreal

Senior Vice President, Editorial and Marketing: Patrick F. Boles
Senior Sponsoring Editor: Natalie Danner
Development Editor: Annette Fantasia
Editorial Assistant: Jill Johnson
Executive Marketing Manager: Nathan L. Wilbur
Operations Manager: Eric M. Kenney
Database Production Manager: Jennifer Berry
Art Director: Renée Sartell
Cover Designer: Kristen Kiley

Cover Art: Courtesy of Michael R. Martin, Darryl Johnson, Photodisk, DK Images, and Prentice-Hall, Inc.

This special edition published in cooperation with Pearson Learning Solutions.

Printed in the United States of America.

Please visit our web site at *www.pearsoncustom.com/*.

Attention bookstores: For permission to return unused stock, contact us at *pe-uscustomreturns@pearson.com*.

Pearson Learning Solutions, 501 Boylston Street, Suite 900, Boston, MA 02116
A Pearson Education Company
www.pearsoned.com

ISBN 10: 0-558-62870-2
ISBN 13: 978-0-558-62870-3

Contents

Microorganisms and Microbiology

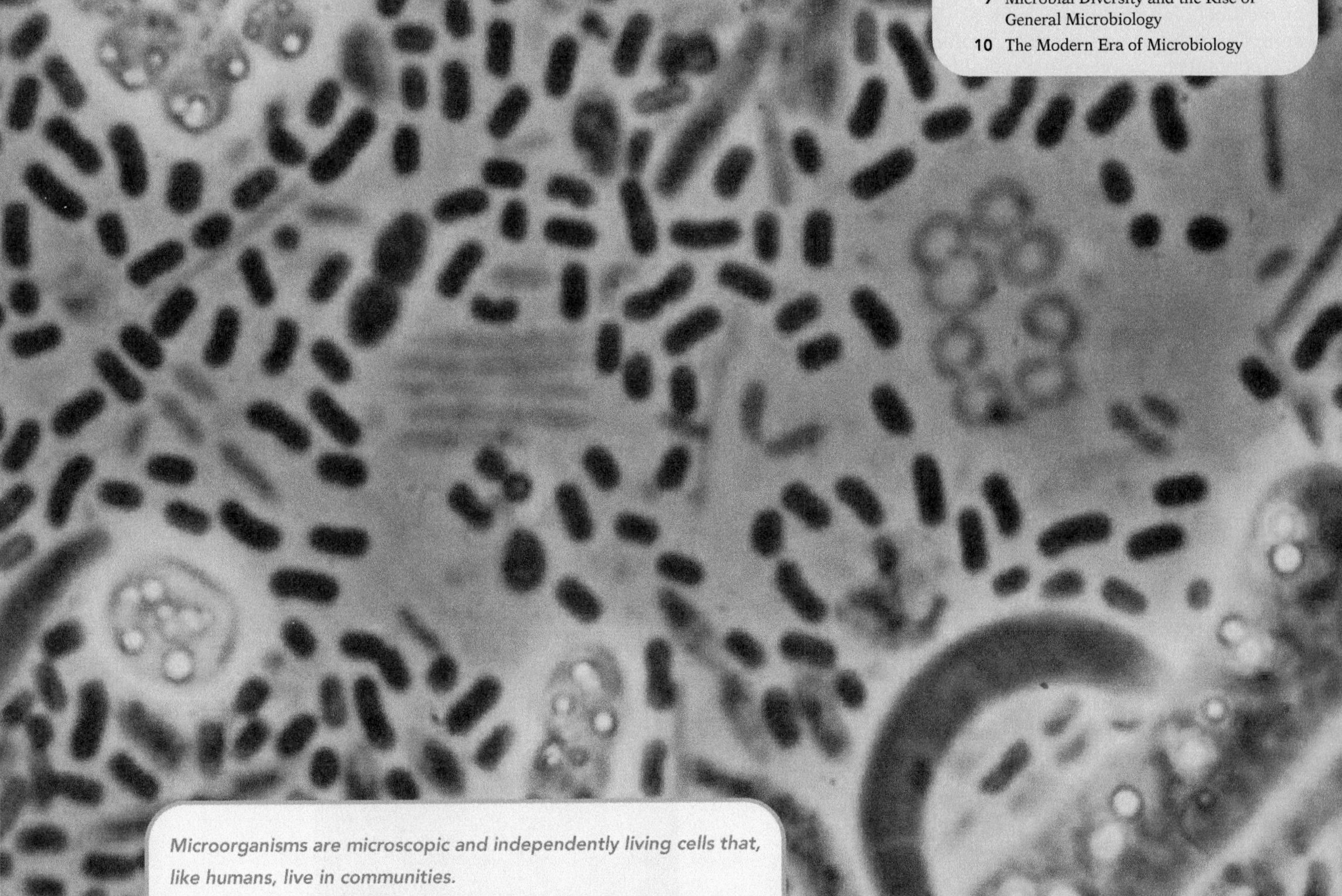

Microorganisms are microscopic and independently living cells that, like humans, live in communities.

D. E. Caldwell

Welcome to microbiology—the study of microorganisms. **Microorganisms** are single-celled microscopic organisms and viruses, which are microscopic but not cellular.

What is microbiology all about? Microbiology is about cells and how they work, especially the bacteria, a large group of cells of enormous basic and practical importance (Figure 1). Microbiology is about diversity and evolution, about how different kinds of microorganisms arose and why. It is about what microorganisms do in the world at large, in soils and waters, in the human body, and in animals and plants. One way or another, microorganisms affect all other life forms on Earth (Figure 1*b*), and thus we may think of microbiology as the foundation of the biological sciences.

Microorganisms differ from the cells of macroorganisms. The cells of macroorganisms such as plants and animals are unable to live alone in nature and exist only as parts of multicellular structures, such as the organ systems of animals or the leaves of leafy plants. By contrast, most microorganisms can carry out their life processes of growth, energy generation, and reproduction independently of other cells.

This chapter begins our journey into the microbial world. Here we discover what microorganisms are and their impact on life. We set the stage for consideration of the structure and evolution of microorganisms that will unfold in the next chapter. We also place microbiology in historical perspective, as a process of scientific discovery. From the landmark contributions of both early microbiologists and scientists practicing today, we can see microbiology at work in medicine, agriculture, the environment, and other everyday aspects of our lives.

I INTRODUCTION TO MICROBIOLOGY

In the first five sections of this chapter we introduce the field of microbiology, look at microorganisms as cells, examine where and how microorganisms live in nature, review the evolutionary history of microbial life, and examine the impact that microorganisms have had and continue to have on human affairs.

1 Microbiology

The science of microbiology revolves around two themes: (1) understanding basic life processes, and (2) applying our understanding of microbiology for the benefit of humankind.

As a basic biological science, microbiology uses and develops tools for probing the fundamental processes of life. Scientists have been able to gain a sophisticated understanding

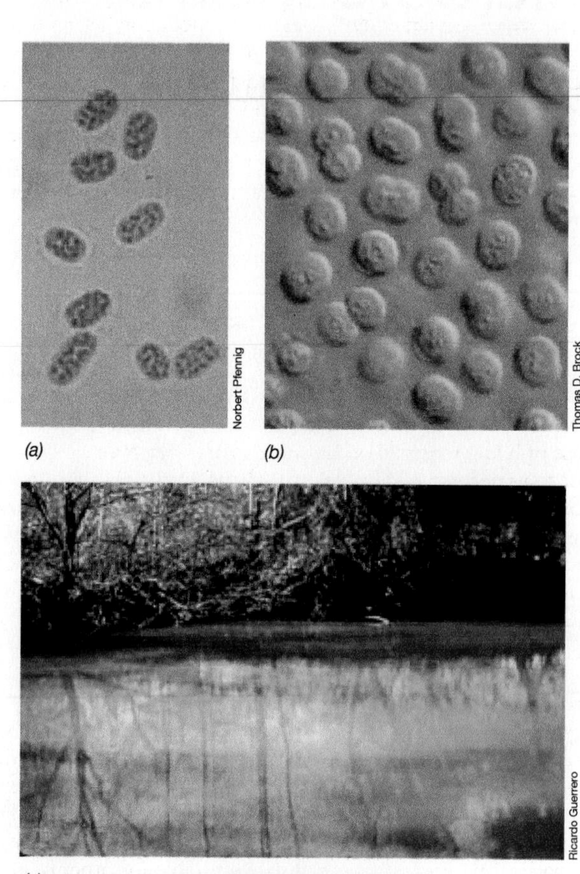

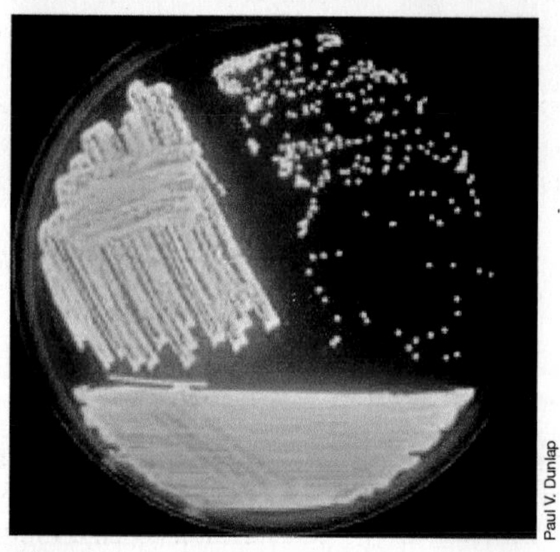

Figure 1 Microorganisms. *(a, b)* A single microbial cell can have an independent existence. Shown are photomicrographs of phototrophic (photosynthetic) microorganisms called (*a*) purple bacteria and (*b*) cyanobacteria. Purple bacteria were among the first phototrophs on Earth; cyanobacteria were the first oxygen-evolving phototrophs. Cyanobacteria oxygenated the atmosphere, opening the way for the evolution of other life forms. *(c, d)* In nature or in the laboratory, bacterial cells can grow to form extremely large populations. Shown are (*c*) a bloom of purple bacteria (compare with Figures 1*a* and 18) in a small lake in Spain, Lake Cisó, and (*d*) bioluminescent (light-emitting) cells of the bacterium *Photobacterium leiognathi* grown in laboratory culture. One milliliter of water from the lake (*c*) or one colony from the plate (*d*) contains more than 1 billion (10^9) individual cells.

of the chemical and physical basis of life from studies of microorganisms because microbial cells share many characteristics with cells of multicellular organisms; indeed, *all* cells have much in common. Moreover, microbial cells can grow to extremely high densities in laboratory culture (Figure 1*d*), making them readily amenable to biochemical and genetic study. These features make microorganisms excellent models for understanding cellular processes in multicellular organisms, including humans.

As an applied biological science, microbiology deals with many important practical problems in medicine, agriculture, and industry. For example, most animal and plant diseases are caused by microorganisms. Microorganisms play major roles as agents of soil fertility and in supporting domestic animal production. Many large-scale industrial processes, such as the production of antibiotics and human proteins, rely heavily on microorganisms. Thus both the detrimental and the beneficial aspects of microorganisms affect the everyday lives of humans.

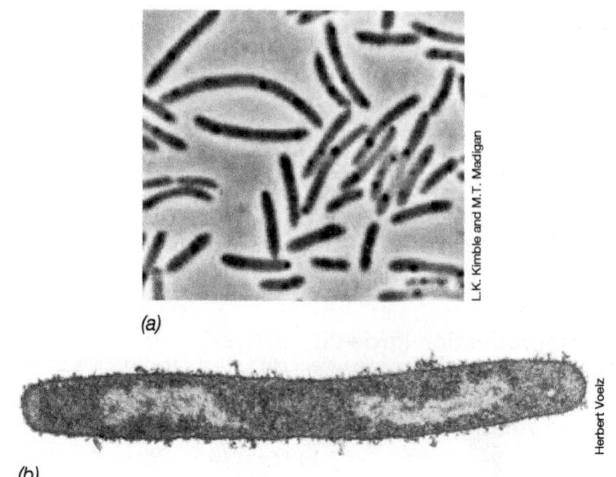

Figure 2 *(a)* Rod-shaped bacterial cells as seen in the light microscope; a single cell is about 1 μm in diameter. *(b)* Longitudinal section through a dividing bacterial cell as viewed with an electron microscope. The two lighter areas are nucleoids, regions in the cell containing aggregated DNA.

The Importance of Microorganisms

Microorganisms play central roles in both human activities and the web of life on Earth. Although microorganisms are the smallest forms of life, collectively they constitute the largest mass of living material on Earth and carry out many chemical processes necessary for other organisms. In the absence of microorganisms, other life forms would never have arisen and could not now be sustained. Indeed, the very oxygen we breathe is the result of past microbial activity (Figure 1*b*). Moreover, humans, plants, and animals are intimately tied to microbial activities for the recycling of key nutrients and for degrading organic matter. No other life forms are as important as microorganisms for the support and maintenance of life on Earth.

Microorganisms existed on Earth for billions of years before plants and animals appeared (see Figure 6), and the diversity of microbial life far exceeds that of the plants and animals. This huge diversity accounts for some of the spectacular properties of microorganisms. For example, we will see how microorganisms can live in places unsuitable for other organisms and how the diverse physiological capacities of microorganisms rank them as Earth's premier chemists. We will trace the evolutionary history of microorganisms and see that three huge groups of cells can be distinguished by their evolutionary relationships. And finally, we will see how microorganisms have established important relationships with other organisms, some beneficial and some harmful.

We begin our study of microbiology with a consideration of the cellular nature of microorganisms.

2 Microorganisms as Cells

The **cell** is the fundamental unit of life. A single cell is an entity, isolated from other cells by a membrane; many cells also contain a cell wall outside the membrane. A cell contains a variety of chemicals and subcellular structures (Figure 2). The membrane forms a compartment or "container" that is necessary to maintain the correct proportions of internal constituents in the cell and to protect it against outside forces. But the fact that a cell is a compartment does not mean that it is a *sealed* compartment. Instead, the membrane is semipermeable and thus the cell is an open, dynamic structure. Cells communicate and exchange materials with their environments, and they are constantly undergoing change.

Cell Chemistry and Key Structures

Cells are highly organized structures that consist of an assortment of four chemical components: proteins, nucleic acids, lipids, and polysaccharides. These large molecules are called **macromolecules**, and, collectively, they make up greater than 95% of the dry weight of a cell (the remainder is a mixture of macromolecular precursors and inorganic ions). It is the precise chemistry and arrangement of macromolecules in different kinds of cells that make them distinct from one another. We can thus say that all cells have much in common but each different kind of cell is chemically unique.

There are a number of key structures in a cell. The **cytoplasmic membrane** (also called the cell membrane) is the barrier that separates the inside of the cell from the outside environment. Inside the cell membrane are various structures and chemicals suspended or dissolved in a fluid called the **cytoplasm**. The "machinery" for cell growth and function in the cytoplasm includes the nucleus or nucleoid, where the cells' **DNA** (the **genome**) is stored, and **ribosomes**, structures consisting of protein and **RNA** upon which new proteins are made in the cell. Most microbial cells also contain a cell wall. It is the cell wall rather than the cell membrane that confers structural strength on the cell and prevents it from osmotic bursting.

1. Compartmentalization and metabolism
Cells take up nutrients from the environment, transform them, and release wastes into the environment. The cell is thus an *open* system.

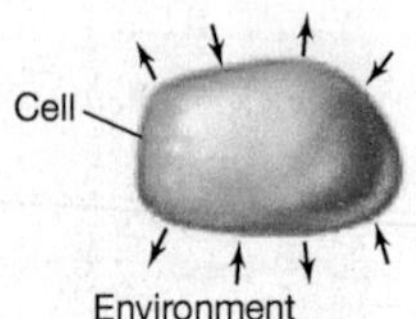

2. Reproduction (growth)
Chemicals from the environment are turned into new cells under the genetic direction of preexisting cells.

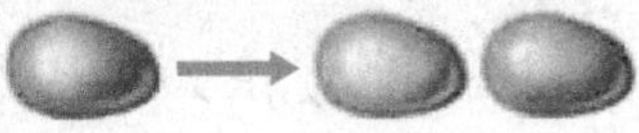

3. Differentiation
Some cells can form new cell structures such as a spore, usually as part of a cellular life cycle.

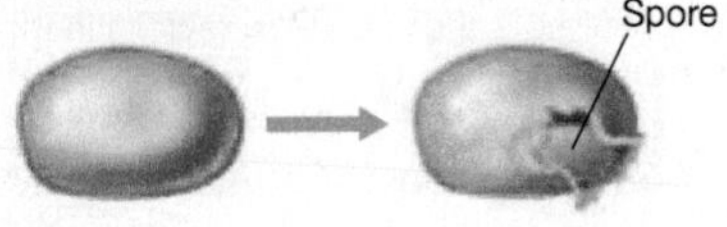

4. Communication
Cells *communicate* or *interact* by means of chemicals that are released or taken up.

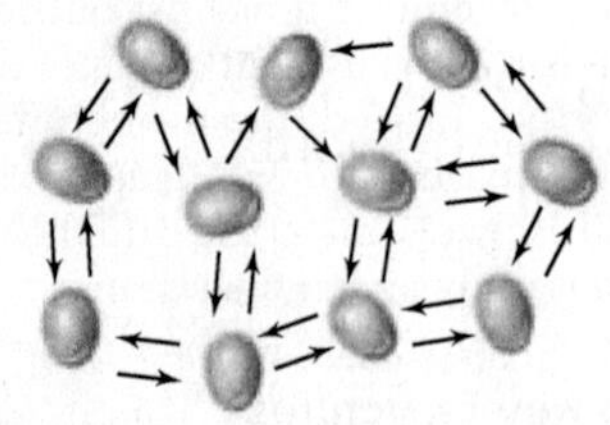

5. Movement
Some cells are capable of self-propulsion.

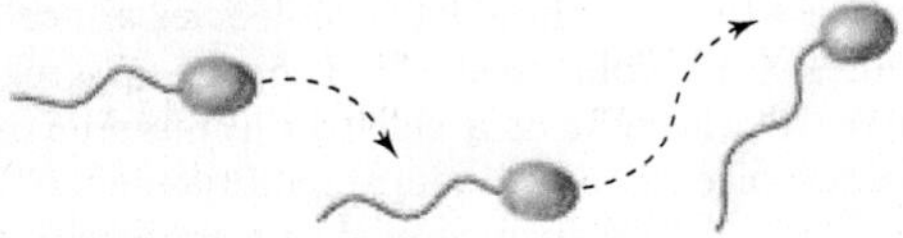

6. Evolution
Cells contain genes and *evolve* to display new biological properties. Phylogenetic trees show the evolutionary relationships between cells.

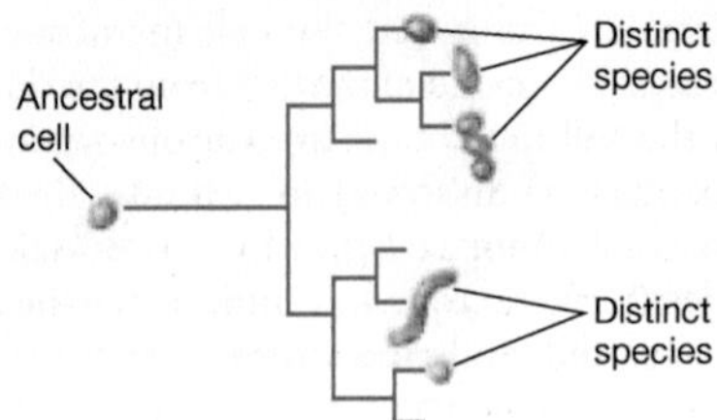

Figure 3 **The characteristics of cellular life.** Only certain cells undergo differentiation or are able to move.

Characteristics of Living Systems

What are the essential characteristics of life? What differentiates cells from inanimate objects? Our concept of a living organism is constrained by what we observe on Earth today and can deduce from the fossil record. But from our knowledge of biology thus far, we can identify several characteristics shared by most living systems. These characteristics of cellular organisms are summarized in Figure 3.

All cellular organisms show some form of **metabolism**. That is, within the framework of the physical container that defines a cell, nutrients are taken up from the environment and chemically transformed. During this process, energy is conserved and waste products eliminated. All cells show regeneration and *reproduction*. That is, a cell can repair and replace its components as needed and then accumulate multiple copies of each component before partitioning them to divide and form two cells. Some cells undergo *differentiation*, a process by which new substances or structures that modify the cell are synthesized. For example, cell differentiation is often part of a cellular life cycle in which cells form special structures, such as spores, involved in reproduction, dispersal, or survival.

Cells respond to chemical signals in their environment, including those produced by other cells. Cells "process" these signals in a variety of ways, which often trigger new activities. Cells thus exhibit *communication*. Many cells are capable of *movement* by self-propulsion; in the microbial world we will see several different mechanisms of motility. Finally, unlike nonliving structures, cells undergo *evolution;* over time, the characteristics of cells change and these changes are transmitted to their offspring.

Cells as Machines and as Coding Devices

The activities of cells can be viewed in two ways. On one hand, cells can be considered to be living machines that carry out chemical transformations. The catalysts of these chemical machines are **enzymes**, proteins that accelerate the rate of chemical reactions within the cell (Figure 4). On the other hand, cells can be considered to be coding devices, like computers. Just as computers store and process *digital* information, cells store and process *genetic* information (DNA) that is eventually passed on to offspring during reproduction (Figure 4).

In reality, cells are both chemical machines and coding devices, and the link between these two cellular attributes is cell growth. Under proper conditions, a cell will grow larger and eventually divide to form two cells (Figure 4). In the events that lead up to cell division, all constituents in the cell double. This requires the chemical machinery of the cell to supply energy and precursors for biosynthesis of macromolecules. Also, when a cell divides, each of the two resulting cells must contain a copy of the genetic information. Thus, DNA must replicate during the growth process (Figure 4). The machine and coding functions of the cell must therefore be

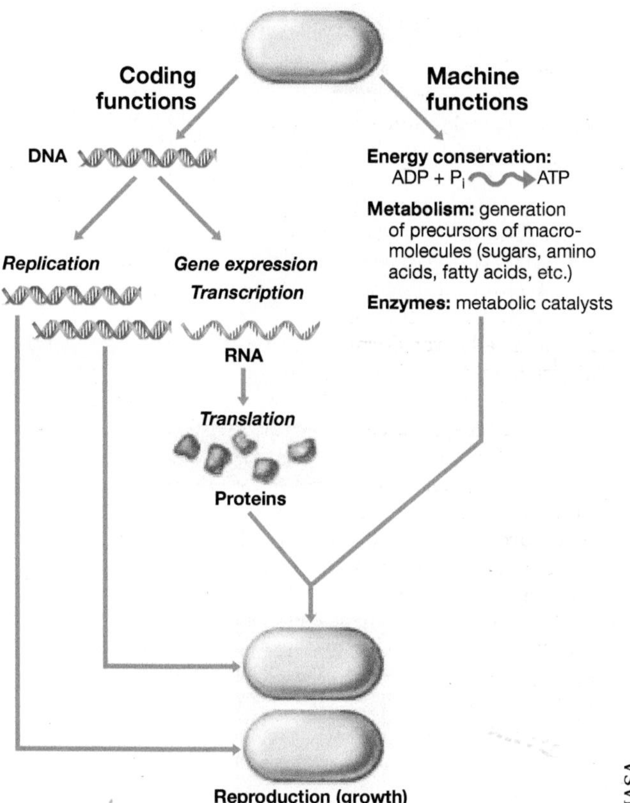

Figure 4 **The machine and coding functions of the cell.** For a cell to reproduce itself there must be energy and precursors for the synthesis of new macromolecules, the genetic instructions must be replicated such that upon division each cell receives a copy, and genes must be expressed to produce proteins and other macromolecules.

highly coordinated. Also, as we will see later, the machine and coding functions are subject to regulation that ensures substances are made in the proper order and concentrations to keep the cell optimally attuned to its environment.

1 and 2 MiniReview

Microorganisms include all microscopic organisms, including viruses. The cytoplasmic membrane is a barrier that partitions the cytoplasm away from the environment. Other major cell structures include the nucleus or nucleoid (genome), cytoplasm, ribosomes, and cell wall. Metabolism and reproduction are key features associated with the living state, and cells can be considered both chemical machines and coding devices.

- List the four classes of cellular macromolecules.
- List six characteristics of living organisms. Why might each characteristic be important to the survival of a cell?
- Compare the machine and coding functions of a microbial cell. Why is neither of value to a cell without the other?

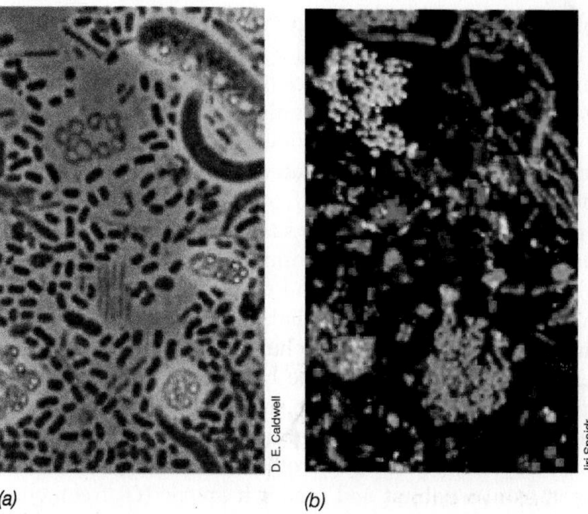

Figure 5 **Microbial communities.** *(a)* A bacterial community that developed in the depths of a small lake (Wintergreen Lake, Michigan), showing cells of various bacteria. *(b)* A bacterial community in a sewage sludge sample. The sample was stained with a series of dyes, each of which stained a specific bacterial group. From R. Amann, J. Snaidr, M. Wagner, W. Ludwig, and K.-H. Schleifer, 1996. *Journal of Bacteriology* 178: 3496–3500, Fig. 2b. © 1996 American Society for Microbiology.

NASA

3 Microorganisms and Their Natural Environments

In nature, microbial cells live in association with other cells in populations. Microbial populations are groups of cells derived from a single parent cell by successive cell divisions. The environment in which a microbial population lives is called its **habitat**. In microbial habitats, a population of cells rarely lives alone. Rather, cell populations live and interact with other populations in assemblages called *microbial communities* (Figure 5). The diversity and abundance of microorganisms in a microbial community is controlled by the resources (foods) and conditions (temperature, pH, oxygen content, and so on) that exist in the environment. The study of microorganisms in their natural environments is called **microbial ecology**.

Microbial Interactions

Microbial populations interact and cooperate in various ways, some beneficial and some harmful. For example, the waste products of the metabolic activities of some organisms can be nutrients for others. Microorganisms also interact with their physical and chemical environment. Habitats differ markedly in their characteristics, and a habitat that is favorable for the growth of one organism may actually be harmful for another. Collectively, we call all the living organisms, together with the physical and chemical constituents of their environment, an **ecosystem**. Major microbial ecosystems are found in aquatic environments (oceans, ponds, lakes, streams, ice, hot springs) and terrestrial environments (soil, deep subsurface environments), and in other organisms such as plants and animals.

An ecosystem is greatly influenced—even controlled—by microbial activities. Microorganisms carrying out metabolic processes remove nutrients from the ecosystem and use them to build new cells. At the same time, they excrete waste products back into the environment. Thus, over time, microbial ecosystems expand and contract, depending on the resources and conditions available; the metabolic activities of microorganisms gradually change these ecosystems, both chemically and physically. The habitat may thus change in significant ways. For example, molecular oxygen (O_2) is a vital nutrient for some microorganisms but a poison to others. If oxygen-consuming (aerobic) microorganisms remove oxygen from a habitat and render it anoxic (O_2-free), conditions may then favor the growth of anaerobic microorganisms that were present in the habitat but previously unable to grow. Thus, as resources and conditions in microbial habitats change, cell populations rise and fall, changing the habitat once again.

3 MiniReview

Microorganisms exist in nature in populations that interact with other populations to form microbial communities. The activities of microorganisms in microbial communities can greatly affect and rapidly change the chemical and physical properties of their habitats.

- What is a microbial habitat? How does a microbial community differ from a microbial population?
- How can microorganisms change the characteristics of their habitats?

4 The Antiquity and Extent of Microbial Life

Microorganisms were the first life forms on Earth to show the basic characteristics of living systems (Figure 3). We have already seen that cyanobacteria paved the way for the evolution of other life forms by producing the oxygen in Earth's atmosphere (Figure 1*b*). But long before cyanobacteria appeared on Earth, the planet was already teeming with life and diverse communities of microorganisms were widespread.

The First Cells

Where did the first cells come from? Were cells as we know them today the first self-replicating structures on Earth?

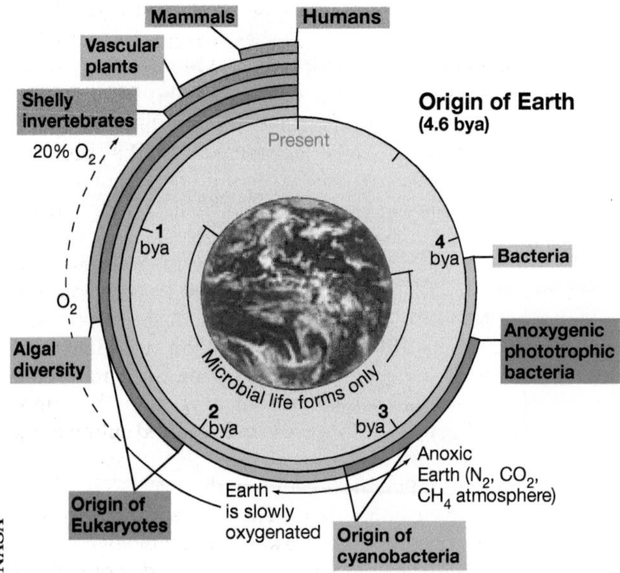

Figure 6 **A summary of life on Earth through time.** Cellular life was present on Earth about 3.8 billion years ago (bya). Cyanobacteria began the slow oxygenation of Earth about 3 bya, but current levels of oxygen in the atmosphere were not achieved until 500–800 million years ago. Eukaryotes are nucleated cells and include both microbial and multicellular organisms.

Because all cells are constructed in similar ways, it is likely that all cells have descended from a common ancestral cell, the *universal ancestor* of all life. However, as we will see later in this book, the first self-replicating entities may not have been cells but instead small molecules of RNA. Eventually, though, evolution selected the cell as the best structural solution for supporting the fundamental characteristics of life. Once the first cells arose from nonliving materials, a process that occurred over hundreds of millions of years, their subsequent growth and division formed cell populations, and these began to interact as microbial communities. Evolution could then select for improvements and diversification of these early cells to yield the highly complex and diverse cells we see today.

Life on Earth through the Ages

Earth is 4.6 billion years old. Scientists have evidence that cells first appeared on Earth between 3.8 and 3.9 billion years ago; these organisms were exclusively microbial. In fact, microorganisms were the only life on Earth for most of its history (Figure 6). Gradually, and over enormous periods of time, higher organisms appeared (we will refer to life forms that evolved after microorganisms as "higher" organisms). What were some of the highlights along the way?

During the first 2 billion years or so of Earth's existence, the atmosphere was anoxic; oxygen was absent, and nitrogen (N_2), carbon dioxide (CO_2), and a few other gases were present. Only microorganisms capable of anaerobic metabolisms could survive under these conditions, but these included many different types of cells, including those that produce methane, called *methanogens*. The evolution of *phototrophic* microorganisms—organisms that harvest energy from sunlight—occurred within a billion years of the formation of Earth. The first phototrophs were relatively simple ones, such as the purple bacteria and their relatives, still widespread in anoxic habitats today (Figure 1*a, c*). Cyanobacteria evolved from these early phototrophs nearly a billion years later and began the long slow process of oxygenating the atmosphere (Figure 6). Triggered by increases in oxygen in the atmosphere, multicellular life forms eventually evolved culminating in the plants and animals we know today (Figure 6).

How do we know that events in the evolution of life occurred as depicted in Figure 6? The answer is that we will probably never know for sure. However, microbiologists have identified key chemical components in present-day organisms that are unique biomarkers for particular groups. Traces of many of these biomarkers can still be found in ancient rocks. The time line shown in Figure 6 pieces together what we know of molecular fossils from rocks of specific ages. Over time, microorganisms diversified and came to colonize every habitat on Earth that would support life, including many habitats unsuitable for other life forms. This brings us to the current distribution of microbial life on Earth. What is this picture like?

The Extent of Microbial Life

Microbial life is all around us. Examination of natural materials such as soil or water invariably reveals microbial cells. But unusual habitats such as boiling hot springs and glacial ice are also teeming with microorganisms. Although widespread on Earth, such tiny cells may seem inconsequential. But if we could count them all, what number would we reach?

Estimates of total microbial cell numbers on Earth are on the order of 5×10^{30} cells. The total amount of carbon present in this very large number of very small cells equals that of all plants on Earth (and plant carbon far exceeds animal carbon). But in addition, the collective contents of nitrogen and phosphorous in microbial cells is more than 10 times that in all plant biomass.

Thus, microbial cells, small as they are, constitute the major portion of biomass on Earth and are key reservoirs of essential nutrients for life. An equally startling revelation is that most microbial cells do not reside on Earth's surface but instead lie underground in the oceanic and terrestrial subsurfaces. Depths up to about 10 km under Earth's surface appear to be hospitable for microbial life. We will see later that these buried microbial habitats support diverse populations of microbial cells that make their livings in unusual ways and grow extremely slowly. However, because Earth's subsurface is a relatively unexplored frontier, there is much left for microbiologists to discover and understand about the life forms that dominate Earth's biology.

4 MiniReview

Diverse microbial populations were widespread on Earth for billions of years before higher organisms appeared, and today the cumulative microbial biomass on Earth exceeds that of higher organisms. Cyanobacteria in particular were important because they oxygenated the atmosphere.

- Were the earliest life forms cellular? Why is it that cellular life is the only form of life we see on Earth today?
- How old is Earth, and when did cellular life forms first appear? How can we use science to reconstruct the sequence of organisms that appeared on Earth?
- Where are most microbial cells located on Earth?

5 The Impact of Microorganisms on Humans

Microbiologists have been highly successful in discovering how microorganisms work, increasing their beneficial effects, and curtailing their harmful effects. Microbiology has thus greatly advanced human health and welfare. An overview of the impact of microorganisms on human affairs is shown in Figure 7.

Microorganisms as Disease Agents

The statistics summarized in Figure 8 show the microbiologist's success in controlling microorganisms. These data compare the present causes of death in the United States with those of 100 years ago. At the beginning of the twentieth century, the major causes of death were infectious diseases, which are caused by microorganisms called **pathogens**. Children and the aged in particular succumbed in large numbers to microbial diseases. Today, however, infectious diseases are much less lethal, at least in developed countries. Control of infectious disease has come from increased understanding of disease processes, improved sanitary and public health practices, and the use of antimicrobial agents. As we will see later in this chapter, the science of microbiology had its roots in the study of infectious disease.

Although many infectious diseases can now be controlled, microorganisms can still be a major threat to survival, even in developed countries. Consider, for example, the individual dying slowly of a microbial infection as a consequence of acquired immunodeficiency syndrome (AIDS) or the individual infected with a multiple drug-resistant pathogen. In many developing countries, microbial diseases are still the major causes of death. Although the worldwide eradication of smallpox was a stunning triumph for medical science, millions still die yearly from other microbial diseases such as malaria, tuberculosis, cholera, African sleeping sickness, measles, pneumonia and other respiratory diseases, and diarrheal syndromes. In addition to these, humans worldwide are under threat from diseases that could emerge suddenly, such as

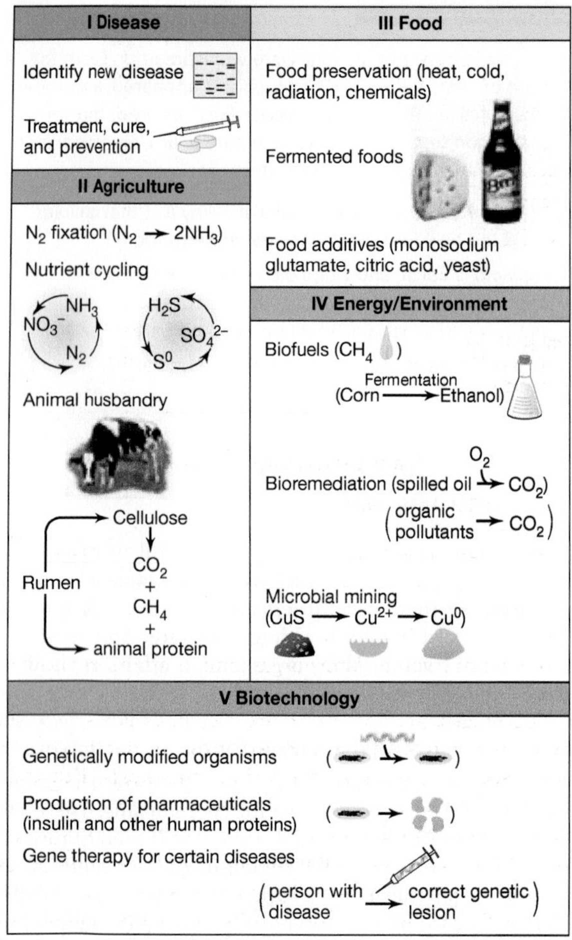

Figure 7 **The impact of microorganisms on humans.** Although many people think of microorganisms in the context of infectious diseases, few microorganisms actually cause disease. Microorganisms do, however, affect many other aspects of our lives as shown here.

bird flu, a viral disease of birds that has the potential to infect alternate hosts and spread through a population quickly. Exotic and rare diseases such as ebola hemorrhagic fever could also spread easily to developed countries because today global travel is so common. And if this weren't enough, consider the threat to humans from those who would deploy microbial bioterrorism agents. Clearly, microorganisms are still serious health threats to humans.

Although we should appreciate the powerful threat posed by microorganisms, in reality, most microorganisms are not harmful to humans. In fact, the vast majority of microorganisms cause no harm whatsoever to higher organisms but instead are beneficial—and in many cases even essential—to human welfare and the functioning of the planet. We consider these aspects of microorganisms now.

Microorganisms and Agriculture

Our whole system of intensive agriculture depends in many important ways on microbial activities (Figure 7). For example, a number of major crops are plants called *legumes*. Legumes live in close association with bacteria that form structures called *nodules* on their roots. In the root nodules, these bacteria convert atmospheric nitrogen (N_2) into fixed nitrogen (NH_3) that the plants use for growth. Thanks to the activities of these nitrogen-fixing bacteria, the legumes have no need for costly and polluting nitrogen fertilizers.

Also of major agricultural importance are the microorganisms that are essential for the digestive process in ruminant animals such as cattle and sheep. These important farm animals have a special digestive vessel called the *rumen* in which dense populations of microorganisms carry out the digestion of cellulose, the major component of plant cell walls. Without these microorganisms, cattle and sheep could not thrive on cellulose-rich but otherwise nutrient-poor substances such as grass and hay.

Microorganisms also play key roles in the cycling of important nutrients in plant nutrition, particularly those of carbon, nitrogen, and sulfur. Microbial activities in soil and water convert these elements to forms that are readily assimilated by plants. However, in addition to benefiting agriculture, microorganisms can also have negative effects; microbial diseases of plants and animals cause major economic losses in the agricultural industry. For example, diseases such as mad cow disease can have dramatic effects on the marketability of beef, and microbial diseases of crop plants can greatly reduce the yield of grain or other valuable plant products.

Microorganisms and Food

Once plants and animals for consumption are produced, they must be delivered in wholesome form to consumers. Microorganisms play important roles in the food industry (Figure 7). Food spoilage alone results in huge economic losses each year. Indeed, the canning, frozen-food, and dried-food industries emerged to preserve foods that would otherwise undergo microbial spoilage. Foodborne disease is also a consideration. Because food fit for human consumption can support the growth of microorganisms including pathogens, foods must be properly prepared and monitored to avoid transmission of disease-causing microorganisms.

However, not all microorganisms in foods have harmful effects on food products or those who eat them. For example, many dairy products depend on microbial transformations, including the fermentations that yield cheeses, yogurt, and buttermilk. Sauerkraut, pickles, and some sausages also owe their existence to microbial fermentations. Moreover, baked goods and alcoholic beverages rely on the fermentative activities of yeast, generating carbon dioxide (CO_2) to raise the dough and alcohol as a key ingredient, respectively.

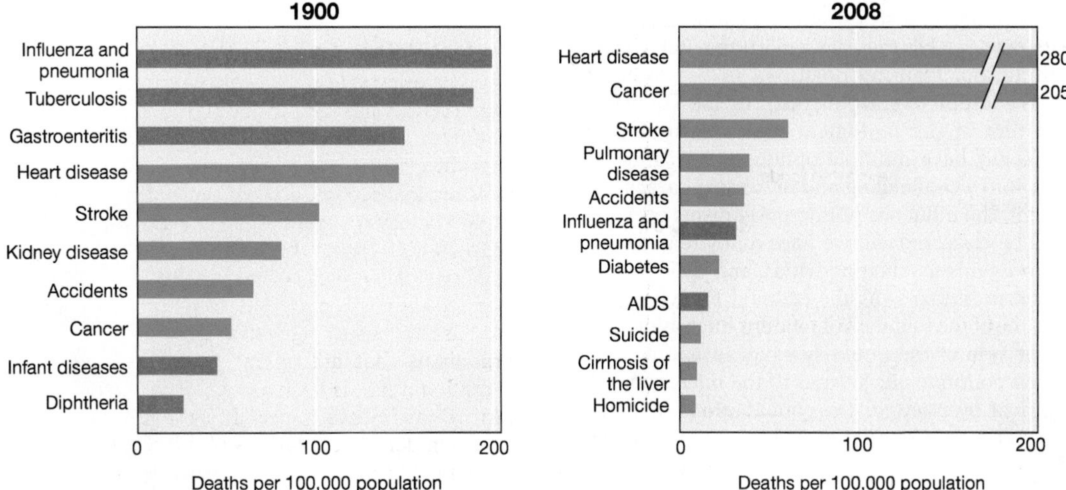

Figure 8 **Death rates for the leading causes of death in the United States: 1900 and 2008** Infectious diseases were the leading causes of death in 1900, whereas today they are much less significant. Microbial diseases are shown in red, nonmicrobial causes of death in green. Data from the United States National Center for Health Statistics.

Microorganisms, Energy, and the Environment

Microorganisms play major roles in energy production (Figure 7). Natural gas (methane) is a product of microbial activity, arising from the metabolism of methanogenic microorganisms. Phototrophic microorganisms can harvest light energy for the production of biomass, energy stored in living organisms. Microbial biomass and waste materials, such as domestic refuse, surplus grain, and animal wastes, can be converted to biofuels, such as methane and ethanol, by the activities of microorganisms. Ethanol produced by the microbial fermentation of glucose from sugarcane or cornstarch is the major motor fuel in some countries, such as Brazil, and is becoming a more important component of fuels in the United States.

Microorganisms can also be used to help clean up pollution created by human activities, a process called *microbial bioremediation* (Figure 7). Microorganisms can be employed to consume spilled oil, solvents, pesticides, and other environmentally toxic pollutants. With time, if the input of pollutants ceases, polluted areas may be cleaned without human intervention through the activities of naturally occurring microorganisms. Bioremediation simply accelerates the natural cleanup process by introducing pollutant-consuming microorganisms or specific nutrients that help microorganisms degrade the pollutants. Within the huge diversity of microorganisms on Earth, vast genetic resources exist. Researchers are now tapping into these genes to develop new solutions to ever more challenging pollution problems.

Microorganisms and Their Genetic Resources

Besides cleaning up the environment, the genetic riches of the microbial world can be put to work to make products of commercial value. Microorganisms have been used for hundreds of years to produce fermented milk products, alcoholic beverages, and the like. More recently, microorganisms have been grown on massive scales for the production of antibiotics, specific enzymes, and various chemicals. But today we live in the world of "biotech." Biotechnology employs genetically modified microorganisms to synthesize products of high commercial value. Biotechnology uses the tools of genetic engineering—the artificial manipulation of genes and gene products (Figure 7). Genes from any source can be manipulated and modified using microorganisms and their enzymes as molecular tools. For instance, human insulin, a hormone found in abnormally low amounts in people with the disease diabetes, is produced today by genetically engineered bacteria into which human insulin genes have been inserted. Using **genomics**, the sequencing and analysis of the genomes of organisms, one can search the genome of any organism for genes encoding proteins of commercial interest. It is now a routine operation to clone a gene of interest into a suitable host and produce the protein it encodes on a scale to meet commercial demand.

Microbiology as a Career

The field of microbiology is ripe with opportunities for those who seek fulfilling and rewarding careers in science. For example, microbiologists are on the front lines of clinical medicine in developing and deploying methods for the diagnosis and treatment of infectious diseases. Research and development in pharmaceutical, chemical and biochemical, and biotechnology companies is often the foundation of these achievements and is itself fueled by the scientific activities of microbiologists. In addition, microbiologists play key roles in the food and beverage industries, public health, government and university research laboratories, environmental research, and in teaching and training positions in the biological sciences. So, in addition to grasping the principles of perhaps the most exciting of the biological sciences, students of microbiology today have multiple options for turning their love of biology into a challenging and rewarding career.

At this point, the influence of microorganisms on human society should be clear. Indeed, we have many reasons to be aware of microorganisms, their activities, and their potential to benefit or harm humans. As the eminent French scientist Louis Pasteur, one of the founders of modern microbiology, expressed it: "The role of the infinitely small in nature is infinitely large." We continue our journey to the microbial world with an historical overview of the contributions of Pasteur and a few others to the science of microbiology as we know it today.

5 MiniReview

Microorganisms can be both beneficial and harmful to humans. Although we tend to emphasize harmful microorganisms (infectious disease agents), many more microorganisms in nature are beneficial than harmful.

- In what ways are microorganisms important in the food and agricultural industries?
- List two fuels that are made by microorganisms.
- What is biotechnology and how might it improve the lives of humans?

II PATHWAYS OF DISCOVERY IN MICROBIOLOGY

Like any science, microbiology owes much to its past. Although able to claim early roots, the science of microbiology didn't really develop until the nineteenth century. Since that time, the field has exploded and spawned several new but related fields. We retrace these pathways of discovery now.

6 The Historical Roots of Microbiology: Hooke, van Leeuwenhoek, and Cohn

Although the existence of creatures too small to be seen with the naked eye had long been suspected, their discovery was linked to the invention of the microscope. Robert Hooke (1635–1703), an English mathematician and natural historian, was also an excellent microscopist. In his famous book *Micrographia* (1665), the first book devoted to microscopic observations, Hooke illustrated, among many other things, the fruiting structures of molds (Figure 9). This was the first known description of microorganisms. The first person to see bacteria was the Dutch draper and amateur microscope

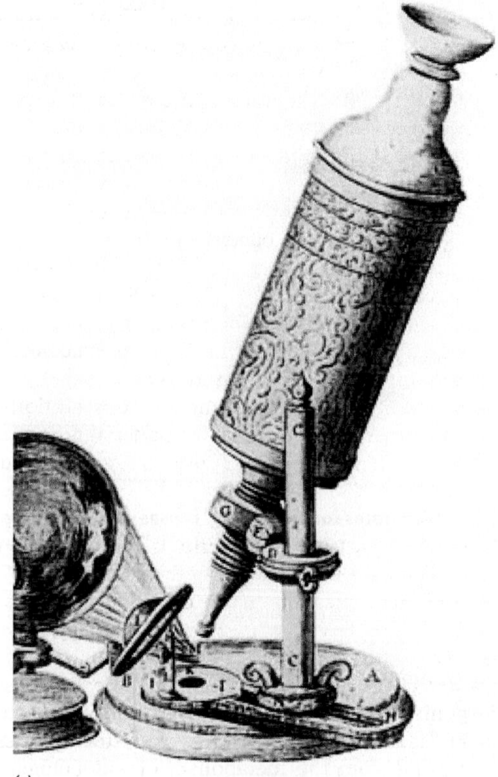

(a)

(b)

Figure 9 Robert Hooke and early microscopy. *(a)* A drawing of the microscope used by Robert Hooke in 1664. The objective lens was fitted at the end of an adjustable bellows (G), with illumination focused on the specimen by a single lens (1). *(b)* A drawing by Robert Hooke. This drawing, published in *Micrographia* in 1655, is the first description of a microorganism. The organism is a bluish-colored mold growing on the surface of leather. The round structures (sporangia) contain spores of the mold.

builder Antoni van Leeuwenhoek (1632–1723). In 1684, van Leeuwenhoek, who was aware of the work of Hooke, used extremely simple microscopes of his own construction (Figure 10) to examine the microbial content of a variety of natural substances.

Van Leeuwenhoek's microscopes were crude by today's standards, but by careful manipulation and focusing he was able to see bacteria, microorganisms considerably smaller than molds. He discovered bacteria in 1676 while studying pepper–water infusions. He reported his observations in a series of letters to the prestigious Royal Society of London, which published them in 1684 in English translation. Drawings of some of van Leeuwenhoek's "wee animalcules," as he referred to them, are shown in Figure 10*b*.

As years went by, van Leeuwenhoek's observations were confirmed by others, but progress in understanding the nature and importance of these tiny organisms remained slow for nearly the next 150 years. Only in the nineteenth century did improved microscopes become widely distributed, and about this time the extent and nature of microbial life forms became more apparent.

In the mid- to late nineteenth century major advances were made in the new science of microbiology, primarily because of the attention that was given to two major questions that pervaded biology and medicine at the time: (1) does spontaneous generation occur and (2) what is the nature of infectious disease. Answers to these penetrating questions emerged from the work of two giants in the fledgling field of microbiology: the French chemist Louis Pasteur and the German physician Robert Koch. But before we explore their work, let us briefly consider the groundbreaking work of a German botanist, Ferdinand Cohn, a contemporary of Pasteur and Koch and the founder of the field we now call *bacteriology*.

Ferdinand Cohn and the Science of Bacteriology

Ferdinand Cohn (1828–1898) was born in Breslau (now in Poland). He was trained as a botanist and became an excellent microscopist. His interests in microscopy naturally led him to the study of unicellular plants—the algae—and later to photosynthetic bacteria. Cohn believed that all bacteria, even those lacking photosynthetic pigments, were members of the plant kingdom, and his microscopic studies gradually drifted away from plants and algae to bacteria, including the large sulfur bacterium *Beggiatoa* (Figure 11).

Cohn was particularly interested in heat resistance in bacteria, which led him to discover the important group of bacteria that form endospores. We now know that bacterial endospores are extremely heat resistant. Cohn described the life cycle of the endospore-forming bacterium *Bacillus* (vegetative cell → endospore → vegetative cell) and discovered that vegetative cells of *Bacillus* but not their endospores were killed by boiling. Indeed, Cohn's discovery of endospores helped explain why his contemporaries, such as the Irish scientist John Tyndall, had found boiling to be an unreliable means of preventing fluid infusions from supporting microbial growth.

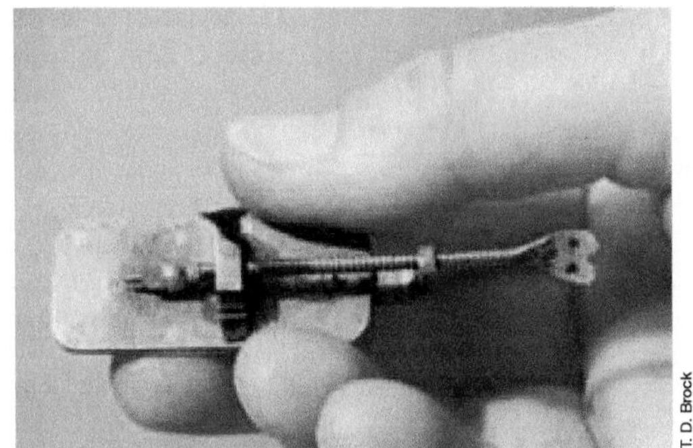

(a)

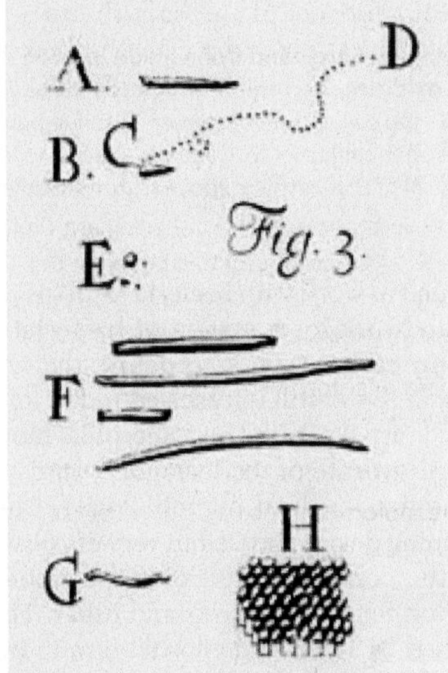

(b)

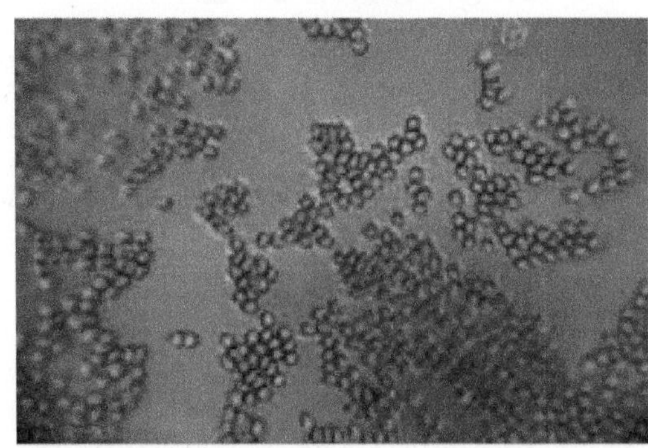

(c)

Figure 10 **The van Leeuwenhoek microscope.** *(a)* A replica of van Leeuwenhoek's microscope. The lens is mounted in the brass plate adjacent to the tip of the adjustable focusing screw. *(b)* Antoni van Leeuwenhoek's drawings of bacteria, published in 1684. Even from these relatively crude drawings we can recognize several shapes of common bacteria: A, C, F, and G, rod shaped; E, spherical or coccus-shaped; H, cocci packets. *(c)* Photomicrograph of a human blood smear taken through a van Leeuwenhoek microscope. Red blood cells are clearly apparent. A single red blood cell is about 6 μm in diameter.

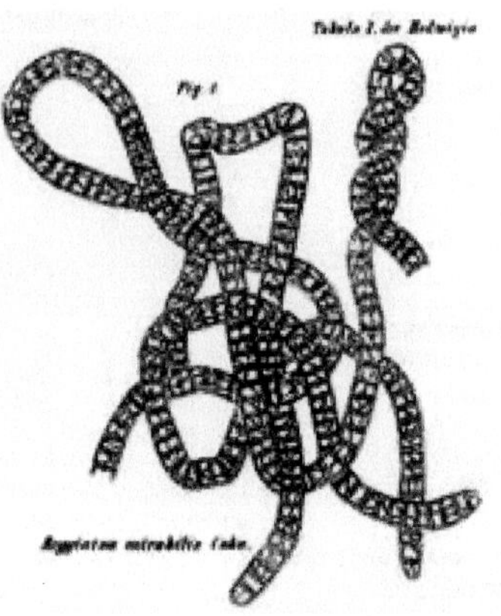

Figure 11 Drawing by Ferdinand Cohn made in 1866 of the large filamentous sulfur-oxidizing bacterium *Beggiatoa mirabilis*. The small granules inside the cell consist of elemental sulfur, produced from the oxidation of hydrogen sulfide (H_2S). Cohn was the first to identify the granules as sulfur. A cell of *B. mirabilis* is about 15 μm in diameter.

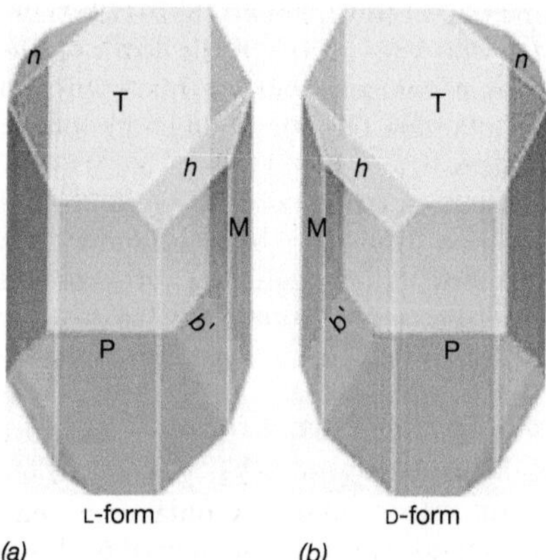

Figure 12 Louis Pasteur's drawings of tartaric acid ($C_4H_6O_6$) crystals that illustrated his famous paper on optical activity. *(a)* Left-handed crystal (L form). *(b)* Right-handed crystal (D form). Note that the two crystals are mirror images. The letters on the faces of the crystals were Pasteur's way of labeling the mirror image faces of the two crystals. Color has been added to show the mirror image faces more clearly.

Cohn continued to work with bacteria until his retirement. He laid the groundwork for a system of bacterial classification, including an early attempt to define the nature of a bacterial species, an issue still unresolved today, and founded a major scientific journal of plant and microbial biology. Cohn was also a strong advocate of the techniques and research of Robert Koch, the first medical microbiologist. Cohn also is credited with helping devise simple but very effective methods for preventing the contamination of culture media, such as the use of cotton for closing flasks and tubes. These methods were later used by Koch and allowed him to make rapid progress in the isolation and characterization of several disease-causing bacteria (Section 8).

6 MiniReview

Robert Hooke was the first to describe microorganisms, and Antoni van Leeuwenhoek was the first to describe bacteria. Ferdinand Cohn founded the field of bacteriology and discovered bacterial endospores.

- What prevented the science of microbiology from developing before the era of van Leeuwenhoek?
- What major discovery emerged from Cohn's study of heat resistance in microorganisms?

7 Pasteur and the Defeat of Spontaneous Generation

The mid- to late nineteenth century saw the science of microbiology blossom. The concept of spontaneous generation was crushed and the science of pure culture microbiology emerged. Several scientific giants emerged in this era, and the first was the Frenchman Louis Pasteur (1822–1895), a contemporary of Cohn.

Optical Isomers and Fermentations

Pasteur was trained as a chemist and was one of the first scientists to recognize the significance of optical isomers. A molecule is optically active if a pure solution or crystal of the molecule diffracts light in only one direction. Pasteur studied crystals of tartaric acid that he separated by hand into those that bent a beam of polarized light to the left and those that bent the beam to the right (Figure 12). Tartrate was chosen because it was an undesirable side product of the wine-making process, and so was readily available in France, and also because solutions of tartaric acid crystallize particularly well. Pasteur found that the mold *Aspergillis* metabolizes only D-tartrate and not its optical isomer L-tartrate. For Pasteur, the fact that a living organism discriminated between optical isomers was of profound significance. He began to see living processes as inherently asymmetric and nonliving chemical processes as not asymmetric. To Pasteur, only living things could selectively produce or consume optical isomers.

Pasteur's thoughts on the asymmetry of life carried over into his work on fermentations and, eventually, spontaneous generation. At the invitation of a local industrialist who was having problems making alcohol by the fermentation of beets, Pasteur began a detailed study of the mechanism of the alcoholic fermentation, at that time thought to be a strictly chemical process. The yeast cells in the fermenting broth were thought to be a complex chemical substance and a result, rather than a catalyst, of the fermentation. One of the side products of the beet fermentation is amyl alcohol, and Pasteur tested the fermenting juice and found the amyl alcohol to be optically active. Microscopic observations and other simple but rigorous experiments convinced Pasteur that the alcoholic fermentation was catalyzed by living yeast cells. Indeed, in Pasteur's own words: ". . . fermentation is associated with the life and structural integrity of the cells and not with their death and decay." From this foundation, Pasteur began a series of classic experiments on spontaneous generation, experiments that are forever linked to his name and to the science of microbiology.

Spontaneous Generation

The concept of **spontaneous generation** had existed since biblical times. The basic idea of spontaneous generation can easily be understood. For example, if food is allowed to stand for some time, it putrefies. When the putrefied material is examined microscopically, it is found to be teeming with bacteria and perhaps even higher organisms such as maggots and worms. Where do these organisms that are not apparent in the fresh food come from? Some people said they developed from seeds or germs that entered the food from air. Others said they arose spontaneously from nonliving materials, that is, spontaneous generation. Who was right? Keen insight was necessary to solve this controversy, and this was exactly the kind of problem that appealed to Louis Pasteur.

Pasteur was a powerful opponent of spontaneous generation. Following his discoveries about fermentation, Pasteur showed that microorganisms closely resembling those observed in putrefying materials could be found in air. Pasteur concluded that the organisms found in putrefying materials originated from microorganisms present in the air and on the surfaces of the containers that held the materials. He postulated that cells are constantly being deposited on all objects and that they grow when conditions are favorable. Furthermore, Pasteur reasoned that if food were treated in such a way as to destroy all living organisms contaminating it, that is, if it were rendered **sterile** and then protected from further contamination, it should not putrefy.

Pasteur used heat to eliminate contaminants. Other workers had shown that when a nutrient solution was sealed in a glass flask and heated to boiling for several minutes, it did not support microbial growth (of course, only if endospores were not present; see discussion of Cohn). Killing all the bacteria or other microorganisms in or on objects is a process we now call *sterilization*. Proponents of spontaneous generation criticized such experiments by declaring that "fresh air" was necessary for the phenomenon to occur. Boiling, so they claimed, in some way affected the air in the sealed flask so that it could no longer support spontaneous generation. In 1864 Pasteur countered this objection simply and brilliantly by constructing a swan-necked flask, now called a *Pasteur flask* (Figure 13). In such a flask nutrient solutions could be heated to boiling and sterilized. However, after the flask was cooled, air was allowed to reenter, but bends in the neck (the "swan neck" design) prevented particulate matter (containing microorganisms) from entering the main body of the flask and causing putrefaction.

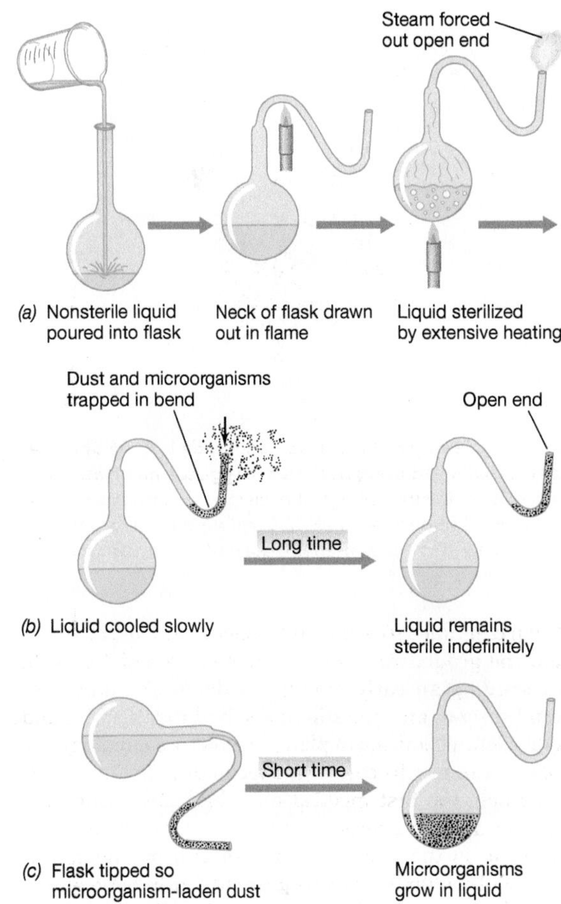
Steam forced out open end
(a) Nonsterile liquid poured into flask
Neck of flask drawn out in flame
Liquid sterilized by extensive heating
Dust and microorganisms trapped in bend
Open end
Long time
(b) Liquid cooled slowly
Liquid remains sterile indefinitely
Short time
(c) Flask tipped so microorganism-laden dust contacts sterile liquid
Microorganisms grow in liquid

Figure 13 **The defeat of spontaneous generation: Pasteur's experiment with the swan-necked flask.** *(a)* Sterilizing the contents of the flask. *(b)* If the flask remained upright, no microbial growth occurred. *(c)* If microorganisms trapped in the neck reached the sterile liquid, microbial growth ensued.

Broth sterilized in a Pasteur flask did not putrefy, and microorganisms never appeared in the flask as long as the neck did not contact the sterile liquid. If, however, the flask was tipped to allow the sterile liquid to contact the contaminated neck of the flask (Figure 13*c*), putrefaction occurred and the liquid soon teemed with microorganisms. This simple experiment effectively settled the controversy surrounding spontaneous generation, and the science of microbiology was able to move ahead on firm footing. Incidentally, Pasteur's work also led to the development of effective sterilization procedures that were eventually refined and carried over into both basic and applied microbiological research. Food science also owes a debt to Pasteur, as his principles are applied today in the canning and preservation of milk and other foods (pasteurization). www.microbiologyplace.com **Online Tutorial 1: Pasteur's Experiment**

(a)

(b)

Figure 14 **Louis Pasteur and symbols of his contributions to microbiology.** *(a)* A French 5-franc note. The note contains a painting of Pasteur and symbols of his many scientific accomplishments. The shepherd boy Jean Baptiste Jupille is shown dispatching a rabid dog who had attacked a group of children. Pasteur's rabies vaccine saved Jupille's life. In France, the franc preceded the euro as a currency. *(b)* The Pasteur Institute, Paris France. Photo of the original structure built for Pasteur by the French government and opened in 1888. The Pasteur Institute today is a campus of several buildings. The Pasteur crypt and museum displaying Pasteur's original swan-neck flasks and other scientific equipment is located in the original building.

Other Accomplishments of Louis Pasteur

Pasteur went on to many other triumphs in microbiology and medicine beyond his seminal work on spontaneous generation. Some highlights include his development of vaccines for the diseases anthrax, fowl cholera, and rabies during a very scientifically productive period in his life from 1880 to 1890. Pasteur's work on rabies was his most famous success, culminating in July of 1885 with the first administration of a rabies vaccine to a human, a young French boy named Joseph Meister who had been bitten by a rabid dog. In those days, a bite from a rabid animal was akin to a death sentence. News of the success of Meister's vaccination, and that of a young shepherd boy, Jean Baptiste Jupille (Figure 14a), administered shortly thereafter, spread quickly, and within a year nearly 2500 people had come to Paris to be treated with Pasteur's rabies vaccine.

Pasteur's fame from his rabies research was legendary and led the French government to build the Pasteur Institute in Paris in 1888. Originally established as a clinical center for treatment of rabies and other contagious diseases, the Pasteur Institute is today a major biomedical research center focused on antiserum and vaccine production (Figure 14*b*). The medical and veterinary breakthroughs of Pasteur were not only highly significant in their own right but helped solidify the concept of the germ theory of disease, whose principles were being developed at about this same time by a second giant of the era, Robert Koch.

7 MiniReview

Louis Pasteur is best remembered for his ingenious experiments showing that living organisms were not spontaneously generated from nonliving matter. Pasteur's work in this area led to many of the basic techniques central to the science of microbiology, including the concept and practice of sterilization.

- Define the term sterile.
- How did Pasteur's swan-neck flask experiment show that the concept of spontaneous generation was invalid?

8 Koch, Infectious Disease, and the Rise of Pure Culture Microbiology

Proof that microorganisms could cause disease provided perhaps the greatest impetus for the development of the science of microbiology. Even in the sixteenth century it was thought that something that induced a disease could be transmitted from a diseased person to a healthy person. After the discovery of microorganisms, it was widely believed that they were responsible, but definitive proof was lacking. Improvements in sanitation by Ignaz Semmelweis and Joseph Lister provided indirect evidence for the importance of microorganisms in causing human diseases, but it was not until the work of a German physician, Robert Koch (1843–1910), that the concept of infectious disease was given experimental support.

The Germ Theory of Disease and Koch's Postulates

In his early work Koch studied anthrax, a disease of cattle and occasionally of humans. Anthrax is caused by an endospore-forming bacterium called *Bacillus anthracis*. By careful microscopy and by using special stains, Koch established that the bacteria were always present in the blood of an animal that was succumbing to the disease. However, Koch reasoned that mere association of the bacterium with the disease was not proof that it actually caused the disease. Instead, the bacterium might be a result of the disease. How could cause and effect be linked? With anthrax Koch sensed an opportunity to study cause and effect experimentally, and his results formed the standard by which infectious diseases have been studied ever since.

Koch used mice as experimental animals. Using all of the proper controls, Koch demonstrated that when a small

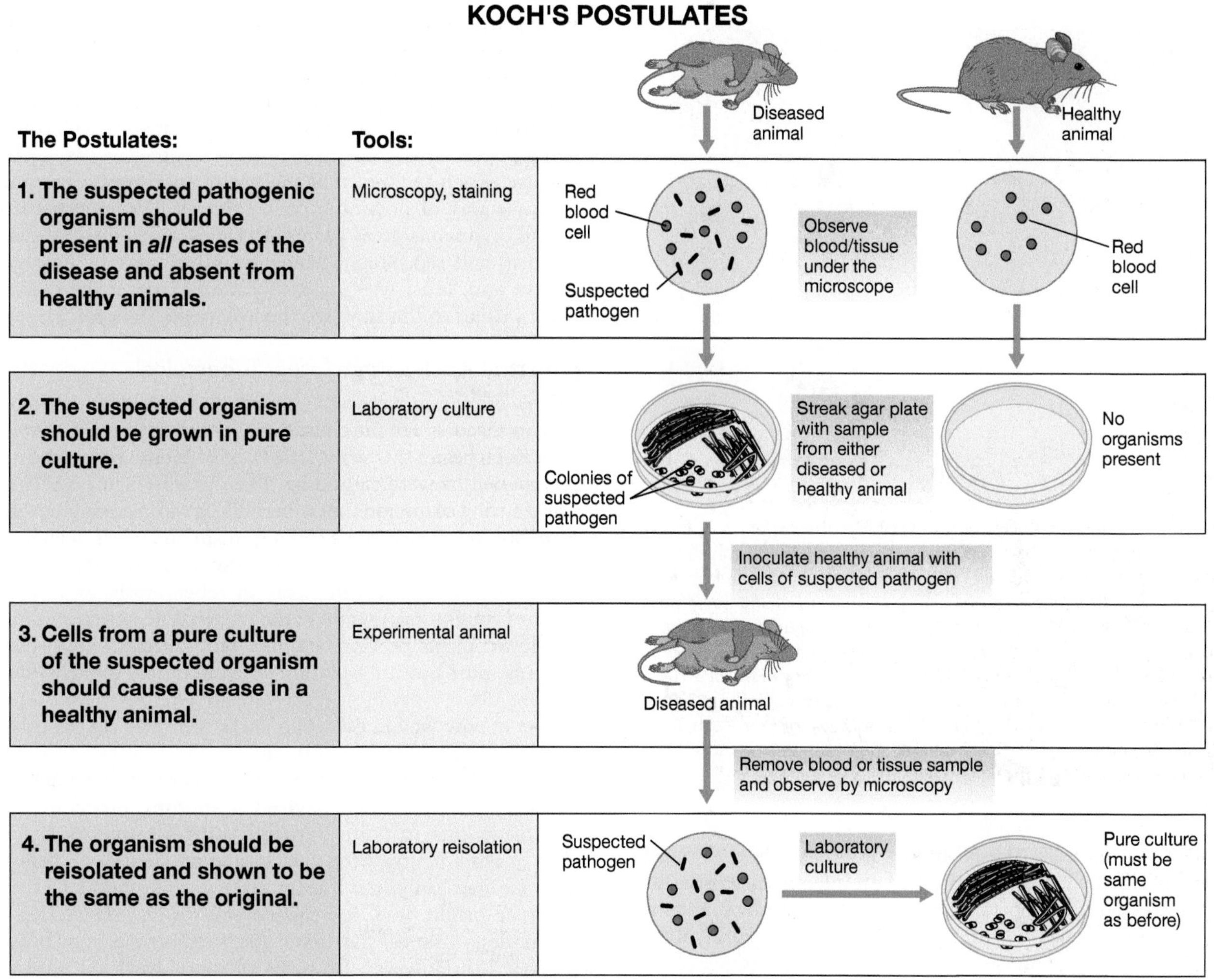

Figure 15 **Koch's postulates for proving that a specific microorganism causes a specific disease.** Note that following isolation of a pure culture of the suspected pathogen, a laboratory culture of the organism should both initiate the disease and be recovered from the diseased animal. Establishing the correct conditions for growing the pathogen is essential, otherwise it will be missed.

amount of blood from a diseased mouse was injected into a healthy mouse, the latter quickly developed anthrax. He took blood from this second animal, injected it into another, and again obtained the characteristic disease symptoms. However, Koch carried this experiment a critically important step further. He discovered that the anthrax bacteria could be grown in nutrient fluids outside the animal body and that even after many transfers in laboratory culture, the bacteria still caused the disease when inoculated into a healthy animal.

On the basis of these and related experiments carried out in his seminal work on the causative agent of tuberculosis, Koch formulated a set of rigorous criteria, now known as **Koch's postulates**, for definitively linking a specific microorganism to a specific disease:

1. The disease-causing organism must always be present in animals suffering from the disease and should not be present in healthy animals.
2. The organism must be cultivated in a pure culture away from the animal body.
3. The isolated organism must cause the disease when inoculated into a healthy susceptible animal.
4. The organism must be reisolated from these experimental animals and cultured again in the laboratory, after which it should still be the same as the original organism.

Koch's postulates are summarized in Figure 15. Koch's postulates were a monumental step forward in the study of

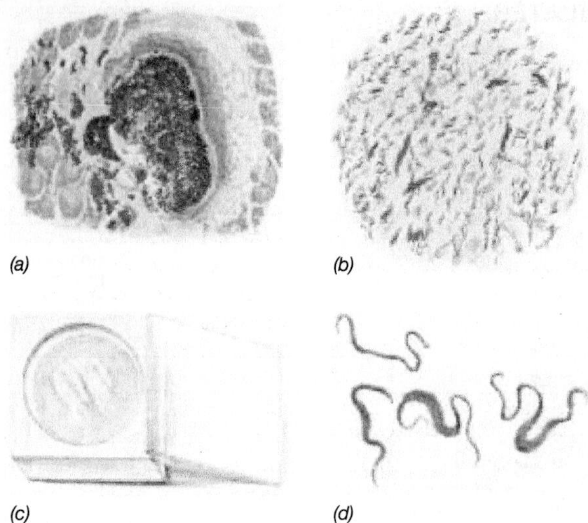

Figure 16 **Robert Koch's drawings of *Mycobacterium tuberculosis*.** Robert Koch was the first to isolate *M. tuberculosis* and to show it causes tuberculosis. *(a)* Section through a tubercle from lung tissue. Cells of *M. tuberculosis* stain blue, whereas the lung tissue stains brown. *(b)* Cells of *M. tuberculosis* in a sputum sample of a tuberculous patient. *(c)* Growth of *M. tuberculosis* on a glass plate of coagulated blood serum inside a glass box (lid open). *(d)* A colony of *M. tuberculosis* cells taken from the plate in *(c)* and observed microscopically at 700×; cells appear as long cordlike forms. Original drawings from Koch, R. 1884. "Die Aetiologie der Tuberkulose." *Mittheilungen aus dem Kaiserlichen Gesundheitsamte* 2:1–88.

infectious diseases. The postulates not only offered a means for linking the cause and effect of an infectious disease, but also stressed the importance of laboratory culture of the putative infectious agent. With these postulates as a guide, Koch, his students, and those that followed them discovered the causative agents of most of the important infectious diseases of humans and other animals. These discoveries led to the development of successful treatments for the prevention and cure of many of these diseases, thereby greatly improving the scientific basis of clinical medicine and human health and welfare (Figure 8).

Koch and Pure Cultures

To link a specific microorganism to a specific disease, the microorganism must first be isolated away from other microorganisms in laboratory culture; in microbiology we say that such a culture is *pure*. This concept was not lost on Robert Koch in formulating his famous postulates (Figure 15), and to accomplish this, he developed several simple but ingenious methods of obtaining bacteria in pure culture (see the Microbial Sidebar, "Solid Media, the Petri Plate, and Pure Cultures").

Koch started in a crude way by using solid nutrients such as a potato slice to culture bacteria. But he quickly developed more reliable methods, many of which are still in use today. Koch observed that when a solid surface such as a potato slice was incubated in air, bacterial colonies developed, each having a characteristic shape and color. He inferred that each colony had arisen from a single bacterial cell that had fallen on the surface, found suitable nutrients, and multiplied. Each colony was a population of identical cells, or in other words, a **pure culture**. Koch realized that the use of solid media provided a simple way of obtaining pure cultures. However, because not all organisms grow on potato slices, Koch devised more uniform and reproducible nutrient solutions solidified with gelatin and, later, with agar, laboratory techniques that remain with us to this day (see the Microbial Sidebar).

A Test of Koch's Postulates: Tuberculosis

Koch's crowning accomplishment in medical bacteriology was his discovery of the causative agent of tuberculosis. At the time Koch began this work (1881), one-seventh of all reported human deaths were caused by tuberculosis (Figure 8). There was a strong suspicion that tuberculosis was a contagious disease, but the suspected causal organism had never been seen, either in diseased tissues or in culture. Koch was determined to demonstrate the causal agent of tuberculosis, and to this end he brought together all of the methods he had so carefully developed in his previous studies with anthrax: microscopy, staining, pure culture isolation, and an animal model system (Figure 15).

As is now well known, the bacterium that causes tuberculosis, *Mycobacterium tuberculosis,* is very difficult to stain because of the large amounts of a waxy lipid present in its cell wall. But Koch devised a staining procedure for *M. tuberculosis* in tissue samples using alkaline methylene blue in conjunction with a second stain (Bismarck brown) that stained only the tissue. Using this method, Koch observed bright blue, rod-shaped cells of *M. tuberculosis* in tuberculous tissues, the tissue itself staining a light brown (Figure 16). However, from his previous work on anthrax, Koch fully realized that simply *identifying* an organism associated with tuberculosis was not enough. He knew he must *culture* the organism in order to prove that it was the specific cause of tuberculosis.

Obtaining cultures of *M. tuberculosis* was not easy, but eventually Koch was successful in growing colonies of this organism on a medium containing coagulated blood serum. Later he used agar, which had just been introduced as a solidifying agent (see the Microbial Sidebar). Under the best of conditions, *M. tuberculosis* grows slowly in culture, but Koch's persistence and patience eventually led to pure cultures of this organism from a variety of human and animal sources.

From here it was relatively easy for Koch to use his postulates (Figure 15) to obtain definitive proof that the organism he had isolated was the cause of the disease tuberculosis. Guinea pigs can be readily infected with *M. tuberculosis* and eventually succumb to systemic tuberculosis. Koch showed that diseased guinea pigs contained masses of *M. tuberculosis* cells in their tissues and that pure cultures obtained from

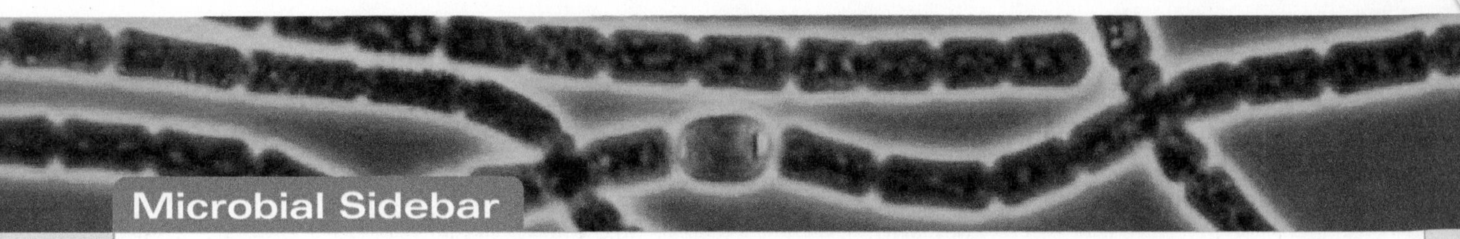

Microbial Sidebar

Solid Media, the Petri Plate, and Pure Cultures

Robert Koch was the first to grow bacteria on solid culture media. Koch's early use of potato slices as solid media was fraught with problems. Besides being rather selective in terms of which bacteria would grow on the slices, the slices were frequently overgrown with molds. Koch thus needed a more reliable and reproducible means of growing bacteria on solid media, and he found the answer in agar.

Koch initially employed gelatin as a solidifying agent for the various nutrient fluids he used to culture bacteria and developed a method for preparing horizontal slabs of solid media that were kept free of contamination by covering them with a bell jar or glass box (see Figure 16c). Nutrient gelatin was a good culture medium for the isolation and study of various bacteria, but it had several drawbacks, the most important being that it did not remain solid at 37°C, the optimum temperature for growth of most human pathogens. Thus, a different solidifying agent was needed.

Agar is a polysaccharide derived from red algae. It was used widely in the nineteenth century as a gelling agent. Walter Hesse, an associate of Koch, first used agar as a solidifying agent for bacteriological culture media (**Figure 1**). The actual suggestion that agar be used instead of gelatin was made by Hesse's wife, Fannie. She had used agar to solidify fruit jellies. When it was tried as a solidifying agent in microbial nutrient media, its superior gelling qualities were immediately evident. Hesse wrote to Koch about this discovery, and Koch quickly adapted agar to his own studies, including his classic studies on the isolation of the bacterium *Mycobacterium tuberculosis,* the cause of the disease tuberculosis (see text and Figure 16).

Agar has many other properties that make it desirable as a gelling agent for microbial culture media. In particular, agar remains solid at 37°C (human body temperature) and, after melting during the sterilization process, remains liquid to about 45°C, at which time it can be poured into sterile vessels. In addition, unlike gelatin, which many bacteria can degrade, causing the medium to liquify, agar is not degraded by most bacteria. Agar also renders most solid culture media transparent, making it easier to differentiate bacterial colonies from inanimate particulate matter suspended in the medium. Hence, agar found its place early in the annals of microbiology and is still used today for obtaining and maintaining pure cultures of bacteria.

In 1887 Richard Petri, a German bacteriologist, published a brief paper describing a modification of Koch's flat plate technique (Figure 16c). Petri's enhancement, which turned out to be amazingly useful, was the development of the transparent double-sided dishes that bear his name (**Figure 2**). The advantages of Petri dishes were immediately apparent. They could easily be stacked and sterilized separately from the medium, and, following the addition of molten culture medium to the smaller of the two dishes, the larger dish could be used as a cover to prevent contamination. Colonies that formed on the surface of the agar in the Petri dish remained fully exposed to air and could easily be manipulated for further study. The original idea of Petri has not been improved on to this day, and the Petri dish, made either of reusable glass and sterilized by heat or of disposable plastic and sterilized by ethylene oxide (a gaseous sterilant), is a mainstay of the microbiology laboratory.

Koch was keenly aware of the implications his pure culture methods had for the study of microbial systematics. He observed that different colonies (differing in color, morphology, size, and the like, see Figure 2) developed on solid media exposed to a contaminated object and that they bred true and could be distinguished from one another by their colony characteristics. Cells from different colonies also differed microscopically and often in their temperature or nutrient requirements as well. Koch realized that these differences among microorganisms met all the requirements that taxonomists had established for the classification of larger organisms, such as plant and animal species. In Koch's own words (translated

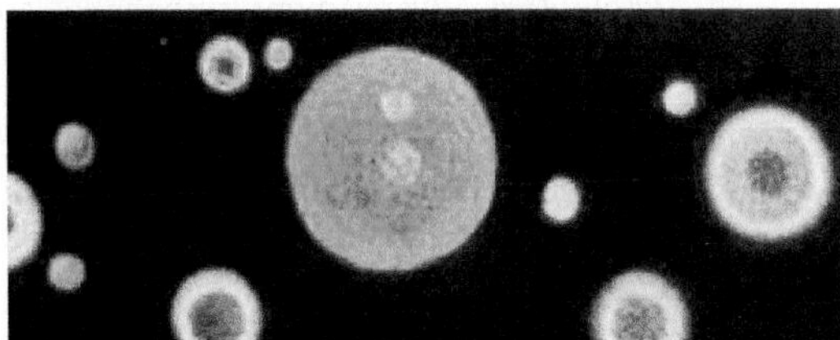

Figure 1 *A hand-colored photograph taken by Walter Hesse of colonies formed on agar. The colonies include those of fungi (molds) and bacteria and were obtained during studies Hesse initiated on the microbiological content of air in Berlin, Germany, in 1882.*

From Hesse, W. 1884. "Ueber quantitative Bestimmung der in der Luft enthaltenen Mikroorganismen," in Struck, H. (ed.), *Mittheilungen aus dem Kaiserlichen Gesundheitsamte.* August Hirschwald.

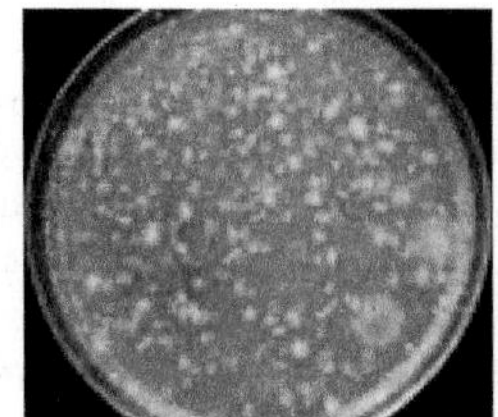

Figure 2 *Photo of a Petri dish containing colonies of marine bacteria. Each colony contains billions of bacterial cells descended from a single cell.*

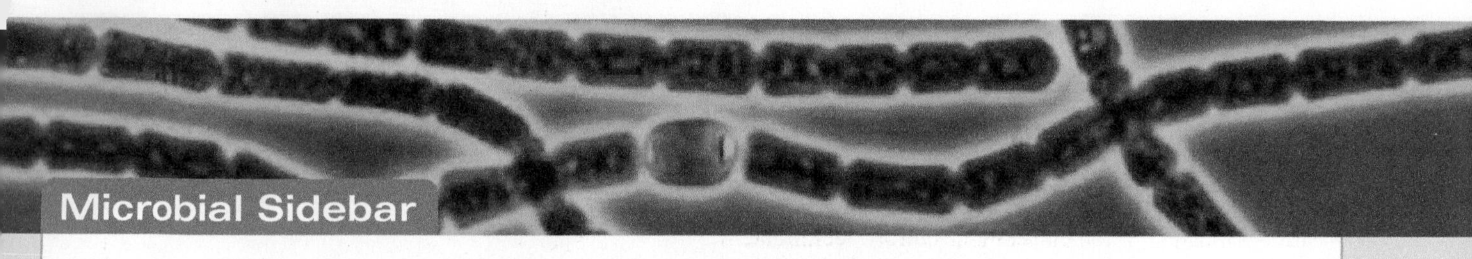

Solid Media, the Petri Plate, and Pure Cultures *(continued)*

from the German): "All bacteria which maintain the characteristics which differentiate one from another when they are cultured on the same medium and under the same conditions, should be designated as species, varieties, forms, or other suitable designation." Koch also realized from the study of pure cultures that one could show that specific organisms have specific effects, not only in causing disease, but in other capacities as well. Such insightful thinking was significant in the relatively rapid acceptance of microbiology as an independent biological science in the early twentieth century.

Koch's discovery of solid culture media and his emphasis on pure culture microbiology reached far beyond the realm of medical bacteriology. His discoveries supplied critically needed tools for development of the fields of bacterial taxonomy, genetics, and several other subdisciplines. Indeed, the entire field of microbiology owes much to Robert Koch and his associates for the intuition they displayed in grasping the significance of pure cultures and developing some of the most basic methods in microbiology.

such animals transmitted the disease to uninfected animals. Thus, Koch successfully satisfied all four of his postulates (Figure 15), and the cause of tuberculosis was understood. Koch announced his discovery of the cause of tuberculosis in 1882 and published a very thorough paper on the subject in 1884. It is in the latter that his postulates are most clearly stated. For his contributions on tuberculosis, Robert Koch was awarded the 1905 Nobel Prize for Physiology or Medicine.

Koch's Postulates Today

For diseases in which an animal model is available it is relatively easy to prove Koch's postulates. In modern clinical medicine, however, this is not always so easy. Even Koch had a hard time satisfying his postulates in some cases. Take cholera, for example. Today there is a suitable animal assay system for cholera, but in Koch's day this was not the case. And since only a fraction of human volunteers fed cells of *Vibrio cholerae,* the bacterium that causes cholera, contract cholera, obtaining definitive proof was difficult.

Even today it is sometimes impossible to satisfy Koch's postulates. For instance, the causative agents of several diseases of humans will not cause disease in any known experimental animals. These include many of the diseases associated with obligately intracellular bacteria, such as the rickettsias and chlamydias, and diseases caused by some viruses and protozoan parasites. Since for most of these diseases it would be unethical to use human volunteers to satisfy Koch's postulates, it is likely that cause and effect will never be unequivocally proven for them. However, for many of these diseases the clinical and epidemiological (disease tracking) evidence provides all but certain proof of the specific cause of the disease. Thus, although Koch's postulates remain the "gold standard" in medical microbiology, it has so far proven impossible to satisfy all of his postulates for every infectious disease.

8 MiniReview

Robert Koch developed criteria for the study of infectious microorganisms and developed the first methods for growth of pure cultures of microorganisms.

- How do Koch's postulates prove cause and effect in a disease?
- What advantages do solid media offer for the culture of microorganisms?
- What is a pure culture?

9 Microbial Diversity and the Rise of General Microbiology

As microbiology advanced out of the nineteenth and into the twentieth century, the initial focus on medical aspects of microbiology broadened to include studies of the microbial diversity of soil and water and the metabolic processes that organisms in these habitats carried out. This was the beginnings of *general microbiology,* a term that refers primarily to the nonmedical aspects of microbiology. Two giants of this era included the Dutchman Martinus Beijerinck and the Russian Sergei Winogradsky.

Martinus Beijerinck and the Enrichment Culture Technique

Martinus Beijerinck (1851–1931), a professor at the Delft Polytechnic School in Holland, was originally trained in botany; he began his career in microbiology studying plants. Beijerinck's greatest contribution to the field of microbiology was his clear formulation of the **enrichment culture technique**. In enrichment cultures microorganisms are isolated from natural samples in a highly selective fashion by manipulating nutrient and incubation conditions. Beijerinck's skill was aptly demonstrated when, following Winogradsky's discovery of the process of nitrogen fixation (see Figure 19), he enriched the aerobic nitrogen-fixing bacterium *Azotobacter* (Figure 17).

Using the enrichment culture technique, Beijerinck isolated the first pure cultures of many soil and aquatic microorganisms, including sulfate-reducing and sulfur-oxidizing bacteria, nitrogen-fixing root nodule bacteria, *Lactobacillus* species, green algae, various anaerobic bacteria, and many others. In his studies of tobacco mosaic disease, Beijerinck used selective filtering techniques to show that the infectious agent (a virus) was smaller than a bacterium and that it somehow became incorporated into cells of the living host plant. In this insightful work, Beijerinck not only described the first virus, but also the basic principles of virology.

Sergei Winogradsky and the Concept of Chemolithotrophy

Sergei Winogradsky (1856–1953) had scientific interests similar to Beijerinck's and was also successful in isolating or at least enriching several key bacteria from natural samples. Winogradsky was particularly interested in bacteria that cycle nitrogen and sulfur compounds, such as the nitrifying bacteria and purple sulfur bacteria (Figure 18). He showed in this work that specific bacteria are linked to specific biogeochemical transformations. For example, bacteria that cycle *nitrogen* compounds do not cycle *sulfur* compounds and vice versa. Moreover, Winogradsky's keen insight into the biology of these organisms revealed the metabolic significance of their biogeochemical transformations. From his studies of sulfur-oxidizing bacteria, for instance, Winogradsky proposed the concept of **chemolithotrophy**, the oxidation of *inorganic* compounds linked to energy conservation (Figure 19*a*). And from his studies of the chemolithotrophic process of nitrification (the oxidation of ammonia to nitrate), Winogradsky showed that the organisms responsible—the nitrifying bacteria—obtained their carbon from CO_2. Winogradsky thus showed that, like phototrophic organisms, the nitrifying bacteria were autotrophs (Figure 19*a*).

Using an enrichment method, Winogradsky performed the first isolation of a nitrogen-fixing bacterium, the anaerobe *Clostridium pasteurianum*, thus formulating the concept of nitrogen fixation (Figure 19*b*). Beijerinck used this discovery to guide his isolation of aerobic nitrogen-fixing bacteria years later (Figure 17). Winogradsky lived to be almost 100, publishing many scientific papers and a major monograph, *Microbiologie du Sol (Soil Microbiology)*. This work, a milestone in microbiology, contains drawings of many of the organisms Winogradsky studied during his lengthy career (Figure 18).

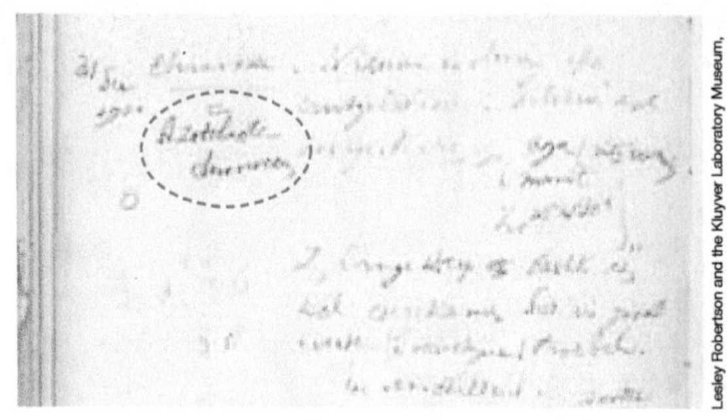

(a)

Lesley Robertson and the Kluyver Laboratory Museum, Delft University of Technology

(b)

Lesley Robertson and the Kluyver Laboratory Museum, Delft University of Technology

Figure 17 **Martinus Beijerinck and *Azotobacter*.** *(a)* Portion of a page from the laboratory notebook of M. Beijerinck dated December 31, 1900, describing his observations on the aerobic nitrogen-fixing bacterium *Azotobacter chroococcum* (name circled in red). It is on this page that Beijerinck uses this name, which is still recognized today, for the first time. *(b)* A painting by M. Beijerinck's sister, Henrëtte Beijerinck, showing cells of *Azotobacter chroococcum*. Beijerinck used such paintings to illustrate his lectures.

9 MiniReview

Beijerinck and Winogradsky studied bacteria inhabiting soil and water and developed the enrichment culture technique for the isolation of various microorganisms. Major new concepts in general microbiology emerged during this period, including enrichment cultures, chemolithotrophy, chemoautotrophy, and nitrogen fixation.

- What is the enrichment culture technique?
- What information in Figure 19 tells you that sulfur oxidation and nitrification are chemolithotrophic (energy-yielding) processes and that nitrogen fixation is not?

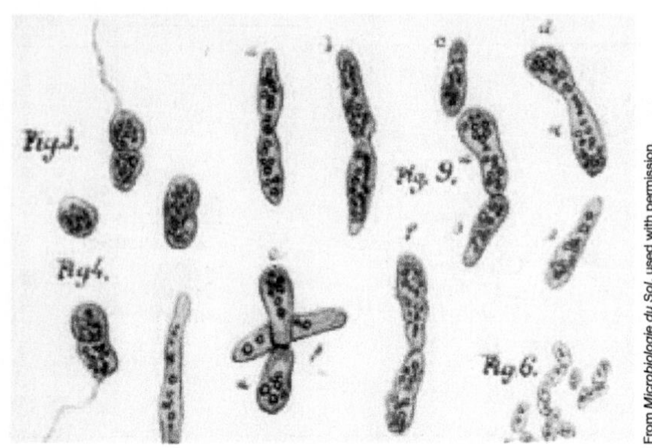

Figure 18 Hand-colored drawings of cells of purple sulfur phototrophic bacteria. The original drawings were made by Sergei Winogradsky about 1887 and then copied and hand-colored by his wife Hèléne. Figures 3 and 4 show cells of the genus *Chromatium,* such as *C. okenii.*

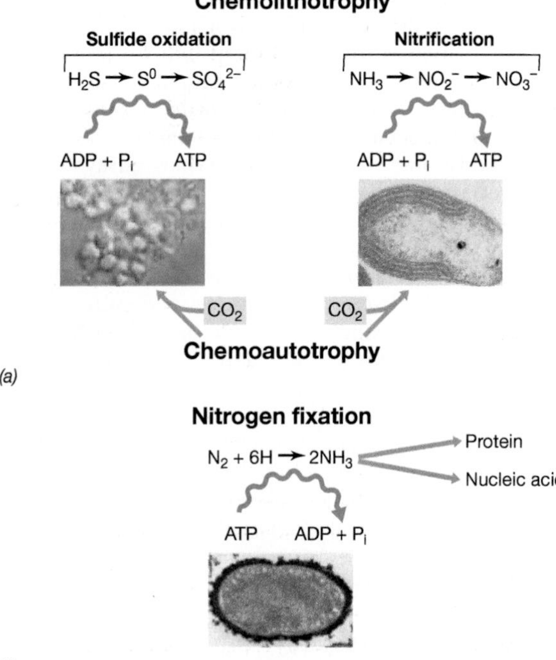

Figure 19 Major concepts conceived by Sergei Winogradsky. *(a)* Chemolithotrophy and chemoautotrophy. Oxidation of the sulfur or nitrogen compounds yields energy (ATP), and the cell obtains carbon from CO_2. Photos, left, the sulfur bacterium *Achromatium;* right, *Nitrobacter,* a bacterium that carries out the first step ($NH_3 \rightarrow NO_2^-$) in nitrification. *(b)* Nitrogen fixation. This process consumes ATP but allows the cell to use nitrogen gas (N_2) for all of its nitrogen needs. Photo, *Azotobacter,* an aerobic nitrogen-fixing bacterium (see also Figure 17).

10 The Modern Era of Microbiology

In the twentieth century, the field of microbiology developed rapidly in two different yet complementary directions—*applied* and *basic*. During this period new laboratory tools to study microorganisms became available, and the science of microbiology began to mature and spawn new subdisciplines. Few of these subdisciplines were purely applied or purely basic. Instead, most had both their discovery (basic) aspects and their problem-solving (applied) aspects. Table 1 summarizes some of the key accomplishments during the first 300 years of microbiology; Figure 20 shows a timeline of major accomplishments from 1975 to the present.

Origin of the Major Subdisciplines of Applied Microbiology

The advances of Robert Koch in understanding the nature of infectious diseases and culturing pathogens in the laboratory were catalysts for development of the fields of *medical microbiology* and *immunology,* both key subdisciplines of microbiology today. Work in these areas resulted in the discovery of many new bacterial pathogens of humans and other animals and elucidation of the mechanisms by which these pathogens infect the body or are resisted by the body's defenses. Other practical advances, bolstered by the discoveries of Beijerinck and Winogradsky, were in the field of *agricultural microbiology,* which began our understanding of microbial processes in the soil, such as nitrogen fixation (Figure 19*b*), that benefit plant growth. Later in the twentieth century, studies of soil microorganisms led to the discovery of antibiotics and other important chemicals. This spawned the field of *industrial microbiology,* the large-scale growth of microorganisms for the production of commercial products.

Advances in soil microbiology also provided the foundation for studies of microbial processes in lakes, rivers, and the oceans—*aquatic microbiology* and *marine microbiology.* One branch of aquatic microbiology deals with treating sewage and other wastewaters to render them harmless to humans and the environment and provide safe drinking water. Marine microbiology is presently enjoying great popularity because of the host of new tools available for studying the diversity and activities of marine microorganisms and the recognition that marine microorganisms likely control many important global parameters, including climate and atmospheric chemistry. As interest in the biodiversity and activities of microorganisms in their natural environments grew, the field of *microbial ecology* emerged in the 1960s and 1970s. Today microbial ecology is enjoying a "golden era" catalyzed by an influx of new molecular tools, in particular those of genomics. These powerful tools allow microbial ecologists to assess the microbial biodiversity and activities of even very complex microbial communities.

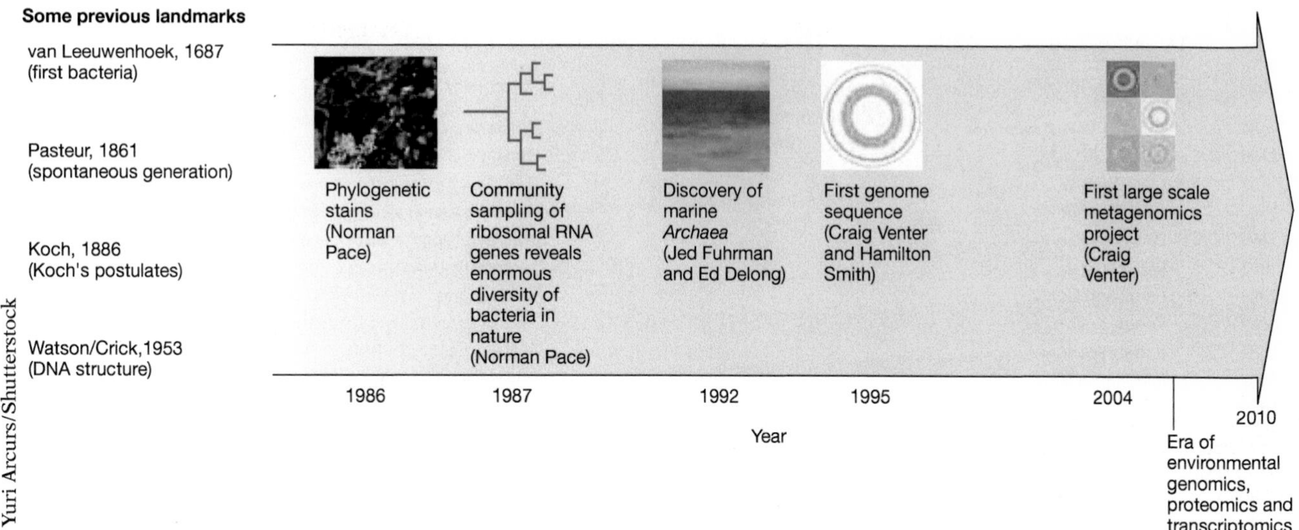

Figure 20 Some landmarks in molecular microbiology since 1985. The icons are representative of the discoveries. Not all contributors to a specific discovery could be listed.

Basic Science Subdisciplines in Microbiology

The twentieth century saw many new basic science subdisciplines develop in microbiology. Since the middle of the twentieth century, many new microorganisms have been cultured, resulting in considerable refinement of *microbial systematics,* the science of grouping and classifying microorganisms. This has culminated in the construction of a phylogenetic tree of life, as we discuss in the next chapter. Microbial ecology has fueled these advances by revealing, in most cases without actually culturing any organisms, that a vast world of unexplored microbial diversity awaits us in virtually any habitat one can examine. *Microbial physiology* studies the nutrients that microorganisms require for metabolism and growth and the products that they make from these nutrients. Enhanced understanding of the structure of microorganisms (*cytology*) and the discovery of microbial enzymes and the chemical reactions they carry out (*microbial biochemistry*) have also greatly influenced how microbiology is practiced today.

A key area of basic research that moved forward rapidly in the mid-twentieth century was the study of heredity and variation in bacteria, the subdiscipline of *bacterial genetics*. Although some aspects of bacterial genetics were known early in the twentieth century, it was not until the discovery of genetic exchange in bacteria around 1950 that bacterial genetics became a major field of study. Bacterial genetics, biochemistry, and physiology shared common roots during the 1950s and even today focus on many of the same scientific questions. By the early 1960s, these fields had provided an advanced understanding of DNA, RNA, and protein synthesis. *Molecular biology* arose to a great extent from studies of bacterial genetics (Figure 20).

Virology, the study of viruses, also blossomed in the twentieth century. Although Beijerinck discovered the first virus more than 100 years ago, it was not until the middle of the twentieth century that viruses were really understood. Much of the relevant work involved viruses that infect bacteria, called *bacteriophages*. Scientists realized that virus infection was a type of genetic transfer, and the relationship between viruses and cells was worked out primarily from research on bacteriophages. Today, animal and plant viruses occupy center stage in virology because of the ever-growing list of pathogenic viruses and the recognition that genetic diversity among these viruses is enormous.

The Era of Molecular Microbiology

By the 1970s, our knowledge of bacterial physiology, biochemistry, and genetics had advanced to the point that cellular genomes could be manipulated. DNA from one organism could be "transplanted" into a bacterium and the proteins encoded by the DNA harvested. This led to development of the field of *biotechnology*. At about this same time, nucleic acid sequencing techniques were developed, and the ramifications of this new technology were felt in all areas of biology. In microbiology, DNA sequencing revealed the phylogenetic (evolutionary) relationships among bacteria, which led to revolutionary new concepts in microbial systematics. DNA sequencing also gave birth in the mid-1990s to the field of *genomics*. The huge amounts of genomic information available today have fueled major advances in medicine, agriculture, biotechnology, and many other areas. And the fast-moving field of genomics has itself spawned new subdisciplines, such as *proteomics* and *metabolomics,* the patterns of protein and metabolic expression in cells, respectively.

Table 1 Three hundred years of microbiology: Some key papers in microbiology, 1684–2000[a]

Year	*Investigator(s)*	*Discovery*
1684	Antoni van Leeuwenhoek	Bacteria
1798	Edward Jenner	Smallpox vaccination
1857	Louis Pasteur	Microbiology of lactic acid fermentation
1860	Louis Pasteur	Role of yeast in alcoholic fermentation
1864	Louis Pasteur	Fallacy of spontaneous generation
1867	Robert Lister	Antiseptic principles in surgery
1876	Ferdinand Cohn	Endospores
1881	Robert Koch	Methods for study of bacteria in pure culture
1882	Robert Koch*	Cause of tuberculosis
1882	Élie Metchnikoff*	Phagocytosis
1884	Robert Koch	Cause of cholera; also first formulation of Koch's postulates
1884	Christian Gram	Gram-staining method
1885	Louis Pasteur	Rabies vaccine
1889	Sergei Winogradsky	Chemolithotrophy
1889	Martinus Beijerinck	Concept of a virus
1890	Emil von Behring* and Shibasaburo Kitasato	Diphtheria antitoxin
1890	Sergei Winogradsky	Autotrophy in chemolithotrophs
1901	Martinus Beijerinck	Enrichment culture method
1901	Karl Landsteiner*	Human blood groups
1908	Paul Ehrlich*	Chemotherapeutic agents
1911	Francis Rous*	First cancer virus
1915/1917	Frederick Twort and Felix d'Hérelle	Bacterial viruses (bacteriophage)
1928	Frederick Griffith	Pneumococcus transformation
1929	Alexander Fleming*	Penicillin
1931	Cornelius van Niel	H_2S (sulfide) as a photosynthetic electron donor
1935	Gerhard Domagk*	Sulfa drugs
1935	Wendall Stanley	Crystallization of tobacco mosaic virus
1941	George Beadle* and Edward Tatum*	One gene–one enzyme hypothesis
1943	Max Delbruck* and Salvador Luria*	Inheritance of genetic characteristics in bacteria
1944	Oswald Avery, Colin Macleod, Maclyn McCarty	DNA is genetic material

New Frontiers

Not only has the 325 years of microbiology since the days of van Leeuwenhoek brought us startling insight into the biology of microorganisms, it has brought new challenges, both good and bad. On the one hand, new emerging diseases, such as SARS (severe acute respiratory syndrome) and bird flu, seem to appear without warning and challenge even our most sophisticated understanding of microbial diseases. On the other hand, new thrusts in microbiology, such as genomics, have given us an unprecedented understanding of how a cell works at the most fundamental level. Microbial research today is close to defining the minimalist genome—the minimum complement of genes necessary for a living cell. When such a genetic blueprint is available, scientists should be able to define precisely, at least in biochemical terms, all of the prerequisites for life. When this day arrives, can the laboratory creation of a living cell be that far off?

As the evolutionary biologist Stephen Jay Gould put it, we are living in the "age of bacteria." What an exciting time to be learning the science of microbiology! Stay tuned. Much more is in store!

10 MiniReview

In the middle to latter part of the twentieth century, basic and applied microbiology worked hand in hand to usher in the current era of molecular microbiology.

- List the subdisciplines of microbiology whose focus is the following: metabolism, enzymology, nucleic acid and protein synthesis, microorganisms and their natural environments, microbial classification, and microbial cell structure.

Table 1 (continued)

Year	Investigator(s)	Discovery
1944	Selman Waksman* and Albert Schatz	Streptomycin
1946	Edward Tatum and Joshua Lederberg*	Bacterial conjugation
1951	Barbara McClintock*	Transposable elements
1952	Joshua Lederberg and Norton Zinder	Bacterial transduction
1953	James Watson,* Francis Crick,* Rosalind Franklin, Maurice Wilkins*	Structure of DNA
1959	Arthur Pardee, François Jacob,* Jacques Monod,* Andre Lwoff*	Gene regulation by repressor proteins
1959	Rodney Porter*	Immunoglobulin structure
1959	F. Macfarlane Burnet	Clonal selection theory
1960	François Jacob, David Perrin, Carmon Sanchez, Jacques Monod	Concept of an operon
1960	Rosalyn Yalow* and Solomon Bernson	Radioimmunoassay (RIA)
1961	Sydney Brenner,* François Jacob,* Matthew Meselson	Messenger RNA and ribosomes as the site of protein synthesis
1966	Marshall Nirenberg* and H. Gobind Khorana*	Genetic code
1967	Thomas Brock	Bacteria inhabit boiling hot springs
1969	Howard Temin,* David Baltimore,* Renato Dulbecco*	Retroviruses/reverse transcriptase
1969	Thomas Brock and Hudson Freeze	*Thermus aquaticus*, source of *Taq* DNA polymerase
1970	Hamilton Smith* and David Nathans*	Restriction enzymes
1973	Stanley Cohen, Annie Chang, Robert Helling, Herbert Boyer, and Paul Berg*	Recombinant DNA technology
1975	Georges Kohler,* Cesar Milstein*	Monoclonal antibodies
1976	Susumu Tonegawa*	Rearrangement of immunoglobulin genes
1977	Carl Woese** and George Fox	*Archaea*
1977	Fred Sanger,* Steven Niklen, Alan Coulson	Methods for sequencing DNA
1981	Stanley Prusiner*	Prions
1982	Karl Stetter	First cultures of hyperthermophiles
1982	Barry Marshall* and Robin Warren*	Cause of peptic ulcers: *Helicobacter pylori*
1983	Luc Montagnier	Human immunodeficiency virus
1985	Kary Mullis*	Polymerase chain reaction (PCR)

[a]Major reference sources here include Brock, T. D. (1961), *Milestones in Microbiology,* Prentice Hall, Englewood Cliffs, NJ; Brock, T. D. (1990), *The Emergence of Bacterial Genetics,* Cold Spring Harbor Press, Cold Spring Harbor, NY. *Year* refers to the year in which the discovery was published.

*Nobel Laureates. The first Nobel Prizes were awarded in 1901 and Robert Koch received the Nobel Prize for Physiology or Medicine in 1905.

**Recipient of Crafoord Prize in Biosciences in 2003.

Review of Key Terms

Cell the fundamental unit of living matter

Chemolithotrophy a form of metabolism in which inorganic compounds are used to generate energy

Cytoplasm the fluid portion of a cell, bounded by the cell membrane

Cytoplasmic membrane a semipermeable barrier that separates the cell interior (cytoplasm) from environment

DNA deoxyribonucleic acid, the genetic material of cells and some viruses

Ecosystem organisms plus their nonliving environment

Enrichment culture technique a method for isolating specific microorganisms from nature using specific culture media and incubation conditions

Enzyme a protein (or in some cases an RNA) catalyst that functions to speed up chemical reactions

Genomics the identification and analysis of genomes

Genome an organism's full complement of genes

Habitat the environment in which a microbial population resides

Koch's postulates a set of criteria for proving that a given microorganism causes a given disease

Macromolecules the proteins, nucleic acids, lipids, and polysaccharides in a cell

Metabolism all biochemical reactions in a cell

Microbial ecology the study of microorganisms in their natural environments

Microorganism a microscopic organism consisting of a single cell or cell cluster, including the viruses

Pathogen a disease-causing microorganism

Pure culture a culture containing a single kind of microorganism

RNA ribonucleic acid, functions in protein synthesis as messenger RNA, transfer RNA, and ribosomal RNA

Ribosome structures composed of RNAs and proteins upon which new proteins are made

Spontaneous generation the hypothesis that living organisms can originate from nonliving matter

Sterile free of all living organisms and viruses

Review Questions

1. List six key properties associated with the living state. Which of these are characteristics of all cells? Which are characteristics of only some types of cells (Sections 1 and 2)?
2. Cells can be thought of as both machines and coding devices. Explain how these two attributes of a cell differ (Section 2).
3. What is needed for translation to occur in a cell? What is the product of the translational process (Section 2)?
4. What is an ecosystem? Do microorganisms live in pure cultures in an ecosystem? What effects can microorganisms have on their ecosystems (Section 3)?
5. Why did the evolution of cyanobacteria change Earth forever (Section 4)?
6. How would you convince a friend that microorganisms are much more than just agents of disease (Section 5)?
7. For what contributions are Hooke and van Leeuwenhoek remembered in microbiology? How did Ferdinand Cohn contribute to bacteriology (Section 6)?
8. Explain the principle behind the use of the Pasteur flask in studies on spontaneous generation (Section 7).
9. What is a pure culture and how can one be obtained? Why was knowledge of how to obtain a pure culture important for development of the science of microbiology (Section 8)?
10. What are Koch's postulates and how did they influence the development of microbiology? Why are they still relevant today (Section 8)?
11. Describe a major contribution to microbiology of the early microbiologist Martinus Beijerinck (Section 9).
12. What major concepts in microbiology do we owe to Sergei Winogradsky (Section 9)?
13. What major advances in microbiology have occurred in the past 60 years (Section 10)?

Application Questions

1. Pasteur's experiments on spontaneous generation were of enormous importance for the advance of microbiology, contributing to the methodology of microbiology, ideas on the origin of life, and techniques for the preservation of food, to name just a few. Explain briefly how Pasteur's experiments affected each of these topics.
2. Describe the lines of proof Robert Koch used to definitively associate the bacterium *Mycobacterium tuberculosis* with the disease tuberculosis. How would his proof have been flawed if any of the tools he developed for studying bacterial diseases had not been available for his study of tuberculosis?
3. Imagine that if by some action all microorganisms suddenly disappeared from Earth. From what you have learned in this chapter, why do you think that animals would eventually disappear from Earth? Why would plants disappear? If by contrast, all higher organisms suddenly disappeared, what aspect of Figure 6 tells you that a similar fate would not befall microorganisms?

A Brief Journey to the Microbial World

The scope of microbial diversity is enormous, and microorganisms are present in every habitat on Earth that will support life and have exploited every means of making a living consistent with the laws of chemistry and physics.

Gernot Arp, Christian Boeker, and Carl Zeis, Jena

I SEEING THE VERY SMALL

Historically, the science of microbiology blossomed as the ability to see microorganisms improved. In other words, *microbiology* and *microscopy* advanced hand-in-hand. This is especially true for the main subject of this chapter—microbial diversity. The microscope is the microbiologist's most important tool, and the student of microbiology needs to have some background on how microscopes work and how microscopy is done. We begin our brief journey to the microbial world by considering different types of microscopes and the applications of microscopy to imaging microorganisms.

1 Some Principles of Light Microscopy

Visualization of microorganisms requires a microscope, either a *light* microscope or an *electron* microscope. In general, light microscopes are used to look at intact cells at relatively low magnifications, and electron microscopes are used to look at internal cell structure and the details of cell surfaces at very high magnification.

All microscopes employ lenses that magnify the original image. Equal in importance to magnification, however, is **resolution**, the ability to distinguish two adjacent objects as distinct and separate. Although magnification can be increased virtually without limit, resolution cannot because it is determined by the physical properties of light. It is thus resolution and not magnification that ultimately dictates what we can see with a microscope.

We begin with the light microscope, for which the limits of resolution are about 0.2 μm (micrometer, 10^{-6} m). We then proceed to the electron microscope, for which resolution is improved over that of the light microscope by about 1,000-fold.

The Compound Light Microscope

The light microscope uses visible light to illuminate cell structures. Several types of light microscopes are commonly used in microbiology: *bright-field, phase-contrast, dark-field,* and *fluorescence*.

With the bright-field microscope specimens are visualized because of the slight differences in contrast (density) that exist between them and their surrounding medium. Contrast differences arise because cells absorb or scatter light to varying degrees. The bright-field microscope is commonly used in laboratory courses in biology and microbiology and consists of two series of lenses (objective lens and ocular lens) that function in unison to form the image. The light source is focused on the specimen by a third lens, the condenser (Figure 1). Bacterial cells are typically difficult to see well with the bright-field microscope because they lack contrast with the surrounding medium. Pigmented microorganisms are an exception

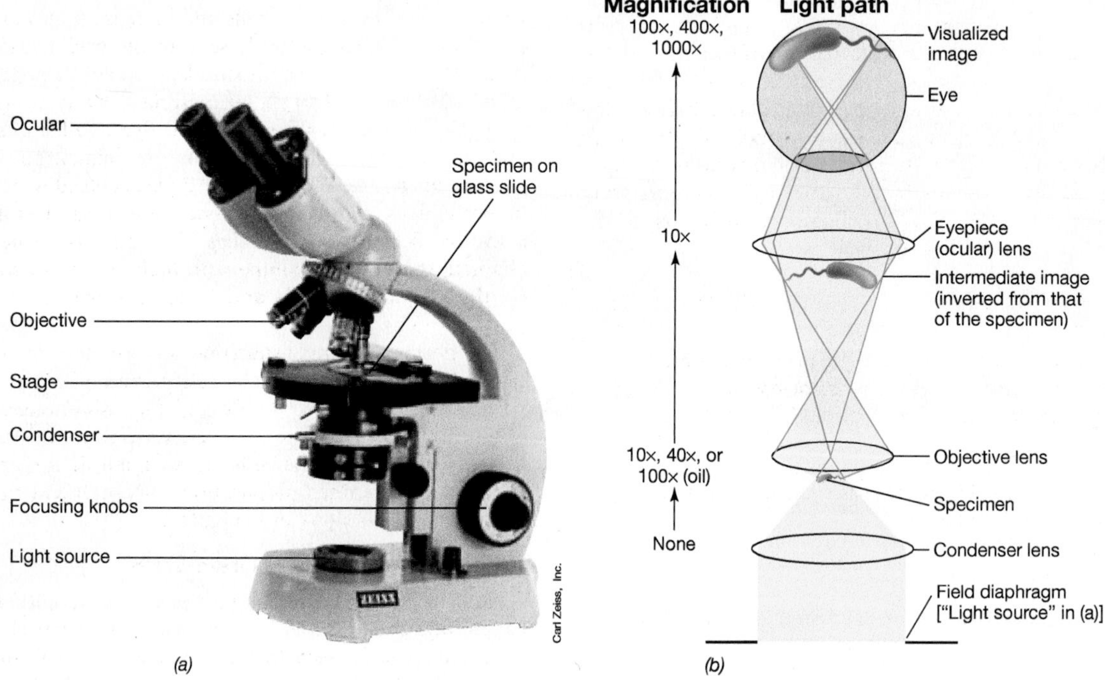

Figure 1 **Microscopy.** *(a)* A compound light microscope. *(b)* Path of light through a compound light microscope. Besides 10×, eyepieces (oculars) are available in 15–30×.

because the color of the organism itself adds contrast, thus improving visualization (Figure 2). For cells lacking pigments there are ways to boost contrast, and we consider these methods in the next section.

Magnification and Resolution

The total magnification of a compound microscope is the product of the magnification of its objective and ocular lenses (Figure 1*b*). Magnifications of about 1500× are the upper limit for a compound light microscope. Above this limit, resolution does not improve. Resolution is a function of the wavelength of light used and a characteristic of the objective lens known as its *numerical aperture* (a measure of light-gathering ability). There is a correlation between the magnification of a lens and its numerical aperture: Lenses with higher magnification typically have higher numerical apertures (the numerical aperture of a lens is stamped on the lens alongside the magnification). The diameter of the smallest object resolvable by any lens is equal to 0.5λ/numerical aperture, where λ is the wavelength of light used. Based on this formula, resolution is greatest when blue light is used to illuminate a specimen (blue light has a shorter wavelength than white or red light) and the objective used has a very high numerical aperture. Many light microscopes come fitted with a blue filter over the condenser lens to improve resolution.

As mentioned, the highest resolution possible in a compound light microscope is about 0.2 μm. What this means is that two objects that are closer together than 0.2 μm cannot be resolved as distinct and separate. Most microscopes used in microbiology have oculars that magnify 10–15× and objectives of 10–100× (Figure 1*b*). At 1000×, objects 0.2 μm in diameter can just be resolved. With a total of the 1000× objective, and with certain other objectives of very high numerical aperture, a special optical oil is placed between the specimen and the objective. Lenses on which oil is used are called *oil-immersion* lenses. Immersion oil increases the light-gathering ability of a lens by allowing rays emerging from the specimen at angles (that would otherwise be lost to the objective lens) to be collected and viewed.

1 MiniReview

Microscopes are essential for studying microorganisms. A bright-field microscope uses a series of lens to magnify and resolve the image.

- Define the term resolution.
- What is the upper limit of magnification for a bright-field microscope? Why is this so?

2 Improving and Adjusting Contrast in Light Microscopy

In microscopy, improving contrast improves the final image observed. Staining is an easy way to improve contrast but there are other ways to do so as well.

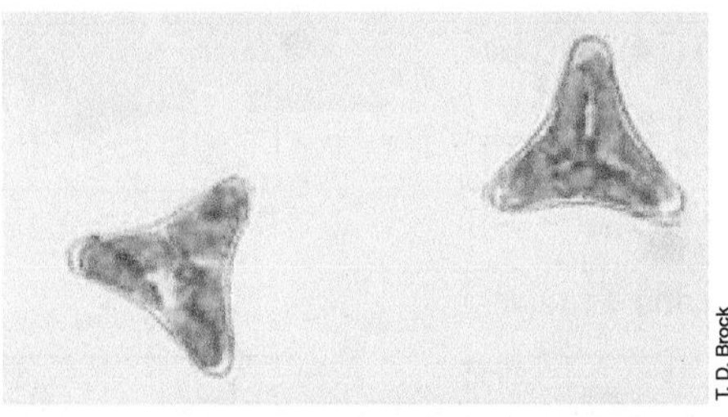

(a)

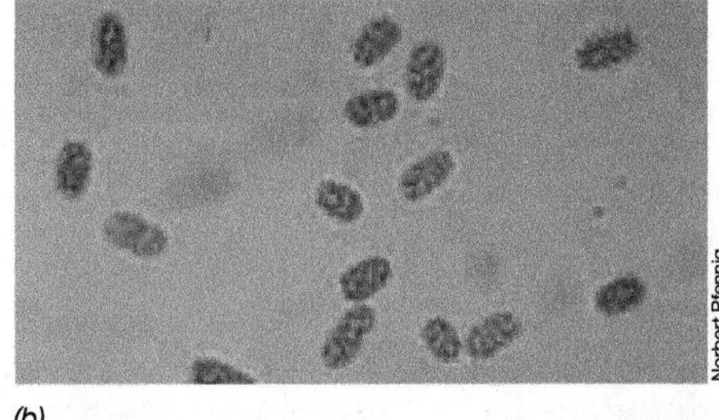

(b)

Figure 2 **Bright-field photomicrographs of pigmented microorganisms.** *(a)* A green alga (eukaryote). The green structures are chloroplasts. *(b)* Purple phototrophic bacteria (prokaryote). The alga cell is about 15 μm wide, and the bacterial cells are about 5 μm wide.

Staining: Increasing Contrast for Bright-Field Microscopy

Dyes can be used to stain cells and increase their contrast so that they can be more easily seen in the bright-field microscope. Dyes are organic compounds, and each class of dye has an affinity for specific cellular materials. Many dyes used in microbiology are positively charged dyes, called *basic dyes,* and bind strongly to negatively charged cellular constituents such as nucleic acids and acidic polysaccharides. Examples of basic dyes include methylene blue, crystal violet, and safranin. Because cell surfaces also tend to be negatively charged, these dyes combine with high affinity to structures on the surfaces of cells and hence are excellent general purpose stains.

To perform a simple stain one begins with dried preparations of cells (Figure 3). A glass slide containing a dried suspension of heat-fixed cells is flooded for a minute or two with a dilute solution of a dye, rinsed several times in water, and blotted dry. Because the cells are so small, it is common to observe dried, stained preparations of bacteria with a high-power (oil-immersion) lens (Figure 3).

Differential Stains: The Gram Stain

Stains that render different kinds of cells different colors are called *differential* stains. An important differential-staining procedure widely used in microbiology is the **Gram stain** (Figure 4a). On the basis of their reaction to the Gram stain, bacteria can be divided into two major groups: *gram positive* and *gram negative*. After Gram staining, **gram-positive bacteria**

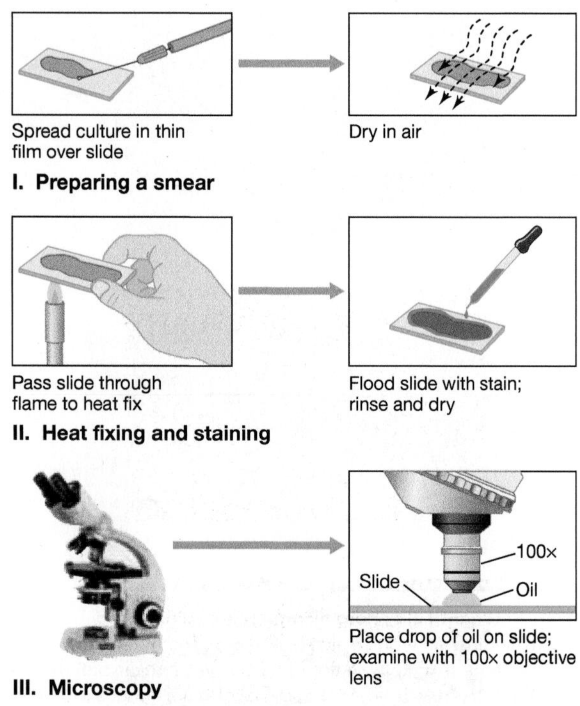
Spread culture in thin film over slide
Dry in air
I. Preparing a smear
Pass slide through flame to heat fix
Flood slide with stain; rinse and dry
II. Heat fixing and staining
100x
Slide
Oil
Place drop of oil on slide; examine with 100x objective lens
III. Microscopy

Figure 3 Staining cells for microscopic observation. Stains improve the contrast between cells and their background.

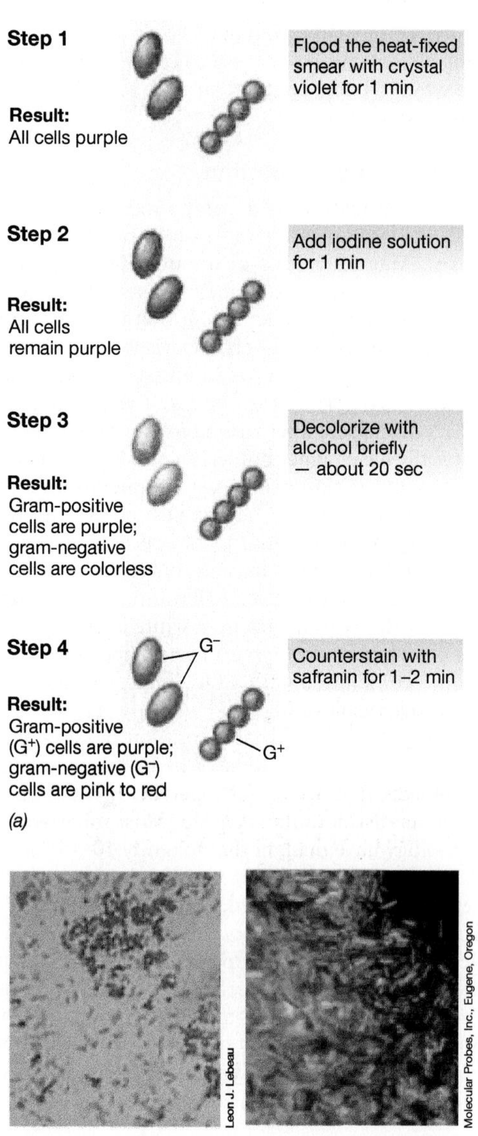
Step 1
Result:
All cells purple
Flood the heat-fixed smear with crystal violet for 1 min
Step 2
Result:
All cells remain purple
Add iodine solution for 1 min
Step 3
Result:
Gram-positive cells are purple; gram-negative cells are colorless
Decolorize with alcohol briefly — about 20 sec
Step 4
Result:
Gram-positive (G^+) cells are purple; gram-negative (G^-) cells are pink to red
G^-
G^+
Counterstain with safranin for 1–2 min
(a)
Leon J. Lebeau
Molecular Probes, Inc., Eugene, Oregon
(b)
(c)

Figure 4 The Gram stain. *(a)* Steps in the Gram-stain procedure. *(b)* Gram-stained *Bacteria* that are gram-positive (purple) and gram-negative (pink). The species are *Staphylococcus aureus* and *Escherichia coli*, respectively. *(c)* Cells of *Pseudomonas aeruginosa* (gram-negative, green) and *Bacillus cereus* (gram-positive, orange) stained with a one-step fluorescent staining method. This method allows for differentiating gram-positive from gram-negative cells in a single staining step.

appear purple and **gram-negative bacteria** appear pink (Figure 4*b*). This difference in reaction to the Gram stain arises because of differences in the cell wall structure of gram-positive and gram-negative cells. After staining with a basic dye, typically crystal violet, treatment with ethanol decolorizes gram-negative but not gram-positive cells. Following counterstaining with a different-colored stain, the two cell types can be distinguished microscopically (Figure 4).

The Gram stain is one of the most useful staining procedures in microbiology. Typically, one begins the characterization of a new bacterium by determining whether it is gram positive or gram negative. If a fluorescent microscope, discussed below, is available, the Gram stain can be reduced to a one-step procedure in which gram-positive and gram-negative cells fluoresce different colors (Figure 4*c*).

Phase-Contrast and Dark-Field Microscopy

Staining, although a widely used procedure in light microscopy, kills cells and can distort their features. Two forms of light microscopy improve contrast without the use of stain. These are phase-contrast microscopy and dark-field microscopy (Figure 5). The phase-contrast microscope is widely used in research because it allows the observation of wet-mount (living) preparations.

Phase-contrast microscopy was invented in 1936 by Frits Zernike, a Dutch mathematical physicist. It is based on the principle that cells differ in refractive index (a factor by which light is slowed as it passes through a material) from their surroundings. Light passing through a cell thus differs in phase from light passing through its surroundings. This subtle difference is amplified by a device in the objective lens of the phase-contrast microscope called the *phase ring*, resulting in a dark image on a light background (Figure 5*b*). The ring

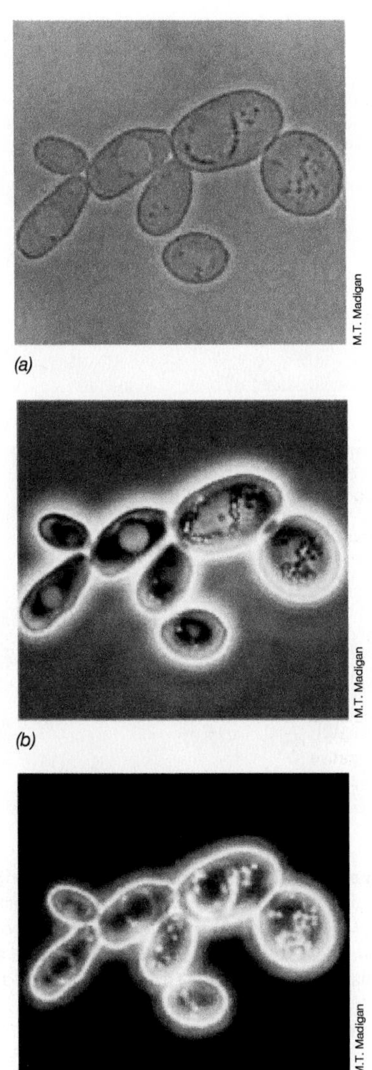

Figure 5 **Cells of the baker's yeast *Saccharomyces cerevisiae* visualized by different types of light microscopy.** *(a)* Bright-field microscopy. *(b)* Phase-contrast microscopy. *(c)* Dark-field microscopy. Cells average 8–10 μm wide.

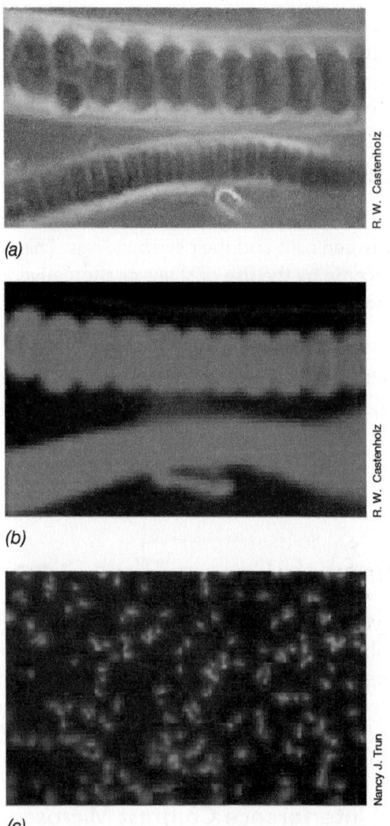

Figure 6 **Fluorescence microscopy.** *(a, b)* Cyanobacteria. *(a)* Cells observed by bright-field microscopy. *(b)* The same cells observed by fluorescence microscopy (cells exposed to light of 546 nm). The cells fluoresce red because they contain chlorophyll *a* and other pigments. *(c)* Fluorescence photomicrograph of cells of *Escherichia coli* made fluorescent by staining with the fluorescent dye, DAPI.

consists of a phase plate—the key discovery of Zernike—that amplifies the minute variation in phase. Zernike's discovery of differences in contrast between cells and their background stimulated other innovations in microscopy, such as fluorescence and confocal microscopy (discussed below). For his invention of phase-contrast microscopy, Zernike was awarded the 1953 Nobel Prize in Physics.

The dark-field microscope is a light microscope in which the light reaches the specimen from the sides only. The only light reaching the lens is scattered by the specimen, and thus the specimen appears light on a dark background (Figure 5*c*). Resolution by dark-field microscopy is somewhat better than by light microscopy, and thus objects can often be resolved by dark-field that cannot be resolved by bright-field or even phase-contrast microscopes. Dark-field microscopy is also an excellent way to observe the motility of microorganisms, as bundles of flagella are often resolvable with this technique.

Fluorescence Microscopy

The fluorescence microscope is used to visualize specimens that fluoresce, that is, emit light of one color when light of another color shines upon them (Figure 6). Cells fluoresce either because they contain naturally fluorescent substances such as chlorophyll or other fluorescing components (autofluorescence) (see Figure 6*a, b*) or because the cells have been stained with a fluorescent dye (Figures 6*c*). DAPI (diamidino-2-phenylindole) is a widely used fluorescent dye, staining cells bright blue (Figure 6*c*). DAPI can be used to identify cells in a complex milieu, such as soil, water, food, or a clinical specimen. Fluorescence microscopy is widely used in clinical diagnostic microbiology and also in microbial ecology for enumerating bacteria in a natural environment or cell suspension (Figure 6*c*).

2 MiniReview

An inherent limitation of bright-field microscopy is its lack of contrast between cells and their surroundings. This problem can be overcome by the use of stains or alternative forms of light microscopy, such as phase contrast or dark field.

- What color will a gram-negative bacterium be after Gram staining by the conventional method?
- What major advantage does phase-contrast microscopy have over staining?
- How can cells be made fluorescent?

3 Imaging Cells in Three Dimensions

Up to now we have discussed forms of microscopy in which the images obtained are two-dimensional. How can this limitation be overcome? We will see in the next section that the scanning electron microscope offers one solution to this problem, but so can certain forms of light microscopy that we consider now.

Differential Interference Contrast Microscopy

Differential interference contrast (DIC) microscopy is light microscopy that employs a polarizer to produce polarized light. The polarized light then passes through a prism that generates two distinct beams. These beams traverse the specimen and enter the objective lens where they are recombined into one. Because the two beams pass through different substances with slightly different refractive indices, the combined beams are not totally in phase but instead create an interference effect. This effect intensifies subtle differences in cell structure. Thus, by DIC microscopy, structures such as the nucleus of eukaryotic cells (Figure 7*a*), and endospores, vacuoles, and granules of prokaryotic cells, take on a three-dimensional appearance. DIC microscopy is particularly useful for observing unstained cells because it can reveal internal cell structures that are less apparent (or even invisible) by bright-field techniques (compare Figure 5*a* with Figure 7*a*).

Atomic Force Microscopy

Another type of microscope useful for three-dimensional imaging of biological structures is the atomic force microscope (AFM). In atomic force microscopy, a tiny stylus is positioned extremely close to the specimen such that weak repulsive forces are established between the probe and atoms in the specimen. During scanning, the stylus rides up and down the "hills and valleys" of the specimen, continually recording its deviations from a flat surface. The pattern that is generated is processed by a series of detectors that feed the digital information into a computer, which outputs an image (Figure 7*b*).

Although the images obtained from an AFM appear similar to those from the scanning electron microscope (compare Figure 7*b* with Figure 10*b*), the AFM has the advantage that the specimen needn't be treated with fixatives or coatings. The AFM thus allows living specimens to be viewed, something that is generally not possible with electron microscopes.

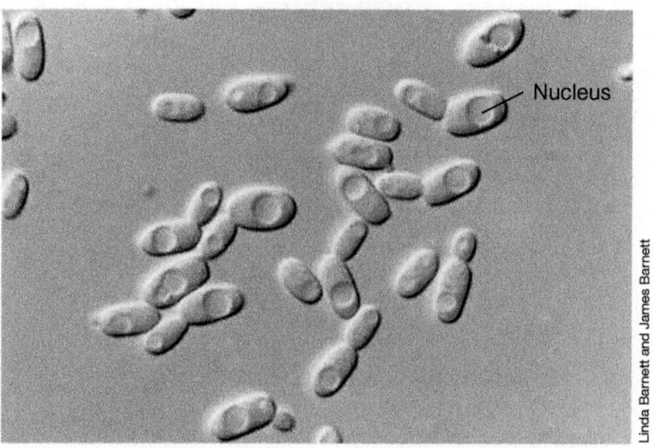

(a)

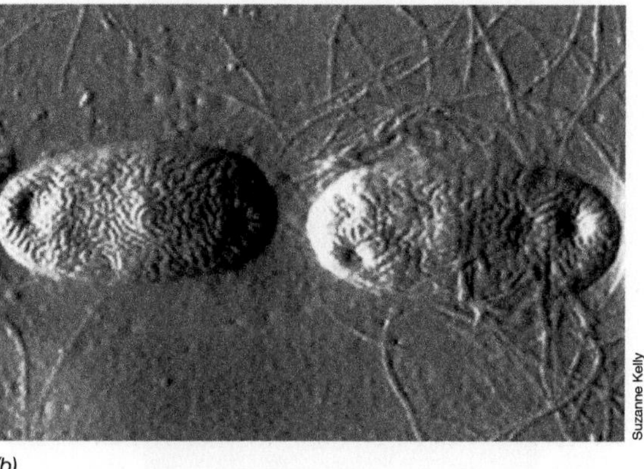

(b)

Figure 7 Three-dimensional imaging of cells. *(a)* Interference contrast microscopy and *(b)* atomic force microscopy. The yeast cells in *(a)* are about 8 μm wide. Note the clearly visible nucleus and compare Figure 5a. The bacterial cells in *(b)* are about 2.2 μm long and are from a natural biofilm that developed on the surface of a glass slide immersed for 24 h in a dog's water bowl. The slide was air dried before viewing with an atomic force microscope.

Confocal Scanning Laser Microscopy

A confocal scanning laser microscope (CSLM) is a computerized microscope that couples a laser source to a light microscope. This generates a three-dimensional digital image of microorganisms and other biological specimens in the sample (Figure 8). The laser beam is precisely adjusted such that only a particular layer within a specimen is visible. By precisely illuminating only a single plane of focus, stray light from other focal planes is eliminated. Thus, when observing a

(a)

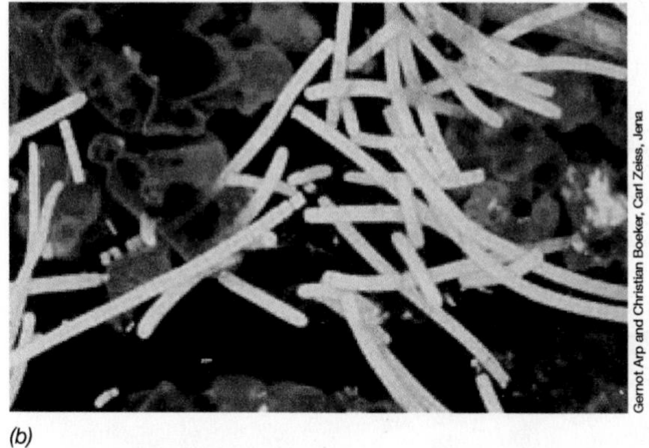

(b)

Figure 8 Confocal scanning laser microscopy. *(a)* Confocal image of a mixed microbial biofilm community cultivated in the laboratory. The green, rod-shaped cells are *Pseudomonas aeruginosa* experimentally introduced into the biofilm. Other cells of different colors are present at different depths in the biofilm. *(b)* Confocal image of a filamentous cyanobacterium growing in a soda lake. Cells are about 5 μm wide.

relatively thick specimen such as a microbial biofilm (Figure 8*a*), not only are cells on the surface of the biofilm apparent, as would be the case with conventional light microscopy, but cells in the various layers can also be observed by adjusting the laser beam. By illuminating a specimen with a laser whose intensity varies as a sine wave, it has been possible to improve on the 0.2-μm resolution of the compound light microscope to a limit of about 0.1 μm.

Cells in CSLM preparations are frequently stained with fluorescent dyes to make them more distinct (Figure 8). Alternatively, false-color images of unstained preparations can be generated such that different layers in the specimen take on different colors. The CLSM comes equipped with computer software that assembles digital images for subsequent image processing. Thus, images obtained from different layers can be stored and then digitally overlaid to reconstruct a three-dimensional image of the entire specimen (Figure 8*a*).

CSLM has found widespread use in microbial ecology, especially for identifying phylogenetically distinct populations of cells present in a microbial habitat or for resolving the different components of a structured microbial habitat, such as a biofilm (Figure 8*a*). CSLM is particularly useful anywhere thick specimens need to be examined for their microbial content throughout their depth.

3 MiniReview

Differential interference contrast (DIC) and confocal scanning (CSLM) are forms of light microscopy that allow for greater three-dimensional imaging than other forms of light microscopy, and CSLM allows imaging through thick specimens. The atomic force microscope (AFM) can yield a detailed three-dimensional image of live preparations.

- What structure in eukaryotic cells is more easily seen in DIC than in bright-field microscopy? (*Hint:* Compare Figures 5*a* and 7*a*).
- How is CSLM able to view different layers in a thick preparation?

4 Electron Microscopy

Electron microscopes use electrons instead of photons to image cells or cell structures. In the *transmission electron microscope* (TEM), electromagnets function as lenses, and the whole system operates in a vacuum (Figure 9). Electron microscopes are fitted with cameras to allow a photograph, called an *electron micrograph*, to be taken.

The TEM is typically used to examine cell structure at very high magnification and resolution. The resolving power of the electron microscope is much greater than that of the

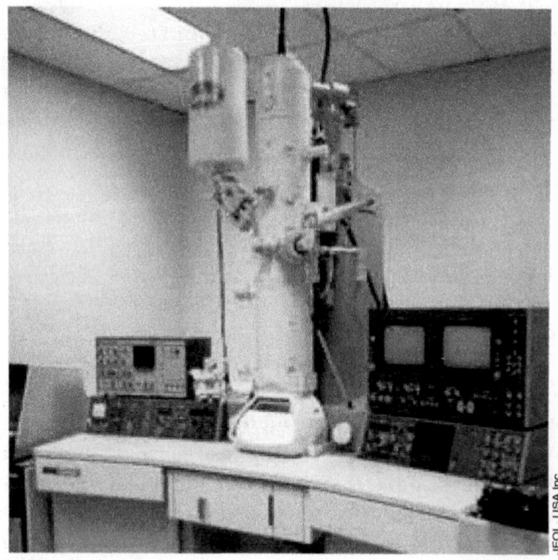

Figure 9 The electron microscope. This instrument encompasses both transmission and scanning electron microscope functions.

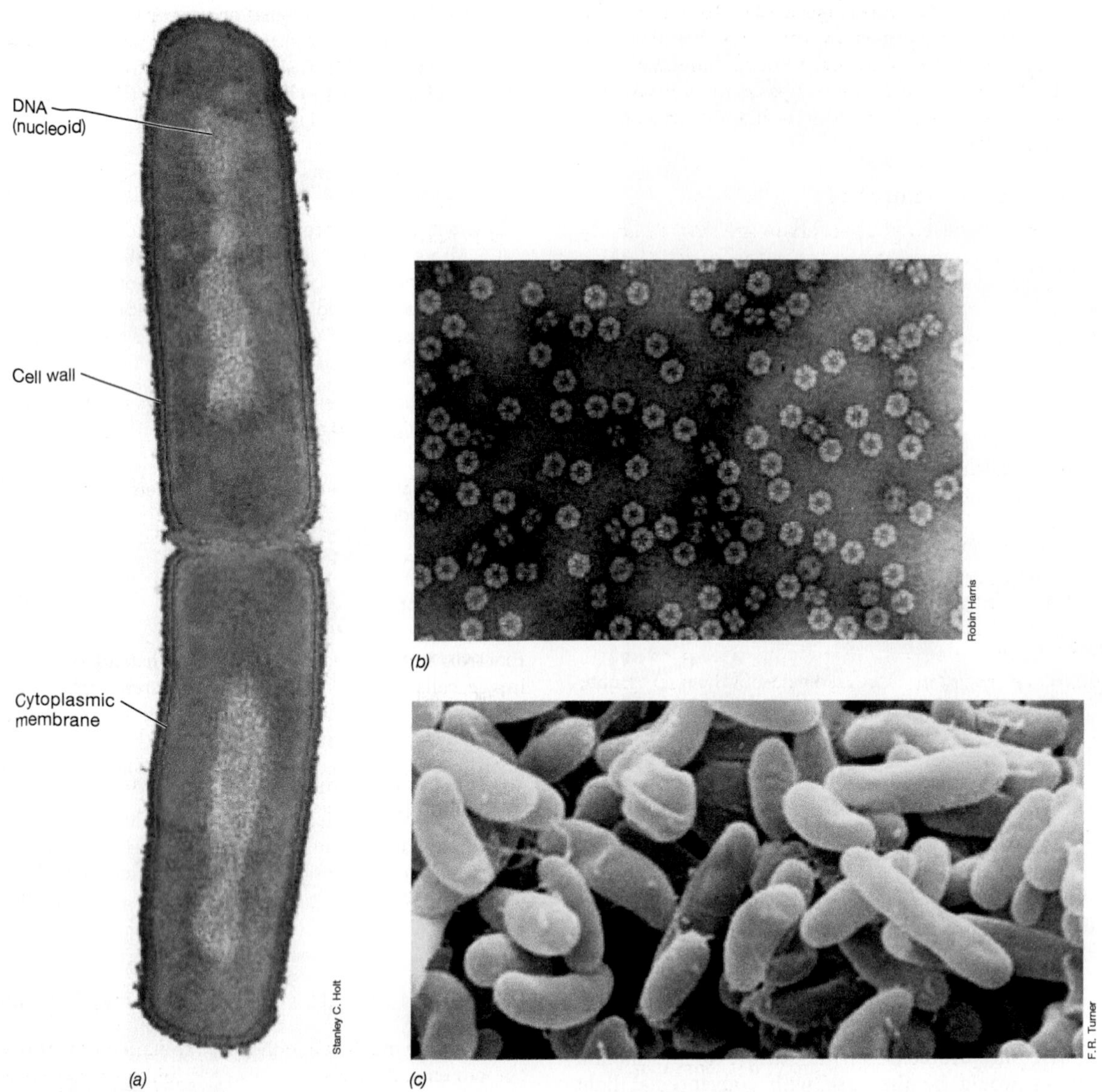

Figure 10 Electron micrographs. *(a)* Micrograph of a thin section of a dividing cell of the gram-positive bacterium, *Bacillus subtilis*, taken by transmission electron microscopy (TEM). Note the DNA forming the nucleoid. The cell is about 0.8 μm wide. *(b)* TEM of negatively stained molecules of hemoglobin from the marine worm *Nereis virens*. Each hexagonal-shaped molecule is about 25 nanometers (nm) in diameter and consists of two donut-shaped rings, a total of 15 nm wide. *(c)* Cells of the phototrophic bacterium *Rhodovibrio sodomensis*. A single cell is about 0.75 μm wide.

light microscope, enabling one to view structures at the molecular level. This is because the wavelength of electrons is much shorter than the wavelength of visible light, and wavelength affects resolution (Section 2). For example, whereas the resolving power of a high-quality light microscope is about 0.2 *micrometers*, the resolving power of a high quality TEM is about 0.2 *nanometers* (nm, 10^{-9}). Thus, even individual molecules, such as proteins and nucleic acids, can be visualized in the transmission electron microscope (Figure 10*b*, and see Figure 14*b*).

Unlike visible light, however, electron beams do not penetrate very well; even a single cell is too thick to reveal its internal contents directly by TEM. Consequently, special techniques of thin sectioning are needed to prepare specimens before observing them. A single bacterial cell, for instance, is cut into many, very thin (20–60 nm) slices, which are then examined individually by TEM (Figure 10*a*). To obtain sufficient contrast, the preparations are treated with stains such as osmic acid, or permanganate, uranium, lanthanum, or lead salts. Because these substances are composed of atoms of high atomic weight, they scatter electrons well and thus improve contrast (Figure 10*b*).

Scanning Electron Microscopy

If only the external features of an organism need to be observed, thin sections are unnecessary. Intact cells or cell components can be observed directly by TEM with a technique called *negative staining* (Figure 10*b*). Alternatively, one can use the *scanning electron microscope* (SEM) (Figure 9).

In scanning electron microscopy, the specimen is coated with a thin film of a heavy metal such as gold. An electron beam from the SEM then scans back and forth across the specimen. Electrons scattered from the metal are collected, and they activate a viewing screen to produce an image (Figure 10*b*). In the SEM, even fairly large specimens can be observed, and the depth of field is extremely good. A wide range of magnifications can be obtained with the SEM, from as low as 15× up to about 100,000×, but only the surface of an object can be visualized.

Electron micrographs taken by either TEM or SEM are black and white images. Often false color is added to these images by manipulating the micrographs with a computer. But false color does not improve resolution of the micrograph; resolution is set by the magnification used to take the original micrograph.

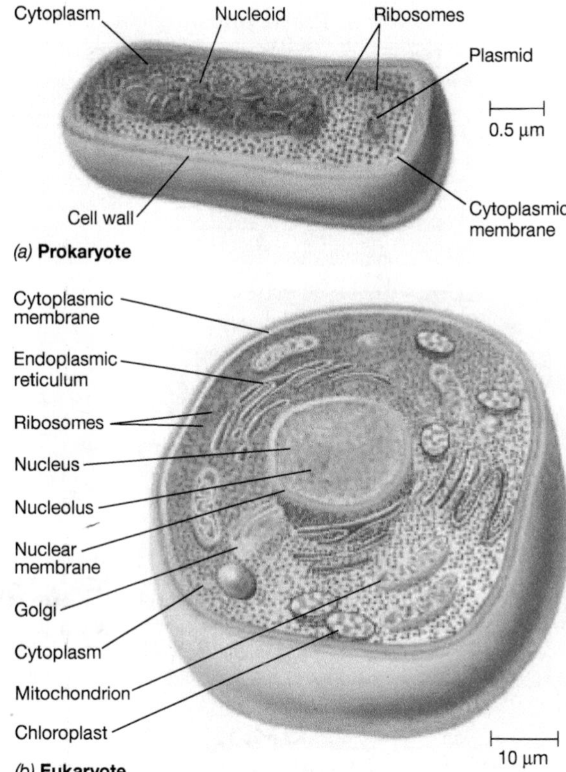

Figure 11 Internal structure of microbial cells. Note differences in scale and internal structure between the prokaryotic and eukaryotic cells.

4 MiniReview

Electron microscopes have far greater resolving power than do light microscopes, the limits of resolution being about 0.2 nm. Two major types of electron microscopy are performed: transmission electron microscopy, for observing internal cell structure down to the molecular level, and scanning electron microscopy, useful for three-dimensional imaging and for examining surfaces.

- What is an electron micrograph? How does an electron micrograph differ from a photomicrograph in terms of how the image is obtained? Why do electron micrographs have so much greater resolution than light micrographs?
- What type of electron microscope would be used to view a cluster of cells? What type would be used to observe the bacterial nucleoid?

II CELL STRUCTURE AND EVOLUTIONARY HISTORY

The next part of this chapter introduces concepts of microbial cell structure and diversity that underlie topics throughout the book. We first compare the internal architecture of microbial cells and differentiate cells from viruses. We then explore the evolutionary tree of life to set the stage for the introduction of the major groups of microorganisms that affect our lives and our planet.

5 Elements of Cell and Viral Structure

All cells have much in common and contain many of the same components. All cells have a permeability barrier called the **cytoplasmic membrane** that separates the inside of the cell, the **cytoplasm**, from the outside (Figure 11). Major components dissolved in the cytoplasm include macromolecules, small organic molecules (mainly precursors of macromolecules), various inorganic ions, and **ribosomes**—the cell's protein-synthesizing structures. Ribosomes interact with cytoplasmic proteins and messenger and transfer RNAs in the key process of protein synthesis (translation).

The **cell wall** gives structural strength to a cell. The cell wall is relatively permeable and located outside the membrane (Figure 11*a*); it is a much stronger layer than the membrane itself. Plant cells and most microorganisms have cell walls, whereas animal cells, with rare exceptions, do not. In place of a cell wall, animal cells are reinforced by molecular scaffolding within the cytoplasm, called the *cytoskeleton*.

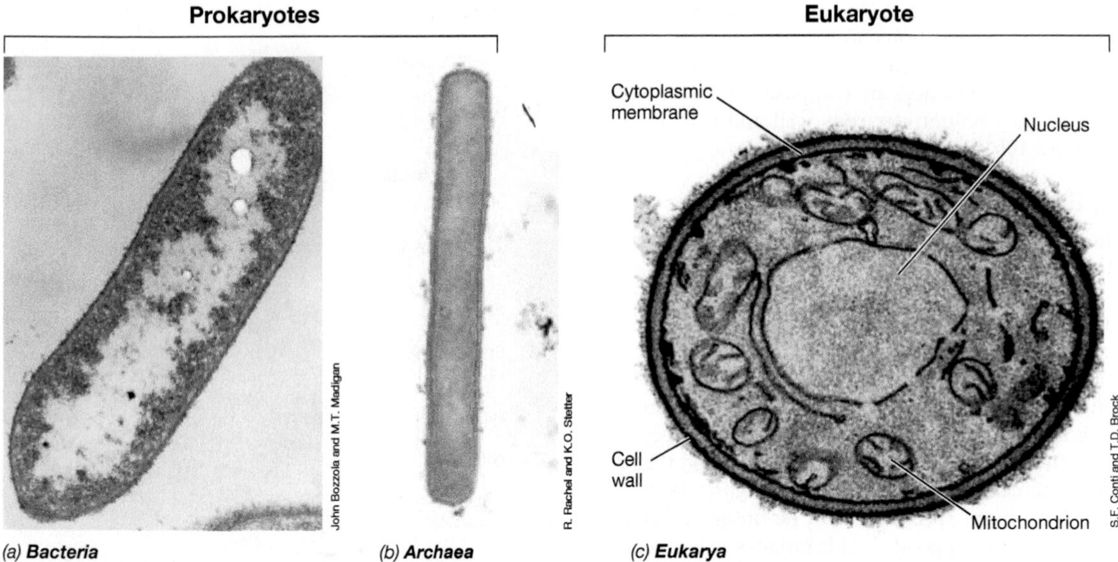

Figure 12 Electron micrographs of sectioned cells from each of the domains of living organisms. *(a) Heliobacterium modesticaldum*; the cell measures 1 × 3 μm. *(b) Methanopyrus kandleri*; the cell measures 0.5 × 4 μm. Reinhard Rachel and Karl O. Stetter, 1981. *Archives of Microbiology* 128:288–293. © Springer-Verlag GmbH & Co. KG. *(c) Saccharomyces cerevisiae*; the cell measures 8 μm in diameter.

Prokaryotic and Eukaryotic Cells

Examination of the internal structure and other features of cells reveal two patterns: **prokaryote** and **eukaryote** (Figure 11 and Figure 12). Eukaryotes have their DNA in a membrane-enclosed **nucleus** and are typically larger and structurally more complex than prokaryotic cells. In eukaryotic cells the key processes of transcription and translation are partitioned; transcription occurs in the nucleus and translation in the cytoplasm. Eukaryotic microorganisms include algae, fungi, and protozoa. All multicellular plants and animals are also constructed of eukaryotic cells.

A major feature of eukaryotic cells is the presence of membrane-enclosed structures called **organelles**. These include, first and foremost, the nucleus, but also mitochondria and chloroplasts (the latter in photosynthetic cells only) (Figures 2*a* and 12*c*). As mentioned, the nucleus houses the genome and is also the site of transcription in eukaryotic cells. Mitochondria and chloroplasts contain their own very small genomes and play specific roles in energy generation by carrying out respiration and photosynthesis, respectively.

In contrast to eukaryotic cells, prokaryotic cells have a simpler internal structure that lacks membrane-enclosed organelles (Figures 11*a* and 12*a*, *b*). Prokaryotes differ from eukaryotes in many other ways as well. For example, prokaryotes couple transcription to translation directly within the cytoplasm because their DNA is not enclosed within a nucleus as it is in eukaryotes (Section 6). Moreover, in contrast to eukaryotes, most prokaryotes use their cytoplasmic membrane to drive energy-conserving reactions and have small, compact genomes consisting of circular DNA (Section 6).

Despite many clearcut differences between prokaryotes and eukaryotes, it is important that we not equate cellular organization with evolutionary relatedness. We will see in Section 7 that the prokaryotic world consists of two large and evolutionarily distinct groups.

Cell Size

In general, microbial cells are very small, particularly prokaryotes. For example, a typical rod-shaped prokaryote is 1–5 μm long and about 1 μm wide and thus is invisible to the naked eye. To conceive of how small a prokaryote is, consider that 500 prokaryotic cells each 1 μm long could be placed end-to-end across the period at the end of this sentence. Eukaryotic cells are typically much larger than prokaryotic cells, but the range of sizes in eukaryotic cells is quite large. Eukaryotic cells are known to have diameters as small as 0.8 μm or as large as several hundred micrometers.

Viruses

Viruses are a major class of microorganisms, but they are not cells (Figure 13). Viruses lack many of the attributes of cells, the most important of which is that they are not dynamic open systems. Instead, a virus particle is static, quite stable, and unable to change or replace its parts. Only when it infects a cell does a virus acquire the key attribute of a living system—replication. Unlike cells, viruses have no metabolic abilities of their own. Although they contain their

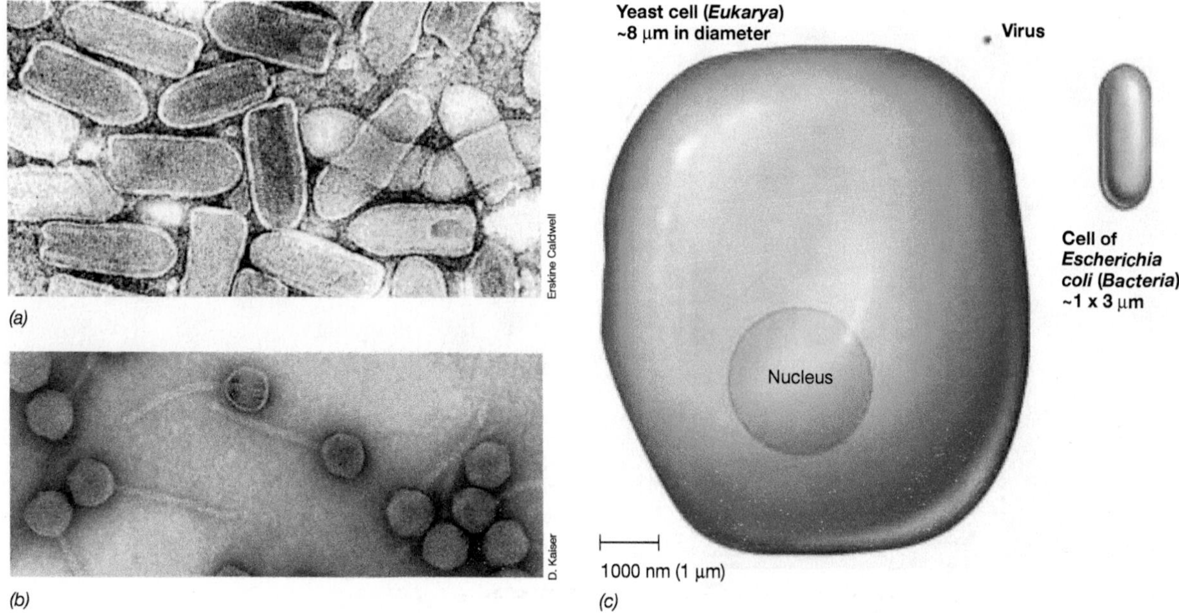

Figure 13 Virus structure and size comparisons of viruses and cells. *(a)* Particles of rhabdovirus (a virus that infects plants and animals). A single virus particle is about 65 nm (0.065 μm) wide. *(b)* Bacterial virus (bacteriophage) lambda. The head of each particle is about 65 nm wide. *(c)* The size of the viruses shown in *(a)* and *(b)* in comparison to a bacterial and eukaryotic cell.

own genomes, viruses lack ribosomes; to synthesize proteins they depend totally on the biosynthetic machinery of the cells they have infected. Moreover, unlike cells, viruses contain only a single form of nucleic acid, either DNA or RNA; thus, some viruses have RNA genomes.

Viruses are known to infect all types of cells, including microbial cells. Many viruses cause disease in the organisms they infect. However, viral infection can have many profound effects on cells other than disease, including genetic alterations that can actually improve the capabilities of the cell. Viruses are also much smaller than cells, even much smaller than prokaryotic cells (Figure 13). Viruses vary in size, with the smallest known viruses being only about 10 nm in diameter.

5 MiniReview

All microbial cells share certain basic structures such as the cytoplasmic membrane and ribosomes; most have a cell wall. Two cell structural patterns are recognized: the prokaryote and the eukaryote. Viruses are not cells but depend on cells for their replication.

- By looking inside a cell how could you tell if it was a prokaryote or a eukaryote?
- What important function do ribosomes play in cells?
- Why are viruses not cells?

6 Arrangement of DNA in Microbial Cells

The life processes of all cells are governed by their complement of genes, their **genome**. A gene can be defined as a segment of DNA that encodes a protein or an RNA molecule. Rapid advances have been made in sequencing and analyzing the genomes of organisms, from viruses through bacteria to humans. These advances have yielded detailed genetic blueprints of hundreds of different organisms and have allowed for extensive and rather revealing comparisons to be made. Here we consider only how genomes are organized in prokaryotic and eukaryotic cells and consider the number of genes and proteins present in a typical bacterial cell.

Nucleus versus Nucleoid

The genomes of prokaryotic and eukaryotic cells are organized differently. In prokaryotic cells, DNA is present in a large double-stranded molecule called the *chromosome*. The chromosome aggregates within the cell to form a mass visible in the electron microscope, called the **nucleoid** (Figure 14). The nucleoid is covalently closed and circular in most prokaryotes.

Most prokaryotes have only a single chromosome. Because of this, they typically contain only a single copy of each gene and are therefore genetically *haploid*. Many prokaryotes

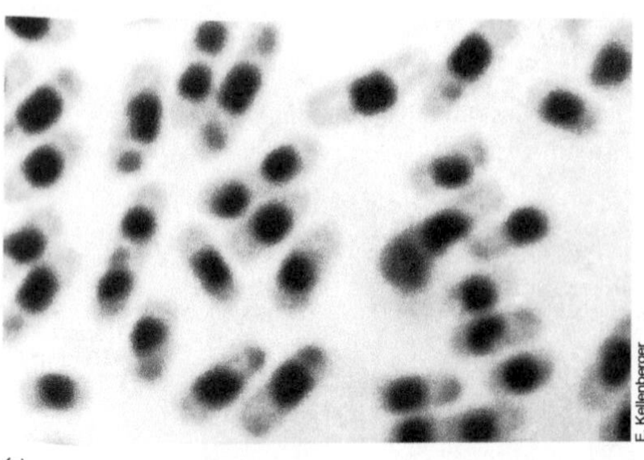

(a)

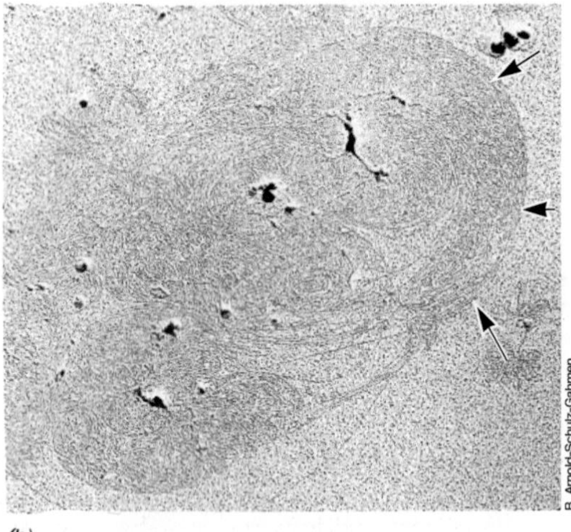

(b)

Figure 14 The nucleoid. *(a)* Photomicrograph of cells of *Escherichia coli* treated in such a way as to make the nucleoid visible. A single cell is about 3 μm in length. *(b)* Transmission electron micrograph of an isolated nucleoid released from a cell of *E. coli*. The cell was gently lysed to allow the highly compacted nucleoid to emerge intact. Arrows point to the edge of DNA strands.

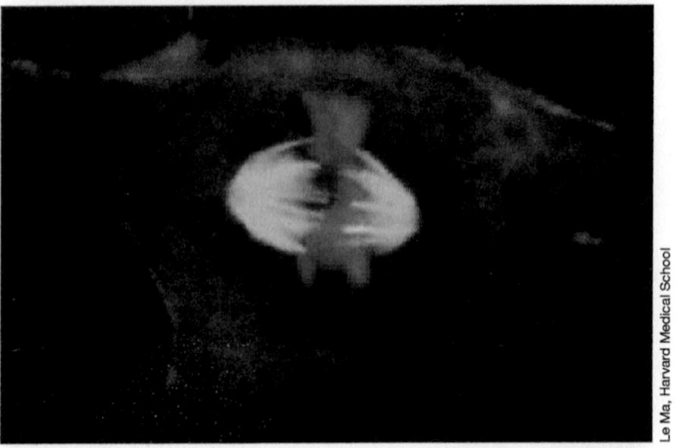

Figure 15 Mitosis in stained kangaroo rat cells. The cell was photographed while in the metaphase stage of mitotic division; only eukaryotic cells undergo mitosis. The green color stains a protein called tubulin, important in pulling chromosomes apart. The blue color is from a DNA-binding dye and shows the chromosomes.

also contain small amounts of circular extrachromosomal DNA called **plasmids**. Plasmids typically contain genes that confer special properties (such as unique metabolisms) on a cell. This is in contrast to essential ("housekeeping") genes, which are needed for basic survival and are located on the chromosome.

In **eukaryotes**, DNA is present in linear molecules within the membrane-enclosed nucleus; the DNA molecules are packaged with proteins and organized to form **chromosomes**. Chromosome number varies considerably. For example, the baker's yeast *Saccharomyces cerevisiae* contains 16 chromosomes arranged in 8 pairs, and human cells contain 46 chromosomes (23 pairs). Chromosomes in eukaryotes contain proteins that assist in folding and packing the DNA and other proteins that are required for gene expression. A key genetic difference between prokaryotes and eukaryotes is that eukaryotes typically contain two copies of each gene and are thus genetically *diploid*. During cell division in eukaryotic cells the nucleus divides (following a doubling of chromosome number) in the process called *mitosis* (Figure 15). Two identical daughter cells result, and each daughter cell receives a full complement of genes.

The diploid genome of eukaryotic cells is halved in the process of *meiosis* to form haploid gametes for sexual reproduction. Fusion of two gametes during zygote formation restores the cell to the diploid state.

Genes, Genomes, and Proteins

How many genes and proteins does a cell have? The genome of *Escherichia coli,* a typical prokaryote, is a single circular chromosome of 4.68 million base pairs of DNA. Because the *E. coli* genome has been completely sequenced, we also know that it contains about 4,300 genes. The genomes of some prokaryotes have nearly three times this many genes, and the genomes of others contain fewer than one-eighth as many. Eukaryotic cells typically have much larger genomes than prokaryotes. A human cell, for example, contains over 1,000 times as much DNA as a cell of *E. coli* and about seven times as many genes.

A single cell of *E. coli* contains about 1,900 different kinds of proteins and a total of about 2.4 million protein molecules. However, some proteins in *E. coli* are very abundant, others are only moderately abundant, and some are present in only one or a very few copies per cell. Thus, *E. coli* has mechanisms for regulating its genes so that not all genes are *expressed* (transcribed and translated, at the same time or to the same extent. Gene regulation is an important mechanism in all cells.

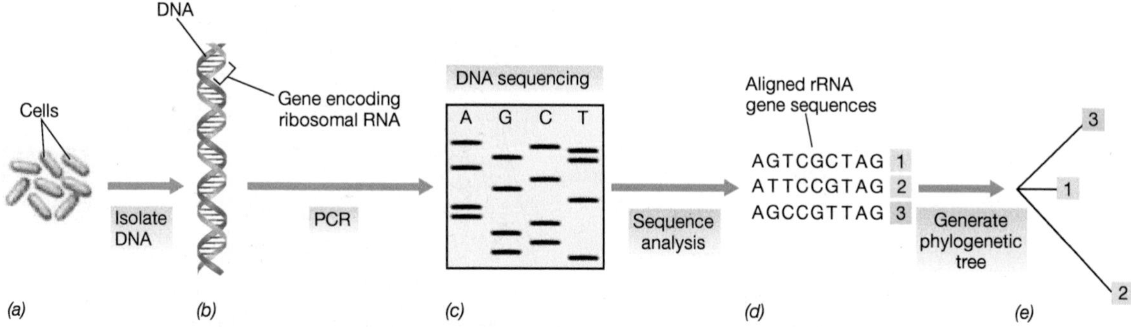

Figure 16 Ribosomal RNA (rRNA) gene sequencing and phylogeny. *(a)* Cells are broken open. *(b)* The gene-encoding rRNA is isolated, and many identical copies are made by the technique called the polymerase chain reaction. *(c, d)* The gene is sequenced, and the sequence obtained is aligned with other rRNA sequences. A computer algorithm makes pairwise comparisons and generates a phylogenetic tree *(e)* that depicts the differences in rRNA sequence between the organisms analyzed. In the example shown, the sequence differences are as follows: organism 1 versus organism 2, three differences; 1 versus 3, two differences; 2 versus 3, four differences. Thus organisms 1 and 3 are closer relatives than are 2 and 3 or 1 and 2.

6 MiniReview

Genes govern the properties of cells, and a cell's complement of genes is called its genome. DNA is arranged in cells to form chromosomes. Most prokaryotic species have a single circular chromosome; eukaryotic species have multiple linear chromosomes.

- Differentiate between the nucleus and the nucleoid.
- How do plasmids differ from chromosomes?
- Why does it make sense that a human cell would have more genes than a bacterial cell?

7 The Evolutionary Tree of Life

Evolution is the process of change in a line of descent over time that results in the appearance of new varieties and species of organisms. Evolution occurs in any self-replicating system in which variation occurs as the result of mutation and selection and differential fitness is a potential result. Thus, over time, all cells and viruses evolve.

Determining Evolutionary Relationships

The evolutionary relationships between organisms are the subject of **phylogeny**. Phylogenetic relationships between cells can be deduced by comparing the genetic information (nucleotide or amino acid sequences) that exists in their nucleic acids or proteins. Macromolecules that form the ribosome, in particular *ribosomal RNAs (rRNA)*, turn out to be excellent tools for determining evolutionary relationships. Because all cells contain ribosomes (and thus rRNA), this molecule can and has been used to construct a phylogenetic tree of all cells, including microorganisms (see Figure 17). Viral phylogenies have also been determined, but because these microorganisms lack ribosomes, other molecules have been used as evolutionary barometers. Carl Woese, an American microbiologist, pioneered the use of rRNA as a barometer of microbial phylogeny and, in so doing, revolutionized our understanding of cellular evolution.

The steps in generating an RNA-based phylogenetic tree are outlined in **Figure 16**. In brief, genes encoding rRNA from two or more organisms are sequenced (that is, the precise order of nucleotides in the molecule are determined), and the sequences are aligned and inspected, base-by-base, using a computer. The greater the rRNA gene sequence variation between any two organisms, the greater their evolutionary divergence. This divergence can then be depicted in a phylogenetic tree (Figure 16).

The Three Domains of Life

From comparative rRNA sequencing, three phylogenetically distinct lineages of cells have been identified. The lineages, called **domains**, are the ***Bacteria*** and the ***Archaea*** (both consisting of prokaryotes) and the ***Eukarya*** (eukaryotes) (**Figure 17**). The domains are thought to have diverged from a common ancestral organism or community of organisms early in the history of life on Earth.

The phylogenetic tree of life reveals two very important evolutionary facts: (1) as previously stated, all prokaryotes are *not* phylogenetically closely related and (2) *Archaea* are more closely related to *Eukarya* than to *Bacteria* (Figure 17). Thus, from the last universal common ancestor of all life, evolutionary diversification initially went in two directions: *Bacteria* and a second main lineage. This second lineage eventually diverged to yield the *Archaea*, which retained a prokaryotic cell structure, and the *Eukarya*, which did not. When we use the word "bacteria" (lower case b and no italics) the reference should be understood to be to some species of the domain *Bacteria*.

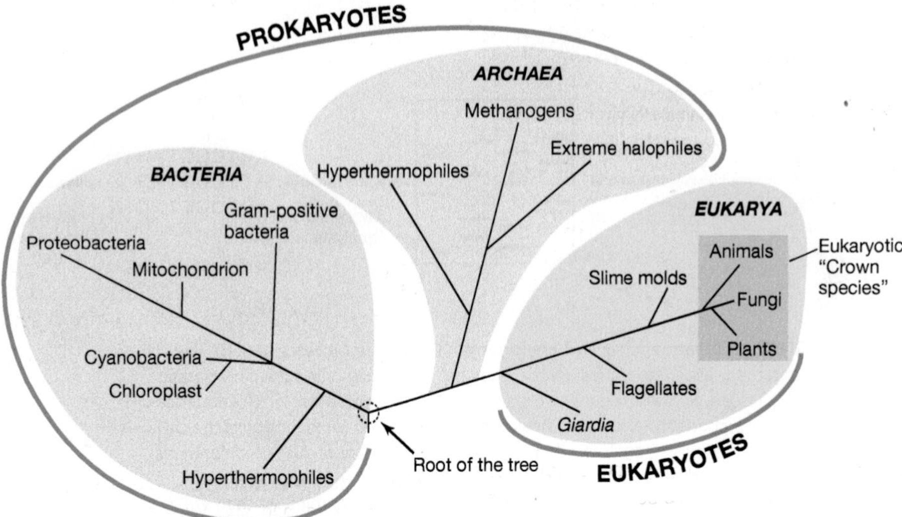

Figure 17 **The phylogenetic tree of life as defined by comparative rRNA gene sequencing.** The tree consists of three domains of organisms: the *Bacteria* and the *Archaea*, cells of which are prokaryotic, and the *Eukarya* (eukaryotes). Only a few of the groups of organisms within each domain are shown. Hyperthermophiles are prokaryotes that grow best at temperatures of 80°C or higher. The groups shaded in red are macroorganisms. All other organisms on the tree of life are microorganisms. Single domain phylogenetic trees can be found in Figures 19, 28, and 32.

Eukarya

Because the cells of animals and plants are all eukaryotic, it follows that eukaryotic microorganisms were the ancestors of multicellular organisms. The tree of life clearly bears this out. As expected, microbial eukaryotes branch off early on the eukaryotic lineage, and plants and animals branch near the tree's crown (Figure 17). However, molecular sequencing and other evidence have shown that eukaryotic cells contain genes from cells of two domains. In addition to the genome in the chromosomes of the nucleus, mitochondria and chloroplasts of eukaryotes contain their own genomes (DNA arranged in circular fashion, as in prokaryotes) and ribosomes. Using rRNA sequencing technology (Figure 16), these organelles have been shown to be highly derived ancestors of specific lineages of *Bacteria* (Figure 17 and Section 9). Mitochondria and chloroplasts were thus once free-living bacterial cells that took up an intracellular existence in cells of *Eukarya* eons ago. The process by which this stable arrangement developed is known as **endosymbiosis**.

Contributions of Molecular Sequencing to Microbiology

Molecular phylogenies have confirmed the evolutionary connections among all cells. Application of molecular sequencing has also created an evolutionary framework for the prokaryotes, something that the science of microbiology had been without since its founding. In addition, RNA-based phylogenies have spawned new tools that have affected many subdisciplines of microbiology. These include, in particular, microbial classification, microbial ecology, and clinical diagnostics. In these areas molecular phylogeny has helped shape our concept of a bacterial species and has given microbial ecologists and clinical microbiologists the tools necessary to identify organisms without actually culturing them. This has greatly improved our picture of microbial diversity and has led to the staggering conclusion that most of the microbial diversity that exists on Earth has yet to be brought into laboratory culture.

7 MiniReivew

Comparative rRNA sequencing has defined the three domains of life: *Bacteria*, *Archaea*, and *Eukarya*. Molecular sequencing has also shown that the organelles of *Eukarya* have evolutionary roots in the *Bacteria* and has yielded new tools for microbial ecology and clinical microbiology.

- How can species of *Bacteria* and *Archaea* be distinguished using molecular biology?
- How did the process of endosymbiosis benefit eukaryotic cells?

III MICROBIAL DIVERSITY

Evolution has molded all life on Earth. The diversity we see in microbial cells today is the result of nearly 4 billion years of evolutionary change. Microbial diversity can be seen in many forms, including cell size and cell morphology (shape), physiology, motility, mechanisms of cell division, pathogenicity, developmental biology, adaptation to environmental extremes, phylogeny, and so on. In the following sections we paint a picture of microbial diversity with a broad brush.

We preface our discussion of *microbial* diversity by first considering *metabolic* diversity. The two are closely linked. Microorganisms have exploited every conceivable means of "making a living" consistent with the laws of chemistry and physics. This enormous versatility has allowed microorganisms to inhabit every conceivable habitat on and in planet Earth.

8 Physiological Diversity of Microorganisms

All cells require energy and a means to conserve it for other uses. Energy can be obtained from three sources in nature: organic chemicals, inorganic chemicals, and light (Figure 18).

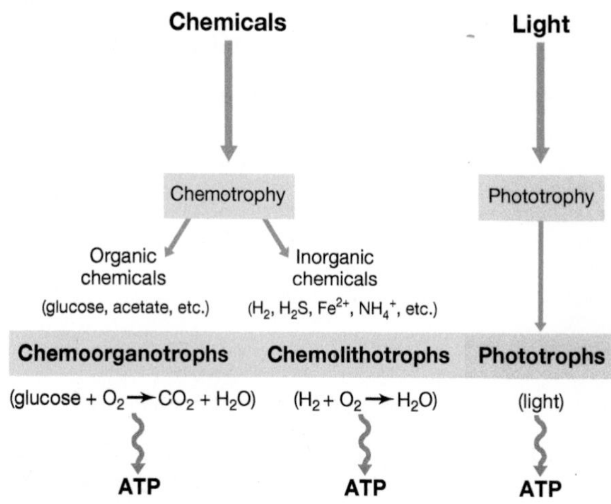

Figure 18 **Metabolic options for conserving energy.** The organic and inorganic chemicals listed here are just a few of the many different chemicals used by various chemotrophic organisms. Chemotrophic organisms oxidize organic or inorganic chemicals, which yields ATP. Phototrophic organisms convert solar energy to chemical energy in the form of ATP.

Chemoorganotrophs

Organisms that obtain energy from chemicals are called *chemotrophs,* and those that use organic chemicals are called **chemoorganotrophs** (Figure 18). Thousands of different organic chemicals can be used by one or another microorganism. Indeed, all natural and even most synthetic organic compounds can be metabolized. Energy is conserved from the oxidation of the compound and is stored in the cell as the energy-rich compound adenosine triphosphate (ATP).

Some microorganisms can extract energy from an organic compound only in the presence of oxygen; these organisms are called *aerobes*. Others can extract energy only in the absence of oxygen (*anaerobes*). Still others can break down organic compounds in either the presence or absence of oxygen. Most microorganisms that have been brought into laboratory culture are chemoorganotrophs.

Chemolithotrophs

Many prokaryotes can tap the energy available in inorganic compounds. This is a form of metabolism called *chemolithotrophy* (discovered by Winogradsky) and is carried out by organisms called **chemolithotrophs** (Figure 18). Chemolithotrophy is a process found only in prokaryotes and is widely distributed among species of *Bacteria* and *Archaea*. The spectrum of different inorganic compounds used is quite broad, but typically, a particular group of prokaryotes specializes in the use of a related group of inorganic compounds.

It should be obvious why the capacity to conserve energy from the oxidation of inorganic chemicals is a good metabolic strategy—competition from chemoorganotrophs is not an issue. But in addition to this, many of the inorganic compounds oxidized by chemolithotrophs, for example H_2 and H_2S, are actually the waste products of chemoorganotrophs. Thus, chemolithotrophs have evolved strategies for exploiting resources that chemoorganotrophs are unable to use.

Phototrophs

Phototrophic microorganisms contain pigments that allow them to use light as an energy source, and thus their cells are colored (Figure 2). Unlike chemotrophic organisms, **phototrophs** do not require chemicals as a source of energy; they synthesize ATP from the energy of sunlight. This is a significant metabolic advantage because competition for energy sources with chemotrophic organisms is not an issue and light is available in a wide variety of microbial habitats.

Two major forms of phototrophy are known in prokaryotes. In one form, called *oxygenic* photosynthesis, oxygen (O_2) is produced. Among microorganisms, oxygenic photosynthesis is characteristic of cyanobacteria, algae, and their phylogenetic relatives. The other form, *anoxygenic* photosynthesis, occurs in the purple and green bacteria and does not result in O_2 production. Both groups of phototrophs use light to make ATP, however, and we will see later the great similarities in their mechanisms of ATP synthesis.

Heterotrophs and Autotrophs

All cells require carbon as a major nutrient. Microbial cells are either **heterotrophs**, which require one or more organic compounds as their carbon source, or **autotrophs**, which use carbon dioxide (CO_2) as their carbon source. Chemoorganotrophs are by definition heterotrophs. By contrast, most

Table 1 Classes and examples of extremophiles[a]

Extreme	Descriptive term	Genus/species	Domain	Habitat	Minimum	Optimum	Maximum
Temperature							
High	Hyperthermophile	*Pyrolobus fumarii*	Archaea	Hot, undersea hydrothermal vents	90°C	**106°C**	113°C[b]
Low	Psychrophile	*Polaromonas vacuolata*	Bacteria	Sea ice	0°C	**48°C**	128°C
pH							
Low	Acidophile	*Picrophilus oshimae*	Archaea	Acidic hot springs	−0.06	**0.7**[c]	4
High	Alkaliphile	*Natronobacterium gregoryi*	Archaea	Soda lakes	8.5	**10**[d]	12
Pressure	Barophile	*Moritella yayanosii*[e]	Bacteria	Deep ocean sediments	500 atm	**700 atm**	>1000 atm
Salt (NaCl)	Halophile	*Halobacterium salinarum*	Archaea	Salterns	15%	**25%**	32% (saturation)

[a]The organisms listed are the current "record holders" for growth at a particular extreme condition.
[b]*Geogemma barossii*, a new species of hyperthermophilic *Archaea*, has been reported to grow at 121°C. However, *Pyrolobus* remains the best-characterized prokaryote growing above 110°C.
[c]*P. oshimae* is also a thermophile, growing optimally at 60°C.
[d]*N. gregoryi* is also an extreme halophile, growing optimally at 20% NaCl.
[e]*Moritella yayanosii* is also a psychrophile, growing optimally at about 4°C.

chemolithotrophs and virtually all phototrophs are autotrophs. Autotrophs are sometimes called *primary producers* because they synthesize organic matter from CO_2 for both their own benefit and that of chemoorganotrophs. The latter either feed directly on the primary producers or live off products they excrete. In one way or another, all organic matter on Earth has been synthesized by primary producers; in particular, by phototrophs.

Habitats and Extreme Environments

Microorganisms are present everywhere on Earth that will support life. These include habitats we are all familiar with—soil, water, animals, and plants—as well as virtually any structures made by humans. Indeed, sterility (the absence of life forms) in a natural sample of any sort is very rare.

Some microbial environments are those that we humans would find too extreme for life. Although these environments can pose challenges to microorganisms as well, extreme environments are often teeming with microbial life. Organisms inhabiting extreme environments are called **extremophiles**, a remarkable group of microorganisms that collectively define the physiochemical limits of life.

Extremophiles abound in such harsh environments as boiling hot springs; on or in the ice covering lakes, glaciers, or the polar seas; in extremely salty bodies of water; and in soils and waters having a pH as low as 0 or as high as 12. These prokaryotes do not just *tolerate* these extremes, but actually *require* the extreme condition in order to grow. That is why they are called extremophiles (the suffix *phile* means "loving"). Table 1 summarizes the current "record holders" among extremophiles and lists the types of habitats in which they reside.

8 MiniReview

Carbon and energy sources are needed by all cells. The terms chemoorganotroph, chemolithotroph, and phototroph refer to organisms that use organic chemicals, inorganic chemicals, or light, respectively, as their source of energy. Autotrophic organisms use CO_2 as their carbon source, and heterotrophs use organic carbon. Extremophiles thrive under environmental conditions that other organisms cannot tolerate.

- How might you distinguish a phototrophic microorganism from a chemotrophic one by simply looking at it under a microscope?
- What are extremophiles?

9 Bacteria

As we have seen, prokaryotes cluster into two phylogenetically distinct domains, the *Archaea* and the *Bacteria* (Figure 17). We begin with the *Bacteria*, because most of the known prokaryotes reside in this domain.

Proteobacteria, Gram-Positive Bacteria, and Cyanobacteria

The domain *Bacteria* contains an enormous variety of prokaryotes. All known disease-causing (pathogenic) prokaryotes are *Bacteria*, as are thousands of nonpathogenic species. There is a large variety of morphologies and physiologies in this domain. The ***Proteobacteria*** make up the largest division of *Bacteria* (Figure 19). Many chemoorganotrophic bacteria are

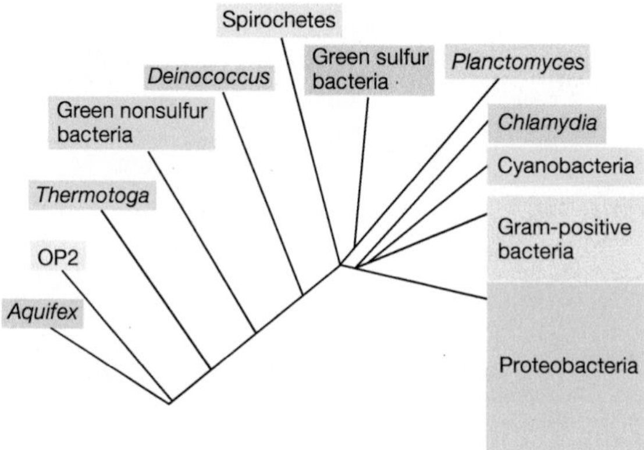

Figure 19 Phylogenetic tree of *Bacteria*. The relative sizes of the colored boxes reflect the number of known genera and species in each of the groups. The *Proteobacteria* are the largest group of *Bacteria* known. The lineage on the tree labeled OP2 does not represent a cultured organism but instead is a sequence of an rRNA gene isolated from an organism in a natural sample. In this example, the closest known relative of OP2 would be *Aquifex*. Although not shown on this tree, many thousands of other environmental sequences are known, and they branch all over the tree. Not all known groups of *Bacteria* are depicted on this tree.

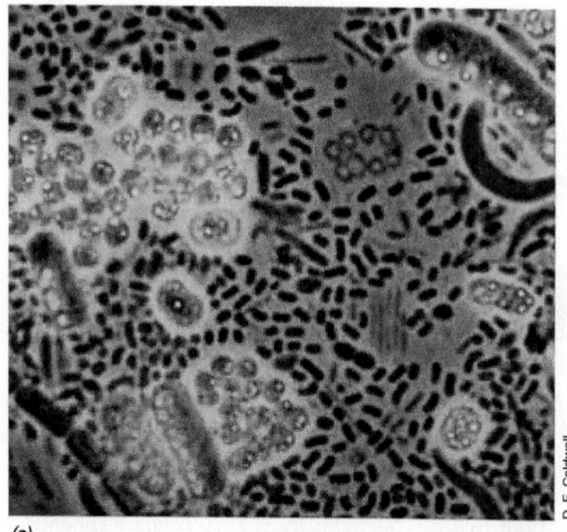

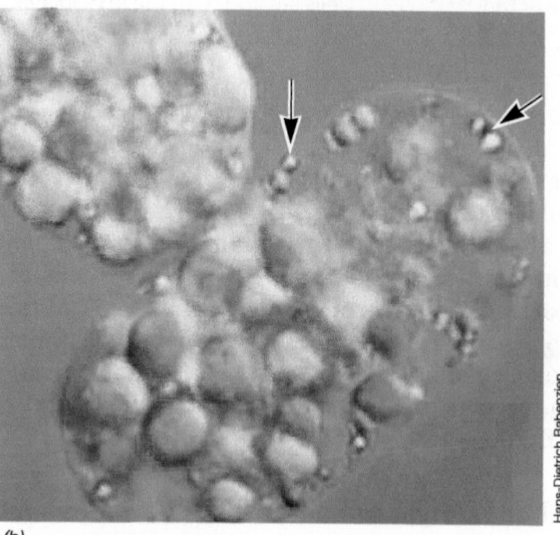

Figure 20 Phototrophic and chemolithotrophic *Proteobacteria*. *(a)* The phototrophic purple sulfur bacterium, *Chromatium* (the large, red-orange, rod-shaped cells in this photomicrograph of a natural microbial community). A cell is about 10 μm wide. (b) The large chemolithotrophic sulfur-oxidizing bacterium, *Achromatium*. A cell is about 20 μm wide. Globules of elemental sulfur can be seen in the cells (arrows). Both of these organisms oxidize hydrogen sulfide (H_2S).

Proteobacteria, including *Escherichia coli*, the model organism of microbial physiology, biochemistry, and molecular biology. Several phototrophic and chemolithotrophic species are also Proteobacteria (Figure 20). Many of these use hydrogen sulfide (H_2S, the smell from rotten eggs) in their metabolism, producing elemental sulfur that is stored within or outside the cell (Figure 20). The sulfur is an oxidation product of H_2S and is further oxidized to sulfate (SO_4^{2-}). The sulfide and sulfur are oxidized to fuel important metabolic functions such as CO_2 fixation (autotrophy) or energy generation (Figure 18).

Several other common prokaryotes of soil and water, and species that live in or on plants and animals in both harmless and disease-causing ways, are members of the *Proteobacteria*. These include species of *Pseudomonas*, many of which can degrade complex and otherwise toxic natural and synthetic organic compounds, and *Azotobacter*, a nitrogen-fixing bacterium. A number of key pathogens are *Proteobacteria*, including *Salmonella*, *Rickettsia*, *Neisseria*, and many others. And finally, it is from within the *Proteobacteria* that the mitochondrion arose by endosymbiosis (Section 7), probably several times during the course of evolution (Figure 17).

As we learned in Section 2, bacteria can be distinguished by the Gram-staining procedure, a technique that stains cells either gram-positive or gram-negative. The gram-positive phylum of *Bacteria* (Figure 19) contains many organisms that are united by their common phylogeny and cell wall structure. Here we find the endospore-forming *Bacillus* (discovered by Ferdinand Cohn) (Figure 21*a*) and *Clostridium* and related spore-forming bacteria such as the antibiotic-producing *Streptomyces*. Also included here are the lactic acid bacteria, common inhabitants of decaying plant material and dairy products that include organisms such as *Streptococcus* (Figure 11*b*) and *Lactobacillus*. Other interesting bacteria that fall among the phylogenetic division of gram-positive bacteria are the mycoplasmas. These bacteria lack a cell wall and have very small genomes; many of them are pathogenic. *Mycoplasma* is a major genus of organisms in this medically important group.

The **cyanobacteria** are phylogenetic relatives of gram-positive bacteria (Figure 19) and are oxygenic phototrophs. The photosynthetic organelle of eukaryotic phototrophs, the chloroplast (Figure 2*a*), is related to the cyanobacteria (Figure 17). Cyanobacteria were critical in the evolution of life, as

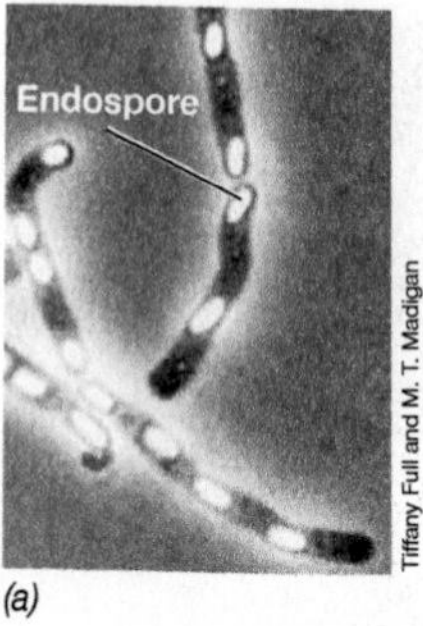

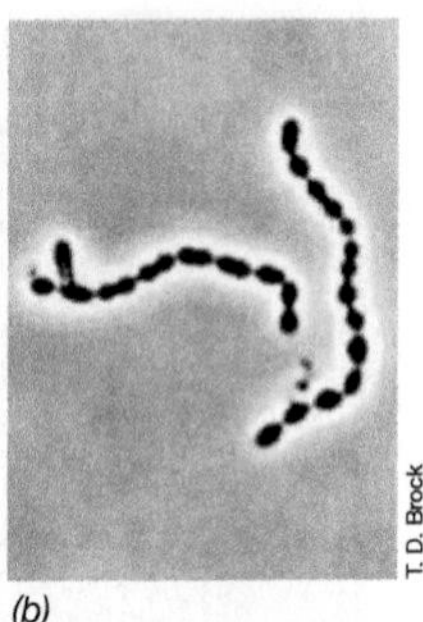

(a) (b)

Figure 21 **Gram-positive bacteria.** *(a)* The rod-shaped endospore-forming bacterium *Bacillus*, here shown as cells in a chain. Note the presence of endospores (bright refractile structures) inside the cells. Endospores are extremely resistant to heat, chemicals, and radiation. Cells are about 16 μm in diameter. *(b) Streptococcus*, a spherical cell that exists in chains. Streptococci are widespread in dairy products, and some are potent pathogens. Cells are about 0.8 μm in diameter.

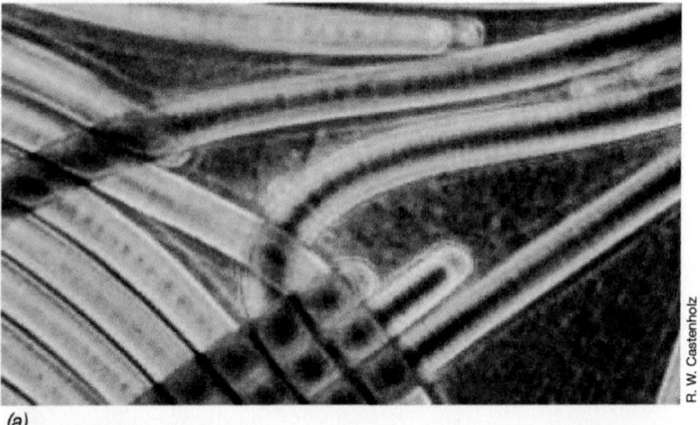

(a)

(b)

Figure 22 **Filamentous cyanobacteria.** *(a) Oscillatoria, (b) Spirulina.* Cells of both organisms are about 10 μm wide.

they were the first oxygenic phototrophs to evolve on Earth. The production of O_2 on an originally anoxic Earth paved the way for the evolution of prokaryotes that could respire using oxygen. The development of higher organisms, such as the plants and animals, followed billions of years later when Earth had a more oxygen-rich environment. Cells of some cyanobacteria join to form filaments (Figure 22). Many other morphological forms of cyanobacteria are known, including unicellular, colonial, and heterocystous cyanobacteria, which contain special structures called *heterocysts* that carry out nitrogen fixation.

Other Major Phyla of Bacteria

Several lineages of *Bacteria* contain species with unique morphologies. These include the aquatic Planctomyces group, characterized by cells with a distinct stalk that allows the organisms to attach to a solid substratum (Figure 23), and the helically shaped spirochetes (Figure 24). Several diseases, most notably syphilis and Lyme disease, are caused by spirochetes.

Two other major lineages of *Bacteria* are phototrophic: the green sulfur bacteria and the green nonsulfur bacteria (*Chloroflexus* group) (Figure 25). Species in both of these lineages contain similar photosynthetic pigments and are also autotrophs. *Chloroflexus* is a filamentous prokaryote that inhabits hot springs and shallow marine bays and is often the dominant organism in stratified microbial mats, laminated microbial communities. *Chloroflexus* is also noteworthy because it is believed to be an important link in the evolution of photosynthesis.

Other major lineages of *Bacteria* include the Chlamydia and Deinococcus groups (Figure 19). The genus *Chlamydia* harbors respiratory and sexually transmitted pathogens of humans. Chlamydia are obligate intracellular parasites. By this it is meant that they live *inside* the cells of higher organisms, in this case, human cells. Several other pathogenic prokaryotes (for example, species of *Rickettsia*, a genus of *Proteobacteria* that causes diseases such as typhus and Rocky Mountain spotted fever, and *Mycobacterium tuberculosis*, a gram-positive bacterium that causes tuberculosis) are also intracellular pathogens. By living inside their host's cells, these pathogens avoid destruction by the host's immune response.

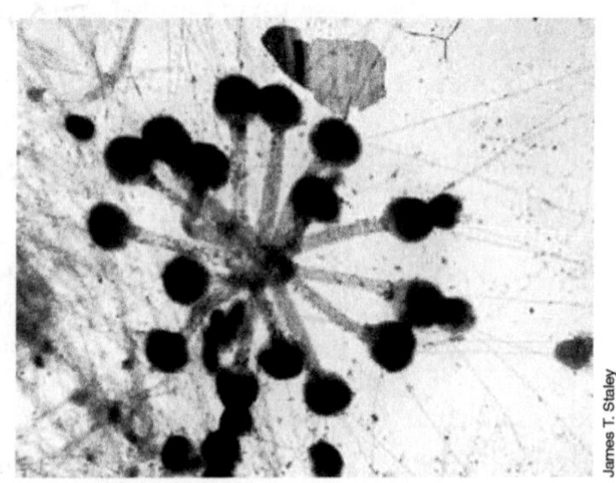

Figure 23 **The morphologically unusual stalked bacterium *Planctomyces.*** Shown are several cells attached by their stalks to form a rosette. Cells are about 1.4 μm wide.

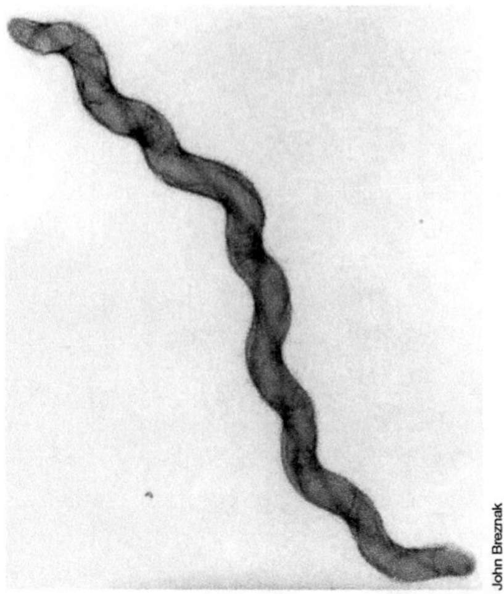

Figure 24 **Spirochetes.** Scanning electron micrograph of a cell of *Spirochaeta zuelzerae*. The cell is about 0.3 μm wide and tightly coiled.

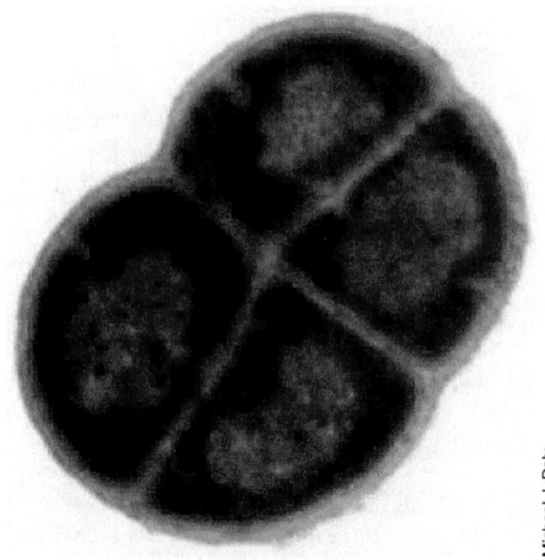

Figure 26 **The highly radiation-resistant bacterium *Deinococcus radiodurans*.** A single cell is about 2.5 μm wide.

The Deinococcus phylum contains species with unusual cell walls and an innate resistance to high levels of radiation; *Deinococcus radiodurans* (Figure 26) is a major species in this group. This organism can survive doses of radiation many-fold greater than that sufficient to kill animals and can even reassemble its chromosome after it has been shattered by radiation.

Finally, several phyla of *Bacteria* branch off very early on the phylogenetic tree, very near the root (Figure 19). Although phylogenetically distinct from one another, these groups are unified by the common property of growth at very high temperature (*hyperthermophily*, Table 1). Organisms such as *Aquifex* (Figure 27) and *Thermotoga* grow in hot springs that are near the boiling point. The early phylogenetic branching of these phyla (Figure 19) is consistent with the hypothesis that the early Earth was much hotter than it is today. Assuming that early life forms were hyperthermophilic, it is not surprising that their closest living relatives would be hyperthermophiles themselves. Interestingly, the phylogenetic trees of both *Bacteria* and *Archaea* support this (Figure 19 and see Figure 28); organisms such as *Aquifex*, *Methanopyrus*, and *Pyrolobus* are thus modern descendants of very ancient cell lineages.

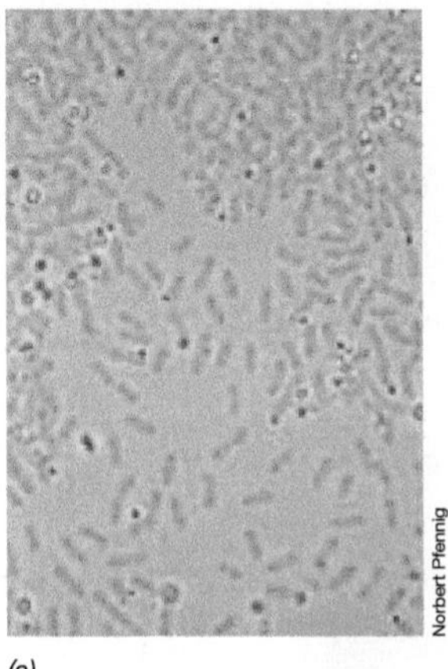

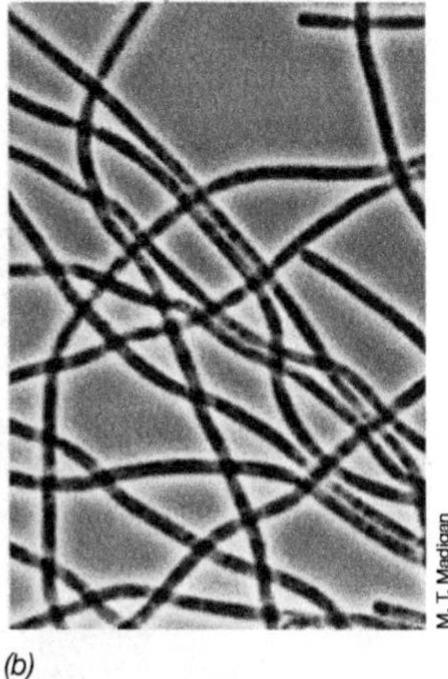

(a) (b)

Figure 25 **Phototrophic green bacteria.** *(a) Chlorobium* (green sulfur bacteria). A single cell is about 0.8 μm wide. *(b) Chloroflexus* (green nonsulfur bacteria). A filament is about 1.3 μm wide. Despite sharing many features such as pigments and photosynthetic membrane structures, these two genera are phylogenetically distinct (Figure 19).

9 MiniReview

Several phyla of *Bacteria* are known, and an enormous diversity of cell morphologies and physiologies are represented.

- What is the largest phylum of *Bacteria*?
- Why can it be said that the cyanobacteria prepared Earth for the evolution of higher life forms?
- What is physiologically unique about *Deinococcus*?

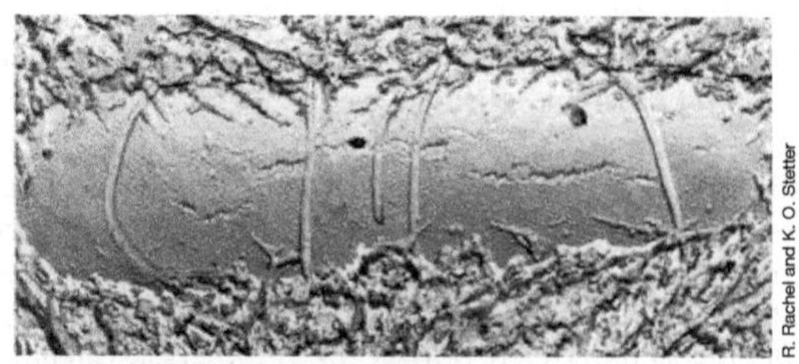

Figure 27 **The hyperthemophile *Aquifex*.** Transmission electron micrograph using a technique called freeze-etching, where a frozen replica of the cell is made and then visualized. The cell is about 0.5 μm wide.

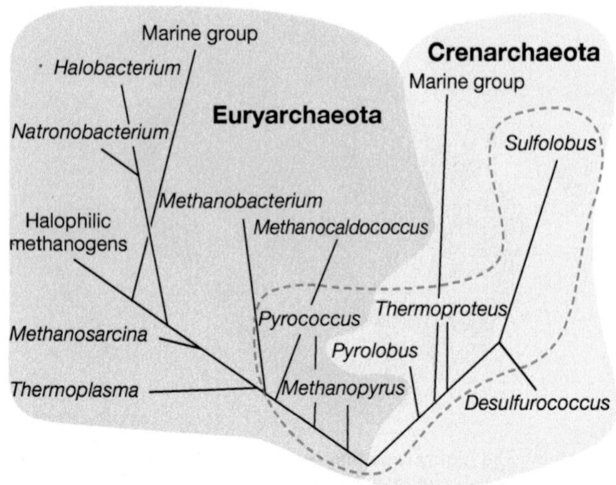

Figure 28 **Phylogenetic tree of *Archaea*.** The organisms circled in red are hyperthermophiles, growing at very high temperatures (*Crenarchaeota*). In pink are shown methanogens and the extreme halophiles and acidophiles (*Euryarchaeota*). The "marine group" sequences are environmental rRNA sequences from marine *Archaea* that are not yet cultured. Not all known groups of *Archaea* are depicted on this tree.

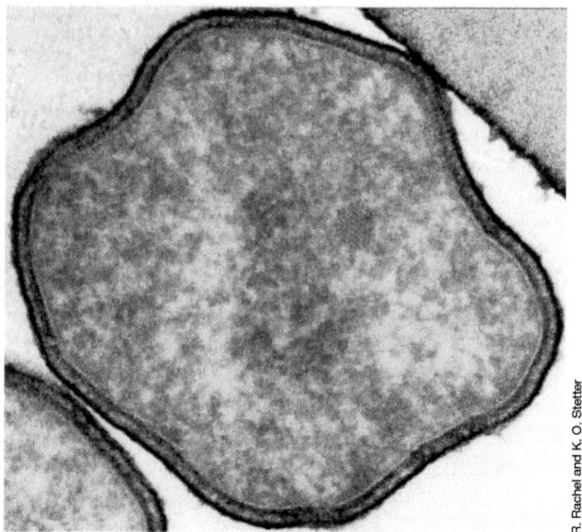

Figure 29 ***Pyrolobus.*** This hyperthermophile grows optimally above the boiling point of water. The cell is 1.4 μm wide.

10 Archaea

Two phyla exist in the domain *Archaea*, the *Euryarchaeota* and the *Crenarchaeota* (Figure 28). Each of these forms a major branch on the archaeal tree. Most cultured *Archaea* are extremophiles, with species capable of growth at the highest temperatures, salinities, and extremes of pH of all known microorganisms. The organism *Pyrolobus* (Figure 29), for example, is one of the most thermophilic of all known prokaryotes (Table 1).

Although all *Archaea* are chemotrophic, *Halobacterium* (to be discussed shortly) can use light to make ATP but in a way quite distinct from that of phototrophic organisms. Some *Archaea* use organic compounds in their energy metabolism. Many others are chemolithotrophs, with hydrogen gas (H_2) being a widely used energy source. Chemolithotrophy is particularly widespread among hyperthermophilic *Archaea*.

Euryarchaeota

The *Euryarchaeota* branch on the tree of *Archaea* (Figure 28) contains three groups of organisms that have dramatically different physiologies, the methanogens, the extreme halophiles, and the thermoacidophiles. Some of these require O_2 whereas others are killed by it, and some grow at the upper or lower extremes of pH (Table 1). Methanogens such as *Methanobacterium* are strict anaerobes. Their metabolism is unique in that energy is conserved during the production of methane (natural gas). Methanogens are important organisms in the anaerobic degradation of organic matter in nature, and most of the natural gas found on Earth is a result of their metabolism.

The extreme halophiles are relatives of the methanogens (Figure 28), but are physiologically distinct from them. Unlike methanogens, which are killed by oxygen, most extreme halophiles require oxygen, and all are unified by their requirement for very large amounts of salt (NaCl) for metabolism and reproduction. It is for this reason that these organisms are called *halophiles* (salt lovers). In fact, organisms like *Halobacterium* are so salt loving that they can actually grow on and within salt crystals (Figure 30).

As we have seen, many prokaryotes are phototrophic and can generate adenosine triphosphate (ATP) from light (Section 8). Although *Halobacterium* species do not produce chlorophyll as phototrophs do, they nevertheless contain

Figure 30 **Extremely halophilic *Archaea*.** A vial of brine with precipitated salt crystals containing cells of the extreme halophile, *Halobacterium*. The organism contains pigments that absorb light and lead to ATP production. Cells of *Halobacterium* can also live within salt crystals themselves.

light-sensitive pigments that can absorb light and trigger ATP synthesis. Extremely halophilic *Archaea* inhabit salt lakes, salterns, and other very salty environments. Some extreme halophiles, such as *Natronobacterium*, inhabit soda lakes, environments characterized by high levels of salt and high pH. Such organisms are *alkaliphilic* and grow at the highest pH of all known organisms (Table 1).

The third group of *Euryarchaeota* are the thermoacidophiles. These include *Thermoplasma* (Figure 31), an organism that, like *Mycoplasma* (Section 9), contains a cytoplasmic membrane but no cell wall. *Thermoplasma* grows best at moderately high temperatures and low pH. The thermoacidophiles also includes *Picrophilus*, the most acidophilic (acid-loving) of all known prokaryotes (Table 1).

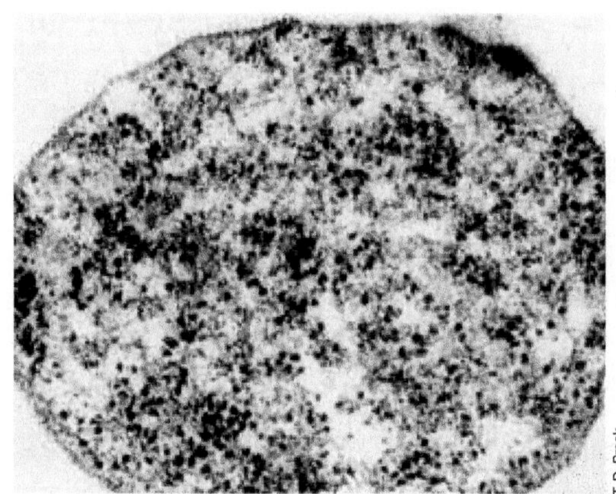

Figure 31 **Extremely acidophilic *Archaea*.** The organism *Thermoplasma* lacks a cell wall. The cell measures 1 μm wide.

Crenarchaeota

The vast majority of cultured *Crenarchaeota* are hyperthermophiles (Figure 29). These organisms are either chemolithotrophs or chemoorganotrophs and grow in such high-temperature environments as hot springs and hydrothermal vents (deep-sea hot springs). For the most part these organisms are anaerobes (because of the high temperature, their habitats are typically anoxic), and many of them use hydrogen gas (H_2) present in their geothermal habitats as an energy source.

Some *Crenarchaeota* inhabit environments that contrast dramatically with high-temperature environments. For example, many of the prokaryotes drifting in the open oceans are *Crenarchaeota:* Their environment is fully oxic and cold (~3°C). Some marine *Crenarchaeota* are chemolithotrophs that use ammonia (NH_3) as their energy source, but we know little about the metabolic activities of most marine *Archaea*. *Crenarchaeota* have also been detected in soil and freshwaters and so appear to be widely distributed in nature.

Phylogenetic Analyses of Natural Microbial Communities

Although microbiologists believe that thus far we have cultured only a small fraction of the *Archaea* and *Bacteria* that exist in nature, we still know a lot about their diversity. This is because it is possible to do phylogenetic analyses on rRNA genes present in a natural sample without first having to culture the organisms that contain them. If a sample of soil or water contains rRNA, it is because organisms that made that rRNA are present in the sample. Thus, if we isolate all of the different rRNA genes from a soil or water sample, we can use the techniques described in Figure 16 to order them on a phylogenetic tree. Conceptually, this is the same as first isolating pure cultures of all of the organisms in the sample and then extracting their rRNA genes. But these powerful techniques skip the culturing step—often the bottleneck in microbial diversity studies—and instead go right for the rRNA genes themselves.

From studies done using these methods of molecular microbial ecology, initially devised by the American microbiologist Norman Pace, it is clear that the extent of microbial diversity is far greater than what laboratory culturing has been able to reveal. A sampling of virtually any habitat typically shows that the vast majority of microorganisms in that habitat have never been in laboratory culture. The phylogeny of these uncultured organisms, known only from environmental rRNA sequences (Figures 19 and 28), is depicted in phylogenetic trees as branches labeled with letters or numbers instead of actual microbial names to identify lineages.

The results of molecular microbial ecology have given new impetus to innovative culturing techniques to grow the great "uncultured majority" of prokaryotes known to exist today. Genomic analyses of uncultured *Archaea* and *Bacteria* (using the techniques of environmental genomics) have helped in this regard. This is because knowledge of the full complement of genes in uncultured organisms often reveals secrets about their metabolic capacities and suggests ways to bring them into laboratory culture.

10 MiniReview

Two major phyla of *Archaea* are known, *Euryarchaeota* and *Crenarchaeota*. Retrieval and analysis of rRNA genes from cells in natural samples have shown that many phylogenetically distinct species of *Archaea* and *Bacteria* exist in nature but have not yet been cultured.

- What is unusual about the genus *Halobacterium*? What group of *Archaea* is responsible for producing the natural gas we use as a fuel? Chemically, what is natural gas?
- How can we know the microbial diversity of a natural habitat without first isolating and growing the organisms it contains?

11 Eukaryotic Microorganisms

Eukaryotic microorganisms are related by their distinct cell structure (Figure 11) and phylogenetic history (Figure 17). Inspection of the domain *Eukarya* (Figure 32) shows plants

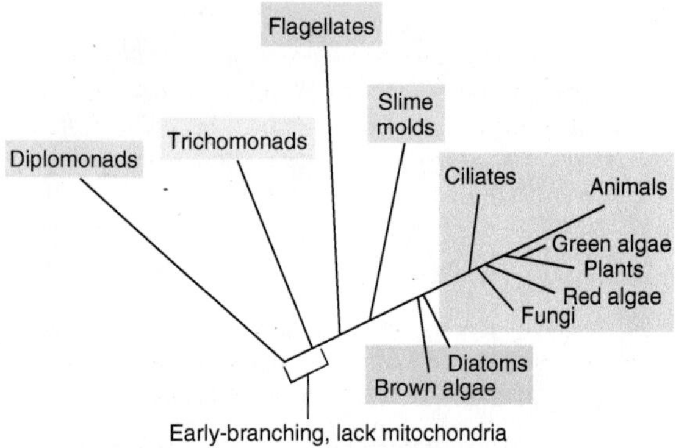

Figure 32 **Phylogenetic tree of *Eukarya*.** Some early-branching species of *Eukarya* lack organelles other than the nucleus. Note that plants and animals branch near the apex of the tree. Not all known lineages of *Eukarya* are depicted.

and animals to be farthest out on the branches of the tree; such late-branching groups are said to be the "most derived." Some of the early-branching *Eukarya* are structurally simple eukaryotes lacking mitochondria and some other organelles. These cells, such as the diplomonad *Giardia,* may be modern descendents of primitive eukaryotic cells that did not engage in endosymbiosis. Alternatively, such cells contained endosymbionts but for reasons that are not yet clear discarded them as they evolved to colonize the habitats we find them in today. Most of these early eukaryotes are parasites of humans and other animals, unable to live a free and independent existence.

Eukaryotic Microbial Diversity

A diverse array of eukaryotic microorganisms is known. Collectively, microbial eukaryotes are called *protists,* and major groups are algae, fungi, protozoa, and slime molds. Some protists, such as the algae (**Figure 33***a*), are phototrophic. Algae contain chloroplasts and can live in environments containing only a few minerals (for example, K, P, Mg, N, S), water, CO_2, and light. Algae inhabit both soil and aquatic habitats and are major primary producers in nature. Fungi (Figure 33*b*) lack photosynthetic pigments and are either unicellular (yeasts) or filamentous (molds). Fungi are major agents of biodegradation in nature and recycle much of the organic matter produced in soils and other ecosystems.

Cells of algae and fungi have cell walls, whereas the protozoa (Figure 33*c*) do not. Protozoans are typically motile, and different species are widespread in nature in aquatic habitats or as pathogens of humans and other animals. Protozoa are spread about the phylogenetic tree of *Eukarya*. Some, like the flagellates, are fairly early-branching species, whereas others, like the ciliates such as *Paramecium* (Figure 33*c*), appear later on the phylogenetic tree (Figure 32).

The slime molds resemble protozoa in that they are motile and lack cell walls. However, slime molds differ from protozoa in both their phylogeny and by the fact that their cells undergo a life cycle. During the slime mold life cycle, motile cells aggregate to form a multicellular structure called a *fruiting body* from which spores are produced that yield new motile cells. Slime molds are the earliest known protists to show the cellular cooperation needed to form multicellular structures.

Lichens are leaflike structures often found growing on rocks, trees, and other surfaces (**Figure 34**). Lichens are an example of microbial mutualism, a situation in which two organisms live together for mutual benefit. Lichens consist of a fungus and a phototrophic partner organism, either an alga (a eukaryote) or a cyanobacterium (a prokaryote). The phototrophic component is the primary producer and the fungus provides an anchor and protection from the elements. Lichens have thus evolved a successful strategy of mutualistic interaction between two quite different microorganisms.

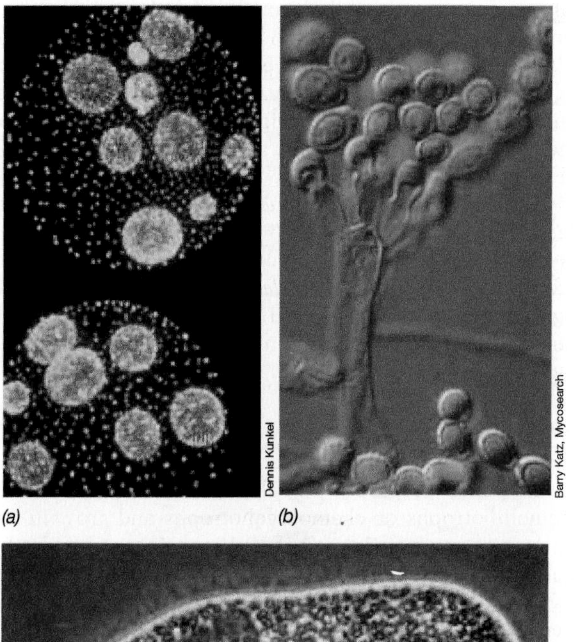

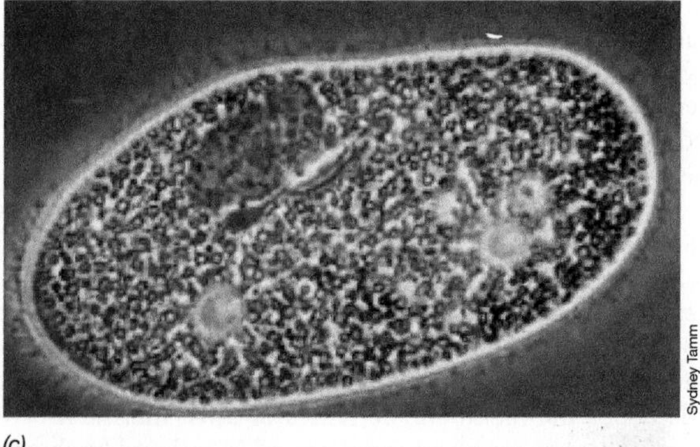

Figure 33 **Microbial *Eukarya*.** *(a)* Algae; the colonial green alga, *Volvox*. Each spherical cell contains several chloroplasts, the photosynthetic organelle of phototrophic eukaryotes. *(b)* Fungi; the spore-bearing structures of a typical mold. Each spore can give rise to a new filamentous fungus. *(c)* Protozoa; the ciliated protozoan *Paramecium*. Cilia function like oars in a boat, conferring motility on the cell.

(a)

(b)

Figure 34 Lichens. *(a)* An orange-pigmented lichen growing on a rock, and *(b)* a yellow-pigmented lichen growing on a dead tree stump, Yellowstone National Park, USA. The color of the lichen comes from the pigmented (algal) component of the lichen structure. Besides chlorophylls, the algal components of lichens contain carotenoid pigments, which can be yellow, orange, brown, red, green, or purple.

Final Remarks

Our tour of microbial diversity here is only an overview of the subject. The viruses were intentionally left out of this overview of diversity. This omission is because viruses are not cells (although they require cells for their replication as mentioned in Section 5).

11 MiniReview

Microbial eukaryotes are a diverse group that includes algae, protozoa, fungi, and slime molds. Some algae and fungi have developed mutualistic associations called lichens.

- List at least two ways algae differ from cyanobacteria.
- List at least two ways algae differ from protozoa.
- How do each of the components of a lichen benefit each other?

Review of Key Terms

Archaea one of two known domains of prokaryotes; compare with *Bacteria*

Autotroph an organism able to grow on carbon dioxide (CO_2) as sole carbon source

Bacteria one of two known domains of prokaryotes; compare with *Archaea*

Cell wall a rigid layer present outside the cytoplasmic membrane that confers structural strength on the cell and protection from osmotic lysis

Chemolithotroph an organism that obtains its energy from the oxidation of inorganic compounds

Chemoorganotroph an organism that obtains its energy from the oxidation of organic compounds

Chromosome a genetic element containing genes essential to cell function

Cyanobacteria prokaryotic oxygenic phototrophs

Cytoplasm the fluid portion of a cell, bounded by the cytoplasmic membrane

Cytoplasmic membrane the cell's permeability barrier; encloses the cytoplasm

Domain the highest level of biological classification

Endosymbiosis the process by which mitochondria and chloroplasts originated from descendants of *Bacteria*

Eukarya the domain of life that includes all eukaryotic cells

Eukaryote a cell having a membrane-bound nucleus and usually other membrane-bound organelles

Evolution change in a line of descent over time leading to new species or varieties within a species

Extremophile an organism that grows optimally under one or more environmental extremes

Genome the complement of genes in an organism

Gram stain a differential staining technique in which cells stain either pink (gram-negative) or purple (gram-positive) depending upon their structural and phylogenetic makeup

Gram-positive bacteria a major phylogenetic lineage of prokaryotic cells that contain mainly peptidoglycan in their cell walls; stain purple in the Gram stain

Gram-negative bacteria prokaryotic cells that contain an outer membrane and peptidoglycan in their cell walls; stain pink in the Gram stain

Heterotroph an organism that requires organic carbon as its carbon source

Nucleoid the aggregated mass of DNA that constitutes the chromosome of cells of *Bacteria* and *Archaea*

Nucleus a membrane-enclosed structure that contains the chromosomes in eukaryotic cells

Organelle a unit membrane-enclosed structure such as a mitochondrion or chloroplast present in the cytoplasm of eukaryotic cells

Phototroph an organism that obtains its energy from light

Phylogeny the evolutionary relationships between organisms

Plasmid an extrachromosomal genetic element nonessential for growth

Prokaryote a cell that lacks a membrane-enclosed nucleus and other organelles

Proteobacteria a large phylum of *Bacteria* that includes many of the common gram-negative bacteria, such as *Escherichia coli*

Resolution in microbiology, the ability to distinguish two objects as distinct and separate under the microscope

Ribosome a cytoplasmic particle that functions in protein synthesis

Virus a genetic element that contains either DNA or RNA and replicates in cells; has an extracellular form

Review Questions

1. What is the function of staining in light microscopy? why are cationic dyes used for general staining purposes (Sections 1 and 2)?
2. What is the advantage of a differential interference contrast microscope over a bright-field microscope? A phase-contrast microscope over a bright-field microscope (Section 3)?
3. What is the major advantage of electron microscopes over light microscopes? What type of electron microscope would be used to view the three-dimensional features of a cell (Section 4)?
4. Why does a cell need a cytoplasmic membrane (Section 5)?
5. Which domains of life have a prokaryotic cell structure? Is prokaryotic cell structure a predictor of phylogenetic status (Section 5)?
6. How long is a cell of the bacterium *Escherichia coli*? How much larger are you than this single cell (Section 5)?
7. How do viruses resemble cells? How do they differ from cells (Section 5)?
8. What is meant by the word genome? How does the chromosome of prokaryotes differ from that of eukaryotes (Section 6)?
9. How many genes does an organism such as *Escherichia coli* have? How does this compare with the number of genes in one of your cells (Section 6)?
10. What is meant by the word endosymbiosis (Section 7)?
11. Molecular studies have shown that many macromolecules in species of *Archaea* resemble their counterparts in various eukaryotes more closely than those in species of *Bacteria*. Explain (Section 7).
12. From the standpoint of energy metabolism, how do chemo-organotrophs differ from chemolithotrophs? What carbon sources do members of each group use? Are they therefore heterotrophs or autotrophs (Section 8)?
13. What domain contains the phylum *Proteobacteria*? What is notable about the *Proteobacteria* (Section 9)?
14. What is unusual about the organism *Pyrolobus* (Sections 8 and 10)?
15. What similarities and differences exist between the following three organisms: *Pyrolobus*, *Halobacterium*, and *Thermoplasma* (Section 10)?
16. Examine Figure 28. What does the lineage "marine group" mean (Section 10)?
17. How does *Giardia* differ from a human cell, both structurally and phylogenetically (Section 11)?

Application Questions

1. Calculate the size of the smallest resolvable object if 600-nm light is used to observe a specimen with a 100× oil-immersion lens having a numerical aperture of 1.32. How could resolution be improved using this same lens?
2. Prokaryotic cells containing plasmids can often be "cured" of their plasmids (that is, the plasmids can be permanently removed) with no ill effects, whereas removal of the chromosome would be lethal. Explain.
3. It has been said that knowledge of the evolution of macroorganisms greatly preceded that of microorganisms. Why do you think that reconstruction of the evolutionary lineage of horses, for example, might have been an easier task than doing the same for any group of prokaryotes?
4. Examine the phylogenetic tree shown in Figure 16. Using the sequence data shown, describe why the tree would be incorrect if its branches remained the same but the positions of organisms 2 and 3 on the tree were switched?
5. Microbiologists have cultured a great diversity of microorganisms but know that an even greater diversity exists, despite the fact that they have never seen these organisms or grown them in the laboratory. Explain.
6. What data from this chapter could you use to convince your friend that extremophiles are not just organisms that were "hanging on" in their respective habitats?
7. Defend this statement: If cyanobacteria had never evolved, life on Earth would have remained strictly microbial.

Microbial Evolution and Systematics

Methane-producing Archaea, such as the cells of Methanocaldococcus jannaschii *shown in this electron micrograph, were probably some of the earliest cells to appear on Earth.*

B. Boonyaratanakornkit & D.S. Clark, G. Vrdoljak

I EARLY EARTH AND THE ORIGIN AND DIVERSIFICATION OF LIFE

A theme that unifies all of biology is **evolution**, DNA sequence change and the inheritance of that change, often under the selective pressures of a changing environment. From the time of its origin about 4.5 billion years ago, Earth has undergone a continual process of physical and geological change. These changes created conditions leading to the origin of life about 4 billion years ago, and they have presented living organisms with new opportunities and challenges from that time to the present. In turn, as microbial metabolisms and physiologies arose to take advantage of and cope with these changes, microbial life has continually altered Earth's biosphere. This chapter focuses on the evolution of microbial life, from the origins of the earliest cells and microbial metabolic diversification to the origin of eukaryotes. Methods for discerning evolutionary relationships among modern-day descendents of early microbial lineages and the emerging concept of a bacterial species are also discussed. The goal of this chapter is to provide an evolutionary and systematic foundation for our examination of the diversity of microbial life to follow in the next four chapters.

1 Formation and Early History of Earth

In these first few sections, we consider the possible conditions under which life arose, the processes that might have given rise to the first cellular life, its divergence into two evolutionary lineages, ***Bacteria*** and ***Archaea***, and the later formation, through endosymbiosis, of a third lineage, the ***Eukarya***. Although much about these events and processes remains speculative, geological and molecular evidence is providing an increasingly clear view of how life might have arisen and diversified.

Origin of Earth

Earth is thought to have formed about 4.5 billion years ago, based on data from slowly decaying radioactive isotopes. Our planet and the other planets of our solar system arose from materials making up a disc-shaped nebular cloud of dust and gases released by the supernova of a massive old star. As a new star—our sun—formed within this cloud, it began to compact, undergo nuclear fusion, and release large amounts of heat and light. Materials left in the nebular cloud began to clump and fuse due to collisions and gravitational pull, forming tiny accretions that gradually grew larger to form clumps that eventually coalesced into planets. Energy released in this process heated the emerging Earth as it formed, as did energy released by radioactive decay within the condensing materials, transforming Earth into a planet of fiery hot magma. As Earth cooled over time, a metallic core, rocky mantle, and a thin lower-density surface crust formed.

The fiery, inhospitable conditions of early Earth, characterized by a molten surface under intense bombardment from space by masses of accreted materials, are thought to have persisted for over 500 million years. Water on Earth originated from innumerable collisions with icy comets and asteroids and from volcanic outgassing of the planet's interior. At this time, water would have been present as vapor due to the heat. No rocks dating to the origin of our planet have yet been discovered, presumably because they have undergone geological metamorphosis. Ancient sedimentary rocks, which form under liquid water, have been found in several locations on Earth. Some of the oldest sedimentary rocks discovered thus far are in the Itsaq Gneiss Complex, in southwestern Greenland, which date to about 3.86 billion years ago. The sedimentary nature of these rocks indicates that at least by that time Earth had cooled sufficiently for the water vapor to have condensed and formed the early oceans.

Even more ancient materials, crystals of the mineral zircon ($ZrSiO_4$), however, have been discovered, and these materials give us a glimpse of even earlier conditions on Earth. Impurities trapped in the crystals and the mineral's isotopic ratios of oxygen indicate that Earth cooled much earlier than previously believed, with solid crust forming and water condensing into oceans perhaps as early as 4.4 to 4.3 billion years ago. The presence of liquid water implies that conditions might have been compatible with life within a few hundred million years after our planet formed.

Evidence for Microbial Life on Early Earth

The fossilized remains of cells and the isotopically "light" carbon abundant in these rocks provide evidence for early microbial life. Some ancient rocks contain what appear to be bacteria-like microfossils, typically as simple rods or cocci (Figure 1).

In rocks of 3.5 billion years old or younger, microbial formations called **stromatolites** are abundant. Stromatolites are fossilized microbial mats consisting of layers of filamentous prokaryotes and trapped sediment (Figure 2). What kind of organisms were these ancient stromatolitic bacteria? By comparing ancient stromatolites with modern stromatolites growing in shallow marine basins (Figure 2*c* and *e*) or in hot springs (Figure 2*d*), it has been concluded that ancient stromatolites were formed by filamentous phototrophic bacteria, perhaps relatives of the green nonsulfur bacterium *Chloroflexus*. Although the microbial nature of the earliest of these fossils is debated, they give an estimate that life, in the form of unicellular microorganisms, was abundant by 3.5 billion years ago.

Figure 3 shows photomicrographs of thin sections of more recent rocks containing cell-like structures remarkably similar to modern filamentous bacteria and green algae. In the oldest stromatolites these organisms were likely anoxygenic (nonoxy-

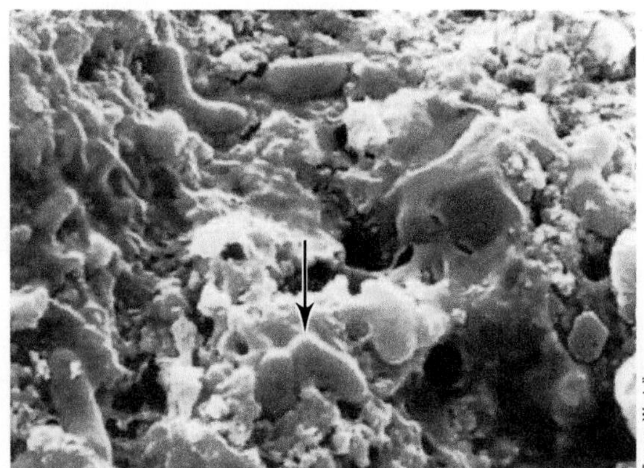

Figure 1 **Ancient microbial life.** Scanning electron micrograph of microfossil bacteria from 3.45 billion-year-old rocks of the Barberton Greenstone Belt, South Africa. Note the rod-shaped bacteria (arrow) attached to particles of mineral matter. The cells are about 0.7 μm in diameter.

Figure 2 **Ancient and modern stromatolites.** *(a)* The oldest known stromatolite, found in a rock about 3.5 billion years old, from the Warrawoona Group in Western Australia. Shown is a vertical section through the laminated structure preserved in the rock. Arrows point to the laminated layers. *(b)* Stromatolites of conical shape from 1.6 billion-year-old dolomite rock of the McArthur basin of the Northern Territory of Australia. *(c)* Modern stromatolites in a warm marine bay, Shark Bay, Western Australia. *(d)* Modern stromatolites composed of thermophilic cyanobacteria growing in a thermal pool in Yellowstone National Park. Each structure is about 2 cm high. *(e)* Another view of modern and very large stromatolites from Shark Bay. Individual structures are 0.5–1 m in diameter.

gen-evolving) phototrophic bacteria rather than the O_2-evolving cyanobacteria that dominate modern stromatolites (Figure 2*c, e*). In summary, it seems likely that *Bacteria* and *Archaea* evolved an impressive morphological and metabolic diversity very early in Earth's history.

1 MiniReview

Planet Earth is approximately 4.5 billion years old. The first evidence for microbial life can be found in rocks 3.86 billion years old. In rocks 3.5 billion years old or younger, microbial formations called stromatolites are abundant.

- Why have rocks dating to the origin of Earth not been found?
- What do crystals of the mineral zircon tell us about when the first oceans may have formed?
- What does the possible presence of liquid water on Earth 4.4 to 4.3 billion years ago suggest about the origin of life?

2 Origin of Cellular Life

Here, we examine some possible ways in which life might have originated, developing from abiotic materials into self-replicating cells. Because all life is cellular, from single-celled bacteria to multicellular animals and plants, our focus here is on the following questions: How might the first cells have arisen? and What might those early cells have been like?

Surface Origin Hypothesis

One hypothesis for the origin of life holds that the first membrane-enclosed, self-replicating cells arose out of a primordial soup rich in organic and inorganic compounds in a "warm little pond." Although there is experimental evidence that organic precursors to living cells can form spontaneously under certain conditions, surface conditions of early Earth are now thought to have been hostile to life and to its inorganic and organic precursors. The dramatic temperature fluctuations and mixing resulting from meteor impacts, dust clouds, and storms, together with the highly oxidizing atmosphere present at the time, make a surface origin for life unlikely.

Subsurface Origin Hypothesis

An alternative hypothesis is that life originated at hydrothermal springs on the ocean floor, well below Earth's surface, where conditions would have been much less hostile and more stable. A steady and abundant supply of energy in the form of reduced inorganic compounds, for example, H_2 and H_2S, may have been available at these spring sites (Figure 4).

When this very warm (90–100°C), alkaline, hydrothermal water flowed up through the crust and mixed with the cooler,

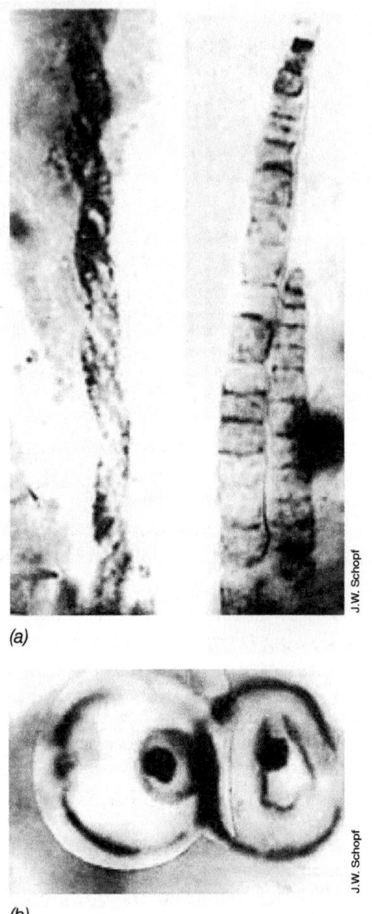

Figure 3 More recent fossil bacteria and eukaryotes. The two photographs in *(a)* show fossil bacteria from the Bitter Springs Formation, a rock formation in central Australia about 1 billion years old. These forms bear a striking resemblance to modern filamentous cyanobacteria, anoxygenic phototrophs, or filamentous sulfur chemolithotrophs. Cell diameters, 5–7 μm. *(b)* Microfossils of eukaryotic cells from the same rock formation. The cellular structure is remarkably similar to that of certain modern green algae, such as *Chlorella* species. Cell diameter, about 15 μm.

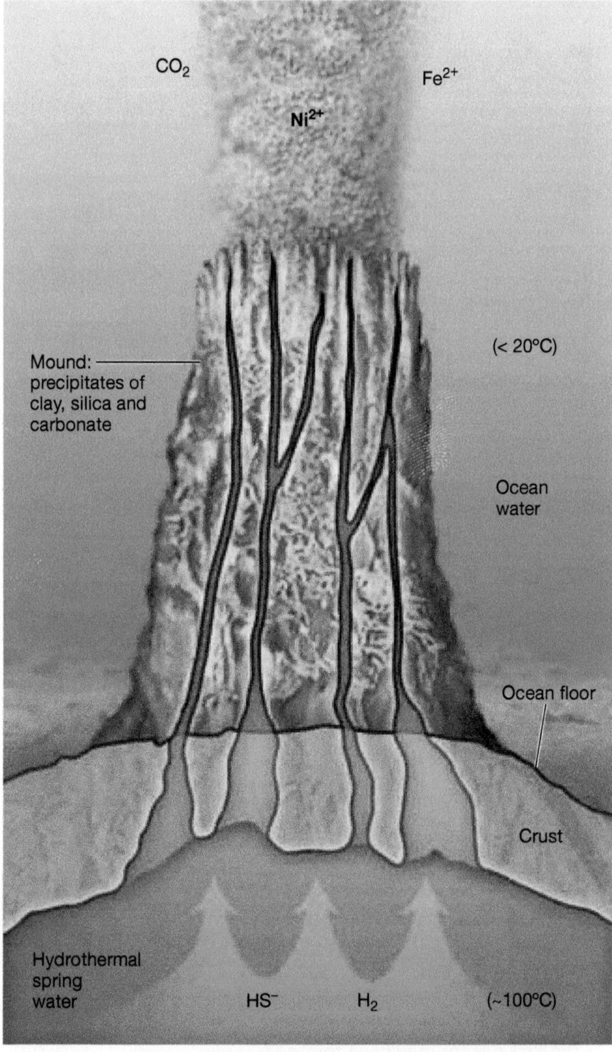

Figure 4 Submarine mound formed at a hydrothermal spring in Earth's early ocean. Hot reduced alkaline hydrothermal fluid mixes with cooler, more oxidized, more acidic ocean water, forming precipitates. The mound is made up of precipitates of Fe and S compounds, clays, silicates, and carbonates. Reaction of H_2 and CO_2 as an early prebiotic metabolism may have led to the generation of organic compounds.

slightly acidic, iron-containing, more oxidized oceanic waters, precipitates of colloidal pyrite (FeS), silicates, carbonates, and magnesium-containing montmorillonite clays formed. These precipitates built up into structured mounds of gel-like adsorptive surfaces containing pore-filled semipermeable enclosures (Figure 5). The surfaces and pores were rich in minerals such as Fe and Ni sulfides, which catalyzed formation of amino acids, simple peptides, sugars, and nitrogenous bases and trapped and concentrated these compounds. With phosphate from seawater, nucleotides such as AMP and ATP were formed, with their polymerization into RNA catalyzed by montmorillonite clay, which has been shown to catalyze various chemical reactions. The flow of reduced inorganic compounds from the crust provided steady sources of electrons for this prebiotic chemistry, which was fed from ocean water by carbon dioxide, phosphate, iron, and other minerals. It was powered by redox and pH gradients developed across the semipermeable FeS membrane-like surfaces, providing a prebiotic proton motive force.

An RNA World and Protein Synthesis

The synthesis and concentration of organic compounds by this prebiotic chemistry set the stage for self-replicating systems, the precursors to cellular life. How might self-replicating

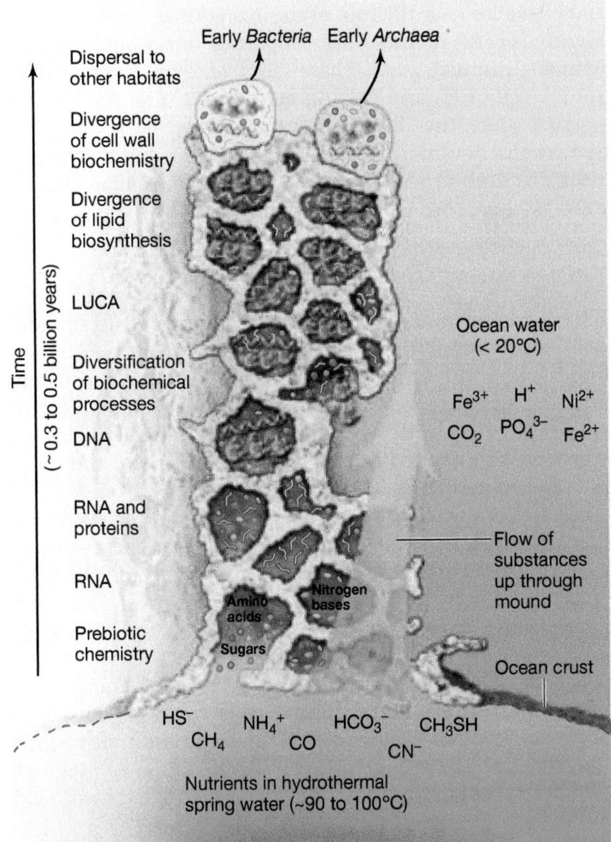

Figure 5 A model for the origin of cellular life and its divergence into early *Bacteria* and early *Archaea*. A portion of the submarine mound from Figure 4 is shown. Transitions from prebiotic chemistry to cellular life are depicted. Key features of the model are self-replicating RNA, enzymatic activity of proteins, and DNA taking on the genetic coding function, leading to early cellular life. This was followed by evolution of biochemical pathways and divergence in lipid biosynthesis and cell wall biochemistry, giving rise to early *Bacteria* and *Archaea*. LUCA, Last Universal Common Ancestor.

systems have arisen? One possibility is that there was an early *RNA world*, in which the first self-replicating systems were molecules of RNA (Figure 5). Although fragile, RNA could have survived in the cooler temperatures of the gel-like precipitates forming at ocean floor springs. RNA can bind small molecules, such as ATP and other nucleotides, and has catalytic activity (ribozymes), so RNA might have catalyzed its own synthesis from the available sugars, bases and phosphate.

RNA also can bind other molecules, such as amino acids, catalyzing the synthesis of primitive proteins. As different proteins were made and accumulated on early Earth they may have coated the inner surfaces of the structured FeS mounds and taken over some of the function of a semipermeable membrane. Later, as different proteins emerged, they took over RNA's catalytic role (Figure 5). Eventually, DNA, more stable than RNA and therefore a better repository of genetic (coding) information, arose and assumed the template role for RNA synthesis. This three-part system—DNA, RNA, and protein—became fixed early on in cellular evolution as the best solution to biological information processing (Figure 5). Following these steps, one can envision a time of extensive biochemical innovation and experimentation in which much of the structural and functional machinery of these earliest self-replicating systems was invented and refined under natural selection.

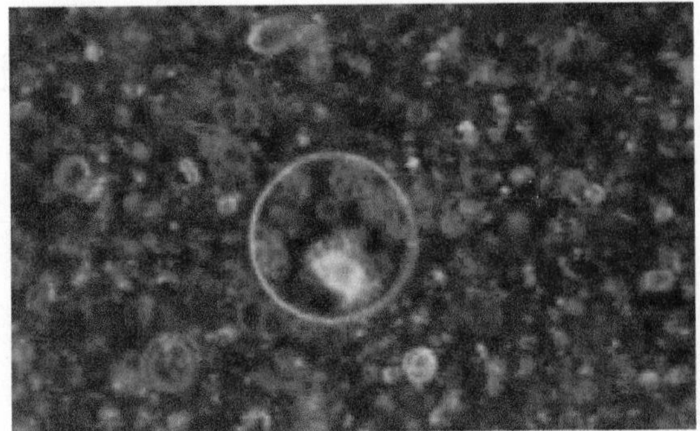

Figure 6 Lipid vesicles made in the laboratory from the fatty acid myristic acid and RNA. The vesicle itself stains green, and the RNA complexed inside the vesicle stains red. Vesicle synthesis is catalyzed by the surfaces of montmorillonite clay particles.

Lipid Membranes and Cellular Life

Other important steps in the emergence of cellular life were the buildup of lipids and the synthesis of phospholipid membrane vesicles that enclosed the cell's biochemical and replication machinery. Proteins embedded in the lipids would have maintained a semipermeable state for the vesicles, shuttling nutrients and wastes across the lipid membrane, setting the stage for evolution of energy-conserving processes and ATP synthesis. By entrapping RNA and DNA, these lipoprotein vesicles, which may have been similar to montmorillonite clay vesicles (Figure 6), may have formed the first self-replicating cells, thereby gaining a measure of independence from the structured FeS precipitate mounds that nurtured them.

From this population of early cells, considered to be the last universal common ancestor (LUCA), cellular life may then have evolved differences in lipid biosynthesis and cell wall biochemistry, diverging into the ancestors of modern day *Bacteria* and *Archaea* (Figure 5). An indication of that early divergence is retained in the stereochemistry of the glycerol-phosphate backbone of phospholipids. In *Bacteria*, phospholipids contain glycerol-3-phosphate, whereas in *Archaea* it is glycerol-1-phosphate, and the enzymes for the synthesis of these different glycerol-phosphates appear to have arisen independently in ancestral *Bacteria* and *Archaea*.

Early Metabolism

From the time of its formation, the early ocean and all of Earth was anoxic. Molecular oxygen did not appear in any

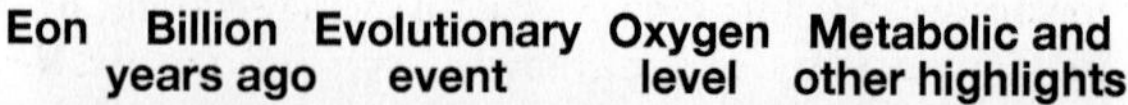

Eon
Billion years ago
Evolutionary event
Oxygen level
Metabolic and other highlights

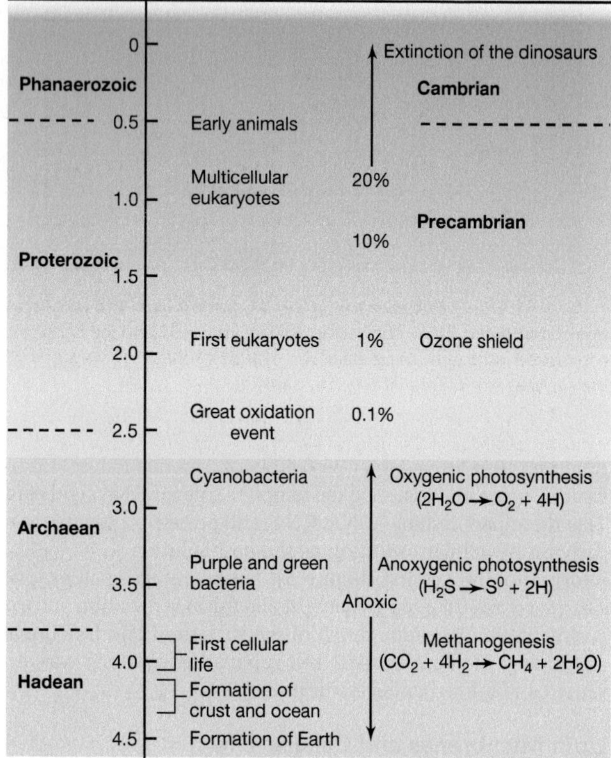

Figure 7 Major landmarks in biological evolution, Earth's changing geochemistry, and microbial metabolic diversification. The maximum time for the origin of life is fixed by the time of the origin of Earth, and the minimum time for the origin of oxygenic photosynthesis is fixed by the Great Oxidation Event, about 2.3 billion years ago. Note how the oxygenation of the atmosphere due to cyanobacterial metabolism was a gradual process, occurring over a period of about 2 billion years. Although full (20%) oxygen levels are required for animals and most other higher organisms, this is not true of *Bacteria*, as many are facultative aerobes or microaerophiles. Thus, *Bacteria* respiring at reduced O_2 levels may have dominated Earth for a period of a billion years or so before Earth's atmosphere reached current levels of oxygen.

significant quantities until much later, following evolution of oxygenic photosynthesis by cyanobacteria (Figure 7). Thus, the energy-generating metabolism of primitive cells would have been exclusively anaerobic. It may also have been autotrophic, because any consumption of abiotically formed organic compounds as sources of carbon for cellular material probably would have exhausted these compounds relatively quickly. The possibility that autotrophy was an early physiological lifestyle is supported also by the discovery of autotrophic *Bacteria* such as *Aquifex*. This member of the *Bacteria* is a hyperthermophile, contains a very small genome, and branches near the root of the evolutionary tree of life (see Figure 16). All of these are properties one would associate with a "primitive" state. These ideas, taken together with the abundance of H_2 and CO_2 on early Earth (Figures 4 and 5), suggest that the first cells may have been anaerobic autotrophs, obtaining their carbon from CO_2 and their energy, electrons used to reduce carbon dioxide to cellular material, from H_2, in accord with the formula:

$$2\,H_2 + CO_2 \rightarrow H_2O + [CH_2O]$$

If life emerged in this way, it would have required an abundant and steady supply of H_2, as well as nitrogen, phosphorus, and various minerals, and it would have produced large amounts of waste, possibly in the form of acetate. A similar situation exists with hyperthermophilic *Archaea*, many of which oxidize H_2 and reduce S^0 and branch near the root of the phylogenetic tree.

Reactions with the substrate ferrous iron, which was abundant on early Earth, also have been proposed as energy-yielding reactions for primitive organisms. For example, the reaction

$$FeS + H_2S \rightarrow FeS_2 + H_2 \qquad \Delta G^{0\prime} = -42\text{kJ}$$

proceeds exergonically with the release of energy. This reaction yields H_2, and primitive cells could have used this powerful electron donor to generate a proton motive force. The H_2 could have fueled a primitive ATPase to yield ATP (Figure 8). Other sources of H_2 may also have been avail-

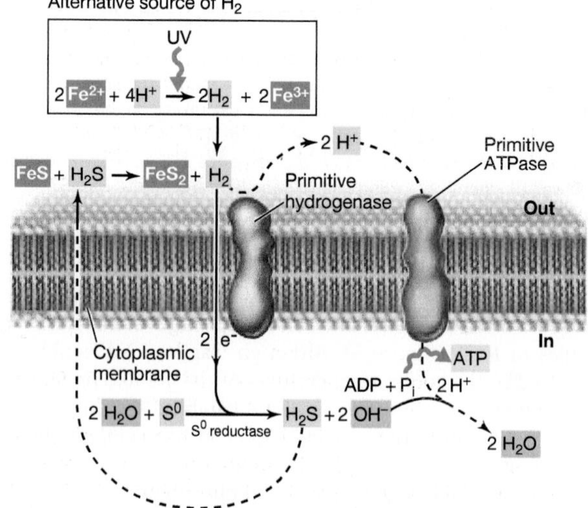

Figure 8 A possible energy-generating scheme for primitive cells. Formation of pyrite leads to H_2 production and S^0 reduction, which fuels a primitive ATPase. Note how H_2S plays only a catalytic role; the net substrates would be FeS and S^0. Also note how few different proteins would be required. The $\Delta G^{0\prime}$ of the reaction $FeS + H_2S \rightarrow FeS_2 + H_2 = -42$ kJ. An alternative source of H_2 could have been the UV-catalyzed reduction of H^+ by Fe^{2+} as shown.

able from ferrous iron on early Earth. For example, Fe^{2+} can reduce protons to hydrogen in the presence of ultraviolet radiation as an energy source (Figure 8). Early oceans were thought to be loaded with ferrous iron, and their surface waters were subject to intense UV radiation.

With H_2 as electron donor, an electron acceptor would also have been required to form a redox pair; this could have been elemental sulfur (S^0). As shown in Figure 8, the oxidation of H_2 with the production of H_2S would have required few enzymes. Moreover, because of the abundance of H_2 and sulfur compounds on early Earth, cells would have had a nearly limitless supply of energy.

These early forms of chemolithotrophic metabolism would have supported the production of large amounts of organic compounds from autotrophic CO_2 fixation. Over time, these organic materials would have accumulated and provided abundant, diverse, and continually renewed sources of reduced organic carbon, triggering the evolution of various chemoorganotrophic bacteria whose metabolic strategies employ organic compounds as electron donors in energy metabolism.

2 MiniReview

Life may have arisen at hydrothermal springs on the early ocean floor. The first life forms may have been self-replicating RNAs that catalyzed synthesis of proteins. Eventually, DNA took over the template role for RNA synthesis, and the three-part system of DNA, RNA, and protein became universal in early cells. Early microbial metabolism was anaerobic and likely chemolithotrophic, exploiting the abundant sources of H_2, FeS, and H_2S present. Carbon metabolism initially may have been autotrophy, followed by heterotrophy as various organic compounds were formed and accumulated.

- What roles did the mounds of mineral-rich materials at warm hydrothermal springs play in the origin of life?
- What important cell structure was necessary for life to proceed from a possible RNA world to cellular life?
- How could cells have obtained energy from FeS + H_2S?

3 Microbial Diversification: Consequences for Earth's Biosphere

Following the origin of cells and the development of early forms of energy and carbon metabolism, microbial life underwent a long process of metabolic diversification, taking advantage of the various and abundant energy resources available on Earth. Undoubtedly, as individual kinds of resources were consumed and became limiting, competition and natural selection drove the evolution of more efficient and new metabolisms. Also, microbial life, through its metabolic activity, altered the chemical environment, depleting some resources and creating others through the production of waste products and cellular material. These changes and new resources in turn presented both challenges to survival and opportunities for utilization. In the following sections, we examine the overall scope of metabolic diversification and focus on one metabolic waste product, oxygen, which had a profound influence on the course of evolution.

Metabolic Diversification

Geological and molecular biological data allow us to look back in time to gain insight into microbial diversification. Molecular evidence, in contrast to geological materials, which can be examined directly, is indirect; phylogenies are based on comparison of DNA sequences that allow us to estimate when the ancestors of modern bacteria may have existed. In Section 5 we describe molecular clocks and DNA sequence-based analysis, but here we use information from DNA to estimate a timescale for when some of the major metabolic groups of bacteria appeared on Earth.

LUCA, the last universal common ancestor, may have existed as early as 4.25 billion years ago (Figure 7). Molecular evidence, however, suggests that ancestors of modern day *Bacteria* and *Archaea* had diverged by 4.1–3.9 billion years ago. As these two lineages diverged, they developed distinct metabolisms. Early *Bacteria* may have used H_2 and CO_2 to produce acetate, or ferrous iron compounds, for energy generation, as noted above. At the same time, early *Archaea* developed the ability to use H_2 and CO_2, or possibly acetate as it accumulated, as substrates for methanogenesis (the production of methane), according to the following formulas:

$$4\ H_2 + CO_2 \rightarrow CH_4 + 2\ H_2O$$

$$H_3C\text{—}COO^- + H_2O \rightarrow CH_4 + HCO_3^-$$

Phototrophy arose somewhat later, about 3.2 billion years ago, and only in *Bacteria*. The ability to use solar radiation as an energy source allowed phototrophs to diversify extensively. With the exception of the early-branching hyperthermophilic *Bacteria, Aquifex,* and *Thermotoga,* the common ancestor of all other *Bacteria* appears to be an anaerobic phototroph, possibly similar to *Chloroflexus*. About 2.7 billion years ago, the cyanobacteria lineage developed a photosystem that could use H_2O in place of H_2S for photosynthetic reduction of CO_2, releasing O_2 instead of S^0 as a waste product. The development of oxygenic photosynthesis dramatically changed the course of evolution.

The Rise of Oxygen: Banded Iron Formations

Molecular and chemical evidence indicates that oxygen-generating cyanobacteria first appeared on Earth about 2.7 billion years ago. Geological evidence, however, indicates that the accumulation of a significant level of oxygen in the atmosphere took another 300 million years. By 2.4 billion years ago, oxygen levels had risen to one part per million, a tiny amount, but enough to initiate what has come to be called the *Great Oxidation Event* (Figure 7). What delayed the buildup of oxygen for so long?

Figure 9 **Banded iron formations.** An exposed cliff about 10 m in height containing layers of iron oxides interspersed with layers containing iron silicates and other silica materials. Brockman Iron Formation, Hammersley Basin, Western Australia. The iron oxides contain iron in the ferric (Fe^{3+}) form produced from ferrous iron (Fe^{2+}) primarily by the oxygen released by cyanobacterial photosynthesis.

The O_2 that cyanobacteria produced did not begin to accumulate in the atmosphere until it reacted with reduced materials, especially iron (such as FeS and FeS_2) in the oceans; these materials react spontaneously with O_2 to produce H_2O. The Fe^{3+} produced in pyrite (FeS_2) oxidation became a prominent marker in the geological record. Much of the iron in rocks of Precambrian origin (>0.5 billion years ago, see Figure 7) exists in banded iron formations (Figure 9), laminated sedimentary rocks formed in deep-water deposits of alternating layers of iron-rich minerals and iron-poor, silica-rich material. The metabolism of cyanobacteria yielded O_2 that oxidized Fe^{2+} to Fe^{3+}. The ferric iron formed various iron oxides that accumulated as banded iron formations (Figure 9). Once the abundant Fe^{2+} on Earth was consumed, the stage was set for O_2 to accumulate in the atmosphere, a major trigger of evolutionary events (Figure 7).

New Metabolisms and the Ozone Shield

The evolution of oxygenic photosynthesis had enormous consequences for Earth because, as O_2 accumulated, the atmosphere gradually changed from anoxic to oxic (Figure 7). *Bacteria* and *Archaea* unable to adapt to this change were increasingly restricted to anoxic habitats because of the toxicity of oxygen and because it oxidized the reduced substances upon which their metabolisms were dependent. The oxic atmosphere, however, also created conditions that led to the evolution of various new metabolic pathways, such as sulfate reduction, nitrification, and iron oxidation. *Bacteria* that developed the ability to respire oxygen, either facultatively or exclusively, gained a tremendous energetic advantage and diversified rapidly thereafter, because with the oxidation of organic compounds they were able to obtain more energy than could anaerobes. With the development of larger cell populations, chances increased for the evolution of new types of organisms and metabolic schemes.

During this time, organelle-containing eukaryotic microorganisms evolved (Section 4), and the rise in oxygen also spurred their rapid evolution. The oldest known eukaryotic microfossil is about 2 billion years old. Multicellular and increasing complex microfossils of algae are evident from 1.9 to 1.4 billion years ago. By 0.6 billion years ago, oxygen was near present levels, and large multicellular organisms, the Ediacaran fauna, were present in the sea (Figure 7). In a relatively short time, multicellular eukaryotes diversified into the ancestors of modern-day algae, plants, fungi, and animals (Section 8).

An important consequence of O_2 for the evolution of life was the formation of ozone, a substance that provides a barrier preventing much of the intense ultraviolet radiation of the sun from reaching the Earth. When O_2 is subject to UV radiation, it is converted to O_3, which strongly absorbs wavelengths up to 300 nm. Until an ozone shield developed in Earth's upper atmosphere, evolution could have continued only beneath the ocean surface and in protected terrestrial environments where organisms were not exposed to the lethal DNA damage by intense UV radiation from the sun. However, after the photosynthetic production of O_2 and subsequent development of an ozone shield, organisms could then range over the surface of Earth, exploiting new habitats and evolving greater diversity. Figure 7 summarizes some major events in biological evolution and changes in the Earth's geochemistry from a highly reducing to a highly oxidizing planet.

3 MiniReview

Early *Bacteria* and *Archaea* may have diverged from a common ancestor 4.1–3.9 billion years ago. Microbial metabolism diversified on early Earth, with the invention of methanogenesis and anoxygenic photosynthesis. Oxygenic photosynthesis led to development of an oxic environment, banded iron formations, and great bursts of biological evolution.

- Why is the advent of cyanobacteria considered a critical step in evolution?
- In what form is iron present in banded iron formations?
- What role did ozone play in biological evolution, and how did cyanobacteria make the production of ozone possible?

4 Endosymbiotic Origin of Eukaryotes

The divergence of the lineages that gave rise to *Bacteria* and *Archaea* was followed by many millions of years of metabolic diversification as the members of these lineages evolved and diversified. Major changes in Earth's biosphere occurred as a consequence of this diversification, most notably the generation of an increasingly oxygenated atmosphere. Up to that point in the evolution of life, all cells apparently lacked a membrane-enclosed nucleus and organelles, as do modern-day *Bacteria* and *Archaea*. Eukaryotes (*Eukarya*), however, are characterized by the presence of a membrane-enclosed nucleus and organelles. Here we probe the origin of *Eukarya*, asking when and how this third domain of life, bearing a membrane-enclosed nucleus and organelles, emerged.

Origin of Eukaryotes

Geological evidence from microfossils (Figure 3) indicates that unicellular eukaryotes arose on Earth about 2 billion years ago (Figure 7). Thus, the lineages that gave rise to modern-day *Bacteria* and *Archaea* had existed as the only life forms on our planet for about 2 billion years before eukaryotes evolved. This timing tells us that the origin of eukaryotes came after the rise in atmospheric oxygen, the invention of respiratory metabolism in *Bacteria*, and the development of enzymes such as superoxide dismutase, by which cells could detoxify oxygen radicals generated as a by-product of aerobic respiration. How might *Eukarya* have arisen and in what ways did the availability of oxygen influence evolution?

Endosymbiosis

A well-supported hypothesis for the origin of the eukaryotic cells is that of **endosymbiosis**, which states that the mitochondria and chloroplasts of modern-day eukaryotes arose from the stable incorporation into another type of cell of a chemoorganotrophic bacterium, which carried out facultatively aerobic metabolism, and a cyanobacterium, which carried out oxygenic photosynthesis. Oxygen was a factor in endosymbiosis through its consumption in energy metabolism by the ancestor of the mitochondrion and its production in photosynthesis by the ancestor of the chloroplast. The greater amounts of energy released by aerobic respiration undoubtedly contributed to rapid evolution of eukaryotes, as did the ability to exploit sunlight for energy.

The overall physiology and metabolism of mitochondria and chloroplasts and the sequence and structures of their genomes support the endosymbiosis hypothesis. For example, both mitochondria and chloroplasts contain ribosomes of the prokaryotic type (70S) and show 16S ribosomal RNA gene sequences (Section 6) characteristic of certain *Bacteria*. Moreover, the same antibiotics that affect ribosome function in free-living *Bacteria* inhibit ribosome function in these organelles. Mitochondria and chloroplasts also contain small amounts of DNA arranged in a covalently closed, circular form, typical of *Bacteria*. Indeed, many telltale signs of *Bacteria* are present in organelles from modern eukaryotic cells. However, there is more to the question of how the eukaryotic cell arose, including the nature of the cell that acquired mitochondria and later chloroplasts and how the nuclear membrane formed.

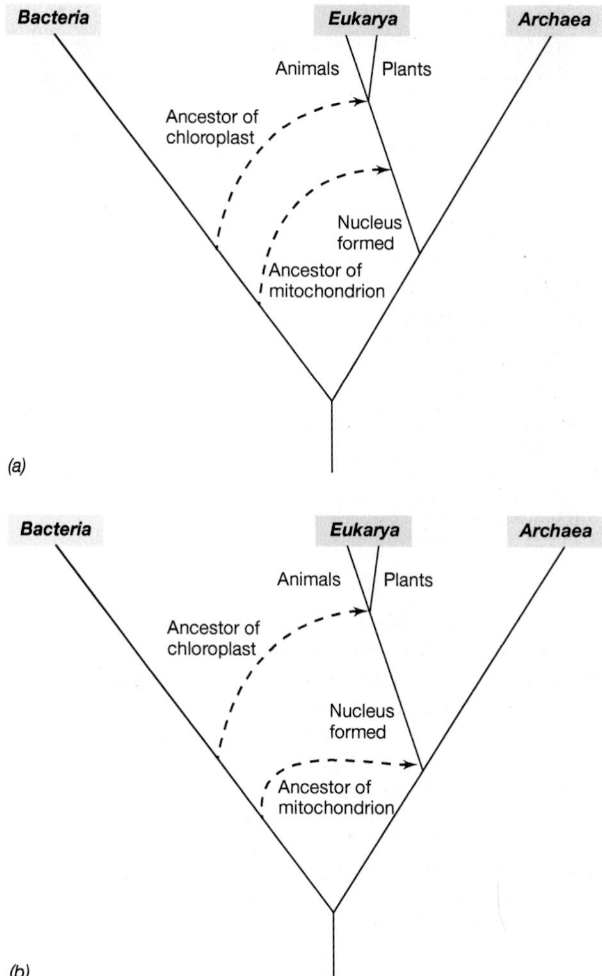

Figure 10 **Models for the origin of the eukaryotic cell.** *(a)* The nucleated line diverged from the archaeal line and later acquired by endosymbiosis the bacterial ancestor of the mitochondrion and then the cyanobacterial ancestor of the chloroplast, at which point the nucleated line diverged into the lineages giving rise to plants and animals. *(b)* In contrast, the bacterial ancestor of the mitochondrion was taken up endosymbiotically by a member of *Archaea*, and from this association, the nucleus later emerged, with a later endosymbiotic acquisition of the cyanobacterial ancestor of the chloroplast. Note the position of the mitochondrion and chloroplast on the universal phylogenetic tree shown in Figure 16.

Formation of the Eukaryotic Cell

Two hypotheses have been put forward to explain the formation of the eukaryotic cell (Figure 10). In one, eukaryotes began as a nucleus-bearing lineage that later acquired mitochondria and chloroplasts by endosymbiosis (Figure 10a). In this scenario, the nucleus-bearing cell line arose from an early kind of cell, and the nucleus is thought to have arisen spontaneously, probably in response to the increasing genome size of the early eukaryote.

Table 1 Major features that group *Bacteria* or *Archaea* with *Eukarya*[a]

Characteristic	Bacteria	Archaea	Eukarya
Membrane lipids	Ester-linked	Ether-linked	Ester-linked
Chlorophyll-based photosynthesis	Yes	No	Yes (in chloroplasts)
Histone proteins present	No[b]	Yes	Yes
Cell wall	Muramic acid present	Muramic acid absent	Muramic acid absent
Initiator tRNA	Formylmethionine	Methionine	Methionine
Ribosome sensitivity to diphtheria toxin	No	Yes	Yes
RNA polymerases	One (4 subunits)	One (8–12 subunits each)	Three (12–14 subunits each)
Transcription factors required	No	Yes	Yes
Promoter structure	−10 and −35 sequences (Pribnow box)	TATA box	TATA box
Sensitivity to chloramphenicol, streptomycin, and kanamycin	Yes	No	No

[a]See also Table 2 for additional features of the three domains.
[b]DNA-binding protein HU is present in *Bacteria*.

The second hypothesis, called the *hydrogen hypothesis*, proposes that the eukaryotic cell arose from an intracellular association between an oxygen-consuming, hydrogen-producing member of *Bacteria*, the symbiont, which gave rise to the mitochondrion, and a member of *Archaea*, the host (Figure 10*b*). The host's dependence on H_2 as an energy source, produced as a waste product of the symbiont's metabolism is thought to have led to this association. In this scenario, the nucleus arose after these two kinds of cells had formed a stable association and genes for lipid synthesis were transferred from the symbiont to the host chromosome. The transfer of these genes to the host chromosome may then have led to synthesis of bacterial (symbiont) lipids by the host, eventually forming an internal membrane system, the endoplasmic reticulum, and the beginnings of the eukaryotic nucleus. Increasing size of the host genome led to compartmentalizing and sequestering the genetic coding information within a membrane away from the cytoplasm to protect it and to permit more efficient replication and gene expression. Later, this mitochondrion-containing, nucleated cell line acquired chloroplasts by endosymbiosis (Figure 10*b*).

Chimeric Nature of the Eukaryotic Cell

Both hypotheses to explain the origin of eukaryotes suggest that the eukaryotic cell is a chimera, a cell made up of attributes of both *Bacteria* and *Archaea*. Indeed, this appears to be the case. Eukaryotes have the type of lipids found in *Bacteria*, but they have a transcription and translation apparatus more similar to that of *Archaea* than that of *Bacteria* (Table 1). However, in energy metabolism—that is, ATP-producing pathways in mitochondria, hydrogenosomes (degenerate mitochondria), and the cytoplasm, as well as glycolytic enzymes in the cytoplasm—they are more similar to *Bacteria* than to *Archaea*.

The development of the eukaryotic cell was a major step in evolution, creating complex, genetically chimeric cells with new capabilities, powered by oxygen-respiring mitochondria and phototrophic, oxygen-generating chloroplasts. Like the origin of the first cells from abiotic materials and the diversification of *Bacteria* and *Archaea*, the evolutionary process by which the eukaryotic cell and its individual components arose took long periods of time and was likely to have undergone many false starts and evolutionary dead ends. Each step along the way, however, created new opportunities for variation to arise and natural selection to work, discarding some functions and attributes while refining others, and inventing wholly new capabilities as a consequence of the progressive genetic integration between symbiont and host. The origin of the eukaryotic cell set the stage for an explosion in biological diversity that built on and followed the massive diversification of *Bacteria* and *Archaea*. The period from about 2 billion years ago to the present saw the rise and diversification of unicellular eukaryotic microorganisms, the origin of multicellularity, and the appearance of structurally complex plant, animal, and fungal life (Figures 7, 10, and see 16).

4 MiniReview

Unicellular eukaryotes arose about 2 billion years ago. The eukaryotic cell may have arisen from the endosymbiosis between a facultatively aerobic H_2-producing *Bacteria* and a H_2-consuming *Archaea*. The eukaryotic cell is believed to be a chimera made up of properties from both *Bacteria* and *Archaea*.

- What evidence supports the idea that the eukaryotic mitochondrion and chloroplast were once free-living members of the domain *Bacteria*?
- How might the eukaryotic nucleus have arisen?
- In what ways are modern eukaryotes a combination of attributes of *Bacteria* and *Archaea*?

II MICROBIAL EVOLUTION

5 The Evolutionary Process

Evolution is descent with modification, a change in the sequence of an organism's genomic DNA and the inheritance of that change by the next generation. In this explicitly Darwinian view of life, all organisms are related through descent from an ancestor that lived in the past. We have outlined an hypothesis for the origin of the most distant of those ancestors, LUCA (Section 2). Since that time, about 4 billion years ago, life has undergone an extensive process of change as new kinds of organisms arose from other kinds existing in the past. Evolution has also led to the loss of life forms, with unsuccessful organisms becoming extinct over time. Evolution accounts not only for the tremendous diversity we see today, but also for the high level of complexity in modern organisms. Indeed, no organism living today is primitive. All extant life forms are modern organisms, well adapted to and successful in their ecological niches, having arisen by the process of evolutionary change under the pressure of natural selection.

Mutations and Selection

DNA sequence variation can arise in a number of different ways. Most important for the way organisms evolve are mutations, changes in the nucleotide sequence of an organism's genome. Mutations occur due to errors in the fidelity of replication, to UV radiation, and other factors, and they are essential in order for life to be able to change and adapt through natural selection. Adaptive mutations are those that improve the **fitness** of an organism, increasing its survival or reproduction compared to competing organisms. By contrast, harmful mutations lower an organism's fitness. Most mutations, however, are neutral, neither benefiting nor causing harm to the cell, and over time these mutations can accumulate in an organism's genome.

Other processes also bring about heritable changes in the sequence of an organism's genome. These include gene duplication, which can set the stage for the evolutionary development of new functions as the sequence of the duplicated gene changes over time; **horizontal gene transfer**, which can bring in genes from distantly related lineages; and gene loss, which can lead to the genome reduction often seen in obligate symbionts and parasites. Also, recombination of homologous DNA that has undergone divergence from closely related strains within a species can contribute to variation.

Regardless of whether a mutation or other genetic change is neutral, beneficial, or harmful, these changes provide the opportunity for selection of organisms whose genomes carry those changes. As environments change and as new habitats arise, cells are presented with new conditions under which they must either survive and successfully compete for nutrients or become extinct. The sequence variation present in a population provides the raw material by which the reproduction of those individuals bearing mutations beneficial under the new circumstances is favored. We will return to these ideas later, in a discussion of bacterial speciation, but here we examine how to track the evolutionary history of an organism.

5 MiniReview

Evolution is descent with modification. Natural selection works by favoring the survival and reproduction of organisms that by chance have mutations that improve fitness under new environmental conditions.

- According to the Darwinian view of life, all organisms are related by ________ .
- What class of mutation—beneficial, neutral, or harmful—is most common?
- How does the accumulation of mutations set the stage for selection?

6 Evolutionary Analysis: Theoretical Aspects

The evolutionary history of a group of organisms is called its **phylogeny**, and a major goal of evolutionary analysis is to understand this history. Because we do not have direct knowledge of the path of evolution, except for certain experimental populations of bacteria in the laboratory, phylogeny is inferred indirectly from nucleotide sequence data. Our premises are that bacteria (and all organisms) are related by descent and that the sequence of a bacterium's genome is an explicit, though sometimes fuzzy, record of the bacterium's ancestry. Because evolution is a process of inherited nucleotide sequence change, analyzing DNA sequence differences among bacteria allows us to reconstruct their phylogenetic history. Here, we examine some of the ways in which this is carried out.

Genes Employed in Phylogenetic Analysis

Various genes are used in molecular phylogenetic studies of microorganisms. Most widely used and useful for defining relationships are the genes encoding 16S rRNA (Figure 11) and its counterpart in eukaryotes, 18S rRNA. These **small subunit ribosomal RNA (SSU rRNA)** genes have been used extensively for sequence-based evolutionary analysis because they are (1) universally distributed, (2) functionally constant, (3) sufficiently conserved (that is, slowly changing), and (4) of adequate length, such that they can provide a view of evolution encompassing all living organisms.

Carl Woese at the University of Illinois pioneered the use of SSU rRNA for phylogenetic studies in the early 1970s. His work established the presence of three domains of life, *Bacteria*, *Archaea*, and *Eukarya*, and provided for the first time a unified phylogenetic framework for bacteria. For his accomplishments, Woese received the 2003 Crafoord Prize, the highest recognition for scientific achievement in biology, from the Royal Swedish Academy of Sciences.

A large and growing database of rRNA gene sequences exists. For example, the **Ribosomal Database Project II**

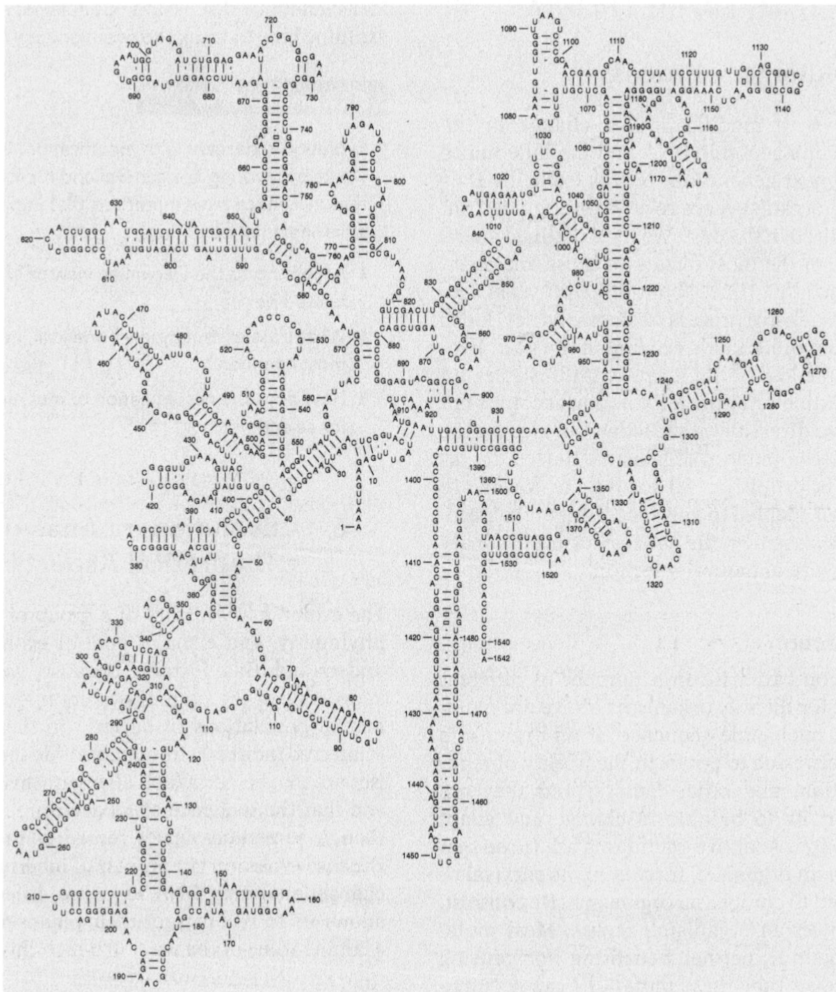

Figure 11 Ribosomal RNA. Primary and secondary structure of 16S rRNA from *Escherichia coli* (*Bacteria*). The16S rRNA from *Archaea* is similar in overall secondary structure (folding) but has numerous differences in primary structure (sequence). The counterpart in *Eukarya* to bacterial 16S rRNA is 18S rRNA, which is present in cytoplasmic ribosomes.

(RDP-II; http://rdp.cme.msu.edu) contains a collection of such sequences, now numbering over 440,000, and provides a variety of analytical programs. The 23S large-subunit rRNA (LSU-rRNA) gene is also phylogenetically highly informative, with its longer sequence providing additional information, though its length makes it more costly and time consuming to sequence. Along with these genes, those for several highly conserved proteins have been used effectively in phylogenetic analysis, including protein synthesis elongation factor Tu, heat-shock protein Hsp60, and several tRNA synthetases.

The highly conserved SSU and LSU genes have changed slowly and provide a view of evolution that is deep enough to encompass all living organisms. This strength, however, is also a limitation, in that the essential functions of rRNAs apparently have limited the amount these genes can change over evolutionary time. Consequently, the amount of variation present in SSU rRNA gene sequences may not be sufficient to provide good discrimination between bacterial species. Another possible problem with using a single gene to study bacterial evolutionary relationships is that a given gene might not be present in all organisms. An example is *recA*, which encodes a recombinase enzyme that facilitates genetic recombination in *Bacteria*. Genes homologous to *recA*, that is, having a shared ancestry with *recA*, are not present in *Archaea* and *Eukarya*, so *recA* would not be suitable for evolutionary studies extending beyond *Bacteria*. We discuss later (Section 8) ways of bypassing these problems in phylogeny and taxonomy by using genes whose sequences have diverged more than the 16S rRNA gene, consequently revealing distinctions between closely related bacteria, and by using multiple genes for evolutionary analysis.

Molecular Clocks

An unresolved question in phylogenetics is whether DNA (and protein) sequences change at a constant rate. If they do, then the amount of change between two homologous sequences would serve as an approximate **molecular clock**, or chronometer, of evolution, allowing the time in the past when the two sequences diverged from a common ancestral sequence to be estimated. Major assumptions of the molecular clock approach are that nucleotide changes accumulate in a sequence in proportion to time, that such changes generally are neutral and do not interfere with gene function, and that they are random. The molecular clock approach has been used to estimate the time of divergence of *Escherichia coli* and *Salmonella typhimurium*, closely related members of the *Gammaproteobacteria*, from a common ancestor about 120–140 million years ago. These data have also been combined with evidence from the geological record on isotopes and specific biological markers to approximate when different metabolic patterns emerged in bacteria (Section 3).

The main problem with the molecular clock approach, however, is that DNA sequences do change at different rates, which means that direct and reliable correlations to a timescale will be difficult to make. However, much of phylogenetic analysis is concerned with relative relationships among organisms, shown by branching order on phylogenetic trees. These relationships are generally discernible regardless of whether different sequences change at similar rates, so the accuracy of the molecular clock approach is not a major concern.

6 MiniReview

The evolutionary history of life, also called phylogeny, can be reconstructed through analysis of DNA sequences. The work of Carl Woese established the presence of three domains of life. Two of the domains, *Bacteria* and *Archaea*, lack a nucleus, whereas the third domain, *Eukarya*, has a nucleus.

- Why are SSU rRNA genes suitable for phylogenetic analysis?
- What information does the RDP-II provide?
- What value do molecular clocks have in phylogenetic analysis?

7 Evolutionary Analysis: Analytical Methods

Modern phylogenetics is based on nucleotide sequence comparisons, for which specific methods have been developed. We consider these methods here.

Obtaining DNA Sequences

Phylogenetic analysis using DNA sequences relies heavily on the polymerase chain reaction (PCR) to obtain sufficient copies of a gene for efficient sequencing. Specific oligonucleotide primers are designed that bind to the ends of the gene of interest, or to DNA flanking the gene, allowing DNA polymerase to bind and copy the gene. The source of DNA bearing a gene of interest typically is genomic DNA purified from individual bacterial strains. The PCR product is then visualized by agarose gel electrophoresis (Figure 12), excised from the gel, extracted and purified from the agarose, and then sequenced, often using the same oligonucleotides as primers for the sequencing reactions.

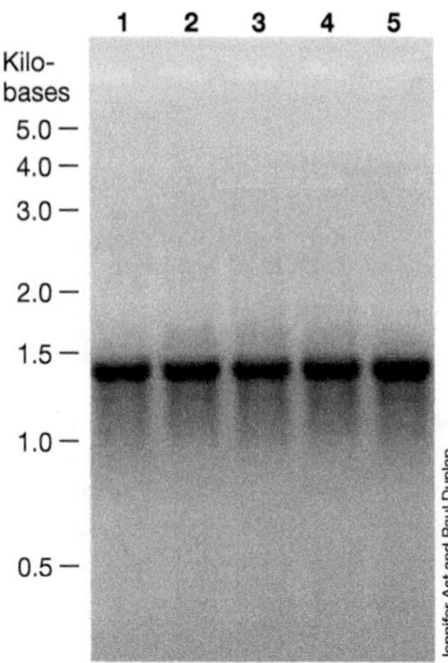

Figure 12 **PCR-amplification of the 16S rRNA gene.** Standard primers complementary to the ends of the 16S rRNA gene 27f (5′-AGAGTTTGATCCTGGCTCAG-3′) and 1492r (5′-TACGGYTACCTTGTTACGACTT-3′) were used to PCR-amplify the 16S rRNA gene from genomic DNA of five different unknown bacterial strains (lanes 1 through 5), and the products were separated by agarose gel electrophoresis (in the primer shown, Y can be either a C or a T). The bands of amplified DNA are approximately 1,465 nucleotides in length. Positions of DNA kilobase size markers are indicated at the left. Excision from the gel and purification of these PCR products is followed by sequencing and analysis to identify the bacteria.

An important aspect of PCR amplification is primer design, deciding what sequence of primers to use to amplify a specific gene. Standard primers exist for many highly conserved genes, such as primers 27f and 1492r, among others, for the 16S rRNA gene of *Bacteria* (Figures 11 and 12). These standard primers allow the 16S rRNA genes of many different *Bacteria* to be amplified for sequencing. Amplification of newly characterized or more highly divergent genes, however, often requires using a computer program, along with some trial and error, to identify primers that will effectively and specifically amplify the gene of interest.

Sequence Alignment

Phylogenetic analysis is based on homology, that is, analysis of DNA sequences that are related by common ancestry. Homologous genes in different organisms may be either

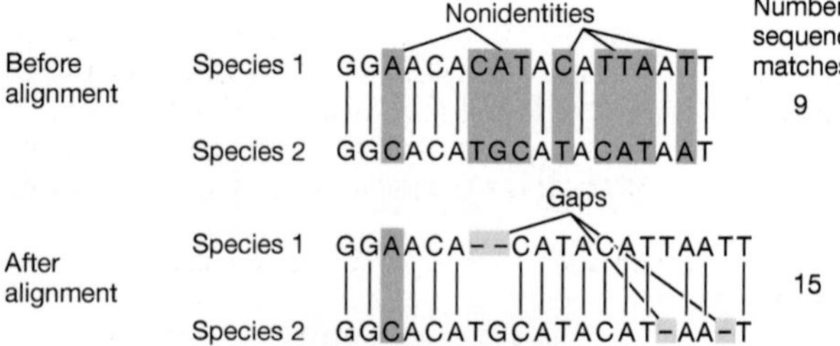

Figure 13 Alignment of DNA sequences. Sequences for a hypothetical region of a gene are shown for two organisms, before alignment and after the insertion of gaps to improve the matchup of nucleotides, indicated by the vertical lines showing identical nucleotides in the two sequences. The insertion of gaps in both sequences substantially improves the alignment.

orthologs, which differ because of sequence divergence as the organisms followed different evolutionary paths, or *paralogs*, which arise through gene duplication. Once the DNA sequence of a gene is obtained, the next step in developing a phylogeny is to align that sequence with sequences of homologous (orthologous) genes from other strains or species. This way, differences between the sequences, that is, nucleotide mismatches and insertions and deletions (gaps), some of which can be phylogenetically informative, can be pinpointed.

Figure 13 gives an example of sequence alignment. The web-based BLAST (*B*asic *L*ocal *A*lignment *S*earch *T*ool) of the National Institutes of Health (http://www.ncbi.nlm.nih.gov/BLAST) does this automatically and can help identify genes homologous to a new sequence from among the many thousands of genes already sequenced. Homologous sequences are then downloaded from GenBank (http://www.ncbi.nih.gov/Genbank), an annotated collection of all publicly available DNA sequences, and aligned. The alignment is critical to phylogenetic analysis, because the assignment of mismatches and gaps is an explicit hypothesis of how the sequences have diverged from a common ancestral sequence. Protein-coding genes usually are aligned with the aid of their inferred amino acid sequences. Other genes, such as those encoding 16S rRNA, can be aligned by eye or through the use of computer programs designed to minimize the number of mismatches and gaps. Secondary structure, for example, the folding of the **16S ribosomal RNA** (Figure 11), is also helpful in making accurate gene alignments.

Phylogenetic Trees

Reconstructing evolutionary history from observed nucleotide sequence differences involves construction of a *phylogenetic tree*, which is a graphic illustration of the relationships among sequences of the organisms under study, much like a family tree. A phylogenetic tree is composed of nodes and branches (Figure 14). The internal nodes represent ancestors, and the tips of the branches, also called nodes, are individual strains of bacterial species that exist now and from which the sequence data were obtained. The internal nodes are points in evolution where an ancestor diverged into two new entities, each of which then began to accumulate

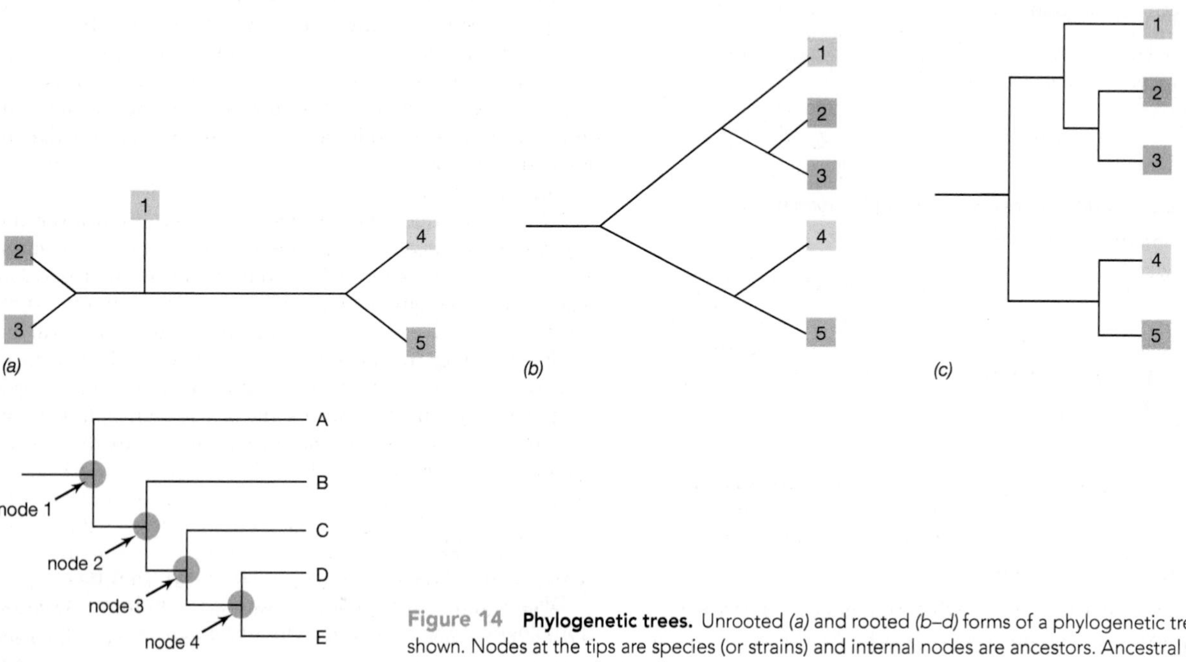

Figure 14 Phylogenetic trees. Unrooted *(a)* and rooted *(b–d)* forms of a phylogenetic tree are shown. Nodes at the tips are species (or strains) and internal nodes are ancestors. Ancestral relationships are revealed by the branching order in rooted trees *(d)*.

differences during its subsequent independent evolution. The branches define (1) the order of descent and (2) the ancestry of the nodes, and the branch length represents the number of changes that have occurred along that branch. Trees can be either *unrooted,* showing the relationships among the bacterial strains under study but not the evolutionary path leading from an ancestor to a strain (Figure 14*a*), or *rooted,* in which case the unique path from an ancestor (internal node) to each strain is defined (Figure 14*b–d*). Trees are rooted by the inclusion in the analysis of an *outgroup,* a bacterium that is less closely related to the organisms under study than the organisms are to each other, but that shares with them homologs of the gene or genes under study.

A phylogenetic tree is a depiction of lines of descent, and the relationship between two organisms therefore should be read in terms of common ancestry. That is, the more recently two species share a common ancestor, the more closely related they are. The tree in Figure 14*d* illustrates this point. Species B is more closely related to species C than it is to species A, because B and C share a more recent common ancestor (node 2) than do B and A (node 1).

Tree Reconstruction

Modern evolutionary analysis uses character-state methods, also called *cladistics,* for tree reconstruction. Character-state methods define phylogenetic relationships by examining changes in nucleotides at individual positions in the sequence, using those characters that are *phylogenetically informative*. These are characters that define a **monophyletic** group. Figure 15 describes how phylogenetically informative characters are recognized. Computer-based analysis of these changes generates a phylogenetic tree, or *cladogram*.

A widely used cladistic method is *parsimony,* which is based on the assumption that evolution is most likely to have proceeded by the path requiring fewest changes. Computer algorithms based on parsimony provide a way of identifying the tree with the smallest number of character changes. Other cladistic methods, *maximum likelihood* and *Bayesian analysis,* proceed like parsimony, but they differ by assuming a model of evolution, for example, that certain kinds of nucleotide changes are more common than others (for example, an A changing into a C happens more often than a change from A to T or G). Inexpensive computer applications, such as PAUP* (*P*hylogenetic *A*nalysis *U*nder *P*arsimony, and Other Methods), guidebooks, and web-accessible tutorials are available for learning the basic procedures of cladistic analysis and tree reconstruction.

7 MiniReview

Analytical methods for evolutionary analysis include sequence alignment and reconstructing phylogenetic trees, which should be read in terms of common ancestry. Character-state methods such as parsimony are used for tree reconstruction.

- How are DNA sequences obtained for phylogenetic analysis?
- What does a phylogenetic tree depict?
- Why is sequence alignment critical to phylogenetic analysis?

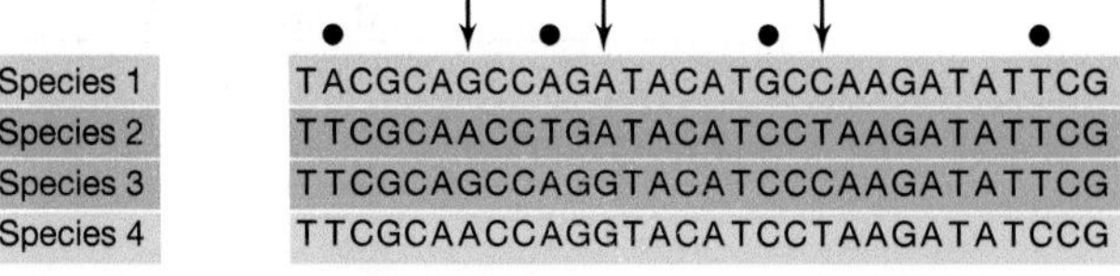

Figure 15 **Identification of phylogenetically informative sites.** Aligned sequences for four species are shown. Invariant sites are unmarked, and phylogenetically neutral sites are indicated by dots. Phylogenetically informative sites, varying in at least two of the sequences, are marked with an arrow.

8 Microbial Phylogeny

Biologists previously grouped living organisms into five kingdoms: plants, animals, fungi, protists, and bacteria. DNA sequence-based phylogenetic analysis, on the other hand, has revealed that the five kingdoms do not represent five primary evolutionary lines. Instead, cellular life on Earth has evolved along three primary lineages, called **domains**, the *Bacteria,* the *Archaea,* and the *Eukarya*. Two of these domains, the *Bacteria* and the *Archaea,* are exclusively microbial and are composed only of cells that lack a membrane-enclosed nucleus (that is, prokaryotic cells). The third lineage contains the eukaryotes (Figure 16) and is primarily microbial (that is, unicellular), and includes all of the original five kingdoms except for bacteria. The terms *Bacteria, Archaea,* and *Eukarya* designate the three domains of life, the domain being the highest biological taxon. Thus, plants, animals, fungi, and protists are all kingdoms within domain *Eukarya*.

A SSU rRNA Gene-Based Phylogeny of Life

The **universal phylogenetic tree** based on SSU rRNA genes (Figure 16) is a genealogy of all life on Earth. It depicts the evolutionary history of the cells of all organisms and clearly reveals the three domains. The root of the universal tree represents a point in evolutionary history when all extant life on Earth shared a common ancestor, LUCA, the *l*ast *u*niversal *c*ommon *a*ncestor.

Whole genome DNA sequences have confirmed the concept of the *Archaea,* species of which contain a large complement of genes that have no counterparts in *Bacteria* or *Eukarya*. The three-domain concept is also supported by analysis of specific genes shared among all organisms. Analysis of over 30 genes present in more than 190 species of *Bacteria, Archaea,* and *Eukarya* whose genomes have been completely sequenced confirms the distinct and unequivocal separation between these three lines of descent. Although branching orders and relationships among some lineages within *Bacteria, Archaea,* and *Eukarya* will be subject to revision as more is learned, analysis of multiple genes from genomic studies supports the basic structure of life proposed by Woese based on sequence analysis of SSU rRNA genes.

The presence of genes in common to *Bacteria, Archaea,* and *Eukarya* raises an interesting question. If these lineages diverged from each other so long ago from a common ancestor, how is it they share so many genes? One hypothesis is that early

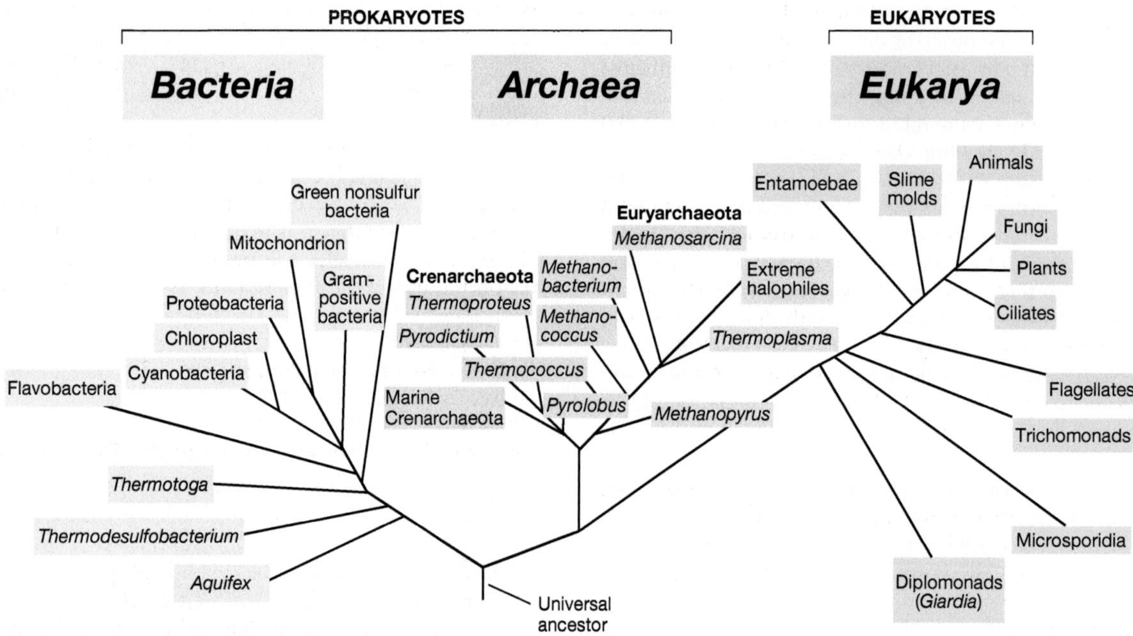

Figure 16 Universal phylogenetic tree as determined from comparative rRNA gene sequence analysis. Only a few key organisms or lineages are shown in each domain. Of the three domains, two (*Bacteria* and *Archaea*) contain only organisms lacking a membrane-enclosed nucleus (prokaryotic cells).

in the history of life, before the primary domains had diverged, horizontal gene transfer was extensive. During this time, genes encoding proteins that conferred exceptional fitness, for example, genes for the core cellular functions of transcription and translation, were promiscuously transferred among a population of primitive organisms derived from a common ancestral cell. If true, this would explain why, as genome analyses have shown, all cells regardless of domain have many core functional genes in common, as would be expected if all cells shared a common ancestor (Figure 16).

But what about the genetic differences observed from complete genome sequences? It is further hypothesized that over time barriers to unrestricted horizontal transfer evolved, perhaps from the selective colonization of habitats (thereby generating reproductive isolation) or as the result of structural or enzymatic (for example, restriction endonuclease) barriers that in some way prevented free genetic exchange. As a result, the previously genetically promiscuous population slowly began to sort out into the primary lines of evolutionary descent, the *Bacteria* and *Archaea* (Figure 16). As each lineage continued to evolve, certain unique biological traits became fixed within each group. Today, after some 4 billion years of microbial evolution (Figure 7), we see the grand result: three domains of cellular life that on the one hand share many common features but on the other hand display distinctive evolutionary histories of their own.

Bacteria

Among *Bacteria*, at least 80 major evolutionary groups (called phyla, singular **phylum**, or divisions) have been discovered thus far; several key ones are shown in the universal tree in Figure 16. Many groups have been defined from environmental sequences only (Section 9). Some of the lineages in the domain *Bacteria* are those previously distinguished by some phenotypic property, such as morphology or physiology; the spirochetes and the cyanobacteria, respectively, are good examples of this. But most major groups of *Bacteria* consist of species that, although specifically related from a phylogenetic standpoint, lack strong phenotypic cohesiveness. The **Proteobacteria** are a good example here; the mixture of physiologies present within this group includes all known forms of microbial physiology. This clearly indicates that physiology and phylogeny are not necessarily linked.

Eukaryotic organelles clearly originated from within the domain *Bacteria*. As shown on the universal tree, mitochondria arose from the *Proteobacteria*, a major group of *Bacteria* (Figure 16), specifically from a relative of *Rhizobium* and the rickettsias. Interestingly, like mitochondria, these organisms live intracellularly, within the cells of either plants or animals. The chloroplast arose from within the cyanobacterial phylum (Figures 10 and 16), as could be predicted because both cyanobacteria and the chloroplast carry out oxygenic photosynthesis.

Archaea

From a phylogenetic perspective, the domain *Archaea* consists of two groups, the *Crenarchaeota* and *Euryarchaeota* (Figure 16). Branching close to the root of the universal tree are hyperthermophilic *Crenarchaeota*, such as *Thermoproteus*, *Pyrolobus*, and *Pyrodictium* (Figure 16). They are followed by the *Euryarchaeota*, the methane-producing (methanogenic) *Archaea* and the extreme halophiles; *Thermoplasma*, an acidophilic, thermophilic member of *Archaea* lacking a cell wall is loosely related to this latter group (Figure 16).

There are some branches in the *Crenarchaeota* lineage (Figure 16) that are known only from environmental sampling of ribosomal genes from the environment (Sections 9). Interestingly, however, these sequences have originated from organisms that inhabit the open oceans, including Antarctic marine waters where temperatures are far colder than in the hot-spring or deep sea hydrothermal vent habitats of known *Crenarchaeota*. Other *Crenarchaeota* sequences have emerged from environmental sampling of soil and lake water.

Eukarya

Phylogenetic trees of species in the domain *Eukarya* are generated from comparative sequence analysis of the 18S rRNA gene, the functional equivalent of the 16S rRNA gene. *Eukarya* include a wide diversity of organisms. At one extreme are the single-celled microsporidia and diplomonads, obligate parasites that live in association with representatives of various groups of eukaryotes (for example, the pathogen *Giardia* is a member of the diplomonad group) and that bear degenerate mitochondria (hydrogenosomes and mitosomes). At another extreme are the multicellular organisms, including the largest and most structurally complex of the *Eukarya*, the plants and animals.

When the fossil record is compared with the phylogenetic tree of *Eukarya*, the beginnings of a rapid evolutionary radiation can be traced to about 2 billion years ago. Geochemical evidence suggests that this is the period in Earth's history in which significant oxygen levels had accumulated in the atmosphere (Figure 7). It is thus likely that the onset of oxic conditions and subsequent development of an ozone shield (which would have greatly expanded the number of surface habitats available for colonization) was a major trigger for the rapid diversification of *Eukarya*.

Distinguishing Characteristics of the Domains of Life

Although the primary domains (*Bacteria*, *Archaea*, and *Eukarya*) were founded on the basis of comparative ribosomal RNA gene sequencing—genetic criteria—each domain can also be characterized by various phenotypic properties. Table 1 listed traits linking *Eukarya* with either *Bacteria* or *Archaea*. Several other traits distinguish *Eukarya* from *Bacteria* and *Archaea*, and these are summarized in Table 2.

Table 2 Major features distinguishing *Bacteria* and *Archaea* from *Eukarya*[a]

Characteristic	Bacteria	Archaea	Eukarya
Morphological and Genetic			
Prokaryotic cell structure	Yes	Yes	No
DNA present in covalently closed and circular form	Yes	Yes	No
Membrane-enclosed nucleus	Absent	Absent	Present
Ribosomes (mass)	70S	70S	80S
Introns in most genes	No	No	Yes
Operons	Yes	Yes	No
Capping and poly(A) tailing of mRNA	No	No	Yes
Plasmids	Yes	Yes	Rare
Physiological/Special Structures			
Dissimilative reduction of S^0 or SO_4^{2-} to H_2S, or Fe^{3+} to Fe^{2+}	Yes	Yes	No
Nitrification	Yes	No[b]	No
Denitrification	Yes	Yes	No
Nitrogen fixation	Yes	Yes	No
Rhodopsin-based energy metabolism	Yes	Yes	No
Chemolithotrophy (Fe, S, H_2)	Yes	Yes	No
Gas vesicles	Yes	Yes	No
Synthesis of carbon storage granules composed of poly-β-hydroxyalkanoates	Yes	Yes	No
Growth above 70°C	Yes	Yes	No

[a]Note that for many features only particular representatives within a domain show the property.
[b]Environmental genomics studies of *Bacteria* and *Archaea* in marine waters strongly suggest that nitrifying *Archaea* exist.

8 MiniReview

Life on Earth evolved along three major lines, domains *Bacteria*, *Archaea*, and *Eukarya*. Each domain contains several major evolutionary groups.

- How does the SSU rRNA tree of life differ from the grouping of life based on five kingdoms?
- What kinds of evidence support the three-domain concept of life?
- How does the universal tree support the hypothesis of endosymbiosis (Figure 10)?

9 Applications of SSU rRNA Phylogenetic Methods

SSU ribosomal RNA gene sequencing has spawned many research tools that employ this technology. These include signature sequences and rRNA probes for use in microbial ecology and diagnostic medicine, and methods for typing bacteria based on the SSU rRNA gene.

Signature Sequences

Computer analyses of ribosomal rRNA sequences have revealed **signature sequences**, short oligonucleotides unique to certain groups of organisms, for example, for each of the domains of cellular life. Moreover, signatures defining a specific group within a domain or, in some cases, a particular genus or even a single species, are also known or can be determined by computer inspection of aligned sequences. Because of their exclusivity, signature sequences are very useful. For example, signature sequences can help place newly isolated or previously misclassified organisms into their correct phylogenetic group. However, the most common use of signature sequences is for the design of specific nucleic acid probes.

Phylogenetic Probes and FISH

Recall that a probe is a strand of nucleic acid that can be labeled and used to hybridize to a complementary nucleic acid from a mixture. Probes can be general or specific. For example, universal SSU rRNA probes are designed to bind to conserved sequences in the rRNA of all organisms, regardless of domain. By contrast, specific probes can be designed that will react only with species of the domain *Bacteria* because of unique signatures found in their RNA. Likewise, archaeal-specific and eukaryl-specific probes will react only with species of *Archaea* or *Eukarya*, respectively. **Phylogenetic probes** can be designed also to target groups within a domain, such as members of individual families, genera, or species.

The binding of probes to cellular ribosomes can be seen microscopically when a fluorescent dye is attached to the probe. By treating cells with the appropriate reagents, membranes become permeable and allow penetration of the probe–dye mixture. After hybridization of the probe directly

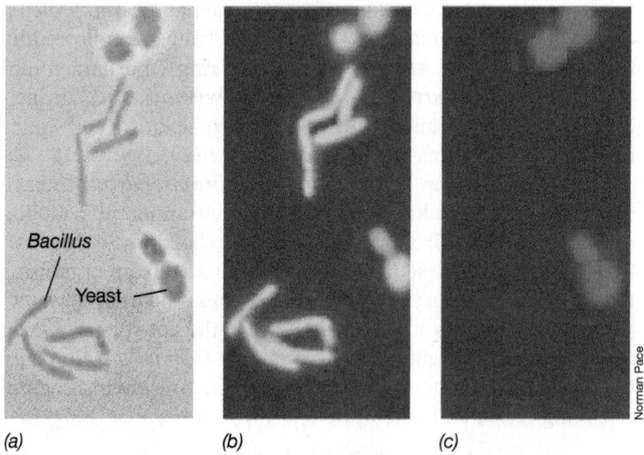

Figure 17 Fluorescently labeled rRNA probes: Phylogenetic stains. *(a)* Phase-contrast photomicrograph of cells of *Bacillus megaterium* (rod, member of the *Bacteria*) and the yeast *Saccharomyces cerevisiae* (oval cells, *Eukarya*). *(b)* Same field; cells stained with a yellow-green universal rRNA probe (this probe reacts with species from any domain). *(c)* Same field; cells stained with a eukaryal probe (only cells of *S. cerevisiae* react). Cells of *B. megaterium* are about 1.5 μm in diameter, and cells of *S. cerevisiae* are about 6 μm in diameter.

to rRNA in ribosomes, the cells become uniformly fluorescent and can be observed under a fluorescent microscope (Figure 17). This technique has been nicknamed **FISH**, for *f*luorescent *i*n *s*itu *h*ybridization, and can be applied directly to cells in culture or in a natural environment (the term *in situ* means "in the environment"). In essence, FISH is a *phylogenetic stain*.

FISH technology is widely used in microbial ecology and clinical diagnostics. In ecology, FISH can be used for the microscopic identification and tracking of organisms directly in the environment. FISH also offers a method for assessing the composition of microbial communities directly by microscopy. In clinical diagnostics, FISH has been used for the rapid identification of specific pathogens from patient specimens. The technique circumvents the need to grow an organism in culture. Instead, microscopic examination of a specimen can confirm the presence of a specific pathogen. In clinical diagnostics this facilitates the rapid diagnosis and treatment of a patient suffering from a microbial infection. By contrast, isolation and identification techniques typically take a minimum of 24 hours to complete and can take much longer.

Microbial Community Analysis

PCR-amplified rRNA genes do not need to originate from a pure culture grown in the laboratory. A phylogenetic snapshot of a natural microbial community can be taken using PCR to amplify the genes encoding SSU rRNA from members of that community. Such genes can easily be sorted out, sequenced, and aligned. From these data, a phylogenetic tree can be generated from these "environmental" sequences that shows the different rRNA genes present in the community. From this tree, specific organisms can be inferred even though none of them were actually cultivated or otherwise identified. Such microbial community analyses, as they have come to be called, are a major thrust of microbial ecology research today and have revealed many key features of microbial community structure and microbial interactions.

Ribotyping

Information from rRNA-based phylogenetic analyses also finds application in a technique for bacterial identification called **ribotyping**. Unlike comparative sequencing methods, however, ribotyping does not involve sequencing. Instead, it reports the specific pattern of bands, or DNA fingerprint, that is generated when DNA from an organism is digested by a restriction enzyme and the fragments are separated and probed with an rRNA gene probe (Figure 18). Differences between organisms in the sequence of their 16S rRNA genes translate into the presence or absence of cut sites recognized by different restriction enzymes. The DNA banding pattern, or *ribotype*, of a particular bacterial species may therefore be unique and diagnostic, allowing discrimination between species (Figure 18) and between different strains of a species, if there are differences in their SSU rRNA gene sequences.

In practice, ribotyping involves digestion of the bacterium's DNA with one or more restriction enzymes and separation of the DNA fragments by gel electrophoresis. The DNA fragments are then transferred from the gel onto nylon membranes and are hybridized with a labeled rRNA gene probe. The pattern generated from the fragments of DNA on the gel is then digitized, and a computer used to make comparisons of this pattern with patterns from reference organisms available from a database (Figure 18). Ribotyping is both highly specific and rapid (because it bypasses the actual sequencing, sequence alignment, and requirements for phylogenetic analysis). For these reasons, ribotyping has found many applications for bacterial identification in clinical diagnostics and for the microbial analyses of food, water, and beverages.

9 MiniReview

Phylogenetic analyses of SSU rRNA genes have led to the development of research tools useful in ecology and medicine.

- What are signature sequences?
- How can oligonucleotide probes be made visible under the microscope? What is this technology called?
- What kinds of questions can be addressed using microbial community analysis?
- How is ribotyping able to distinguish between different bacteria?

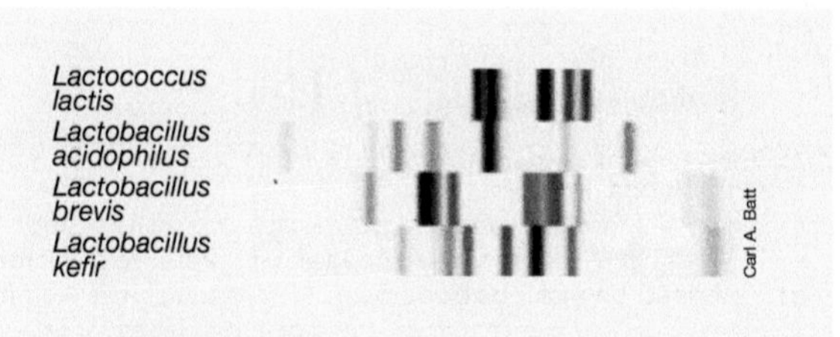

Figure 18 **Ribotyping.** Ribotype results from four different lactic acid bacteria. For each species there is a unique pattern of DNA fragments generated from restriction enzyme digestion of DNA taken from a colony of each bacterium and then probed with a 16S rRNA gene probe. Variations in both position and intensity of the bands are important in identification.

III MICROBIAL SYSTEMATICS

Systematics is the study of the diversity of organisms and their relationships. It links together phylogeny, just discussed, with **taxonomy**, in which organisms are characterized, named, and placed into groups according to their natural relationships. Bacterial taxonomy traditionally has focused on practical aspects of identification and description, activities that have relied heavily on phenotypic comparisons. At present, the growing use of genetic information, especially DNA sequence data, is allowing taxonomy to increasingly reflect phylogenetic relationships. Ideally, as Charles Darwin stated in his famous monograph, *On the Origin of Species*, "Our classifications will come to be, as far as they can be so made, genealogies." In the sections that follow, we consider basic elements of bacterial taxonomy—the identification of bacteria, species concepts, and bacterial classification and nomenclature.

Bacterial taxonomy has changed substantially in the past few decades, incorporating new methods for the identification of bacteria and additional criteria for the description of new species. This *polyphasic* approach to taxonomy uses three kinds of methods, phenotypic, genotypic, and phylogenetic, for the identification and description of bacteria. Phenotypic analysis examines the morphological, metabolic, physiological, and chemical characteristics of the cell. Genotypic analysis considers comparative aspects of cells at the level of the genome. These two kinds of analysis group organisms on the basis of similarities. They are complemented by phylogenetic analysis, which seeks to place organisms in a framework of evolutionary relationships. There is also growing recognition of the importance of information on the bacterium's habitat and ecology in polyphasic taxonomy.

10 Phenotypic Analysis

The observable characteristics of a bacterium provide many traits that can be used to differentiate between species. Typically, in describing a new species, and also to identify a bacterium, several of these traits are determined for the strain or strains of interest. The results are then compared with known organisms as controls, either examined in parallel

Table 3 Some phenotypic characteristics of taxonomic value

Major category	*Components*
Morphology	Colony morphology; Gram reaction; cell size and shape; pattern of flagellation; presence of spores, inclusion bodies (e.g., PHB[a] granules, gas vesicles, magnetosomes); stalks or appendages; fruiting-body formation
Motility	Nonmotile; gliding motility; swimming (flagellar) motility; swarming; motile by gas vesicles
Metabolism	Mechanism of energy conservation (phototroph, chemoorganotroph, chemolithotroph); utilization of individual carbon, nitrogen, or sulfur compounds; fermentation of sugars; nitrogen fixation; growth factor requirements
Physiology	Temperature, pH, and salt ranges for growth; response to oxygen (aerobic, facultative, anaerobic); presence of catalase or oxidase; production of extracellular enzymes
Cell chemistry	Fatty acids; polar lipids; respiratory quinones
Other traits	Pigments; luminescence; antibiotic sensitivity; serotype

[a]PHB, poly-β-hydroxybutyric acid.

with the unknowns or from published information. The specific traits used depend on the kind of organism, and which traits are chosen for testing may arise from substantial prior knowledge of the bacterial group to which the new organism likely belongs as well as on the investigator's purpose. For example, in applied situations, such as in clinical diagnostic microbiology, where identification may be an end in itself and speed may be critical, a well-defined subset of traits often is used that quickly discriminates among likely or possible identifications. Table 3 lists general categories and examples of some phenotypic traits used in identifications and species descriptions, and we examine one of these examples here.

Fatty Acid Analyses: FAME

The types and proportions of fatty acids present in cytoplasmic membrane and outer membrane (gram-negative bacteria) lipids of cells are major phenotypic traits. The technique for determining these fatty acids has been nicknamed **FAME**, for *f*atty *a*cid *m*ethyl *e*ster and is in widespread use in clinical, public health, and food and water inspection laboratories where the identification of pathogens or other bacterial hazards needs to be done on a routine basis. It is widely used in the characterization of new species of bacteria.

The fatty acid composition of *Bacteria* can be highly variable, including differences in chain length, the presence or absence of double bonds, rings, branched chains, or hydroxy groups (Figure 19a). Hence, a fatty acid profile can often identify a particular bacterial species. For the analyses, fatty acids, extracted from cell hydrolysates of a culture grown under standardized conditions, are chemically derivatized to form their corresponding methyl esters. These now volatile derivatives are then identified by gas chromatography. A chromatogram showing the types and amounts of fatty acids

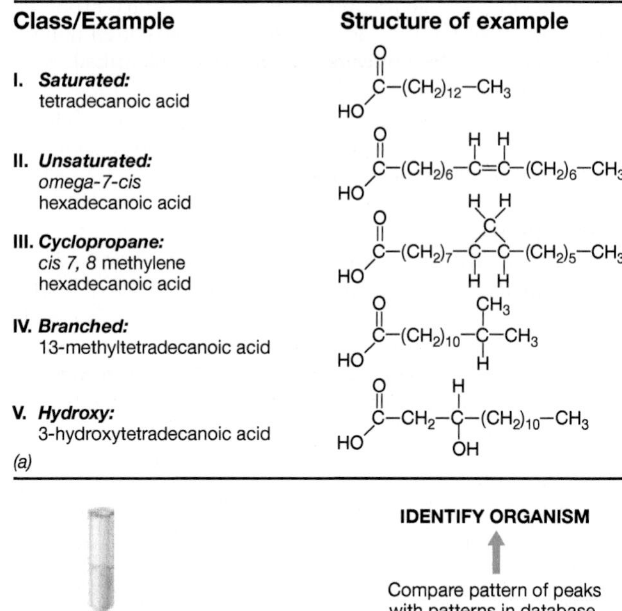

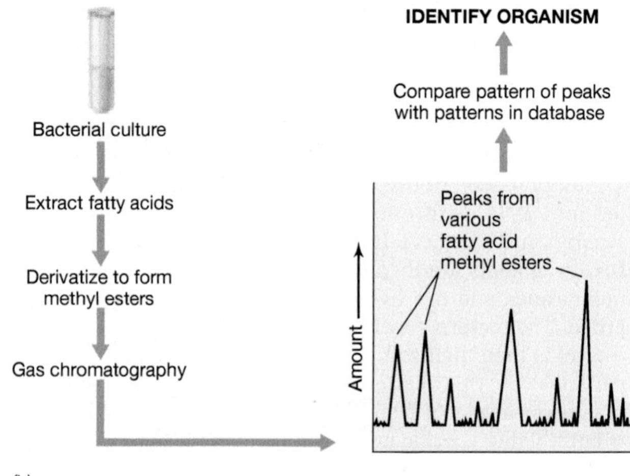

Figure 19 **Fatty acid methyl ester (FAME) analysis in bacterial identification.** *(a)* Classes of fatty acids in *Bacteria*. Only a single example is given of each class, but in fact, more than 200 different fatty acids have been discovered from bacterial sources. A methyl ester contains a methyl group (CH_3) in place of the proton on the carboxylic acid group (COOH) of the fatty acid. *(b)* Procedure. Each peak from the gas chromatograph is due to one particular fatty acid methyl ester, and the peak height is proportional to the amount.

from the unknown bacterium is then compared with a database containing the fatty acid profiles of thousands of reference bacteria grown under the same conditions. The best matches to that of the unknown are then selected (Figure 19*b*).

As a phenotypic trait for species identification and description, FAME does have some drawbacks. In particular, FAME analyses require rigid standardization because fatty acid profiles of an organism, like many phenotypic traits, can vary as a function of temperature, growth phase (exponential versus stationary), and to a lesser extent, growth medium. Thus, for consistent results, it is necessary to grow the unknown organism

Table 4 Some genotypic methods used in bacterial taxonomy

Method	Description/application
DNA–DNA hybridization	A genomewide comparison of sequence similarity. Useful to distinguish species within a genus
DNA profiling	Ribotyping (Section 9), AFLP, rep-PCR. Rapid method to distinguish between species and strains within a species
MLST	Strain typing using DNA sequences of multiple genes. High resolution, useful for distinguishing even very closely related strains within a species
GC ratio	Percentage of guanine plus cytosine base pairs in the genome. Less commonly used in taxonomy because of poor resolution. If the GC ratio of two organisms differs by more than about 5%, they cannot be closely related, and organisms with similar or even identical GC ratios may be unrelated

on a specific medium and at a specific temperature in order to compare its fatty acid profile with those of organisms from the database that have been grown in the same way. For many organisms this is impossible, of course, and thus FAME analyses are limited to those organisms that can be grown under the specified conditions. In addition, the extent of variation in FAME profiles among strains of a species, a necessary consideration in studies to discriminate between species, is not yet well documented.

10 MiniReview

Systematics is the study of the diversity and relationships of living organisms. Polyphasic taxonomy is based on phenotypic, genotypic, and phylogenetic information. Phenotypic traits useful in taxonomy include morphology, motility, metabolism, and cell chemistry, especially lipid analyses.

- What is FAME analysis?
- What are some of the drawbacks of FAME analysis?
- Do these drawbacks apply to other kinds of phenotypic traits?

11 Genotypic Analysis

Comparative analysis of the genome also provides many traits for discriminating between species of bacteria. Genotypic analysis has particular appeal in microbial taxonomy because of the insights it provides at the DNA level. Several methods of genotypic analysis are used (as listed in Table 4) depending on the questions posed, with DNA–DNA hybridization and DNA profiling among the more commonly used in microbial taxonomy.

DNA–DNA Hybridization

When two organisms share many highly similar (or identical) genes, their DNAs would be expected to hybridize to one another in approximate proportion to the similarities in their gene sequences. In this way, measurement of **DNA–DNA hybridization** between the genomes of two organisms provides a rough index of their similarity to each other. DNA–DNA hybridization therefore is useful for differentiating between organisms as a complement to SSU rRNA gene sequencing.

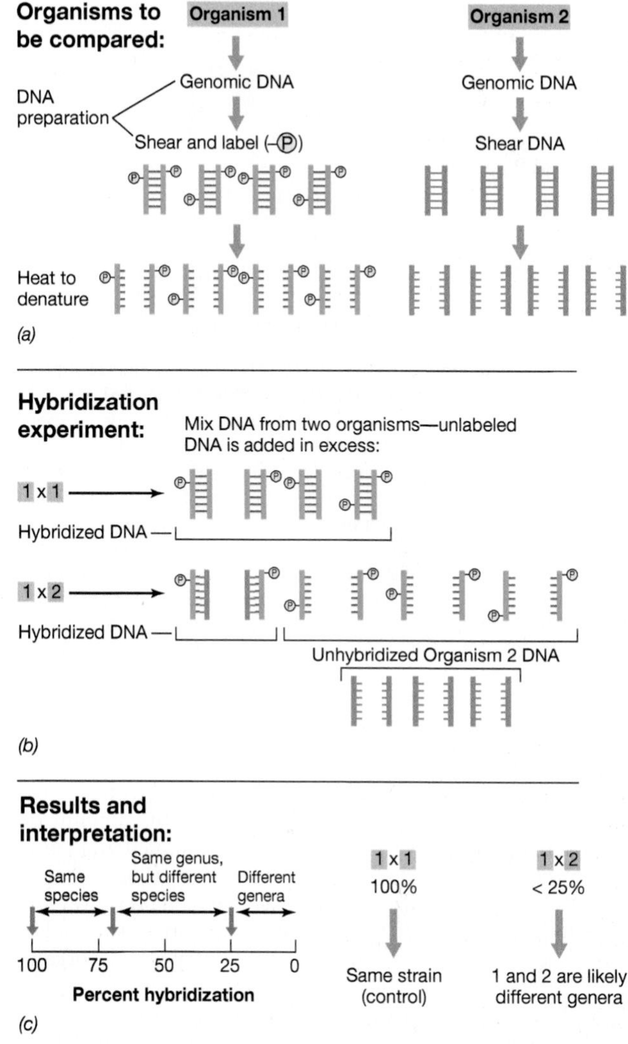

Figure 20 **Genomic hybridization as a taxonomic tool.** *(a)* Genomic DNA is isolated from test organisms. One of the DNAs is labeled (shown here as radioactive phosphate in the DNA of Organism 1). *(b)* Excess unlabeled DNA is added to prevent labeled DNA from reannealing with itself. Following hybridization, hybridized DNA is separated from unhybridized DNA before measuring radioactivity in the hybridized DNA only. *(c)* Radioactivity in the control (Organism 1 DNA hybridizing to itself) is taken as the 100% hybridization value.

In a hybridization experiment, genomic DNA isolated from one organism is made radioactive with ^{32}P or ^{3}H, sheared to a relatively small size, heated to separate the two strands, and mixed with an excess of unlabeled DNA prepared in the same way from a second organism (Figure 20). The DNA mixture is then cooled to allow the single strands to

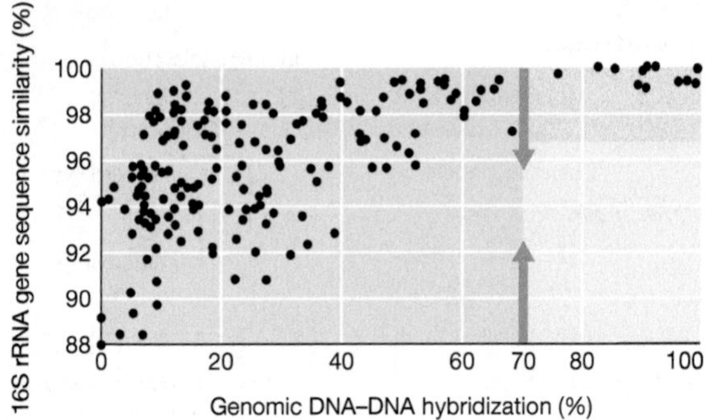

Figure 21 Relationship between 16S rRNA gene sequence similarity and genomic DNA-hybridization for different pairs of organisms. These data are the results from several independent experiments with various species of the domain *Bacteria*. Points in the orange box represent combinations for which 16S rRNA gene sequence similarity and genomic hybridization were both very high; thus, in each case, the two organisms tested were clearly the same species. Points in the green box represent combinations that detected different species, and both methods show this. The blue box shows examples of organisms that seemed to be different species as measured by genomic DNA–DNA hybridization but not by 16S rRNA gene sequence. Note that above 70% DNA–DNA hybridization, no 16S rRNA gene similarities were found that were less than 97%.

Data from Rosselló-Mora, R., and R. Amann. 2001. *FEMS Microbiol. Revs.* 25:39–67.

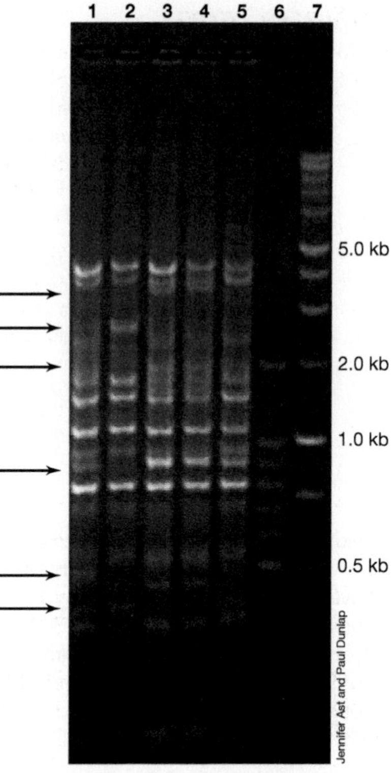

Figure 22 DNA fingerprinting with rep-PCR. Genomic DNAs from five strains (1–5) of a single species of bacteria were PCR-amplified using REP (repetitive extragenic palidromic) primers, REP1R-I (5′-IIIICGICGICATCIGGC-3′) and REP2-I (5′-ICGICTTATCIGGCCTAC-3′), and the PCR products were separated by gel electrophoresis on the basis of size to generate DNA fingerprints (in the primers shown, "I" can be any nucleotide). Arrows indicate some of the different bands in each strain. Strains 3 and 4 have very similar DNA profiles. Lanes 6 and 7 are 100-bp and 1-kbp DNA size ladders, respectively, used in estimating sizes of DNA fragments.

reanneal. The double-stranded DNA is separated from any remaining unhybridized DNA. Following this, the amount of radioactivity in the hybridized DNA is determined and compared with the control, which is taken as 100% (Figure 20).

DNA–DNA hybridization is a sensitive method for revealing subtle differences in the genomes of two organisms and is often therefore useful for differentiating very similar organisms. Although there is no fixed convention as to how much hybridization between two DNAs is necessary to assign two organisms to the same taxonomic rank, hybridization values of 70% or greater are recommended for considering two isolates to be of the same species. By contrast, values of at least 25% are required to argue that two organisms should reside in the same genus. DNAs from more distantly related organisms, for example, *Clostridium* (gram-positive) and *Salmonella* (gram-negative), hybridize at only background levels, 10% or less (Figure 21).

DNA Profiling Methods

Several methods can be used to generate DNA fragment patterns for analysis of genotypic similarity among bacterial strains. One of these DNA-profiling methods, ribotyping, was described in Section 9 on applications of SSU sequence analysis. Other commonly used methods for rapid genotyping of bacteria include *repetitive extragenic palindromic PCR (rep-PCR)* and *amplified fragment length polymorphism (AFLP)*. In contrast to ribotyping, which focuses on a single gene, rep-PCR and AFLP assay for variations in DNA sequence throughout the genome.

The rep-PCR method is based on the presence of highly conserved repetitive DNA elements interspersed randomly around the bacterial chromosome. The number and positions of these elements differ between strains of a species that have diverged in genome sequence. Oligonucleotide primers, designed to be complementary to these elements, enable PCR amplification of different genomic fragments, generating a pattern of bands from genomic DNA. The pattern of bands differs for different strains, giving a strain-specific DNA "fingerprint" (Figure 22).

AFLP is based on the digestion of genomic DNA with one or two restriction enzymes and selective PCR-amplification of resulting fragments, which are separated by agarose gel electrophoresis. Strain-specific banding patterns similar to that of rep-PCR or other DNA fingerprinting methods are generated, with the large number of bands giving a high degree of discrimination between strains within a species. A similar technique to AFLP called T-RFLP is widely used in phylogenetic analyses of natural microbial communities.

Multilocus Sequence Typing

One of the limitations of both ribosomal RNA gene sequence analysis and ribotyping (but not of strain typing with rep-PCR or AFLP) is that these analyses focus on only a single gene, which may not provide sufficient information for unequivocal discrimination between bacterial strains. **Multilocus sequence typing (MLST)** circumvents this problem and is a powerful technique for characterizing strains within a species.

MLST involves sequencing several different "housekeeping genes" from an organism and comparing their sequences with sequences of the same genes from different strains of the same organism. Recall that housekeeping genes encode essential functions in cells and are located on the chromosome rather than on a plasmid. For each gene, an approximately 450-bp sequence is amplified using PCR and is then sequenced. Each nucleotide along the sequence is compared and differences are noted. Each difference, or sequence variant, is considered an **allele** and is assigned a number. A given strain will then be assigned a series of numbers, its allelic profile, or multilocus sequence type. In MLST, strains with identical sequences for a given gene will have the same allele number for that gene, and two strains with identical sequences for all the genes would have the same allelic profile (and would be considered identical by this method). The relatedness between each allelic profile is expressed in a dendrogram of linkage distances that vary from 0 (strains are identical) to 1 (strains are only distantly related) (Figure 23).

MLST has sufficient resolving power to distinguish even very closely related strains. In practice, strains can be discriminated on the basis of a single nucleotide change in just one of the several analyzed genes. MLST is not useful, however, for comparing organisms above the species level; its resolution is too sensitive to yield meaningful information for higher order groups, that is, genera or families.

MLST has made a variety of impacts in microbiology. In clinical microbiology, it has been effective for differentiating strains of a particular pathogen. This is important because some strains within a species—*Escherichia coli* K-12, for example—may be harmless, whereas others, such as strain O157:H7, can cause serious and even fatal infections. MLST is also quite useful for epidemiological studies, to track a virulent strain of a bacterial pathogen as it moves through a population, and for environmental studies, to define the geographic distributions of strains.

MLST analyses also have revealed some interesting genetic patterns in bacteria. For example, some *Bacteria*, such as *Staphylococcus aureus*, show very little MLST variation, whereas other organisms, such as *Neisseria meningititis*, show great variability by MLST analyses. This difference implies that organisms such as *N. meningitidis* have undergone much greater horizontal gene flow in the past than has *S. aureus*, or that their genes accumulate mutations at a faster rate.

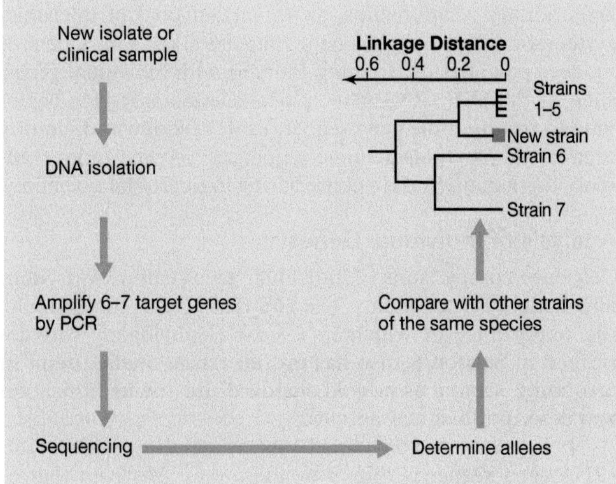

Figure 23 **Multilocus sequence typing.** Steps in MLST leading to a similarity phenogram are shown. Strains 1–5 are virtually identical, whereas strains 6 and 7 are both distinct from one another and from strains 1–5.

GC Ratios

Another method used to compare and describe bacteria is their **GC ratios**. The GC ratio is the percentage of guanine plus cytosine in an organism's genomic DNA. GC ratios vary over a wide range, with values as low as 20% and as high as nearly 80% among *Bacteria* and *Archaea*, a range that is somewhat broader than for eukaryotes. It is generally considered that if two organisms' GC ratios differ by more than about 5%, they will share few DNA sequences in common and are therefore unlikely to be closely related. However, two organisms can have identical GC ratios and yet turn out to be quite unrelated, because very different nucleotide sequences are possible from DNA of the same overall base composition. In this case, the identical GC ratios are taxonomically misleading. Because gene sequence data are increasingly easy to obtain, GC ratios may find less application in bacterial taxonomy in the future.

11 MiniReview

Genotypic analysis examines traits of the genome. Bacterial species can be distinguished genotypically on the basis of DNA–DNA hybridization and DNA profiling.

- What is DNA fingerprinting and how is it useful for distinguishing bacteria?
- Hybridization of less than 25% between two organisms' DNA indicates that they are ______.
- How do AFLP and MLST differ from ribotyping?

12 Phylogenetic Analysis

Phylogenetic data are being used increasingly in microbial taxonomy to complement phenotypic and genotypic information. In addition, phylogenetic analysis permits organisms to be placed in a unified classification system structured on their evolutionary relationships, an important goal of microbial systematics. Thus, phylogenetic data are a key component of modern polyphasic taxonomy. Starting with individual genes, such as the SSU rRNA gene, phylogenetic analysis is beginning to use multiple gene sequences to describe and identify organisms. As whole-genome sequences become more common, these data, too, are contributing to microbial taxonomy.

Analysis of Individual Genes

Sequence comparisons of individual genes can provide valuable insight for taxonomy. The 16S rRNA gene, for example, the importance of which in microbial phylogeny was described in Section 6, also has proven exceptionally useful in taxonomy, serving as a "gold standard" for the identification and description of new species.

It is generally considered that a bacterium whose 16S rRNA gene sequence differs by more than 3% from that of other organisms should be considered a new species. This proposal is supported by the observation that genomic DNA from two microorganisms whose 16S rRNA gene sequences are less than 97% identical typically hybridize to less than 70%, a minimal value considered evidence for two organisms being of the same species (Figure 20). The relationship between these methods is depicted in Figure 21. The proposed cutoff value serves as a guide for discriminating between strains at the species level, and it provides widely used data for the practical description of a new species. What constitutes a genus, the next level in taxonomic hierarchy (Section 11), is more a matter of judgment than for species, but 16S rRNA gene sequence differences of more than 5% from other organisms have been taken as support for an organism being a new genus. Other highly conserved genes, such as *recA*, which encodes a recombinase protein, and *gyrB*, which encodes a DNA gyrase protein, also can be useful for distinguishing bacteria at the species level.

Reliance in taxonomy, as well as in phylogeny, on the sequence of a single gene, however, can have pitfalls. The lack of divergence of the 16S rRNA gene, for example, can limit its effectiveness in discriminating between bacteria at the species level. This problem can be overcome by analysis of genes that are more highly divergent but that still reliably reflect systematic relationships, when such genes can be identified for the bacterial group under study. Individual genes also may be subject to horizontal gene transfer, however, which would invalidate taxonomic conclusions based on their sequences. For these reasons, a *multi-gene* approach is being used more frequently now in bacterial taxonomy and phylogeny.

Multi-Gene Sequence Analysis

The use of multiple genes for the identification and description of bacteria can avoid problems associated with reliance on individual genes. Multi-gene sequence analysis is similar to MLST, except that complete gene sequences are obtained when possible and comparisons are made using cladistic methods. By sequencing a few to several functionally unrelated genes, one can obtain a sampling of the genome that is more representative than a single gene, and instances of horizontal gene transfer can be detected and those genes excluded from further consideration. Taxonomic descriptions based on multiple genes therefore can provide a more reliable measure of the bacterium's systematic relationships.

Whole-Genome Sequence-Based Analysis

Rapid progress in sequencing the whole genomes of *Bacteria*, *Archaea*, and *Eukarya* has the potential of providing new tools for bacterial taxonomy. At this time, more than 670 genomes have been completely sequenced, over 550 of which are *Bacteria*. Approximately 2,300 additional genome sequencing projects are in progress. When the genome of a bacterium is sequenced, computational methods can be used to compare its genes with those of any and all other sequenced organisms.

Whole-genome sequences provide many traits for comparative genotypic analysis. For example, major physical differences between species in genome structure, including size and number of chromosomes, their GC content, and whether the chromosomes are linear or circular may have taxonomic significance. Comparative analyis of gene content (the presence or absence of genes) and the order of those genes in the genome also will undoubtedly provide insights with implications for taxonomy, as will MLST and phylogenetic analysis based on identification of genes found to be universally present in the organisms of interest. One can envision a time in the not too distant future when descriptions of new bacterial species will include, along with phenotypic, genotypic, phylogenetic, and ecological data, the sequence of the bacterium's genome.

12 MiniReview

Phylogenetic approaches to bacterial taxonomy can be based on sequence analysis of individual genes, multiple genes, or potentially on the whole genome. Phylogenetic analysis is an important aspect of modern polyphasic taxonomy.

- What limits the value of the 16S rRNA gene (or any gene) in taxonomy?
- Why is the *recA* gene not suitable for phylogenetic analysis in *Archaea*?
- What distinguishes multi-gene phylogenetic analysis from MLST?

13 The Species Concept in Microbiology

At present, there is no universally accepted concept of **species** for prokaryotes. We have seen that microbial taxonomy combines phenotypic, genotypic, and sequence-based phylogenetic data, and that, as will be discussed in the following section, certain standards and guidelines are in place for distinguishing bacteria as separate species. These standards and guidelines provide an effective framework for the practice of describing and identifying prokaryotes, but they leave unaddressed the question of what constitutes a prokaryotic

Table 5 Taxonomic hierarchy for the purple sulfur bacterium *Allochromatium warmingii*

Taxonomic division	*Name*	*Properties*	*Confirmed by*
Domain	*Bacteria*	Bacterial cells; ribosomal RNA gene sequences typical of *Bacteria*	Microscopy; 16S rRNA gene sequence analysis; presence of unique biomarkers, for example, peptidoglycan
Phylum	*Proteobacteria*	rRNA gene sequence typical of *Proteobacteria*	16S rRNA gene sequence analysis
Class	*Gammaproteobacteria*	Gram-negative bacteria; rRNA sequence typical of *Gammaproteobacteria*	Gram-staining, microscopy
Order	*Chromatiales*	Phototrophic purple bacteria	Characterizing pigments (Figure 20.3)
Family	*Chromatiaceae*	Purple sulfur bacteria	Ability to oxidize H_2S and store S^0 within cells; observe culture microscopically for presence of S^0 (see photo)
Genus	*Allochromatium*	Rod-shaped purple sulfur bacteria	Microscopy (see photo)
Species	*warmingii*	Cells 3.5–4.0 μm × 5–11 μm; store sulfur mainly in poles of cell (see photo)	Measure cells in microscope using a micrometer; look for position of S^0 globules in cells (see photo)

Sulfur (S^0) globules

Norbert Pfennig

Photomicrograph of cells of the purple sulfur bacterium Allochromatium warmingii.

species. Because species are the fundamental units of biological diversity, this question has importance for our perception of and interaction with the microbial world. How the concept of species is defined in microbiology determines how we distinguish and classify the units of diversity that make up the microbial world.

Current Definition of Prokaryotic Species

A prokaryotic species presently is defined operationally as a collection of strains sharing a high degree of similarity in several independent traits. In polyphasic taxonomy, phenotypic, genotypic, and phylogenetic data are used to describe a new species. Traits currently considered most important for grouping strains together as a species include 70% or greater DNA–DNA hybridization and 97% or greater 16S rRNA gene sequence identity (Sections 10 and 11). Table 5 gives an example of species definition in practice, listing relevant traits for the hierarchical classification of the phototrophic bacterium *Allochromatium warmingii*. Based on these kinds of criteria, nearly 7,000 species of *Bacteria* and *Archaea* have been formally recognized.

There is substantial interest in microbiology, however, in moving beyond a reliance on practical methods for identification to develop a prokaryotic species concept that is grounded in fundamental principles of biology and evolution. The biological species concept, which states that a species is an interbreeding population of organisms that are reproductively isolated from other interbreeding populations, is widely accepted as effective for grouping many eukaryotic organisms in a biologically meaningful way. However, the biological species concept is not effective or meaningful for the vast majority of life's diversity—the *Bacteria* and *Archaea*, which are haploid and do not undergo sexual reproduction. Even if we factor in acquisition of homologous DNA by recombination and acquisition of nonhomologous DNA by horizontal gene transfer and illegitimate recombination, descent in prokaryotes is predominantly vertical, and there is no true sexual reproduction, the fusion of haploid gametes to form a diploid cell, in bacteria. For these organisms, one haploid cell reproduces to form two new haploid cells that are identical genetically or essentially identical except for mutations. Therefore, a species definition based on sexual reproduction and reproductive isolation is not suitable for *Bacteria* and *Archaea*.

An alternative to the biological species concept that seems suitable for haploid organisms is the genealogical species concept (also referred to as the phylogenetic species concept). According to the genealogical species concept, a prokaryotic species is a group of strains that—based on DNA sequences of multiple genes—cluster closely with each other phylogenetically and are distinct from other groups of strains. In other

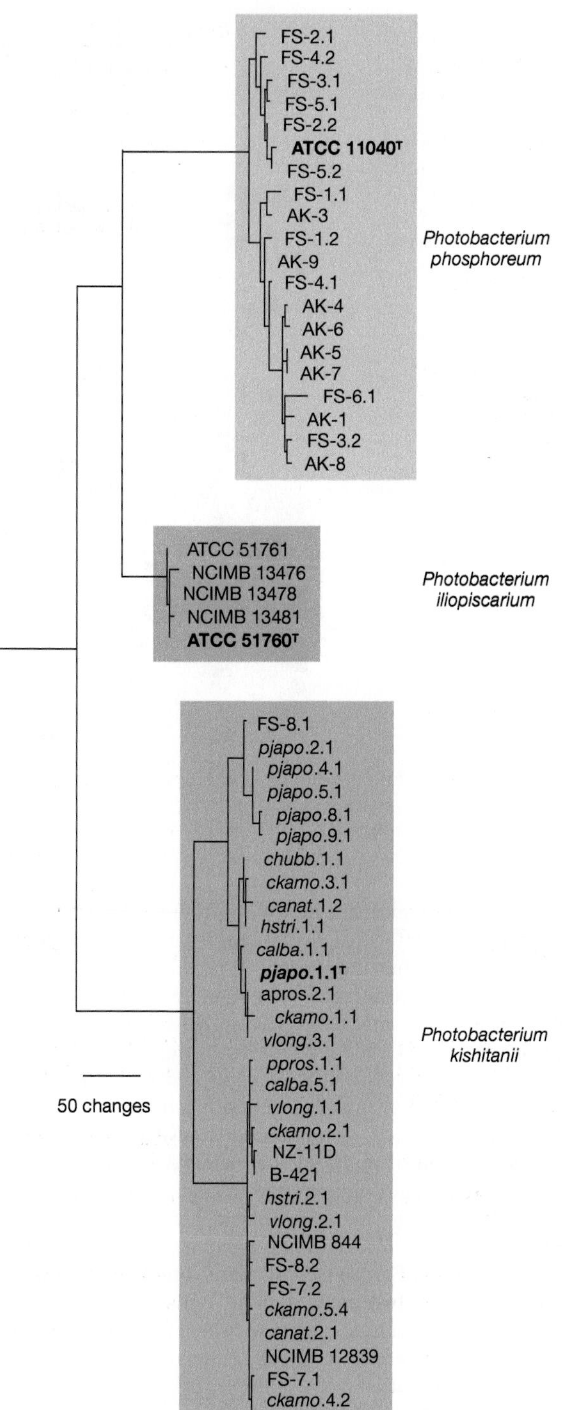

Figure 24 Multi-gene phylogenetic analysis. A phylogeny is shown for strains in the genus *Photobacterium* (*Gammaproteobacteria*) based on combined parsimony analysis of the 16S rRNA gene, *gyrB* (a housekeeping gene that encodes DNA gyrase subunit B), and the *luxABFE* genes (encoding the light-emitting enzyme luciferase and other luminescence enzymes). Although 16S rRNA gene sequences alone do not distinguish among these bacteria, due to the lack of divergence in the sequence of this gene, the combined analysis, due to the greater sequence divergences of the *gyrB* and *luxABFE* genes, resolves them as three evolutionarily distinct clades (that is, species), *P. phosphoreum*, *P. iliopiscarium*, and *P. kishitanii*. The scale bar indicates the branch length equal to 50 nucleotide changes. Type strains of each species, designated with a superscript "T" appended to their strain designations, are shown in bold.

words, each of these groups of strains is monophyletic, having descended from a different common ancestor. An example of the use multiple gene sequences to define separate species is shown in Figure 24. The analysis shown here uses the 16S rRNA gene, the sequence of which has diverged very little and which therefore provides good family and genus level resolution, but not good species level resolution. For good species level resolution, the *gyrB* gene, which encodes DNA gyrase subunit B, and the *luxABFE* genes, which encode luminescence enzymes, are included in the analysis. The *gyrB* and *luxABFE* genes are less constrained functionally; that is, their sequences can change more than that of the 16S rRNA gene without a loss of function of the proteins they encode. The combined analysis (Figure 24) separates closely related, phenotypically similar strains of *Photobacterium*, a genus of *Bacteria*, into three evolutionarily distinct clades (that is, *species*). In this way, through its reliance on multiple gene sequence analysis, the genealogical species concept has the potential to provide a strong evolutionary framework for species descriptions that are based on polyphasic taxonomy.

Speciation in Prokaryotes

How might new prokaryotic species arise? One possibility is by the process of periodic selection. Imagine a population of bacteria that originated from a single cell and that occupies a particular niche in a habitat. If cells in this population share a particular resource (for example, a key nutrient), this population of cells can be called an **ecotype**. Different ecotypes can coexist in a habitat, but each is only successful within its prime niche in the habitat.

Within each ecotype population, random mutations will occur over time in the genomes of the cells as they reproduce. Most of the mutations are neutral and have no effect. If there is a beneficial mutation, one that increases fitness, in a cell in one of the ecotypes, that cell may reproduce better than other kinds, so its progeny, which carry the mutation, will become dominant. In time, this may purge the population of the less well-adapted cells. Repeated rounds of mutation and selection in this ecotype may lead it to become more and more distinct genetically from the other ecotypes. Given enough time and sufficient changes, cells of this lineage would likely be identified by various traits as a new species (Figure 25). Selection of strains bearing beneficial mutations can proceed gradually, or it can occur quite suddenly due to rapid environmental change. Note that this series of events within an ecotype has no effect on other ecotypes, because different ecotypes do not compete for the same resources (Figure 25). It is also possible that a new genetic capability in an ecotype may arise from genes obtained from cells of another ecotype by horizontal gene transfer, rather than from mutation and selection.

The extent of horizontal gene transfer among bacteria is variable. Genome sequence analyses have revealed examples in which horizontal tranfer of genes has apparently been frequent and others in which it has been rare. In addition, MLST (Section 11) has revealed that genetic exchange within some species, called intraspecific recombination, is widespread, but virtually nonexistent within other species. Despite the impact of horizontal gene transfer, speciation in *Bacteria* and *Archaea* is thought to be driven primarily by mutation and periodic selection (Figure 25) rather than by horizontal gene transfer. This is because horizontal gene transfer occurs rarely in most bacteria and may confer only temporary benefits; the transferred genes can readily be lost if the selective pressure to retain them decreases.

How Many Prokaryotic Species Are There?

The result of over 4 billion years of evolution (Figure 7) is the prokaryotic world we see today. Microbial taxonomists agree that no firm estimate of the number of prokaryotic species can be given at present, in part because of uncertainty about what delimits a species. However, they also agree that in the final analysis, this number will be very large. Nearly 7,000 species of *Bacteria* and *Archaea* are already known, and thousands more, perhaps as many as 100,000–1,000,000 in total, are thought likely to exist. If we factor in application of the genealogical species concept, which provides better resolution of evolutionarily distinct monophyletic groups (species) (Figure 24), the estimate increases many fold.

It is important to remember that microbial community analyses (Section 9) indicate that we have only scratched the surface in our ability to culture the diversity of *Bacteria* and *Archaea* in nature. With more exacting tools, both molecular and cultural, for revealing diversity, it is possible that the large number of species already predicted will be an underestimate. The reality today is that an accurate estimate of prokaryotic species is simply out of reach of current understanding and technology. But as with other things in microbiology, this will likely change. The area of microbial systematics is just beginning to open up, and many exciting discoveries will be made over the next several years.

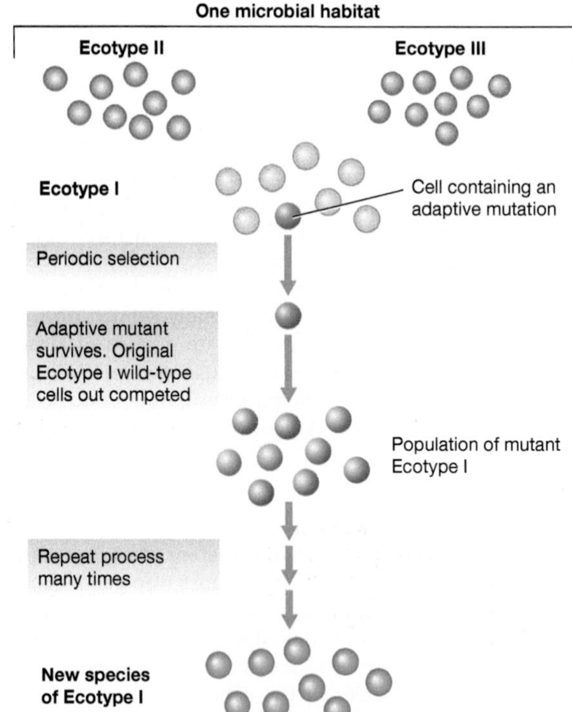

Figure 25 A model for bacterial speciation. Several ecotypes can coexist in a single microbial habitat, each occupying its own prime ecological niche. A cell within an ecotype that has a beneficial mutation may become a population that eventually replaces the original ecotype. As this occurs repeatedly within a given ecotype, a genetically distinct population of cells arises that represents a new species. Because other ecotypes do not compete for the same resources, they are unaffected by genetic and selection events outside of their prime niche.

13 MiniReview

A prokaryotic species presently is defined operationally. The biological species concept is not suitable for *Bacteria* and *Archaea*, because the members of these domains do not undergo true sexual reproduction. Prokaryotes may speciate as a result of repeated periodic selection for favorable traits within an ecotype.

- How does the genealogical species concept compare to an operational definition of a bacterial species?
- What is meant by the term monophyletic?
- What is an ecotype?
- How many species of *Bacteria* and *Archaea* are already known? How many likely exist?

14 Classification and Nomenclature

We conclude this chapter with a brief description of how *Bacteria* and *Archaea* are classified and named. Information is presented also on culture collections, which serve as repositories for scientific deposition of cultures, on some key taxonomic resources available for microbiology, and on some of the procedures for naming new species. The formal description of a new prokaryotic species and deposition of living cultures into a culture collection form an important foundation for prokaryotic systematics.

Classification

Classification is the organization of organisms into progressively more inclusive groups on the basis of either phenotypic similarity or evolutionary relationship. The hierarchical nature of classification is shown in Table 5, which presents the taxonomic ranks by which prokaryotes are classified, from domain to species. A new species is usually defined from the characterization of several strains, with groups of similar species then collected into genera (singular, genus). Groups of similar genera are collected into families, families into orders, orders into classes, up to the domain, the taxon of highest level.

Nomenclature

Nomenclature is the application of formal rules for naming organisms. Following the **binomial system** of nomenclature used throughout biology, prokaryotes are given genus names and species epithets. The terms used are Latin or Latinized Greek derivations, often of some descriptive property appropriate for the organism, and are set in print in *italics*. For example, over 100 species of the genus *Bacillus* have been described, including *Bacillus subtilis*, *Bacillus cereus*, and *Bacillus megaterium*. These species epithets mean "slender," "waxen," and "big beast," respectively, and refer to key morphological, physiological, or ecological traits characteristic of each organism. By classifying organisms into groups and naming them, we order the natural word and make it possible to communicate effectively about all aspects of individual organisms, including their behavior, ecology, physiology, pathogenesis, and evolutionary relationships.

In contrast to classification, nomenclature is subject to specific rules. The assignment of names for species and higher groups of *Bacteria* and *Archaea* is regulated by the Bacteriological Code—*The International Code of Nomenclature of Bacteria*. This source presents the formal framework by which *Bacteria* and *Archaea* are to be officially named and the procedures by which existing names can be changed, for example, when new data warrants taxonomic rearrangements. There are even rules for rejecting names if errors were made in the original naming process or a name has otherwise become invalid. The Bacteriological Code deals only with procedures for assigning names to organisms, not with issues of taxonomic methods or interpretation.

Bergey's Manual and *The Prokaryotes*

Because taxonomy is largely a matter of scientific judgment, there is no "official" classification of *Bacteria* and *Archaea*. Presently, the classification system most widely accepted by microbiologists is the "Taxonomic Outline of the Prokaryotes" arising out of the second edition of *Bergey's Manual of Systematic Bacteriology*, a major taxonomic treatment of *Bacteria* and *Archaea*. Widely used, *Bergey's Manual* has served the community of microbiologists since 1923 and is a compendium of information on all recognized species of bacteria. Each chapter, written by experts, contains tables, figures, and other systematic information useful for identification purposes. Volume I of the second edition of *Bergey's Manual* appeared in 2001, Volume 2 in 2005, and three additional volumes in 2007. The second edition of *Bergey's Manual* has incorporated many of the concepts that have emerged from SSU rRNA gene sequencing and genomic studies and blends this with a wealth of phenotypic information as well.

A second major reference in bacterial diversity is *The Prokaryotes*, which provides detailed information on the enrichment, isolation, and culture of the many groups of *Bacteria* and *Archaea* assembled by experts on each microbial group. This work, with more than 4,100 pages (four volumes) in its second edition (1992), is now available in a third edition (2006) of seven volumes. Collectively, *Bergey's Manual* and *The Prokaryotes* offer microbiologists the foundations as well as the details of the taxonomy and phylogeny of *Bacteria* and *Archaea* as we know it today. Typically they are the primary resources for microbiologists characterizing newly isolated organisms.

Culture Collections

National microbial culture collections are an important foundation of microbial systematics (as well as industrial microbiology). These permanent collections catalog and store microorganisms and provide them upon request, usually for a fee, to researchers in academia, medicine, and industry. They play an important role as repositories for the natural diversity of bacteria, through the deposition of new kinds of microorganisms by the scientists who discover them. In this way, these collections serve to maintain and protect microbial biodiversity, much in the same way that museums maintain plant and animal specimens for future study. However, microbial culture collections store the deposited microorganisms, not as chemically preserved or dried, dead specimens, but as *viable* cultures, typically frozen at very low temperatures or as a freeze-dried culture. These storage methods maintain the bacteria essentially indefinitely as viable cultures in their original state.

A related and key role of culture collections is as repositories for *type strains*. When a new species of bacteria is described in a scientific journal, a strain is designated as the nomenclatural type of the taxon for future taxonomic comparison with other strains of that species. Deposition of this type strain in the national culture collections of at least two countries, thereby making the strain publicly available, is a prerequisite for validation of the new species name. Some of the large national culture collections are listed in Table 6. Their web sites contain searchable databases of strain holdings, together with information on the environmental sources of strains and publications on them.

Describing New Species

When a new prokaryote is isolated from nature and thought to be unique, a decision must be made as to whether it is

Table 6 Some national microbial culture collections

Collection	*Name*	*Location*	*Web address*
ATCC	American Type Culture Collection	Manassas, Virginia	http://www.atcc.org
BCCM/LMG	Belgium Coordinated Collection of Microorganisms	Ghent, Belgium	http://bccm.belspo.be
CIP	Collection de l'Institut Pasteur	Paris, France	http://www.pasteur.fr
DSMZ	Deutsche Sammlung von Mikroorganismen und Zellkulturen	Braunschweig, Germany	http://www.dsmz.de
JCM	Japan Collection of Microorganisms	Saitama, Japan	http://www.jcm.riken.go.jp
NCCB	Netherlands Culture Collection of Bacteria	Utrecht, The Netherlands	http://www.cbs.knaw.nl/nccb
NCIMB	National Collection of Industrial, Marine and Food Bacteria	Aberdeen, Scotland	http://www.ncimb.com

sufficiently different from other species to be described as novel, or perhaps even sufficiently different from all described genera to warrant description as a new genus (in which case a new species name is automatically created). To achieve formal validation of taxonomic standing as a new genus or species, a detailed description of the organism's characteristics and distinguishing traits, along with its proposed name, is published, and viable cultures of the organism are deposited in at least two international culture collections. The description and new name should be published in the *International Journal of Systematic and Evolutionary Microbiology (IJSEM),* the official publication of record for the taxonomy and classification of *Bacteria* and *Archaea*. Alternatively, if the new organism is published in a different journal, a copy of the publication and additional supporting information can be submitted to *IJSEM* to request validation of the name and formal acceptance as a new taxon. In each issue, the *IJSEM* publishes an approved list of newly validated names. By providing validation of newly proposed names, publication in *IJSEM* paves the way for their inclusion in *Bergey's Manual of Systematic Bacteriology*. Two web sites provide listings of valid, approved bacterial names: List of Prokaryotic Names with Standing in Nomenclature (http:// www.bacterio.cict.fr), and Bacterial Nomenclature Up-to-Date (http://www.dsmz.de/bactnom/bactname.htm).

The International Committee on Systematics of Prokaryotes (ICSP) is responsible for overseeing nomenclature and taxonomy of *Bacteria* and *Archaea*. The ICSP oversees the publication of *IJSEM* and the Bacteriological Code, and it guides several subcommittees tasked with setting up minimal standards for the description of new species in the different groups.

14 MiniReview

Formal recognition of a new prokaryotic species requires depositing a sample of the organism in culture collections and official publication of the new species name and description. *Bergey's Manual of Systematic Bacteriology* and *The Prokaryotes* are major taxonomic compilations of *Bacteria* and *Archaea*.

- What roles do culture collections play in microbial systematics?
- What is the *IJSEM* and what taxonomic function does it fulfill?
- Why might viable cell cultures be of more use in microbial taxonomy than preserved specimens?

Review of Key Terms

Allele a sequence variant of a given gene

Archaea a group of phylogenetically related prokaryotes distinct from *Bacteria*

Bacteria a group of phylogenetically related prokaryotes distinct from *Archaea*

Binomial system the system devised by Linnaeus for naming living organisms by which an organism is given a genus name and a species epithet

Cladistics phylogenetic methods that group organisms by their evolutionary relationships, not by their phenotypic similarities

Domain in a taxonomic sense, the highest level of biological classification

DNA–DNA hybridization the experimental determination of genomic similarity by measuring the extent of hybridization of DNA from the genome of one organism with that of another

Ecotype a population of genetically identical cells sharing a particular resource within an ecological niche

Endosymbiosis the theory that a chemo-organotrophic bacterium and a cyanobacterium, respectively, were stably incorporated into another cell type to give rise to the mitochondria and chloroplasts of modern-day eukaryotes

Eukarya all eukaryotes: algae, protists, fungi, slime molds, plants, and animals

Evolution descent with modification; DNA sequence variation and the inheritance of that variation

FAME fatty acid methyl ester

FISH fluorescent *in-situ* hybridization

Fitness the capacity of an organism to survive and reproduce as compared to competing organisms

GC ratio in DNA from an organism, the percentage of the total nucleic acid that consists of guanine and cytosine bases

Horizontal gene transfer the transfer of DNA from one cell to another, often distantly related, cell

Molecular clock a gene, such as for ribosomal RNA, whose DNA sequence can be used as a comparative temporal measure of evolutionary divergence

Monophyletic in phylogeny, a group descended from one ancestor

Multilocus sequence typing (MLST) a taxonomic tool for classifying organisms on the basis of gene sequence variations in several housekeeping genes

Phylogenetic probe an oligonucleotide, sometimes made fluorescent by attachment of a dye, complementary in sequence to some ribosomal RNA signature sequence

Phylogeny the evolutionary history of an organism

Phylum a major lineage of cells in one of the three domains of life

Proteobacteria a large group of phylogenetically related gram-negative *Bacteria*

Ribosomal Database Project (RDP) a large database of small subunit ribosomal RNA sequences that can be retrieved electronically and used in comparative ribosomal RNA sequence studies

Ribotyping a means of identifying microorganisms from analysis of DNA fragments generated from restriction enzyme digestion of genes encoding their 16S rRNA

Signature sequence short oligonucleotides of defined sequence in SSU ribosomal RNA characteristic of specific organisms or a group of phylogenetically related organisms; useful for constructing probes

16S ribosomal RNA a large polynucleotide (~1,500 bases) that functions as part of the small subunit of the ribosome of *Bacteria* and *Archaea* and from whose gene sequence evolutionary information can be obtained; eukaryotic counterpart, 18S rRNA

Small subunit (SSU) RNA ribosomal RNA from the 30S ribosomal subunit of *Bacteria* and *Archaea* or the 40S ribosomal subunit of eukaryotes, that is 16S or 18S ribosomal RNA, respectively

Species defined in microbiology as a collection of strains that all share the same major properties and differ in one or more significant properties from other collections of strains; defined phylogenetically as monophyletic, exclusive groups based on DNA sequence

Stromatolite a laminated microbial mat, typically built from layers of filamentous *Bacteria* and other microorganisms, which can become fossilized

Systematics the study of the diversity organisms and their relationships; includes taxonomy and phylogeny

Taxonomy the science of identification, classification, and nomenclature

Universal phylogenetic tree a tree that shows the position of representatives of all domains of living organisms

Review Questions

1. What is the age of planet Earth? When did the oceans form, and what is the age of the earliest known microfossils (Section 1)?
2. Under what conditions did life likely originate? What were the steps leading from prebiotic chemistry to living cells? (Section 2)?
3. What kind of energy and carbon metabolisms likely characterized early cellular life (Section 2)?
4. Why was the evolution of cyanobacteria of such importance to the further evolution of life on Earth? What component of the geological record is used to date the evolution of cyanobacteria (Section 3)?
5. What is the hydrogen hypothesis and how does it relate to the endosymbiotic origin of the eukaryotic cell (Section 4)?
6. What does the phrase "descent with modification" imply about natural relationships among living organisms (Secton 5)?
7. Why are SSU rRNA genes good choices for phylogenetic studies, and what are their limitations (Section 6)?
8. What is the fundamental basis for character-state methods of phylogenetic analysis (Section 7)?
9. What major evolutionary finding has emerged from the study of rRNA sequences? How did this modify the classic view of evolution? How has this discovery supported previous beliefs on the origin of eukaryotic organisms (Section 8)?
10. What major physiological and biochemical properties do *Archaea* share with *Eukarya*? With *Bacteria* (Section 8)?
11. What are signature sequences and of what phylogenetic value are they? How are signature sequences discerned (Section 9)?
12. What is FISH technology? Give an example of how it would be used (Section 9).
13. What major phenotypic and genotypic properties are used to classify organisms in bacterial taxonomy (Sections 10 and 11)?
14. What is measured in FAME analyses (Section 10)?
15. How does 16S rRNA gene sequence analysis differ from multilocus sequence typing as an identification tool (Section 11)?
16. How is multi-gene phylogenetic analysis an improvement over analyses based on individual genes (Section 12)?
17. How is it thought that new bacterial species arise? How many bacterial species are there? Why don't we know this number more precisely (Section 13)?
18. What roles do microbial culture collections play in microbial systematics (Section 14)?

Application Questions

1. Compare and contrast the physical and chemical conditions on Earth at the time life first arose with conditions today. From a physiological standpoint, discuss at least two reasons why *animals* could not have existed on early Earth.
2. Why is it highly unlikely that life could originate today as it did billions of years ago?
3. Imagine that you are debating someone who is arguing against the theory of endosymbiosis. What evidence would you use to support the view that endosymbiosis did occur? (You may wish to review Section 4 before writing your answer.)
4. In what ways has microbial metabolism altered Earth's biosphere? How might life on Earth be different if oxygenic photosynthesis had not evolved?
5. For the following sequences, identify the phylogenetically informative sites. Identify also the phylogenetically neutral sites and those that are invariant.

   Taxon 1: TCCGTACGTTA
   Taxon 2: TCCCCACGGTT
   Taxon 3: TCGGTACCGTA
   Taxon 4: TCGGTACCGTA
6. Imagine that you are doing lipid analyses of two microorganisms along the lines shown in Figure 22. Your results on culture A show an abundance of short-chain unsaturated fatty acids. Analyses of cells in culture B show ether-linked phytanyl lipids to be present. Based on this information, to which phylogenetic domain do organisms A and B belong? Also, if you were told that these organisms were both extremophiles and that one originated from a boiling hot spring and one from polar sea ice, which would be which? Finally, based on your lipid analyses and knowledge of where most lipid is located in a cell, describe how the substances you detected might benefit each organism in thriving in its extreme environment.
7. Imagine that you have been given several bacterial strains from various countries around the world and that all the strains are thought to cause the same gastrointestinal disease and to be genetically identical. Upon carrying out a DNA fingerprint analysis of the strains, you find that four different strain types are present. What methods could you use to test whether the different strains are actually members of the same species?
8. What reference resource(s) would you check for information on the taxonomy and phylogeny of *Bacteria* and *Archaea*? On enrichment, isolation, and culture? If your library has these sources, compare their tables of contents. Which has the greater emphasis on classification and nomenclature?
9. Imagine that you have discovered a new form of microbial life, one that appears to represent a fourth domain. How would you go about characterizing the new organism and determining if it actually is evolutionarily distinct from *Bacteria, Archaea,* and *Eukarya*?

Chemistry of Cellular Components

Chemistry of Cellular Components

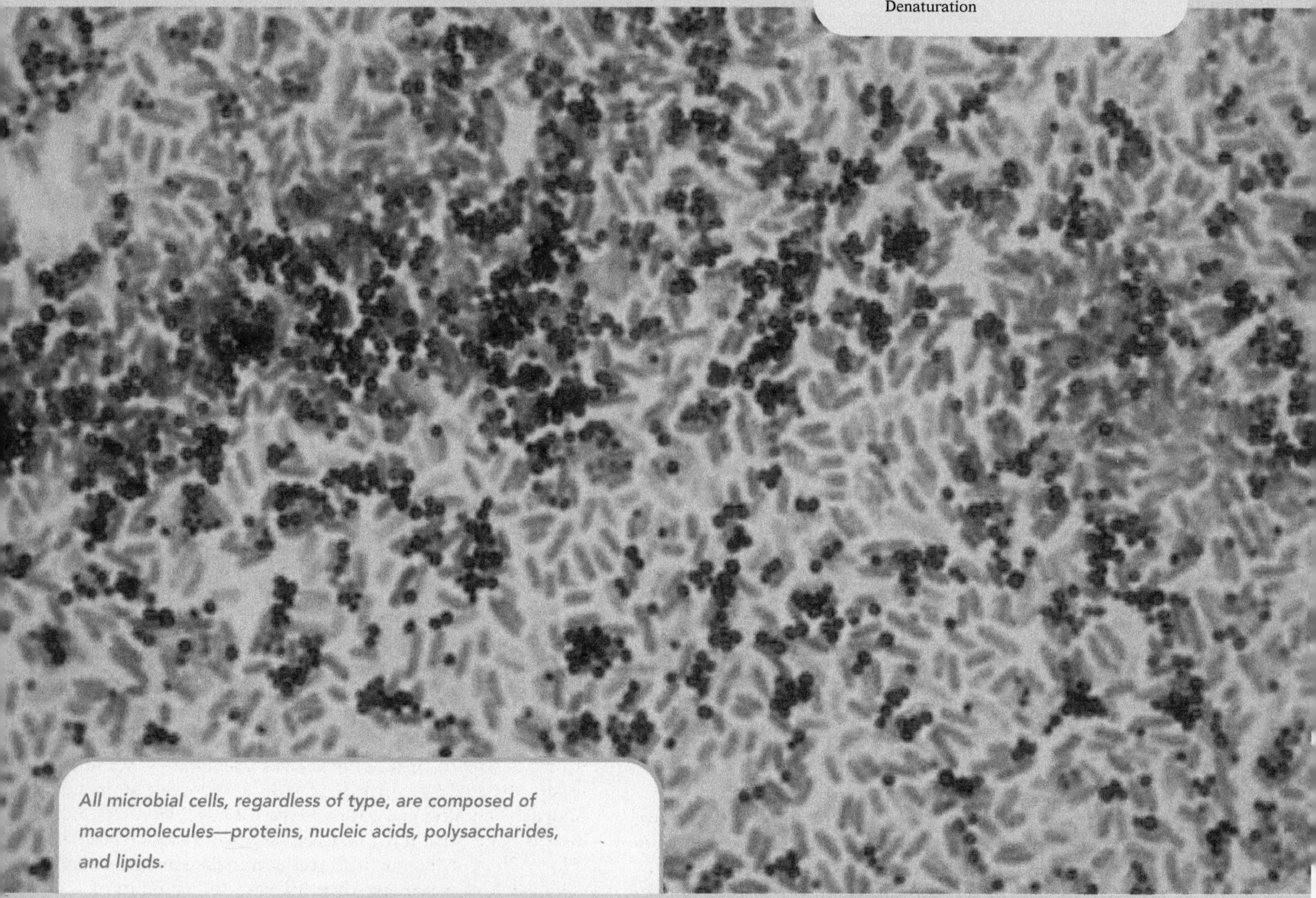

All microbial cells, regardless of type, are composed of macromolecules—proteins, nucleic acids, polysaccharides, and lipids.

Brent Selinger, Pearson Benjamin Cummings

I CHEMICAL BONDING, MACROMOLECULES, AND WATER

All cells have much in common. The heart of microbial diversity lies in the variations that cells display in the chemistry and arrangement of their cellular components. These variations confer special properties on each type of cell and allow the cell to carry out specific functions.

To really understand how a cell works, it is necessary to know the molecules that are present and the chemical processes that take place. Molecules, especially macromolecules, are the "guts" of the cell and are the subject of this chapter. It is assumed that the reader has some background in elementary chemistry, especially regarding the nature of atoms and atomic bonding. Here we will expand on this background with a primer on relevant biochemical bonds, followed by a discussion of the structure and function of the four classes of macromolecules.

1 Strong and Weak Chemical Bonds

The major chemical elements in living things include hydrogen, oxygen, carbon, nitrogen, phosphorus, and sulfur. These elements bond in various ways to form the molecules of life. A **molecule** consists of two or more atoms chemically bonded to one another. Thus, two oxygen (O) atoms can combine to form a molecule of oxygen (O_2). Likewise, carbon (C), hydrogen (H), and O atoms can combine to form glucose, $C_6H_{12}O_6$, a hexose sugar (see Figure 4).

Covalent Bonds

In living things, chemical elements typically form strong bonds in which electrons are shared more or less equally between atoms. These are called **covalent bonds**. To envision a covalent bond, consider the formation of a molecule of water from the elements O and H:

$$\ddot{\underset{..}{O}} + 2H\cdot \longrightarrow H:\ddot{\underset{..}{O}}:H$$

Oxygen has six electrons in its outermost shell, and hydrogen contains only a single electron. When O and 2H combine to form H_2O, covalent bonds maintain the three atoms in tight association as a water molecule. In some compounds, double and even triple covalent bonds can form (Figure 1). The strength of these bonds increases dramatically with their number. In cells single and double covalent bonds are most common; triply bonded substances are rare.

Chemical elements bond in different combinations to form **monomers**, small molecules that in turn bond with each other to form larger molecules called **polymers**. Covalently bonded polymers in living things are called **macromolecules**. Thousands of different monomers are known but only a relatively small number play important roles in the four classes of macromolecules. To a large extent it is the chemical properties of monomers that give macromolecules their distinctive structure and function.

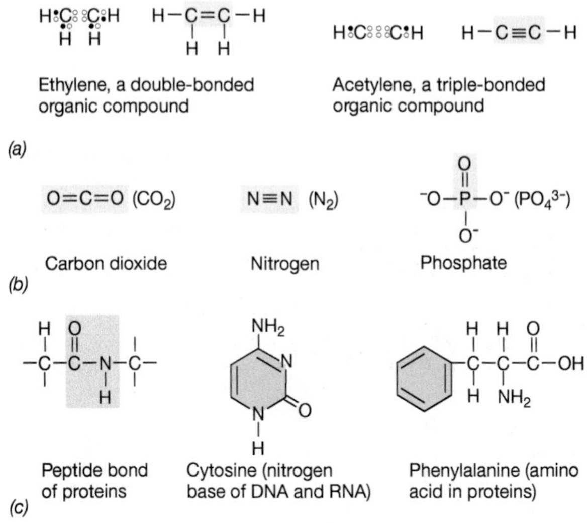

Figure 1 Covalent bonding of some molecules containing double or triple bonds. *(a)* For acetylene and ethylene, both the electronic configuration of the molecules and the conventional shorthand for bonds is shown. *(b)* Some inorganic compounds with double bonds. *(c)* Some organic compounds with double bonds.

Hydrogen Bonding and Polarity

In addition to covalent bonds, several weaker chemical bonds also play an important role in biological molecules. Foremost among these are hydrogen bonds. **Hydrogen bonds** form as the result of weak electrostatic interactions between hydrogen atoms and more electronegative (electron attracting) atoms, such as oxygen or nitrogen (Figure 2). For example, because an oxygen atom is electronegative but a hydrogen atom is not, in the covalent bond between oxygen and hydrogen the shared electrons orbit slightly nearer the oxygen nucleus than the hydrogen nucleus. Because electrons carry a negative charge, this creates a slight charge separation, oxygen slightly negative and hydrogen slightly positive; this bridge is the hydrogen bond. An individual hydrogen bond by itself is very weak. However, when many hydrogen bonds form within and between molecules, overall stability of the molecules can increase dramatically.

Water is a **polar** substance. Because of this, water molecules tend to associate with one another and remain apart from **nonpolar** (hydrophobic) molecules. Water is extensively hydrogen bonded. As water molecules orient themselves in solution, the slight positive charge on a hydrogen atom can bridge the negative charges on oxygen atoms (Figure 2*a*). Hydrogen bonds also form between atoms in macromolecules (Figure 2*b*,*c*). As these weak forces accumulate in a large molecule such as a protein, they increase the stability of the molecule and can also affect its overall structure. We will see in Sections 5, 7, and 8 that hydrogen bonds play major roles in the biological properties of proteins (Figure 2*b*) and nucleic acids (Figure 2*c*).

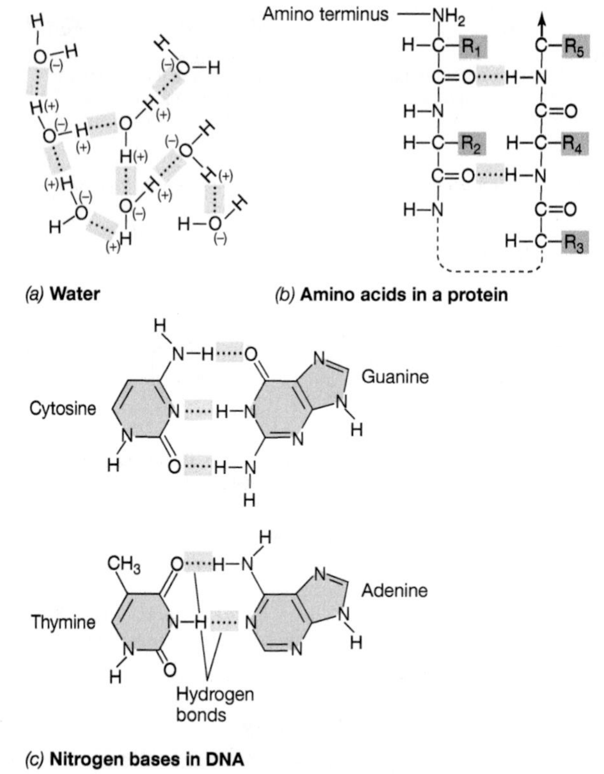

Figure 2 Hydrogen bonding in water and organic compounds. Hydrogen bonds are shown as highlighted dotted lines. *(b)* Proteins. R represents the side chain of the amino acid (Figure 12). *(c)* Hydrogen bonds formed during complementary base pairing in DNA.

Other Weak Bonds

Weak interactions other than hydrogen bonds are also important in cells. For instance, *van der Waals forces* are weak attractive forces that occur between atoms when they become closer than about 3–4 angstroms (Å); van der Waals forces can play significant roles in the binding of substrates to enzymes and in protein–nucleic acid interactions.

Ionic bonds, such as that between Na^+ and Cl^- in NaCl, are weak electrostatic interactions that support ionization in aqueous solution. Many important biomolecules, such as carboxylic acids and phosphates (Table 1), are ionized at cytoplasmic pH (typically pH 6–8) and thus can be dissolved to high levels in the cytoplasm.

Hydrophobic interactions are also considered weak bonds. Hydrophobic interactions occur when nonpolar molecules or nonpolar regions of molecules associate tightly in a polar environment. Hydrophobic interactions can play major roles in controlling the folding of proteins (Sections 7 and 8). Like van der Waals forces, hydrophobic interactions help bind substrates to enzymes. In addition, hydrophobic interactions often control how different subunits in a multisubunit protein associate with one another (quaternary structure, Section 8) to form the biologically active molecule, and they also help stabilize RNA and cytoplasmic membranes.

Bonding Patterns in Biological Molecules

The element carbon is a major component of all macromolecules. Carbon can bond not only with itself, but with many other elements as well, to yield large structures of considerable diversity and complexity. Different organic (carbon-containing) compounds have different bonding patterns. Each of these patterns, called *functional groups*, has unique chemical properties that are important in determining their biological role within the cell. An awareness of key functional groups will make our later discussion of macromolecular structure, cell physiology, and biosynthesis easier to follow. Table 1 lists several functional groups of biochemical importance and examples of molecules or macromolecules that contain them.

1 MiniReview

Covalent bonds are strong bonds that bind elements in macromolecules. Weak bonds, such as hydrogen bonds, van der Waals forces, and hydrophobic interactions, also affect macromolecular structure, but they do so through more subtle atomic interactions. Various functional groups are common in biomolecules.

- Why are covalent bonds stronger than hydrogen bonds?
- How can a hydrogen bond play a role in macromolecular structure?

2 An Overview of Macromolecules and Water as the Solvent of Life

If you were to chemically analyze a cell of the common intestinal bacterium *Escherichia coli*, what would you find? You would find water as the major constituent, but after removing the water, you would find large amounts of macromolecules, much smaller amounts of monomers, and a variety of inorganic ions (Table 2). About 95% of the dry weight of a cell consists of macromolecules, and of these, proteins are by far the most abundant class (Table 2).

Proteins are polymers of monomers called **amino acids**. Proteins are found throughout the cell, playing both structural and enzymatic roles (Figure 3*a*). An average cell will have over a thousand different types of proteins and multiple copies of each (Table 2).

Nucleic acids are polymers of **nucleotides** and are found in the cell in two forms, RNA and DNA. After proteins, ribonucleic acids (RNAs) are the next most abundant macromolecule in an actively growing cell (Table 2 and Figure 3*b*). This is because there are thousands of ribosomes (the "machines" that make new proteins) in each cell, and

Table 1 Some functional groups of biochemical importance

Functional group	*Structure*[a]	*Biological relevance*	*Example*
Carboxylic acid	$-\overset{\overset{\displaystyle O}{\|}}{C}-OH$	Organic, amino, and fatty acids; lipids; proteins	Acetate[b]
Aldehyde	$-\overset{\overset{\displaystyle O}{\|}}{C}-H$	Functional group of reducing sugars such as glucose; aldehydes	Formaldehyde
Alcohol	$-\underset{\underset{\displaystyle H}{\|}}{\overset{\overset{\displaystyle H}{\|}}{C}}-OH$	Lipids; carbohydrates	Glucose
Keto	$-\overset{\overset{\displaystyle O}{\|}}{C}-$	Citric acid cycle intermediates	α-ketoglutarate
Ester	$-\overset{\overset{\displaystyle O}{\|}}{C}-O-\underset{\underset{\displaystyle H}{\|}}{\overset{\overset{\displaystyle H}{\|}}{C}}-$	Triglycerides	Lipids of *Bacteria* and *Eukarya*
Phosphate ester	$^{-}O-\underset{\underset{\displaystyle O}{\|}}{\overset{\overset{\displaystyle O^{-}}{\|}}{P}}-O-\underset{\|}{\overset{\|}{C}}-$	Nucleic acids	DNA, RNA
Thioester	$-\overset{\overset{\displaystyle O}{\|}}{C}\sim S-$	Energy metabolism; biosynthesis of fatty acids	Acetyl-CoA
Ether	$-\underset{\underset{\displaystyle H}{\|}}{\overset{\overset{\displaystyle H}{\|}}{C}}-O-\underset{\underset{\displaystyle H}{\|}}{\overset{\overset{\displaystyle H}{\|}}{C}}-$	Certain types of lipids	Lipids of *Archaea*
Acid anhydride	$-\overset{\overset{\displaystyle O}{\|}}{C}\sim O-\underset{\underset{\displaystyle O^{-}}{\|}}{\overset{\overset{\displaystyle O^{-}}{\|}}{P}}=O$	Energy metabolism	Acetyl phosphate
Phosphoanhydride	$^{-}O-\underset{\underset{\displaystyle O}{\|}}{\overset{\overset{\displaystyle O^{-}}{\|}}{P}}\sim O-\underset{\underset{\displaystyle O}{\|}}{\overset{\overset{\displaystyle O^{-}}{\|}}{P}}-O^{-}$	Energy metabolism	Adenosine triphosphate (ATP)
Peptide	$R-C-\overset{\overset{\displaystyle O}{\|}}{C}-N-C-R$	Proteins	Cellular proteins

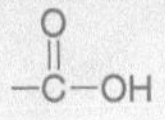

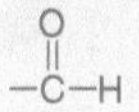

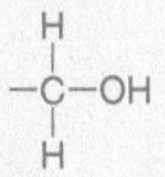

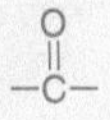

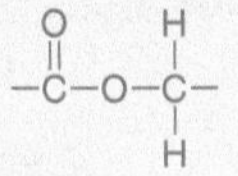

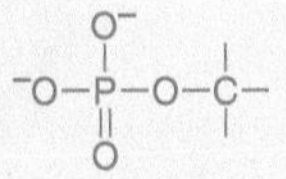

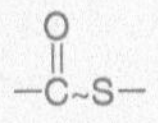

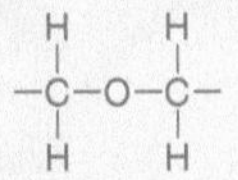

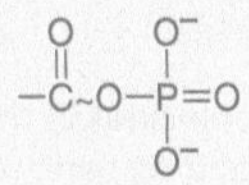

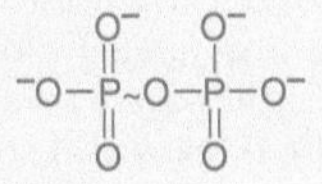

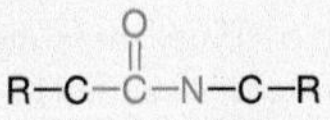

[a]A squiggle-type bond depiction (~) indicates an "energy-rich" bond.
[b]Acetate (H_3CCOO^-) is the ionized form of acetic acid (H_3CCOOH).

ribosomes are composed of a mixture of RNAs and protein. In addition, smaller amounts of RNA are present in the form of messenger and transfer RNAs, other key players in protein synthesis. In contrast to RNA, DNA makes up a small fraction of the bacterial cell (Table 2).

Lipids have both hydrophobic and hydrophilic properties and play crucial roles in the cell as the backbone of membranes and as storage depots for excess carbon (Figure 3*d*). **Polysaccharides** are polymers of sugars and are present in the cell, primarily in the cell wall. Like lipids, however, polysaccharides such as glycogen (discussed in the next section) can be major forms of carbon and energy storage in the cell (Figure 3*c*).

Water as a Biological Solvent

Macromolecules and all other molecules in cells are bathed in water. Water has several important features that make it an ideal biological solvent. Two key features are its polarity and cohesiveness.

The polar properties of water are important because many biologically important molecules (Table 2) are themselves polar and thus readily dissolve in water. Dissolved substances are continually passing into and out of the cell through transport activities of the cytoplasmic membrane. These substances include nutrients needed to build new cell material and waste products of metabolic processes.

Table 2 Chemical composition of a prokaryotic cell[a]

Molecule	*Percent of dry weight[b]*	*Molecules per cell (different kinds)*
Total macromolecules	96	24,610,000 (~2,500)
Protein	55	2,350,000 (~1,850)
Polysaccharide	5	4,300 (2)[c]
Lipid	9.1	22,000,000 (4)[d]
Lipopolysaccharide	3.4	1,430,000 (1)
DNA	3.1	2.1 (1)
RNA	20.5	255,500 (~660)
Total monomers	3.0	—[e](~350)
Amino acids and precursors	0.5	—(~100)
Sugars and precursors	2	—(~50)
Nucleotides and precursors	0.5	—(~200)
Inorganic ions	1	—(18)
Total	100%	—

[a]Data from Neidhardt, F.C., et al. (eds.), 1996. *Escherichia coli* and *Salmonella typhimurium—Cellular and Molecular Biology*, 2nd edition. American Society for Microbiology, Washington, DC.

[b]Dry weight of an actively growing cell of *E. coli* = 2.8×10^{-13}g; total weight (70% water) = 9.5×10^{-13} g.

[c]Assuming peptidoglycan and glycogen to be the major polysaccharides present.

[d]There are several classes of phospholipids, each of which exists in many kinds because of variability in fatty acid composition between species and because of different growth conditions.

[e]Reliable estimates of monomer and inorganic ion composition are lacking.

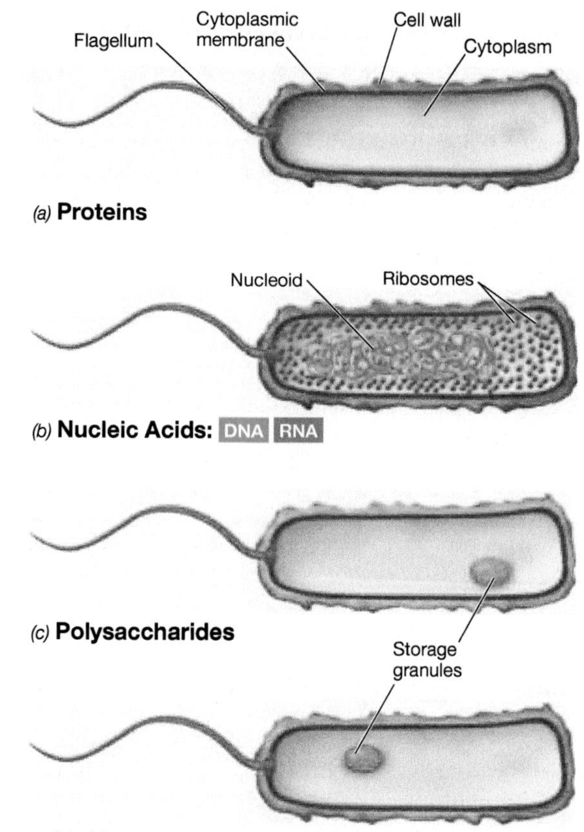

Figure 3 Macromolecules in the cell. *(a)* Proteins (brown) are found throughout the cell both as parts of cell structures and as enzymes. The flagellum is a structure involved in swimming motility. *(b)* Nucleic acids. DNA (green) is found in the nucleoid of prokaryotic cells and in the nucleus of eukaryotic cells. RNA (orange) is found in the cytoplasm (mRNA, tRNA) and in ribosomes (rRNA). *(c)* Polysaccharides (yellow) are located in the cell wall and occasionally in internal storage granules. *(d)* Lipids (blue) are found in the cytoplasmic membrane, the cell wall, and in storage granules.

The polar properties of water also promote the stability of large molecules because of the increased opportunities for hydrogen bonding. Water forms three-dimensional networks, both with itself (Figure 2*a*) and within macromolecules. By so doing, water molecules help to position atoms within biomolecules for potential interaction. The high polarity of water is also beneficial to the cell because it forces nonpolar substances to aggregate and remain together. Membranes, for example, contain large amounts of lipids, which have major nonpolar (hydrophobic) components, and these aggregate in such a way as to prevent the unrestricted flow of polar molecules into and out of the cell.

The polar nature of water makes it highly cohesive. This means that water molecules have a high affinity for one another and form ordered arrangements in which hydrogen bonds (Figure 2*a*) are constantly forming, breaking, and reforming. The cohesiveness of water is responsible for some of its biologically important properties, such as high surface tension and high specific heat (heat required to raise the temperature 1°C). Also, the fact that water expands on freezing to yield a less dense solid form (ice) has a profound effect on life in temperate and polar aquatic environments. In a lake, for example, ice on the surface insulates the water beneath the ice and prevents it from freezing, thus allowing aquatic organisms to survive under the overlying ice.

Life originated in water about 3.9 billion years ago, and virtually anywhere on Earth where liquid water exists, microorganisms are likely to be found. With these important properties of water in mind, we now consider the structure of the major macromolecules of life (Table 2 and Figure 3) in more detail.

2 MiniReview

Proteins are the most abundant class of macromolecule in the cell. Other macromolecules include the nucleic acids, lipids, and polysaccharides. Water is an excellent solvent for life because of its polarity and cohesiveness.

- Why do protein and RNA make up such a large proportion of an actively growing cell?
- Why does the high polarity of water make it useful as a biological solvent?

II NONINFORMATIONAL MACROMOLECULES

In this unit we examine the structure and function of noninformational macromolecules—polysaccharides and lipids. The sequence of monomers in these macromolecules does not carry genetic information, but the macromolecules themselves play important roles in the cell, primarily as structural or reserve materials.

3 Polysaccharides

Carbohydrates (sugars) are organic compounds that contain carbon, hydrogen, and oxygen in a ratio of 1:2:1. The structural formula for glucose, the most abundant sugar on Earth is $C_6H_{12}O_6$ (Figure 4). The most biologically relevant carbohydrates are those containing four, five, six, and seven carbon atoms (designated as C_4, C_5, C_6, and C_7). C_5 sugars (pentoses) are of special significance because of their role as structural backbones of nucleic acids. Likewise, C_6 sugars (hexoses) are the monomeric constituents of cell wall polymers and energy reserves. Figure 4 shows the structure of a few common sugars.

Derivatives of simple carbohydrates are common in cells. When other chemical species replace one or more of the hydroxyl groups on the sugar, derivatives are formed. For example, the important bacterial cell wall polymer *peptidoglycan* contains the glucose derivative *N*-acetylglucosamine (Figure 5). Besides sugar derivatives, sugars having the same *structural* formula can differ in their *stereoisomeric* properties. For example, a polysaccharide composed of D-glucose differs from one containing L-glucose (Section 6). Hence, a large number of different sugars are available to the cell for the construction of polysaccharides.

The Glycosidic Bond

Polysaccharides are carbohydrates containing many (sometimes hundreds or even thousands) of monomeric units called *monosaccharides*. The latter are connected by covalent bonds called **glycosidic bonds** (Figure 6). If two monosaccharides are bonded by a glycosidic linkage, the resulting molecule is a disaccharide. The addition of one more monosaccharide yields a trisaccharide, and several more an oligosaccharide. An extremely long chain is then a *polysaccharide*.

Glycosidic bonds can form in two different geometric orientations, alpha (α) and beta (β) (Figure 6*a*). Polysaccharides with a repeating structure composed of glucose units bonded between carbons 1 and 4 in the alpha orientation (for example, glycogen and starch, Figure 6*b*) function as important carbon and energy reserves in bacteria, plants, and animals. Glucose units joined by β-1,4 linkages are present in cellulose (Figure 6*b*), a stiff plant and algal cell wall component. Thus, even though both starch and cellulose contain only D-glucose, their functional properties differ because of the different configurations, α or β, of their glycosidic bonds.

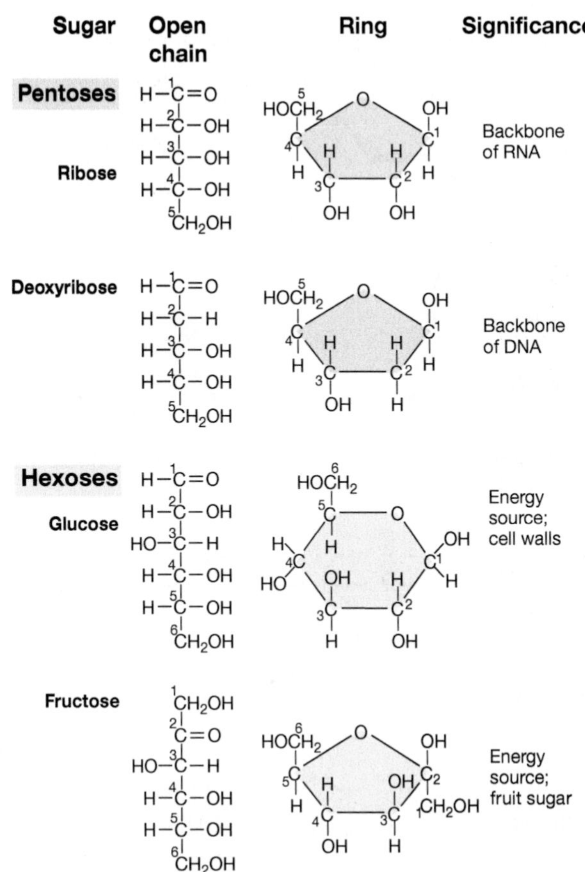

Figure 4 **Structural formulas of a few common sugars.** The formulas can be depicted in two alternate ways, open chain and ring. The open chain is easier to visualize, but the ring form is the commonly used structure. Note the numbering system on the ring. Glucose and fructose are isomers of one another; they have the same molecular composition but have different structures (Section 6).

Complex Polysaccharides

Polysaccharides can also combine with other classes of macromolecules, such as proteins and lipids, to form complex polysaccharides—*glycoproteins* and *glycolipids*. These

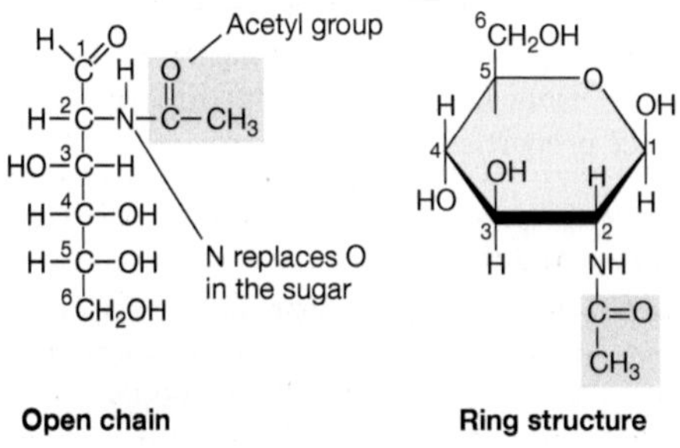

Acetyl group
N replaces O in the sugar
Open chain
Ring structure

Figure 5 ***N*-acetylglucosamine, a derivative of glucose.** The O on C-2 is replaced with an *N*-acetyl group.

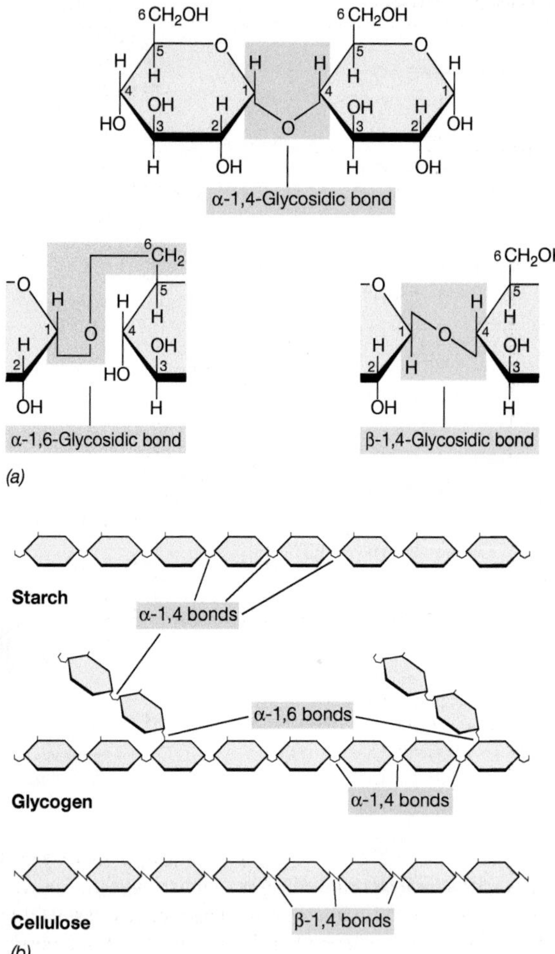

Figure 6 **The glycosidic bond and polysaccharides.** *(a)* Structure of different glycosidic bonds. Note that both the linkage (position on the ring of the carbon atoms bonded) and the geometry (α or β) of the linkage can vary about the glycosidic bond. *(b)* Structures of some common polysaccharides. Compare color coding to (a).

compounds play important roles in cells, in particular as cell-surface receptor molecules in cytoplasmic membranes. The compounds typically reside on the external surfaces of the membrane where they are in contact with the environment. Glycolipids constitute a major portion of the cell wall of gram-negative bacteria and, as such, impart a number of unique surface properties to these organisms.

3 MiniReview

Sugars can form long polymers called polysaccharides. The two different orientations of the glycosidic bonds that link sugar residues impart different properties to the resultant molecules. Polysaccharides can also contain other molecules such as protein or lipid, forming complex polysaccharides.

- How can glycogen and cellulose differ so much in their physical properties when they both consist of 100% D-glucose?

4 Lipids

Lipids are essential components of cells and are *amphipathic* macromolecules, meaning that they show both hydrophilic and hydrophobic character. Lipid structure varies between the domains of life, and even within a domain many different lipids are known. **Fatty acids** are major constituents of *Bacteria* and *Eukarya* lipids. By contrast, lipids of *Archaea* contain a hydrocarbon (phytanyl) side chain not composed of fatty acids.

Fatty acids contain both hydrophobic and hydrophilic components. Palmitate (the ionized form of palmitic acid), is a common fatty acid in membrane lipids. Palmitate is a 16-carbon fatty acid composed of a chain of 15 saturated (fully hydrogenated and thus highly hydrophobic) carbon atoms and a single carboxylic acid group (the hydrophilic portion) (Figure 7). Other common fatty acids in the lipids of *Bacteria* include saturated or monounsaturated forms, from C_{12} to C_{20} (Figure 7).

Triglycerides and Complex Lipids

Simple lipids (fats) consist of fatty acids (or phytanyl units in *Archaea*) bonded to the C_3 alcohol glycerol (Figure 7*a, b*). Simple lipids are also called *triglycerides* because three fatty acids are linked to the glycerol molecule. We will see when we consider membrane structure that the bond between glycerol and the hydrophobic side chain is an *ester* bond (Table 1) in cells of *Bacteria* and *Eukarya* but an *ether* bond (Table 1) in *Archaea*.

Complex lipids are simple lipids that contain additional elements such as phosphorus, nitrogen, or sulfur, or small hydrophilic organic compounds such as sugars (Figure 7*d*), ethanolamine (Figure 7*c*), serine, or choline. Lipids containing a phosphate group, called *phospholipids*, are an important class of complex lipids because they play a major structural role in the cytoplasmic membrane.

The amphipathic property of lipids makes them ideal structural components of membranes. Lipids aggregate to form membranes; the hydrophilic (glycerol) portion is in contact with the cytoplasm and the external environment whereas the hydrophobic portion remains buried away inside the membrane. Because of this property, membranes are ideal permeability barriers. The inability of polar substances to flow through the hydrophobic region of the lipids renders the membrane impermeable and prevents leakage of cytoplasmic constituents. However, this also means that polar substances necessary for cell function do not leak *in*, either.

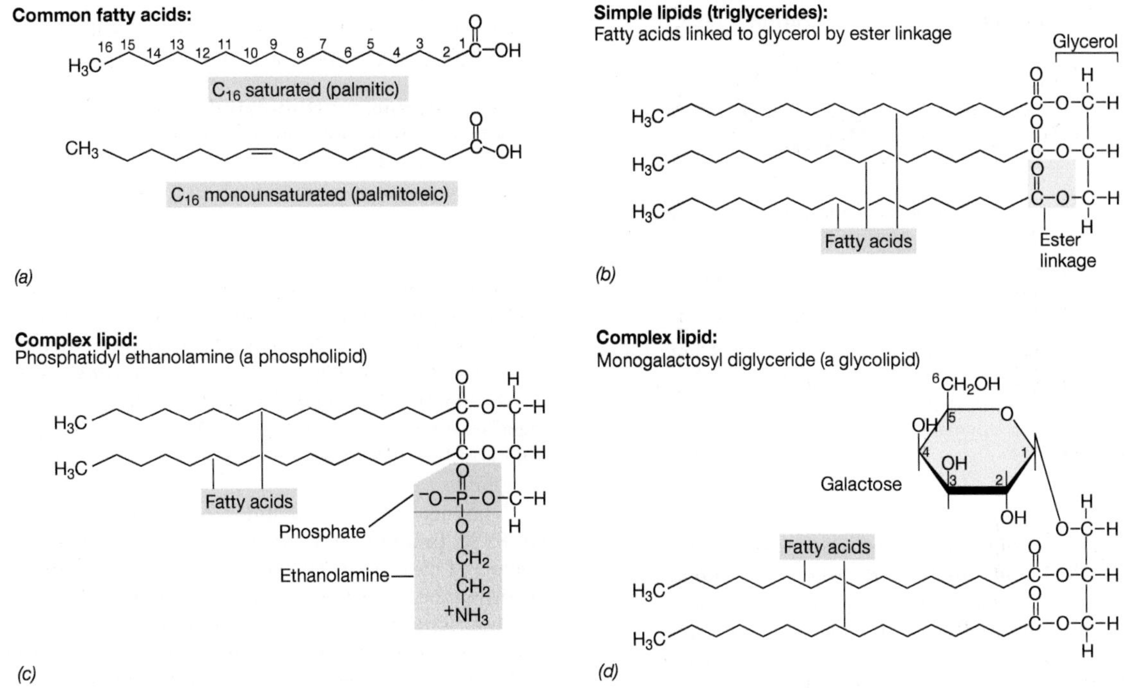

Common fatty acids:

C_{16} saturated (palmitic)

C_{16} monounsaturated (palmitoleic)

(a)

Simple lipids (triglycerides):
Fatty acids linked to glycerol by ester linkage

Glycerol

Fatty acids

Ester linkage

(b)

Complex lipid:
Phosphatidyl ethanolamine (a phospholipid)

Fatty acids

Phosphate

Ethanolamine

(c)

Complex lipid:
Monogalactosyl diglyceride (a glycolipid)

Galactose

Fatty acids

(d)

Figure 7 **Lipids.** *(a)* Fatty acids differ in length, in position, and in number of double bonds. *(b)* Simple lipids are formed by a dehydration reaction between fatty acids and glycerol to yield an ester linkage. The fatty acid composition of a cell varies with growth temperature. *(c, d)* Complex lipids are simple lipids containing other molecules.

4 MiniReview

Lipids contain both hydrophobic and hydrophilic components; their chemical properties make them ideal structural components for cytoplasmic membranes.

- What part of a fatty acid molecule is hydrophobic? Hydrophilic?
- How does a phospholipid differ from a triglyceride?
- Draw the chemical structure of butyrate, a C4 fully saturated fatty acid.

III INFORMATIONAL MACROMOLECULES

The sequence of monomers in nucleic acids carries genetic information, and the sequence of monomers in proteins carries structural and functional information. In contrast to polysaccharides and lipids, nucleic acids and proteins are thus *informational* macromolecules.

5 Nucleic Acids

The **nucleic acids** deoxyribonucleic acid, **DNA**, and ribonucleic acid, **RNA**, are macromolecules composed of monomers called *nucleotides*. Therefore, DNA and RNA are **polynucleotides**. As we already know, DNA carries the genetic blueprint for the cell and RNA is the intermediary molecule that converts the blueprint into defined amino acid sequences in proteins.

A nucleotide is composed of three components: a pentose sugar, either ribose (in RNA) or deoxyribose (in DNA), a nitrogen base, and a molecule of phosphate, PO_4^{3-}. The general structure of nucleotides of both DNA and RNA is very similar (Figure 8).

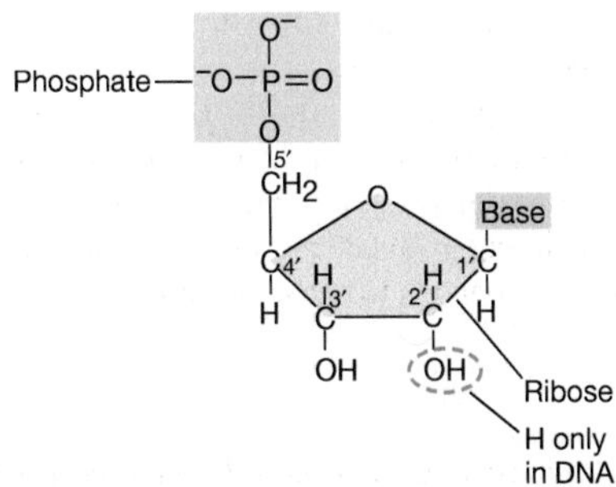

Figure 8 **Nucleotides.** The numbers on the sugar contain a prime (′) after them because the ring structure in the nitrogen base is also numbered (Figure 9).

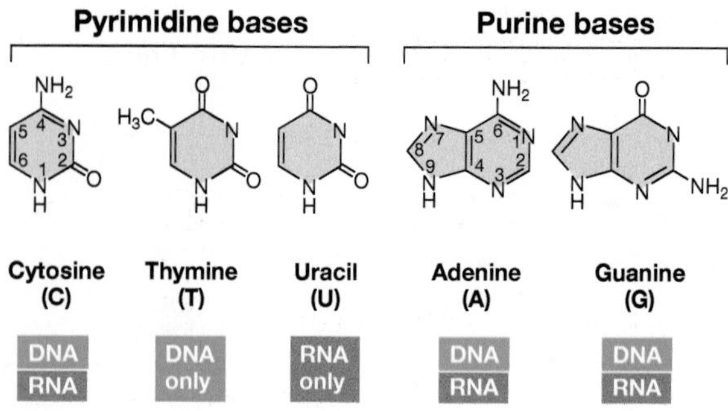

Figure 9 Structure of the nitrogen bases of DNA and RNA. Note the numbering system of the rings. In attaching itself to the 1′ carbon of the sugar phosphate shown in Figure 8, a pyrimidine base bonds through N-1 and a purine base bonds at N-9.

Nucleotides

The nitrogen bases of nucleic acids belong to one of two chemical classes. **Purine** bases—*adenine* and *guanine*—contain two fused heterocyclic rings (a heterocyclic ring contains more than one kind of atom). **Pyrimidine** bases—*thymine, cytosine,* and *uracil*—contain a single six-membered heterocyclic ring (Figure 9). Guanine, adenine, and cytosine are present in both DNA and RNA. Thymine is present (with minor exceptions) only in DNA, and uracil is present only in RNA.

Nucleotides consist of a nitrogen base attached to a pentose sugar by a glycosidic linkage between carbon atom 1 of the sugar and a nitrogen atom of the base, either the nitrogen atom labeled 1 (in a pyrimidine base) or 9 (in a purine base). Without the phosphate, a nitrogen base bonded to its sugar is called a *nucleoside*. Nucleotides are thus nucleosides containing one or more phosphates (Figure 10).

Nucleotides play other roles in the cell besides their major role as components of nucleic acids. Nucleotides, especially adenosine triphosphate (ATP) (Figure 10), are key forms of chemical energy within the cell, releasing sufficient energy during the hydrolysis of a phosphate bond to drive energy-requiring reactions in the cell. Other

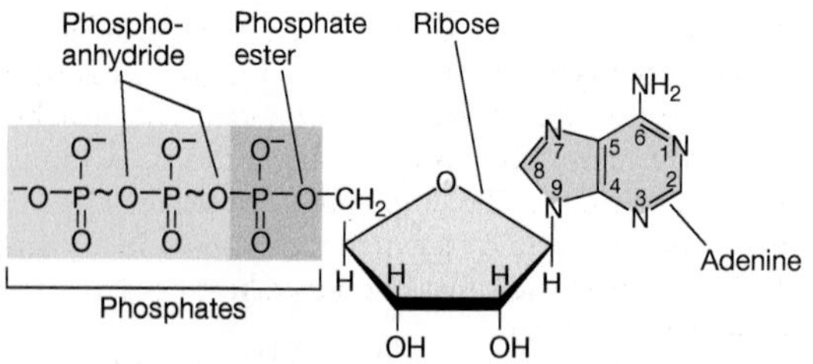

Figure 10 Components of the important nucleotide, adenosine triphosphate. The energy of hydrolysis of a phosphoanhydride bond (shown as squiggles) is greater than that of a phosphate ester bond, which is significant in bioenergetics. With the phosphate group removed, the molecule would be the nucleoside adenosine.

nucleotides or nucleotide derivatives function in oxidation–reduction reactions in the cell as carriers of sugars in the biosynthesis of polysaccharides and as regulatory molecules inhibiting or stimulating the activities of certain enzymes or metabolic events. However, we discuss here only the role of nucleotides as building blocks of nucleic acids, the major informational function of nucleotides.

Nucleic Acids

The nucleic acid backbone is a polymer of alternating sugar and phosphate molecules. Polynucleotides consist of nucleotides covalently bonded via phosphate from carbon 3—called the 3′ (3 prime) carbon—of one sugar to the 5′ carbon of the adjacent sugar (Figure 11*a*). The phosphate linkage is called a **phosphodiester bond** because a phosphate molecule connects two sugar molecules by ester linkage (Figure 11*a*; Table 1).

The sequence of nucleotides in a DNA or RNA molecule is called its **primary structure**. As we have discussed, the sequence of bases in a DNA or RNA molecule is informational, encoding the sequence of amino acids in proteins or encoding specific ribosomal or transfer RNAs. The replication of DNA and the synthesis of RNA are key events in the life of a cell. We will see later that a virtually error-free mechanism is employed to ensure the faithful transfer of genetic traits from one generation to another.

DNA

In the genome of cells, DNA is *double-stranded*. Each chromosome consists of two strands of DNA, with each strand containing hundreds of thousands to several million nucleotides linked by phosphodiester bonds. The strands associate with one another by hydrogen bonds that form between the nitrogen bases in nucleotides of one strand and the nitrogen bases in nucleotides of the other strand. When positioned adjacent to one another, purine and pyrimidine bases can undergo hydrogen bonding (see Figure 2*c*).

Hydrogen bonding is most stable when guanine (G) bonds with cytosine (C) and adenine (A) bonds with thymine (T) (see Figure 2*c*). Specific base pairing, A with T and G with C, thus ensures that the two strands of DNA are *complementary* in base sequence; that is, wherever a G is found in one strand, a C is found in the other, and wherever a T is present in one strand, its complementary strand has an A (Figure 11*b*).

RN3A

With a few exceptions, all RNAs are *single-stranded* molecules. However, RNAs typically fold back upon themselves in regions where complementary base pairing is possible to form folded structures. This pattern of folding in RNA is called its **secondary structure** (Figure 11*c*). In certain very large RNA molecules, such as ribosomal RNA, some parts of the molecule contain only primary structure but others

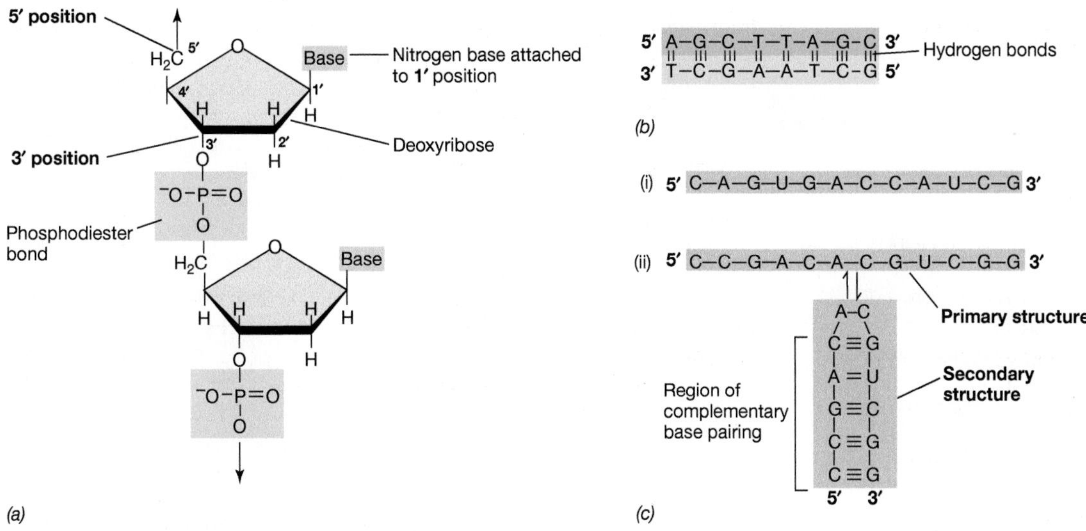

Figure 11 Nucleic acids: DNA and RNA. *(a)* Structure of part of a DNA chain. The nitrogen bases can be adenine, guanine, cytosine, or thymine. In RNA, an OH group is present on the 2′ carbon of the pentose sugar (see Figure 8) and uracil replaces thymine. *(b)* Simplified structure of DNA in which only the nitrogen bases are shown. The two strands are complementary in base sequence, with A joined to T by two hydrogen bonds and G joined to C by three hydrogen bonds (note that the hydrogen bonds are indicated by two and three lines rather than by dots as in Figure 2). *(c)* RNA: (i) a sequence showing only primary structure; (ii) a sequence that allows for secondary structure. In RNA, secondary structures form when opportunities for *intra*strand base pairing arise, as shown here.

contain both primary and secondary structure. This leads to highly folded and twisted molecules whose biological function is critically dependent on their final three-dimensional shape.

At least four classes of RNA exist in cells. *Messenger RNA* (mRNA) carries the genetic information of DNA in a single-stranded molecule complementary in base sequence to that of DNA. *Transfer RNAs* (tRNAs) convert the genetic information present in mRNA into the language of amino acids, the building blocks of proteins. *Ribosomal RNAs* (rRNAs), of which there are several types, are important structural and catalytic components of the ribosome, the protein-synthesizing system of the cell. In addition to these, a variety of *small RNAs* exist in cells. These RNAs function to regulate the production or activity of other RNAs.

5 MiniReview

The informational content of a nucleic acid is determined by the sequence of nitrogen bases along the polynucleotide chain. Both RNA and DNA are informational macromolecules. RNA can fold into various configurations to obtain secondary structure.

- What components are found in a nucleotide?
- How does a nucleo*side* differ from a nucleo*tide*?
- Distinguish between the primary and secondary structure of RNA.

6 Amino Acids and the Peptide Bond

Amino acids are the monomers of **proteins**. Most amino acids consist of carbon, hydrogen, oxygen, and nitrogen only, but 2 of the 22 genetically encoded amino acids also contain sulfur, and 1 contains selenium. All amino acids contain two important functional groups, a carboxylic acid group (—COOH) and an amino group (—NH_2) (Table 1 and Figure 12*a*). These groups are key to the structure of proteins because covalent bonds can form between the carboxyl carbon of one amino acid and the amino nitrogen of a second amino acid (with elimination of a molecule of water) to form the **peptide bond** (Figure 13).

Structure of Amino Acids

All amino acids have the general structure shown in Figure 12*a*. But each type of amino acid is unique because of its unique side group (abbreviated R in Figure 12*a*) attached to the α-carbon. The α-carbon is the carbon atom adjacent to the carboxylic acid group. The side chains vary considerably in structure, from as simple as a hydrogen atom in the amino acid glycine to aromatic rings in phenylalanine, tyrosine, and tryptophan (Figure 12*b*).

The chemical properties of an amino acid are governed by its side chain. Amino acids that have similar chemical properties are grouped into related amino acid "families" as shown in Figure 12*b*. For example, the side chain may contain a carboxylic acid group, such as in aspartic acid or glutamic acid,

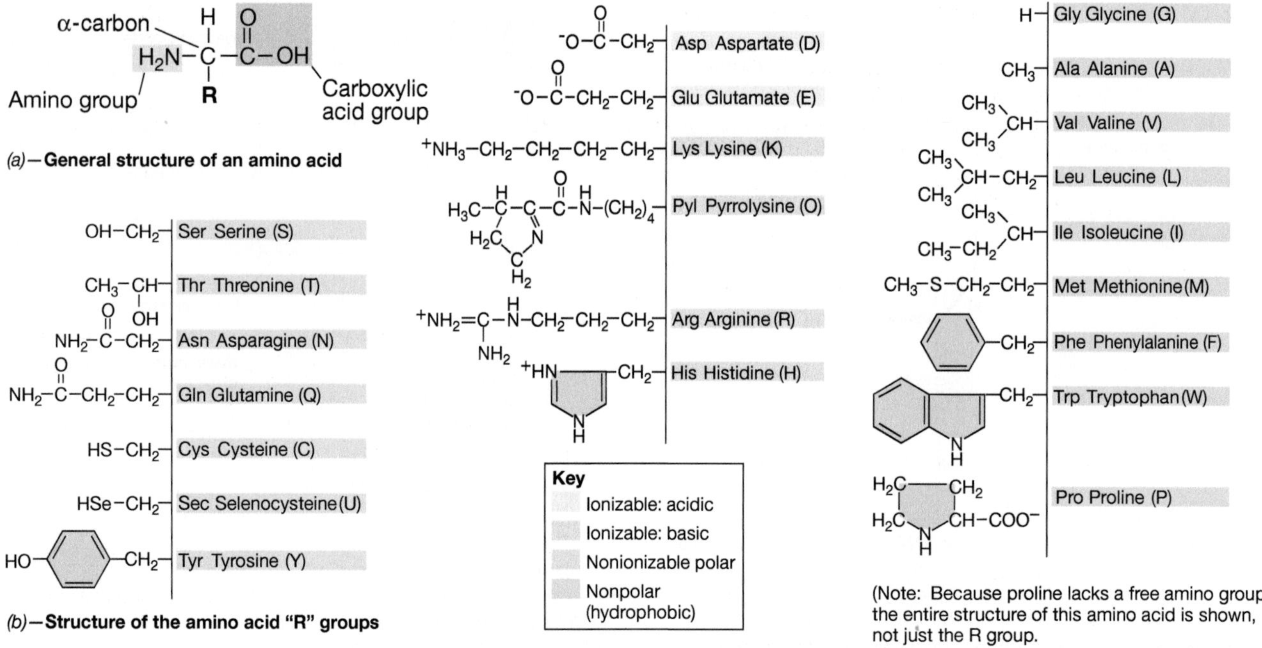

Figure 12 Structure of the 22 genetically encoded amino acids. *(a)* General structure. *(b)* R group structure. The three-letter codes for the amino acids are to the left of the names, and the one-letter codes are in parentheses to the right of the names. Pyrrolysine has thus far been found only in certain methanogenic *Archaea.*

rendering the amino acid acidic. Others contain additional amino groups, rendering them basic. Alternatively, several amino acids contain hydrophobic side chains and are grouped together as nonpolar amino acids. The amino acid cysteine contains a sulfhydryl group (—SH). Sulfhydryl groups can connect one chain of amino acids to another by disulfide linkage (R—S—S—R) through two cysteine molecules, one from each chain.

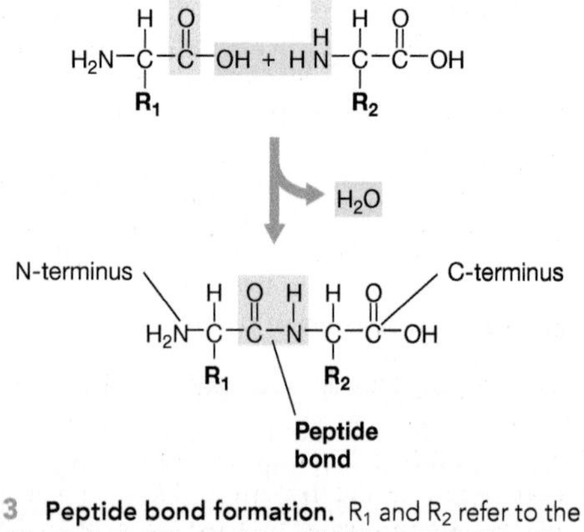

Figure 13 Peptide bond formation. R_1 and R_2 refer to the variable portions (side chains) of the amino acids (Figure 12). Note how, following peptide bond formation, a free OH group is present at the C-terminus for formation of the next peptide bond.

The diversity of chemically distinct amino acids makes possible an enormous number of unique proteins with widely different biochemical properties. For example, if one assumes that an average polypeptide contains 100 amino acids, there are 22^{100} different polypeptide sequences that are theoretically possible. No cell has anywhere near this many different proteins. However, a cell of *Escherichia coli* contains almost 2,000 different kinds of proteins (Table 2). These include different soluble and membrane-integrated enzymes, structural proteins, transport proteins, sensory proteins, and many others.

Isomers

Two molecules may have the same molecular formula but exist in different structural forms. These related but nonidentical molecules are called **isomers**. For example, the hexose sugars glucose and fructose (Figure 4) are isomers. Louis Pasteur, the famous early microbiologist who quashed the theory of spontaneous generation, began his scientific career as a chemist studying a class of isomers called *optical* isomers. Optical isomers that have the same molecular and structural formulas, except that one is a "mirror image" of the other (just as the left hand is a mirror image of the right), are called **enantiomers**. The enantiomers of a given compound can never be superimposed one over the other and are designated as either D or L (Figure 14), depending on whether a pure solution rotates light to the right or left, respectively. Sugars of the D enantiomer predominate in biological systems.

Amino acids also have D or L enantiomers. However, in proteins cells employ the L-amino acid rather than the D form (Figure 14*c*). Nevertheless, D-amino acids are occasionally found in cells, most notably in the cell wall polymer peptidoglycan and in certain peptide antibiotics. Cells can interconvert certain enantiomers by the activity of enzymes called *racemases*. For instance, some prokaryotes can grow on L-sugars or D-amino acids because they have racemases that can convert these forms into the opposite enantiomer before metabolizing them.

6 MiniReview

Twenty-two different amino acids are found in cells and can bond to each other via the peptide bond. Mirror image (enantiomeric) forms of sugars and amino acids exist, but only one optical isomer of each is found in most cell polysaccharides and proteins.

- Why can it be said that all amino acids are structurally similar yet different simultaneously?
- Draw the complete structure of a dipeptide containing the amino acids alanine and tyrosine. Outline the peptide bond.
- Which enantiomeric forms of sugars and amino acids are commonly found in living organisms? Why doesn't the amino acid glycine have different enantiomers? (*Hint:* Look carefully at Figure 14*c* and replace the alanine shown with glycine.)

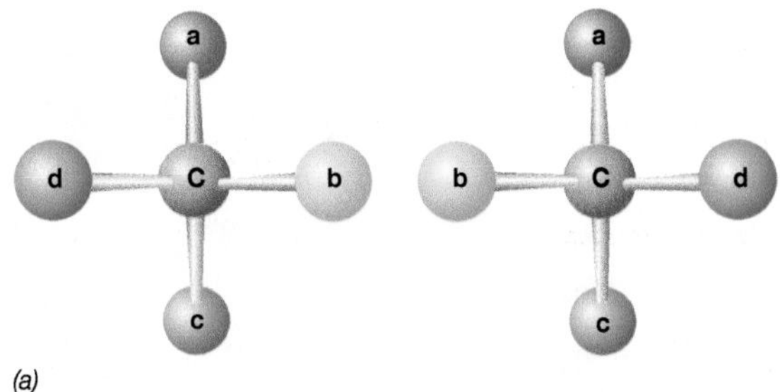

(a)

D-Glucose

H–C=O
H–C–OH
HO–C–H
H–C–OH
H–C–OH
CH_2OH

L-Glucose

H–C=O
HO–C–H
H–C–OH
HO–C–H
HO–C–H
CH_2OH

(b)

L-Alanine

COOH
H_2N–C–H
CH_3

D-Alanine

COOH
H–C–NH_2
CH_3

COOH
H_2N C H
CH_3

COOH
H C NH_2
CH_3

Three-dimensional projection

(c)

Figure 14 **Isomers.** *(a)* Ball-and-stick model showing mirror images. *(b)* Enantiomers of glucose. *(c)* Enantiomers of the amino acid alanine. In the three-dimensional projection the arrow should be understood as coming *toward* the viewer and the dashed line indicates a plane *away* from the viewer. Note that no matter how the three-dimensional views are rotated, the L and D forms can never be superimposed. This is a characteristic of enantiomers.

7 Proteins: Primary and Secondary Structure

Proteins play several key roles in cell function. In essence, a cell is what it is and does what it does because of the kinds and amounts of proteins it contains; that is, every different type of cell has a different complement of proteins. An understanding of protein structure is therefore essential for understanding how cells work.

Two major classes of proteins are *catalytic* proteins (enzymes) and *structural* proteins. **Enzymes** are the catalysts for chemical reactions that occur in cells. By contrast, structural proteins are integral parts of the major structures of the cell: membranes, walls, cytoplasmic components, and so on. However, all proteins show certain basic features in common, and we discuss these now.

Primary Structure

As we have said, proteins are polymers of amino acids covalently bonded by *peptide bonds* (Figure 13). Two amino acids bonded by peptide linkage constitute a dipeptide, three amino acids, a tripeptide, and so on. When many amino acids are covalently linked via peptide bonds, they form a **polypeptide**.

A protein consists of one or more polypeptides. The number of amino acids differs greatly from one protein to another; proteins containing as few as 15 or as many as 10,000 amino acids are known. Because proteins differ in their composition, sequence, and number of amino acids, it is obvious that enormous variation in protein structure (and thus function) is possible.

The linear array of amino acids in a polypeptide is called its **primary structure**. The primary structure of a polypeptide is critical to its final function because it is consistent with only certain types of folding patterns. And it is only the final, folded polypeptide that assumes biological activity. The two ends of a polypeptide are so designated by whether a free carboxylic acid group or a free amino group exists; the terms "C-terminus" and "N-terminus" are used to describe these two ends, respectively (Figure 2*b*).

Secondary Structure

Once formed, a polypeptide does not remain a linear structure. Instead it *folds* to form a more stable structure. Interactions of the R groups on the amino acids in a polypeptide force the molecule to twist and fold in a specific way. This forms the **secondary structure**. Hydrogen bonds, the weak noncovalent linkages discussed earlier (Section 1), play

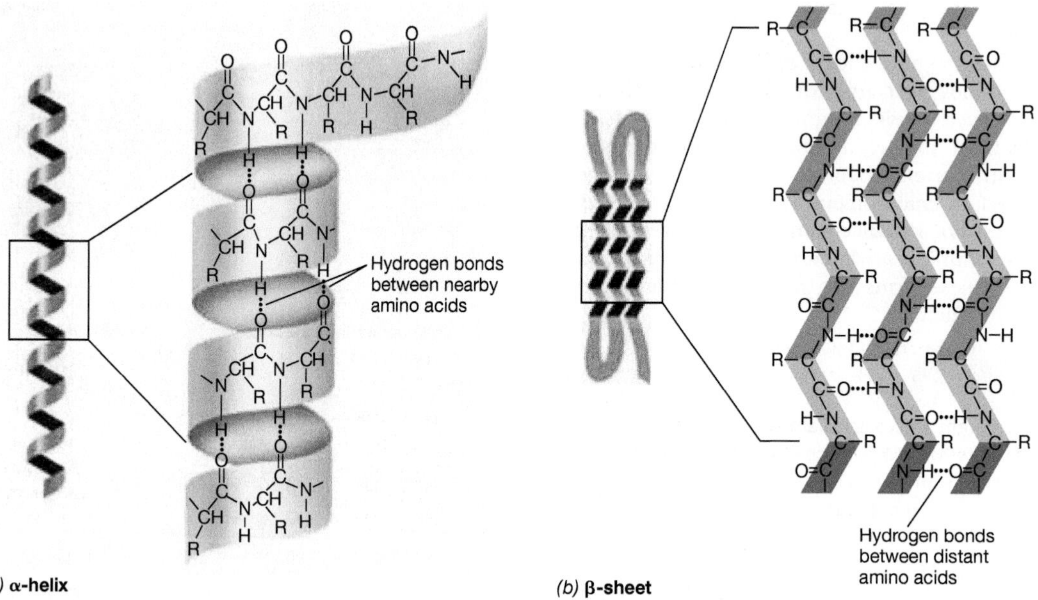

Figure 15 Secondary structure of polypeptides. *(a)* α-helix secondary structure. *(b)* β-sheet secondary structure. Note that the hydrogen bonding is between atoms in the peptide bonds and does not involve the R groups.

important roles in polypeptide secondary structure. One common type of secondary structure is the *α-helix*. To envision an α-helix, imagine a linear polypeptide wound around a cylinder (Figure 15*a*). In this twisted structure, oxygen and nitrogen atoms from different amino acids become positioned close enough to allow hydrogen bonding. These hydrogen bonds give the α-helix its inherent stability (Figure 15*a*).

The primary structure of some polypeptides induces a different type of secondary structure, called a *β-sheet*. In the β-sheet, the chain of amino acids in the polypeptide folds back and forth upon itself instead of forming a helix. However, as in the α-helix, the folding in a β-sheet exposes hydrogen atoms that can undergo hydrogen bonding (Figure 15*b*). Typically, a β-sheet secondary structure yields a polypeptide that is rather rigid and α-helical secondary structures are more flexible. Thus, an enzyme, for example, whose activity may depend on its being rather flexible, may contain a high degree of α-helix secondary structure. By contrast, a structural protein that functions in cellular scaffolding may contain large regions of β-sheet secondary structure.

Many polypeptides contain regions of both α-helix *and* β-sheet secondary structure, the type of folding and its location in the molecule being determined by the primary structure and the available opportunities for hydrogen bonding and hydrophobic interactions (see Figure 16). A typical protein is thus made up of many **domains**, as they are called, regions of the protein that have a specific structure and function in the final, biologically active, molecule.

8 Proteins: Higher Order Structure and Denaturation

Once a polypeptide has achieved secondary structure it continues to fold to form an even more stable molecule. This folding results in a unique three-dimensional shape called the **tertiary structure** of the protein.

Like secondary structure, tertiary structure is ultimately determined by primary structure. However, tertiary structure is also governed to some extent by the secondary structure of the molecule because the side chain of each amino acid in the polypeptide is positioned in a specific way (Figure 15). If additional hydrogen bonds, covalent bonds, hydrophobic interactions, or other atomic interactions are able to form, the polypeptide will fold to accommodate them (Figure 16). The tertiary folds of the polypeptide ultimately form exposed regions or grooves in the molecule (Figure 16 and see Figure 17) that are important for binding other molecules (for example, in the binding of a substrate to an enzyme or the binding of DNA to a specific regulatory protein).

Frequently a polypeptide folds in such a way that adjacent sulfhydryl groups of cysteine residues are exposed. These free —SH groups can form a disulfide bond between the two amino acids. If the two cysteine residues are located in different polypeptides in a protein, the disulfide bond covalently links the two molecules (Figure 16*a*). In addition, a single polypeptide chain can fold and bond to itself if a disulfide bond can form within the molecule.

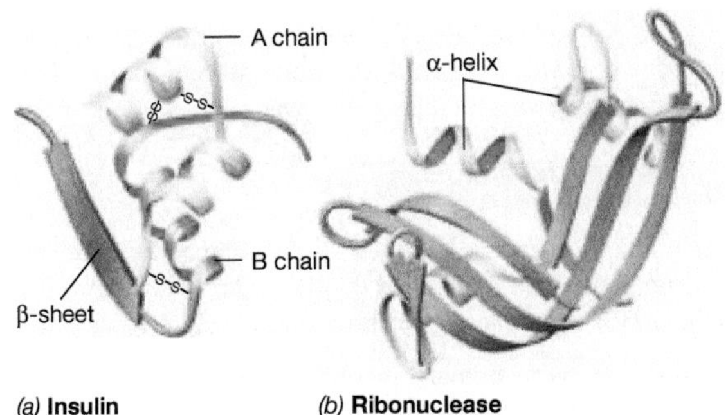

Figure 16 **Tertiary structure of polypeptides.** *(a)* Insulin, a protein containing two polypeptide chains; note how the B chain contains both α-helix and β-sheet secondary structure and how disulfide linkages (S–S) help in dictating folding patterns (tertiary structure). *(b)* Ribonuclease, a large protein with several regions of α-helix and β-sheet secondary structure.

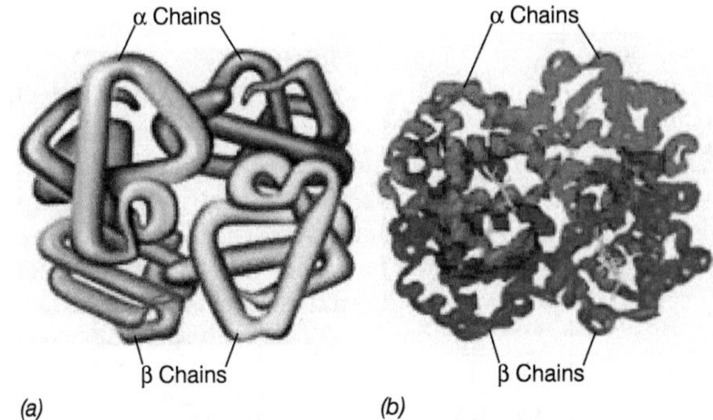

Figure 17 **Quaternary structure of human hemoglobin.** *(a)* There are two kinds of polypeptide in human hemoglobin, α chains (shown in blue and red) and β chains (shown in orange and yellow), but a total of four polypeptides in the final protein molecule (two α chains and two β chains). Separate colors are used to distinguish each chain. *(b)* Molecular structure of human hemoglobin as determined by X-ray crystallography. In this view each α chain is red and each β chain is blue.

Quaternary Structure

If a protein consists of two or more polypeptides, and many proteins do, the number and type of polypeptides that form the final protein molecule are referred to as its **quaternary structure** (Figure 17). In proteins showing quaternary structure, each polypeptide, called a *subunit*, contains primary, secondary, and tertiary structure. Some proteins contain multiple copies of a single subunit. A protein containing two identical subunits, for example, would be called a *homodimer*. Other proteins may contain nonidentical subunits, each present in one or more copies (a heterodimer, for example, contains one copy each of two different polypeptides). The subunits in multisubunit proteins are held together by noncovalent interactions (hydrogen bonding, van der Waals forces, and hydrophobic interactions) or by covalent linkages, typically disulfide bonds.

Denaturation

When proteins are exposed to extremes of heat or pH or to certain chemicals or metals that affect their folding, they may undergo **denaturation** (Figure 18). Denaturation causes the polypeptide chain to unfold, destroying the higher order (secondary, tertiary, and quaternary, if relevant) structure of the molecule. Depending on the severity of the denaturant or denaturing conditions, the polypeptide may refold after the denaturant is removed (Figure 18). Typically, however, denatured proteins unfold such that their hydrophobic regions become exposed and stick together to form protein aggregates that lack biological activity.

The biological properties of a protein are usually lost when it is denatured. Peptide bonds (Figure 13) are unaffected, however, and so a denatured molecule retains its primary structure. This shows that biological activity is not inherent in the primary structure of a protein but instead is a function of the uniquely folded form of the molecule as ultimately directed by primary structure. In other words, folding

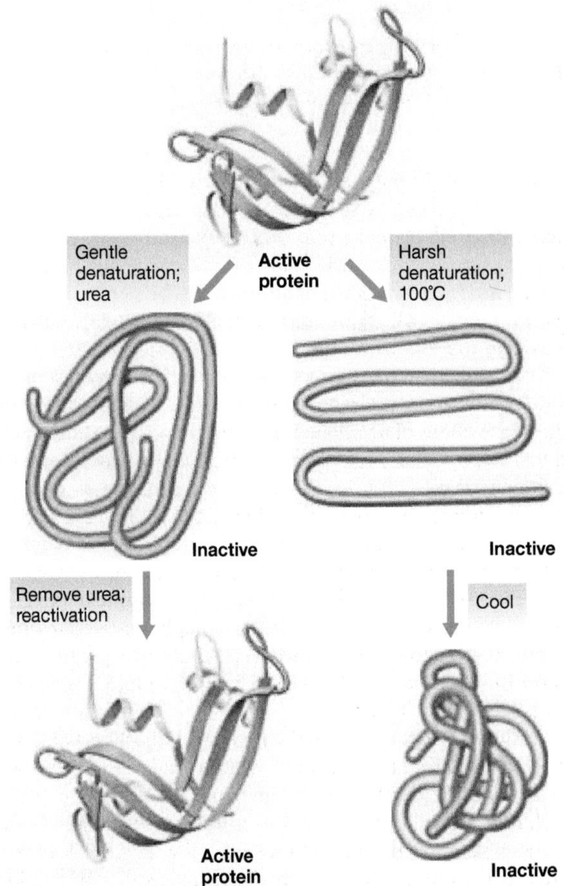

Figure 18 **Denaturation of the protein ribonuclease.** Ribonuclease structure was shown in Figure 16*b*. Note how harsh denaturation permanently destroys a molecule (from the standpoint of biological function) because of improper folding but primary structure is retained.

of a polypeptide confers upon it a unique shape that is compatible with a *specific* biological function.

Denaturation of proteins is a major means of destroying microorganisms. For example, alcohols such as phenol and ethanol are effective disinfectants because they readily penetrate cells and irreversibly denature their proteins. Such chemical agents are thus useful for disinfecting inanimate objects such as surfaces and have enormous practical value in household, hospital, and industrial disinfectant applications.

Moving On

Now that we have reviewed the chemistry of cellular components, we are in a better position to understand the structural details of cells. Metabolism, the *machine* function of a cell, drives the biosynthesis and assembly of new copies of macromolecules; these processes result in cell growth. The metabolic events themselves are directed by the *coding* functions of the cell, the essential genetic events carried out by all cells.

As the contemporary microbiologist Norman Pace has put it, "life is fundamentally *chemistry*." And as any microbiologist will attest, a feeling for the biochemistry of proteins, lipids, nucleic acids, and polysaccharides is essential to a grasp of modern microbiology and will accelerate the understanding of both basic and more advanced principles.

7 and 8 MiniReview

The primary structure of a protein is determined by its amino acid sequence, but the folding (higher order structure) of the polypeptide determines how the protein functions in the cell.

- Define the terms primary, secondary, and tertiary with respect to protein structure.
- How does a polypeptide differ from a protein?
- What secondary structural features tend to make β-sheet proteins more rigid than α-helices?
- Describe the number and kinds of polypeptides present in a homotetrameric protein.
- Describe the structural and biological effects of the denaturation of a protein. Of what practical value is knowledge of protein denaturation?

Review of Key Terms

Amino acid one of the 22 different monomers that make up proteins; chemically, a two-carbon carboxylic acid containing an amino group and a characteristic substituent on the alpha carbon

Covalent bond a chemical bond in which electrons are shared between two atoms

Denaturation destruction of the folding properties of a protein leading (usually) to protein aggregation and loss of biological activity

Domain in the context of proteins, a portion of the protein typically possessing a specific structure or function

DNA (deoxyribonucleic acid) a polymer of deoxyribonucleotides linked by phosphodiester bonds that carries genetic information

Enantiomer a form of a molecule that is the mirror image of another form of the same molecule

Enzyme a protein or an RNA that catalyzes a specific chemical reaction in a cell

Fatty acid an organic acid containing a carboxylic acid group and a hydrocarbon chain of various lengths; major components of lipids of *Bacteria* and *Eukarya*

Glycosidic bond a covalent bond linking sugars together in a polysaccharide

Hydrogen bond a weak chemical interaction between a hydrogen atom and a second, more electronegative element, usually an oxygen or nitrogen atom

Isomers two molecules with the same molecular formula but a difference in structure

Lipid a polar compound such as glycerol bonded to fatty acids or other hydrophobic molecules by ester or ether linkage, often also containing other groups, such as phosphate or sugars

Macromolecule a polymer of covalently linked monomeric units, such as DNA, RNA, polysaccharides, and lipids

Molecule two or more atoms chemically bonded to one another

Monomer a small molecule that is a building block for larger molecules

Nonpolar possessing hydrophobic (water-repelling) characteristics and not easily dissolved in water

Nucleic acid DNA or RNA

Nucleotide a monomer of a nucleic acid containing a nitrogen base (adenine, guanine, cytosine, thymine, or uracil), one or more molecules of phosphate, and a sugar, either ribose (in RNA) or deoxyribose (in DNA)

Peptide bond a type of covalent bond linking amino acids in a polypeptide

Phosphodiester bond a type of covalent bond linking nucleotides together in a polynucleotide

Polar possessing hydrophilic (water-loving) characteristics and generally water soluble

Polymer a large molecule made up of monomers

Polynucleotide a polymer of nucleotides bonded to one another by covalent bonds called phosphodiester bonds

Polypeptide a polymer of amino acids bonded to one another by peptide bonds

Polysaccharide a polymer of sugar units bonded to one another by glycosidic bonds

Primary structure in an informational macromolecule such as a polypeptide or a nucleic acid, the precise sequence of monomeric units

Protein a polypeptide or group of polypeptides forming a molecule of specific biological function

Purine one of the nitrogen bases of nucleic acids that contain two fused rings; adenine and guanine

Pyrimidine one of the nitrogen bases of nucleic acids that contain a single ring; cytosine, thymine, and uracil

Quaternary structure in proteins, the number and types of individual polypeptides in the final protein molecule

RNA (ribonucleic acid) a polymer of ribonucleotides linked by phosphodiester bonds that plays many roles in cells, in particular, during protein synthesis

Secondary structure the initial pattern of folding of a polypeptide or a polynucleotide, usually dictated by opportunities for hydrogen bonding

Tertiary structure the final folded structure of a polypeptide that has previously attained secondary structure

Review Questions

1. Which are the major elements found in living organisms? Why are oxygen and hydrogen particularly abundant in living organisms (Section 1)?
2. Define the word "molecule." How many atoms are in a molecule of hydrogen gas? How many atoms are in a molecule of glucose (Sections 1 and 3)?
3. Refer to the structure of the nitrogen base cytosine shown in Figure 1. Draw this structure and then label the positions of all single bonds and double bonds in the cytosine molecule (Section 1).
4. Compare and contrast the words "monomer" and "polymer." Give three examples of biologically important polymers and list the monomers of which they are composed. Which classes of macromolecules are most abundant (by weight) in a cell (Sections 1 and 2)?
5. List the components that would make up a simple lipid. How does a triglyceride differ from a complex lipid (Section 4)?
6. Examine the structures of the triglyceride and of phosphatidyl ethanolamine shown in Figure 7. How might the substitution of phosphate and ethanolamine for a fatty acid alter the chemical properties of the lipid (Section 4)?
7. RNA and DNA are similar types of macromolecules but show distinct differences as well. List three ways in which RNA differs chemically or physically from DNA. What is the cellular function of DNA and RNA (Section 5)?
8. Why are amino acids so named? Write a general structure for an amino acid. What is the importance of the R group to final protein structure? Why does the amino acid cysteine have special significance for protein structure (Section 6)?
9. What type of reaction between two amino acids leads to formation of the peptide bond (Section 6)?
10. Define the types of protein structure: primary, secondary, tertiary, and quaternary. Which of these structures are altered by denaturation (Sections 7 and 8)?
11. Fill in the blanks. A glycosidic bond is to a __________ as a __________ bond is to a polypeptide and a __________ is to a nucleic acid. All of these bonds are examples of __________ bonds, which are chemically much stronger than weak bonds, such as __________, __________, and __________

Application Questions

1. Observe the following nucleotide sequences of RNA: (*a*) GUCAAAGAC, (*b*) ACGAUAACC. Can either of these RNA molecules have secondary structure? If so, draw the potential secondary structure(s).
2. A few soluble (cytoplasmic) proteins contain a high content of hydrophobic amino acids. How would you predict these proteins would fold into their tertiary structure and why?
3. Cells of the genus *Halobacterium*, an organism that lives in very salty environments, contain over 5 molar (M) potassium (K^+). Because of this high K^+ content, many cytoplasmic proteins of *Halobacterium* cells are enriched in two specific amino acids that are present in much higher proportions in *Halobacterium* proteins than in functionally similar proteins from *Escherichia coli* (which has only very low levels of K^+ in its cytoplasm). Which amino acids are enriched in *Halobacterium* proteins and why? (*Hint:* Which amino acids could best neutralize the positive charges due to K^+?)
4. When a culture of the bacterium *Escherichia coli*, an inhabitant of the human gut, is placed in a beaker of boiling water, significant changes in the cells occur almost immediately. However, when a culture of *Pyrodictium*, a hypothermophile that grows optimally in boiling hot springs is put in the same beaker, similar changes do not occur. Explain.
5. Review Figure 6*b* and then describe the differences that make each of these polymers unique. If all of the glycosidic bonds in these polymers were hydrolyzed, what single molecule would remain?
6. Review Figure 12*b*. Of all the amino acids shaded in blue, what is it about their chemistry that unites them as a "family"?

Cell Structure and Function in *Bacteria* and *Archaea*

Cell Structure and Function in *Bacteria* and *Archaea*

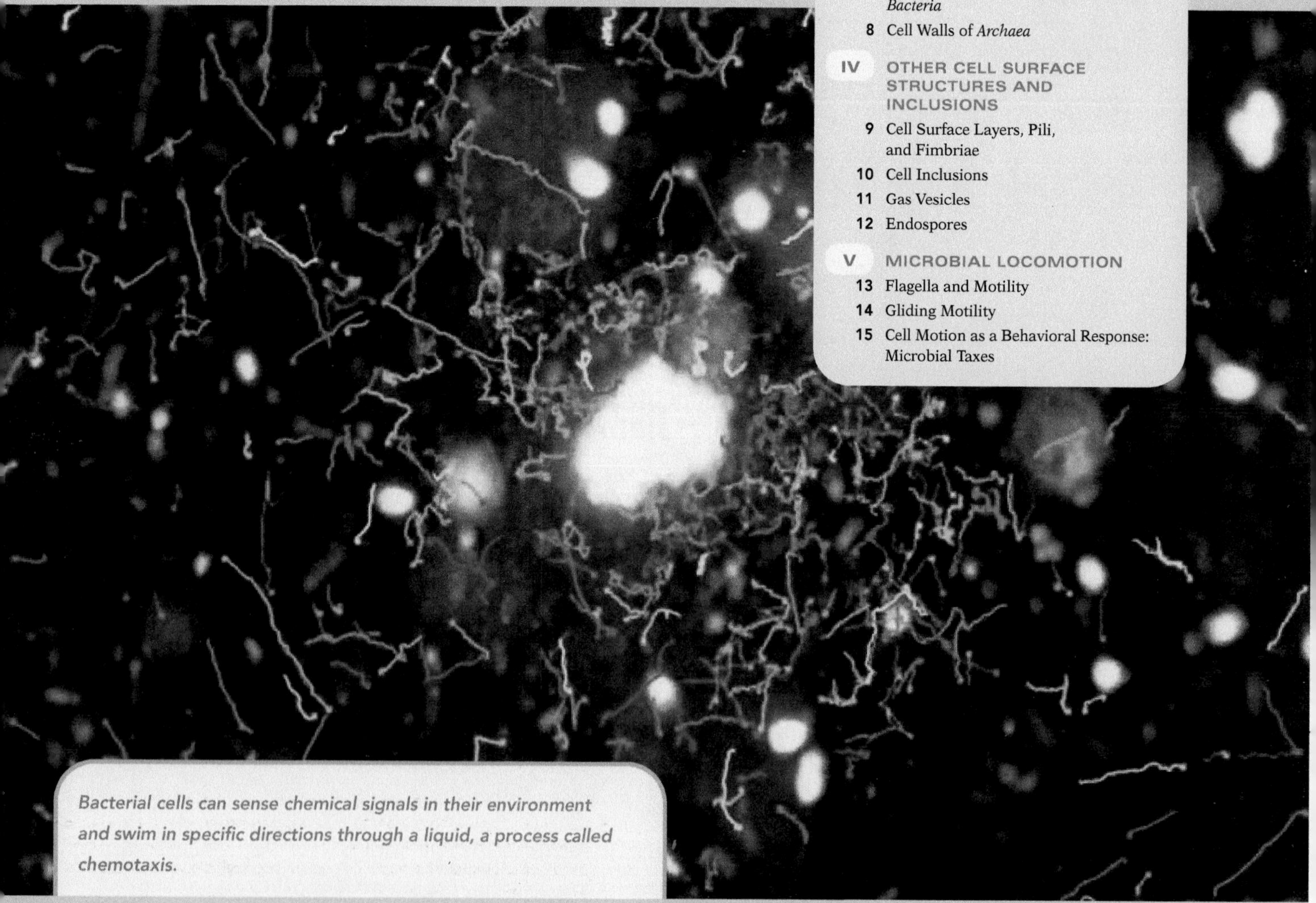

Bacterial cells can sense chemical signals in their environment and swim in specific directions through a liquid, a process called chemotaxis.

Nicholas Blackburn

I CELL SHAPE AND SIZE

In this chapter we examine how macromolecules combine to form the key components of the cell: the cytoplasmic membrane, the cell wall, cell inclusions, the flagellum, and so on. Our theme in this chapter will be structure and function. There is an old saying in biology that "form follows function." That is, the structure (form) of a biological component evolved as it did because it was better than the alternatives at carrying out a specific function, either within the cell or within the whole organism. Microorganisms are no exception in this regard as the key structures of microbial cells evolved because they carry out specific functions effectively.

We begin this chapter by discussing two key features of prokaryotic cells—their shape and small size. Prokaryotes typically have defined shapes and are extremely small cells. Shape is useful for differentiating prokaryotic cells and size has profound effects on their biology.

1 Cell Morphology

In microbiology, the term **morphology** means cell shape. Several morphologies are known among prokaryotes, and the most common ones are described by terms that are part of the essential lexicon of the microbiologist.

Major Cell Morphologies

Examples of bacterial morphologies are shown in Figure 1. A bacterium that is spherical or ovoid in morphology is called a *coccus* (plural, *cocci*). A bacterium with a cylindrical shape is called a *rod*. Some rods twist into spiral shapes and are called *spirilla*. The cells of many prokaryotic species remain together in groups or clusters after cell division, and the arrangements are often characteristic of certain genera. For instance, some cocci form long chains (for example, the bacterium *Streptococcus*), others occur in three-dimensional cubes (*Sarcina*), and still others in grapelike clusters (*Staphylococcus*).

Several groups of bacteria are immediately recognizable by the unusual shapes of their individual cells. Examples include spirochetes, which are tightly coiled bacteria, appendaged bacteria, which possess extensions of their cells as long tubes or stalks, and filamentous bacteria, which form long, thin cells or chains of cells (Figure 1).

The cell shapes in Figure 1 should be examined with the understanding that they are *representative* morphologies for prokaryotic cells. Many variations of these basic morphological types are known. Thus there are fat rods, thin rods, short rods, and long rods, a rod simply being a cell that is longer in one dimension than in the other. As we will see, there are even square bacteria and star-shaped bacteria! Cell morphologies thus form a continuum, with some shapes very common and others more unusual.

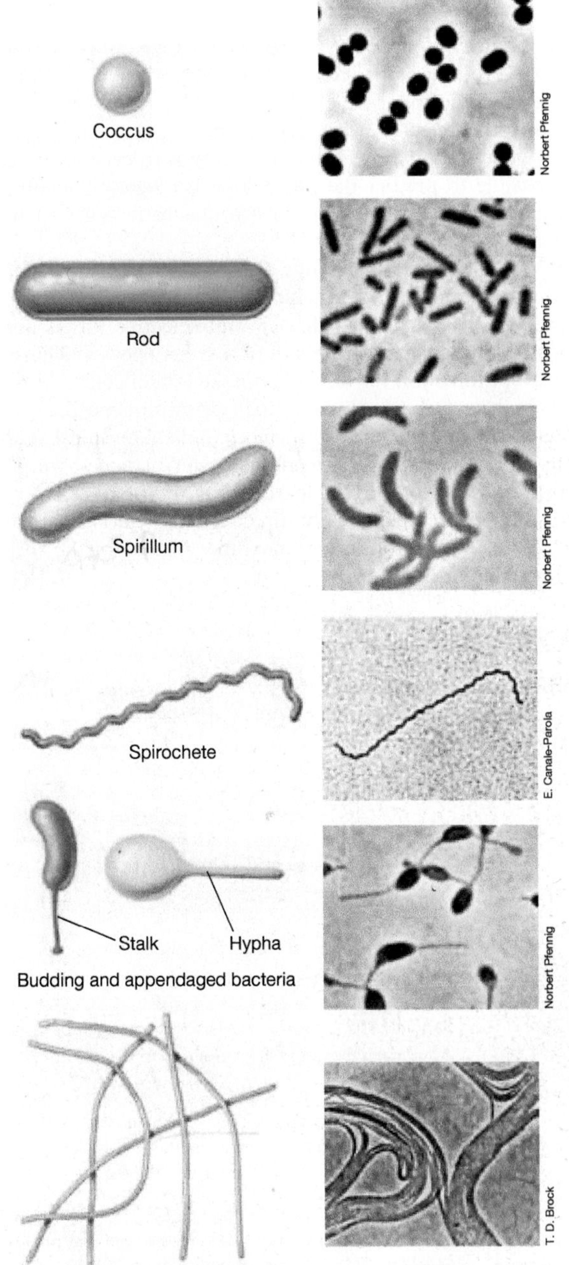

Figure 1 Representative cell morphologies of prokaryotes. Next to each drawing is a phase-contrast photomicrograph showing an example of that morphology. Organisms are coccus, *Thiocapsa roseopersicina* (diameter of a single cell = 1.5 μm); rod, *Desulfuromonas acetoxidans* (diameter = 1 μm); spirillum, *Rhodospirillum rubrum* (diameter = 1 μm); spirochete, *Spirochaeta stenostrepta* (diameter = 0.25 μm); budding and appendaged, *Rhodomicrobium vannielii* (diameter = 1.2 μm); filamentous, *Chloroflexus aurantiacus* (diameter = 0.8 μm).

Morphology and Biology

Although cell morphology is easily recognized, it is in general a poor predictor of a cell's other properties. For example, under the microscope many rod-shaped *Archaea* look identical to rod-shaped *Bacteria,* yet we know they are of different phylogenetic domains. Thus, with very rare exceptions, it is impossible to predict the physiology, ecology, phylogeny, or virtually any other property of a prokaryotic cell by simply knowing its morphology.

What sets the morphology of a particular species? This is an interesting question to which we don't have firm answers. However, it is suspected that several selective forces are in play in setting the morphology of a given species. These include optimization for nutrient uptake (small cells and those with high surface-to-volume ratios), swimming motility in viscous environments or near surfaces (helical or spiral-shaped cells), gliding motility (filamentous bacteria), and so on. Thus morphology is not a trivial feature of a microbial cell. A cell's morphology is a genetically directed characteristic and has been selected by evolution to maximize fitness for the species in a particular habitat.

1 MiniReview

There are prokaryotic cells of many different shapes. Rods, cocci, and spirilla are common cell morphologies.

- Write a single sentence that describes how cocci and rods differ in morphology.
- Is cell morphology a good predictor of other properties of the cell?

2 Cell Size and the Significance of Smallness

Prokaryotes vary in size from cells as small as about 0.2 μm in diameter to those more than 700 μm in diameter (Table 1). The vast majority of rod-shaped prokaryotes that have been cultured in the laboratory are between 0.5 and 4 μm wide and less than 15 μm long, but a few very large prokaryotes, such as *Epulopiscium fishelsoni*, are huge, with cells being longer than 600 μm (0.6 millimeter). This bacterium, phylogenetically related to the endospore-forming bacterium *Clostridium* and found in the gut of the surgeonfish, is interesting not only because it is so large, but also because it has an unusual form of cell division and contains multiple copies of its genome. Multiple offspring are formed and are then released from the *Epulopiscium* "mother cell" (Figure 2a shows a mother cell). A mother cell of *Epulopiscium* contains several thousand genome copies, each of which is about the same size as the genome of *Escherichia coli* (4.6 megabase pairs, or Mbp). The many

Table 1 Cell size and volume of prokaryotic cells, from the largest to the smallest

Organism	*Characteristics*	*Morphology*	*Size[a] (μm)*	*Cell volume (μm^3)*	E. coli volumes
Thiomargarita namibiensis	Sulfur chemolithotroph	Cocci in chains	750	200,000,000	10^8
Epulopiscium fishelsoni	Chemoorganotroph	Rods with tapered ends	80 × 600	3,000,000	1.5×10^6
Beggiatoa sp.	Sulfur chemolithotroph	Filaments	50 × 160	1,000,000	5×10^5
Achromatium oxaliferum	Sulfur chemolithotroph	Cocci	35 × 95	80,000	4×10^4
Lyngbya majuscula	Cyanobacterium	Filaments	8 × 80	40,000	2×10^4
Prochloron sp.	Prochlorophyte	Cocci	30	14,000	7×10^3
Thiovulum majus	Sulfur chemolithotroph	Cocci	18	3,000	1.5×10^3
Staphylothermus marinus	Hyperthermophile	Cocci in irregular clusters	15	1,800	9×10^2
Titanospirillum velox	Sulfur chemolithotroph	Curved rods	5 × 30	600	3×10^2
Magnetobacterium bavaricum	Magnetotactic bacterium	Rods	2 × 10	30	15
Escherichia coli	Chemoorganotroph	Rods	1 × 2	2	1
Pelagibacter ubique	Marine chemoorganotroph	Rods	0.2 × 0.5	0.014	1.4×10^{-2}
Mycoplasma pneumoniae	Pathogenic bacterium	Pleomorphic[b]	0.2	0.005	2.5×10^{-3}

[a]Where only one number is given, this is the diameter of spherical cells. The values given are for the largest cell size observed in each species. For example, for *T. namibiensis*, an average cell is only about 200 μm in diameter. But on occasion, giant cells of 750 μm are observed. Likewise, an average cell of *S. marinus* is about 1 μm in diameter.

[b]*Mycoplasma* is a cell wall-less bacterium and can take on many shapes (*pleomorphic* means "many shapes").

Source: Data obtained from Schulz, H.N., and B.B. Jørgensen. 2001. *Ann. Rev. Microbiol. 55:* 105–137.

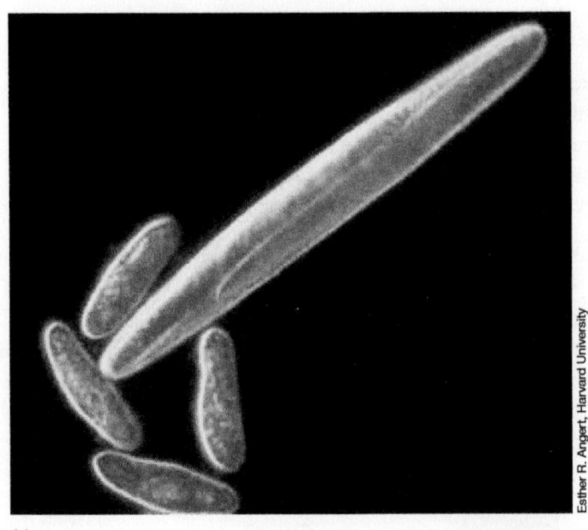

(a)

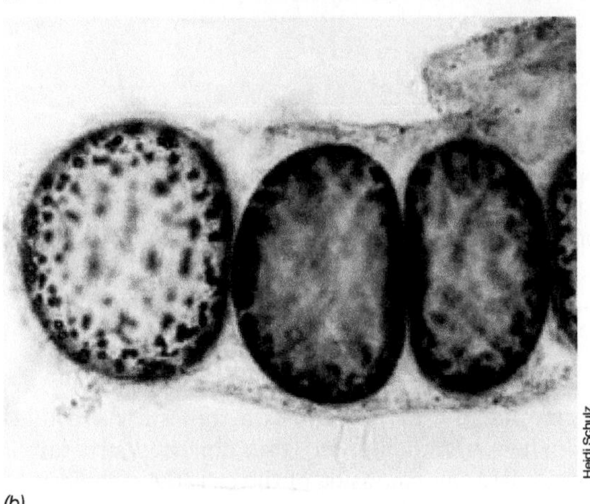

(b)

Figure 2 Some very large prokaryotes. *(a)* Dark-field photomicrograph of a giant prokaryote, the surgeonfish symbiont *Epulopiscium fishelsoni*. The rod-shaped *E. fishelsoni* cell in this field is about 600 μm (0.6 mm) long and 75 μm wide and is shown with three cells of the protist (eukaryote) *Paramecium*, each of which is about about 150 μm long. *E. fishelsoni* is a member of the *Bacteria* and phylogenetically related to *Clostridium* species. *(b) Thiomargarita namibiensis*, a large sulfur chemolithotroph (phylum *Proteobacteria* of the *Bacteria*) and currently the largest known prokaryote. Each ovoid-shaped cell is about 400 μm wide.

copies are apparently necessary because the cell volume of *Epulopiscium* is so large that a single copy of its genome wouldn't be sufficient to support the transcriptional and translational needs of the cell.

Cells of the largest known prokaryote, the sulfur chemolithotroph *Thiomargarita* (Figure 2*b*), can be 750 μm in diameter, nearly visible to the naked eye. Most very large prokaryotes are either sulfur chemolithotrophs or cyanobacteria (Table 1). Why these cells are so large is not well understood, although for sulfur bacteria large cell size may be a mechanism for storing sulfur (an energy source). It is thought that limitations in nutrient uptake ultimately dictate upper limits for the size of prokaryotic cells. The metabolic rate of a cell varies inversely with the square of its size. Thus for very large cells uptake processes eventually limit metabolism to the point that the cell is no longer competitive with smaller cells.

Very large cells are not the norm in the prokaryotic world. By contrast to *Thiomargarita* or *Epulopiscium* (Figure 2), the dimensions of an average rod-shaped prokaryote, the bacterium *E. coli*, for example, are about 1 × 2 μm; these dimensions are typical of prokaryotes. For comparison, average eukaryotic cells can be 10 to more than 200 μm in diameter. In general, then, prokaryotes are very small cells compared with eukaryotes.

Surface-to-Volume Ratios, Cell Growth Rates, and Evolution

There are significant advantages to being a small cell. Small cells contain more surface area relative to cell volume than do large cells; that is, they have a higher surface-to-volume ratio. Consider a spherical coccus. The volume of such a cell is a function of the cube of its radius ($V = 4/3\pi r^3$), and its surface area is a function of the square of the radius ($S = 4\pi r^2$). Therefore, the (S/V) ratio of a spherical coccus is $3/r$ (Figure 3). As a cell increases in size, its S/V ratio decreases. To illustrate this, consider the S/V ratio for some of the cells of different sizes listed in Table 1: *Pelagibacter ubique*, 22; *E. coli*, 4.5; and *E. fishelsoni*, 0.05.

The S/V ratio of a cell affects several aspects of its biology, including evolution. For instance, because a cell's growth rate depends, among other things, on the rate of nutrient exchange, the higher S/V ratio of smaller cells supports greater nutrient exchange per unit of cell volume

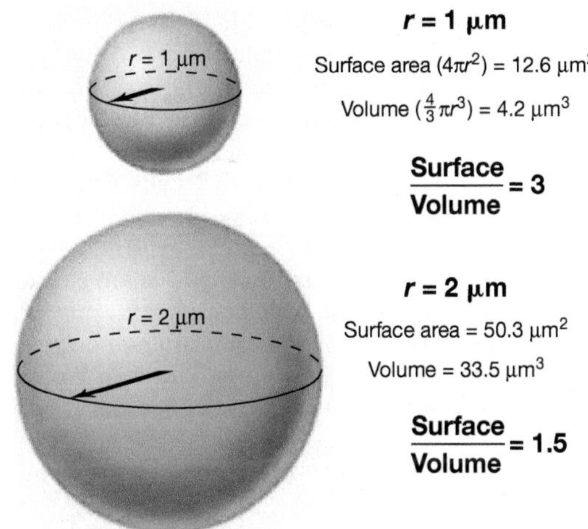

Figure 3 Surface area and volume relationships in cells. As a cell increases in size, its S/V ratio decreases.

in comparison with larger cells. Because of this, smaller cells, in general, grow faster than larger cells. In addition, a given amount of resources (the nutrients available to support growth) will support a larger population of small cells than of large cells. Why is this important? Each time a cell divides, its chromosome replicates as well. As DNA is replicated, occasional errors, called *mutations*, occur. Because mutation rates appear to be roughly the same in all cells, large or small, the more chromosome replications that occur, the greater the *total number* of mutations in the population. Mutations are the "raw materials" of evolution; the larger the pool of mutations, the greater the evolutionary possibilities. Thus, because prokaryotic cells are quite small and are also genetically haploid (allowing mutations to be expressed immediately), they have, in general, the capacity for more rapid growth and evolution than larger, genetically diploid cells.

In the larger diploid cells, not only is the S/V ratio smaller, but the effects of a mutation in one gene can be masked by a second unmutated gene copy. These fundamental differences between prokaryotic and eukaryotic cells support the observations that prokaryotes are often seen to adapt quite rapidly to changing environmental conditions and can more easily exploit new habitats than can eukaryotic cells.

Lower Limits of Cell Size

From the discussion above, it may seem that smaller and smaller bacteria will have greater and greater selective advantages in nature. Obviously, there must be lower limits to cell size, but what are they? Some microbiologists have proposed from observations of soil and other habitats that very small bacteria exist in nature, cells called *nanobacteria* (the word "nano" comes from Greek, meaning "dwarf"). The sizes reported for nanobacteria are 0.1 μm in diameter and smaller. This is extremely small, even by prokaryotic standards (Table 1). If one considers the volume needed to house the essential biomolecules of a free-living cell, a structure of 0.1 μm or less is insufficient to do the job, and structures 0.15 μm in diameter are on the borderline in this regard. Thus, whether nanobacteria are really living cells is an unanswered question. If such tiny cells actually exist, they would be by far the smallest known cells.

Regardless of the status of nanobacteria, many very small prokaryotic cells are known and many have been grown in the laboratory. The open oceans, for example, contain 10^4–10^5 prokaryotic cells per milliliter, and these tend to be very small cells, 0.2–0.4 μm in diameter. We will see later that many pathogenic bacteria are very small as well. Thus, very small cells are not uncommon, but cellular organisms smaller than 0.15 μm in diameter are unlikely to exist.

2 MiniReview

Prokaryotes are typically smaller in size than eukaryotes, although some very large and some very small prokaryotes are known. The typical small size of prokaryotic cells affects their physiology, growth rate, ecology, and evolution. The lower limit of cell diameter is probably about 0.15 μm.

- What physical property of cells increases as cells become smaller?
- Using the formula for volume, calculate the volume of a nanobacterium 0.1 μm in diameter (the cell radius is half of its diameter). How many nanobacteria this size could fit into a cell of *Mycoplasma pneumoniae*, the smallest known prokaryote (see Table 1)?

II THE CYTOPLASMIC MEMBRANE AND TRANSPORT

We now consider an extremely important cell structure, the cytoplasmic membrane, and review the major functions that the membrane has, in particular, in the transport of substances into and out of the cell.

3 The Cytoplasmic Membrane in *Bacteria* and *Archaea*

The **cytoplasmic membrane** is a thin structure that surrounds the cell. Although very thin, this vital structure is the barrier separating the inside of the cell (the cytoplasm) from its environment. If the membrane is broken, the integrity of the cell is destroyed, the cytoplasm leaks into the environment, and the cell dies. The cytoplasmic membrane is also a highly selective permeability barrier, enabling a cell to concentrate specific metabolites and excrete waste materials.

Composition of Membranes

The general structure of biological membranes is a phospholipid bilayer (Figure 4). Phospholipids contain both hydrophobic (fatty acid) and hydrophilic (glycerol–phosphate) components and can exist in many different chemical forms as a result of variation in the groups attached to the glycerol backbone. As phospholipids aggregate in an aqueous solution, they naturally form bilayer structures. In a phospholipid membrane, the fatty acids point inward toward each other to form a hydrophobic environment, and the hydrophilic portions remain exposed to the external environment or the cytoplasm (Figure 4*a*).

The cytoplasmic membrane, which is 6–8 nanometers wide, can be seen with the electron microscope, where it appears as two light-colored lines separated by a darker area

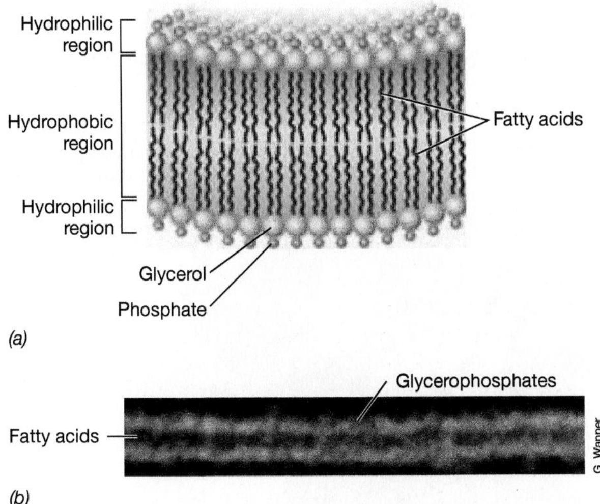

Figure 4 **Structure of a phospholipid bilayer.** *(b)* Transmission electron micrograph of a membrane from the bacterium *Halorhodospira halochloris*. The dark inner area is the hydrophobic region of the model membrane shown in *(a)*.

(Figure 4*b*). This *unit membrane,* as it is called (because each phospholipid leaf forms half of the "unit"), consists of a phospholipid bilayer with proteins embedded in it (Figure 5). The overall structure of the cytoplasmic membrane is stabilized by hydrogen bonds and hydrophobic interactions. In addition, Mg^{2+} and Ca^{2+} help stabilize the membrane by forming ionic bonds with negative charges on the phospholipids.

Although in a diagram the cytoplasmic membrane may appear rather rigid (Figure 5), in reality it is somewhat fluid, having a viscosity approximating that of a light-grade oil. Membrane biologists used to think that membranes were highly fluid, with proteins free to float around within a "sea" of lipid. We now know that this model is incorrect; some movement in the membrane is likely, although how extensive this is and how important it is to membrane function is unknown.

Membrane Proteins

The major proteins of the cytoplasmic membrane have hydrophobic surfaces in their regions that span the membrane and hydrophilic surfaces in their regions that contact the environment and the cytoplasm (Figure 5). The outer surface of the cytoplasmic membrane faces the environment and in certain bacteria interacts with a variety of proteins that bind substrates or process large molecules for transport into the cell (periplasmic proteins, discussed in Section 7). The inner side of the cytoplasmic membrane faces the cytoplasm and interacts with proteins involved in energy-yielding reactions and other important cellular functions.

Many membrane proteins are firmly embedded in the membrane and are called *integral* membrane proteins. Other proteins have one portion anchored in the membrane and extramembrane regions that point into or out of the cell (Figure 5). Still other proteins, called *peripheral* membrane proteins, are not embedded in the membrane at all but are nevertheless firmly associated with membrane surfaces. Some of these peripheral membrane proteins are lipoproteins, proteins that contain a lipid tail that anchors the protein into the membrane. These proteins typically interact with integral membrane proteins in important cellular processes such as energy metabolism and transport.

Proteins in the cytoplasmic membrane are arranged in patches (Figure 5); instead of being distributed evenly, proteins are clustered, a strategy that allows the grouping of proteins that interact or that have similar function. The overall protein content of the membrane is also quite high membrane proteins are indeed rather crowded—and it is thought that the lipid bilayer varies in thickness from 6 to 8 nm to accommodate thicker and thinner patches of proteins.

Membrane-Strengthening Agents: Sterols and Hopanoids

One major eukaryotic–prokaryotic difference in cytoplasmic membrane composition is that eukaryotes have **sterols** in their membranes (Figure 6a). Sterols are absent from the membranes of almost all prokaryotes (methanotrophic bacteria and mycoplasmas are exceptions). Depending on the cell type, sterols can make up as little as 5% or as much as 25% of the total lipids of eukaryotic membranes.

Sterols are rigid, planar molecules, whereas fatty acids are flexible. The presence of sterols in a membrane thus strengthens and stabilizes it and makes it less flexible. Molecules similar to sterols, called *hopanoids,* are present in the membranes of many *Bacteria* and likely play a role there similar to that of sterols in eukaryotic cells. One widely distributed hopanoid is the C_{30} hopanoid diploptene (Figure 6*b*). As far as is known, hopanoids are not present in *Archaea*.

Archaeal Membranes

The membrane lipids of *Archaea* differ from those of *Bacteria* and *Eukarya*. In contrast to the lipids of *Bacteria* and *Eukarya* in which *ester* linkages bond the fatty acids to glycerol (Figure 7a), the lipids of *Archaea* contain *ether* bonds between glycerol and their hydrophobic side chains (Figure 7*b*). In addition, archaeal lipids lack fatty acids. Instead, the side chains are composed of repeating units of the five-carbon hydrocarbon isoprene (Figure 7*c*). Despite these chemical differences, the fundamental construction of the cytoplasmic membrane of *Archaea*—inner and outer hydrophilic surfaces and a hydrophobic interior—is the same as that of membranes in *Bacteria* and *Eukarya*.

The major lipids of *Archaea* are glycerol diethers, which have 20-carbon side chains (the 20-C unit is called a *phytanyl*

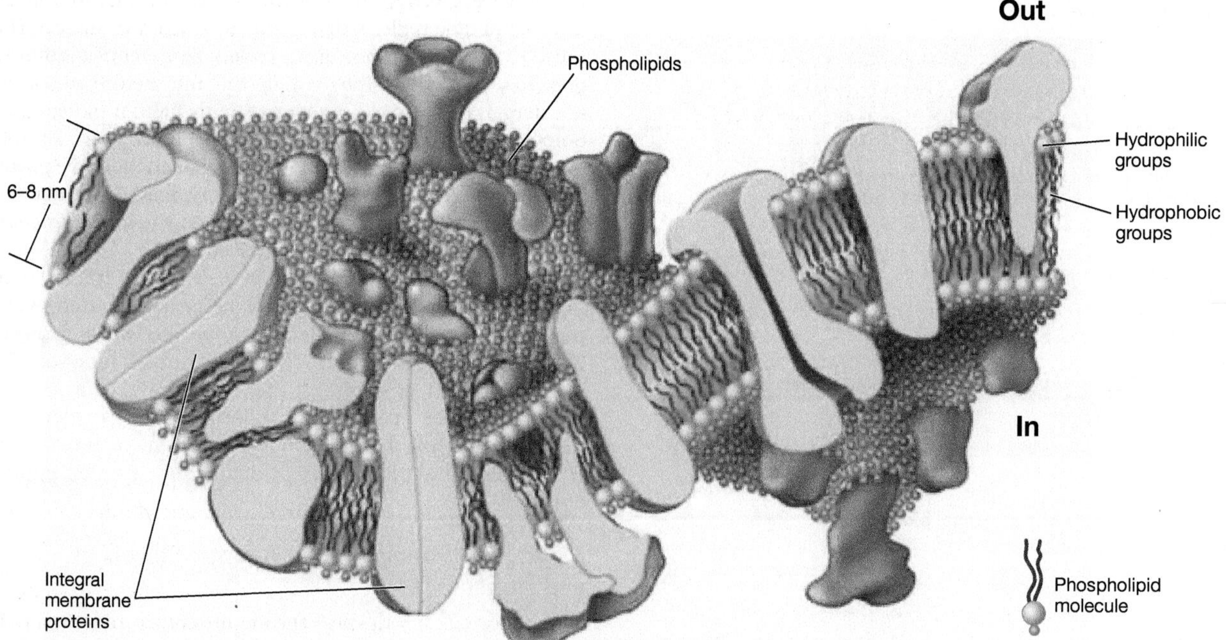

Figure 5 Structure of the cytoplasmic membrane. The inner surface (**In**) faces the cytoplasm and the outer surface (**Out**) faces the environment. Phospholipids compose the matrix of the cytoplasmic membrane, with the hydrophobic groups directed inward and the hydrophilic groups toward the outside, where they associate with water. Embedded in the matrix are proteins that are hydrophobic in the region that traverses the fatty acid bilayer. Hydrophilic proteins and other charged substances, such as metal ions, may attach to the hydrophilic surfaces. Although there are some chemical differences, the overall structure of the cytoplasmic membrane shown is similar in both prokaryotes and eukaryotes (but an exception to the bilayer design is shown in Figure 8*d*).

group), and diglycerol tetraethers, which have 40-carbon side chains (**Figure 8*a,b***). In the tetraether lipid, phytanyl side chains from each glycerol molecule are covalently linked (Figure 8*b*). Within a membrane this structure yields a lipid *monolayer* instead of a lipid *bilayer* membrane (Figure 8*c, d*). Unlike lipid bilayers, lipid monolayers are quite resistant to peeling apart. Not surprisingly, then, monolayer membranes are widespread among hyperthermophilic *Archaea*, prokaryotes that grow at temperatures so high that the heat could peel apart lipid bilayers, causing cell lysis.

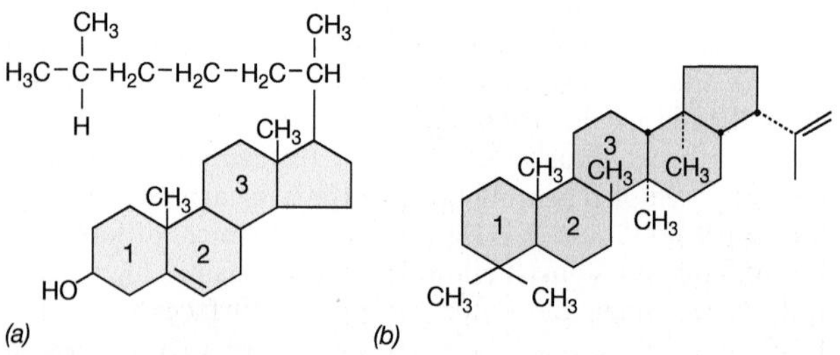

Figure 6 Sterols and hopanoids. *(a)* The structure of cholesterol, a typical sterol. *(b)* The structure of the hopanoid diploptene. Sterols are found in the membranes of eukaryotes and hopanoids in the membranes of some prokaryotes. The intraring labels 1, 2, and 3 highlight similarities in the parent structure of sterols and hopanoids.

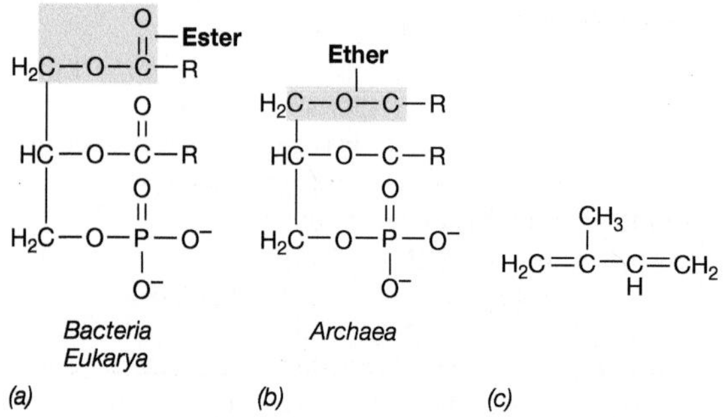

Figure 7 General structure of lipids. *(a)* The ester linkage. *(b)* The ether linkage. *(c)* Isoprene, the parent structure of the hydrophobic side chains of archaeal lipids. By contrast, in lipids of *Bacteria* and *Eukarya*, the side chains are composed of fatty acids.

3 MiniReview

The cytoplasmic membrane is a highly selective permeability barrier constructed of lipids and proteins that form a bilayer with hydrophilic exteriors and a hydrophobic interior. Other molecules, such as sterols and hopanoids, may strengthen the membrane. Unlike *Bacteria* and *Eukarya*, *Archaea* contain ether-linked lipids, and some species have membranes of monolayer instead of bilayer construction.

- Draw the basic structure of a lipid bilayer.
- Why should compounds like sterols and hopanoids be good at stabilizing the cytoplasmic membrane?
- Contrast the linkage between glycerol and the hydrophobic portion of lipids in *Bacteria* and *Archaea*.

4 The Functions of Cytoplasmic Membranes

The cytoplasmic membrane is more than just a barrier separating the inside from the outside of the cell. The membrane plays critical roles in cell function. First and foremost, the membrane functions as a permeability barrier, preventing the passive leakage of substances into or out of the cell (Figure 9). Secondly, the membrane is an anchor for many proteins. Some of these are enzymes that catalyze bioenergetic reactions and others transport substances into and out of the cell. The cytoplasmic membrane is also a major site of energy conservation in the cell. The membrane has an energetically charged form in which protons (H^+) are separated from hydroxyl ions (OH^-) across its surface (Figure 9). This charge separation is a form of energy, analogous to the potential energy present in a charged battery. This energy source, called the proton motive force, is responsible for driving many energy-requiring functions in the cell, including some forms of transport, motility, and biosynthesis of the cell's energy currency, ATP.

The Cytoplasmic Membrane as a Permeability Barrier

The interior of the cell (the cytoplasm) consists of an aqueous solution of salts, sugars, amino acids, nucleotides, vitamins, coenzymes, and other soluble materials. The hydrophobic internal portion of the cytoplasmic membrane (Figure 5) is a tight barrier to diffusion. Although some small hydrophobic molecules can pass through the membrane by diffusion, polar

Ether linkage
Phytanyl
H_2C-O-C
$HC-O-C$
$H_2COPO_3^{2-}$
CH_3
CH_3
CH_3 groups
Isoprene unit

***(a)* Glycerol diether**

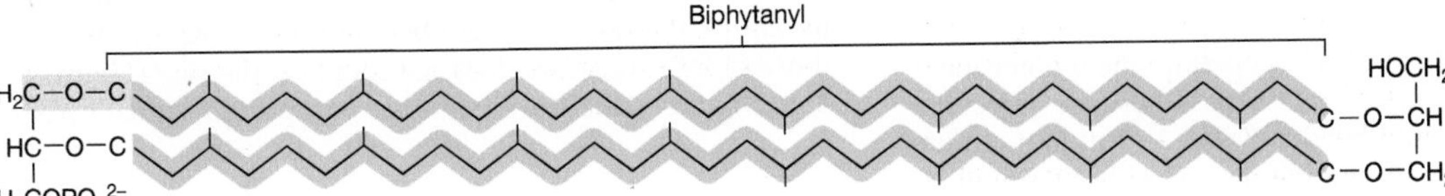

***(b)* Diglycerol tetraether**

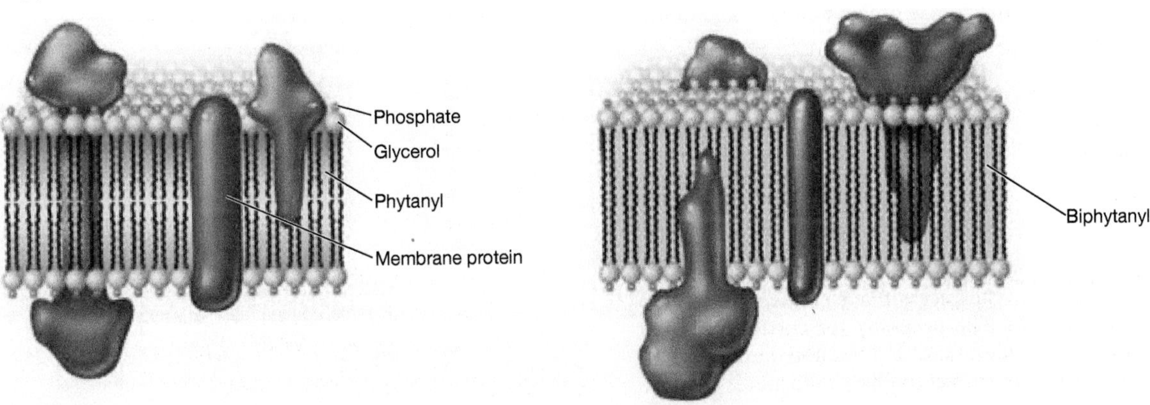

***(c)* Lipid bilayer**

***(d)* Lipid monolayer**

Figure 8 Major lipids of *Archaea* and the structure of archaeal cytoplasmic membranes. Note that in both *(a)* and *(b)*, the hydrocarbon of the lipid is attached to the glycerol by an ether linkage. The hydrocarbon in *(a)* is phytanyl (C_{20}) and in *(b)* biphytanyl (C_{40}). *(c, d)* Membrane structure in *Archaea*. The monolayer structure is the result of the tetraether composition of the membrane.

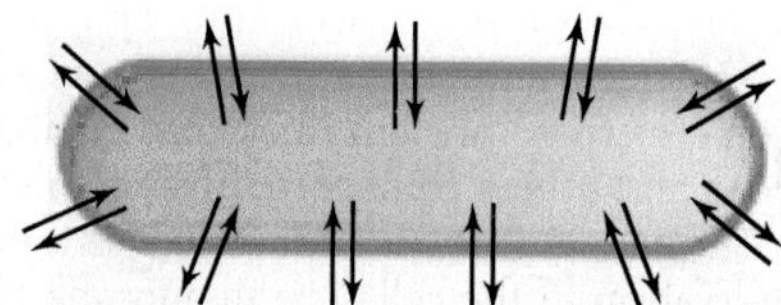

1. **Permeability Barrier** – Prevents leakage and functions as a gateway for transport of nutrients into and out of the cell

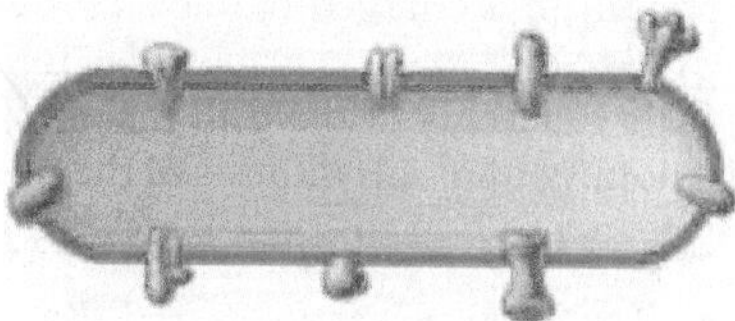

2. **Protein Anchor** – Site of many proteins involved in transport, bioenergetics, and chemotaxis

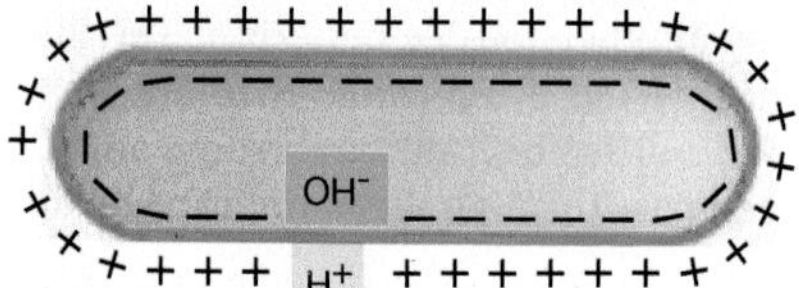

3. **Energy Conservation** – Site of generation and use of the proton motive force

Figure 9 **The major functions of the cytoplasmic membrane.** Although structurally weak, the cytoplasmic membrane has many important cellular functions.

and charged molecules do not pass through but instead must be specifically transported. Because the cytoplasmic membrane is charged, even a substance as small as a proton cannot diffuse across the cytoplasmic membrane.

One molecule that does freely penetrate the membrane is water, which is sufficiently small to pass between phospholipid molecules in the lipid bilayer (Table 2). But in addition, water movement through the membrane is accelerated by transport proteins called *aquaporins*. These proteins form membrane-spanning channels that specifically transport water into or out of the cytoplasm. For example, aquaporin AqpZ of *Escherichia coli* imports or exports water depending on whether osmotic conditions in the cytoplasm are high or low, respectively. The relative permeability of a few biologically relevant substances is shown in Table 2. As can be seen, most substances do not passively enter the cell and thus must be transported.

The Necessity for Transport Proteins

Transport proteins do more than just ferry substances across the membrane—they *accumulate* solutes against the concentration gradient. The necessity for carrier-mediated transport is easy to understand. If diffusion were the only way that solutes entered a cell, cells would never achieve the intracellular concentrations necessary to carry out biochemical reactions. This is for two reasons. First, as we have seen, few things diffuse across the cytoplasmic membrane. But secondly, even if solutes could diffuse across the membrane, their rate of uptake and their intracellular concentration would only be proportional to their external concentration (Figure 10), which in nature is often quite low. Hence, cells must have mechanisms for accumulating solutes, most of which are vital nutrients, to levels higher than those in their habitats, and this is the role of transport systems.

Table 2 Comparative permeability of membranes to various molecules

Substance	*Rate of permeability*[a]	*Potential for diffusion into a cell*
Water	100	Excellent
Glycerol	0.1	Good
Tryptophan	0.001	Fair/Poor
Glucose	0.001	Fair/Poor
Chloride ion (Cl^-)	0.000001	Very poor
Potassium ion (K^+)	0.0000001	Extremely poor
Sodium ion (Na^+)	0.00000001	Extremely poor

[a]Relative scale—permeability with respect to permeability of water given as 100. Permeability of the membrane to water may be affected by aquaporins (see text)

Properties of Transport Proteins

Carrier-mediated transport systems show several characteristic properties. First, in contrast with simple diffusion, transport systems show a *saturation effect*. If the concentration of substrate is high enough to saturate the carrier, which can occur at even the very low substrate concentrations found in nature, the rate of uptake becomes maximal and the addition of more substrate does not increase the rate (Figure 10). This characteristic feature of transport proteins greatly assists

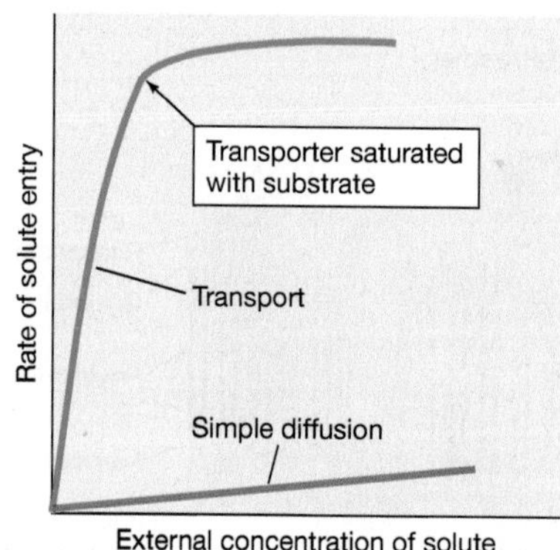

Figure 10 **Transporters versus diffusion.** In transport, the uptake rate shows saturation at relatively low external concentrations.

cells in concentrating nutrients from an often very dilute environment.

A second characteristic of carrier-mediated transport is the *high specificity* of the transport event. Many carrier proteins react only with a single molecule, and others show affinities for a closely related class of molecules such as sugars or amino acids. This economy in uptake reduces the need for separate transport proteins for each different amino acid or sugar.

Another major characteristic of transport systems is that biosynthesis of the transport proteins is typically *regulated* by the cell. That is, the specific complement of transporters present in the membrane at any given time is a function of both the nutrients present in the environment and their concentrations. Biosynthetic control is important because a particular nutrient may need to be transported by one transporter when the nutrient is at high concentration and by a different, higher-affinity transporter, when at low concentration.

4 MiniReview

The major functions of the cytoplasmic membrane are permeability, transport, and energy conservation. To accumulate nutrients against the concentration gradient, specific transport mechanisms are employed.

- List two reasons why a cell cannot depend on diffusion as a means of acquiring nutrients.
- Why is physical damage to the cytoplasmic membrane a more critical problem for the cell than damage to some other cell component?

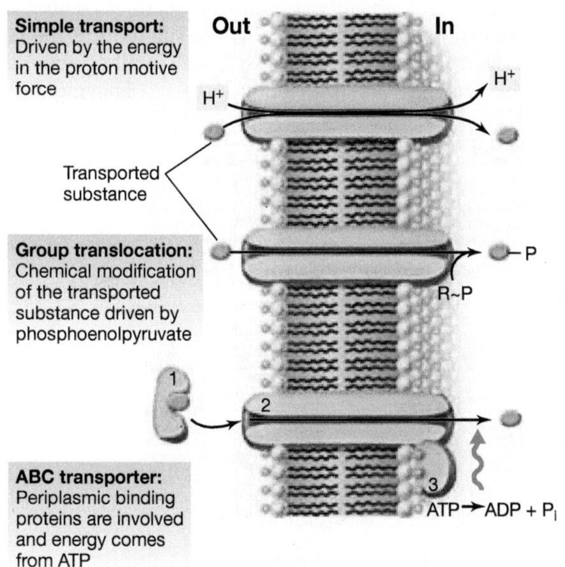

Figure 11 **The three classes of membrane transport systems.** Note how simple transporters and the ABC system transport substances without chemically modifying them, whereas group translocation results in the chemical modification (phosphorylation) of the transported substance. The three proteins of the ABC system are labeled 1, 2, and 3.

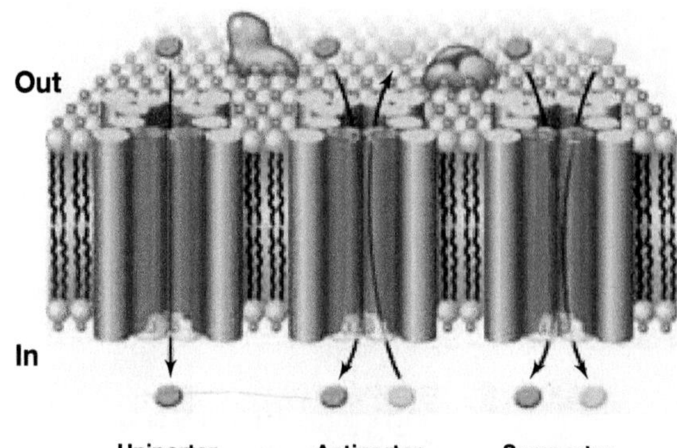

Figure 12 **Structure of membrane-spanning transporters and types of transport events.** In prokaryotes, membrane-spanning transporters typically contain 12 α-helices (each shown here as a cylinder) that aggregate to form a channel through the membrane. Shown here are three transporters with differing types of transport events. For antiporters and symporters, the cotransported substance is shown in yellow.

5 Transport and Transport Systems

Nutrient transport is a vital cellular event. Different mechanisms for transport exist in prokaryotes, each with its own unique features. We explore this subject here.

Structure and Function of Membrane Transport Proteins

At least three transport systems exist in prokaryotes: **simple transport**, **group translocation**, and the **ABC system**. Simple transport consists only of a membrane-spanning transport protein, group translocation involves a series of proteins in the transport event, and the ABC system consists of three components: a substrate-binding protein, a membrane-integrated transporter, and an ATP-hydrolyzing protein (Figure 11). All transport systems require energy in some form, either from the proton motive force or ATP (or some other energy-rich organic compound).

Figure 11 contrasts transport systems of prokaryotes. Regardless of the system, the membrane-spanning components typically show significant similarities in amino acid sequence, an indication of the common evolutionary roots of all transport systems. Membrane transporters contain 12 α-helix domains that weave back and forth through the membrane to form a channel. It is through this channel that the solute is actually carried into the cell (Figure 12). The transport event involves a conformational change in the transport protein after it binds its solute. Like a gate swinging open, the conformational change then brings the solute into the cell.

Three transport events are possible: uniport, symport, and antiport (Figure 12). *Uniporters* are proteins that transport a molecule unidirectionally across the membrane. *Symporters* are proteins that function as cotransporters; they transport

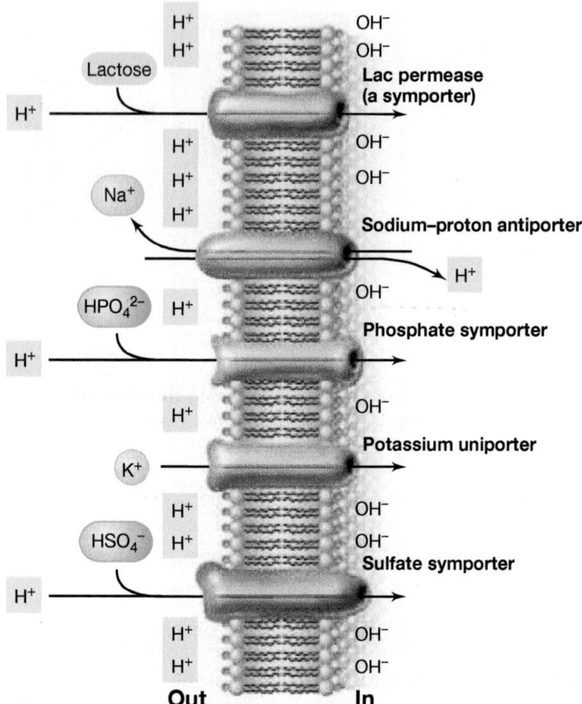

Figure 13 **Function of the Lac permease symporter of *Escherichia coli* and several other well-characterized simple transporters.** Although for simplicity the membrane-spanning proteins are drawn here in globular form, note that their structure is actually as depicted in Figure 12.

one molecule along with another substance, typically a proton. *Antiporters* are proteins that transport a molecule across the membrane while simultaneously transporting a second molecule in the opposite direction (Figure 12).

Simple Transport: Lac Permease of *Escherichia coli*

The bacterium *Escherichia coli* metabolizes the disaccharide sugar lactose. Lactose is transported into cells of *E. coli* by the activity of a simple transporter, *lac permease,* a symporter. This is shown in Figure 13, where the activity of lac permease is compared with that of some other simple transporters, including uniporters and antiporters. We will see later that lac permease is one of three proteins required to metabolize lactose in *E. coli* and that the synthesis of these proteins is highly regulated by the cell.

Activity of lac permease is energy driven. As each lactose molecule is transported into the cell, the energy in the proton motive force (Figure 9) is diminished by the cotransport of protons into the cytoplasm. The strength of the proton motive force is reestablished through energy-yielding reactions The net result of the activity of lac permease is the accumulation of lactose within the cell coupled to the consumption of energy.

Group Translocation: The Phosphotransferase System

Group translocation is a form of transport in which the substance transported is chemically modified during its uptake across the membrane. The best-studied group translocation system transports the sugars glucose, mannose, and fructose in *E. coli*. These compounds are modified by phosphorylation during transport by the *phosphotransferase system*.

The phosphotransferase system consists of a family of proteins, five of which are necessary to transport a given sugar. Before the sugar is transported, the proteins in the phosphotransferase system are themselves alternately phosphorylated and dephosphorylated in cascading fashion until the actual transporter, Enzyme II$_c$, phosphorylates the sugar during the transport event (Figure 14). A small protein called *HPr,* the enzyme that phosphorylates it (Enzyme I), and

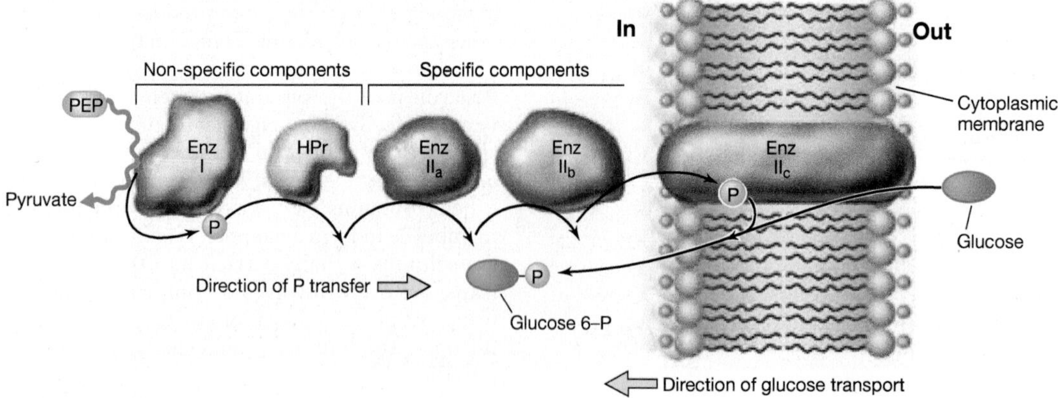

Figure 14 **Mechanism of the phosphotransferase system of *Escherichia coli.*** For glucose uptake, the system consists of five proteins: Enzyme (Enz) I, Enzymes II$_a$, II$_b$, and II$_c$, and HPr. Sequential phosphate transfer occurs from phosphoenolpyruvate (PEP) through the proteins shown to Enzyme II$_c$, which actually transports and phosphorylates the sugar. Proteins HPr and Enz I are nonspecific and will transport any sugar. The Enz II components are specific for each particular sugar.

Enzyme II_a are all cytoplasmic proteins. By contrast, Enzyme II_b lies on the inner surface of the membrane and Enzyme II_c is an integral membrane protein (Figure 14). HPr and Enzyme I are nonspecific components of the phosphotransferase system and participate in the uptake of various sugars. A specific Enzyme II exists for each different sugar transported (Figure 14).

Energy for the phosphotransferase system comes from the energy-rich compound phosphoenolpyruvate. Although energy in the form of one energy-rich phosphate bond is consumed in the process of transporting the glucose molecule (Figure 14), the phosphorylation of glucose to glucose-6-P is the first step in its intracellular metabolism anyway (glycolysis). Thus, the phosphotransferase system prepares glucose for immediate entry into this major metabolic pathway.

Periplasmic-Binding Proteins and the ABC System

We will learn a bit later in this chapter that gram-negative bacteria contain a region called the *periplasm* that lies between the cytoplasmic membrane and a second membrane layer called the *outer membrane* (Section 7). The periplasm contains many different proteins, several of which function in transport and are called *periplasmic-binding proteins*. Transport systems that contain periplasmic-binding proteins along with a membrane transporter and ATP-hydrolyzing proteins are called *ABC transport systems,* the "ABC" being an acronym for *A*TP-*b*inding *c*assette, a structural feature of proteins that bind ATP (Figure 15). More than 200 different ABC transport systems have been identified in prokaryotes. ABC transporters exist for the uptake of organic compounds such as sugars and amino acids, inorganic nutrients such as sulfate and phosphate, and trace metals.

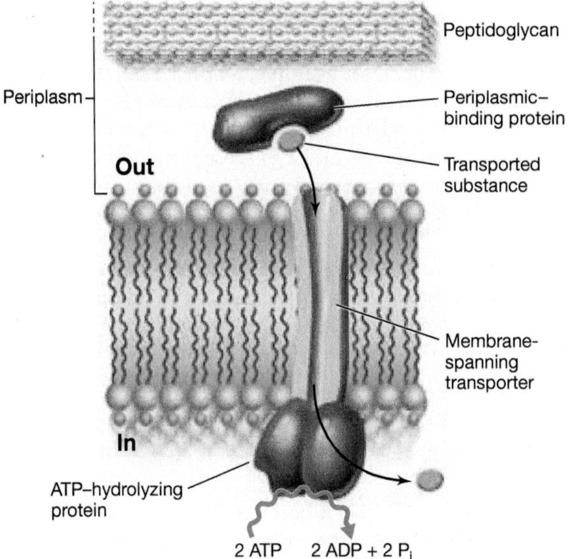

Figure 15 **Mechanism of an ABC transporter.** The periplasmic-binding protein has high affinity for substrate, the membrane-spanning proteins form the transport channel, and the cytoplasmic ATP-hydrolyzing proteins supply the energy for the transport event.

One of the characteristic properties of ABC transporters is the typically high substrate affinity of the periplasmic-binding proteins. These proteins can bind their substrate even when the substrate is present at extremely low concentration. For example, substrates present at concentrations as low as 1 micromolar (10^{-6} M) can easily be trapped by periplasmic-binding proteins. Once its substrate is bound, the periplasmic-binding protein interacts with its respective membrane-spanning transporter to transport the substrate driven by the energy of ATP hydrolysis (Figure 15).

Interestingly, even though gram-positive bacteria lack a periplasm, they have ABC systems. In gram-positive bacteria, however, specific substrate-binding proteins are anchored to the external surface of the cytoplasmic membrane. Nevertheless, as in gram-negative bacteria, once these proteins bind substrate, they interact with a membrane transporter to catalyze uptake of the substrate at the expense of ATP hydrolysis, just as they do in gram-negative bacteria (Figure 15).

Protein Export

Thus far our discussion of transport has focused on small molecules. What about the transport of large molecules, such as proteins? To function properly, many proteins need to be either transported outside the cytoplasmic membrane or inserted into the membrane in a specific way. Proteins are exported through and inserted into prokaryotic membranes by the activities of proteins called *translocases,* a key one being the Sec (for secretory) system. The Sec system both exports proteins and inserts integral membrane proteins into the membrane. Proteins destined for transport are recognized by the Sec system because they are tagged in a specific way. We discuss this process later.

The Sec translocase system consists of seven proteins, with SecYEG constituting the actual transmembrane transporter. Other components of the Sec system include SecA, an ATP-hydrolyzing enzyme that provides energy for the process; SecB, a protein that prevents folding of proteins in the cytoplasm; and Sec D and F, proteins that assist in the translocation process while consuming energy from the proton motive force.

Protein export is important to bacteria because many bacterial enzymes function outside the cell (exoenzymes). For example, hydrolytic exoenzymes such as amylase or cellulase are excreted directly into the environment where they cleave starch or cellulose, respectively, into glucose, which is then used by the cell as a carbon and energy source. In gram-negative bacteria, many enzymes are localized to the periplasm, and these must get past the cytoplasmic membrane and into the periplasm in order to function. Moreover, many pathogenic bacteria excrete protein toxins or other harmful proteins into the host during infection. Many toxins are excreted by a second translocase system called the *type III secretion system*. This system differs from the Sec system in that the secreted protein is translocated from the bacterial cell directly into the host, for example, a human cell. However, all of these large molecules need to move through the cytoplasmic membrane, and translocases such as SecYEG and the type III secretion system assist in these transport events.

5 MiniReview

At least three functional classes of transporters are known: simple transporters, phosphotransferase-type transporters, and ABC systems. Transport requires energy from the proton motive force, ATP, or some other energy-rich substance.

- Contrast simple transporters, the phosphotransferase system, and ABC transporters in terms of (1) energy source, (2) chemical alterations of the substrate transported, and (3) number of proteins involved.
- Which transport system is best suited for the transport of nutrients present in the environment at extremely low levels, and why?
- How are proteins exported from the cell?

III CELL WALLS OF PROKARYOTES

6 The Cell Wall of *Bacteria*: Peptidoglycan

Because of the activities of transport systems, the cytoplasm of bacterial cells maintains a high concentration of dissolved solutes. This causes significant osmotic pressure to develop—about 2 atmospheres in a bacterium such as *Escherichia coli*. This is roughly the same as the pressure in an automobile tire. To withstand these pressures and prevent bursting—a process called *lysis*—bacteria have cell walls. Besides preventing osmotic lysis, cell walls also give shape and rigidity to the cell.

Species of bacteria can be divided into two major groups, called **gram-positive** and **gram-negative**. The distinction between gram-positive and gram-negative bacteria is based on the **Gram stain** reaction. But differences in cell wall structure are at the heart of the Gram-staining reaction. The appearance of the cell walls of gram-positive and gram-negative cells in the electron microscope differs markedly, as is shown in Figure 16. The gram-negative cell wall is a multilayered structure and quite complex, whereas the gram-positive cell wall is typically much thicker and consists almost entirely of a single type of molecule.

The focus of this section is on the polysaccharide component of the cell walls of *Bacteria*, both gram positive and gram negative. In Section 7 we describe the special wall components found in gram-negative *Bacteria*. And finally, in Section 8 we describe the various cell walls of *Archaea*.

Peptidoglycan

The cell walls of *Bacteria* have a rigid layer that is primarily responsible for the strength of the wall. In gram-negative bacteria, additional layers are present outside this rigid layer. The rigid layer, called **peptidoglycan**, is a polysaccharide composed of two sugar derivatives—*N-acetylglucosamine* and *N-acetylmuramic acid*—and a few amino acids, including L-alanine, D-alanine, D-glutamic acid, and either lysine or diaminopimelic acid (DAP) (Figure 17). These constituents are connected to form a repeating structure, the glycan tetrapeptide (Figure 18).

Long chains of peptidoglycan are biosynthesized adjacent to one another to form a sheet surrounding the cell. The chains are connected through cross-links of amino acids. The glycosidic bonds connecting the sugars in the glycan strands are covalent bonds, but these can provide rigidity to the structure in only one direction. Only after cross-linking is peptidoglycan strong in both the X and Y directions (Figure 19). Cross-linking occurs to different extents in different species of *Bacteria*, with greater rigidity the result of more extensive cross-linking.

In gram-negative bacteria, peptidoglycan cross-linkage occurs by peptide bond formation from the amino group of DAP of one glycan chain to the carboxyl group of the terminal D-alanine on the adjacent glycan chain (Figure 19). In gram-positive bacteria, cross-linkage occurs by way of a peptide interbridge, the kinds and numbers of amino acids in the interbridge varying from organism to organism. For example, in *Staphylococcus aureus*, a well-studied gram-positive bacterium, the interbridge peptide consists of five glycine residues (Figure 19*b*). The overall structure of a peptidoglycan molecule is shown in Figure 19*c*.

Diversity of Peptidoglycan

Peptidoglycan is present only in species of *Bacteria*—the sugar *N*-acetylmuramic acid and the amino acid DAP have never been found in the cell walls of *Archaea* or *Eukarya*. However, not all *Bacteria* examined have DAP in their peptidoglycan. This amino acid analog is present in peptidoglycan from all gram-negative bacteria and some gram-positive species; however, most gram-positive cocci contain lysine instead of DAP (Figure 19*b*), and a few other gram-positive bacteria have other amino acids. Another unusual feature of peptidoglycan is the presence of two amino acids that have the D configuration, D-alanine and D-glutamic acid. In cellular proteins amino acids are always of the L stereoisomer.

More than 100 different peptidoglycans are known, with the diversity focused on the chemistry of the peptide cross-links and interbridge. In each different peptidoglycan the glycan portion is constant; only the sugars *N*-acetylglucosamine and *N*-acetylmuramic are present. Moreover, these sugars are always connected in β-1,4 linkage (Figure 18). The tetrapeptide of the repeating unit shows major variation in only one amino acid, the lysine–DAP alternation. However, the D-glutamic acid at position 2 is hydroxylated in the peptidoglycan of some organisms, and there are substitutions

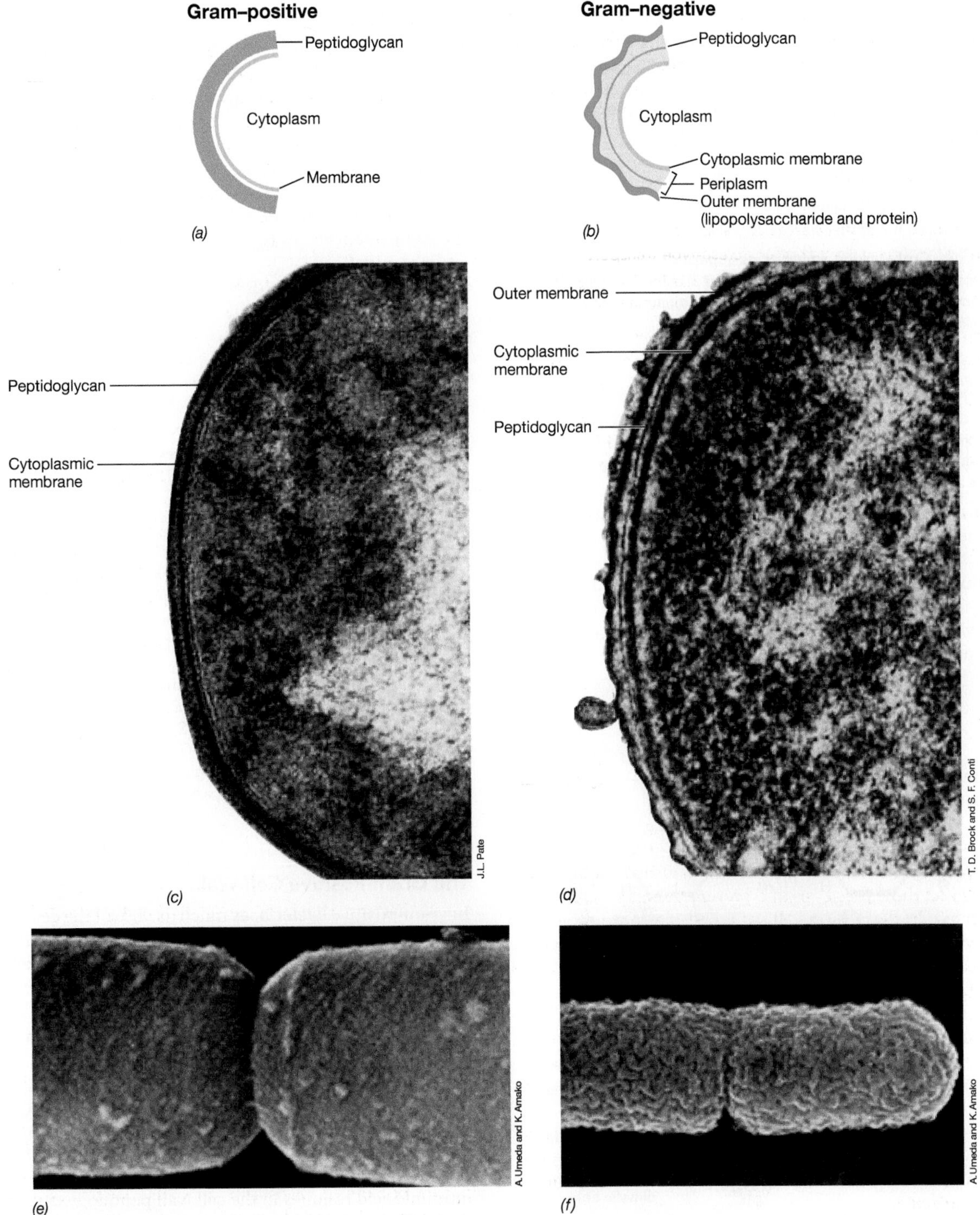

Figure 16 **Cell walls of *Bacteria*.** *(a, b)* Schematic diagrams of gram-positive and gram-negative cell walls. Transmission electron micrographs showing the cell wall of *(c)* a gram-positive bacterium, *Arthrobacter crystallopoietes*, and *(d)* a gram-negative bacterium, *Leucothrix mucor*. *(e, f)* Scanning electron micrographs of gram-positive (*Bacillus subtilis*) and gram-negative (*Escherichia coli*) bacteria. Note differences in the surface texture in the cells shown in *(e)* and *(f)*. A single cell of *B. subtilis* or *E. coli* is about 1 μm wide.

(a) **Diaminopimelic acid** (b) **Lysine**

Figure 17 **Cross-linking amino acids in peptidoglycan.** The only difference in the two molecules is highlighted in color. Besides these two amino acids, several other amino acids are found in peptidoglycan cross-links (Figure 18).

in amino acids at positions 1 and 3 in some others. Any of the amino acids present in the tetrapeptide can also occur in the interbridge. In addition, several other amino acids such as glycine, threonine, serine, and aspartic acid can be in the interbridge. However, branched-chain amino acids, aromatic amino acids, sulfur-containing amino acids, and histidine, arginine, and proline have never been found in the interbridge.

Thus, although the peptide chemistry of peptidoglycan varies, the backbone of peptidoglycan—alternating repeats of N-acetylglucosamine and N-acetylmuramic acid—is the same in all species of *Bacteria*.

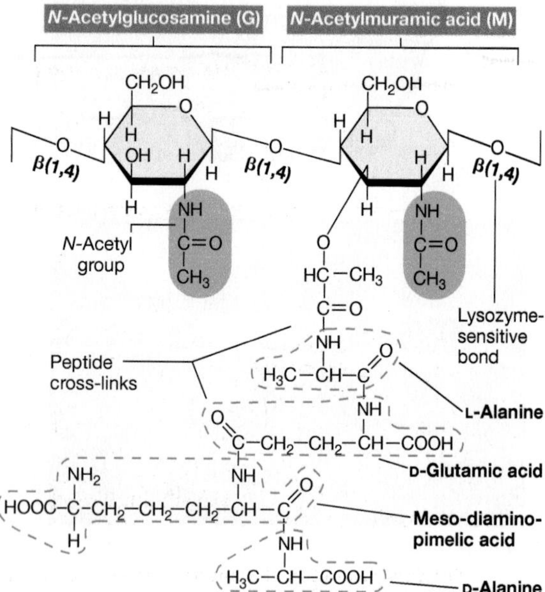

Figure 18 **Structure of the repeating unit in peptidoglycan, the glycan tetrapeptide.** The structure given is that found in *Escherichia coli* and most other gram-negative *Bacteria*. In some *Bacteria*, other amino acids are found.

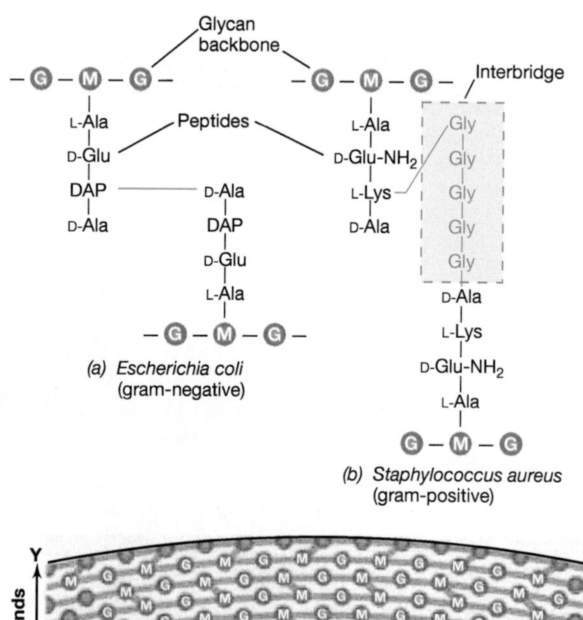

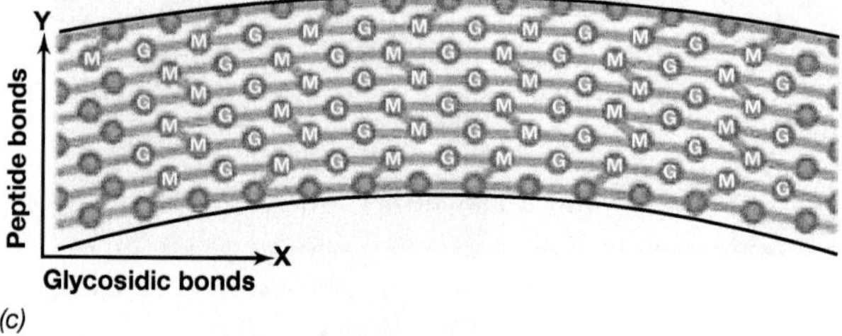

Figure 19 **Peptidoglycan in *Escherichia coli* and *Staphylococcus aureus*.** *(a)* No interbridge is present in *E. coli* and other gram-negative *Bacteria*. *(b)* The glycine interbridge in *S. aureus* (gram-positive). *(c)* Overall structure of peptidoglycan. G, *N*-acetylglucosamine; M, *N*-acetylmuramic acid. Note how glycosidic bonds confer strength to peptidoglycan in the X direction whereas peptide bonds confer strength in the Y direction.

The Gram-Positive Cell Wall

In gram-positive bacteria, as much as 90% of the cell wall consists of peptidoglycan. And, although some bacteria have only a single layer of peptidoglycan surrounding the cell, many bacteria, especially gram-positive bacteria, have several (up to about 25) sheets of peptidoglycan stacked one upon another.

Many gram-positive bacteria have acidic substances called **teichoic acids** embedded in their cell wall. Teichoic acids include all cell wall, cytoplasmic membrane, and capsular polymers containing glycerophosphate or ribitol phosphate residues. These polyalcohols are connected by phosphate esters and usually have other sugars and D-alanine attached (Figure 20a). Teichoic acids are covalently bonded to muramic acid residues in the cell wall peptidoglycan. Because they are negatively charged, teichoic acids are partially responsible for the negative charge of the cell surface. Teichoic acids also function to bind Ca^{2+} and Mg^{2+} for eventual transport into the cell. Certain teichoic acids are covalently bound to membrane lipids; thus they have been called *lipoteichoic acids*.

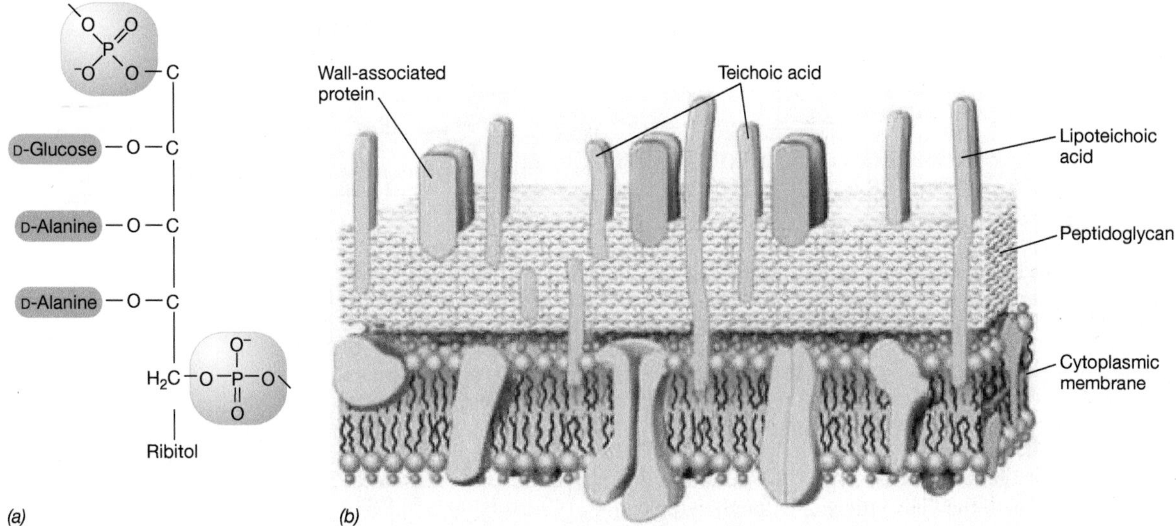

Figure 20 Teichoic acids and the overall structure of the gram-positive bacterial cell wall. *(a)* Structure of the ribitol teichoic acid of *Bacillus subtilis*. The teichoic acid is a polymer of the repeating ribitol units shown here. *(b)* Summary diagram of the gram-positive bacterial cell wall.

Figure 20*b* summarizes the structure of the cell wall of gram-positive *Bacteria* and shows how teichoic acids and lipoteichoic acids are arranged in the overall wall structure.

Lysozyme and Protoplasts

Peptidoglycan can be destroyed by certain agents. One such agent is the enzyme *lysozyme*, a protein that breaks the β-1,4-glycosidic bonds between *N*-acetylglucosamine and *N*-acetylmuramic acid in peptidoglycan (Figure 18), thereby weakening the wall. Water then enters the cell and the cell swells and eventually bursts (cell lysis) (Figure 21*a*). Lysozyme is found in animal secretions including tears, saliva, and other body fluids, and functions as a major line of defense against bacterial infection.

If a solute that does not penetrate the cell, such as sucrose, is added to a cell suspension containing lysozyme, the solute concentration outside the cell balances the concentration inside (these conditions are called *isotonic*). Under isotonic conditions, if lysozyme is used to digest peptidoglycan, water does not enter the cell and lysis does not occur. Instead, a **protoplast** (a bacterium that has lost its cell wall) is formed (Figure 21*b*). If such sucrose-stabilized protoplasts are placed in water, they immediately lyse. The word *spheroplast* is often used as a synonym for protoplast, although the two words have slightly different meanings. Protoplasts are cells that are free of residual cell wall material, whereas spheroplasts contain pieces of wall material attached to the otherwise membrane-enclosed structure.

Cells That Lack Cell Walls

Although most prokaryotes cannot survive in nature without their cell walls, some are able to do so. These include the mycoplasmas, a group of pathogenic bacteria that causes a variety of infectious diseases in humans and other animals, and the *Thermoplasma* group, species of *Archaea* that naturally lack cell walls. These prokaryotes are essentially free-living protoplasts, and they are able to survive without

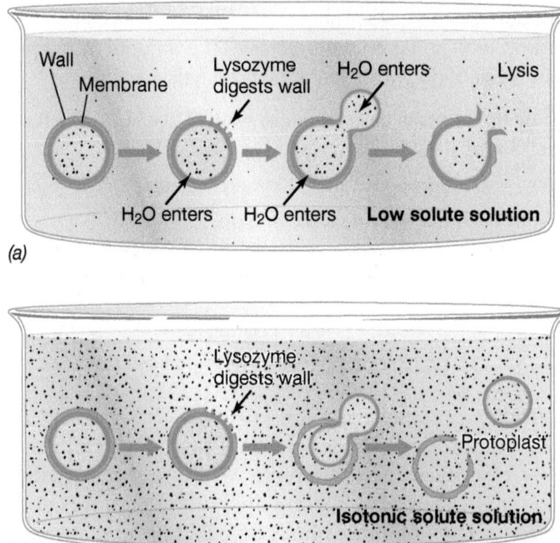

Figure 21 Protoplasts and their formation. Lysozyme breaks the β-1,4 glycosidic bonds in peptidoglycan (Figure 18). *(a)* In dilute solutions, breakdown of the cell wall is immediately followed by cell lysis because the cytoplasmic membrane is structurally very weak. *(b)* In a solution containing an isotonic concentration of a solute such as sucrose, water does not enter the protoplast and it remains stable.

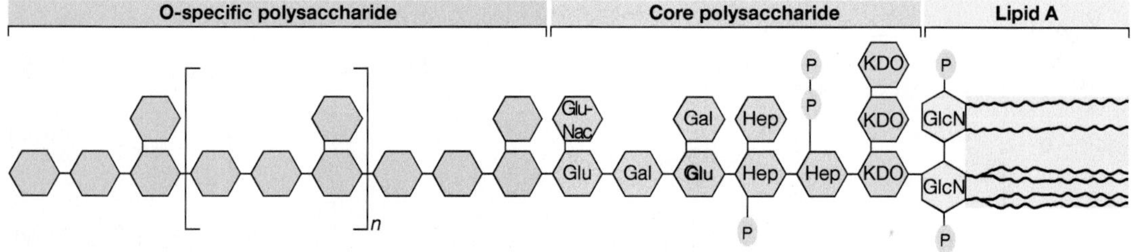

Figure 22 **Structure of the lipopolysaccharide of gram-negative *Bacteria*.** The chemistry of lipid A and the polysaccharide components varies among species of gram-negative *Bacteria*, but the major components (lipid A–KDO–core–O-specific) are typically the same. The O-specific polysaccharide varies greatly among species. KDO, ketodeoxyoctonate; Hep, heptose; Glu, glucose; Gal, galactose; GluNac, *N*-acetylglucosamine; GlcN, glucosamine; P, phosphate. Glucosamine and the lipid A fatty acids are linked through the amine groups. The lipid A portion of LPS can be toxic to animals and comprises the endotoxin complex. Compare this figure with Figure 23 and follow the LPS components by the color-coding.

cell walls either because they have unusually tough cytoplasmic membranes or because they live in osmotically protected habitats such as the animal body. Most mycoplasmas have sterols in their cytoplasmic membranes, and these probably function to add strength and rigidity to the membrane as they do in the cytoplasmic membranes of eukaryotic cells (Section 3).

6 MiniReview

The cell walls of *Bacteria* contain a polysaccharide called peptidoglycan. Peptidoglycan consists of alternating repeats of *N*-acetylglucosamine and *N*-acetylmuramic acid, which forms the glycan tetrapeptide with strands cross-linked by short peptides. One to several sheets of peptidoglycan can be present, depending on the organism. The enzyme lysozyme destroys peptidoglycan, leading to cell lysis.

- Why do bacterial cells need cell walls? Do all bacteria have cell walls?
- Why is peptidoglycan such a strong molecule?
- What does the enzyme lysozyme do?

7 The Outer Membrane of Gram-Negative *Bacteria*

In gram-negative bacteria such as *Escherichia coli* only about 10% of the total cell wall consists of peptidoglycan. Instead, most of the cell wall is composed of the **outer membrane**. This layer is effectively a second lipid bilayer, but it is not constructed solely of phospholipid and protein as is the cytoplasmic membrane (Figure 5). The gram-negative cell outer membrane also contains polysaccharide. The lipid and polysaccharide are linked in the outer membrane to form a complex. Because of this, the outer membrane is called the **lipopolysaccharide** layer, or simply **LPS**.

Chemistry of LPS

The chemistry of LPS from several bacteria is known. As seen in Figure 22, the polysaccharide portion of LPS consists of two components, the *core polysaccharide* and the *O-polysaccharide*. In *Salmonella* species, where LPS has been best studied, the core polysaccharide consists of ketodeoxyoctonate (KDO), seven-carbon sugars (heptoses), glucose, galactose, and *N*-acetylglucosamine. Connected to the core is the O-polysaccharide, which typically contains galactose, glucose, rhamnose, and mannose (all hexoses), as well as one or more unusual dideoxy sugars such as abequose, colitose, paratose, or tyvelose. These sugars are connected in four- or five-membered sequences, which often are branched. When the sequences repeat, the long O-polysaccharide is formed.

The relationship of the O-polysaccharide to the rest of the LPS is shown in Figure 23. The lipid portion of the LPS, called *lipid A*, is not a typical glycerol lipid (see Figure 7*a*), but instead the fatty acids are connected through the amine groups from a disaccharide composed of glucosamine phosphate (Figure 22). The disaccharide is attached to the core polysaccharide through KDO (Figure 22). Fatty acids commonly found in lipid A include caproic (C_6), lauric (C_{12}), myristic (C_{14}), palmitic (C_{16}), and stearic (C_{18}) acids.

LPS replaces most of the phospholipids in the outer half of the outer membrane; the structure of the inner half more closely resembles that of the cytoplasmic membrane. However, a lipoprotein complex is also present on the inner half of the outer membrane (Figure 23*a*). Lipoprotein functions as an anchor between the outer membrane and peptidoglycan. Thus, although the outer membrane is considered a lipid bilayer, its structure is distinct from that of the cytoplasmic membrane, especially in the outer half in contact with the environment (compare Figures 5 and 23*a*).

Endotoxin

Although the major function of the outer membrane is undoubtedly structural, one of its important biological properties is its toxicity to animals. Gram-negative bacteria that

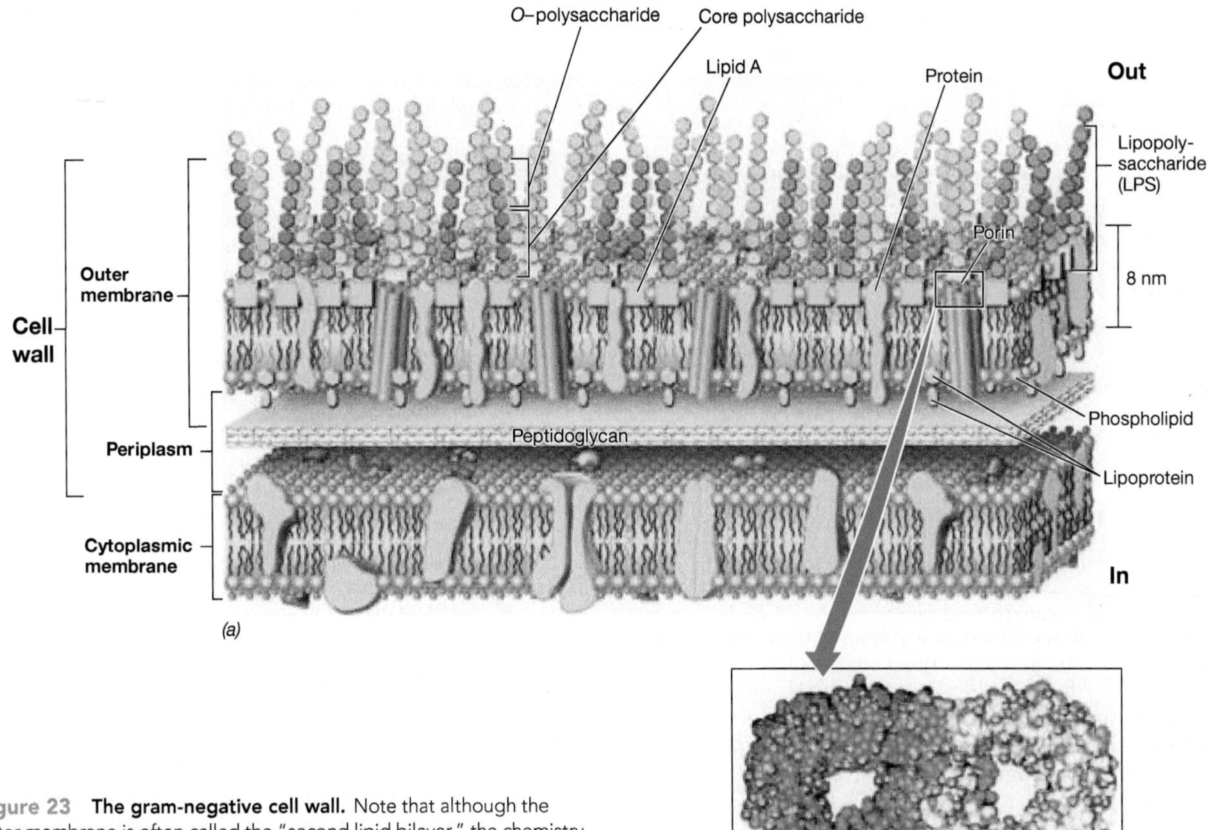

Figure 23 **The gram-negative cell wall.** Note that although the outer membrane is often called the "second lipid bilayer," the chemistry and architecture of this layer differ in many ways from that of the cytoplasmic membrane. *(a)* Arrangement of lipopolysaccharide, lipid A, phospholipid, porins, and lipoprotein in the outer membrane. See Figure 22 for details of the structure of LPS. *(b)* Molecular model of porin proteins. Note the four pores present, one within each of the proteins forming a porin molecule and a smaller central pore between the porin proteins. The view is perpendicular to the plane of the membrane. Model based on X-ray diffraction studies of *Rhodobacter blasticus* porin.

are pathogenic for humans and other mammals include species of *Salmonella, Shigella,* and *Escherichia,* among others, and some of the intestinal symptoms these pathogens typically elicit in their hosts are due to their toxic outer membrane.

The toxic properties are associated with the LPS layer, in particular, lipid A. The term *endotoxin* refers to this toxic component of LPS. Some endotoxins cause violent symptoms in humans, including severe gastrointestinal distress (gas, diarrhea, vomiting). Endotoxins are responsible for a number of bacterial illnesses, including *Salmonella* food infection. Interestingly, LPS from several nonpathogenic bacteria have also been shown to have endotoxin activity. Thus, the organism itself need not be pathogenic to contain toxic outer membrane components.

Porins

Unlike the cytoplasmic membrane, the outer membrane of gram-negative bacteria is relatively permeable to small molecules even though it is basically a lipid bilayer. This is because proteins called *porins* are present in the outer membrane that function as channels for the entrance and exit of hydrophilic low-molecular-weight substances (Figure 23). Several different porins exist, including both specific and nonspecific classes.

Nonspecific porins form water-filled channels through which any small substance can pass. By contrast, specific porins contain a binding site for only one or a small group of structurally related substances. Porins are transmembrane proteins that contain three identical subunits (Figure 23*a*). Besides the channel present in each barrel of the porin, the barrels of the porin proteins associate in such a way that a small hole about 1 nm (10^{-9} m) in diameter is formed in the

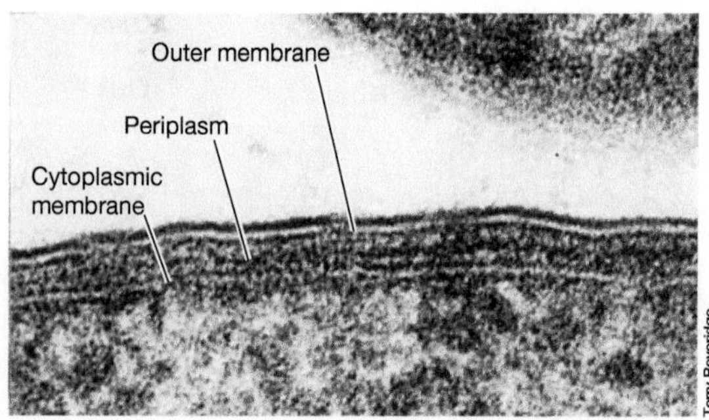

Figure 24 The cell wall of *Escherichia coli* as seen by the electron microscope. High-magnification thin section transmission electron micrograph of the cell envelope of *E. coli* showing the periplasm bounded by the outer and cytoplasmic membranes.

outer membrane through which very small substances can travel (Figure 23*b*).

The Periplasm

Although permeable to small molecules, the outer membrane is not permeable to enzymes or other large molecules. In fact, one of the major functions of the outer membrane is to keep proteins that are present outside the cytoplasmic membrane from diffusing away from the cell. These proteins are present in a region called the **periplasm** (see Figure 23 and Figure 24). This space, located between the outer surface of the cytoplasmic membrane and the inner surface of the outer membrane, is about 15 nm wide. The periplasm contents are gel-like in consistency because of the high concentration of proteins present there.

The periplasm can contain several different classes of proteins. These include hydrolytic enzymes, which function in the initial degradation of food molecules; binding proteins, which begin the process of transporting substrates (Section 5); and chemoreceptors, which are proteins involved in the chemotaxis response (Section 15). Most of these proteins reach the periplasm by way of the Sec protein exporting transport system in the cytoplasmic membrane (Section 5).

Relationship of Cell Wall Structure to the Gram Stain

The structural differences between the cell walls of gram-positive and gram-negative *Bacteria* are thought to be responsible for differences in the Gram stain reaction. In the Gram stain, an insoluble crystal violet–iodine complex forms inside the cell. This complex is extracted by alcohol from gram-negative but not from gram-positive bacteria. As we have seen, gram-positive bacteria have very thick cell walls consisting of several layers of peptidoglycan (Figure 20); these become dehydrated by the alcohol, causing the pores in the walls to close and preventing the insoluble crystal violet–iodine complex from escaping. By contrast, in gram-negative bacteria, alcohol readily penetrates the lipid-rich outer membrane and extracts the crystal violet–iodine complex from the cell. After alcohol treatment, gram-negative cells are nearly invisible unless they are counterstained with a second dye, a standard procedure in the Gram stain.

7 MiniReview

In addition to peptidoglycan, gram-negative bacteria have an outer membrane consisting of LPS, protein, and lipoprotein. Proteins called porins allow for permeability across the outer membrane. The space between the outer and cytoplasmic membranes is the periplasm, which contains various proteins involved in important cellular functions.

- What components constitute the LPS layer of gram-negative bacteria?
- What is the function of porins and where are they located in a gram-negative cell wall?
- What component of the cell has endotoxin properties?
- Why does alcohol readily decolorize gram-negative but not gram-positive bacteria?

8 Cell Walls of *Archaea*

Peptidoglycan, the "signature" molecule in the cell walls of *Bacteria*, is absent from the cell walls of *Archaea*. An outer membrane is typically lacking in *Archaea* as well. Instead, a variety of chemistries are found in the cell walls of *Archaea*, including polysaccharides, proteins, and glycoproteins.

Pseudomurein

The cell walls of certain methanogenic *Archaea* (species that produce methane, natural gas), contain a polysaccharide that is very similar to peptidoglycan, a polysaccharide called *pseudomurein* (the term "murein" has Latin roots meaning "wall" and was an old term for peptidoglycan; Figure 25). The backbone of pseudomurein is composed of alternating repeats of *N*-acetylglucosamine (also found in peptidoglycan) and *N*-acetyltalosaminuronic acid; the latter replaces the *N*-acetylmuramic acid of peptidoglycan (compare Figures 18 and 25). Pseudomurein also differs from peptidoglycan in that the glycosidic bonds between the sugar derivatives are β-1,3 instead of β-1,4, and the amino acids are all of the L stereoisomer.

Peptidoglycan and pseudomurein are remarkably similar molecules, yet they are chemically distinct. It is likely that they arose either by convergent evolution after the two prokaryotic domains of life had separated or by divergence from a common polysaccharide present in the cell walls of prokaryotic cells before the divergence of the domain *Bacteria* from the domain *Archaea*.

Other Polysaccharide Cell Walls

Cell walls of some other *Archaea* lack pseudomurein and contain other polysaccharides. For example, *Methanosarcina*

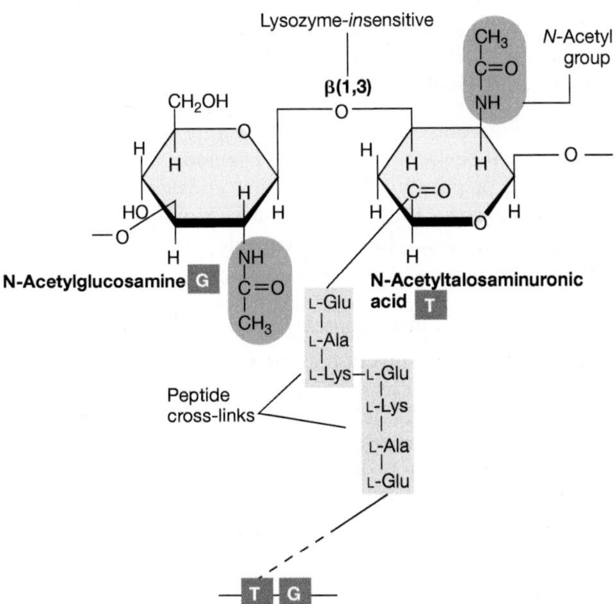

Figure 25 **Pseudomurein.** Structure of pseudomurein, the cell wall polymer of *Methanobacterium* species. Note the similarities and differences between pseudomurein and peptidoglycan (Figure 18).

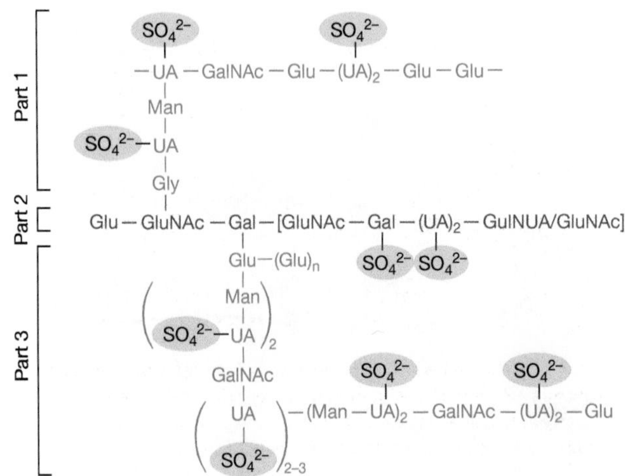

Figure 26 **Polysaccharide cell walls of *Archaea*.** Shown is the cell wall structure of *Halococcus*, an extreme halophile. The wall consists of a repeating three-part structure. UA, uronic acid; Glu, glucose; Gal, galactose; GluNAc, *N*-acetylglucosamine, GalNAc, *N*-acetylgalactosamine; Gly, glycine; GulNUA, *N*-acetylgulosaminuronic acid; Man, mannose.

species have thick polysaccharide walls composed of glucose, glucuronic acid, uronic acid galactosamine, and acetate. Extremely halophilic (salt-loving) *Archaea* such as *Halococcus* have cell walls similar to that of *Methanosarcina* but which contain, in addition, sulfate (SO_4^{2-}) (Figure 26). The negatively charged sulfate groups bind the high concentration of Na^+ present in the habitats of *Halococcus,* salt evaporation ponds and saline seas and lakes, helping to stabilize the cell wall in such polar environments. We will see later that *Methanosarcina* and the extreme halophiles are phylogenetically closely related, so their similarities in cell wall structure are not surprising.

S-Layers

The most common cell wall type among the *Archaea* is the paracrystalline surface layer, or **S-layer**. S-layers consist of protein or glycoprotein and show an ordered appearance when viewed with the electron microscope (Figure 27). The paracrystalline structure of S-layers becomes arranged into various symmetries, such as hexagonal, tetragonal, or trimeric, depending upon the number and structure of the protein or glycoprotein subunits of which they are composed. S-layers have been found in representatives of all major groups of *Archaea,* the extreme halophiles, the methanogens, and the hyperthermophiles. Several species of *Bacteria* also have S-layers on their outer surfaces (Figure 27).

The cell walls of some *Archaea,* for example that of the methanogen *Methanococcus jannaschii,* consist of only a single S-layer. Thus, S-layers are themselves sufficiently strong to withstand osmotic bursting. However, in many organisms S-layers are present in addition to other cell wall components, usually polysaccharides. For example, in *Bacillus brevis,* a species of *Bacteria*, an S-layer is present along with peptidoglycan. When an S-layer is present along with other wall components, the S-layer is always the outermost wall layer. Besides serving as structural reinforcement, S-layers may have other functions. For example, as the interface between the cell and its environment, it is likely that the S-layer functions as a selective sieve, allowing the passage of low-molecular-weight substances and excluding large molecules and structures (such as viruses). The S-layer may also function to retain proteins near the cell surface, much as the outer membrane (Section 7) does in gram-negative bacteria.

Other Archaeal Cell Walls

Natronococcus is a haloalkaliphilic species of *Archaea* that thrives in highly alkaline and saline habitats, such as soda lakes. *Natronococcus* contains a glycoprotein cell wall that is not a typical S-layer. This is because the glycoprotein contains only a single type of amino acid, L-glutamate, as a backbone from which glucose and glucose derivatives are linked. Interestingly, polyglutamate protein surface layers are known from some *Bacteria* as well, most notably, that of *Bacillus anthracis,* the causative agent of anthrax. But a glycoprotein containing glutamic acid as the sole amino acid has been found only in *Natronococcus*.

In species of *Archaea* we thus see several cell wall chemistries, varying from molecules that closely resemble peptidoglycan to those lacking a polysaccharide component. But with rare exception, all *Archaea* contain a cell wall of some

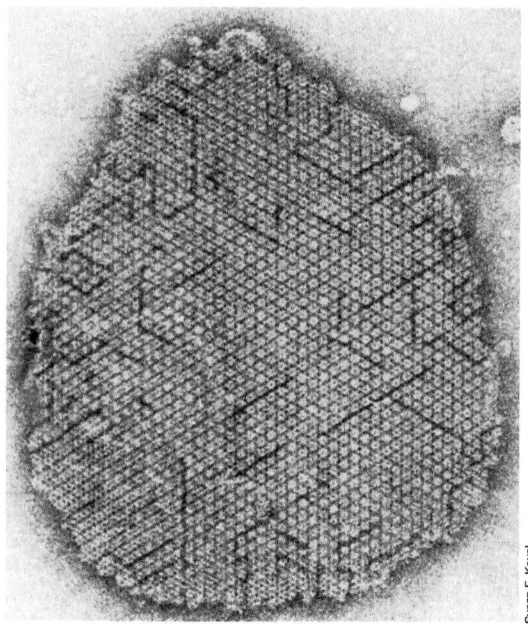

Figure 27 **The S-Layer.** Transmission electron micrograph of an S-layer showing the paracrystalline structure. Shown is the S-layer from *Aquaspirillum serpens* (a species of *Bacteria*); this S-layer shows hexagonal symmetry as is common in S-layers of *Archaea* as well.

sort, and as in *Bacteria*, the archaeal cell wall functions to prevent osmotic lysis and gives the cell its shape. In addition, because they lack peptidoglycan in their cell walls, *Archaea* are naturally resistant to the activity of lysozyme (Section 6) and the antibiotic penicillin, agents that either destroy peptidoglycan or prevent its proper synthesis.

8 MiniReview

The cell walls of *Archaea* are of several types, including pseudomurein, various types of polysaccharides, S-layers, and other protein or glycoprotein cell walls.

- How does pseudomurein resemble peptidoglycan? How do the two molecules differ?
- What is the composition of an S-layer?
- Why are *Archaea* insensitive to penicillin?

IV OTHER CELL SURFACE STRUCTURES AND INCLUSIONS

In addition to cell walls, prokaryotic cells can have other outer layers or structures in contact with the environment. Moreover, cells often contain one or more types of cellular inclusions. We examine some of these structures here.

9 Cell Surface Layers, Pili, and Fimbriae

Many prokaryotic organisms secrete slimy or sticky materials on their cell surface. These materials consist of either polysaccharide or protein. These are not considered part of the cell wall because they do not confer significant structural strength on the cell. The terms "capsule" and "slime layer" are used to describe these layers.

Capsules and Slime Layers

Capsules and slime layers may be thick or thin and rigid or flexible, depending on their chemistry and degree of hydration. If the material is organized in a tight matrix that excludes small particles, such as India ink, it is called a **capsule** (Figure 28). If the material is more easily deformed, it will not exclude particles and is more difficult to see; this form is called a *slime layer*. In addition, capsules are typically

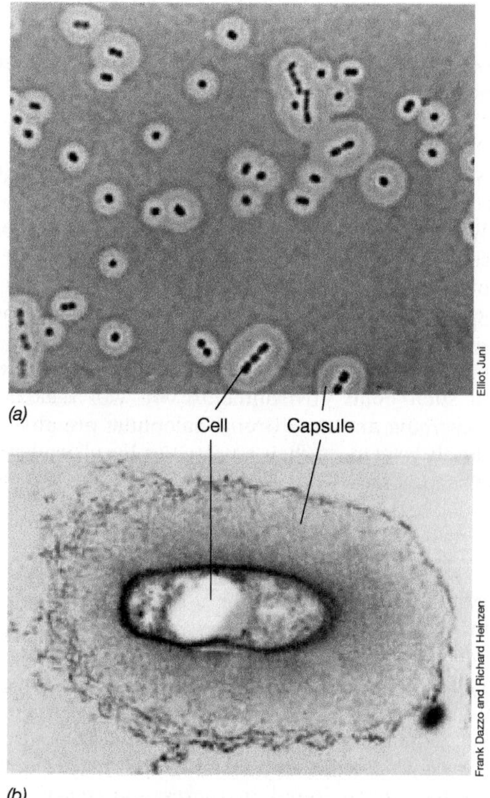

Figure 28 **Bacterial capsules.** *(a)* Capsules of *Acinetobacter* species observed by negative staining cells with India ink and phase-contrast microscopy. India ink does not penetrate the capsule and so the capsule appears as a light area surrounding the cell, which appears black. *(b)* Electron micrograph of a thin section of a cell of *Rhizobium trifolii* stained with ruthenium red to reveal the capsule. The diameter of the cell proper (not including the capsule) is about 0.7 μm.

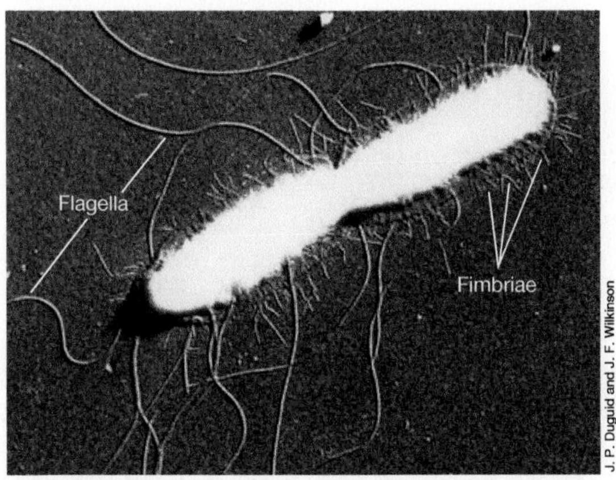

Figure 29 **Fimbriae.** Electron micrograph of a dividing cell of *Salmonella typhi*, showing flagella and fimbriae. A single cell is about 0.9 μm wide.

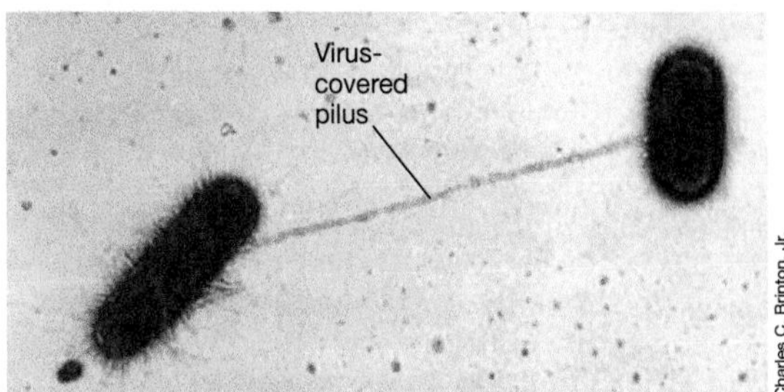

Figure 30 **Pili.** The pilus on an *Escherichia coli* cell that is undergoing genetic transfer with a second cell is revealed by the viruses that have adhered to it. The cells are about 0.8 μm wide.

firmly attached to the cell wall, whereas slime layers are loosely attached and can be lost from the cell surface.

Polysaccharide layers have several functions in bacteria. Surface polysaccharides assist in the attachment of microorganisms to solid surfaces. As we will see later, pathogenic microorganisms that enter the animal body by specific routes usually do so by first binding specifically to surface components of host tissues. This binding is often mediated by surface polysaccharides on the bacterial cell. Many nonpathogenic bacteria also bind to solid surfaces in nature, sometimes forming a thick layer of cells called a *biofilm*. Extracellular polysaccharides play a key role in the development of biofilms.

Polysaccharide outer layers play other roles as well. For example, encapsulated pathogenic bacteria are typically more difficult for phagocytic cells of the immune system to recognize and subsequently destroy. In addition, because outer polysaccharide layers bind a significant amount of water, it is likely that these layers play some role in resistance of the cell to desiccation.

Fimbriae and Pili

Fimbriae and pili are filamentous structures composed of protein that extend from the surface of a cell and can have many functions. *Fimbriae* (Figure 29) enable organisms to stick to surfaces, including animal tissues in the case of some pathogenic bacteria, or to form pellicles (thin sheets of cells on a liquid surface) or biofilms on surfaces. Notorious among human pathogens in which these structures assist in the disease process include *Salmonella* species (salmonellosis), *Neisseria gonorrhoeae* (gonorrhea), and *Bordetella pertussis* (whooping cough).

Pili are similar to fimbriae but are typically longer structures, and only one or a few pili are present on the surface of a cell. Because pili can be receptors for certain types of viruses, they can best be seen under the electron microscope when they become coated with virus particles (Figure 30). Although they may attach to surfaces as do fimbriae, pili also have other functions. A very important function is facilitating genetic exchange between prokaryotic cells in the process of conjugation.

Many classes of pili are known, distinguished by their structure and function. One class, called *type IV pili*, performs an unusual form of cell motility called *twitching motility*. Type IV pili are 6 nm in diameter and can extend for several micrometers away from the cell surface. Twitching motility is a type of gliding motility, movement along a solid surface (Section 14). In twitching motility, extension of the pili followed by their retraction drag the cell along a solid surface. Energy for twitching motility is supplied by ATP hydrolysis. Certain species of *Pseudomonas* and *Moraxella* are well known for their twitching motility.

Unlike other pili, type IV pili are present only at the poles of rod-shaped cells. Type IV pili have been implicated as key colonization factors for certain human pathogens, including *Vibrio cholerae* (cholera) and *Neisseria gonorrhoeae*. The twitching motility of these pathogens presumably assists the organisms in their movement across host tissues. Type IV pili are also thought to mediate genetic transfer by the process of transformation.

9 MiniReview

Many prokaryotic cells contain capsules, slime layers, pili, or fimbriae. These structures have several functions, including attachment, genetic exchange, and twitching motility.

- Could a bacterial cell dispense with a cell wall if it had a capsule? Why or why not?
- How do fimbriae differ from pili, both structurally and functionally?

10 Cell Inclusions

Granules or other inclusions are often present in prokaryotic cells. Inclusions function as energy reserves or as a reservoir of structural building blocks such as carbon. Inclusions can

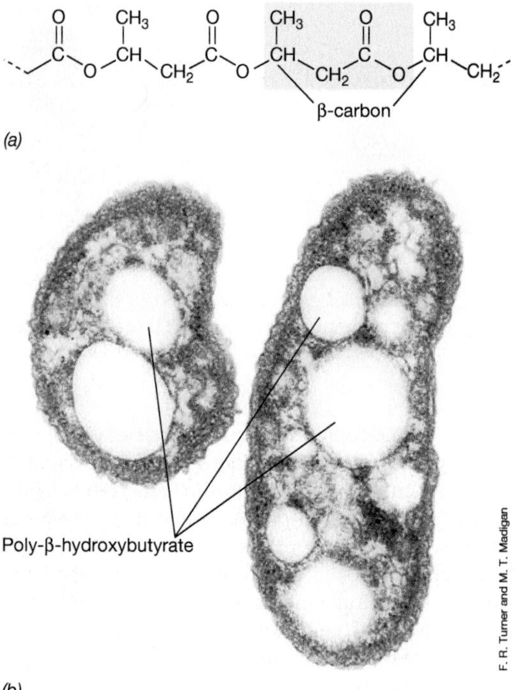

Figure 31 Poly-β-hydroxybutyrate (PHB). *(a)* Chemical structure of PHB, a common poly-β-hydroxyalkanoate. A monomeric unit is shown in color. Other alkanoate polymers are made by substituting longer-chain hydrocarbons for the $-CH_3$ group on the β carbon. *(b)* Electron micrograph of a thin section of cells of the phototrophic bacterium *Rhodovibrio sodomensis* containing granules of PHB.

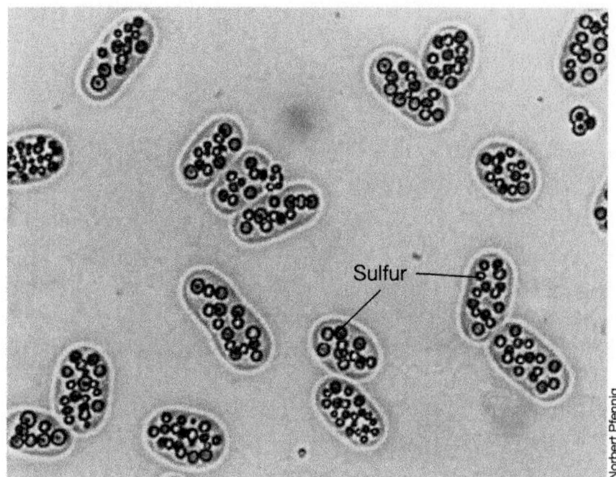

Figure 32 Sulfur globules. Bright-field photomicrograph of cells of the purple sulfur bacterium *Isochromatium buderi*. The intracellular inclusions are sulfur globules formed from the oxidation of hydrogen sulfide (H_2S). A single cell measures 4 × 7 μm.

often be seen directly with the light microscope and are typically enclosed by structurally atypical membranes that partition them off in the cell. Storing carbon or other substances in an insoluble form is advantageous to the cell because it reduces the osmotic stress that would be encountered if the same amount of the substance was stored in soluble form within the cytoplasm.

Carbon Storage Polymers

One of the most common inclusion bodies in prokaryotic organisms consists of **poly-β-hydroxybutyric acid (PHB)**, a lipid that is formed from β-hydroxbutyric acid units (Figure 31*a*). The monomers of PHB bond by ester linkage to form the long PHB polymer, and then the polymer aggregates into granules (Figure 31*b*). The length of the monomer in the polymer can vary considerably, from as short as C_4 to as long as C_{18}. Thus, the more generic term poly-β-hydroxyalkanoate (PHA) is used to describe this whole class of carbon- and energy-storage polymers. PHAs are synthesized when there is an excess of carbon and are broken down for use as carbon skeletons for biosynthesis or to make ATP when conditions warrant. Many prokaryotes, including species of both *Bacteria* and *Archaea*, produce PHAs.

Another storage product is *glycogen,* which is a polymer of glucose. Like PHAs, glycogen is a storehouse of both carbon and energy. Glycogen is produced when carbon is in excess in the environment and is consumed when carbon is limited. Glycogen resembles starch, the major storage reserve of plants, but differs from starch in the manner in which the glucose units are linked together.

Polyphosphate and Sulfur

Many microorganisms accumulate inorganic phosphate (PO_4^{2-}) in the form of granules of *polyphosphate*. These granules can be degraded and used as sources of phosphate for nucleic acid and phospholipid biosyntheses and in some organisms can be used to make the energy-rich compound ATP. Phosphate is often a limiting nutrient in natural environments. Thus if a cell happens upon an excess of phosphate, it is advantageous to store it as polyphosphate for future use.

Many gram-negative prokaryotes can oxidize reduced sulfur compounds, such as hydrogen sulfide (H_2S). The oxidation of sulfide is linked to either reactions of energy metabolism (chemolithotrophy) or phototrophic CO_2 fixation (autotrophy). In either case, *elemental sulfur* may accumulate inside the cell in readily visible globules (Figure 32). These globules of elemental sulfur remain as long as the source of reduced sulfur is still present. However, as the reduced sulfur source becomes limiting, the sulfur in the granules is oxidized to sulfate (SO_4^{2-}), and the granules slowly disappear as this reaction proceeds.

It has been shown that the sulfur globules of sulfur bacteria actually form in the periplasm of the cell rather than in the cytoplasm. The periplasm expands outward to accommodate the globules as H_2S is oxidized to S^0. The periplasm then contracts inward as S^0 is oxidized to SO_4^{2-}. It is likely that some of the other "cytoplasmic" inclusions that form in gram-negative bacteria are actually periplasmic as well. For example, granules of PHA in gram-negative cells (Figure 31) are almost certainly located in the periplasm.

Magnetic Storage Inclusions: Magnetosomes

Some bacteria can orient themselves specifically within a magnetic field because they contain **magnetosomes**. These structures are intracellular particles of the iron mineral magnetite—Fe_3O_4 (Figure 33). Magnetosomes impart a magnetic dipole on a cell, allowing it to respond to a magnetic field. Bacteria that produce magnetosomes exhibit *magnetotaxis,* the process of orienting and migrating along Earth's magnetic field lines. Although the suffix "*-taxis*" is used in the word magnetotaxis, there is no evidence that magnetotactic bacteria employ the sensory systems of chemotactic or phototactic bacteria (Section 15). Instead, the alignment of magnetosomes in the cell simply imparts a magnetic moment upon it, which then orients the cell in a particular direction in its environment.

The major function of magnetosomes is unknown. However, magnetosomes have been found in several aquatic organisms that grow best in laboratory cultures at low O_2 concentrations. It has thus been hypothesized that one function of magnetosomes may be to guide these aquatic cells downward (the direction of Earth's magnetic field) toward the sediments where O_2 levels are lower.

Magnetosomes are surrounded by a membrane containing phospholipids, proteins, and glycoproteins (Figure 33*b, c*). This membrane is not a unit membrane, as is the cytoplasmic membrane (Figure 5), but instead is a nonunit membrane, like that surrounding granules of PHB (Figure 31). Magnetosome membrane proteins probably play a role in precipitating Fe^{3+} (brought into the cell in soluble form by chelating agents) as Fe_3O_4 in the developing magnetosome. The morphology of magnetosomes appears to be species specific, varying in shape from square to rectangular to spike-shaped in different species, forming into chains inside the cell (Figure 33).

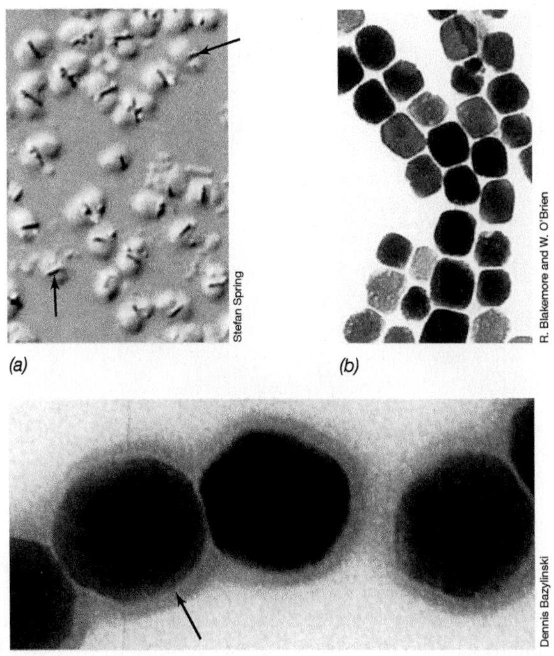

Figure 33 Magnetotactic bacteria and magnetosomes. *(a)* Differential interference contrast micrograph of coccoid magnetotactic bacteria. Note magnetosomes (arrows). A single cell is 2.2 μm wide. *(b)* Magnetosomes isolated from the magnetotactic bacterium *Magnetospirillum magnetotacticum*. Each particle is about 50 nm long. *(c)* Transmission electron micrograph of magnetosomes from a magnetic coccus. The arrow points to the membrane surrounding each magnetosome. A single magnetosome is about 90 nm wide.

10 MiniReview

Prokaryotic cells often contain inclusions of sulfur, polyphosphate, carbon polymers, or magnetosomes. These substances function as storage materials or in magnetotaxis.

- Under what growth conditions would you expect PHAs or glycogen to be produced?
- Why would it be impossible for gram-positive bacteria to store sulfur as sulfur-oxidizing chemolithotrophs can?
- What form of iron is present in magnetosomes?

11 Gas Vesicles

Some prokaryotes are *planktonic,* meaning that they live a floating existence within the water column of lakes and the oceans. These organisms can float because they contain **gas vesicles**. These structures confer buoyancy on cells, allowing them to position themselves in a water column in response to environmental factors.

The most dramatic examples of gas-vesiculate bacteria are cyanobacteria that form massive accumulations called *blooms* in lakes or other bodies of water (Figure 34). Gas-vesiculate cells rise to the surface of the lake and are blown by winds into dense masses. Certain purple and green phototrophic bacteria have gas vesicles, as do some nonphototrophic bacteria that live in lakes and ponds. Some *Archaea* also contain gas vesicles. Gas vesicles are absent from eukaryotes.

General Structure of Gas Vesicles

Gas vesicles are spindle-shaped gas-filled structures made of protein; they are hollow yet rigid and of variable length and diameter. Gas vesicles in different organisms vary in length from about 300 to more than 1000 nm and in width from 45 to 120 nm, but the vesicles of a given organism are more or less of constant size (Figure 35).

Figure 34 Buoyant cyanobacteria. Flotation of gas-vesiculate cyanobacteria in a bloom that formed in a nutrient-rich lake, Lake Mendota, Madison, Wisconsin, USA.

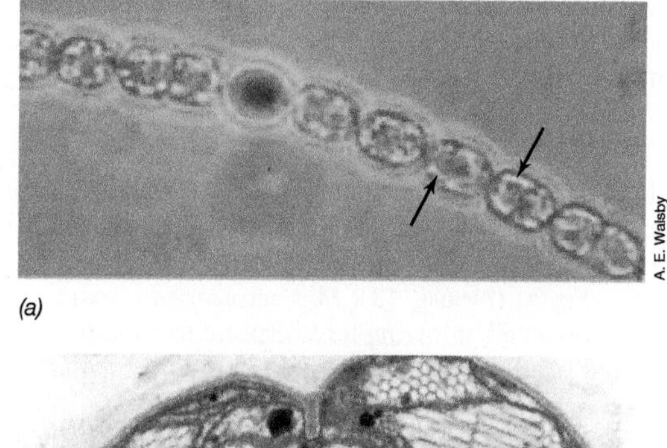

(a)

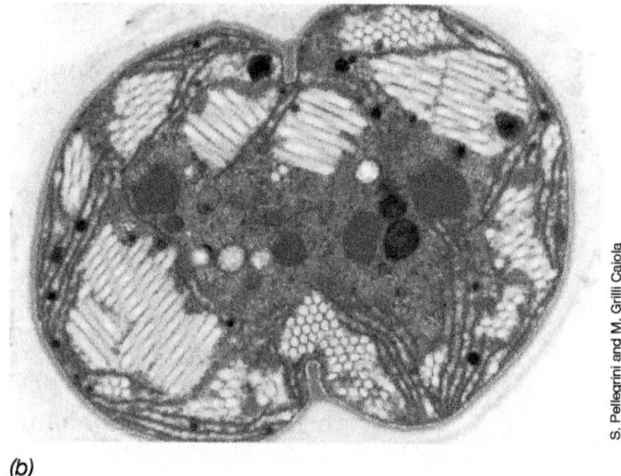

(b)

Figure 36 Gas vesicles of the cyanobacteria *Anabaena* and *Microcystis*. *(a) Anabaena flosaquae.* The dark cell in the center (a heterocyst) lacks gas vesicles. In the other cells, the vesicles group together as phase-bright clusters called gas vacuoles (arrows). *(b)* Transmission electron micrograph of the cyanobacterium *Microcystis.* Gas vesicles are arranged in bundles, here observable in both longitudinal and cross section.

Gas vesicles may number from a few to hundreds per cell. The gas-vesicle membrane is composed of protein, is about 2 nm thick, and is impermeable to water and solutes but permeable to gases. The presence of gas vesicles in cells can be determined either by light microscopy, where clusters of vesicles, called *gas vacuoles*, appear as irregular bright inclusions (Figure 34), or by electron microscopy (Figure 36).

Molecular Structure of Gas Vesicles

A gas vesicle is composed of two different proteins (Figure 37). The major gas vesicle protein, called *GvpA*, is a small, highly hydrophobic and very rigid protein. The rigidity is essential for the structure to resist the pressures exerted on it from outside. GvpA makes up the gas vesicle shell and composes 97% of total gas vesicle protein. The minor protein, called *GvpC,* functions to strengthen the shell of the gas vesicle.

Gas vesicles are biosynthesized when copies of GvpA align to form parallel "ribs" yielding a watertight shell. The GvpA ribs are strengthened by GvpC protein. GvpC cross-links GvpA at an angle, binding several GvpA molecules together like a clamp (Figure 37). The final shape of the gas vesicle can vary in different organisms from long and thin to short and fat (compare Figures 35 and 36*b*) and is a function of how the GvpA and GvpC proteins are arranged to form the intact vesicle.

How do gas vesicles confer buoyancy and what ecological benefit does buoyancy confer? The composition and

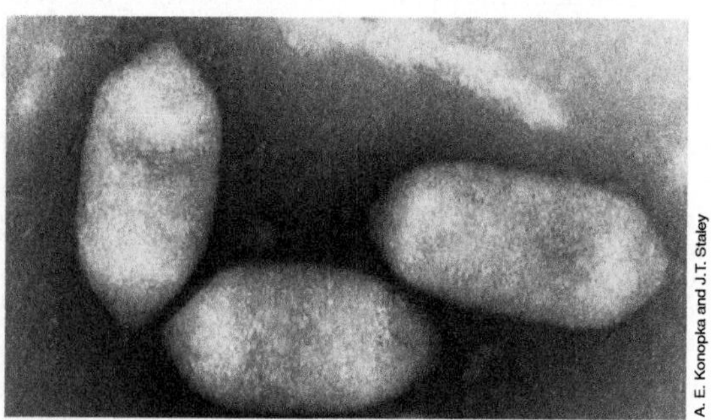

Figure 35 Gas vesicles. Transmission electron micrographs of gas vesicles purified from the bacterium *Ancyclobacter aquaticus* and examined in negatively stained preparations. A single gas vesicle is about 100 nm in diameter. [Reproduced with permission from *Archives of Microbiology* 112: 133–140 (1977).]

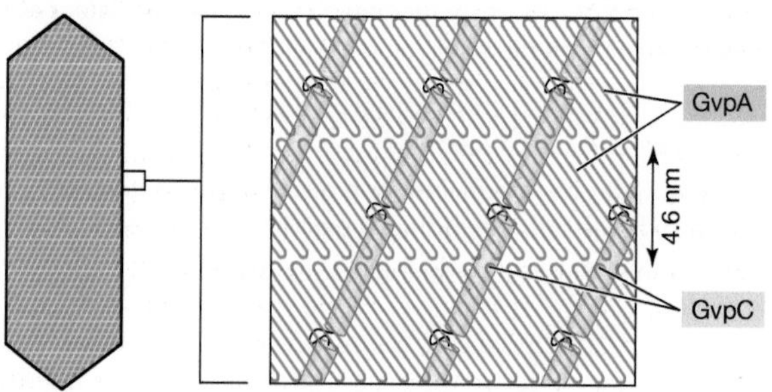

Figure 37 Gas vesicle proteins. Model of how the two proteins making up the gas vesicle, GvpA and GvpC, interact to form a watertight but gas-permeable structure. GvpA, a rigid β-sheet, makes up the rib, and GvpC, an α-helix structure, is the cross-linker.

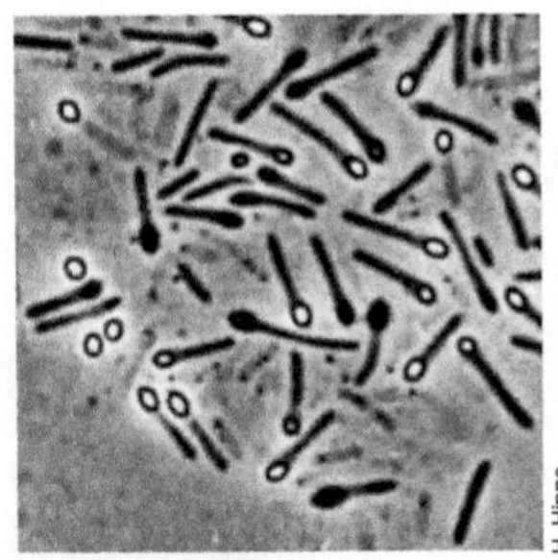

(*a*) **Terminal spores**

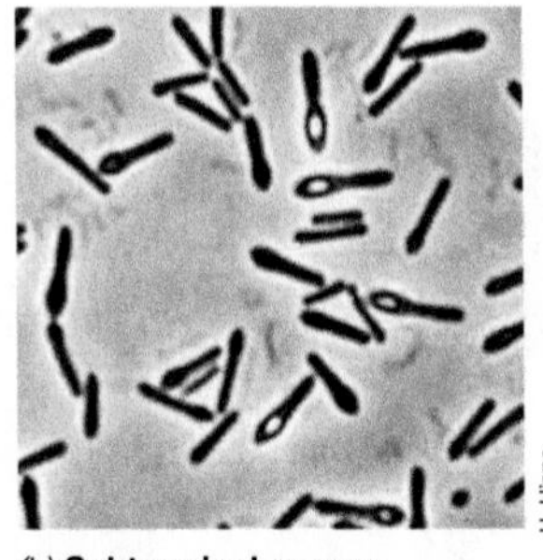

(*b*) **Subterminal spores**

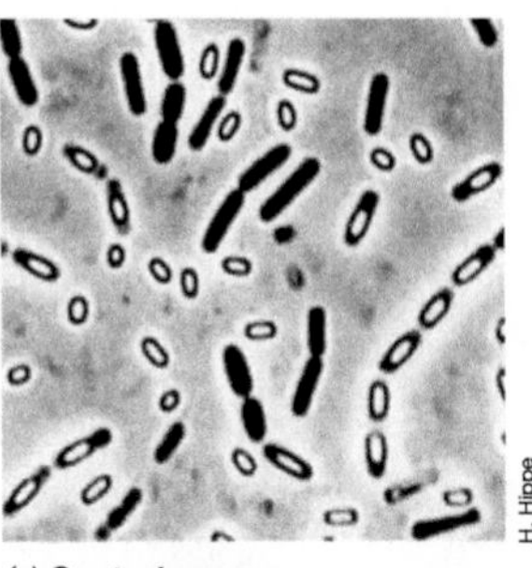

(*c*) **Central spores**

Figure 38 **The bacterial endospore.** Phase-contrast photomicrographs illustrating endospore morphologies and intracellular locations in different species of endospore-forming bacteria.

pressure of the gas inside a gas vesicle is the same as that of the gas in which the organism is suspended. However, because the inflated gas vesicle has a density of only some 5–20% of that of the cell proper, gas vesicles decrease the density of the cell, thereby increasing its buoyancy. Phototrophic organisms in particular can benefit from gas vesicles because they allow cells to adjust their position vertically in a water column to regions where the light intensity for photosynthesis is optimal.

11 MiniReview

Gas vesicles are intracellular gas-filled structures composed of proteins that function to confer buoyancy on cells. Gas vesicles contain two different proteins arranged to form a gas-permeable but watertight structure.

- What might be the benefit of gas vesicles to phototrophic cells? (*Hint*: What do phototrophs need to grow?).
- How are the two proteins that make up the gas vesicle, GvpA and GvpC, arranged to form such a water-impermeable structure?

12 Endospores

Certain species of *Bacteria* produce structures called **endospores** (Figure 38) during a process called *sporulation*. Endospores (the prefix "endo" means "within") are highly differentiated cells that are extremely resistant to heat, harsh chemicals, and radiation. Endospores function as survival structures and enable the organism to endure difficult times, including but not limited to extremes of temperature, drying, or nutrient depletion. Endospores can thus be thought of as the dormant stage of a bacterial life cycle: vegetative cell → endospore → vegetative cell. Endospores are also ideal structures for dispersal of an organism by wind, water, or through the animal gut. Endospore-forming bacteria are found most commonly in the soil, and the genera *Bacillus* and *Clostridium* are the best studied of endospore-forming bacteria.

Endospore Formation and Germination

During endospore formation, a vegetative cell is converted into a nongrowing, heat-resistant structure (Figure 39). Cells do not sporulate when they are actively growing but only when growth ceases owing to the exhaustion of an essential nutrient. Thus, cells of *Bacillus*, a typical endospore-forming bacterium, cease vegetative growth and begin sporulation when, for example, a key nutrient such as carbon or nitrogen becomes limiting.

An endospore can remain dormant for years, but it can convert back to a vegetative cell relatively rapidly. This process involves three steps: *activation*, *germination*, and *outgrowth* (Figure 40). Activation is most easily accomplished by heating freshly formed endospores for several minutes at an elevated but sublethal temperature. Activated endospores are then conditioned to germinate when placed in the presence of specific nutrients, such as certain amino acids (alanine is a particularly good trigger of endospore germination). Germination,

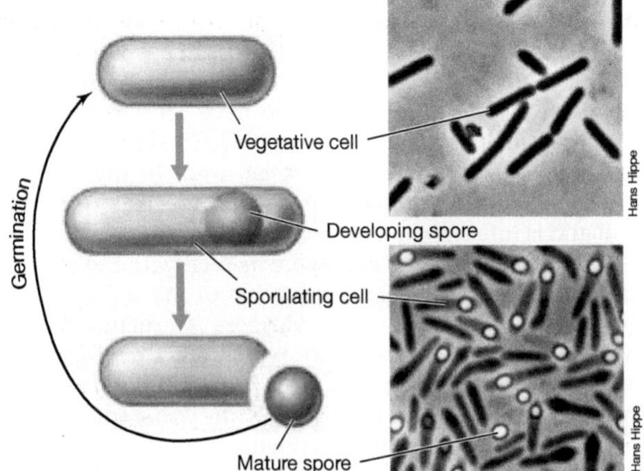

Figure 39 **The life cycle of an endospore-forming bacterium.** The phase-contrast photomicrographs are of cells of *Clostridium pascui*. A cell is about 0.8 μm wide.

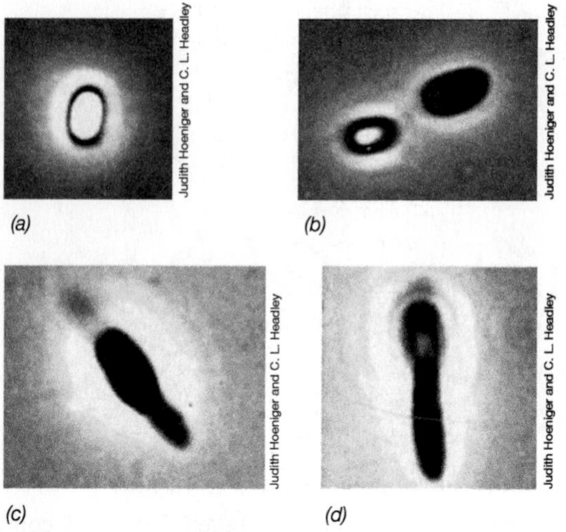

Figure 40 Endospore germination in *Bacillus*. Conversion of an endospore into a vegetative cell. The series of photomicrographs shows the sequence of events starting from a highly refractile mature endospore *(a)*. *(b)* (Activation) refractility is being lost. *(c)*, *(d)* The new vegetative cell is emerging (outgrowth).

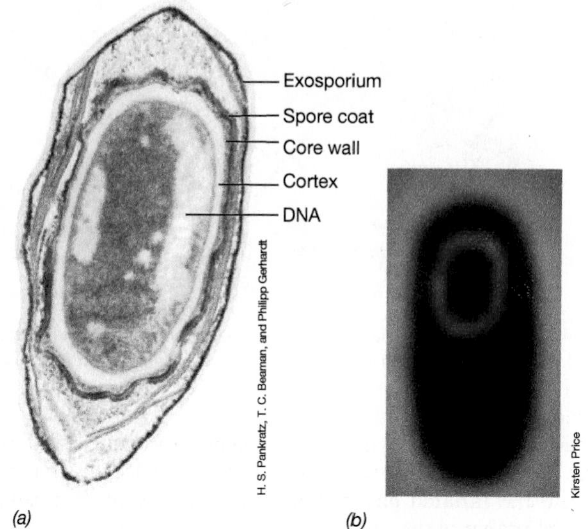

Figure 41 Structure of the bacterial endospore. *(a)* Transmission electron micrograph of a thin section through an endospore of *Bacillus megaterium*. *(b)* Fluorescent photomicrograph of a cell of *Bacillus subtilis* undergoing sporulation. The green area is due to a dye that specifically stains a sporulation protein in the spore coat.

usually a rapid process (on the order of several minutes), involves loss of microscopic refractility of the endospore, increased ability to be stained by dyes, and loss of resistance to heat and chemicals. The final stage, outgrowth, involves visible swelling due to water uptake and synthesis of new RNA, proteins, and DNA. The cell emerges from the broken endospore and begins to grow (Figure 40). The cell then remains in vegetative growth until environmental signals once again trigger sporulation.

Endospore Structure

Endospores stand out under the light microscope as strongly refractile structures (see Figures 38–40). Endospores are impermeable to most dyes, so occasionally they are seen as unstained regions within cells that have been stained with basic dyes such as methylene blue. To stain endospores, special stains and procedures must be used. In the classical endospore-staining protocol, malachite green is used as a stain and is infused into the spore with steam.

The structure of the endospore as seen with the electron microscope differs distinctly from that of the vegetative cell (Figure 41). In particular, the endospore is structurally more complex in that it has many layers that are absent from the vegetative cell. The outermost layer is the *exosporium*, a thin protein covering. Within this are the *spore coats*, composed of layers of spore-specific proteins (Figure 41*b*). Below the spore coat is the *cortex*, which consists of loosely cross-linked peptidoglycan, and inside the cortex is the *core*, which contains the core wall, cytoplasmic membrane, cytoplasm, nucleoid, ribosomes, and other cellular essentials. Thus, the endospore differs structurally from the vegetative cell primarily in the kinds of structures found outside the core wall.

One substance that is characteristic of endospores but absent from vegetative cells is **dipicolinic acid** (Figure 42*a*). This substance has been found in the endospores of all endospore-forming bacteria examined and is located in the core. Endospores are also enriched in calcium (Ca^{2+}), most of which is complexed with dipicolinic acid (Figure 42*b*). The calcium–dipicolinic acid complex of the core represents about 10% of the dry weight of the endospore. The complex functions to reduce water availability within the endospore, thus helping to dehydrate it. In addition, the complex intercalates (inserts between bases) in DNA, and in so doing stabilizes DNA to heat denaturation.

The Endospore Core and SASPs

Although both contain a copy of the chromosome and other essential cellular components, the core of a mature endospore differs greatly from the vegetative cell from which it was formed. Besides the high levels of calcium dipicolinate (Figure 42), which help reduce the water content of the core, the core becomes greatly dehydrated during the sporulation process. The core of a mature endospore contains only 10–25% of the water content of the vegetative cell, and thus the consistency of the core cytoplasm is that of a gel. Dehydration of the core greatly increases the heat resistance of macromolecules within the spore. Some bacterial endospores survive heating to temperatures as high as 150°C, although 121°C, the standard for microbiological sterilization (121°C is autoclave temperature) kills the endospores of most species.

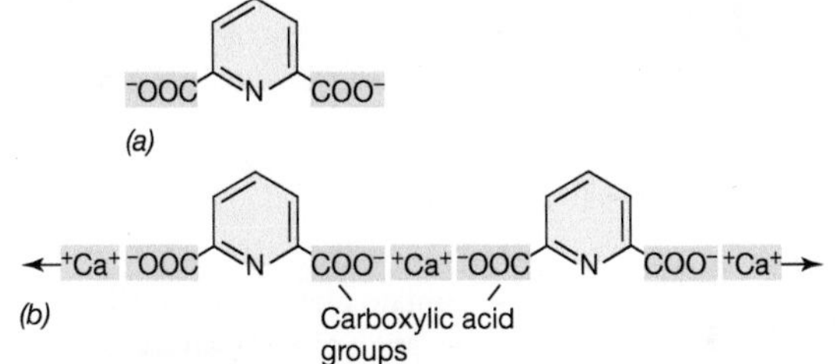

Figure 42 Dipicolinic acid (DPA). *(a)* Structure of DPA. *(b)* How Ca^{2+} cross-links DPA molecules to form a complex.

Boiling has essentially no negative effect on endospores. Dehydration has also been shown to confer resistance in the endospore to chemicals, such as hydrogen peroxide (H_2O_2) and causes enzymes remaining in the core to become inactive. In addition to the low water content of the endospore, the pH of the core is about one unit lower than that of the vegetative cell cytoplasm.

The endospore core contains high levels of *small acid-soluble proteins* (SASPs). These proteins are made during the sporulation process and have at least two functions. SASPs bind tightly to DNA in the core and protect it from potential damage from ultraviolet radiation, desiccation, and dry heat. Ultraviolet resistance is conferred when SASPs change the molecular structure of DNA from the normal "B" form to the more compact "A" form. A-form DNA is more resistant to the formation of pyrimidine dimers by UV radiation, a means of mutation, and to the denaturing effects of dry heat. In addition, SASPs function as a carbon and energy source for the outgrowth of a new vegetative cell from the endospore during germination.

The Sporulation Process

Sporulation is a complex series of events in cellular differentiation; many genetically directed changes in the cell underlie the conversion from vegetative growth to sporulation. The structural changes occurring in sporulating cells of *Bacillus* are shown in Figure 43. Sporulation can be divided into several stages. In *Bacillus subtilis*, where detailed studies have been done, the entire sporulation process takes about 8 hours and begins with asymmetric cell division (Figure 43). Genetic studies of mutants of *Bacillus*, each blocked at one of the stages of sporulation shown in Figure 43, indicate that more than 200 genes are specific to the process. Sporulation requires that the synthesis of many proteins needed for vegetative cell functions cease and that specific endospore proteins be made. This is accomplished by the activation of several families of endospore-specific genes in response to an environmental trigger to sporulate. The proteins encoded by these genes catalyze the series of events leading from a moist,

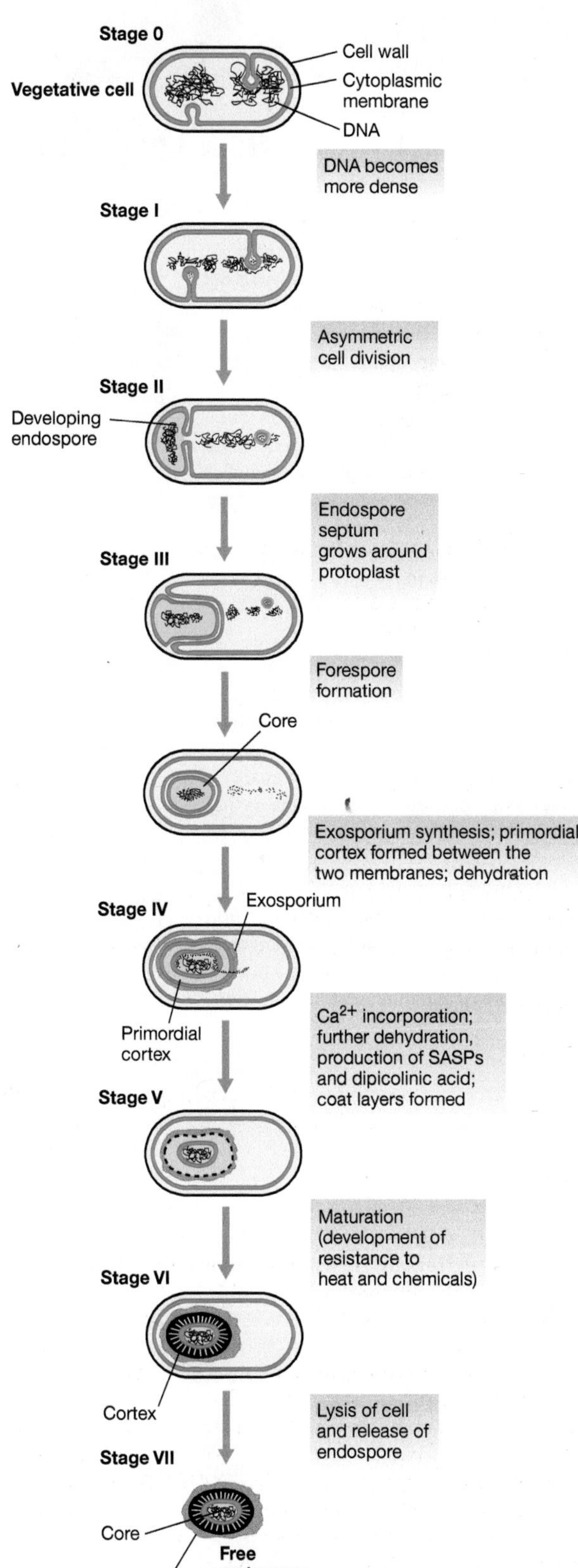

Figure 43 Stages in endospore formation. Stages 0 through VII are defined from genetic studies and microscopic analyses of sporulation in *Bacillus subtilis*.

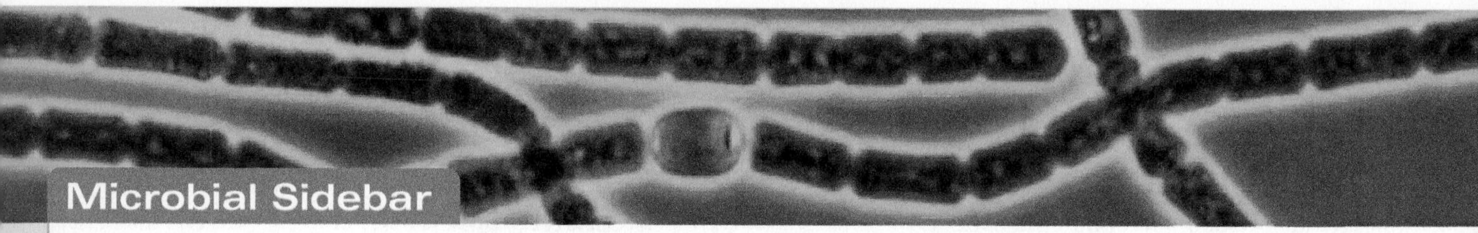

How Long Can an Endospore Survive?

In this chapter we have discussed the dormancy and resistance properties of bacterial endospores and have pointed out that endospores can survive for long periods in a dormant state. But how long is *long*?

Evidence for endospore longevity suggests that these structures can remain viable (that is, capable of germination into vegetative cells) for at least several decades and probably for much longer than that. For example, a suspension of endospores of the bacterium *Clostridium aceticum* (Figure 1a) prepared in 1947 was placed in sterile growth medium in 1981, 34 years later, and in less than 12 h growth commenced, leading to a robust culture. *C. aceticum* was originally isolated by the Dutch scientist K.T. Wieringa in 1940 but was thought to have been lost until this vial of *C. aceticum* endospores was found in a storage room at the University of California at Berkeley and revived.[1] *C. aceticum* is an acetogen, a bacterium that makes acetate from $CO_2 + H_2$ or from glucose.

Other more dramatic examples of endospore longevity have been documented. Bacteria of the genus *Thermoactinomyces* are thermophilic endospore formers that are widespread in nature in soil, plant litter,

Figure 1 Longevity of endospores. *(a) A tube containing endospores from the bacterium* Clostridium aceticum *prepared on May 7, 1947. After remaining dormant for over 30 years, the endospores were suspended in a culture medium after which growth occurred within 12 h. (b) Halophilic bacteria trapped within salt crystals. These crystals (about 1 cm in diameter) were grown in the laboratory in the presence of* Halobacterium *cells (orange) that remain viable in the crystals. Crystals similar to these but of Permian age ($\approx$250 million years old) were reported to contain viable halophilic endosporulating bacteria.*

and fermenting plant material. Microbiological examination of a Roman archaeological site in the United Kingdom that was dated to more than 2,000 years ago yielded significant numbers of viable *Thermoactinomyces* endospores in various pieces of debris. Additionally, *Thermoactinomyces* endospores were recovered in fractions of sediment cores from a Minnesota lake known to be over 7,000 years old. Although contamination is always a possibility in such studies, samples in both of these cases were processed in such a way as to virtually rule out contamination with "recent" endospores.[2] Thus, endospores can probably last for several thousands of years, but is this the limit?

What factors could limit the age of an endospore? Cosmic radiation has been considered a major factor because it can introduce mutations in DNA.[2] It has been hypothesized that over periods of thousands of years, the cumulative effects of cosmic radiation could introduce so many mutations into the genome of an organism that even highly radiation-resistant structures such as endospores would succumb to the genetic damage. However, extrapolations from experimental assessments of the effect of

metabolizing, vegetative cell to a relatively dry, metabolically inert, but extremely resistant endospore (Table 3 and Figure 43).

Diversity and Phylogenetic Aspects of Endospore Formation

Nearly 20 genera of *Bacteria* have been shown to form endospores, although the process has only been studied in detail in a few species of *Bacillus* and *Clostridium*. Nevertheless, many of the secrets to endospore survival, like the formation of calcium–dipicolinate complexes (Figure 42) and the production of endospore-specific proteins, seem universal. Thus, although some of the details of sporulation may vary from one organism to the next, the general principles are likely the same in all endospore-forming bacteria.

From a phylogenetic perspective, the capacity to produce endospores is found only in a particular sublineage of the gram-positive bacteria. Despite this, the physiologies of endospore-forming bacteria are highly diverse and include anaerobes, aerobes, phototrophs, and chemolithotrophs. Considering this physiological diversity, the actual triggers for endospore formation may vary with different species and could include signals other than simple nutrient starvation, the major trigger for endospore formation in *Bacillus* and *Clostridium* species. Interestingly, no species of *Archaea* have

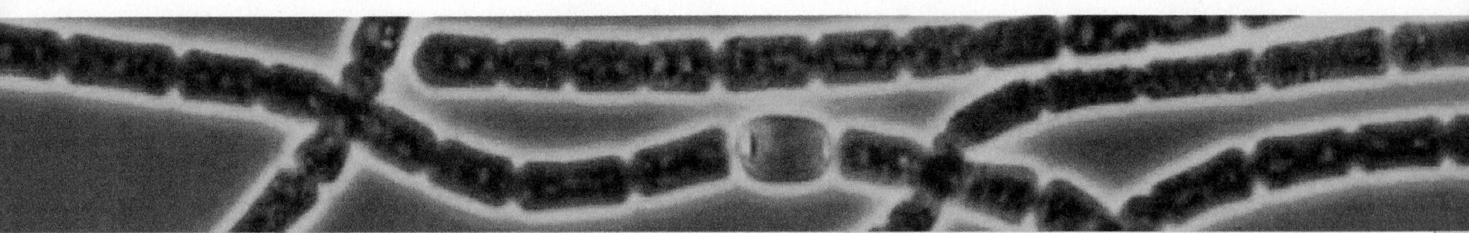

(continued)

natural radiation on endospores suggest that if suspensions of endospores were partially shielded from cosmic radiation, for example, by being embedded in layers of organic matter, such as in the Roman archaeological dig or the lake sediments described above, they could retain viability over periods as great as several hundred thousand years. Amazing, but is *this* the upper limit?

In 1995 a group of scientists reported the revival of bacterial endospores they claimed were 25–40 million years old.[3] The endospores were allegedly preserved in the gut of an extinct bee trapped in amber of known geological age. The presence of endospore-forming bacteria in these bees was previously suspected because electron microscopic studies of the insect gut showed endospore-like structures (Figure 41*a*) and because *Bacillus*-like DNA was recovered from the insect. Incredibly, samples of bee tissue incubated in a sterile culture medium quickly yielded endospore-forming bacteria. Rigorous precautions were taken to demonstrate that the endospore-forming bacterium revived from the amber-encased bee was not a modern-day contaminant. Subsequently, an even more spectacular claim was made that halophilic (salt-loving) endospore-forming bacteria had been isolated from fluid inclusions in salt crystals of Permian age, over 250 million years old.[4] Presumably, these cells were trapped in brines within the crystal (Figure 1*b*) as it formed eons ago and remained viable for more than a quarter billion years! Molecular experiments on even older material, 425 million-year-old halite, showed evidence for prokaryotic cells as well.[5]

If these astonishing claims are supported by repetition of the results in independent laboratories (and such confirmation is crucial in science for verifying controversial findings), then it appears that endospores stored under the proper conditions can remain viable indefinitely. This is remarkable testimony to a structure that probably evolved as a means of surviving relatively brief dormant periods or as a mechanism to withstand drying but that turned out to be so well designed that survival for millions of years may be possible.

[1]Braun, M., F. Mayer, and G. Gottschalk. 1981. *Clostridium aceticum* (Wieringa), a microorganism producing acetic acid from molecular hydrogen and carbon dioxide. *Arch. Microbiol. 128:* 288–293.

[2]Gest, H., and J. Mandelstam. 1987. Longevity of microorganisms in natural environments. *Microbiol. Sci. 4:* 69–71.

[3]Cano, R. J., and M. K. Borucki. 1995. Revival and identification of bacterial spores in 25- to 40-million-year-old Dominican amber. *Science 268:* 1060–1064.

[4]Vreeland, R.H., W.D. Rosenzweig, and D.W. Powers. 2000. Isolation of a 250 million-year-old halotolerant bacterium from a primary salt crystal. *Nature 407:* 897–900.

[5]Fish, S.A., T.J. Shepherd, T.J. McGenity, and W.D. Grant. 2002. Recovery of 16S ribosomal RNA gene fragments from ancient halite. *Nature 417:* 432–436.

been shown to form endospores, suggesting that the capacity to produce endospores evolved sometime after the major prokaryotic lineages diverged billions of years ago.

12 MiniReview

The endospore is a highly resistant and differentiated bacterial cell produced by certain gram-positive *Bacteria*. Endospores are highly dehydrated and contain essential macromolecules and various protective substances, including calcium dipicolinate and small acid-soluble proteins, absent from vegetative cells. Endospores can remain dormant indefinitely but can germinate quickly when conditions warrant.

- What is dipicolinic acid and where is it found?
- What are SASPs and what is their function?
- What happens when an endospore germinates?

V MICROBIAL LOCOMOTION

We finish our survey of microbial structure and function by examining cell locomotion. Many cells can move under their own power. Motility allows cells to reach different parts of their environment. In the struggle for survival, movement to a new location may offer a cell new resources and opportunities and spell the difference between life and death.

Table 3 Differences between endospores and vegetative cells

Characteristic	*Vegetative cell*	*Endospore*
Structure	Typical gram-positive cell; a few gram-negative cells	Thick spore cortex; Spore coat; exosporium
Microscopic appearance	Nonrefractile	Refractile
Calcium content	Low	High
Dipicolinic acid	Absent	Present
Enzymatic activity	High	Low
Metabolism (O_2 uptake)	High	Low or absent
Macromolecular synthesis	Present	Absent
mRNA	Present	Low or absent
DNA and ribosomes	Present	Present
Heat resistance	Low	High
Radiations resistance	Low	High
Resistance to chemicals (for example, H_2O_2) and acids	Low	High
Stainability by dyes	Stainable	Stainable only with special methods
Action of lysozyme	Sensitive	Resistant
Water content	High, 80–90%	Low, 10–25% in core
Small acid-soluble proteins (product of *ssp* genes)	Absent	Present
Cytoplasmic pH	About pH 7	About pH 5.5–6.0 (in core)

We examine here the two major types of cell movement, *swimming* and *gliding*. We then consider how motile cells are able to move in a directed fashion toward or away from particular stimuli (phenomena called *taxes*) and present examples of these simple behavioral responses.

13 Flagella and Motility

Many prokaryotes are motile by swimming, and this function is typically due to a structure called the **flagellum** (plural, flagella) (Figure 44). We see here that the flagellum functions by rotation to push or pull the cell through a liquid medium.

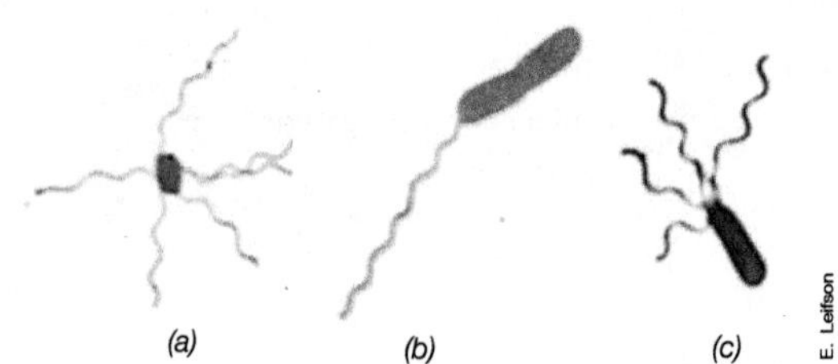

Figure 44 **Bacterial flagella.** Light photomicrographs of prokaryotes containing different arrangements of flagella. Cells are stained with Leifson flagella stain. *(a)* Peritrichous. *(b)* Polar. *(c)* Lophotrichous.

Flagella of *Bacteria*

Bacterial flagella are long, thin appendages free at one end and attached to the cell at the other end. Bacterial flagella are so thin (15–20 nm, depending on the species) that a single flagellum can be seen with the light microscope only after being stained with special stains that increase their diameter (Figure 44). However, flagella are easily seen with the electron microscope (Figure 45).

Flagella can be attached to cells in different patterns. In **polar flagellation**, the flagella are attached at one or both ends of the cell (Figures 44*b* and 45*a*). Occasionally a tuft (group) of flagella may arise at one end of the cell, a type of polar flagellation called *lophotrichous* ("lopho" means "tuft"; "trichous" means "hair") (Figure 44*c*). Tufts of flagella of this type can be seen in living cells by dark-field microscopy (Figure 46*a*), where the flagella appear light and are attached to light-colored cells against a dark background. In relatively large prokaryotes, tufts of flagella can also be observed by phase-contrast microscopy (Figure 46*b*). When a tuft of flagella emerges from both poles, flagellation is called *amphitrichous*. In **peritrichous flagellation** (Figures 44*a* and 45*b*), flagella are inserted at many locations around the cell surface ("*peri*" means "around"). The type of flagellation, polar or peritrichous, is a characteristic used in the classification of bacteria.

Flagellar Structure

Flagella are not straight but are helical. When flattened, flagella show a constant distance between adjacent curves, called

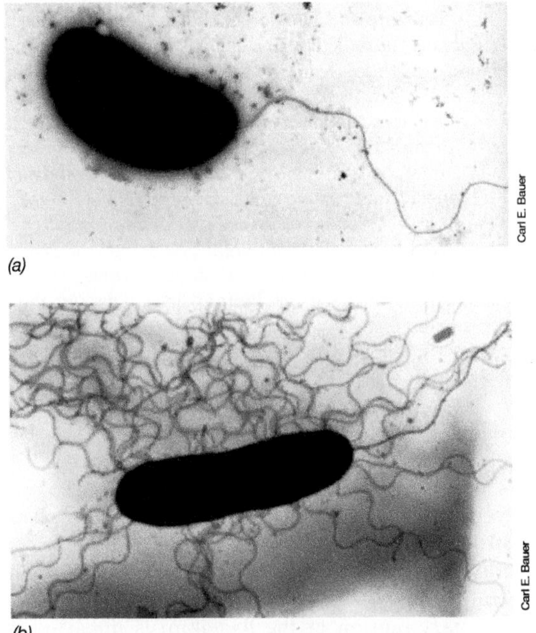

Figure 45 **Bacterial flagella as observed by negative staining in the transmission electron microscope.** *(a)* A single polar flagellum. *(b)* Peritrichous flagella. Both micrographs are of cells of the phototrophic bacterium *Rhodospirillum centenum*, which are about 1.5 μm wide. Cells of *R. centenum* are normally polarly flagellated but under certain growth conditions form peritrichously flagellated "swarmer" cells. See also Figure 55*b*.

the *wavelength*, and this wavelength is characteristic for the flagella of any given species (Figures 44–46). The filament of bacterial flagella is composed of many copies of a protein called *flagellin*. The shape and wavelength of the flagellum are in part determined by the structure of the flagellin protein and also to some extent by the direction of rotation of the filament. Flagellin is highly conserved in amino acid sequences in species of *Bacteria*, suggesting that flagellar motility has deep roots within this evolutionary domain.

A flagellum consists of several components and moves by rotation, much like a propeller of a boat motor. The base of the flagellum is structurally different from the filament (Figure 47a). There is a wider region at the base of the filament called the *hook*. The hook consists of a single type of protein and connects the filament to the motor portion in the base.

The motor is anchored in the cytoplasmic membrane and cell wall. The motor consists of a central rod that passes through a series of rings. In gram-negative bacteria, an outer ring, called the *L ring*, is anchored in the lipopolysaccharide layer. A second ring, called the *P ring*, is anchored in the peptidoglycan layer of the cell wall. A third set of rings, called the *MS* and *C rings*, are located within the cytoplasmic membrane and the cytoplasm, respectively (Figure 47*a*). In gram-positive bacteria, which lack an outer membrane, only the inner pair of rings is present. Surrounding the inner ring and anchored in the cytoplasmic membrane are a series of proteins called *Mot proteins*. A final set of proteins, called the *Fli proteins* (Figure 47*a*), function as the motor switch, reversing the direction of rotation of the flagella in response to intracellular signals.

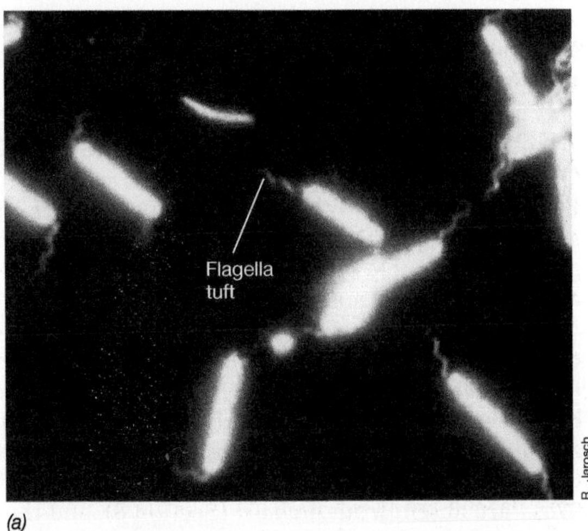

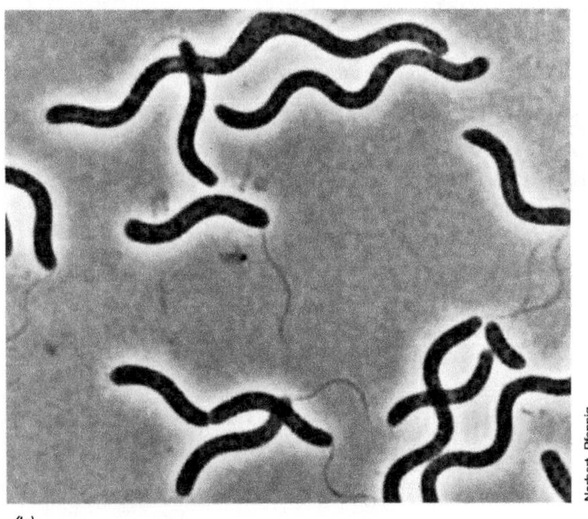

Figure 46 **Bacterial flagella observed in living cells.** *(a)* Dark-field photomicrograph of a group of large rod-shaped bacteria with flagellar tufts at each pole. A single cell is about 2 μm wide. *(b)* Phase-contrast photomicrograph of cells of the large phototrophic purple bacterium *Rhodospirillum photometricum* with lophotrichous flagella that emanate from one of the poles. A single cell measures about 3 × 30 μm.

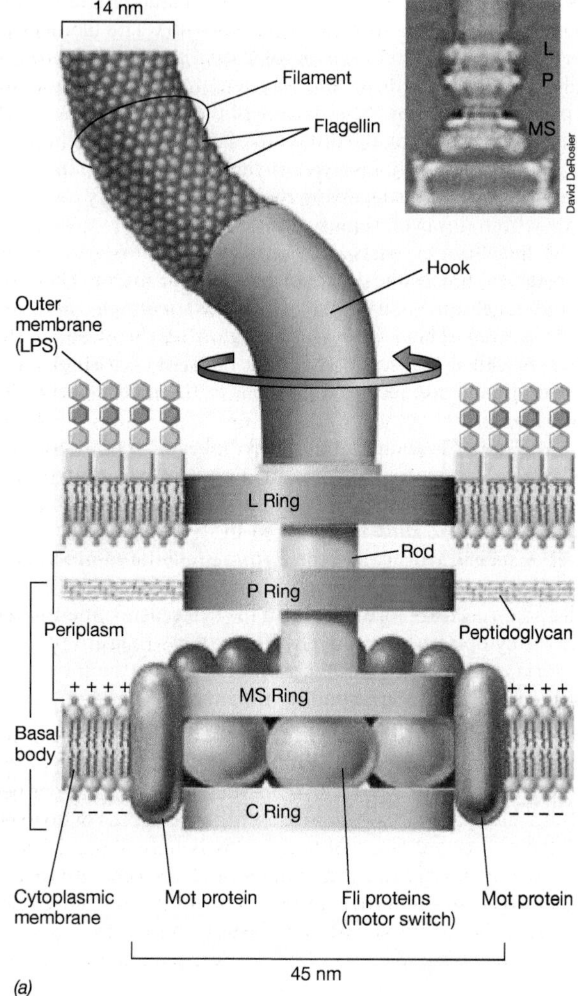

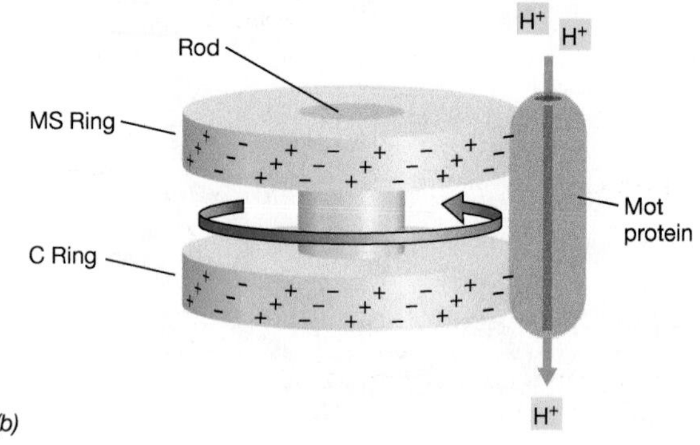

Figure 47 **Structure and function of the flagellum in gram-negative *Bacteria*.** *(a)* Structure. The L ring is embedded in the LPS and the P ring in peptidoglycan. The MS ring is embedded in the cytoplasmic membrane and the C ring in the cytoplasm. A narrow channel exists in the rod and filament through which flagellin molecules diffuse to reach the site of flagellar synthesis. The Mot proteins function as the flagellar motor, whereas the Fli proteins function as the motor switch. The flagellar motor rotates the filament to propel the cell through the medium. Inset: transmission electron micrograph of a flagellar basal body from *Salmonella enterica* with the various rings labeled. *(b)* Function. A "proton turbine" model has been proposed to explain rotation of the flagellum. Protons, flowing through the Mot proteins, may exert forces on charges present on the C and MS rings, thereby spinning the rotor. Electron micrograph from *J. Bacteriol. 183*: 6404–6412 (2001).

Flagellar Movement

The flagellum is a tiny rotary motor. How does this motor work? Rotary motors typically contain two main components: the *rotor* and the *stator*. In the flagellar motor, the rotor consists of the central rod and the L, P, C, and MS rings. Collectively, these structures make up the **basal body**. The stator consists of the Mot proteins that surround the basal body and function to generate torque.

The rotary motion of the flagellum is imparted by the basal body. The energy required for rotation of the flagellum comes from the proton motive force. Proton movement across the cytoplasmic membrane through the Mot complex (Figure 47) drives rotation of the flagellum; about 1000 protons are translocated per rotation of the flagellum. How this actually occurs is not yet known. However, a "proton turbine" model has been proposed to explain the results of experiments on flagellar function. In this model, protons flowing through channels in the stator exert electrostatic forces on helically arranged charges on the rotor proteins. Attractions positive and negative charges cause the basal body to rotate as protons flow though the stator (Figure 47*b*). www.microbiologyplace.com **Online Tutorial 1: The Prokaryotic Flagellum**

Archaeal Flagella

Flagellar motility is widespread among *Archaea*, as representatives of all of the major physiological and phylogenetic groups are capable of swimming motility. Archaeal flagella are significantly thinner than bacterial flagella, measuring only 10–14 nm in width (Figure 48). Archaeal flagella clearly rotate as they do in *Bacteria*, but the structure of the archaeal flagellar motor is not yet known. Recall that the components of the cell wall that play an important role in anchoring the flagellum in gram-negative *Bacteria*—peptidoglycan and the outer membrane in particular (Figure 47*a*)—are absent from *Archaea* (Section 8), and thus differences in the archaeal structure should be expected.

Unlike the situation in most *Bacteria* in which a single flagellin protein is present in the flagellar filament, several different flagellin proteins exist in *Archaea*. In addition, unlike those of most *Bacteria*, some archaeal flagellins are glycoproteins. The amino acid sequences of archaeal flagellins bear no relationship to that of bacterial flagellin. However, archaeal

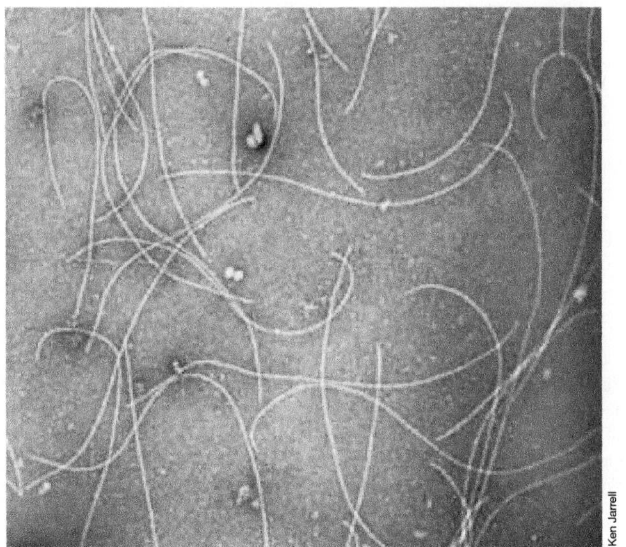

Figure 48 **Archaeal flagella.** Transmission electron micrograph of flagella isolated from cells of the methanogen *Methanococcus maripaludis*. A single flagellum is about 12 nm wide.

flagellins share certain molecular features with bacterial type IV pili, which function in other forms of motility (Sections 9 and 14). Studies of swimming cells of the extreme halophile *Halobacterium* show that they swim at speeds only about one-tenth that of cells of *Escherichia coli*. Whether this is typical for *Archaea* is unknown, but the significantly smaller diameter of the archaeal flagellum compared to the bacterial flagellum likely reduces the torque and, ultimately, the power of the flagellar motor such that slower swimming speeds would not be surprising.

Flagellar Synthesis

Several genes are required for flagellar synthesis and subsequent motility in *Bacteria*. In *E. coli* and *Salmonella typhimurium*, where studies have been most extensive, over 50 genes are involved in motility. These genes have several functions, including encoding structural proteins of the flagellar apparatus, export of flagellar components through the cytoplasmic membrane to the outside of the cell, and regulation of the many biochemical events surrounding the synthesis of new flagella.

A flagellar filament grows not from its base, as does an animal hair, but from its tip. The MS ring is synthesized first and inserted into the cytoplasmic membrane. Then other anchoring proteins are synthesized along with the hook before the filament forms (Figure 49). Flagellin molecules synthesized in the cytoplasm pass up through a 3-nm channel inside the filament and add on at the terminus to form the mature flagellum. At the end of the growing flagellum a protein "cap" exists. Cap proteins assist flagellin molecules that have diffused through the channel to organize at the flagellum termini to form new filament (Figure 49). Approximately 20,000 flagellin molecules are needed to make one filament. The flagellum grows more-or-less continuously until it reaches its final length. Broken flagella still rotate and can be repaired with new flagellin units passed through the filament channel to replace the lost ones.

Cell Speed and Motion

Flagella do not rotate at a constant speed but instead can increase or decrease their speed in relation to the strength of the proton motive force. They can rotate at up to 300 revolutions per second and can move cells through a liquid at speeds of up to 60 cell lengths/second (sec). Although this is only about 0.00017 kilometer/hour (km/h), when comparing this speed with that of higher organisms in terms of the number of lengths moved per second, it is extremely fast. The fastest animal, the cheetah, moves at a maximum rate of about 110 km/h, but this represents

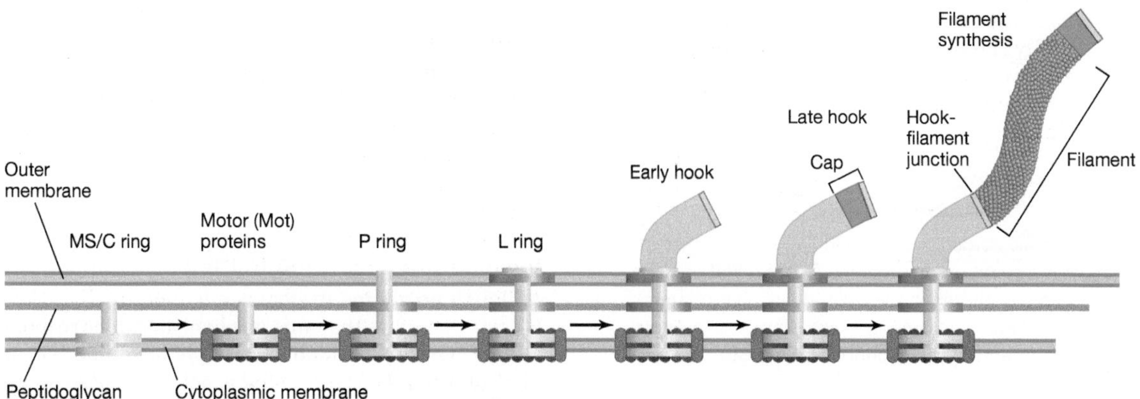

Figure 49 **Flagella biosynthesis.** Synthesis begins with assembly of MS and C rings in the cytoplasmic membrane. Then the other rings, the hook and the cap, form. At this point, flagellin protein flows through the hook to form the filament. Flagellin molecules are guided into position by cap proteins to ensure that the growing filament develops evenly.

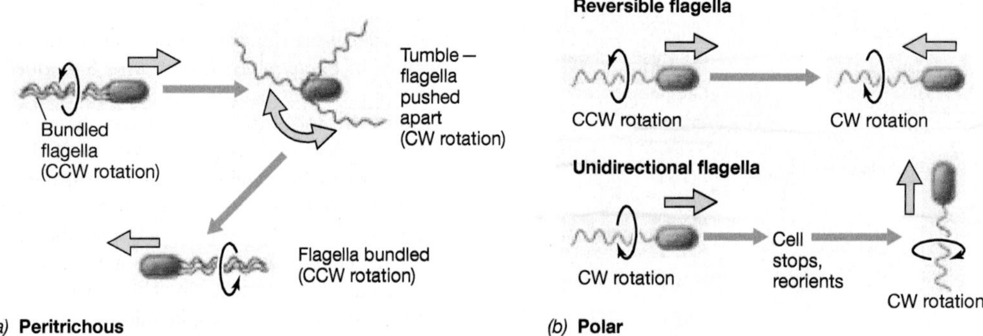

Figure 50 Movement in peritrichously and polarly flagellated prokaryotes. *(a)* Peritrichous: Forward motion is imparted by all flagella rotating counterclockwise (CCW) in a bundle. Clockwise (CW) rotation causes the cell to tumble, and then a return to counterclockwise rotation leads the cell off in a new direction. *(b)* Polar: Cells change direction by reversing flagellar rotation (thus pulling instead of pushing the cell) or, with unidirectional flagella, by stopping periodically to reorient, and then moving forward by clockwise rotation of its flagella. The yellow arrows show the direction the cell is traveling.

only about 25 body lengths/sec. Thus, when size is accounted for, prokaryotic cells swimming at 50–60 lengths/sec are actually moving faster than larger organisms!

The swimming motions of polarly and lophotrichously flagellated organisms differ from those of peritrichously flagellated organisms, and these can be distinguished by observing swimming cells under the microscope (Figure 50). Peritrichously flagellated organisms typically move in a straight line in a slow, deliberate fashion. Polarly flagellated organisms, on the other hand, move more rapidly, spinning around and seemingly dashing from place to place. The different behavior of flagella on polar and peritrichous organisms, including differences in reversibility of the flagellum, is illustrated in Figure 50.

Swimming speed is a genetically governed property because different motile species, even different species that have the same cell size, can swim at different maximum speeds. Moreover, when assessing the capacity of an organism for swimming motility and swimming speed, observations should only be made on young cultures. In old cultures, otherwise motile cells often stop swimming and the culture may appear to be nonmotile.

13 MiniReview

Motility in most microorganisms is due to flagella. In prokaryotes the flagellum is a complex structure made of several proteins, most of which are anchored in the cell wall and cytoplasmic membrane. The flagellum filament, which is made of a single kind of protein, rotates at the expense of the proton motive force, which drives the flagellar motor.

- How do flagella of *Bacteria* and *Archaea* compare?
- How does a bacterial flagellum move a cell forward? What is flagellin and where is it found?
- How does polar flagellation differ from peritrichous flagellation?

14 Gliding Motility

Some prokaryotes are motile but lack flagella. These nonswimming yet motile bacteria move across solid surfaces in a process called *gliding*. Unlike flagellar motility, in which cells stop and then start off in a different direction, gliding motility is a slower and smoother form of movement and typically occurs along the long axis of the cell. Gliding motility is widely distributed among *Bacteria* but has been well studied in only a few groups. The gliding movement itself—up to 10 μm/sec in some gliding bacteria—is considerably slower than propulsion by flagella but still offers the cell a means of moving about its habitat.

Gliding prokaryotes are filamentous or rod-shaped cells (Figure 51), and the gliding process requires that the cells be in contact with a solid surface. The morphology of colonies of a typical gliding bacterium (colonies are masses of bacterial cells that form from successive cell divisions of a single cell, are distinctive, because cells glide out and move away from the center of the colony (Figure 51*c*). Perhaps the most well-known gliding bacteria are the filamentous cyanobacteria (Figure 51*a, b*), certain gram-negative *Bacteria*, such as *Myxococcus* and other myxobacteria, and species of *Cytophaga* and *Flavobacterium* (Figure 51*c, d*).

Mechanisms of Gliding Motility

Although no gliding mechanism is thoroughly understood, it is clear that more than one mechanism can be responsible for gliding motility. Cyanobacteria (phototrophic bacteria, Figure 51*a, b*) glide by secreting a polysaccharide slime on the outer surface of the cell. The slime contacts both the cell surface and the solid surface against which the cell moves. As the excreted slime adheres to the surface, the cell is pulled along. This mechanism is supported by the identification of slime-excreting pores on the cell surface of gliding

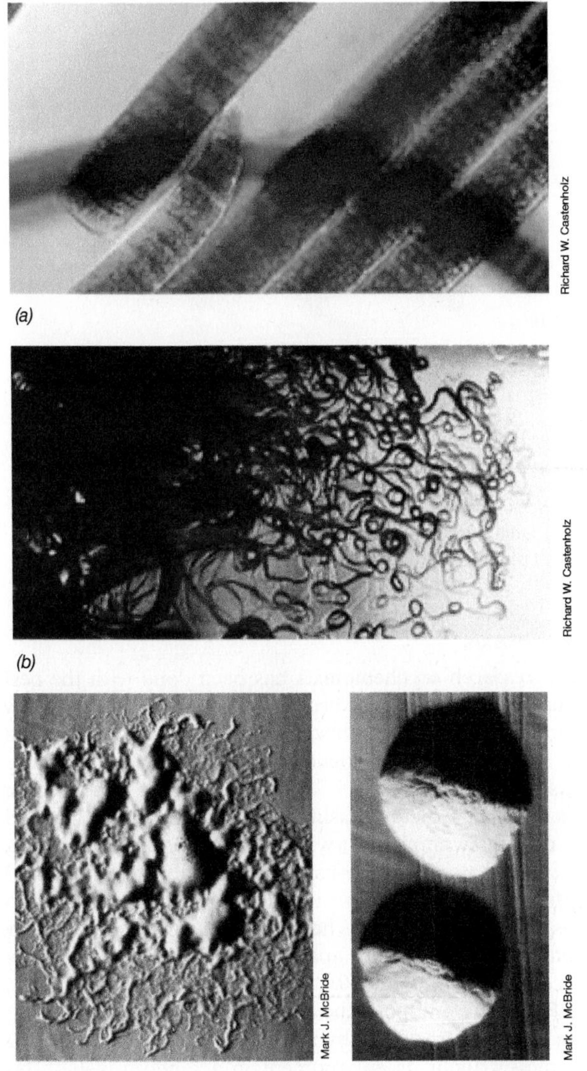

Figure 51 Gliding bacteria. *(a, b)* The large filamentous cyanobacterium *Oscillatoria princeps. (a)* A cell is about 35 μm wide. *(b)* Filaments of *O. princeps* gliding on an agar surface. *(c, d)* The gliding bacterium *Flavobacterium johnsoniae. (c)* Masses of cells gliding away from the center of the colony (the colony is about 2.7 mm wide). *(d)* Nongliding mutant strain showing typical colony morphology of nongliding bacteria (the colonies are 0.7–1 mm in diameter). See also Figure 52.

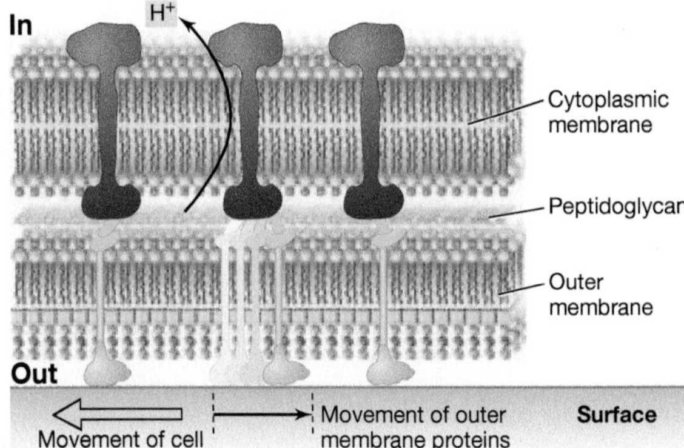

Figure 52 Gliding motility in *Flavobacterium johnsoniae*. Tracks (yellow) are thought to exist in the peptidoglycan that connect cytoplasmic proteins (brown) to outer membrane proteins (orange) and propel the outer membrane proteins along the solid surface. Note that the outer membrane proteins and the cell proper move in opposite directions.

filamentous cyanobacteria. The nonphototrophic gliding bacterium *Cytophaga* also moves at the expense of slime excretion, rotating along its long axis as it does.

As previously mentioned, cells capable of "twitching motility," also display a form of gliding motility using a mechanism by which repeated extension and retraction of type IV pili propel the cell along a surface (Section 9). The gliding myxobacterium *Myxococcus xanthus* has two forms of gliding motility. One form is driven by type IV pili whereas the other is distinct from either the type IV pili or the slime extrusion methods. In this form of *M. xanthus* motility a protein adhesion complex is formed at one pole of the rod-shaped cell and remains at a fixed position on the surface as the cell glides forward. This means that the adhesion complex moves in the direction opposite that of the cell, presumably fueled by some sort of cytoplasmic motility engine perhaps linked to the cell cytoskeleton. These different forms of motility can be expressed at the same time and are somehow coordinated by the cell, presumably in response to various signals from the environment (Section 15).

Neither slime extrusion nor twitching is the mechanism of gliding in other gliding bacteria. In *Flavobacterium johnsoniae* (Figure 51*c*), for example, no slime is excreted and the cells lack type IV pili. Instead, the movement of proteins on the cell surface may be the mechanism of gliding in this organism. Specific motility proteins anchored in the cytoplasmic and outer membranes are thought to propel cells of *F. johnsoniae* forward by a ratcheting mechanism (Figure 52). Movement of gliding-specific proteins in the cytoplasmic membrane is driven by energy from the proton motive force that is somehow transmitted to gliding-specific proteins in the outer membrane. It is thought that movement of these proteins against the solid surface literally pulls the cell forward (Figure 52).

Like other forms of motility, gliding motility has significant ecological relevance. Gliding allows a cell to exploit new resources and to interact with other cells. In the latter regard, it is of interest that myxobacteria, such as *Myxococcus xanthus*, have a very social and cooperative lifestyle. In these bacteria gliding motility may play an important role in cell-to-cell interactions that are necessary to complete a very elaborate life cycle.

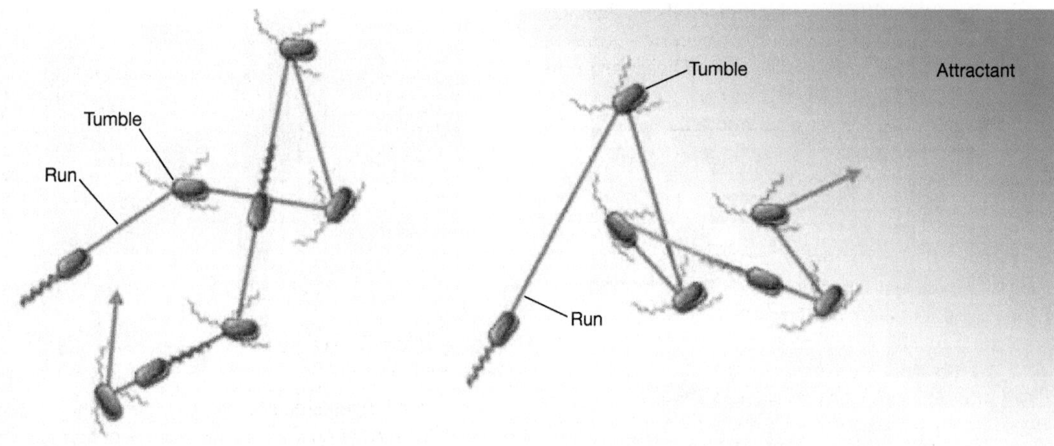

(a) **No attractant present: Random movement** *(b)* **Attractant present: Directed movement**

Figure 53 **Chemotaxis in a peritrichously flagellated bacterium such as *Escherichia coli.*** *(a)* In the absence of a chemical attractant the cell swims randomly in runs, changing direction during tumbles. *(b)* In the presence of an attractant runs become biased, and the cell moves up the gradient of the attractant.

14 MiniReview

Bacteria that move by gliding motility do not employ rotating flagella but instead creep along a solid surface by any of several possible mechanisms.

- How does gliding motility differ from swimming motility in both mechanism and requirements?
- Contrast the mechanism of gliding motility in a filamentous cyanobacterium and in *Flavobacterium*.

15 Cell Motion as a Behavioral Response: Microbial Taxes

Prokaryotes often encounter gradients of physical or chemical agents in nature and have evolved means to respond to these gradients by moving either toward or away from the agent. Such a directed movement is called a *taxis* (plural, taxes). **Chemotaxis**, a response to chemicals, and **phototaxis**, a response to light, are two well-studied taxes. Here we discuss these taxes in a general way.

Chemotaxis has been well studied in swimming bacteria, and much is known at the genetic level concerning how the chemical state of the environment is communicated to the flagellar assembly. Our discussion here will thus deal solely with swimming bacteria. However, some gliding bacteria (Section 14) are also chemotactic, and there are phototactic movements in filamentous cyanobacteria (Figure 51*b*). In addition, although they reside in a different evolutionary domain, many species of *Archaea* are also chemotactic, and many of the proteins that control chemotaxis in *Bacteria* are present in these *Archaea* as well.

Chemotaxis

Much research on chemotaxis has been done with the peritrichously flagellated bacterium *E. coli*. To understand how chemotaxis affects the behavior of *E. coli*, consider the situation in which a cell experiences a gradient of some chemical in its environment (Figure 53). In the absence of a gradient, cells move in a random fashion that includes *runs*, in which the cell is swimming forward in a smooth fashion, and *tumbles*, when the cell stops and jiggles about (Figure 53*a*). During forward movement in a run, the flagellar motor rotates counterclockwise. When flagella rotate clockwise, the bundle of flagella pushes apart, forward motion ceases, and the cells tumble (Figure 50).

Following a tumble, the direction of the next run is random (Figure 53*a*). Thus, by means of runs and tumbles, the cell moves about its environment in a random fashion but does not really go anywhere. However, if a gradient of a chemical attractant is present, these random movements become biased. As the organism senses that it is moving toward higher concentrations of the attractant, runs become longer and tumbles are less frequent. The result of this behavioral response is that the organism moves up the concentration gradient of the attractant (Figure 53*b*). If the organism senses a repellent, the same general mechanism applies, although in this case it is the decrease in concentration of the repellent (rather than the increase in concentration of an attractant) that promotes runs.

Prokaryotic cells are too small to sense a gradient of a chemical along the length of a single cell. Instead, while moving, the cell monitors its environment, comparing its chemical or physical state with that sensed a few moments before. Bacterial cells are thus responding to *temporal* rather than *spatial* differences in the concentration of a chemical as they swim. This information is fed through an elaborate cascade of proteins that eventually affect the direction of rotation of the flagellar motor. The attractants and repellants are sensed by a series of membrane proteins called *chemoreceptors*. These proteins bind the chemicals and begin the process of sensory transduction to the flagellum. In a way, chemotaxis can thus be considered a sensory response system, analogous to sensory responses in the nervous system of animals.

Chemotaxis in Polarly Flagellated Bacteria

Chemotaxis in polarly flagellated cells shows similarities to and differences from that in peritrichously flagellated cells such as *E. coli*. Many polarly flagellated bacteria, such as *Pseudomonas* species, can reverse the direction of rotation of their flagella and in so doing reverse their direction of movement (Figure 50*b*). However, some polarly flagellated bacteria, such as the phototrophic bacterium *Rhodobacter sphaeroides*, have flagella that rotate only in a clockwise direction. How do such cells change direction, and are they chemotactic?

In cells of *R. sphaeroides*, which have only a single flagellum inserted subpolarly, rotation of the flagellum stops periodically. When it stops, the cell becomes reoriented in a random way by Brownian motion. As the flagellum begins to rotate again, the cell moves in a new direction. Nevertheless, cells of *R. sphaeroides* are strongly chemotactic to certain organic compounds and also show tactic responses to oxygen and light. *R. sphaeroides* cannot reverse its flagellar motor and tumble as *E. coli* can, but there is a similarity in that the cells maintain runs as long as they sense an increasing concentration of attractant; movement ceases if the cells sense a decreasing concentration of attractant. By random reorientation, a cell eventually finds a path of increasing attractant and maintains a run until either its chemoreceptors are saturated or it begins to sense a decrease in the level of attractant.

Measuring Chemotaxis

Bacterial chemotaxis can be demonstrated by immersing a small glass capillary tube containing an attractant in a suspension of motile bacteria that does not contain the attractant. From the tip of the capillary, a gradient forms into the surrounding medium, with the concentration of chemical gradually decreasing with distance from the tip (Figure 54*a*). When an attractant is present, the bacteria will move toward it, forming a swarm around the open tip (Figure 54*c*) with many of the bacteria swimming into the capillary. Of course, because of random movements some bacteria will move into the capillary even if it contains a solution of the same composition as the medium (Figure 54*b*). However, when an attractant is present, movement becomes biased. The concentration of bacteria within the capillary can be many times higher than the external concentration. If the capillary is removed after a time period and the cells are counted and compared with a control, attractants and repellants can easily be identified (Figure 54*e*).

If the inserted capillary contains a repellent, the concentration of bacteria within the capillary will be considerably

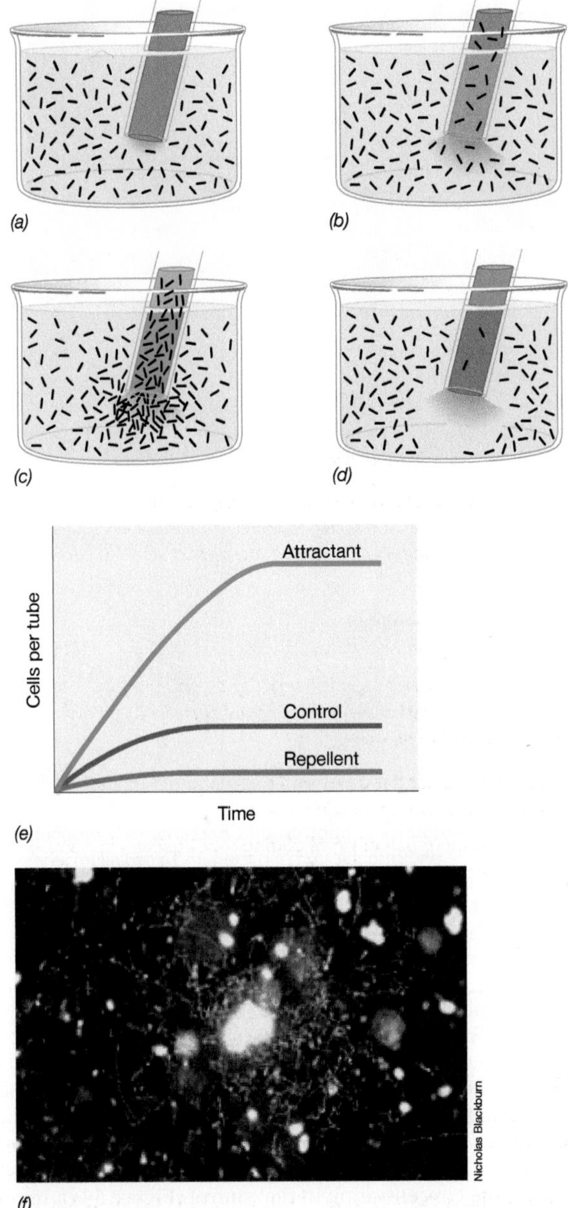

Figure 54 Measuring chemotaxis using a capillary tube assay. *(a)* Insertion of the capillary into a bacterial suspension. As the capillary is inserted, a gradient of the chemical begins to form. *(b)* Control capillary contains a salt solution that is neither an attractant nor a repellent. Cell concentration inside the capillary becomes the same as that outside. *(c)* Accumulation of bacteria in a capillary containing an attractant. *(d)* Repulsion of bacteria by a repellent. *(e)* Time course showing cell numbers in capillaries containing various chemicals. *(f)* Tracks of motile bacteria in seawater swarming around an algal cell (large white spot, center) photographed with a tracking video camera system attached to a microscope. Note how the bacterial cells are showing positive aerotaxis by moving toward the oxygen-producing algal cell. The average velocity of the cells was about 25 μm/sec. The alga is about 60 μm in diameter.

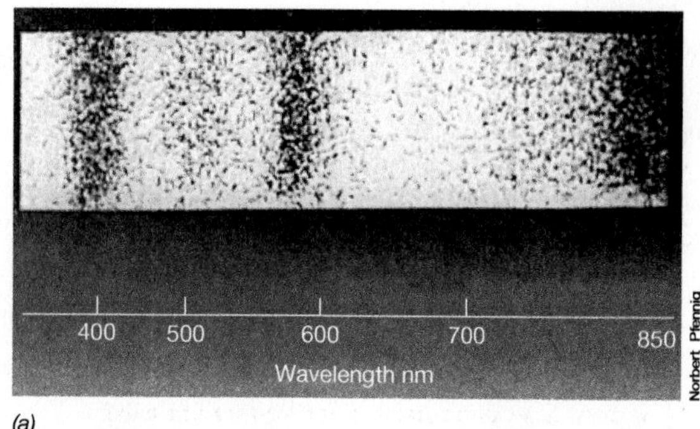

(a)

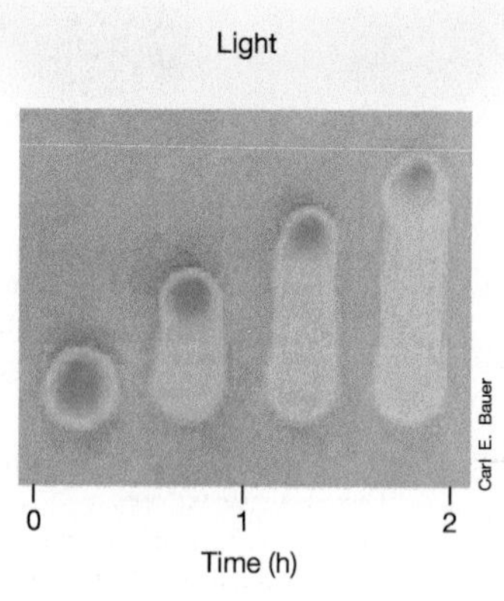

(b)

Figure 55 Phototaxis of phototrophic bacteria. *(a)* Scotophobic accumulation of the phototrophic purple bacterium *Thiospirillum jenense* at wavelengths of light at which its pigments absorb. A light spectrum was displayed on a microscope slide containing a dense suspension of the bacteria; after a period of time, the bacteria had accumulated selectively and the photomicrograph was taken. The wavelengths at which the bacteria accumulated are those at which the photosynthetic pigment bacteriochlorophyll *a* absorbs. *(b)* Phototaxis of an entire colony of the purple phototrophic bacterium *Rhodospirillum centenum.* These strongly phototactic cells move in unison toward the light source at the top. See Figure 45 for electron micrographs of *R. centenum* cells.

less than the concentration in the control (Figure 54*d*). In this case, the cell senses an increasing gradient of repellent, and the appropriate chemoreceptors affect flagellar rotation to move the cell away from the repellent (Figure 54*d*). Using the capillary method, it is possible to screen chemicals to see if they are attractants or repellents for a given bacterium.

Chemotaxis can also be observed visually under a microscope. Using a video camera that captures the position of bacterial cells with time and shows the motility tracks of each cell, it is possible to see the chemotactic movements of cells (Figure 54*f*). This method has been adapted to studies of chemotaxis of bacteria in natural environments. In nature it is thought that the major chemotactic agents for bacteria are nutrients excreted from larger microbial cells or from live or dead macroorganisms. Algae, for example, produce both organic compounds and oxygen (O_2, from photosynthesis) that can trigger chemotactic movements of bacteria toward an algal cell (Figure 54*f*).

Phototaxis

Many phototrophic microorganisms can move toward light, a process called *phototaxis*. The advantage of phototaxis for a phototrophic organism is that it allows the organism to orient itself most efficiently to receive light for photosynthesis. This can be seen if a light spectrum is spread across a microscope slide on which there are motile phototrophic bacteria. On such a slide the bacteria accumulate at wavelengths at which their photosynthetic pigments absorb (Figure 55*a*).

Two different light-mediated taxes are observed in phototrophic bacteria. One, called *scotophobotaxis*, can be observed only microscopically and occurs when a phototrophic bacterium happens to swim outside the illuminated field of view of the microscope into darkness. Entering darkness negatively affects the energy state of the cell and signals it to tumble, reverse direction, and once again swim in a run, thus reentering the light.

True phototaxis differs from scotophobotaxis. Phototaxis is analogous to chemotaxis except the attractant in this case is light instead of a chemical. In some species, such as the highly motile phototrophic organism *Rhodospirillum centenum* (Figure 45), entire colonies of cells show phototaxis and move in unison toward the light (Figure 55*b*).

Several components of the regulatory system that govern chemotaxis also control phototaxis. This conclusion has emerged from the study of mutants of phototrophic bacteria defective in phototaxis; such mutants show defective chemotaxis systems as well. A *photoreceptor*, a protein that functions similar to a chemoreceptor but senses a gradient of light instead of chemicals, is the initial sensor in the phototaxis response. The photoreceptor then interacts with the same cytoplasmic proteins that control flagellar rotation in chemotaxis, maintaining the cell in a run if it is swimming toward an increasing intensity of light. Thus, although the stimulus in chemotaxis and phototaxis differs—chemicals versus light—the same molecular machinery is employed in the cytoplasm to process both signals.

Other Taxes

Other bacterial taxes, such as movement toward or away from oxygen (*aerotaxis*, see Figure 54*f*) or toward or away from conditions of high ionic strength (*osmotaxis*), are known among various swimming prokaryotes. Like chemotaxis and phototaxis, these are simple forms of behavior, and it appears that a common molecular mechanism controls each of these behavioral responses. Cells periodically sample their environment for chemicals, light, oxygen, salt, or other substances, and then process the results through a network of proteins that ultimately control the direction of flagellar rotation. In some gliding cyanobacteria (Figure 51*a*,*b*), an unusual taxis, *hydrotaxis*, also occurs. This allows gliding cyanobacteria inhabiting dry environments, such as soils, to glide up a gradient of increasing hydration.

From our coverage of microbial taxes it should be clear that motile prokaryotes do not just swim around at random, but instead are keenly attuned to the chemical and physical state of their habitat. Indeed, regular and periodic "assays" of their environment are probably a key to ecological success for prokaryotes. By being able to move toward or away from various stimuli, prokaryotic cells have a better chance of competing successfully for resources and avoiding the harmful effects of substances that could damage or kill them.

15 MiniReview

Motile bacteria can respond to chemical and physical gradients in their environment. In swimming prokaryotes, movement of the cell can be biased either toward or away from a stimulus by control of runs and tumbles. Tumbles are controlled by the direction of rotation of the flagellum, which in turn is controlled by a network of sensory and response proteins.

- Define the word chemotaxis. How does chemotaxis differ from aerotaxis?
- What causes a run versus a tumble?
- How does scotophobotaxis differ from phototaxis?

Review of Key Terms

ABC (ATP-binding cassette) transport system a membrane transport system consisting of three proteins, one of which hydrolyzes ATP, which transports specific nutrients into the cell

Basal body the "motor" portion of the bacterial flagellum, embedded in the cytoplasmic membrane and wall

Capsule a polysaccharide or protein outermost layer, usually rather slimy, present on some bacteria

Chemotaxis directed movement of an organism toward (positive chemotaxis) or away from (negative chemotaxis) a chemical gradient

Cytoplasmic membrane the permeability barrier of the cell, separating the cytoplasm from the environment

Dipicolinic acid a substance unique to endospores that confers heat resistance on these structures

Endospore a highly heat-resistant, thick-walled, differentiated structure produced by certain gram-positive *Bacteria*

Flagellum a long, thin cellular appendage capable of rotation and responsible for swimming motility in prokaryotic cells

Gas vesicles gas-filled cytoplasmic structures bounded by protein and conferring buoyancy on cells

Gram-negative a prokaryotic cell whose cell wall contains small amounts of peptidoglycan, and an outer membrane, containing lipopolysaccharide, lipoprotein, and other complex macromolecules

Gram-positive a prokaryotic cell whose cell wall consists chiefly of peptidoglycan and lacks the outer membrane of gram-negative cells

Gram stain A differential staining procedure that stains cells either purple (gram-positive cells) or pink (gram-negative cells)

Group translocation an energy-dependent transport system in which the substance transported is chemically modified during the transport process

Lipopolysaccharide (LPS) a combination of lipid with polysaccharide and protein that forms the major portion of the outer membrane in gram-negative *Bacteria*

Magnetosome a particle of magnetite (Fe_3O_4) organized into a nonunit membrane-enclosed structure in the cytoplasm of magnetotactic *Bacteria*

Morphology the *shape* of a cell—rod, coccus, spirillum, and so on

Outer membrane a phospholipid- and polysaccharide-containing unit membrane that lies external to the peptidoglycan layer in cells of gram-negative *Bacteria*

Peptidoglycan a polysaccharide composed of alternating repeats of *N*-acetylglucosamine and *N*-acetylmuramic acid arranged in adjacent layers and cross-linked by short peptides

Periplasm a gel-like region between the outer surface of the cytoplasmic membrane and the inner surface of the lipopolysaccharide layer of gram-negative *Bacteria*

Peritrichous flagellation flagella located in many places around the surface of the cell

Phototaxis movement of an organism toward light

Pili thin, filamentous structures that extend from the surface of a cell and, depending on type, facilitate cell attachment, genetic exchange, or twitching motility

Polar flagellation having flagella emanating from one or both poles of the cell

Poly-β-hydroxybutyrate (PHB) a common storage material of prokaryotic cells consisting of a polymer of β-hydroxybutyrate or another β-alkanoic acid or mixtures of β-alkanoic acids

Protoplast an osmotically protected cell whose cell wall has been removed

S-layer an outermost cell surface layer composed of protein or glycoprotein present on some *Bacteria* and *Archaea*

Simple transport system a transporter that consists of only a membrane-spanning protein and typically driven by energy from the proton motive force

Sterol a hydrophobic heterocyclic ringed molecule that strengthens the cytoplasmic membrane of eukaryotic cells and a few prokaryotes

Teichoic acid a phosphorylated polyalcohol found in the cell wall of some gram-positive *Bacteria*

Review Questions

1. What are the major morphologies of prokaryotes? Draw cells for each morphology you list (Section 1).
2. How large can a prokaryote be? How small? Why is it that we likely know the lower limit more accurately than the upper limit? What are the dimensions of the rod-shaped bacterium *Escherichia coli* (Section 2)?
3. Describe in a single sentence the structure of a unit membrane (Section 3).
4. Describe a major chemical difference between membranes of *Bacteria* and *Archaea* (Section 3).
5. Explain in a single sentence why ionized molecules do not readily pass through the cytoplasmic membrane of a cell. How do such molecules get through the cytoplasmic membrane (Sections 4 and 5)?
6. Cells of *Escherichia coli* take up lactose via lac permease, glucose via the phosphotransferase system, and maltose via an ABC-type transporter. For each of these sugars describe: (1) the components of their transport system and (2) the source of energy that drives the transport event (Section 5).
7. Why is the bacterial cell wall rigid layer called peptidoglycan? What are the chemical reasons for the rigidity that is conferred on the cell wall by the peptidoglycan structure (Section 6)?
8. Why is sucrose able to stabilize bacterial cells from lysis by lysozyme (Section 6)?
9. List several functions of the outer membrane in gram-negative *Bacteria*. What is the chemical composition of the outer membrane (Section 7)?
10. What cell wall polysaccharide common in *Bacteria* is absent from *Archaea*? What is unusual about S-layers compared to other cell walls of prokaryotes ? What types of cell walls are found in *Archaea* (Section 8)?
11. What function(s) do non-cell wall polysaccharide layers have in prokaryotes (Section 9)?
12. What types of cytoplasmic inclusions are formed by prokaryotes? How does an inclusion of poly-β-hydroxybutyric acid differ from a magnetosome in composition and metabolic role (Section 10)?
13. What is the function of gas vesicles? How are these structures made such that they can remain gas tight (Section 11)?
14. In a few sentences, indicate how the bacterial endospore differs from the vegetative cell in structure, chemical composition, and ability to resist extreme environmental conditions (Section 12).
15. Define the following terms: mature endospore, vegetative cell, and germination (Section 12).
16. Describe the structure and function of a bacterial flagellum. What is the energy source for the flagellum (Section 13)? How do the flagella of *Bacteria* differ from those of *Archaea* in both size and composition?
17. How does the mechanism and energy requirements for motility in *Flavobacterium* differ from that in *Escherichia coli* (Sections 13 and 14)?
18. In a few sentences, write an explanation describing how a motile bacterium is able to sense the direction of an attractant and move toward it (Section 15).

Application Questions

1. Calculate the surface-to-volume ratio of a spherical cell 15 μm in diameter and a cell 2 μm in diameter. What are the consequences of these differences in surface-to-volume ratio for cell function?
2. Assume you are given two cultures, one of a species of gram-negative *Bacteria* and one of a species of *Archaea*. Other than by phylogenetic analyses, discuss at least four different ways you could tell which culture was which.
3. Calculate the amount of time it would take a cell of *Escherichia coli* (1 × 3 μm) swimming at maximum speed (60 cell lengths per second) to travel all the way up a 3-cm-long capillary tube containing a chemical attractant.
4. Assume you are given two cultures of rod-shaped bacteria, one gram positive and the other gram negative. How could you differentiate them using (a) light microscopy; (b) electron microscopy; (c) chemical analyses of cell walls; and (d) phylogenetic analyses?

Essentials of Molecular Biology

Molecular biology begins with the genome, shown here being released from a bacterial cell, and includes all of the fundamental molecular processes that flow from the genome, including transcription (the production of RNA) and translation (protein synthesis).

G. Murti/Photo Researchers, Inc.

As chemical machines, cells accumulate and transform their vast array of macromolecules into new cells. As coding devices, they store, process, and use genes, the genetic information of the cell. Genes and gene expression are the subject of molecular biology. In particular, the review of molecular biology in this chapter includes the chemical nature of genes, the structure and function of DNA and RNA, and the replication of DNA. We then consider the biosynthesis of proteins, macromolecules that play important roles in both the structure and the functioning of the cell. Our focus in this chapter is on these processes as they occur in *Bacteria*. In particular, *Escherichia coli*, a member of the *Bacteria*, is the model organism for molecular biology and is the main example used.

I GENES AND GENE EXPRESSION

1 Macromolecules and Genetic Information

The functional unit of genetic information is the **gene**. All microorganisms, indeed all life forms, contain genes, and thus a fundamental understanding of what a gene is and what it does is important for understanding the structure and behavior of cells and viruses. Physically, genes are located on chromosomes or other large molecules known collectively as **genetic elements**. Nowadays, in the "genomics era," biology is tending to define cells in terms of their complement of genes. Thus, we must understand the process of biological information flow if we are to understand how microorganisms function.

Genes and the Steps in Information Flow

In all cells genes are composed of deoxyribonucleic acid (DNA). The information in the gene is present as the sequence of bases—purine (adenine and guanine) and pyrimidines (thymine and cytosine)—in the DNA. The information stored in DNA is transferred to ribonucleic acid (RNA). RNA may act as an informational intermediate (a messenger), as a structural component, or even as an enzyme. Finally, information carried by RNA is used to manufacture proteins. Because all three of these molecules, DNA, RNA, and protein, contain genetic information in their sequences, they are called **informational macromolecules**.

The molecular processes underlying genetic information flow can be divided into three stages (Figure 1).

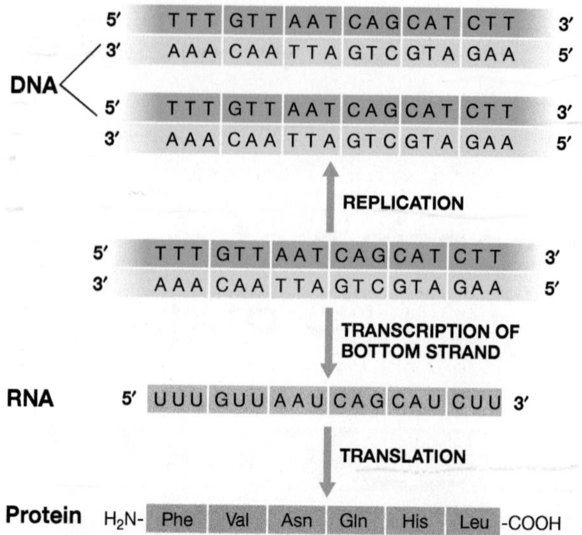

Figure 1 Synthesis of the three types of informational macromolecules. Note that for any particular gene only one of the two strands of the DNA double helix is transcribed.

1. **Replication**. The DNA molecule is a double helix of two long chains. During replication, DNA is duplicated, producing two double helices (Figure 1).
2. **Transcription**. DNA participates in protein synthesis through an RNA intermediate. Transfer of the information to RNA is called transcription, and the RNA molecule that encodes one or more polypeptides is called **messenger RNA** (mRNA). Some genes contain information for other types of RNA, in particular **transfer RNA** (tRNA) and **ribosomal RNA** (rRNA). These play roles in protein synthesis but do not themselves encode the genetic information for making proteins.
3. **Translation**. The sequence of amino acids in a polypeptide is determined by the specific sequence of bases in the mRNA. There is a linear correspondence between the base sequence of a gene and the amino acid sequence of a polypeptide (Figure 1). Each group of three bases on an mRNA molecule encodes a single amino acid, and each such triplet of bases is called a **codon**. This genetic code is translated into protein by means of the protein-synthesizing system. This system consists of ribosomes (which are themselves made up of proteins and rRNA), tRNA, and a number of proteins known as translation factors.

The three steps shown in Figure 1 are used in all cells and constitute the central dogma of molecular biology (DNA → RNA → protein). Note that many different RNA molecules are each transcribed from a relatively short region of the long DNA molecule. In eukaryotes, each gene is transcribed to give a single mRNA, whereas in prokaryotes, a single messenger RNA may carry genetic information from several genes, that is, more than one coding region (Figure 2). Some viruses violate the central dogma. This includes instances where RNA is the viral genetic material and either functions as mRNA directly or encodes mRNA. This also occurs in retroviruses such as HIV—the causative agent of AIDS—where an RNA genome encodes the production of DNA, a process called reverse transcription. Note that in both of these cases information transfer remains from nucleic acid to nucleic acid but not in the way originally stated by the central dogma.

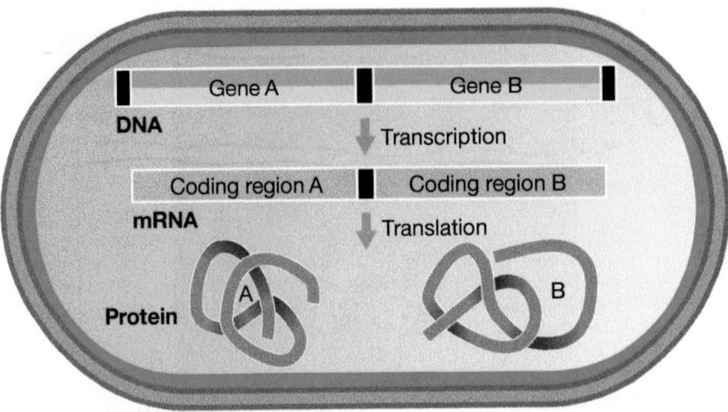

Figure 2 **Transcription in prokaryotes.** A single mRNA often contains more than one coding region.

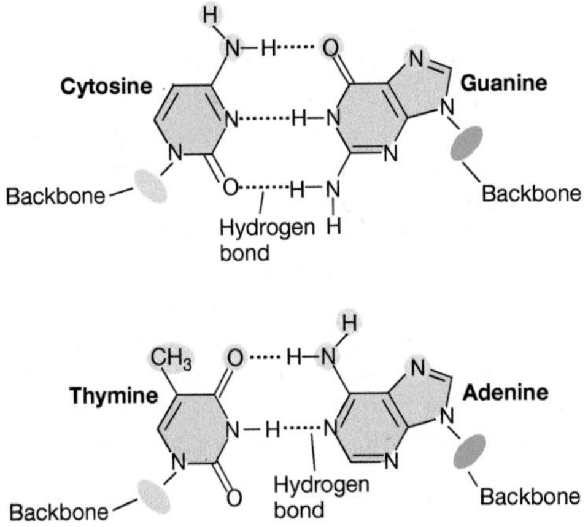

Figure 3 **Specific pairing between adenine (A) and thymine (T) and between guanine (G) and cytosine (C) via hydrogen bonds.** These are the typical base pairs found in double-stranded DNA. Atoms that are found in the major groove of the double helix and that interact with proteins are highlighted in pink. The deoxyribose phosphate backbones of the two strands of DNA are also indicated. Note the different shades of green for the two strands of DNA, a convention used throughout this book.

1 MiniReview

The three key processes of macromolecular synthesis are: (1) DNA replication; (2) transcription (the synthesis of RNA from a DNA template); and (3) translation (the synthesis of proteins using messenger RNA as template).

- What three informational macromolecules are involved in genetic information flow?
- In all cells there are three processes involved in genetic information flow. What are they?

II DNA STRUCTURE

In the next few sections of this chapter we discuss the details of DNA structure, including the types of genetic elements containing DNA that are found in cells. With this information as a foundation, we can then discuss how DNA is replicated, transcribed into RNA, and translated into protein.

2 The Double Helix

Four nucleic acid bases are found in DNA: adenine (A), guanine (G), cytosine (C), and thymine (T). The backbone of the DNA chain consists of alternating repeats of phosphate and the pentose sugar deoxyribose; connected to each sugar is one of the nucleic acid bases. Recall especially the numbering system for the positions of sugar and base. The phosphate connecting two sugars spans from the 3′-carbon of one sugar to the 5′-carbon of the adjacent sugar (see Figure 4). At one end of each DNA strand the sugar has a phosphate on the 5′-hydroxyl whereas at the other end the sugar has a free hydroxyl at the 3′-position.

DNA as a Double Helix

In all cells and many viruses, DNA exists as a double-stranded molecule with two polynucleotide strands whose base sequences are **complementary**. (The genomes of some viruses are single-stranded.) The complementarity of DNA arises because of the specific pairing of the purine and pyrimidine bases: Adenine always pairs with thymine, and guanine always pairs with cytosine (Figure 3). The two strands in the resulting double-stranded molecule are arranged in an **antiparallel** fashion (Figure 3 and Figure 4, distinguished as two shades of green). For example, in Figure 4 the strand on the left is arranged 5′ to 3′ (top to bottom), whereas the other strand is 5′ to 3′ (bottom to top).

The two strands of DNA are wrapped around each other to form a double helix (Figure 5). In the double helix, DNA forms two distinct grooves, the *major groove* and the *minor groove*. Of the many proteins that interact specifically with DNA, most bind in the major groove, where there is a considerable amount of space. Because of the regularity of the double helix, some atoms of each base are always exposed in the major groove (and some in the minor groove). Key regions of nucleotides that are important in interactions with proteins are shown in Figure 3.

Several double-helical structures are possible for DNA. The Watson and Crick double helix is known as the B-form or *B-DNA* to distinguish it from the A- and Z-forms. The A-form is shorter and fatter than the B-form of the double helix; has 11 base pairs per turn, and the major groove is narrower and deeper. Double-stranded RNA or hybrids of one RNA plus one DNA strand often form the A-helix. The Z-DNA double helix has 12 base pairs per turn and is left-handed. Its sugar phosphate backbone is a zigzag line rather than a smooth curve. Z-DNA is found in GC- or GT-rich regions, especially when negatively supercoiled. Occasional enzymes and regulatory proteins bind preferentially to Z-DNA.

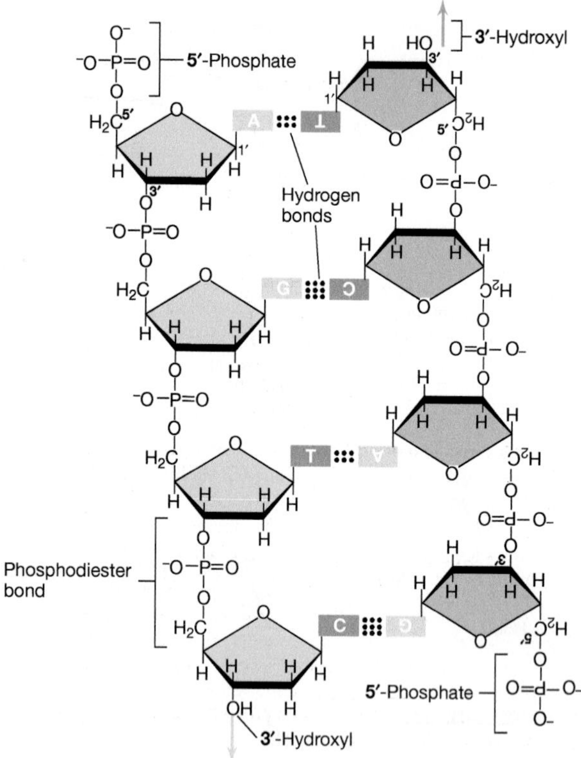

Figure 4 **DNA structure.** Complementary and antiparallel nature of DNA. Note that one chain ends in a 5′-phosphate group, whereas the other ends in a 3′-hydroxyl. The red bases represent the pyrimidines cytosine (C) and thymine (T), and the yellow bases represent the purines adenine (A) and guanine (G).

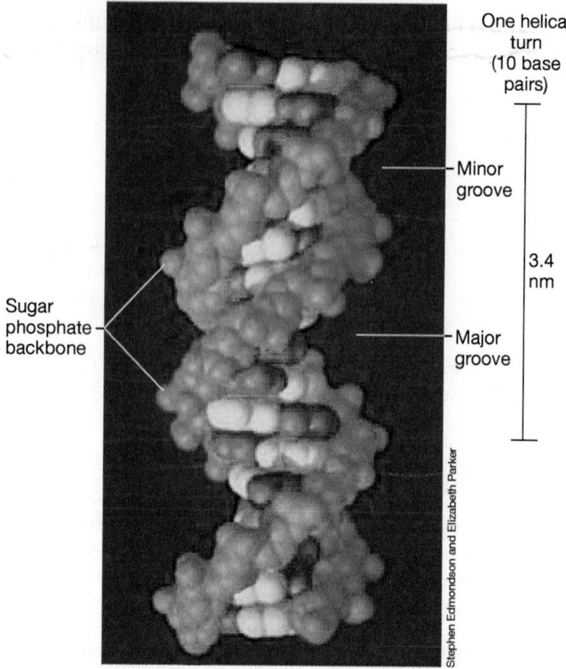

Figure 5 **A computer model of a short segment of DNA showing the overall arrangement of the double helix.** One of the sugar–phosphate backbones is shown in blue and the other in green. The pyrimidine bases are shown in red and the purines in yellow. Note the locations of the major and minor grooves (compare with Figure 3). One helical turn contains 10 base pairs.

Size of a DNA Molecule

The size of a DNA molecule can be expressed as the number of thousands of nucleotide bases or base pairs per molecule. Thus, a DNA molecule with 1000 bases is 1 kilobase (kb) of DNA. If the DNA is a double helix, then one speaks of *kilobase pairs* (kbp). Thus, a double helix 5000 base pairs in size would be 5 kbp. The bacterium *Escherichia coli* has about 4640 kbp of DNA in its chromosome. Since many genomes are quite large, it is easiest to speak of millions of base pairs, or *megabase pairs* (Mbp). The genome of *E. coli* is thus 4.64 Mbp.

In terms of actual length, each base pair takes up 0.34 nanometer (nm) in length along the helix, and each turn of the helix contains approximately 10 base pairs. Therefore, 1 kb of DNA has 100 turns of the helix and is 0.34 μm long. Calculations such as this can be very interesting, as we shall soon see.

Secondary Structure, Inverted Repeats, and Stem-Loops

Long DNA molecules are quite flexible, but stretches of DNA less than 100 base pairs are more rigid. Some short segments of DNA can be bent by proteins that interact with them. However, certain base sequences themselves cause DNA to bend. The sequences of this bent DNA often have several runs of five or six adenines (in the same strand), each separated by four or five other bases. In addition, some sequences contribute to the ability of DNA to bend when certain proteins interact with the DNA. DNA bending is one mechanism for the regulation of gene expression (the turning on and off of genes).

Short, repeated sequences are often found in DNA molecules. Many proteins interact with regions of DNA containing repeated sequences that are arranged in inverse orientation. This type of repeat is called an inverted repeat and gives the DNA sequence a twofold symmetry. As shown in Figure 6, nearby inverted repeats can lead to the formation of stem-loop structures. The stems are short double-helical regions with normal base pairing and antiparallel strands. The loop consists of the unpaired bases between the two repeat units.

The production of stem-loop structures in DNA itself is relatively rare in cells. However, the production of stem-loop structures in the RNA produced from DNA following transcription is common. Such secondary structure formed by base pairing within a single strand of nucleic acid is critical to the functioning of transfer RNA (Section 14) and ribosomal RNA

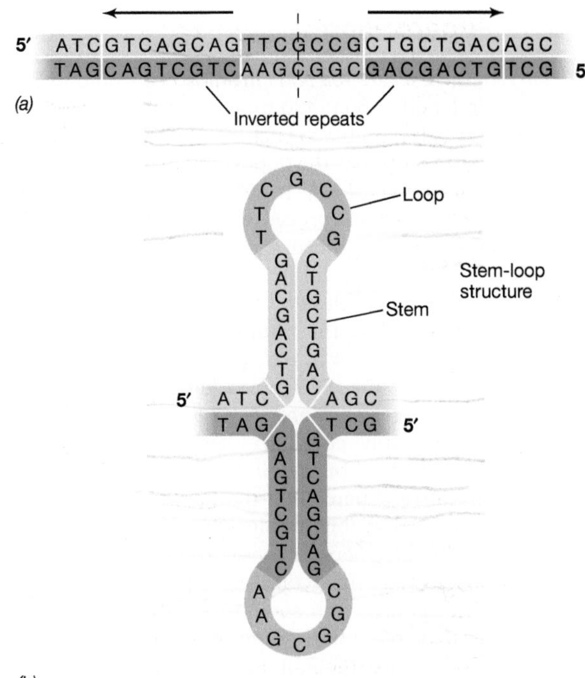

Figure 6 **Inverted repeats and the formation of a stem-loop structure.** *(a)* Nearby inverted repeats in DNA. The arrows indicate the symmetry around the imaginary axis (dashed line). *(b)* Formation of stem-loop structures by pairing of complementary bases on the same strand. Note how if RNA was formed from either strand of DNA, the RNA could form a single stem-loop (compare with Figure 23).

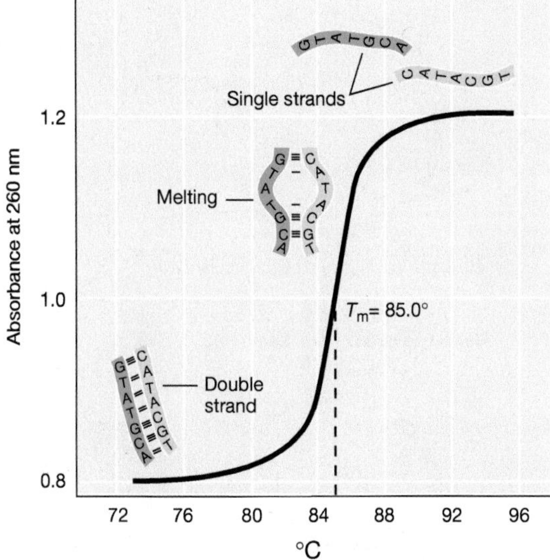

Figure 7 **Thermal denaturation of DNA.** DNA absorbs more ultraviolet radiation at 260 nm as the double helix is denatured. The transition is quite abrupt, and the temperature of the midpoint, T_m, is proportional to the GC content of the DNA. Although the denatured DNA can be renatured by slow cooling, the process does not follow a similar curve. Renaturation becomes progressively more complete at temperatures well below the T_m and then only after a considerable incubation time.

(Section 15). Even if a stem-loop does not form, inverted repeats in DNA are often binding sites for specific DNA-binding proteins that regulate transcription.

The Effect of Temperature on DNA Structure

Although the hydrogen bonds between the base pairs are individually very weak, many such bonds in a long DNA molecule effectively hold the two strands together. There may be millions or even hundreds of millions of hydrogen bonds in a DNA molecule, depending on the number of base pairs present. Recall from Figure 3 that each adenine-thymine base pair has *two* hydrogen bonds, while each guanine-cytosine base pair has *three*. This makes GC pairs stronger than AT pairs.

When isolated from cells and kept near room temperature and at physiological salt concentrations, DNA remains in a double-stranded form. However, if the temperature is raised, the hydrogen bonds will break but the covalent bonds holding a chain together will not, and so the two DNA strands will separate. This process is called denaturation (melting) and can be measured experimentally because single-stranded and double-stranded nucleic acids differ in their ability to absorb ultraviolet radiation at 260 nm (Figure 7).

DNA with a high percentage of GC pairs melts at a higher temperature than a similar-sized molecule with more AT pairs. If the heated DNA is allowed to cool slowly, the double-stranded DNA can reform, a process called annealing. This can be used not only to reform native DNA but also to form hybrid molecules whose two strands come from different sources. Hybridization, the artificial construction of a double-stranded nucleic acid by complementary base pairing of two single strands, is a powerful technique in molecular biology.

2 MiniReview

DNA is a double-stranded molecule that forms a helix. Its length is measured in terms of numbers of base pairs. The two strands in the double helix are antiparallel, but inverted repeats allow for the formation of secondary structure. The strands of a double-helical DNA molecule can be denatured by heat and allowed to reassociate following cooling.

- Explain what the word antiparallel means in terms of the structure of double-stranded DNA.
- Define the term complementary when used to refer to two strands of DNA.
- Define the terms denaturation, reannealing, and hybridization as they apply to nucleic acids.

(a) Relaxed, covalently closed circular DNA

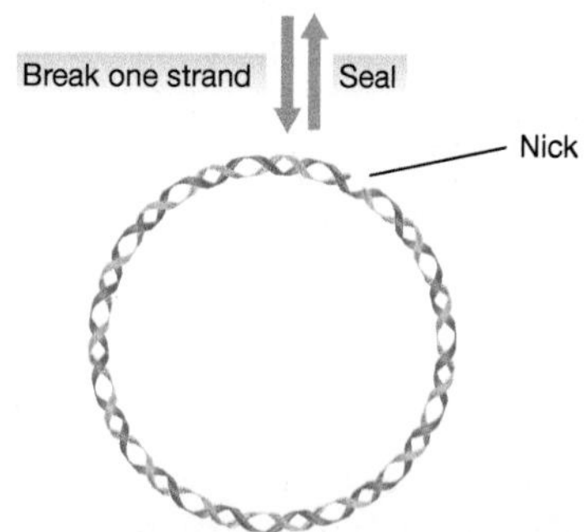

(b) Relaxed, nicked circular DNA

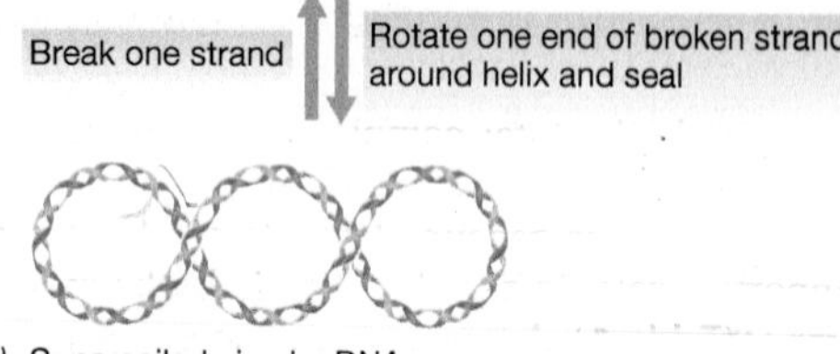

(c) Supercoiled circular DNA

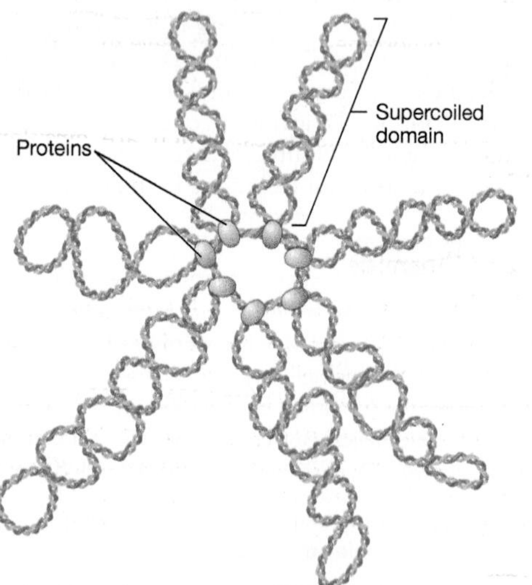

(d) Chromosomal DNA with supercoiled domains

Figure 8 Supercoiled DNA. Parts *(a)*, *(b)*, and *(c)* show supercoiled circular DNA and relaxed, nicked circular DNA. A nick is a break in a phosphodiester bond of one strand. *(d)* In fact, the double-stranded DNA in the bacterial chromosome is arranged not in one supercoil but in several supercoiled domains, as shown here.

3 Supercoiling

If linearized, the *Escherichia coli* chromosome would be more than 1 mm in length, about 400 times longer than the *E. coli* cell itself! How is it possible to pack so much DNA into such a little space? The solution is the imposition of a kind of "higher order" structure on the DNA, in which the double-stranded DNA is further twisted in a process called *supercoiling*. Figure 8 shows how supercoiling occurs in a circular DNA duplex. If a circular DNA molecule is linearized, any supercoiling is lost and the DNA becomes "relaxed." Thus, a relaxed DNA molecule is one with exactly the number of turns of the helix predicted from the number of base pairs.

Supercoiling puts the DNA molecule under torsion, much like the added tension to a rubber band that occurs when it is twisted. DNA can be supercoiled in either a positive or negative manner. In positive supercoiling the double helix is overwound, whereas in negative supercoiling the double helix is underwound. Negative supercoiling results when the DNA is twisted about its axis in the opposite sense from the right-handed double helix. Negatively supercoiled DNA is the form predominantly found in nature, with some interesting exceptions in certain species of *Archaea*. In *Escherichia coli* more than 100 supercoiled domains are thought to exist, each of which is stabilized by binding to specific proteins.

Topoisomerases: DNA Gyrase

Supercoils may be introduced or removed by enzymes known as topoisomerases. Two major classes of topoisomerase exist and each functions by a different mechanism. Class I topoisomerases make a single-stranded break in the DNA that allows the rotation of one strand of the double helix around the other. Each such rotation adds or removes a single supercoil. After this, the nick is resealed. Class II topoisomerases make double-stranded breaks, pass the intact double helix through the break, and finally reseal the break. Each such operation adds or removes two supercoils. Insertion of supercoils into DNA requires ATP to provide energy, whereas releasing supercoils does not.

In *Bacteria* and most *Archaea*, there is an enzyme called **DNA gyrase** that introduces negative supercoils into DNA. DNA gyrase belongs to the group of type II topoisomerases. Its operation occurs in several stages. First, the circular DNA molecule is twisted; then, where the two chains touch, a double-stranded break is made in one chain. Next, the intact chain is passed through the break, and then the broken double helix is resealed (Figure 9). It is worth noting that some of the antibiotics that affect *Bacteria*, such as the quinolone nalidixic acid, the fluoroquinolone ciprofloxacin, and novobiocin, inhibit the activity of DNA gyrase. Novobiocin is also effective against several species of *Archaea*, where it also seems to inhibit DNA gyrase.

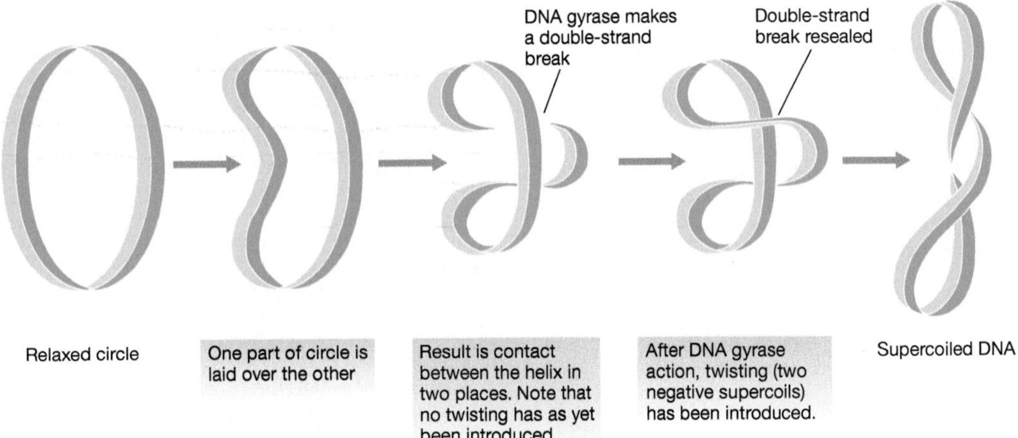

Figure 9 DNA gyrase. Introduction of negative supercoiling into circular DNA by the activity of DNA gyrase (topoisomerase II), which makes double-strand breaks.

The removal of surplus supercoiling in DNA is generally done by topoisomerase I. This enzyme introduces a single-stranded break in the DNA and causes the rotation of one strand of the double helix around the other. As was shown in Figure 8, a break in the backbone (a nick) of either strand allows the DNA to return to the relaxed state. However, to prevent the entire bacterial chromosome from becoming relaxed every time a nick is made, the chromosome contains supercoiled domains as shown in Figure 8*d*. A nick in the DNA in one of these domains does not relax DNA in the others. It is unclear precisely how these domains are formed, although specific DNA-binding proteins are involved.

Through the activity of topoisomerases, the DNA molecule can be alternately supercoiled and relaxed. Because supercoiling is necessary for packing the DNA into the cell and relaxation is necessary for DNA replication and transcription, the complementary processes of supercoiling and relaxation play an important role in the biology of the cell. In most prokaryotes, the extent of negative supercoiling is the result of a balance between the activity of DNA gyrase and topoisomerase I. In addition to replication, however, supercoiling also affects gene expression. Certain genes are more actively transcribed when DNA is supercoiled, whereas transcription of other genes is inhibited by excessive supercoiling.

3 MiniReview

Very long DNA molecules can be packaged into cells because they are supercoiled. In prokaryotes this supercoiling is brought about by enzymes called topoisomerases. DNA gyrase is a key enzyme in prokaryotes and introduces negative supercoils into the DNA.

- Why is supercoiling important?
- What function do topoisomerases serve inside cells?

4 Chromosomes and Other Genetic Elements

Structures containing genetic material (DNA in most organisms, but RNA in some viruses) are called *genetic elements*. The **genome** is the total complement of genes in a cell or virus. Although the main genetic element in prokaryotes is the **chromosome**, other genetic elements are known and these play important roles in gene function in both prokaryotes and eukaryotes (Table 1). A typical prokaryote has a single circular chromosome containing all (or most) of the genes found inside the cell. Although a single chromosome is the rule among prokaryotes, there are exceptions. A few prokaryotes contain two chromosomes. Eukaryotes have multiple chromosomes making up their genome. Also, the DNA in all known eukaryotic chromosomes is linear in contrast to most prokaryotic chromosomes, which are circular DNA molecules.

Viruses and Plasmids

Besides the chromosome, a number of other genetic elements are known, including virus genomes, plasmids, organellar genomes, and transposable elements.

Viruses contain genomes, *either* DNA or RNA, that control their own replication and their transfer from cell to cell. Both linear and circular viral genomes are known. In addition, the nucleic acid in viral genomes may be single-stranded or double-stranded. Viruses are of special interest because they often cause disease.

Plasmids are genetic elements that replicate separately from the chromosome. The great majority of plasmids are double-stranded DNA, and although most plasmids are circular, some are linear. Plasmids differ from viruses in two ways: (1) they do not cause cellular damage (generally they are

Table 1 Kinds of genetic elements

Organism	*Element*	*Type of nucleic acid*	*Description*
Prokaryote	Chromosome	Double-stranded DNA	Extremely long, usually circular
Eukaryote	Chromosome	Double-stranded DNA	Extremely long, linear
All organisms	Plasmid[a]	Double-stranded DNA	Relatively short circular or linear molecule, extrachromosomal
All organisms	Transposable element	Double-stranded DNA	Always found inserted into another DNA molecule
Mitochondrion or chloroplast	Genome	Double-stranded DNA	Medium length, usually circular
Virus	Genome	Single- or double-stranded DNA or RNA	Relatively short, circular or linear

[a]Plasmids are uncommon in eukaryotes.

beneficial), and (2) they do not have extracellular forms, whereas viruses do. Although only a few eukaryotes contain plasmids, one or more plasmids have been found in most prokaryotic species and can be of profound importance.

Some plasmids contain genes whose protein products confer important properties on the host cell, such as resistance to antibiotics. What is the difference, then, between a large plasmid and a chromosome? A chromosome is a genetic element that contains genes whose products are necessary for essential cellular functions. Such essential genes are called *housekeeping genes.* Some of these encode essential proteins, such as DNA and RNA polymerases, and others encode essential RNAs, such as ribosomal and transfer RNA. By contrast to the chromosome, plasmids are often expendable and rarely contain genes required for growth under all conditions. There are many genes on a chromosome that are unessential as well, but the presence of *essential* genes is necessary for a genetic element to be called a chromosome.

Transposable Elements

Transposable elements are segments of DNA that can move from one site on a DNA molecule to another site on the same molecule or on a different DNA molecule. Chromosomes, plasmids, virus genomes, and any other type of DNA molecule may act as host molecules for transposable elements. Transposable elements are not found as separate molecules of DNA but are inserted into other DNA molecules including chromosomes, plasmids, or virus genomes. Transposable elements are found in both prokaryotes and eukaryotes and play important roles in genetic variation. In prokaryotes there are three main types of transposable elements: insertion sequences, transposons, and some special viruses. Insertion sequences are the simplest type of transposable element and carry no genetic information other than that required for them to move about the chromosome. Transposons are larger and contain other genes. The unique feature common to all transposable elements is that they replicate as part of some other molecule of DNA.

4 MiniReview

In addition to the chromosome, a number of other genetic elements exist in cells. Plasmids are DNA molecules that exist separately from the chromosome of the cell. Viruses contain a genome, either DNA or RNA, that controls their own replication. Transposable elements exist as a part of other genetic elements.

- What is a genome?
- What genetic material is found in all cellular chromosomes?
- What defines a chromosome in prokaryotes?

III DNA REPLICATION

The flow of biological information begins with DNA replication. DNA replication is necessary for cells to divide, whether to reproduce new organisms, as in unicellular microorganisms, or to produce new cells as part of a multicellular organism. The process of DNA replication must occur at sufficiently high accuracy so that the daughter cells are genetically identical to the mother cell (or nearly so). This involves a host of special enzymes and processes.

5 Templates and Enzymes

DNA exists in cells as a double helix with complementary base pairing (Figures 3 and 4). If the DNA double helix is opened up, a new strand can be synthesized as the complement of each of the parental strands. As shown in Figure 10, replication is **semiconservative**, meaning that the two resulting double helices consist of one newly made strand and one parental strand. The DNA strand that is copied is called the template, and in DNA replication each parental strand is a template for one newly synthesized (and complementary) daughter strand (Figure 10).

The chemistry of DNA, the nature of its precursors, and the activities of the enzymes involved in replication place some important restrictions on the manner in which new strands are synthesized. The precursor of each new nucleotide in the chain is a deoxynucleoside 5′-triphosphate, from which the two terminal phosphates are removed and the internal phosphate is attached covalently to deoxyribose of the growing chain (Figure 11). The addition of the nucleotide to the grow-

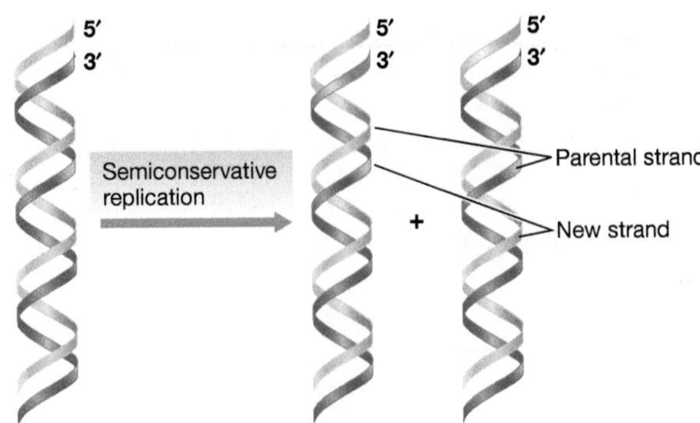

Figure 10 **Overview of DNA replication.** DNA replication is a semiconservative process in both prokaryotes and eukaryotes. Note that the new double helices each contain one new (shown topped in red) and one parental strand.

ing chain requires the presence of a free hydroxyl group, which is available only at the 3′ end of the molecule. This restriction leads to an important principle that is at the basis of DNA replication: DNA replication always proceeds from the 5′ end to the 3′ end, the 5′ -phosphate of the incoming nucleotide being attached to the 3′-hydroxyl of the previously added nucleotide.

DNA Polymerase and Primase

Enzymes that catalyze the addition of deoxynucleotides are called **DNA polymerases**. Several such enzymes exist, and each has a specific function. There are five different DNA polymerases in *Escherichia coli,* called DNA polymerases I, II, III, IV, and V. DNA polymerase III (Pol III) is the primary enzyme for replicating chromosomal DNA. DNA polymerase I (Pol I) is also involved in chromosomal replication, though to a lesser extent (see below). The other DNA polymerases help repair damaged DNA.

All known DNA polymerases synthesize DNA in the 5′ → 3′ direction. However, no known DNA polymerase can initiate a new chain; all of these enzymes can only add a nucleotide onto a preexisting 3′-OH group. Therefore, to start a new chain a **primer**, a nucleic acid molecule to which DNA polymerase can attach the first nucleotide, is required. In most cases this primer is a short stretch of RNA.

When the double helix is opened at the beginning of replication, an RNA-polymerizing enzyme makes the RNA primer. This enzyme, called *primase,* synthesizes a short stretch of RNA of around 11–12 nucleotides that is complementary in base pairing to the template DNA. At the growing end of this RNA primer is a 3′-OH group to which DNA polymerase can add the first deoxyribonucleotide. Continued extension of the molecule thus occurs as DNA rather than RNA. The newly synthesized molecule has a structure like that shown in Figure 12. The primer will eventually be removed and replaced with DNA, as described later. We will examine the details of DNA replication next.

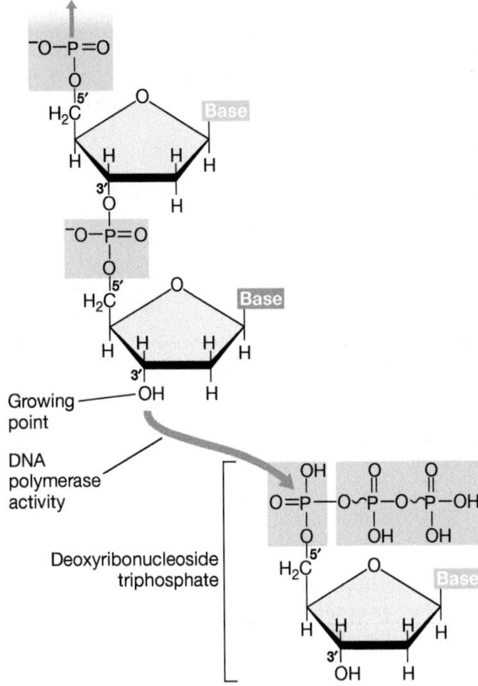

Figure 11 **Structure of the DNA chain and mechanism of growth by addition of a deoxyribonucleoside triphosphate at the 3′-end of the chain.** Growth proceeds from the 5′-phosphate to the 3′-hydroxyl end. The enzyme DNA polymerase catalyzes the addition reaction. The four precursors are deoxythymidine triphosphate (dTTP), deoxyadenosine triphosphate (dATP), deoxyguanosine triphosphate (dGTP), and deoxycytidine triphosphate (dCTP). Upon nucleotide insertion, the two terminal phosphates of the triphosphate are split off as pyrophosphate (PP_i). Thus, two energy-rich phosphate bonds are consumed in the addition of a single nucleotide.

5 MiniReview

Both strands of the DNA helix serve as templates for the synthesis of two new strands (semiconservative replication). The two progeny double helices each contain one parental strand and one new strand. The new strands are elongated by addition of deoxyribonucleotides to the 3′ end. DNA polymerases require a primer made of RNA.

- To which end (5′ end or 3′ end) of a newly synthesized strand of DNA does polymerase add a base?
- Why is a primer required for DNA replication?

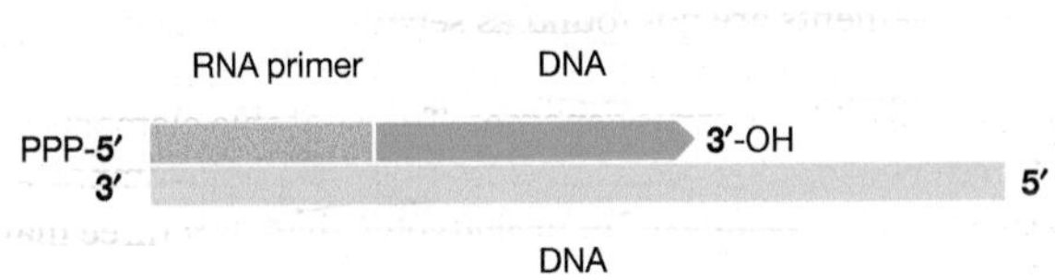

Figure 12 **The RNA primer.** Structure of the RNA–DNA combination formed at the initiation of DNA synthesis.

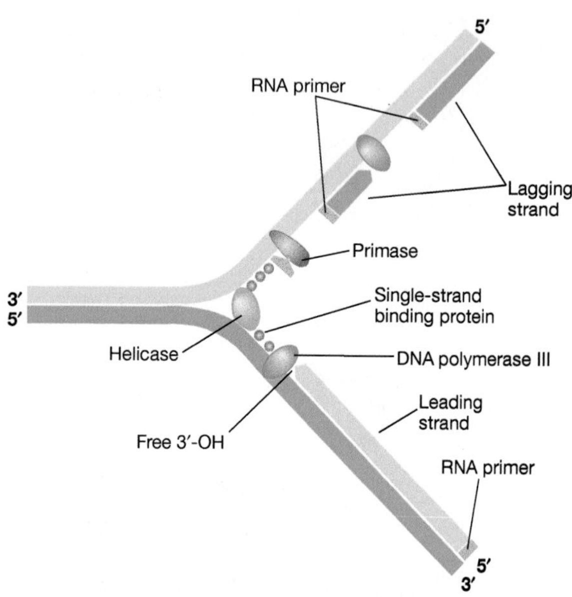

Figure 13 **Events at the DNA replication fork.** Note the polarity and antiparallel nature of the DNA strands.

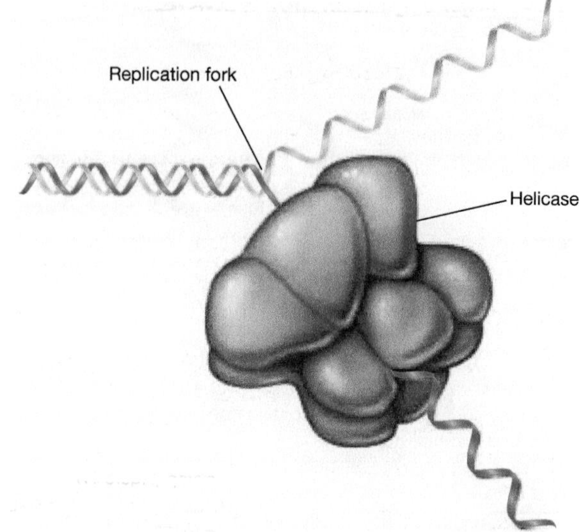

Figure 14 **DNA helicase unwinding a double helix.** In this figure, the protein and DNA molecules are drawn to scale. Simple diagrams are often used to give an idea of molecular events in the cell, but they may give the incorrect impression that most proteins are relatively small compared to DNA. Although DNA molecules are generally extremely long, they are relatively thin compared to many proteins.

6 The Replication Fork

Much of our understanding of the mechanism of DNA replication has been obtained from studying the bacterium *Escherichia coli,* and the following discussion deals primarily with this organism. However, the process of DNA replication is probably quite similar in all *Bacteria*. By contrast, although most species of *Archaea* have circular chromosomes, many events in DNA replication resemble those in eukaryotic cells more than those in *Bacteria*. This again reflects the phylogenetic affiliation between *Archaea* and *Eukarya*.

Initiation of DNA Synthesis

Before DNA polymerase can synthesize new DNA, the preexisting double helix must be unwound to expose the template strands. The zone of unwound DNA where replication occurs is known as the **replication fork**. An enzyme known as DNA helicase unwinds the DNA double helix and exposes a short single-stranded region (Figures 13 and 14). The energy required by helicases for unwinding DNA comes from the hydrolysis of ATP. Helicases move along the helix and separate the strands just in advance of the replication fork. The single-stranded region is complexed with a special protein, the single-strand binding protein, which stabilizes the single-stranded DNA, preventing the formation of intrastrand hydrogen bonds and reversion to the double helix.

In prokaryotes, there is a single location on the chromosome where DNA synthesis is initiated, the origin of replication. This consists of a specific DNA sequence of about 250 bases that is recognized by specific initiation proteins, in particular a protein called DnaA (Table 2), which binds to this region and opens up the double helix to expose the individual strands to the replication machinery. Next to assemble is the helicase (also known as DnaB), which is helped onto the DNA by the helicase loader protein (or DnaC). Two helicases are loaded, one onto each strand, facing in opposite directions. Next, two primase and then two DNA polymerase enzymes are loaded onto the DNA behind the helicases. Initiation of DNA replication then begins on the two single strands. As replication proceeds, the replication fork appears to move along the DNA (Figure 13). www.microbiologyplace.com **Online Tutorial 1: DNA Replication**

Leading and Lagging Strands

Figure 13 shows an important distinction in replication of the two DNA strands due to the fact that replication always proceeds from 5′ → 3′ (always adding a new nucleotide to the 3′-OH of the growing chain). On the strand growing from the 5′-PO_4^{2-} to the 3′-OH, called the **leading strand**, DNA synthesis occurs continuously because there is always a free 3′-OH at the replication fork to which a new nucleotide can be added. But on the opposite strand, called the **lagging strand**, DNA synthesis occurs discontinuously because there is no 3′-OH at the replication fork to which a new nucleotide can attach. Where is the 3′-OH on this strand? It is located at the opposite end, away from the replication fork. Therefore, on

Table 2 Major enzymes involved in DNA replication in *Bacteria*

Enzyme	*Encoding genes*	*Function*
DNA gyrase	*gyrAB*	Unwinds supercoils ahead of replisome
Origin-binding protein	*dnaA*	Binds origin of replication; aids DNA melting to open double helix
Helicase loader	*dnaC*	Loads helicase at origin
Helicase	*dnaB*	Unwinds double helix at replication fork
Single-strand binding protein	*ssb*	Prevents single strands from annealing
Primase	*dnaG*	Primes new strands of DNA
DNA polymerase III		Main polymerizing enzyme
Sliding clamp	*dnaN*	Holds Pol III on DNA
Clamp loader	*holA–E*	Loads Pol III onto sliding clamp (Figure 19)
Dimerization subunit	*dnaX*	Holds together the two core enzymes for the leading and lagging strands
Polymerase subunit	*dnaE*	Strand elongation
Proofreading subunit	*dnaQ*	Proofreading
DNA polymerase I	*polA*	Excises RNA primer and fills in gaps
DNA ligase	*ligA, ligB*	Seals nicks in DNA
Tus protein	*tus*	Binds terminus and blocks progress of the replication fork
Topoisomerase IV	*parCE*	Unlinking of interlocked circles

the lagging strand, RNA primers must be synthesized by primase multiple times to provide free 3′-OH groups. By contrast, the leading strand is primed only once, at the origin. As a result, the lagging strand is made in short segments, called *Okazaki fragments,* after their discoverer, Reiji Okazaki. These fragments are joined together later to give a continuous strand of DNA.

DNA Replication: Synthesis of the New DNA Strands

After synthesizing the RNA primer, primase is replaced by Pol III. This enzyme is a complex of several proteins (Table 2), including the polymerase core enzyme itself. Each polymerase is held on the DNA by a sliding clamp, which encircles and slides along the single template strands of DNA. Consequently, the replication fork contains two polymerase core enzymes and two sliding clamps, one set for each strand. However, there is only a single clamp-loader complex. This is needed to assemble the sliding clamps onto the DNA. After assembly on the lagging strand, the elongation component of

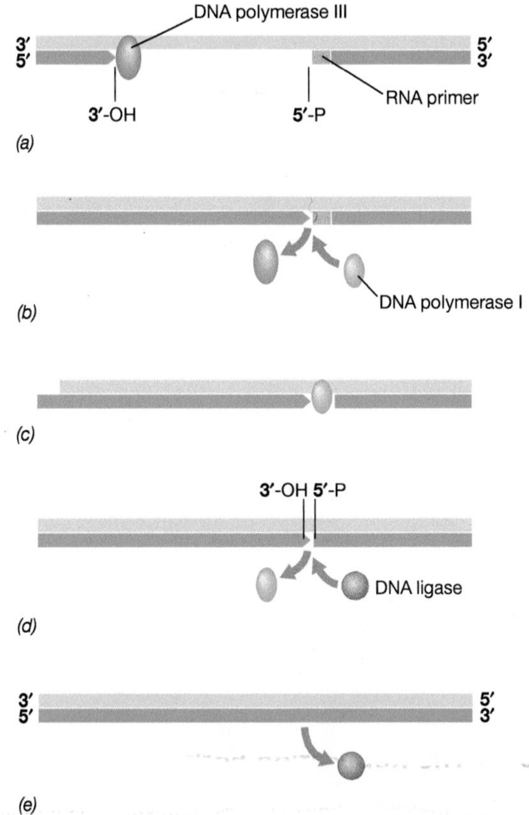

Figure 15 Sealing two fragments on the lagging strand. *(a)* DNA polymerase III is synthesizing DNA in the 5′ → 3′ direction toward the RNA primer of a previously synthesized fragment on the lagging strand. *(b)* On reaching the fragment, DNA polymerase III leaves and is replaced by DNA polymerase I. *(c)* DNA polymerase I continues synthesizing DNA while removing the RNA primer from the previous fragment. *(d)* DNA ligase replaces DNA polymerase I after the primer has been removed. *(e)* DNA ligase seals the two fragments together.

Pol III, DnaE, then adds deoxyribonucleotides until it reaches previously synthesized DNA (Figure 15). At this point, the activity of Pol III stops.

The next enzyme to take part, Pol I, has more than one enzymatic activity. Besides synthesizing DNA, Pol I has a 5′ → 3′ exonuclease activity that removes the RNA primer preceding it (Figure 15). When the primer has been removed and replaced with DNA, Pol I is released. The last phosphodiester bond is made by an enzyme called *DNA ligase.* This enzyme seals nicks in DNAs that have an adjacent 5′-PO_4^{2-} and 3′-OH (something that Pol III is unable to do), and along with Pol I, it also participates in DNA repair. DNA ligase also plays an important role in sealing genetically manipulated DNA in the process of molecular cloning.

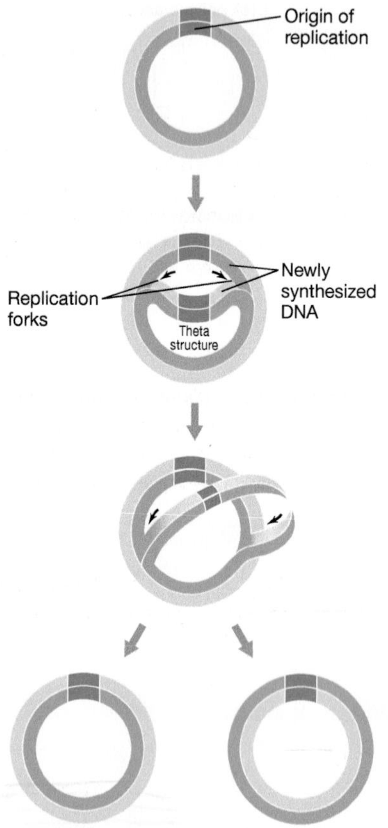

Figure 16 **Replication of circular DNA: the theta structure.** In circular DNA, bidirectional replication from an origin forms an intermediate structure resembling the Greek letter theta (θ).

6 MiniReview

DNA synthesis begins at a unique location called the origin of replication. The double helix is unwound by helicase and is stabilized by single-strand binding protein. Extension of the DNA occurs continuously on the leading strand but discontinuously on the lagging strand. The fragments of the lagging strand are joined together later.

- Why are there leading and lagging strands?
- What recognizes the origin of replication?
- What enzymes take part in joining the fragments of the lagging strand?

7 Bidirectional Replication and the Replisome

The circular nature of the chromosome of *Escherichia coli* and most other prokaryotes creates an opportunity for speeding up replication. Here we consider how this fits into the overall scheme of replication and cell division.

Bidirectional Chromosome Replication

In *E. coli,* and probably in all prokaryotes with circular chromosomes, replication is *bidirectional* from the origin of replication, as shown in Figures 16 and 17. There are thus two replication forks on each chromosome moving in opposite directions. In circular DNA, bidirectional replication leads to the formation of characteristic structures called theta structures (Figure 16). Most large DNA molecules, whether from prokaryotes or eukaryotes, have bidirectional replication from fixed origins. In fact, a single eukaryotic chromosome has many origins. Close inspection of the replicating DNA shows that during bidirectional replication, synthesis is occurring in both a leading and lagging fashion on each template strand (Figure 17).

Bidirectional DNA synthesis along a circular chromosome allows DNA to replicate as rapidly as possible. Even taking this into account and considering that Pol III can add nucleotides to a growing DNA strand at the rate of about 1,000 per second, chromosome replication in *E. coli* still takes about 40 min. Interestingly, under the best growth conditions, *E. coli* can grow with a doubling time of about 20 min. However, under these conditions, chromosome replication still takes 40 min. The solution to this conundrum is that cells of *E. coli* growing at doubling times shorter than 40 min contain multiple DNA replication forks. That is, a new round of DNA replication begins before the last round has been completed (Figure 18). Only in this way can a generation time shorter than the chromosome replication time be maintained.

The Replisome

While DNA is being synthesized at the replication fork, the coiling of the DNA is changing due to the activities of topoisomerases (Section 3). Unwinding is an essential feature of DNA replication, and because supercoiled DNA is under tension, it unwinds more easily than DNA that is not supercoiled. Thus, by regulating the degree of supercoiling, topoisomerases may regulate the process of replication (and also transcription, as discussed later).

Figure 13 shows the differences in replication of the leading and the lagging strands and the enzymes involved. From such a simplified drawing it would appear that each replication fork contains a host of different proteins all working independently. Actually, this is not the case. The highly dynamic proteins aggregate to form a large replication complex called the *replisome* (Figure 19). The lagging strand of DNA loops out to allow the replisome to move smoothly along both strands, and the replisome literally pulls the DNA template through it as replication occurs (Figure 18). Therefore, it is the DNA, and not DNA polymerase, that moves during replication. Note also in the replisome how helicase and primase form a subcomplex, called the *primosome,* which aids their

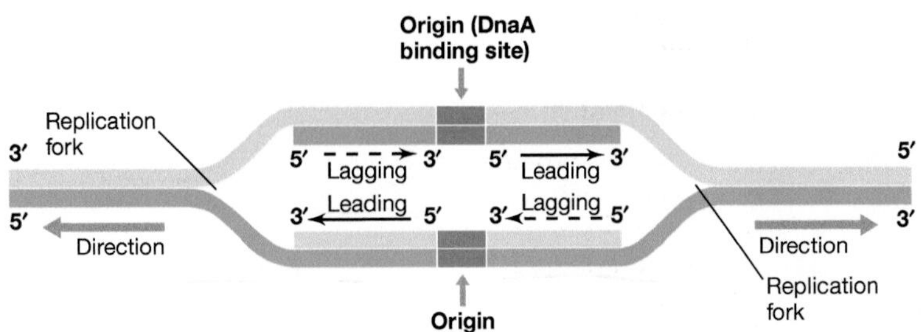

Figure 17 Dual replication forks in the circular chromosome. At an origin of replication that directs bidirectional replication, two replication forks must start. Therefore, two leading strands must be primed, one in each direction. In *Escherichia coli*, the origin of replication is identified by the binding of a specific protein, DnaA.

working in close association during the replication process (Figure 19).

In summary, in addition to Pol III, the replisome contains several key replication proteins: (1) DNA gyrase, which removes supercoils; (2) DNA helicase and primase (the primosome), which unwind and prime the DNA; and (3) single-strand binding protein, which prevents the separated template strands from re-forming a double helix (Figure 19). Table 2 summarizes the properties of proteins essential for DNA replication.

7 MiniReview

Starting from a single origin, DNA synthesis proceeds in both directions around circular chromosomes. Therefore, there are two replication forks in operation simultaneously. The proteins at the replication fork form a large complex known as the replisome.

- What is the replisome and what are its components?
- How does *Escherichia coli* manage to carry out cell division in less time than it takes to duplicate its chromosome?

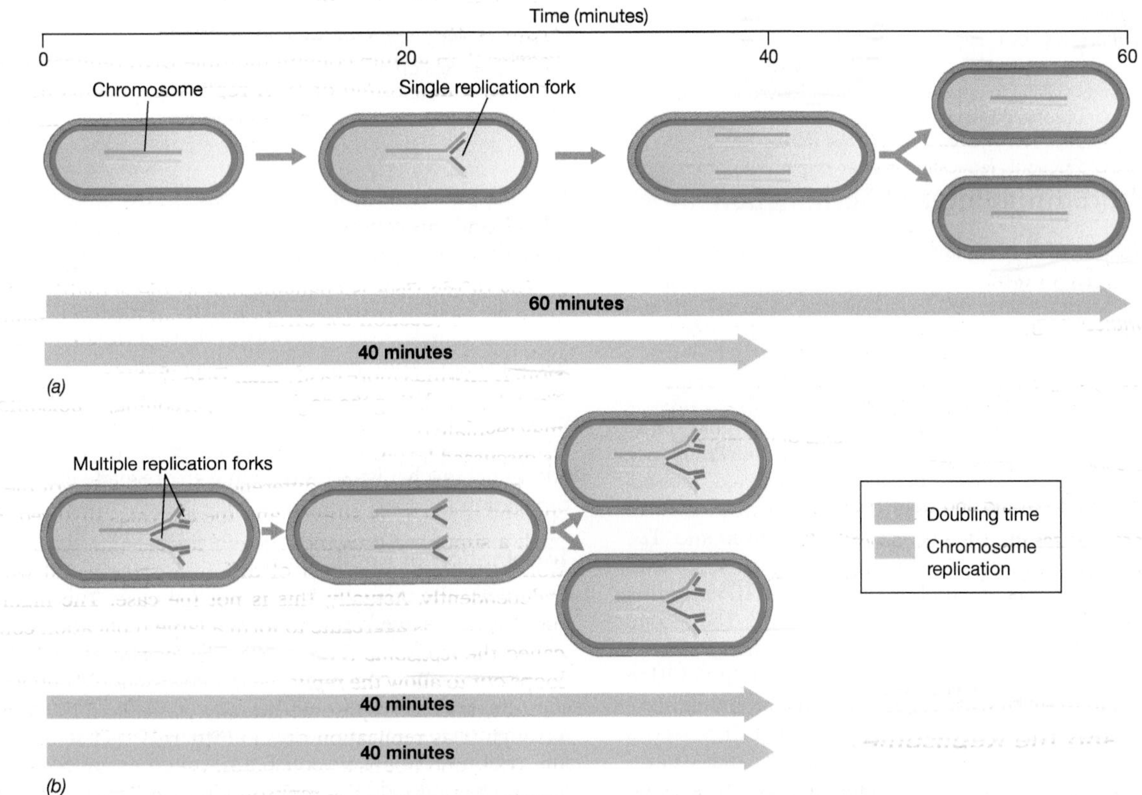

Figure 18 Cell division versus chromosome duplication. *(a)* Cells of *Escherichia coli* take approximately 40 min to replicate the chromosome and an additional 20 min for cell division. *(b)* When cells double in less than 60 min, a new round of chromosome replication must be initiated before the previous round is finished.

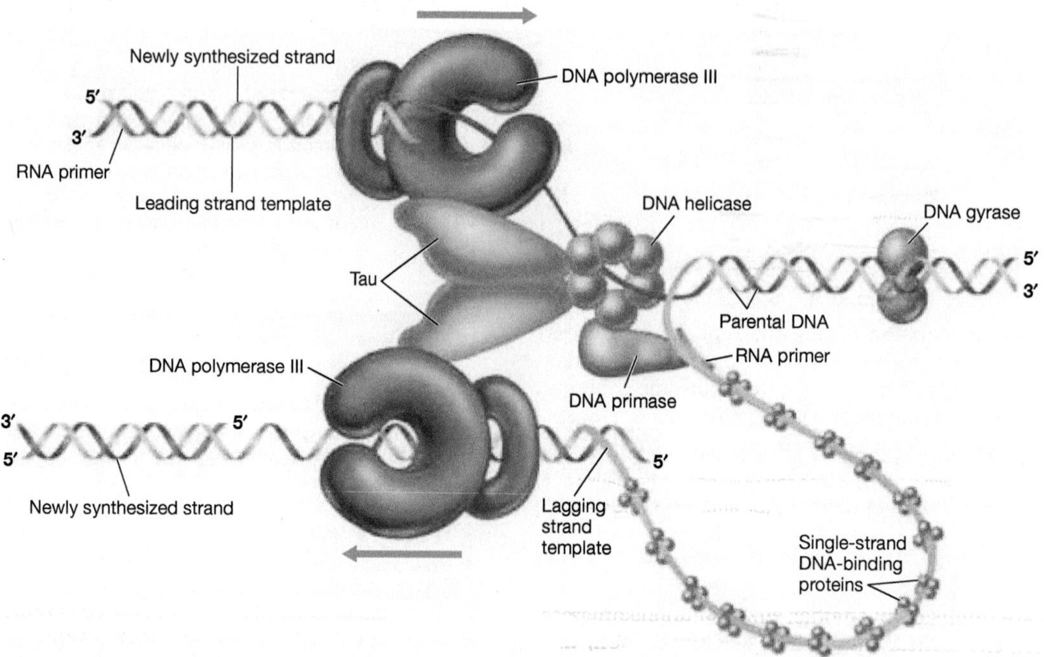

Figure 19 **The replisome.** The replisome consists of two copies of DNA polymerase III, plus helicase and primase (together forming the primosome), and many copies of single-strand DNA-binding protein. The tau subunits hold the two DNA polymerase assemblies and helicase together. Just upstream of the replisome, DNA gyrase removes supercoils in the DNA to be replicated. Note that the two polymerases are replicating the two individual strands of DNA in opposite directions. Consequently, the lagging-strand template loops around so that the whole replisome moves in the same direction along the chromosome.

8 Proofreading and Termination

DNA replicates with a remarkably low error rate. Nevertheless, when errors do occur, a back-up mechanism exists to detect and correct them. After considering this, we will discuss how DNA synthesis is terminated.

Fidelity of DNA Replication: Proofreading

Errors in DNA replication introduce mutations, changes in DNA sequence. Mutation rates in cells are remarkably low, between 10^{-8} and 10^{-11} errors per base pair inserted. This accuracy is possible partly because DNA polymerases get two chances to incorporate the correct base at a given site. The first chance follows the insertion of complementary bases opposite the bases on the template strand by Pol III according to the base-pairing rules, A with T and G with C. The second chance depends upon a second enzymatic activity of both Pol I and Pol III, called *proofreading* (Figure 20). In Pol III, a separate protein subunit, DnaQ, performs the proofreading.

How does proofreading work? Pol I and Pol III possess a $3' \rightarrow 5'$ exonuclease (exo means "end") activity that can remove a misinserted nucleotide. Proofreading activity occurs if an incorrect base has been inserted because this creates a mismatch in base pairing. The polymerase senses this because a misinserted nucleotide does not form the correct hydrogen-bonding pattern with its partner base in the complementary strand, and this causes a slight distortion in the double helix. After the removal of a mismatched nucleotide, Pol III gets a second chance to insert the correct nucleotide (Figure 20).

Proofreading exonuclease activity is distinct from the $5' \rightarrow 3'$ exonuclease activity of Pol I that is used to remove the RNA primer from both the leading and lagging strands (Figure 15). Only Pol I has this latter activity. Exonuclease proofreading occurs in prokaryotes, eukaryotes, and viral DNA replication systems. However, many organisms have additional mechanisms for reducing errors made during DNA replication.

Termination of Replication

Eventually the process of DNA replication is finished. How does the replisome know when to stop? On the opposite side of the circular chromosome from the origin is a site called the terminus of replication. Here the two replication forks collide as the new circles of DNA are completed. The details of termination are not completely known. However, in the terminus region there are several DNA sequences called *Ter* sites that are recognized by a protein called Tus, whose function is to block progress of the replication forks. When replication of the circular chromosome is complete (Figure 16), the two circular molecules are linked together, much like the links of a

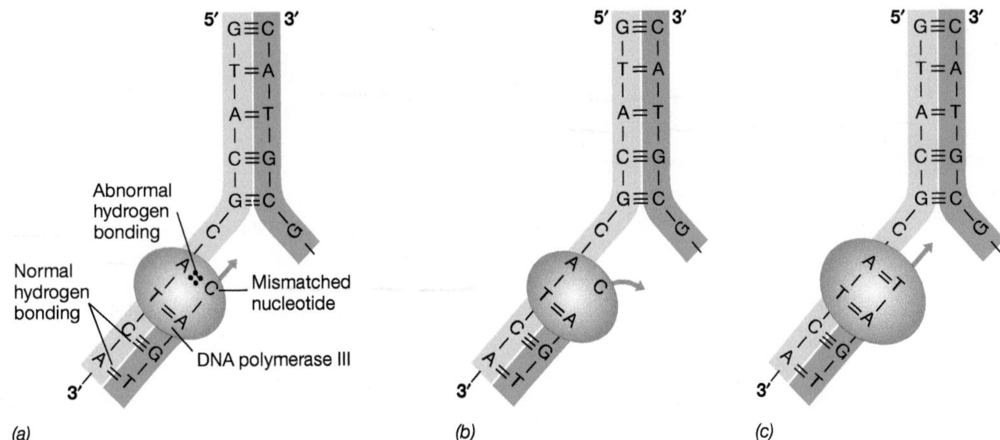

Figure 20 **Proofreading by the 3′ → 5′ exonuclease activity of DNA polymerase III.** A mismatch in base pairing at the terminal base pair *(a)* causes the polymerase to pause briefly. This is a signal for the proofreading activity to excise the mismatched nucleotide *(b)*, after which the correct base is incorporated by the polymerase activity *(c)*.

chain. They are unlinked by another enzyme, topoisomerase IV. Obviously, it is critical that, after DNA replication, the DNA is partitioned so that each daughter cell receives a copy of the chromosome. This process may be assisted by the important cell division protein FtsZ, which helps orchestrate several key events of cell division.

8 MiniReview

Most errors in base pairing that occur during replication are corrected by the proofreading functions of DNA polymerases. Incorrect nucleotides are removed and replaced. Finally, DNA replication terminates when the replication forks meet at a special terminus region on the chromosome.

- How is proofreading carried out during DNA replication?
- What brings the replication forks to a halt in the terminus region of the chromosome?

IV RNA SYNTHESIS: TRANSCRIPTION

Ribonucleic acid (RNA) plays a number of important roles in the cell. There are three key differences in the chemistry of RNA and DNA: (1) RNA contains the sugar ribose instead of deoxyribose; (2) RNA contains the base uracil instead of thymine; and (3) except in certain viruses, RNA is not double-stranded. A change from deoxyribose to ribose affects the chemistry of a nucleic acid; enzymes that act on DNA usually have no effect on RNA, and vice versa. However, the change from thymine to uracil does not affect base pairing, as these two bases pair with adenine equally well.

Three major types of RNA are involved in protein synthesis: *messenger RNA (mRNA), transfer RNA (tRNA),* and *ribosomal RNA (rRNA).* Several other types of RNA are also found that are mostly involved in regulation. These RNA molecules are all products of the transcription of DNA. It should be emphasized that RNA plays a role at two levels, genetic and functional. At the genetic level, mRNA carries the genetic information from the genome to the ribosome. In contrast, rRNA has both a functional and a structural role in ribosomes and tRNA has an active role in carrying amino acids for protein synthesis. Some RNA even has catalytic (enzymatic) activity (ribozymes). In this section we focus on how RNA is synthesized in species of *Bacteria,* using *Escherichia coli* as our model organism.

9 Overview of Transcription

Transcription of genetic information from DNA to RNA is carried out by the enzyme **RNA polymerase**. Like DNA polymerase, RNA polymerase catalyzes the formation of phosphodiester bonds but in this case between ribonucleotides rather than deoxyribonucleotides. RNA polymerase requires DNA as a template. The precursors of RNA are the ribonucleoside triphosphates ATP, GTP, UTP, and CTP.

The mechanism of RNA synthesis is much like that of DNA synthesis (Figure 11). That is, during elongation of an RNA chain, ribonucleoside triphosphates are added to the 3′-OH of the ribose of the preceding nucleotide. Polymerization is driven by the release of energy from the two energy-rich phosphate bonds of the incoming ribonucleoside triphosphates. In both DNA replication and RNA transcription the overall direction of chain growth is from the 5′ end to the 3′ end, thus the newly synthesized strand is antiparallel to the template strand. Unlike DNA polymerase, however, RNA polymerase

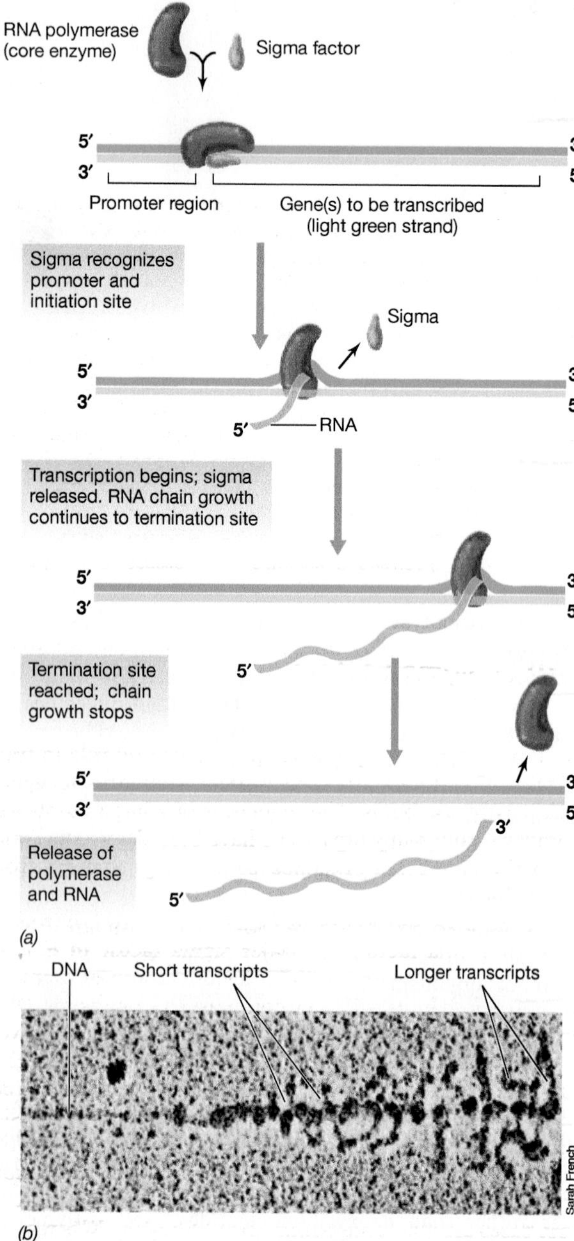

Figure 21 **Transcription.** *(a)* Steps in RNA synthesis. The initiation site (promoter) and termination site are specific nucleotide sequences on the DNA. RNA polymerase moves down the DNA chain, temporarily opening the double helix and transcribing one of the DNA strands. *(b)* Electron micrograph of transcription along a gene on the *Escherichia coli* chromosome. The region of active transcription is about 2 kb pairs of DNA. Transcription is proceeding from left to right, with the shorter transcripts on the left becoming longer as transcription proceeds.

can initiate new strands of nucleotides on its own; consequently, no primer is necessary.

RNA Polymerases

The template for RNA polymerase is a double-stranded DNA molecule, but only one of the two strands is transcribed for any given gene. Nevertheless, genes are present on both strands of DNA and thus DNA sequences on both strands are transcribed, although at different locations. Although these principles are true for transcription in all organisms, there are significant differences among RNA polymerase from *Bacteria, Archaea,* and *Eukarya.* The following discussion deals only with RNA polymerase from *Bacteria,* which has the simplest structure and about which most is known.

RNA polymerase from *Bacteria* has five different subunits, designated β, β′, α, ω (omega) and σ (sigma), with α present in two copies. The β and β′ (beta prime) subunits are similar but not identical. The subunits interact to form the active enzyme, called the RNA polymerase holoenzyme, but the sigma factor is not as tightly bound as the others and easily dissociates, leading to the formation of the RNA polymerase core enzyme, $\alpha_2\beta\beta'\omega$. The core enzyme alone synthesizes RNA, whereas the sigma factor recognizes the appropriate site on the DNA for RNA synthesis to begin. The omega subunit is needed for assembly of the core enzyme but is not required for RNA synthesis. RNA synthesis carried out by RNA polymerase and sigma is illustrated in Figure 21. www.microbiologyplace.com **Online Tutorial 2: Transcription**

Promoters

RNA polymerase is a large protein and makes contact with many bases of the DNA simultaneously. Proteins such as RNA polymerase can interact specifically with DNA because portions of the bases are exposed in the major groove (Figure 5). However, in order to initiate RNA synthesis correctly, RNA polymerase must first recognize the initiation sites on the DNA. These important sites, called **promoters,** are recognized by the sigma factor (Figure 22).

Once the RNA polymerase has bound to the promoter, transcription can proceed. In this process, the DNA double helix at the promoter is opened up by the RNA polymerase to form a transcription bubble. As the polymerase moves, it unwinds the DNA in short segments. This transient unwinding exposes the template strand and allows it to be copied into the RNA complement. Thus, promoters can be thought of as pointing RNA polymerase in one direction or the other along the DNA. If a region of DNA has two nearby promoters pointing in opposite directions, then transcription from one of the promoters will proceed in one direction (on one of the strands) while transcription from the other promoter will proceed in the opposite direction (on the other strand).

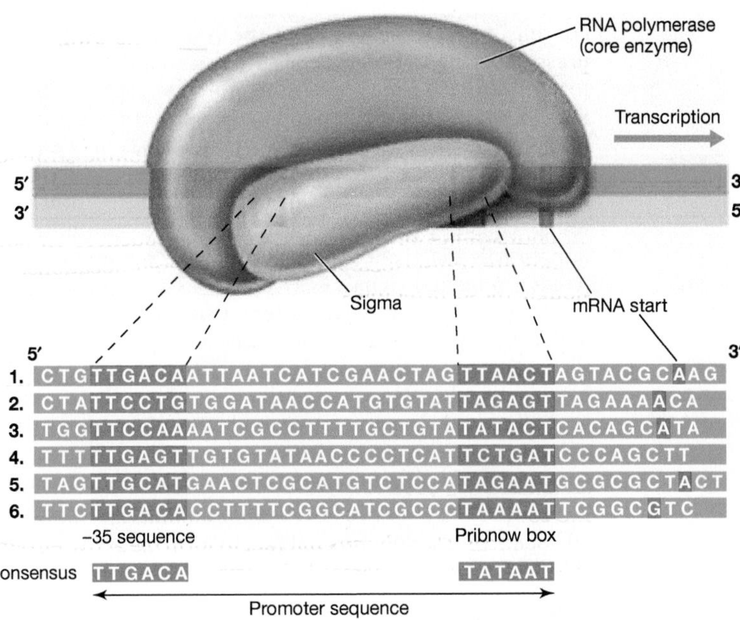

Figure 22 The interaction of RNA polymerase with the promoter. Shown below the RNA polymerase and DNA are six different promoter sequences identified in *Escherichia coli*, a species of *Bacteria*. The contacts of the RNA polymerase with the −35 sequence and the Pribnow box (−10 sequence) are shown. Transcription begins at a unique base just downstream from the Pribnow box. Below the actual sequences at the −35 and Pribnow box regions are consensus sequences derived from comparing many promoters. Note that although sigma recognizes the promoter sequences on the 5′ → 3′ (dark green) strand of DNA, the RNA polymerase core enzyme will actually transcribe the light green strand running 3′ → 5′ because core enzyme works only in a 5′ → 3′ direction.

Once a short stretch of RNA has been formed, the sigma factor dissociates. Elongation of the RNA molecule is then carried out by the core enzyme alone (Figure 21). Sigma is only involved in forming the initial RNA polymerase–DNA complex at the promoter. As the newly made RNA dissociates from the DNA, the opened DNA closes back into the original double helix. Transcription stops at specific sites called transcription terminators (Section 11).

Unlike DNA replication, which copies entire genomes, transcription involves much smaller units of DNA, often as little as a single gene. This system allows the cell to transcribe different genes at different frequencies, depending on the needs of the cell for different proteins. In other words, gene expression is regulated. Regulation of transcription is an important and elaborate process that uses many different mechanisms and is very efficient at controlling gene expression and conserving cell resources.

9 MiniReview

The three major types of RNA are messenger RNA (mRNA), transfer RNA (tRNA), and ribosomal RNA (rRNA). Transcription of RNA from DNA is due to the enzyme RNA polymerase, which adds nucleotides onto 3′ ends of growing chains. Unlike DNA polymerase, RNA polymerase needs no primer and recognizes a specific start site on the DNA called the promoter.

- In which direction (5′ → 3′ or 3′ → 5′) along the template strand does transcription occur?
- What is a promoter? What protein recognizes the promoters in *Escherichia coli*?

10 Sigma Factors and Consensus Sequences

As we have noted, the promoter plays a central role in transcription. Promoters are specific DNA sequences to which RNA polymerase binds. The sequences of a large number of promoters from many organisms have been determined, and Figure 22 shows the sequence of a few promoters from *Escherichia coli.*

All the DNA sequences in Figure 22 are recognized by the same sigma factor, the major sigma factor in *E. coli*, called σ^{70} (the superscript 70 indicates the size of this protein, 70 kilodaltons). If you compare the promoter DNA sequences, you will see that they are not identical. However, two shorter sequences within the promoter region are highly conserved between promoters, and it is these that sigma recognizes. Both sequences precede (are upstream of) the site where transcription starts. One is a region 10 bases before the start of transcription, the −10 region, called the *Pribnow box*. Notice that although each promoter is slightly different, most bases are the same within the −10 region. When comparing the −10 regions of all the promoters recognized by this sigma factor to determine which base occurs most often at each position, one arrives at the consensus sequence: TATAAT. In our example, each promoter has from three to five matches for these bases. The second region of conserved sequence in the promoter is about 35 bases from the start of transcription. The consensus sequence in the −35 region is TTGACA (Figure 22). Once again, most of the sequences are not exactly the same as the consensus sequence, but are very close.

Table 3 Sigma factors in *Escherichia coli*

Name[a]	Upstream consensus recognition sequence[b]	Function
σ^{70} RpoD	TTGACA	For most genes, major sigma factor during normal growth
σ^{54} RpoN	TTGGCACA	Nitrogen assimilation
σ^{38} RpoS	CCGGCG	Major sigma factor during stationary phase, also for genes involved in oxidative and osmotic responses
σ^{32} RpoH	TNTCNCCTTGAA[c]	Heat shock response
σ^{28} FliA	TAAA	For genes involved in flagella synthesis
σ^{24} RpoE	GAACTT	Response to misfolded proteins in periplasm
σ^{19} FecI	AAGGAAAAT	For certain genes in iron transport

[a]Superscript number in name indicates size of protein in kilodaltons. Many factors also have other names, for example, σ^{70} is also called σ^{D}.

[b]For a discussion of consensus sequences, see Sections 10 and 11 and Figure 30.

[c]N = any nucleotide.

Note that in Figure 22 the promoter sequence is shown for only one strand of the DNA. By convention, the strand shown is the one oriented with its 5′ end upstream (therefore, it is not the strand used as the template by RNA polymerase). Showing the sequence of only one strand is simply "shorthand" for writing DNA sequences. In reality, DNA is double-stranded, and RNA polymerase binds to double-stranded DNA and then unwinds it. A single strand of the unwound DNA, the transcribed strand is then used as template by the core RNA polymerase. Although it binds to both DNA strands, sigma recognizes the specific sequences in the −10 and −35 regions on the nontranscribed strand with which it makes most of its contacts.

Some sigma factors in other bacteria are much more specific as regards binding sequences than the example shown in Figure 22. In such cases, very little leeway is allowed in the critical bases that are recognized. In *E. coli*, promoters that are most like the consensus sequence are usually more effective in binding RNA polymerase. These more effective promoters are called strong promoters and are very useful in genetic engineering.

Alternative Sigma Factors in *Escherichia coli*

Most genes in *E. coli* require the standard sigma factor, known as σ^{70}, for transcription and have promoters like those shown in Figure 22. However, several alternative sigma factors are known that recognize different consensus sequences (Table 3). Each of these alternative sigma factors is specific for a group of genes required under special circumstances. Thus σ^{38}, also known as RpoS, recognizes a consensus sequence found in the promoters of genes expressed during stationary phase. Consequently, it is possible to control the expression of each family of genes by regulating the level of the corresponding sigma factor. This may be done by changing either the rate of synthesis or the rate of degradation of the sigma factor. In addition, the activity of alternative sigma factors can be modulated by other proteins called *anti-sigma factors*. These proteins can temporarily inactivate a particular sigma factor in response to environmental signals.

In total there are seven different sigma factors in *E. coli*, and each recognizes different consensus sequences (Table 3). Sigma factors were originally named according to their molecular weight. More recently, they have been named according to their roles, for example, RpoN stands for "*R*NA *po*lymerase—*N*itrogen." Most of these sigma factors have counterparts in other *Bacteria*. The endospore-forming bacterium *Bacillus subtilis* has 14 sigma factors, with 4 different sigma factors dedicated to the transcription of endospore-specific genes.

10 MiniReview

In *Bacteria*, promoters are recognized by the sigma subunit of RNA polymerase. Regions of DNA recognized by a particular DNA-binding protein have very similar sequences. Alternative sigma factors allow joint regulation of large families of genes in response to growth conditions.

- What is a consensus sequence?
- To what parts of the promoter region does sigma bind?
- How may families of genes required during specialized conditions be controlled as a group using sigma factors?

11 Termination of Transcription

Only those genes that need to be expressed should be transcribed. Therefore it is important to terminate transcription at the correct position. **Termination** of RNA synthesis is governed by specific base sequences on the DNA. In *Bacteria* a common termination signal on the DNA is a GC-rich sequence containing an inverted repeat with a central nonrepeating segment (see Section 2 and Figure 6 for an explanation of inverted repeats). When such a DNA sequence is transcribed, the RNA forms a stem-loop structure by intrastrand base pairing (Figure 23). Such stem-loop structures, followed by a run of adenosines in the DNA template and therefore a run of uridines in the mRNA, are effective transcription terminators. This is due to the formation of a stretch of U:A base pairs that holds the RNA and DNA template together. This structure is very weak as U:A base pairs have only two hydrogen bonds each. The RNA polymerase pauses at the stem-loop, and the

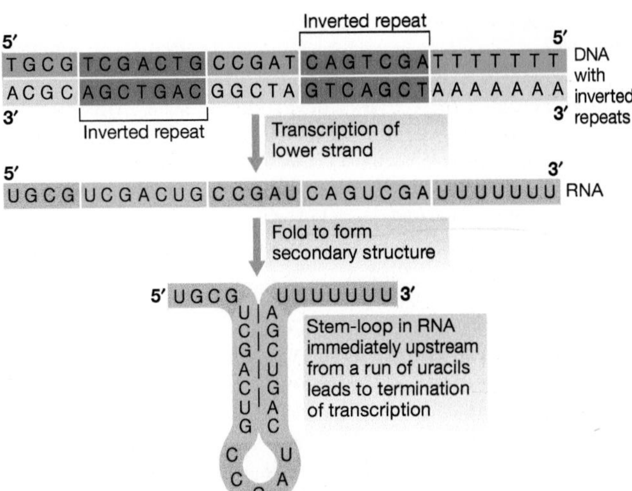

Figure 23 Inverted repeats and transcription termination. Inverted repeats in transcribed DNA form a stem-loop structure in the RNA that terminates transcription when followed by a run of uracils.

DNA and RNA come apart at the run of uridines. This terminates transcription. Sequence patterns that terminate transcription without addition of any extra factors are referred to as intrinsic terminators.

Rho-Dependent Termination

The other mechanism for transcription termination uses a specific protein factor, known in *Escherichia coli* as Rho. Rho does not bind to RNA polymerase or to the DNA, but binds tightly to RNA and moves down the chain toward the RNA polymerase–DNA complex. Once RNA polymerase has paused at a Rho-dependent termination site (a specific sequence on the DNA template), Rho causes both the RNA and RNA polymerase to be released from the DNA, thus terminating transcription. Although the termination sequences function at the level of RNA, remember that RNA is transcribed from DNA. Consequently, transcription termination is ultimately determined by specific nucleotide sequences on the DNA.

11 MiniReview

RNA polymerase stops transcription at specific sites called transcription terminators. Although encoded by DNA, these terminators function at the level of RNA. Some are intrinsic terminators and require no accessory proteins beyond RNA polymerase itself. In *Bacteria* these sequences are usually stem-loops followed by a run of uridines. Other terminators require proteins such as Rho.

- What is an intrinsic terminator?
- What is a stem-loop structure?

12 The Unit of Transcription

Chromosomes are organized into units that are bounded by sites where transcription of DNA into RNA is initiated and terminated: units of transcription. One might assume that each unit of transcription includes only a single gene. Although this is true in some instances, it is not always the case. Some units of transcription contain two or more genes. These genes are then said to be cotranscribed, yielding a single RNA molecule.

Ribosomal and Transfer RNAs and RNA Longevity

As we learned in Section 1, most genes encode proteins, but others encode RNAs that are not translated, such as ribosomal RNA (rRNA) and transfer RNA (tRNA). There are several different types of rRNA in an organism (with a ribosome having one copy of each type; Section 13). Prokaryotes have three types: 16S rRNA, 23S rRNA, and 5S rRNA. As shown in Figure 24, there are clusters containing one gene for each of these rRNAs, and the genes in such a cluster are cotranscribed. The situation is similar in eukaryotes. Therefore, in all organisms the unit of transcription for most rRNA is longer than a single gene. In prokaryotes tRNA genes are often cotranscribed with each other or even, as shown in Figure 24, with genes for rRNA. However, these cotranscribed transcripts must be processed (cleaved into individual units) to yield mature (functional) rRNAs or tRNAs (Figure 24). RNA

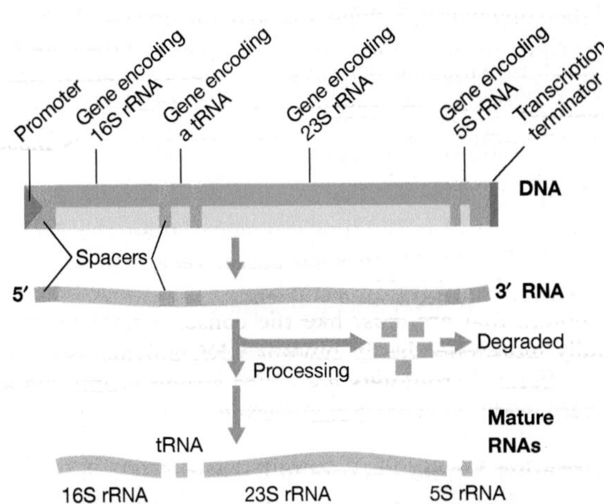

Figure 24 A ribosomal rRNA transcription unit from *Bacteria* and its subsequent processing. In *Bacteria* all rRNA transcription units have the genes in the order 16S rRNA, 23S rRNA, and 5S rRNA (shown approximately to scale). Note that in this particular transcription unit the "spacer" between the 16S and 23S rRNA genes contains a tRNA gene. In other transcription units this region may contain more than one tRNA gene. Often one or more tRNA genes also follow the 5S rRNA gene and are cotranscribed. *Escherichia coli* contains seven rRNA transcription units.

Table 4 The genetic code as expressed by triplet base sequences of mRNA

Codon	Amino acid	Codon	Amino acid	Codon	Amino acid	Codon	Amino acid
UUU	Phenylalanine	UCU	Serine	UAU	Tyrosine	UGU	Cysteine
UUC	Phenylalanine	UCC	Serine	UAC	Tyrosine	UGC	Cysteine
UUA	Leucine	UCA	Serine	UAA	None (stop signal)	UGA	None (stop signal)
UUG	Leucine	UCG	Serine	UAG	None (stop signal)	UGG	Tryptophan
CUU	Leucine	CCU	Proline	CAU	Histidine	CGU	Arginine
CUC	Leucine	CCC	Proline	CAC	Histidine	CGC	Arginine
CUA	Leucine	CCA	Proline	CAA	Glutamine	CGA	Arginine
CUG	Leucine	CCG	Proline	CAG	Glutamine	CGG	Arginine
AUU	Isoleucine	ACU	Threonine	AAU	Asparagine	AGU	Serine
AUC	Isoleucine	ACC	Threonine	AAC	Asparagine	AGC	Serine
AUA	Isoleucine	ACA	Threonine	AAA	Lysine	AGA	Arginine
AUG (start)[a]	Methionine	ACG	Threonine	AAG	Lysine	AGG	Arginine
GUU	Valine	GCU	Alanine	GAU	Aspartic acid	GGU	Glycine
GUC	Valine	GCC	Alanine	GAC	Aspartic acid	GGC	Glycine
GUA	Valine	GCA	Alanine	GAA	Glutamic acid	GGA	Glycine
GUG	Valine	GCG	Alanine	GAG	Glutamic acid	GGG	Glycine

[a]AUG encodes *N*-formylmethionine at the beginning of polypeptide chains of *Bacteria*.

processing is rare in prokaryotes but common in eukaryotes, as we will see later.

In prokaryotes, most messenger RNAs have a short half-life (on the order of a few minutes), after which they are degraded by cellular ribonucleases. This is in contrast to rRNA and tRNA, which are stable RNAs. The stability occurs because tRNAs and rRNAs form highly folded structures that prevent them from being degraded by ribonucleases. By contrast, normal mRNA does not form such structures and is susceptible to ribonuclease attack. The rapid turnover of prokaryotic mRNAs is likely a mechanism that permits the cell to quickly adapt to new environmental conditions and halt translation of messages whose products are no longer needed.

Polycistronic mRNA and the Operon

In prokaryotes, genes encoding related enzymes are often clustered together (Figure 2). RNA polymerase proceeds through such clusters and transcribes the whole group of genes into a single, long mRNA molecule. An mRNA encoding such a group of cotranscribed genes is called a *polycistronic mRNA*. When this is translated, several polypeptides are synthesized, one after another, by the same ribosome.

A group of related genes that are transcribed together to give a single polycistronic mRNA is known as an **operon**. Assembling genes for the same biochemical pathway or genes needed under the same conditions into an operon allows their expression to be regulated in a coordinated manner. Despite this, eukaryotes do not have operons and polycistronic mRNA. Often, transcription of an operon is controlled by a specific region of the DNA found just upstream of the protein-coding region of the operon.

12 MiniReview

The unit of transcription in prokaryotes often contains more than a single gene. Several genes are then transcribed into a single mRNA molecule that contains information for more than one polypeptide. A cluster of genes that are transcribed together from a single promoter constitute an operon. In all organisms, genes encoding rRNA are cotranscribed but then processed to form the final rRNA species.

- What is messenger RNA (mRNA)?
- What is a polycistronic mRNA?
- What are operons and why are they useful to prokaryotes?

V PROTEIN SYNTHESIS

In the first two steps in biological information transfer, replication and transcription, nucleic acids are synthesized on nucleic acid templates. In the last step, **translation**, there is synthesis on a nucleic acid template, but in this case the final product is a *protein* rather than a *nucleic acid.*

13 The Genetic Code

Before we describe the mechanism of translation, we need to discuss the heart of biological information transfer: the

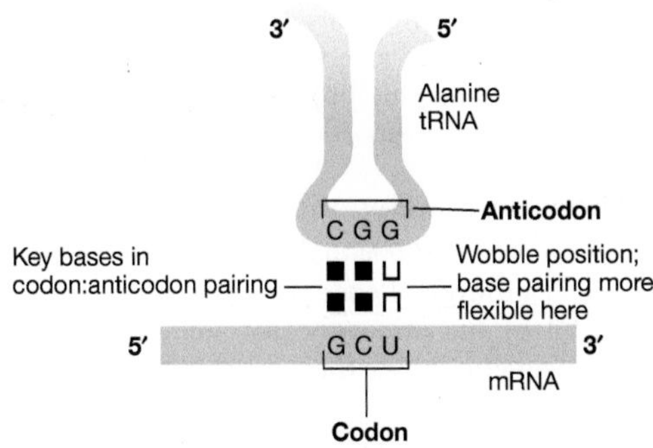

Figure 25 **The wobble concept.** Base pairing is more flexible for the third base of the codon than for the first two. Only a portion of the tRNA is shown (the structure of the whole tRNA is shown in Figure 27).

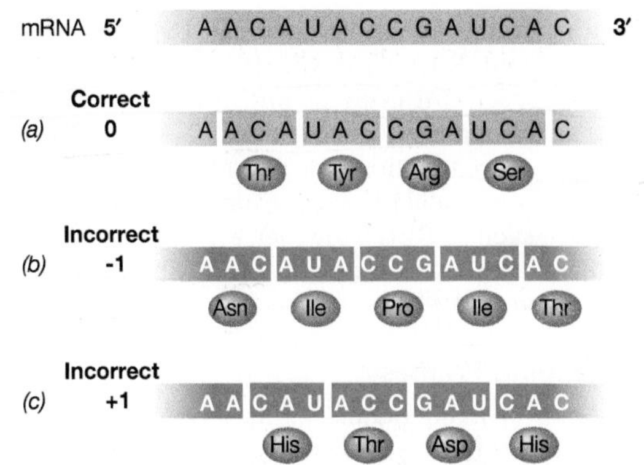

Figure 26 **Possible reading frames in an mRNA.** An interior sequence of an mRNA is shown. *(a)* The amino acids that would be encoded if the ribosome is in the correct reading frame (designated the "0" frame). *(b)* The amino acids that would be encoded by this region of the mRNA if the ribosome were in the −1 reading frame. *(c)* The amino acids that would be encoded if the ribosome were in the +1 reading frame.

correspondence between the nucleic acid template and the amino acid sequence of the polypeptide product. This is known as the **genetic code**. As we mentioned in Section 1, a triplet of three bases called a *codon* encodes a specific amino acid. The genetic code is written as mRNA rather than as DNA because it is mRNA that is translated. The 64 possible codons (four bases taken three at a time, 4^3) of mRNA are shown in Table 4. Note that in addition to the codons specifying the various amino acids, there are also specific codons for starting and stopping translation.

Properties of the Genetic Code

One of the most interesting features of the genetic code is that many amino acids are encoded by more than one codon. In these cases there is no one-to-one correspondence between the amino acid and the codon. Consequently, knowing the amino acid at a given location does not mean that the codon at that location is automatically known. A code such as this in which there is no one-to-one correspondence between word and code is called a degenerate code. The converse is true, however. Knowing the DNA sequence and the correct reading frame, one can specify the amino acid in the protein. This permits the determination of amino acid sequences from DNA base sequences and is at the heart of genomics. Interestingly, in most cases where multiple codons encode the same amino acid, the multiple codons are closely related in RNA sequence (Table 4).

A codon is recognized by specific base-pairing with a complementary sequence of three bases called the **anticodon**, a sequence found on tRNAs. If this base-pairing were always the standard pairing of A with U and G with C, then at least one specific tRNA would exist for each codon. In some cases, this is true. For instance, there are six different tRNAs in *Escherichia coli* that carry the amino acid leucine, one for each codon (Table 4). By contrast, some tRNAs can recognize more than one codon. For instance, although there are two lysine codons in *E. coli,* there is only one lysyl tRNA whose anticodon can base-pair with either AAA or AAG (see Table 4).

In these special cases, tRNA molecules form standard base pairs at only the first two positions of the codon while tolerating irregular base pairing at the third position. This phenomenon is called **wobble** and is illustrated in Figure 25 where it can be seen that pairing between G and U (rather than G with C) is allowed at the wobble position.

Stop and Start Codons

A few codons do not encode an amino acid (Table 4). These codons (UAA, UAG, and UGA) are the **stop codons**, and they signal the termination of translation of a protein-coding sequence on the mRNA (Section 15). Stop codons are also called **nonsense codons**, because they interrupt the "sense" of the growing polypeptide when they terminate translation.

Messenger RNA is translated beginning with the **start codon (AUG)**, which encodes a chemically modified methionine, *N*-formylmethionine. Although AUG at the beginning of a coding region encodes *N*-formylmethionine, AUG within the coding region encodes methionine. Two different tRNAs are involved in this process (see below). With a triplet code it is critical for translation to begin at the correct nucleotide. If it does not, the whole reading frame of the mRNA will be shifted and thus an entirely different protein will be made. If the shift introduces a stop codon into the reading frame, the protein will terminate prematurely. By convention the reading frame that is translated to give the protein encoded by the gene is called the 0 frame. As can be seen in Figure 26, the other two possible reading frames (−1 and +1) do not encode the same amino acid sequence. Therefore it is essential that the ribosome finds the correct start codon to begin translation and, once it has, that it moves down the mRNA exactly three bases at a time. How is the correct reading frame ensured?

Reading frame fidelity is governed by interactions between mRNA and rRNA within the ribosome. Ribosomal RNA recognizes a specific AUG on the mRNA as a start codon with the aid of an upstream sequence in the mRNA called the Shine–Dalgarno sequence (Section 15). This alignment requirement explains why occasional messages from *Bacteria* can use other start codons, such as GUG. However, even these unusual start codons direct the incorporation of *N*-formylmethionine as the initiator amino acid.

Open Reading Frames

The genomes of many organisms have been sequenced. But these mountains of sequence data would be useless unless scientists can determine the location of protein-encoding genes. One common method of identifying protein encoding genes is to examine each strand of the DNA sequence for **open reading frames (ORF)**. Remember that mRNA is transcribed from DNA, so that if one knows the sequence of DNA, one also knows the sequence of RNA that is transcribed from it. If an RNA can be translated, it contains an open reading frame: a start codon (typically AUG) followed by a number of codons and then a stop codon in the same reading frame as the start codon. In practice, only ORFs long enough to encode a protein of realistic length are accepted as true coding sequences. Although most functional proteins are at least 100 amino acids in length, a few protein hormones and regulatory peptides are much shorter. Consequently, it is not always possible to tell from sequence data alone whether a relatively short ORF is merely due to chance or encodes a genuine, albeit short, protein.

A computer can be programmed using the above guidelines to scan long DNA base sequences to look for open reading frames. In addition to looking for start and stop codons, the search may include promoters and Shine–Dalgarno ribosome-binding sequences as well. The search for ORFs is very important in genomics. If an unknown piece of DNA has been isolated and sequenced, the presence of an open reading frame indicates that it can encode protein.

Codon Bias

Several amino acids are encoded by multiple codons. One might assume that such multiple codons would be used at equal frequencies. However, this is not the case, and sequence data show major **codon bias**. In other words, some codons are greatly preferred over others even though they encode the same amino acid. Moreover, this bias is organism specific. In *E. coli*, for instance, only about 1 out of 20 isoleucine residues in proteins is encoded by the isoleucine codon AUA, the other 19 being encoded by the other isoleucine codons, AUU and AUC (Table 4). Codon bias is correlated with a corresponding bias in the concentration of different tRNA molecules. Thus a tRNA corresponding to a rarely used codon will be in relatively short supply.

The origin of codon bias is unclear, but it is easily recognized and may be taken into account in practical uses of gene sequence information. For example, a gene from one organism whose codon usage differs dramatically from that of another may not be translated well if the gene is cloned into the latter using genetic engineering. This is due to a shortage of the tRNA for codons that are rare in the host but frequent in the cloned gene. However, this problem can be corrected or at least compensated for by genetic manipulation.

Modifications to the Genetic Code

All cells appear to use the same genetic code. Therefore, the genetic code is a universal code. However, this view has been tempered a bit by the discovery that some organelles and a few cells use genetic codes that are slight variations of the "universal" genetic code.

Alternative genetic codes were first discovered in the genomes of animal mitochondria. These modified codes typically use nonsense codons as sense codons. For example, animal (but not plant) mitochondria use the codon UGA to encode tryptophan instead of using it as a stop codon (Table 4). Several organisms are known that also use slightly different genetic codes. For example, in the genus *Mycoplasma (Bacteria)* and the genus *Paramecium (Eukarya)*, certain nonsense codons encode amino acids. These organisms simply have fewer nonsense codons because one or two of them are used as sense codons. In a few rare cases, nonsense codons encode unusual amino acids rather than one of the 20 common amino acids (see below).

13 MiniReview

The genetic code is expressed as RNA, and a single amino acid may be encoded by several different but related codons. In addition to the nonsense codons, there is also a specific start codon that signals where the translation process should begin.

- Why is it important for the ribosome to read "in frame"?
- Describe an open reading frame. If you were given a nucleotide sequence, how would you find ORFs?

14 Transfer RNA

Recall from Section 13 that it is the anticodon portion of the tRNA that base-pairs with the codon. However, a tRNA is much more than simply an anticodon (Figure 27). A tRNA is specific for both a codon and its cognate amino acid (that is, the amino acid corresponding to the anticodon of the tRNA). The tRNA and its specific amino acid are brought together by specific enzymes that ensure that a particular tRNA receives its correct amino acid. These enzymes, called **aminoacyl-tRNA synthetases**, have the important function of recognizing both the cognate amino acid and the specific tRNA for that amino acid.

General Structure of tRNA

There are about 60 different tRNAs in bacterial cells and 100–110 in mammalian cells. Transfer RNA molecules are short, single-stranded molecules that contain extensive secondary structure and have lengths of 73–93 nucleotides.

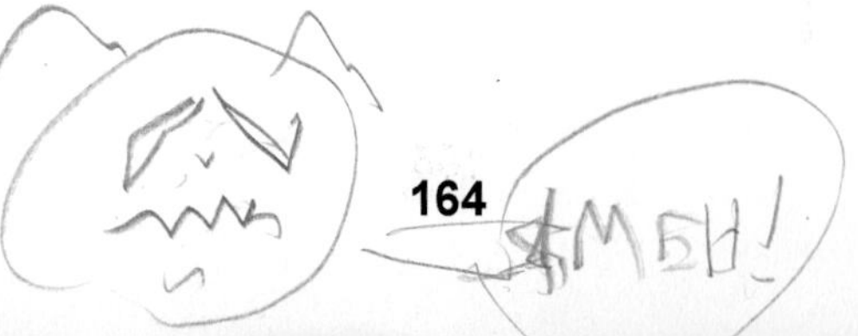

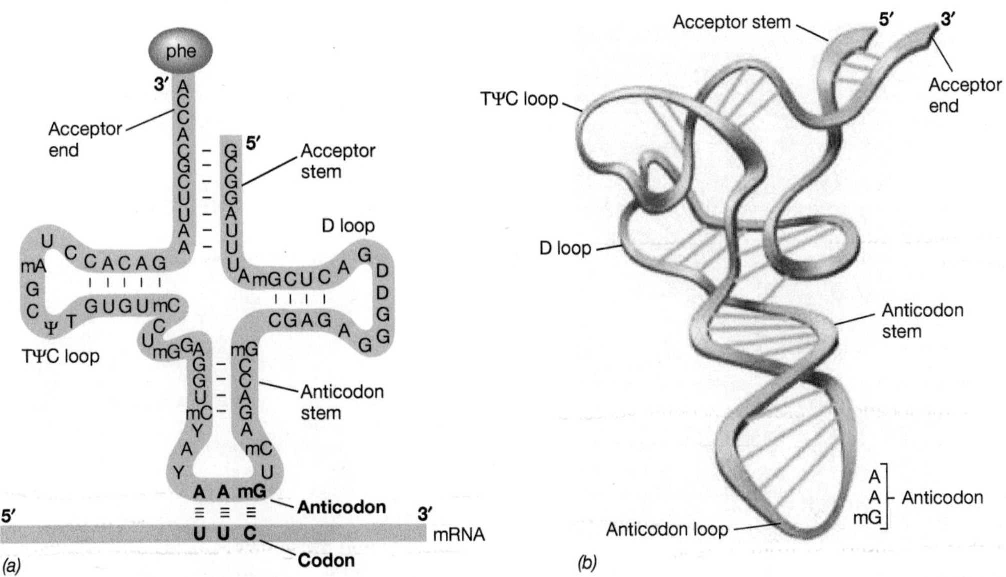

Figure 27 Structure of a transfer RNA. *(a)* The conventional cloverleaf structure of yeast phenylalanine tRNA. The amino acid is attached to the ribose of the terminal A at the acceptor end. A, adenine; C, cytosine; U, uracil; G, guanine; T, thymine; ψ, pseudouracil; D, dihydrouracil; m, methyl; Y, a modified purine. *(b)* In fact, the tRNA molecule folds so that the D loop and TψC loops are close together and associate by hydrophobic interactions.

Certain bases and secondary structures are constant for all tRNAs, whereas other parts are variable. Transfer RNA molecules also contain some purine and pyrimidine bases that differ slightly from the normal bases found in RNA because they are chemically modified. These modifications are made to the bases after transcription. Some of these unusual bases are pseudouridine, inosine, dihydrouridine, ribothymidine, methyl guanosine, dimethyl guanosine, and methyl inosine. The final mature and active tRNA not only contains unusual bases but also extensive double-stranded regions within the molecule. This secondary structure forms by internal base-pairing when the single-stranded molecule folds back on itself (Figure 27).

The structure of a tRNA can be drawn in a cloverleaf fashion, as in Figure 27*a*. Some regions of tRNA secondary structure are named after the bases most often found there (the TψC and D loops) or after their specific functions (anticodon loop and acceptor stem). The three-dimensional structure of a tRNA is shown in Figure 27*b*. Note that bases that appear widely separated in the cloverleaf model are actually closer together when viewed in three dimensions. This allows some of the bases in the loops to pair with bases in other loops.

The Anticodon and Amino Acid-Binding Site

One of the key variable parts of the tRNA molecule is the anticodon, the group of three bases that recognizes the codon on the mRNA. The anticodon is found in the anticodon loop (Figure 27). The three nucleotides of the anticodon recognize the codon by specifically pairing with its three bases (Section 13 and Figure 25). By contrast, other portions of the tRNA interact with both the rRNA and protein components of the ribosome, nonribosomal translation proteins, and the aminoacyl synthetase enzyme.

At the 3′-end, or acceptor stem, of all tRNAs, are three unpaired nucleotides. The sequence of these three nucleotides is always cytosine-cytosine-adenine (CCA), and they are absolutely essential for function. Curiously, in most organisms these three nucleotides are not encoded by the tRNA genes on the chromosome. Instead they are added, one after another, by an enzyme called the CCA-adding enzyme, using CTP and ATP as substrates. The cognate amino acid is covalently attached to the terminal adenosine of the CCA end by an ester linkage to the ribose sugar. As we shall see, from this location on the tRNA, the amino acid is incorporated into the growing polypeptide chain on the ribosome by a mechanism described in the next section.

Recognition, Activation, and Charging of tRNAs

Recognition of the correct tRNA by an aminoacyl-tRNA synthetase involves specific contacts between key regions of the tRNA and the synthetase (Figure 28). As might be expected because of its unique sequence, the anticodon of the tRNA is important in recognition by the synthetase. However, other contact sites between the tRNA and the synthetase are also important. Studies of tRNA binding to aminoacyl-tRNA synthetases, in which specific bases in the tRNA have been changed by mutation, have shown that only a small number of key nucleotides in a tRNA in addition to the anticodon region, are involved in recognition. These other key recognition

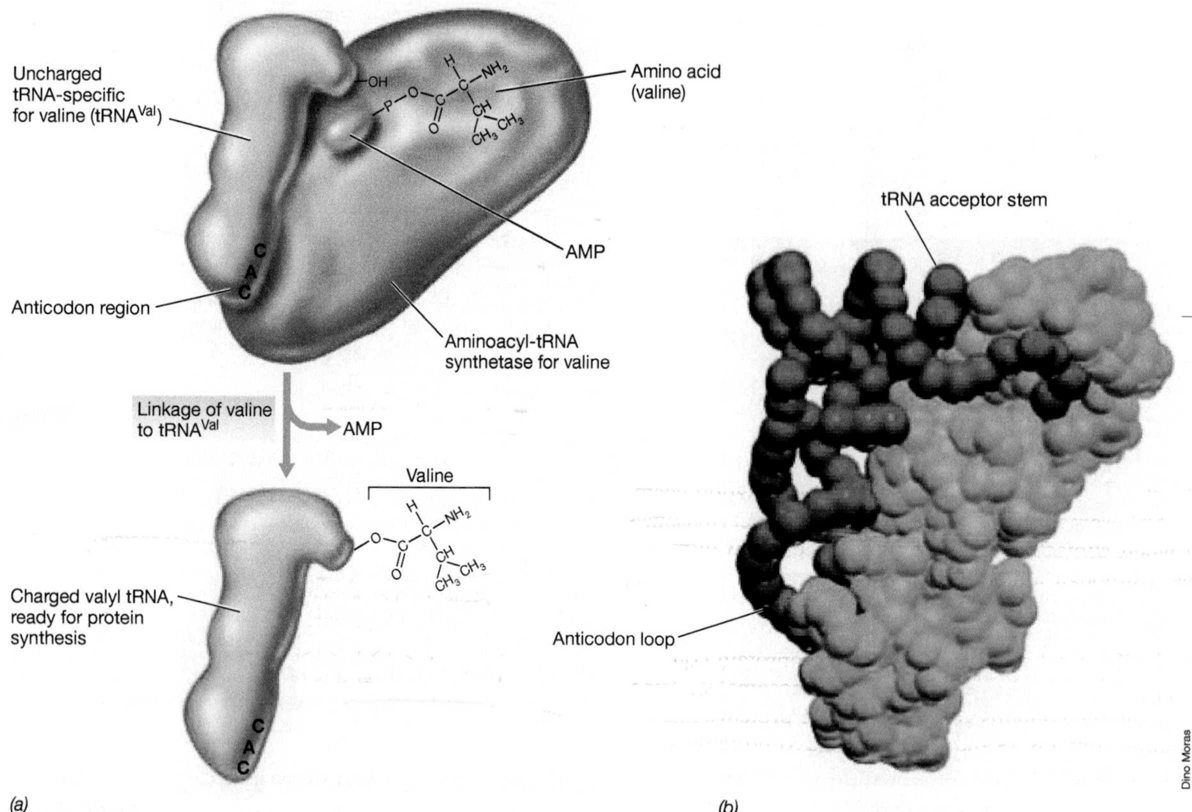

Figure 28 Aminoacyl-tRNA synthetase. *(a)* Mode of activity of an aminoacyl-tRNA synthetase. Recognition of the correct tRNA by a particular synthetase involves contacts between specific nucleic acid sequences in the D-loop and acceptor stem of the tRNA and specific amino acids of the synthetase. In this diagram, valyl-tRNA synthetase is shown catalyzing the final step of the reaction, where the valine in valyl-AMP is transferred to tRNA. *(b)* A computer model showing the interaction of glutaminyl-tRNA synthetase (blue) with its tRNA (red). Reprinted with permission from M. Ruff et al. 1991. *Science* 252: 1682–1689. © 1991, AAAS.

nucleotides are often part of the acceptor stem or D-loop of the tRNA molecule (Figure 27). It should be emphasized that the fidelity of this recognition process is crucial, for if the wrong amino acid is attached to the tRNA, it will be inserted into the growing polypeptide, likely leading to the synthesis of a faulty protein.

The specific reaction between amino acid and tRNA catalyzed by the aminoacyl-tRNA synthetase begins with activation of the amino acid by reaction with ATP:

$$\text{Amino acid} + \text{ATP} \longleftrightarrow \text{aminoacyl—AMP} + \text{P—P}$$

The aminoacyl-AMP intermediate formed normally remains bound to the enzyme until collision with the appropriate tRNA molecule. Then, as shown in Figure 28*a*, the activated amino acid is attached to the tRNA to form a charged tRNA:

$$\text{Aminoacyl—AMP} + \text{tRNA} \longleftrightarrow \text{aminoacyl—tRNA} + \text{AMP}$$

The pyrophosphate (PP_i) formed in the first reaction is split by a pyrophosphatase, giving two molecules of inorganic phosphate. Because ATP is used and AMP is formed in these reactions, a total of two energy-rich phosphate bonds are needed to charge a tRNA with its cognate amino acid. After activation and charging, the aminoacyl-tRNA leaves the synthetase and travels to the ribosome where the polypeptide is synthesized.

14 MiniReview

One or more tRNAs exist for each amino acid incorporated into proteins by the ribosome. Enzymes called aminoacyl-tRNA synthetases attach amino acids to their cognate tRNAs. Once the correct amino acid is attached to its tRNA, further specificity resides primarily in the codon–anticodon interaction.

- What is the function of the anticodon of a tRNA?
- What is the function of the acceptor stem of a tRNA?

15 Translation: The Process of Protein Synthesis

It is the amino acid sequence that determines the structure, and hence the function, of a protein. Thus, it is vital for proper functioning of proteins that the correct amino acids are inserted at the proper locations in the polypeptide chain. This is the task of the protein-synthesizing machinery, the ribosome.

Ribosomes

Ribosomes are the sites of protein synthesis. A cell may have many thousand ribosomes, the number being positively correlated with growth rate. Each ribosome is constructed of two subunits (Figure 29a). Prokaryotes possess 30S and 50S ribosome subunits, yielding intact 70S ribosomes. The S-values are Svedberg units, which refer to the sedimentation coefficients of ribosome subunits (30S and 50S) or intact ribosomes (70S) when subjected to centrifugal force in an ultracentrifuge. (Although larger particles have larger S-values, the relationship is not linear and S-values cannot be added together.)

Each ribosomal subunit is a ribonucleoprotein complex made up of specific ribosomal RNAs and ribosomal proteins. The 30S subunit contains 16S rRNA and 21 proteins, and the 50S subunit contains 5S and 23S rRNA and 31 proteins. Thus, in *Escherichia coli,* there are 52 distinct ribosomal proteins, most present at one copy per ribosome. The ribosome is a dynamic structure whose subunits alternately associate and dissociate and also interact with many other proteins. There are several proteins that are essential for ribosome function and interact with the ribosome at various stages of translation (discussed below), but that are not considered "ribosomal proteins," per se.

Steps in Protein Synthesis

Protein is synthesized in a cycle in which the various ribosomal components play specific roles. Although protein synthesis is a continuous process, it can be broken down into a number of steps: initiation, elongation, and termination. In addition to mRNA, tRNA, and ribosomes, the process requires a number of proteins designated initiation, elongation, and termination factors. The energy-rich compound guanosine triphosphate (GTP) provides the necessary energy for the process. The key steps in protein synthesis are shown in Figure 29*b*.

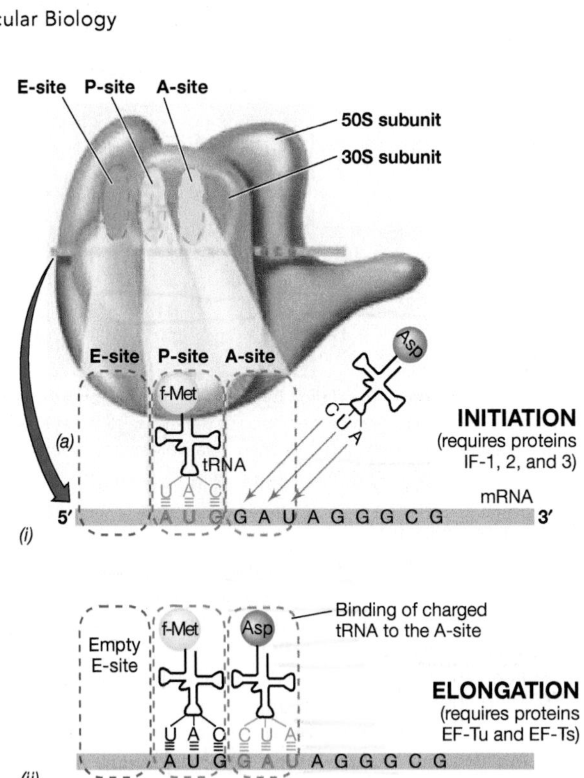

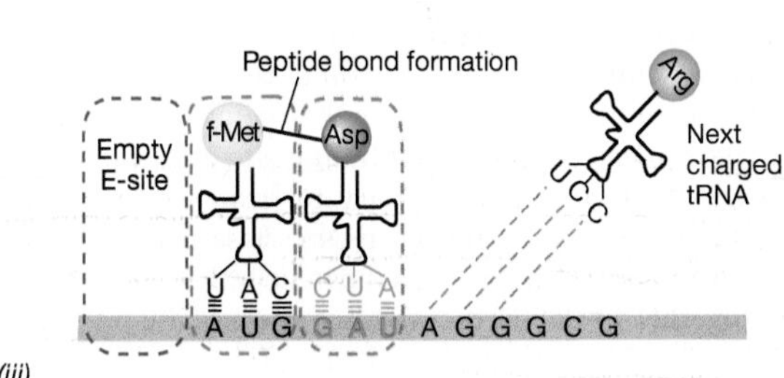

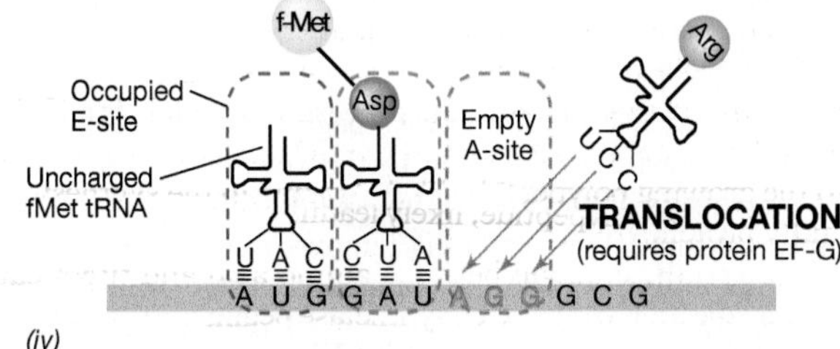

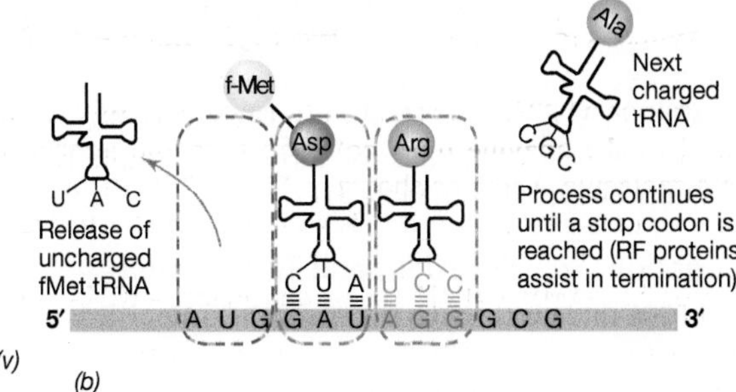

Figure 29 **The ribosome and protein synthesis.** *(a)* Structure of the ribosome, showing the position of the A (acceptor) site, the P (peptide) site, and the E (exit) site. *(b)* Translation. Initiation and elongation. (i, ii) Interaction between the codon and anticodon brings the correct charged tRNAs into position—in this case the initiator tRNA and the second charged tRNA. (iii) The formation of a peptide bond between amino acids on adjacent tRNA molecules completes elongation. (iv) Translocation of the ribosome from one codon to the next occurs with release of the tRNA from the E site. (v) The next charged tRNA binds to the A site.

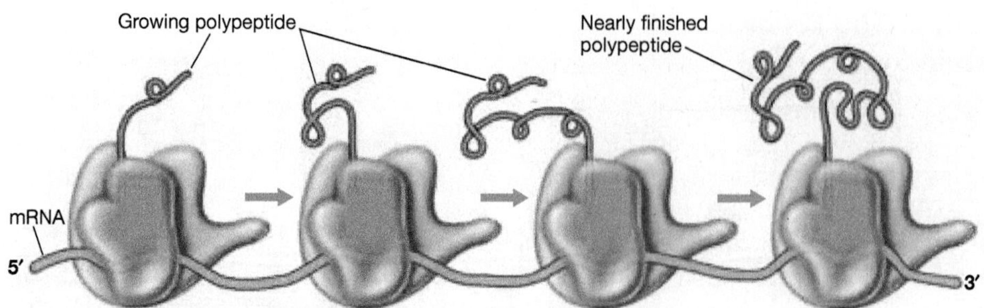

Figure 30 **Polysomes.** Translation by several ribosomes on a single messenger RNA forms the polysome. Note how the ribosomes nearest the 5′-end of the message are at an earlier stage in the translation process than ribosomes nearer the 3′-end, and thus only a relatively short portion of the final polypeptide has been made.

Initiation of Translation

In *Bacteria,* such as *E. coli,* initiation of protein synthesis always begins with a free 30S ribosomal subunit. From this, an initiation complex forms consisting of the 30S subunit, plus mRNA, formylmethionine tRNA, and several initiation proteins called IF1, IF2, and IF3. GTP is also required for this step. Next, a 50S ribosomal subunit is added to the initiation complex to form the active 70S ribosome. At the end of the translation process, the ribosome separates again into 30S and 50S subunits.

Just preceding the start codon on the mRNA is a sequence of three to nine nucleotides called the Shine–Dalgarno sequence or ribosome-binding site that helps bind the mRNA to the ribosome. The ribosome binding site is at the 5′-end of the mRNA and is complementary in base sequence to sequences in the 3′-end of the 16S rRNA. Base-pairing between these two molecules holds the ribosome–mRNA complex securely together in the correct reading frame. The presence of the Shine–Dalgarno sequence on the mRNA and its specific interaction with 16S rRNA allow bacterial ribosomes to translate polycistronic mRNA because the ribosome can find each initiation site within a message by binding to its Shine–Dalgarno site (Section 13).

Translational initiation always begins with a special initiator aminoacyl-tRNA binding to the start codon, AUG. In *Bacteria* this is formylmethionyl-tRNA. After polypeptide completion, the formyl group is removed. Consequently, the N-terminal amino acid of the completed protein will be methionine. However, in many proteins this methionine is removed by a specific protease. Because the Shine–Dalgarno sequences (and other possible interactions between the rRNA and the mRNA) direct the ribosome to the proper start site, prokaryotic mRNAs can use a start codon other than AUG. The most common alternative start codon is GUG. When used in this context, however, GUG calls for formylmethionine initiator tRNA (and not valine, see Table 3).

Elongation, Translocation, and Termination

The mRNA threads through the ribosome primarily bound to the 30S subunit. The ribosome contains other sites where the tRNAs interact. Two of these sites are located primarily on the 50S subunit, and they are termed the A site and the P site (Figure 29*b*). The A site, the acceptor site, is the site on the ribosome where the new charged tRNA first attaches. Travel and attachment of a tRNA to the A site is assisted by one of a series of elongation factor (EF) proteins called EF-Tu.

The P site, the peptide site, is the site where the growing polypeptide is held by a tRNA. During peptide bond formation, the growing polypeptide chain moves to the tRNA at the A site as a new peptide bond is formed. Several nonribosomal proteins are required for elongation, especially the elongation factors, EF-Tu and EF-Ts, as well as more GTP (to simplify Figure 29*b*, the elongation factors are omitted and only a portion of the ribosome is shown). Following elongation, the tRNA holding the polypeptide is translocated (moved) from the A site to the P site, thus opening up the A site for another charged tRNA (Figure 29*b*).

Translocation requires a specific EF protein called EF-G and one molecule of GTP for each translocation event. At each translocation step the ribosome advances three nucleotides, exposing a new codon at the A site. Translocation pushes the now empty tRNA to a third site, called the E site. It is from this exit site that the tRNA is actually released from the ribosome (Figure 29*b*). The precision of the translocation step is critical to the accuracy of protein synthesis. The ribosome must move exactly one codon at each step. Although during this process mRNA appears to be moving through the ribosome complex, in reality, the ribosome is moving along the mRNA. Thus, the three sites on the ribosome that we have identified in Figure 29 are not static locations but instead are moving parts of a complex biomolecular machine.

Several ribosomes can simultaneously translate a single mRNA molecule, forming a complex called a polysome (Figure 30). Polysomes increase the speed and efficiency of translation, and because the activity of each ribosome is independent of that of its neighbors, each ribosome in a polysome complex makes a complete polypeptide. Note in Figure 30 how ribosomes closest to the 5′-end (the beginning) of the mRNA molecule have short polypeptides attached to them because only a few codons have been read, while ribosomes closest to the 3′-end of the mRNA have nearly finished polypeptides.

Protein synthesis terminates when the ribosome reaches a nonsense codon (stop codon). No tRNA binds to a nonsense codon. Instead, specific proteins called *release factors* (RFs) recognize the stop codon and cleave the attached polypeptide from the final tRNA, releasing the finished product. Following this, the ribosome subunits dissociate, and the 30S and 50S subunits are then free to form new initiation complexes and repeat the process.

Role of Ribosomal RNA in Protein Synthesis

Ribosomal RNA plays a vital role in all stages of protein synthesis, from initiation to termination. The role of the many proteins present in the ribosome, although less clear, may be to act as a scaffold to position key sequences in the ribosomal RNAs.

As already discussed, in prokaryotes it is clear that 16S rRNA is involved in initiation through base-pairing with the Shine–Dalgarno sequence on the mRNA. There are also other mRNA–rRNA interactions during elongation. On either side of the codons in the A and P sites, the mRNA is held in position by binding to 16S rRNA and ribosomal proteins. Ribosomal RNA also plays a role in ribosome subunit association, as well as in positioning tRNA in the A and P sites on the ribosome (Figure 29*b*). Although charged tRNAs that enter the ribosome recognize the correct codon by codon–anticodon base pairing, they are also bound to the ribosome by interactions of the anticodon stem-loop of the tRNA with specific sequences within 16S rRNA. Moreover, the acceptor end of the tRNA (Figure 27) base-pairs with sequences in the 23S rRNA.

In addition to all of this, the actual formation of peptide bonds is catalyzed by rRNA. This happens on the 50S subunit of the ribosome during the peptidyl transferase reaction. This reaction is catalyzed by the 23S rRNA itself, rather than by any of the ribosomal proteins. The 23S rRNA also plays a role in translocation, and in this regard, the EF proteins are known to interact specifically with 23S rRNA. Thus, besides its role as the structural backbone of the ribosome, ribosomal RNA plays a major catalytic role in the translation process as well. www.microbiologyplace.com **Online Tutorial 3: Translation**

Freeing Trapped Ribosomes

A defective mRNA that lacks a stop codon causes a problem in translation. Such a defect may arise, for example, from a mutation that removed the stop codon, defective synthesis of the mRNA, or partial degradation of the mRNA. If a ribosome reaches the end of an mRNA molecule and there is no stop codon, release factor cannot bind and the ribosome cannot be released from the mRNA. The ribosome is trapped.

Bacterial cells contain a small RNA molecule, called *tmRNA*, that frees stalled ribosomes (Figure 31). The "tm" in its name refers to the fact that tmRNA mimics both tRNA, in that it carries the amino acid alanine, and mRNA, in that it contains a short stretch of RNA that can be translated. When tmRNA collides with a stalled ribosome, it binds alongside the defective mRNA. Protein synthesis can then proceed, first by adding the alanine on the tmRNA and then by translating the short tmRNA message. Finally, tmRNA contains a stop codon that allows release factor to bind and disassemble the ribosome. The protein made as a result of this rescue operation is defective and is subsequently degraded. The short sequence of amino acids, encoded by tmRNA and added to the end of the defective protein, is a signal for a specific protease to degrade the protein. Thus, through the activity of tmRNA, stalled ribosomes are freed up to participate in protein synthesis once again.

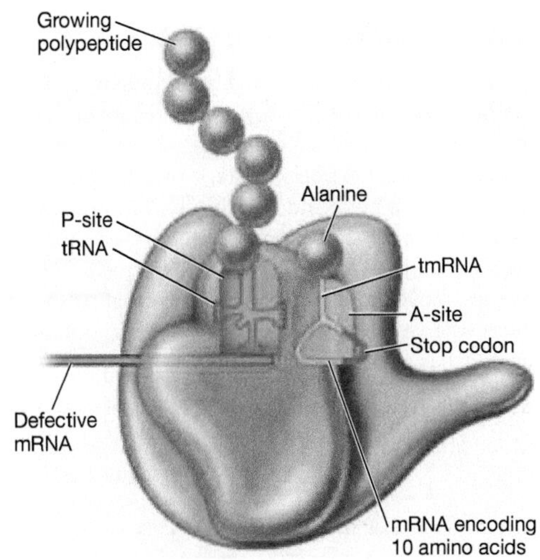

Figure 31 **Freeing of a stalled ribosome by tmRNA.** A defective mRNA lacking a stop codon stalls a ribosome that has a partly synthesized polypeptide attached to a tRNA (blue) in the P site. Binding of tmRNA (yellow) in the A site releases the polypeptide. Translation then continues up to the stop codon provided by the tmRNA.

Effect of Antibiotics on Protein Synthesis

A large number of antibiotics inhibit translation by interacting with the ribosome. These interactions are quite specific, and many have been shown to involve rRNA. Several of these antibiotics are clinically useful, and several are also effective research tools because they are specific for different steps in protein synthesis. For instance, streptomycin inhibits initiation. By contrast, puromycin, chloramphenicol, cycloheximide, and tetracycline inhibit elongation. Adding to their clinical usefulness is the fact that many antibiotics specifically inhibit ribosomes of organisms from only one or two of the phylogenetic domains. Of the antibiotics just listed, for example, chloramphenicol and streptomycin are specific for the ribosomes of *Bacteria* and cycloheximide for ribosomes of *Eukarya*.

15 MiniReview

The ribosome plays a key role in the translation process, bringing together mRNA and aminoacyl tRNAs. There are three sites on the ribosome: the acceptor site, where the charged tRNA first combines; the peptide site, where the growing polypeptide chain is held; and an exit site. During each step of amino acid addition, the ribosome advances three nucleotides (one codon) along the mRNA and the tRNA that is in the acceptor site moves to the peptide site. Protein synthesis terminates when a nonsense codon, which does not encode an amino acid, is reached.

- What are the components of a ribosome?
- What functional roles does rRNA play in protein synthesis?

16 The Incorporation of Nonstandard Amino Acids

The Variety of Amino Acids

The universal genetic code has codons for 20 amino acids (Table 4). However, many proteins contain other amino acids. In fact, more than 100 different amino acids have been found in various proteins. Most of these are made by modifying one of the standard amino acids after it is incorporated into a protein molecule, a process called *posttranslational modification.* However, at least two nonstandard amino acids are inserted into proteins during protein synthesis itself. These exceptions are selenocysteine and pyrrolysine, the 21st and 22nd genetically encoded amino acids.

Selenocysteine and Pyrrolysine

Selenocysteine has the same structure as cysteine except it contains a selenium rather than a sulfur atom. It is formed by modifying a serine after it has been attached to selenocysteine tRNA by the aminoacyl-tRNA synthetase. Pyrrolysine is a lysine derivative with an extra aromatic ring. In this case, pyrrolysine is fully synthesized and only then joined to pyrrolysyl tRNA by the corresponding aminoacyl-tRNA synthetase.

Both selenocysteine and pyrrolysine are encoded by stop codons (UGA and UAG, respectively). Both have their own tRNAs that contain anticodons that read these stop codons. Both selenocysteine and pyrrolysine also have specific aminoacyl-tRNA synthetases to charge the tRNA with the amino acids. Note that these amino acids are used by organisms that use the universal genetic code; in other words, most stop codons in these organisms do indeed indicate stop. However, occasional stop codons are recognized as encoding selenocysteine or pyrrolysine. How can a codon sometimes be a nonsense codon and sometimes a sense codon? The answer in the case of selenocysteine is well understood and depends on a recognition sequence just downstream of the selenocysteine-encoding UGA codon. This forms a stem-loop structure that binds a special protein factor, the SelB protein. The SelB protein also binds charged selenocysteine tRNA and brings it to the ribosome when needed during translation. Similarly, pyrrolysine incorporation relies on a recognition sequence just downstream of the pyrrolysine-encoding UAG codon.

Selenocysteine and pyrrolysine are both relatively rare. *Escherichia coli* makes only a handful of proteins with selenocysteine, including two different formate dehydrogenase enzymes. It was sequencing the genes for these enzymes that led to the discovery of selenocysteine and its incorporation mechanism. Most organisms, including plants and animals, have a small number of proteins that contain selenocysteine. Pyrrolysine is rarer still. It has been found in certain *Archaea* and *Bacteria* but was first discovered in species of methanogenic *Archaea,* organisms whose metabolism generates natural gas (methane). In certain methanogens the enzyme methylamine methyltransferase contains a pyrrolysine residue. Whether there are still other genetically encoded amino acids that use reassigned nonsense codons, or perhaps even reassigned sense codons, remains a possibility.

16 MiniReview

Many nonstandard amino acids are found in proteins as a result of posttranslational modification. In contrast, the two rare amino acids selenocysteine and pyrrolysine are inserted into growing polypeptide chains during protein synthesis. They are both encoded by special stop codons that have a nearby recognition sequence that is specific for insertion of selenocysteine or pyrrolysine.

- Explain the term posttranslational modification.
- What specific components (apart from a ribosome and a stop codon) are needed for the insertion of selenocysteine into a growing polypeptide chain?

17 Folding and Secreting Proteins

Thus far we have described how genetic information present in the sequence of bases in DNA is replicated into an identical copy, transcribed into a sequence of bases in RNA, and translated into a sequence of amino acids in a polypeptide chain. For a protein to function, however, it must be folded correctly, and it must also end up in the correct location in the cell. Here we briefly discuss these two processes.

Protein Folding

Most polypeptides fold spontaneously into their active form while they are being synthesized. However, some do not and require assistance from other proteins called **molecular chaperones** or **chaperonins** for proper folding or for assembly into larger complexes. The chaperonins themselves do not become part of the assembled proteins but only assist in folding. Indeed, one important function of chaperones is to prevent improper aggregation of proteins.

There are several different kinds of molecular chaperones. Some help newly synthesized proteins fold correctly. Other chaperonins are very abundant in the cell, especially under growth conditions that put protein stability at risk (for example, high temperatures). Chaperonins are widespread in all domains of life, and their sequences are highly conserved among all organisms.

Four key chaperones in *Escherichia coli* are the proteins DnaK, DnaJ, GroEL, and GroES. DnaK and DnaJ are ATP-dependent enzymes that bind to newly formed polypeptides and keep them from folding too abruptly, a process that increases the risk of improper folding (Figure 32). Slower folding thus improves the chances of correct folding. If the DnaKJ complex is unable to fold the protein properly, it may transfer the partially folded protein to the two multi-subunit proteins, GroEL and GroES. The protein first enters GroEL, a large barrel-shaped protein that, using the energy of ATP hydrolysis, properly folds the protein. GroES assists in this (Figure 32). It is estimated that only about 100 of the several thousand proteins of *E. coli* need help in folding from the GroEL/GroES complex and of these approximately a dozen are essential for survival of the bacteria.

In addition to folding newly synthesized proteins, chaperones can also refold proteins that have partially denatured in the cell. A protein may denature for many reasons, but often it is because the organism has temporarily experienced high temperatures. Chaperones are thus one type of *heat shock protein*, and their synthesis is greatly accelerated when a cell is stressed by excessive heat. The heat shock response is an attempt by the cell to refold its partially denatured proteins for re-use before proteases recognize them as improperly folded and destroy them. Refolding is not always successful, and cells contain proteases whose function is to specifically target and destroy misfolded proteins, which then frees their amino acids to make new proteins.

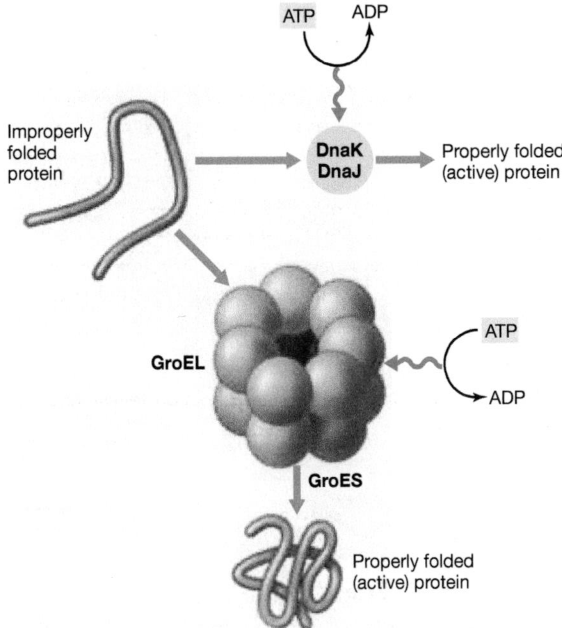

Figure 32 **The activity of molecular chaperones.** An improperly folded protein can be refolded by either the DnaKJ complex or by the GroEL/ES complex. In both cases, energy for refolding comes from ATP.

Protein Secretion and the Signal Recognition Particle

Many proteins carry out their function in the cytoplasmic membrane, in the periplasm of gram-negative cells, or even outside the cell proper. Such proteins must get from their site of synthesis on ribosomes into or through the cytoplasmic membrane. How is it possible for a cell to selectively transfer some proteins across a membrane while leaving most proteins in the cytoplasm?

Most proteins that must be transported into or through membranes are synthesized with an amino acid sequence of about 15–20 residues, called the **signal sequence**, at the beginning of the protein molecule. Signal sequences are quite variable, but typically have a few positively charged residues at the beginning, a central region of hydrophobic residues, and then a more polar region. The signal sequence "signals" the cell's secretory system that this particular protein is to be exported and also helps prevent the protein from completely folding, a process that could interfere with its secretion. Because the signal sequence is the first part of the protein to be synthesized, the early steps in export may actually begin before the protein is completely synthesized (Figure 33).

Proteins to be exported are identified by their signal sequences either by the *SecA protein* or the *signal recognition particle (SRP)* (Figure 33). Generally, SecA binds proteins that are fully exported across the membrane into the periplasm whereas the SRP binds proteins that are inserted into the membrane but are not released on the other side. SRPs are found in all cells. In *Bacteria,* they contain a single protein and a small noncoding RNA molecule (4.5S RNA). Both SecA and the SRP deliver proteins to be secreted to the membrane secretion complex. In bacteria this is normally the Sec system, whose channel consists of the three proteins SecYEG. The protein is exported across the cytoplasmic membrane through this channel. It may then either remain in the membrane or be released into the periplasm or the environment (Figure 33). After crossing the membrane, the signal sequence is removed by a protease.

Secretion of Folded Proteins: The Tat System

In the Sec system of protein transport, the transported proteins are threaded through the cytoplasmic membrane in an unfolded state and only fold afterwards (Figure 33). However, there are a small number of proteins that must be transported outside the cell after they have already achieved their final folded structure. Usually this is because they contain small cofactors that must be inserted into the protein

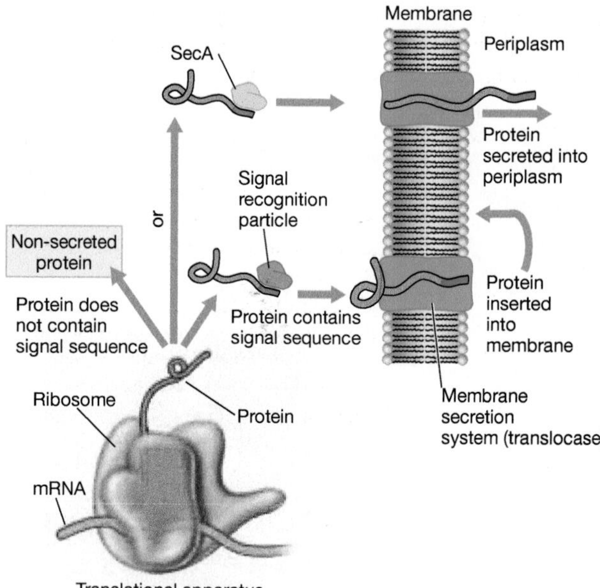

Figure 33 Export of proteins via the major secretory system. The signal sequence is recognized either by SecA or by the signal recognition particle, which carries the protein to the membrane secretion system. The signal recognition particle binds proteins that are inserted into the membrane whereas SecA binds proteins that are secreted across the membrane. In gram-negative bacteria, the latter proteins will be secreted into the periplasmic space.

as it folds into its final form. Such proteins fold in the cytoplasm and then are exported by a transport system distinct from Sec, called the *Tat protein export system.*

The acronym Tat stands for "twin arginine translocase" because the transported proteins contain a short signal sequence containing a pair of arginine residues. This signal sequence on a folded protein is recognized by the TatBC proteins, which carries the protein to TatA, the membrane transporter. Energy is required for the actual transport event, and this is supplied by the proton motive force. A wide variety of proteins are transported by the Tat system, especially proteins required for energy metabolism that function in the periplasm. This includes iron-sulfur proteins and several other "redox" type proteins. In addition, the Tat pathway transports proteins needed for outer membrane biosynthesis and a few proteins that do not contain cofactors but only fold properly within the cytoplasm.

17 MiniReview

Proteins must be properly folded in order to function correctly. Folding may occur spontaneously but may also involve other proteins called molecular chaperones. Many proteins also need to be transported into or through membranes. Such proteins are synthesized with a signal sequence that is recognized by the cellular export apparatus and is removed either during or after export.

- What is a molecular chaperone?
- Why do some proteins have a signal sequence?
- What is a signal recognition particle?

In this chapter we have covered the essentials of the key molecular processes that occur in bacteria. We next consider how archaeal and eukaryotic cells carry out the same processes. There are many similarities but also some major differences, in replication, transcription, and translation, among organisms in the three domains of life.

Review of Key Terms

Aminoacyl-tRNA synthetase an enzyme that catalyzes attachment of an amino acid to its cognate tRNA

Anticodon a sequence of three bases in a tRNA molecule that base-pairs with a codon during protein synthesis

Antiparallel in reference to double-stranded DNA, the two strands run in opposite directions (one runs $5' \rightarrow 3'$ and the complementary strand $3' \rightarrow 5'$)

Chaperonin or molecular chaperone a protein that helps other proteins fold or refold from a partly denatured state

Chromosome a genetic element, usually circular in prokaryotes, carrying genes essential to cellular function

Codon a sequence of three bases in mRNA that encodes an amino acid

Codon bias nonrandom usage of multiple codons encoding the same amino acid

Complementary nucleic acid sequences that can base-pair with each other

DNA gyrase an enzyme found in most prokaryotes that introduces negative supercoils in DNA

DNA polymerase an enzyme that synthesizes a new strand of DNA in the $5' \rightarrow 3'$ direction using an antiparallel DNA strand as a template

Gene a segment of DNA specifying a protein (via mRNA), a tRNA, an rRNA, or any other non-coding RNA

Genetic code correspondence between nucleic acid sequence and amino acid sequence of proteins

Genetic element a structure that carries genetic information, such as a chromosome, a plasmid, or a virus genome

Genome the total complement of genes contained in a cell or virus

Informational macromolecule any large polymeric molecule that carries genetic information, including DNA, RNA, and protein

Lagging strand the new strand of DNA that is synthesized in short pieces during DNA replication and then joined together later

Leading strand the new strand of DNA that is synthesized continuously during DNA replication

Messenger RNA (mRNA) an RNA molecule that contains the genetic information to encode one or more polypeptides

Nonsense codon another name for a stop codon

Open reading frame (ORF) a sequence of DNA or RNA that could be translated to give a polypeptide

Operon a cluster of genes that are cotranscibed to give a single messenger RNA

Primer an oligonucleotide to which DNA polymerase can attach the first deoxyribonucleotide during DNA replication

Promoter a site on DNA to which RNA polymerase binds to commence transcription

Replication synthesis of DNA using DNA as a template

Replication fork the site on the chromosome where DNA replication occurs and where the enzymes replicating the DNA are bound to untwisted, single-stranded DNA

Ribosomal RNA (rRNA) types of RNA found in the ribosome; some participate actively in the process of protein synthesis

Ribosome a cytoplasmic particle composed of ribosomal RNA and protein and whose function is to synthesize proteins

RNA polymerase an enzyme that synthesizes RNA in the $5' \rightarrow 3'$ direction using a complementary and antiparallel DNA strand as a template

Semiconservative replication DNA synthesis yielding new double helices, each consisting of one parental and one progeny strand

Signal sequence a special N-terminal sequence of approximately 20 amino acids that signals that a protein should be exported across the cytoplasmic membrane

Start codon a special codon, usually AUG, that signals the start of a protein

Stop codon a codon that signals the end of a protein

Termination stopping the elongation of an RNA molecule at a specific site

Transcription the synthesis of RNA using a DNA template

Transfer RNA (tRNA) a small RNA molecule used in translation that possesses an anticodon at one end and has the corresponding amino acid attached to the other end

Translation the synthesis of protein using the genetic information in RNA as a template

Wobble less rigid form of base pairing allowed only in codon–anticodon pairing

Review Questions

1. Describe the central dogma of molecular biology (Section 1).
2. Genes were discovered before their chemical nature was known. Define a gene without mentioning its chemical nature. Of what is a gene composed (Section 1)?
3. Inverted repeats can give rise to stem-loops. Show this by giving the sequence of a double-stranded DNA containing an inverted repeat and show how the transcript from this region can form a stem-loop (Section 2).
4. Is the sequence 5′-GCACGGCACG-3′ an inverted repeat? Explain your answer (Section 2).
5. DNA molecules that are AT-rich separate into two strands more easily when the temperature is raised than do DNA molecules that are GC-rich. Explain this observation based on the properties of AT and GC base pairing (Section 2).
6. Describe how DNA, which when linearized, is many times the length of a cell, fits into the cell (Section 3).
7. List the major genetic elements known in microorganisms (Section 4).
8. A structure commonly seen in circular DNA during replication is the theta structure. Draw a diagram of the replication process and show how a theta structure could arise (Sections 5–7).
9. Why are errors in DNA replication so rare? What enzymatic activity, in addition to polymerization, is associated with DNA polymerase III and how does it reduce errors (Section 8)?
10. Do genes for tRNAs have promoters? Do they have start codons? Explain (Sections 12 and 13).
11. The start and stop sites for mRNA synthesis (on the DNA) are different from the start and stop sites for protein synthesis (on the mRNA). Explain (Sections 10 and 13).
12. What is "wobble" and what makes it necessary in protein synthesis (Section 13 and 14)?
13. What are aminoacyl-tRNA synthetases and what types of reactions do they carry out? Approximately how many different types of these enzymes are present in the cell? How does a synthetase recognize its correct substrates (Section 14)?
14. The activity that forms peptide bonds on the ribosome is called peptidyl transferase. What catalyzes this reaction (Section 15)?
15. Sometimes misfolded proteins can be correctly refolded, but sometimes they cannot and are destroyed. What kinds of proteins are involved in refolding misfolded proteins? What kinds of enzymes are involved in destroying misfolded proteins (Section 17)?
16. How does a cell know which of its proteins are designed to function outside of the cell (Section 17)?

Application Questions

1. The genome of the bacterium *Neisseria gonorrhoeae* consists of one double-stranded DNA molecule that contains 2220 kilobase pairs. Calculate the length of this DNA molecule in centimeters. If 85% of this DNA molecule is made up of the open reading frames of genes encoding proteins, and the average protein is 300 amino acids long, how many protein-encoding genes does *Neisseria* have? What kind of information do you think might be present in the other 15% of the DNA?
2. Compare and contrast the activity of DNA and RNA polymerases. What is the function of each? What are the substrates of each? What is the main difference in the behavior of the two polymerases?
3. What would be the result (in terms of protein synthesis) if RNA polymerase initiated transcription one base upstream of its normal starting point? Why? What would be the result (in terms of protein synthesis) if translation began one base downstream of its normal starting point? Why?
4. By inspecting Table 4, discuss how the genetic code has evolved to help minimize the impact of mutations.

Regulation of Gene Expression

Regulation of Gene Expression

Bacteria regulate gene expression in response to environmental signals. Here bioluminescent bacterial colonies emit light following accumulation of a triggering molecule produced by the cells themselves.

Timothy C. Johnston

The genetic information stored as a sequence of nucleotides in a gene can be transcribed into RNA in cells of the three domains of life. This information is then translated to yield a specific polypeptide. Collectively, these processes are called **gene expression**. Most proteins are enzymes that carry out the hundreds of different biochemical reactions needed for cell growth. However, to succeed in nature, microorganisms must respond rapidly to changes in their environment. To efficiently orchestrate the numerous reactions that occur in a cell and make maximal use of available resources, cells need to *regulate* the kinds and amounts of macromolecules they make. Such metabolic regulation is the focus of this chapter.

I OVERVIEW OF REGULATION

Some proteins and RNA molecules are needed in the cell at about the same level under all growth conditions. The expression of these molecules is said to be *constitutive*. However, it is more common for a particular macromolecule to be needed under some conditions but not others. For instance, enzymes required for the catabolism of the sugar lactose are useful to the cell only if lactose is present in its environment. Microbial genomes encode many more proteins than are actually present in the cell under any particular condition. Thus, regulation is a major process in all cells and a mechanism for conserving energy and resources.

1 Major Modes of Regulation

There are two major levels of regulation in the cell. One controls the *activity* of preexisting enzymes, and one controls the *amount* of an enzyme (Figure 1). The activity of a protein can be regulated only after it has been synthesized (that is, post-translationally). By contrast, the amount of protein synthesized can be regulated at either the level of transcription, by varying the amount of messenger RNA (mRNA) made, or at the level of translation, by translating or not translating the mRNA.

Regulation of enzyme *activity* in prokaryotes is typically a very rapid process (occurring in seconds or less), whereas the regulation of enzyme *synthesis* is a relatively slow process (taking a few minutes). If a new enzyme needs to be synthesized, it will take some time before it is present in the cell in amounts sufficient to affect metabolism. Alternatively, if synthesis of an enzyme is stopped, a considerable amount of time may elapse before the existing enzyme is diluted sufficiently to no longer affect metabolism. However, working together, regulating enzyme activity and enzyme synthesis efficiently control cell metabolism.

Systems that control the level of expression of particular genes are varied, and genes can be regulated by more than one system. The processes that regulate the activity of preformed enzymes have already been discussed. Here we consider how the synthesis of RNA and proteins is controlled.

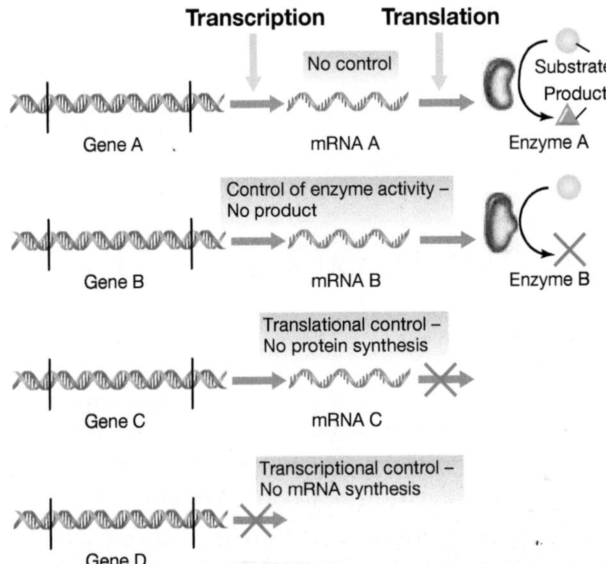

Figure 1 **An overview of mechanisms of regulation.** The product of gene A is enzyme A, which in this example is synthesized constitutively and carries out its reaction. Enzyme B is also synthesized constitutively, but its activity can be inhibited. The synthesis of the gene C product can be prevented by control at the level of translation. The synthesis of the gene D product can be prevented by control at the level of transcription.

1 MiniReview

Most genes encode proteins, and most proteins are enzymes. Expression of an enzyme-encoding gene is regulated by controlling the activity of the enzyme or controlling the amount of enzyme produced.

- What steps in the synthesis of protein might be subject to regulation?
- Which is likely to be more rapid, the regulation of activity or the regulation of synthesis? Why?

II DNA-BINDING PROTEINS AND REGULATION OF TRANSCRIPTION

The amount of a protein present in a cell may be controlled at the level of transcription, at the level of translation, or, occasionally, by protein degradation. Our discussion focuses on control at the level of transcription because this is the major means of regulation in prokaryotes.

Recall that the half-life of a typical mRNA in prokaryotes is short, only a few minutes at best. Because the half-life of a mRNA is so short, prokaryotes can exploit this to respond quickly to changing environmental parameters. Although there are energy costs in resynthesizing mRNAs that have been translated only a few times before being degraded, there

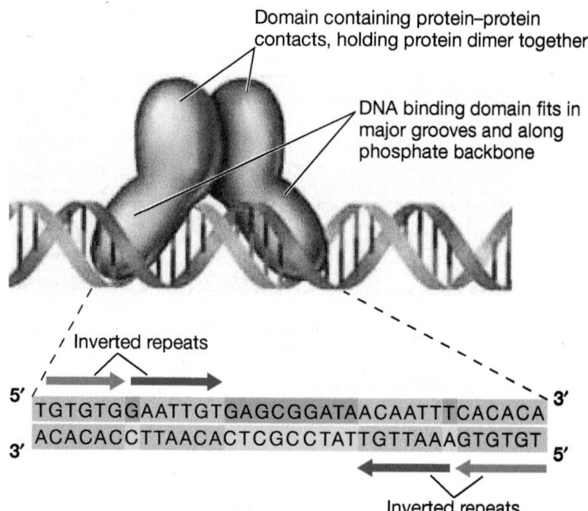

Figure 2 DNA-binding proteins. Many such proteins are dimers that combine specifically with two sites on the DNA. The specific DNA sequences that interact with the protein are inverted repeats. The nucleotide sequence of the operator gene of the lactose operon is shown, and the inverted repeats, which are sites at which the *lac* repressor makes contact with the DNA, are shown in shaded boxes.

are benefits from removing mRNAs rapidly when they are no longer needed, as this prevents the production of unneeded proteins. In the growing cell, transcription and mRNA degradation are thus coexisting processes.

For a gene to be transcribed, RNA polymerase must recognize a specific promoter on the DNA and begin functioning. Regulation of transcription, both the turning on and turning off, typically requires proteins that can bind to DNA. Thus, before discussing specific regulatory mechanisms, we must consider DNA-binding proteins.

2 DNA-Binding Proteins

Small molecules are often involved in the regulation of transcription. However, they rarely do so directly. Instead, they typically influence the binding of certain proteins, called *regulatory proteins,* to specific sites on the DNA. It is these proteins that actually regulate transcription.

Interaction of Proteins with Nucleic Acids

Interactions between proteins and nucleic acids are central to replication, transcription, and translation, as well as to the regulation of these processes. Protein–nucleic acid interactions may be nonspecific or specific, depending on whether the protein attaches anywhere along the nucleic acid or whether the interaction is sequence specific. Histones are good examples of nonspecific binding proteins. Histones are universally present in *Eukarya* and are also present in many *Archaea.* Because they are positively charged, histones combine strongly and relatively nonspecifically with negatively charged DNA. If the DNA is covered with histones, RNA polymerase is unable to bind and transcription cannot occur. However, removal of histones does not automatically lead to transcription, but simply leaves genes in a position to be activated by other factors. For example, even after binding and beginning transcription, eukaryotic RNA polymerases need several protein factors to help them elongate through the histone-coated DNA.

Most DNA-binding proteins interact with DNA in a sequence-specific manner. Specificity is provided by interactions between specific amino acid side chains of the proteins and specific chemical groups on the bases and the sugar–phosphate backbone of the DNA. Because of its size, the *major groove* of DNA is the main site of protein binding. To achieve high specificity, the binding protein must interact simultaneously with more than one nucleotide, frequently several. In practice, this means that a specific binding protein binds only to DNA containing a specific base sequence.

We have already described a structure in DNA called an *inverted repeat*. Such inverted repeats are frequently the locations at which regulatory proteins bind specifically to DNA (Figure 2). Note that this interaction does not involve the formation of stem-loop structures in the DNA. DNA-binding proteins are typically homodimeric, meaning they are composed of two identical polypeptides. On each polypeptide chain is a domain that interacts specifically with a region of DNA in the major groove. When protein dimers interact with inverted repeats on DNA, each of the polypeptides binds to one of the inverted repeat regions and, in doing so, combines with each of the DNA strands (Figure 2). The DNA-binding protein does not recognize base sequences, per se, but instead recognizes molecular contacts associated with specific base sequences.

Structure of DNA-Binding Proteins

Studies of the structure of several DNA-binding proteins from both prokaryotes and eukaryotes have revealed several classes of protein domains that are critical for proper binding of these proteins to DNA. One of these is called the *helix-turn-helix motif* (Figure 3). The helix-turn-helix-motif consists of two segments of polypeptide chain with an α-helix secondary structure connected by a short sequence forming the "turn." The first helix is the *recognition helix* that interacts specifically with DNA. The second helix, the *stabilizing helix,* stabilizes the first helix by interacting hydrophobically with it. The turn linking the two helices consists of three amino acid residues, the first of which is typically a glycine (Figure 3*a*). Sequences are recognized by noncovalent interactions, including hydrogen bonds and van der Waals contacts, between the recognition helix of the protein and specific chemical groups in the sequence of base pairs on the DNA.

Many different DNA-binding proteins from *Bacteria* contain the helix-turn-helix structure. These include many repressor proteins, such as the *lac* and *trp* repressors of *Escherichia coli* (Section 3), and some bacteriophage proteins, such as the phage lambda repressor (Figure 3*b*). Indeed, there

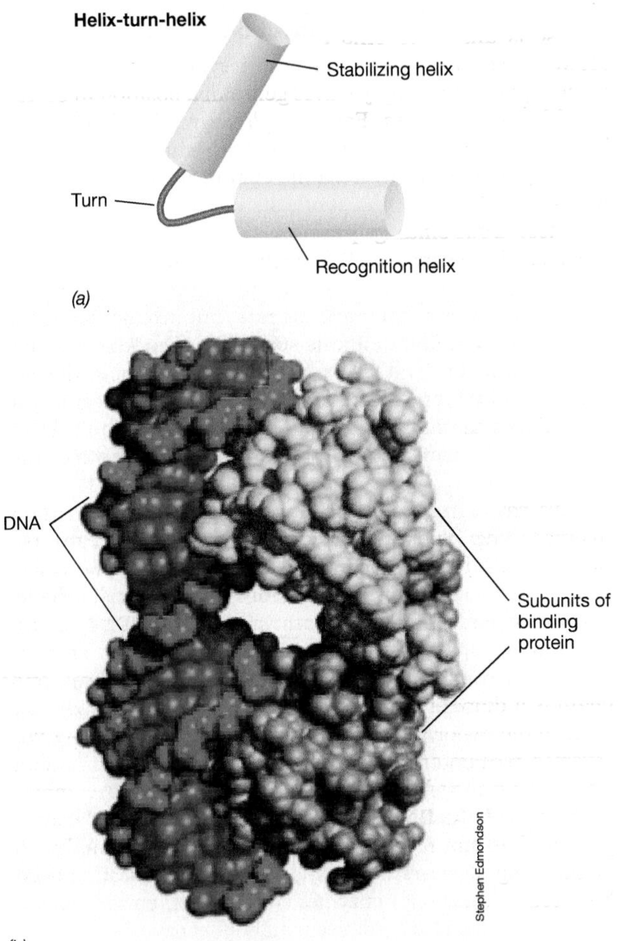

Figure 3 **The helix-turn-helix structure of some DNA-binding proteins.** *(a)* A simple model of the helix-turn-helix components. *(b)* A computer model of the bacteriophage lambda repressor, a typical helix-turn-helix protein, bound to its operator. DNA is red and blue, and one subunit of the dimeric repressor is brown and the other yellow. One subunit of the dimeric repressor is shown in dark brown and the other in dark yellow. Each subunit contains a helix-turn-helix structure. The coordinates used to generate this image were downloaded from the Protein Data Base, Brookhaven, NY (www.pdb.org/pdb/home/).

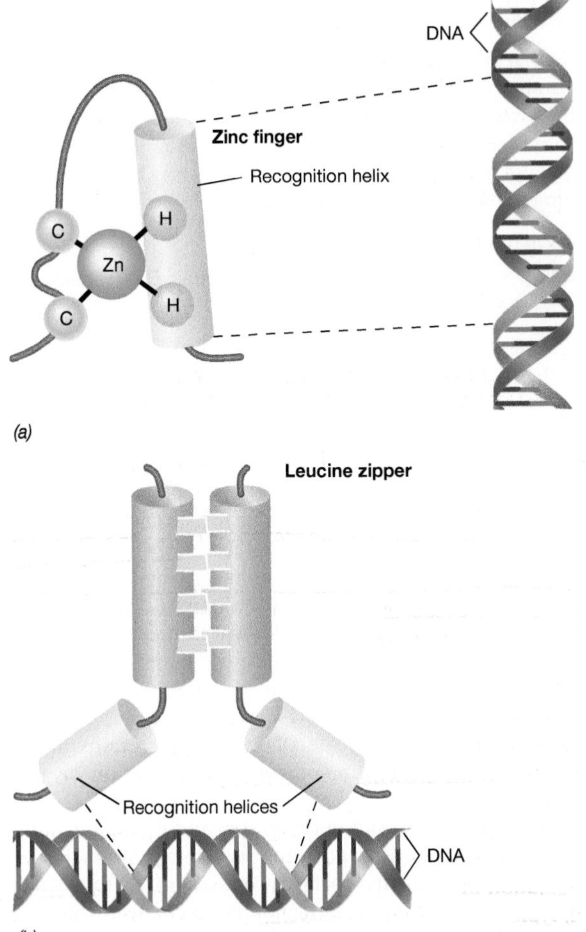

Figure 4 **Simple models of protein substructures found in eukaryotic DNA-binding proteins.** α-Helices are represented by cylinders. Recognition helices are the domains that bind DNA. *(a)* The zinc finger structure. The amino acids holding the Zn^{2+} ion always include at least two cysteine residues (C), with the other residues being histidine (H). *(b)* The leucine zipper structure. The leucine residues (yellow) are spaced exactly every seven amino acids. The interaction of the leucine side chains helps hold the two helices together.

are over 250 different proteins known with this motif that bind to DNA to regulate transcription in *E. coli.*

Two other types of protein domains are commonly found in DNA-binding proteins. One of these, the *zinc finger,* is frequently found in regulatory proteins in eukaryotes. The zinc finger is a protein structure that, as its name implies, binds a zinc ion (Figure 4*a*). Part of the "finger" of amino acids that is created forms an α-helix, and this recognition helix interacts with DNA in the major groove. There are typically at least two or three zinc fingers on proteins that use them for DNA binding.

The other protein domain commonly found in DNA-binding proteins is the *leucine zipper*. These proteins contain regions in which leucine residues are spaced every seven amino acids, somewhat resembling a zipper. Unlike the helix-turn-helix structure and the zinc finger, the leucine zipper does not interact with DNA itself but functions to hold two recognition helices in the correct orientation to bind DNA (Figure 4*b*).

Once a protein binds at a specific site on the DNA, a number of outcomes are possible. In some cases, the DNA-binding protein is an enzyme that catalyzes a specific reaction on the DNA, such as transcription by RNA polymerase. In other cases, however, the binding event can either block transcription (negative regulation, Section 3) or activate it (positive regulation, Section 4).

2 MiniReview

Certain proteins can bind to DNA because of interactions between specific domains of the proteins and specific regions of the DNA molecule. In most cases the interactions are sequence-specific. Proteins that bind to nucleic acid may be enzymes that use nucleic acid as substrates, or they may be regulatory proteins that affect gene expression.

- What is a protein domain?
- Why are some interactions specific to certain DNA sequences?

3 Negative Control of Transcription: Repression and Induction

Transcription is the first step in biological information flow (Figure 1); because of this, it is relatively easy to affect gene expression at this point. If one gene is transcribed more frequently than another, there will be more of its mRNA available for translation and therefore a greater amount of its protein product in the cell. Several different mechanisms for controlling gene expression are known in bacteria, and all of them are greatly influenced by the environment in which the organism is growing, in particular by the presence or absence of specific small molecules. These molecules can interact with specific proteins such as the DNA-binding proteins just described. The result is the control of transcription or, more rarely, translation.

We begin by describing repression and induction, simple forms of regulation that govern gene expression at the level of transcription. In this section we deal only with **negative control** of transcription, a regulatory mechanism that stops transcription (hence, the term *negative*).

Enzyme Repression and Induction

Often the enzymes that catalyze the synthesis of a specific product are not synthesized if the product is present in the medium in sufficient amounts. For example, the enzymes needed to synthesize the amino acid arginine are made only when arginine is absent from the culture medium; an excess of arginine represses the synthesis of these enzymes. This event is called enzyme **repression**.

As can be seen in Figure 5, if arginine is added to a culture growing exponentially in a medium devoid of arginine, growth continues at the previous rate, but production of the enzymes for arginine synthesis stops. Note that this is a specific effect, as the synthesis of all other enzymes in the cell continues at the previous rate. This is because the enzymes affected by a particular repression event make up only a tiny fraction of the entire complement of proteins in the cell at that time.

Enzyme repression is widespread in bacteria as a means of controlling the synthesis of enzymes required for the biosynthesis of amino acids and the nucleotide precursors purines and pyrimidines. In most cases, it is the final product of a particular biosynthetic pathway that represses the enzymes of the pathway. In these cases repression is quite specific and usually has no effect on the synthesis of enzymes other than those in the specific biosynthetic pathway (Figure 5). The benefit of enzyme repression should be obvious. It ensures that the organism does not waste energy and nutrients synthesizing unneeded enzymes.

Enzyme **induction** is conceptually the opposite of enzyme repression. In enzyme induction an enzyme is made only when its substrate is present. Enzyme repression typically affects biosynthetic (anabolic) enzymes. In contrast, enzyme induction usually affects degradative (catabolic) enzymes.

Consider, for example, the utilization of the sugar lactose as a carbon and energy source by *Escherichia coli*. Figure 6

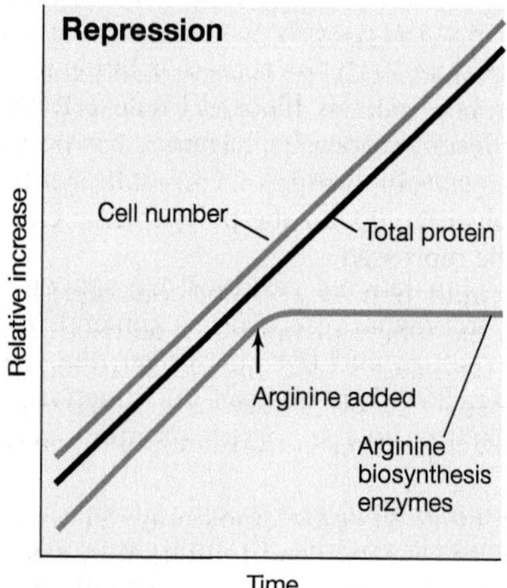

Figure 5 **Enzyme repression.** The addition of arginine to the medium specifically represses production of enzymes needed to make arginine. Net protein synthesis is unaffected.

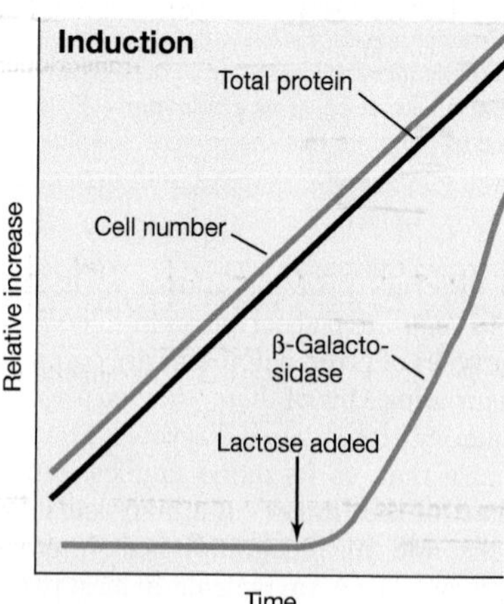

Figure 6 **Enzyme induction.** The addition of lactose to the medium specifically induces synthesis of the enzyme β-galactosidase. Net protein synthesis is unaffected.

shows the induction of β-galactosidase, the enzyme that cleaves lactose into glucose and galactose. This enzyme is required for *E. coli* to grow on lactose. If lactose is absent from the medium, the enzyme is not synthesized, but synthesis begins almost immediately after lactose is added. The three genes in the *lac* operon encode three proteins, including β-galactosidase, that are induced simultaneously upon adding lactose. One can immediately see the value to the organism of such a control mechanism; it provides a means to synthesize specific enzymes only when they are needed.

Inducers and Corepressors

The substance that induces enzyme synthesis is called an *inducer,* and a substance that represses enzyme synthesis is called a *corepressor*. These substances, which are normally small molecules, are collectively called *effectors*. Interestingly, not all inducers and corepressors are actual substrates or end products of the enzymes involved. For example, structural analogs may induce or repress even though they are not substrates of the enzyme. Isopropyl-thiogalactoside (IPTG), for instance, is an inducer of β-galactosidase even though IPTG cannot be hydrolyzed by this enzyme. In nature, however, inducers and corepressors are probably normal cell metabolites. However, detailed studies of lactose utilization in *E. coli* have shown that the actual inducer of β-galactosidase, is not lactose, but instead the structurally similar compound *allolactose,* a derivative made by the cell from lactose. www.microbiologyplace.com **Online Tutorial 9.1: Negative Control of Transcription and the *lac* Operon**

Mechanism of Repression and Induction

How can inducers and corepressors affect transcription in such a specific manner? They do this indirectly by binding to specific DNA-binding proteins, which, in turn, affect transcription. In the case of a repressible enzyme (Figure 5), the corepressor (in this case, arginine) binds to a specific **repressor protein**, the arginine repressor, which is present in the cell (Figure 7). The repressor protein is itself an allosteric protein; that is, its conformation is altered when the corepressor binds to it.

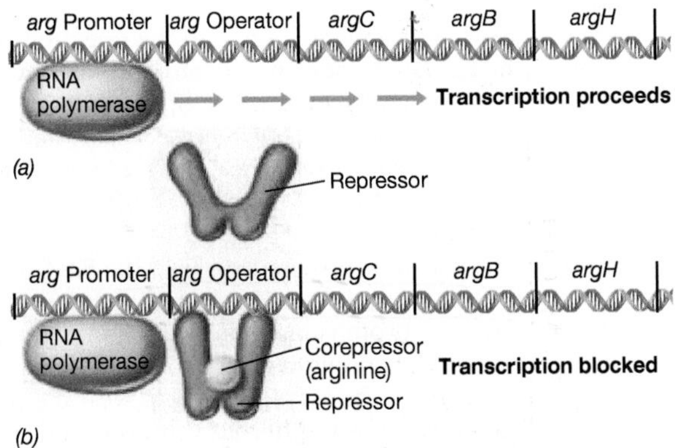

Figure 7 **The process of enzyme repression using the arginine operon as an example.** *(a)* The operon is transcribed because the repressor is unable to bind to the operator. *(b)* After a corepressor (small molecule) binds to the repressor, the repressor binds to the operator and blocks transcription; mRNA and the proteins it encodes are not made. For the *argCBH* operon, the amino acid arginine is the corepressor that binds to the arginine repressor.

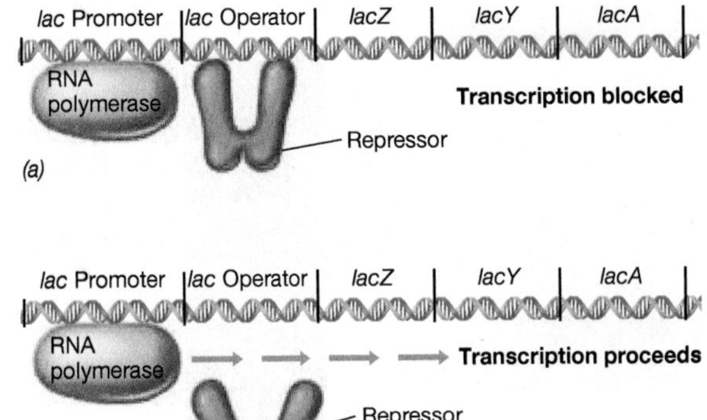

Figure 8 **The process of enzyme induction using the lactose operon as an example.** *(a)* A repressor protein binds to the operator region and blocks the binding of RNA polymerase. *(b)* An inducer molecule binds to the repressor and inactivates it so that it no longer can bind to the operator. RNA polymerase then transcribes the DNA and makes an mRNA for that operon. For the *lac* operon, the sugar allolactose is the inducer that binds to the lactose repressor.

By binding its effector, the repressor protein becomes active and can then bind to a specific region of the DNA near the promoter of the gene, the *operator*. This region gave its name to the **operon**, a cluster of genes arranged in a linear and consecutive fashion whose expression is under the control of a single operator. All of the genes in an operon are transcribed as a single unit yielding a single mRNA. The operator is located downstream of the promoter where synthesis of mRNA is initiated (Figure 7). If the repressor binds to the operator, transcription is physically blocked because RNA polymerase can neither bind nor proceed. Hence, the polypeptides encoded by the genes in the operon cannot be synthesized. If the mRNA is polycistronic, all the polypeptides encoded by this mRNA will be repressed.

Enzyme induction may also be controlled by a repressor. In this case, the repressor protein is active in the absence of the inducer, completely blocking transcription. When the inducer is added, it combines with the repressor protein and inactivates it; inhibition is overcome and transcription can proceed (Figure 8).

All regulatory systems employing repressors have the same underlying mechanism: inhibition of mRNA synthesis by the activity of specific repressor proteins that are themselves under the control of specific small effector molecules. And, as previously noted, because the repressor's role is inhibitory, regulation by repressors is called *negative control*.

3 MiniReview

The amount of a specific enzyme in the cell can be controlled by increasing (induction) or decreasing (repression) the amount of mRNA that encodes the enzyme. This transcriptional regulation is carried out by allosteric regulatory proteins that bind to DNA. For negative control of transcription, the regulatory protein is called a repressor, and it functions by inhibiting mRNA synthesis.

- Why is "negative control" so named?
- How does a repressor inhibit the synthesis of a specific mRNA?

4 Positive Control of Transcription

In negative control, the controlling element—the repressor protein—brings about repression of mRNA synthesis. By contrast, in **positive control** of transcription, a regulator protein activates the binding of RNA polymerase to DNA. An excellent example of positive regulation is the catabolism of the disaccharide sugar maltose in *Escherichia coli.*

Maltose Catabolism in *Escherichia coli*

The enzymes for maltose catabolism in *E. coli* are synthesized only after the addition of maltose to the medium. The expression of these enzymes thus follows the pattern shown for β-galactosidase in Figure 6 except that maltose rather than lactose is required to affect gene expression. However, control of the synthesis of maltose-degrading enzymes is not under negative control as in the *lac* operon, but under positive control; transcription requires the binding of an **activator protein** to the DNA.

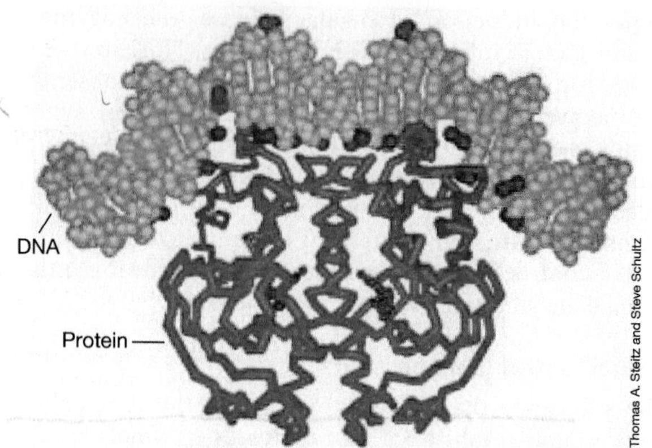

Figure 10 Computer model of the interaction of a positive regulatory protein with DNA. This model shows the cyclic AMP-binding protein (CRP protein; Section 9), a regulatory protein that helps control several operons. The α-carbon backbone of this protein is shown in blue and purple. The protein is binding to a DNA double helix (green and light blue). Note that binding of the CRP protein to DNA has bent the DNA.

The maltose activator protein cannot bind to the DNA unless this protein first binds maltose, the inducer (also called an effector). When the maltose activator protein binds to DNA, it allows RNA polymerase to begin transcription (Figure 9). Like repressor proteins, activator proteins bind specifically only to certain sequences on the DNA. However, the region on the DNA that is the site of the activator is not called an operator (Figures 7 and 8), but instead an *activator-binding site* (Figure 9). Nevertheless, the genes controlled by this activator-binding site are still called an operon.

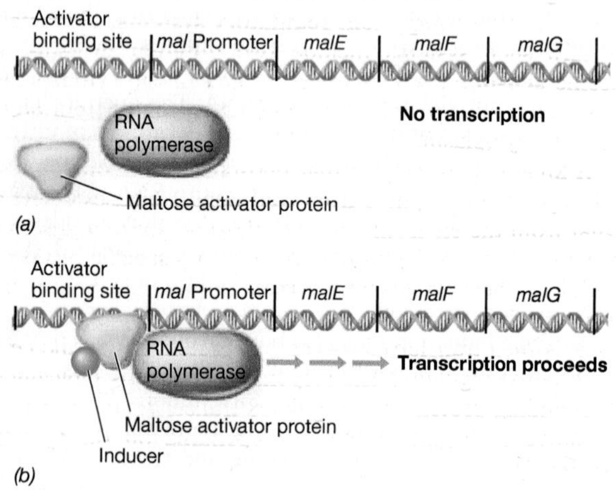

Figure 9 Positive control of enzyme induction using the maltose operon as an example. *(a)* In the absence of an inducer, neither the activator protein nor the RNA polymerase can bind to the DNA. *(b)* An inducer molecule (for the *malEFG* operon it is the sugar maltose) binds to the activator protein (MalT), which in turn binds to the activator-binding site. This allows RNA polymerase to bind to the promoter and begin transcription.

Binding of Activator Proteins

In negative control, the repressor binds to the operator and blocks transcription. How does an activator protein work? The promoters of positively controlled operons have nucleotide sequences that bind RNA polymerase weakly and are poor matches to the consensus sequence. Thus, even with the correct sigma factor, the RNA polymerase has difficulty binding to these promoters.

The role of the activator protein is to help the RNA polymerase recognize the promoter and begin transcription. For example, the activator protein may cause a change in the structure of the DNA by bending it (Figure 10), allowing the RNA polymerase to make the correct contacts with the promoter to begin transcription. Alternatively, the activator protein may interact directly with the RNA polymerase. This can happen either when the activator-binding site is close to the promoter (Figure 11a) or when it is several hundred base pairs away from the promoter, a situation in which DNA looping is required to make the necessary contacts (Figure 11*b*).

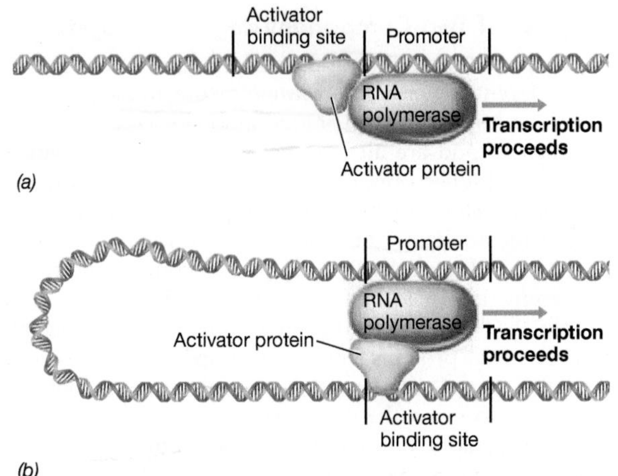

Figure 11 Activator protein interactions with RNA polymerase. *(a)* The activator-binding site is near the promoter. *(b)* The activator-binding site is several hundred base pairs from the promoter. In this case, the DNA must be looped to allow the activator and the RNA polymerase to contact.

Many genes in *E. coli* have promoters under positive control, and many have promoters under negative control. In addition, many operons have a promoter with multiple types of control and some have more than one promoter, each with its own control system! Thus, the rather simple picture outlined above is not typical of all operons. Multiple control features are common in the operons of virtually all prokaryotes, and thus their overall regulation can be very complex.

Operons versus Regulons

In *E. coli,* the genes required for maltose utilization are spread out over the chromosome in several operons, each of which has an activator-binding site to which a copy of the maltose activator protein can bind. Therefore, the maltose activator protein actually controls the transcription of more than one operon. When more than one operon is under the control of a single regulatory protein, these operons are collectively called a **regulon.** Therefore, the enzymes for maltose utilization are encoded by the maltose regulon.

Regulons are also known for operons under negative control as well. For example, the arginine biosynthetic enzymes (Section 3) are encoded by the arginine regulon, whose operons are all under the control of the arginine repressor protein (only one of the arginine operons was shown in Figure 7). However, in regulon control a specific DNA-binding protein binds only at those operons it controls regardless of whether it is functioning as an activator or repressor; other operons are not affected.

4 MiniReview

Positive regulators of transcription are called activator proteins. They bind to activator-binding sites on the DNA and stimulate transcription. As for repressors, the activity of activating proteins is modified by inducers. For positive control of enzyme induction, the inducer promotes the binding of the activator protein and thus stimulates transcription.

- Compare and contrast the activities of an activator protein and a repressor protein.
- Distinguish between an operon and a regulon.

III SENSING AND SIGNAL TRANSDUCTION

5 Two-Component Regulatory Systems

Prokaryotes regulate cell metabolism in response to environmental fluctuations, including temperature changes, changes in pH and oxygen availability, changes in the availability of nutrients, and even changes in the number of cells present. Therefore, there must be mechanisms by which cells receive signals from the environment and transmit them to the specific target to be regulated.

We have seen in preceding sections that some signals can be small molecules that enter the cell and function as effectors. However, in many cases the external signal is not transmitted directly to the regulatory protein but instead is detected by a sensor that transmits it to the rest of the regulatory machinery, a process called **signal transduction.**

Sensor Kinases and Response Regulators

Most signal transduction systems contain two parts and are thus called **two-component regulatory systems.** Characteristically, such systems include two different proteins: a specific **sensor kinase protein** located in the cytoplasmic membrane and a partner **response regulator protein** present in the cytoplasm.

A kinase is an enzyme that phosphorylates compounds, typically using phosphate from ATP. Sensor kinases detect a signal from the environment and phosphorylate themselves (a process called autophosphorylation) at a specific histidine residue on their cytoplasmic surface (Figure 12). Sensor kinases are thus also called *histidine kinases*. The phosphoryl group is then transferred to another protein inside the cell, the response regulator. The response regulator is typically a DNA-binding protein that regulates transcription, either in a positive or negative fashion, depending on the system (Figure 12).

A balanced regulatory system must have a feedback loop, that is, a way to complete the regulatory circuit and terminate the initial signal. This resets the system for another cycle. This feedback loop involves a phosphatase, an enzyme activity that removes the phosphoryl group from the response regulator protein at a constant rate. In many systems this reaction is carried out by the response regulator

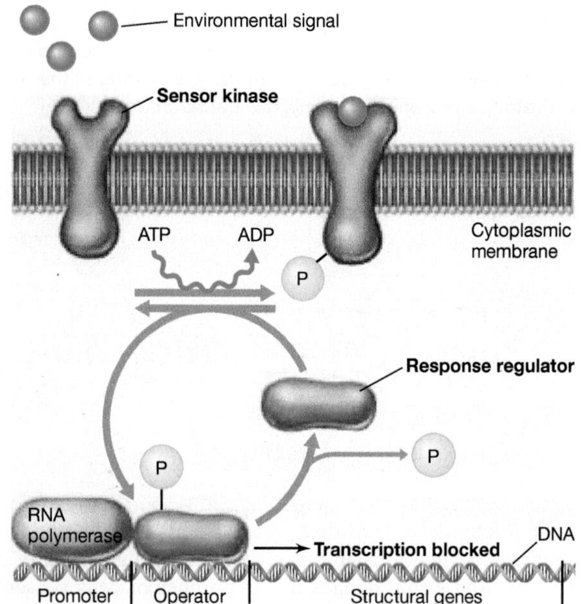

Figure 12 The control of gene expression by a two-component regulatory system. The main components of the system include a sensor kinase in the cytoplasmic membrane that phosphorylates itself in response to an environmental signal. The phosphoryl group is then transferred to the other main component, a response regulator. In the system shown here the phosphorylated response regulator is a repressor protein. The phosphatase activity of the response regulator slowly releases the phosphate from the response regulator and closes the circuit.

itself, although in many other cases separate proteins are present that stimulate this reaction (Figure 12). Phosphatase activity is typically a slower process than response regulator phosphorylation. However, if phosphorylation ceases due to reduced sensor kinase activity, phosphatase activity eventually returns the response regulator to the fully unphosphorylated state.

Examples of Two-Component Regulatory Systems

Two-component systems regulate a large number of genes in many different bacteria. Interestingly, two-component systems seem to be less widely distributed among species of *Archaea* than *Bacteria* and are all but absent in bacteria that live as parasites of higher organisms. A few key examples of two-component systems include those for phosphate assimilation, nitrogen metabolism, and response to osmotic pressure. In *Escherichia coli* almost 50 different two-component systems are present, and a few of them are listed in Table 1. For example, the osmolarity of the environment controls the relative levels of the proteins OmpC and OmpF in the *E. coli* outer membrane. OmpC and OmpF are porins, proteins that allow metabolites to cross the outer membrane of gram-negative bacteria. If osmotic pressure is low, the synthesis of OmpF, a porin with a larger pore, increases; if osmotic pressure is higher, OmpC, a porin with a smaller pore, is made in larger amounts. The response regulator of this system is OmpR. When OmpR is phosphorylated, it activates transcription of the *ompC* gene and represses transcription of the *ompF* gene. The *ompF* gene in *E. coli* is also controlled by antisense RNA (Section 14).

Some signal transduction systems have multiple regulatory elements. For instance, in the Ntr regulatory system, which regulates nitrogen assimilation in many *Bacteria*, including *E. coli*, the response regulator is the activator protein NRI (nitrogen regulator I). NRI activates transcription from promoters recognized by RNA polymerase using σ^{54} (RpoN), an alternative sigma factor. The sensor kinase in the Ntr system, NRII (nitrogen regulator II), fills a dual role as both kinase and phosphatase. The activity of NRII is in turn regulated by the addition or removal of uridine monophosphate groups from another protein, PII.

The Nar regulatory system (Table 1) controls a set of genes that allow the use of nitrate and/or nitrite as alternative electron acceptors during anaerobic respiration. The Nar system contains two different sensor kinases and two different response regulators. In addition, all of the genes

Table 1 Examples of two-component regulatory systems that regulate transcription in *Escherichia coli*

System	*Environmental signal*	*Sensor kinase*	*Response regulator*	*Activity of response regulator*[a]
Arc system	Oxygen	ArcB	ArcA	Repressor/activator
Nitrate and nitrite respiration (Nar)	Nitrate and nitrite	NarX	NarL	Activator/repressor
		NarQ	NarP	Activator/repressor
Nitrogen utilization (Ntr)	Shortage of organic nitrogen	NRII (=GlnL)	NRI (=GlnG)	Activator of promoters requiring RpoN/σ^{54}
Pho regulon	Inorganic phosphate	PhoR	PhoB	Activator
Porin regulation	Osmotic pressure	EnvZ	OmpR	Activator/repressor

[a]Note that many response regulator proteins act as both activators and repressors depending on the genes being regulated. Although ArcA can function as either an activator or a repressor, it functions as a repressor on most operons that it regulates.

regulated by this system are also controlled by the FNR protein, a global regulator for genes involved in anaerobic respiration (see Table 3). This type of multiple regulation is not uncommon in systems of central importance to the metabolism of a cell.

Genomic analyses allow for the ready detection of genes encoding two-component regulatory systems because the histidine kinases show significant amino acid sequence conservation. Some species of *Archaea,* in particular the methanogens, also possess two-component regulatory systems genes. Two-component systems closely related to those in *Bacteria* are also present in microbial eukaryotes, such as the yeast *Saccharomyces cerevisiae*, and even in plants. However, most eukaryotic signal transduction pathways rely on phosphorylation of serine, threonine and tyrosine residues of proteins that are unrelated to those of bacterial two-component systems.

5 MiniReview

Signal transduction systems transmit environmental signals to the cell. In prokaryotes signal transduction is typically carried out by a two-component regulatory system that includes a membrane-integrated sensor kinase and a cytoplasmic response regulator. The activity of the response regulator depends on its state of phosphorylation.

- What are kinases and what is their role in two-component regulatory systems?
- After depletion of an environmental signal, how are the two components reset for a second stimulus response?

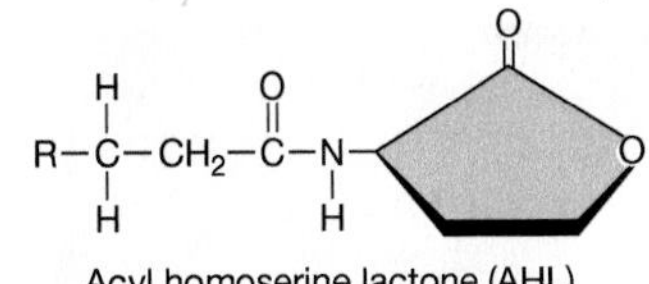

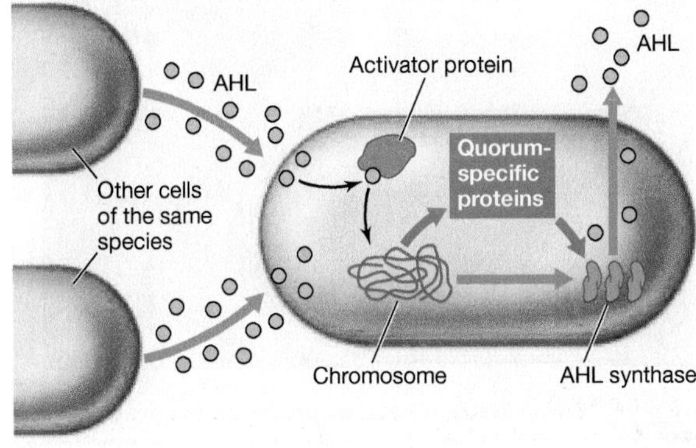

Figure 13 **Quorum sensing.** *(a)* General structure of an acyl homoserine lactone (AHL). Different AHLs are variants of this parent structure. R = alkyl group (C_1–C_{17}); the carbon next to the R group is often modified to a keto group (C=O). *(b)* A cell capable of quorum sensing expresses acyl homoserine lactone synthase at basal levels. This enzyme makes the cell's specific AHL. When cells of the same species reach a certain density, the concentration of AHL rises sufficiently to bind to the activator protein, which activates transcription of quorum-specific genes.

6 Quorum Sensing

As previously mentioned, organisms regulate genes in response to signals in the environment. One potential signal that prokaryotes can respond to is the presence of other cells of the same species in their surroundings. Some prokaryotes have regulatory pathways that are controlled by the density of cells of their own kind. This type of control is called **quorum sensing** (the word "quorum" in this sense means "sufficient numbers").

Mechanism of Quorum Sensing

Quorum sensing is a mechanism by which bacteria assess their population density. This is of practical use to ensure that sufficient cell numbers of a given species are present before initiating a response that requires a certain cell density to have an effect. For example, a pathogenic (disease-causing) bacterium that secretes a toxin can have no effect as a single cell; production of the toxin by that cell alone would be a waste of resources. However, if there is a sufficiently high population of cells present, the coordinated expression of the toxin may successfully initiate disease.

Quorum sensing is widespread among gram-negative bacteria but is also found in gram-positive bacteria. Each species that employs quorum sensing synthesizes a specific signal molecule called an **autoinducer**. This molecule diffuses freely across the cell envelope in either direction. Because of this, the autoinducer reaches high concentrations inside the cell only if there are many cells nearby, each making the same autoinducer. Inside the cell, the autoinducer binds to a specific activator protein and in so doing triggers transcription of specific genes (Figure 13*b*).

There are several different classes of autoinducers (Table 2). The first to be identified were the *acyl homoserine lactones* (AHLs) (Figure 13*a*). Several different AHLs, with acyl groups of different lengths, are found in different species of gram-negative bacteria. In addition, many gram-negative bacteria make AI-2 (*auto*inducer *2*; a cyclic furan derivative). This is apparently used as a common autoinducer between many species of bacteria. Among gram-positive bacteria, certain short peptides function as autoinducers.

Quorum sensing was first discovered as the mechanism of regulating light emission in bioluminescent bacteria. Several bacterial species can emit light, including the marine bacterium *Aliivibro fischeri*. Figure 14 shows bioluminescent colonies of *A. fischeri.* The light is due to the activity of an enzyme called luciferase. The *lux* operons, which encode the proteins needed for bioluminescence, are under control of the activator protein LuxR and are induced when the concentration of the specific *A. fischeri* AHL, *N*-3-oxohexanoyl

Figure 14 Bioluminescent bacteria producing the enzyme luciferase. Cells of the bacterium *Aliivibrio fischeri* were streaked on nutrient agar in a Petri dish and allowed to grow overnight. The photograph was taken in a darkened room using only the light generated by the bacteria.

homoserine lactone, becomes high enough. This AHL is synthesized by the enzyme encoded by the *luxI* gene.

Examples of Quorum Sensing

A variety of genes are controlled by a quorum-sensing system, including some in pathogenic bacteria. For example, pseudomonads use 4-hydroxy-alkyl quinolines as autoinducers to induce genes involved in virulence and related activities. In *Pseudomonas aeruginosa*, for instance, quorum sensing triggers the expression of a large number of unrelated genes when the population density becomes sufficiently high. These genes assist cells of *P. aeruginosa* in the transition from growing freely suspended in liquid to growing in a semisolid matrix called a *biofilm*. The biofilm, formed from specific polysaccharides produced by *P. aeruginosa*, increases the pathogenicity of this organism and prevents the penetration of antibiotics.

The pathogenesis of *Staphylococcus aureus* involves, among many other things, the production and secretion of small cell-surface and extracellular peptides that damage host cells or that interfere with the immune system. The genes encoding these virulence factors are under the control of a quorum-sensing system that responds to a peptide produced by the organism. The regulation of these genes is quite complex and requires a regulatory RNA molecule discussed below. The *S. aureus* quorum-sensing system also uses regulatory proteins that are part of a signal-transduction system (Section 5).

Quorum sensing probably exists in *Archaea*, in particular haloalkaliphilic *Archaea*, organisms that inhabit alkaline saline habitats, although the reports are preliminary and the details are unclear. However, quorum sensing also occurs in microbial eukaryotes. For example, in the eukaryotic budding yeast, *Saccharomyces cerevisiae*, specific aromatic alcohols are produced as autoinducers and control the transition between growth of *S. cerevisiae* as single cells and as elongated filaments. Similar transitions are seen in other fungi, some of which, such as *Candida*, whose quorum sensing is mediated by the long chain alcohol farnesol, cause disease in humans.

6 MiniReview

Quorum sensing allows cells to monitor their environment for cells of their own kind. Quorum sensing depends on the sharing of specific small molecules known as autoinducers. Once a sufficient concentration of the autoinducer is present, specific gene expression is triggered.

- What are the properties required for a molecule to function as an autoinducer?
- In terms of autoinducers, how does quorum sensing differ between gram-negative and gram-positive bacteria?

Table 2 Examples of quorum sensing and autoinducers

Organism	*Autoinducer*	*Receptor*[a]	*Process regulated*
Proteobacteria	Acyl homoserine lactones	LuxR protein	Diverse processes
Many diverse bacteria	AI-2 (furanone ± borate)[b]	LuxQ protein	Diverse processes
Pseudomonads	4-Hydroxy alkyl quinolines	?	Virulence; biofilms
Streptomyces	Gamma-butyrolactones	ArpA repressor	Antibiotic synthesis; sporulation
Gram-positive bacteria	Oligopeptides (linear or cyclic)	Two-component systems	Diverse processes
Yeast	Aromatic alcohols	?	Filamentation

[a]The details of how many of the quorum-sensing systems operate is complex. Some involve two-component regulatory systems (Section 5).

[b]The AI-2 autoinducer exists in several slightly different structures, some of which have an attached borate group.

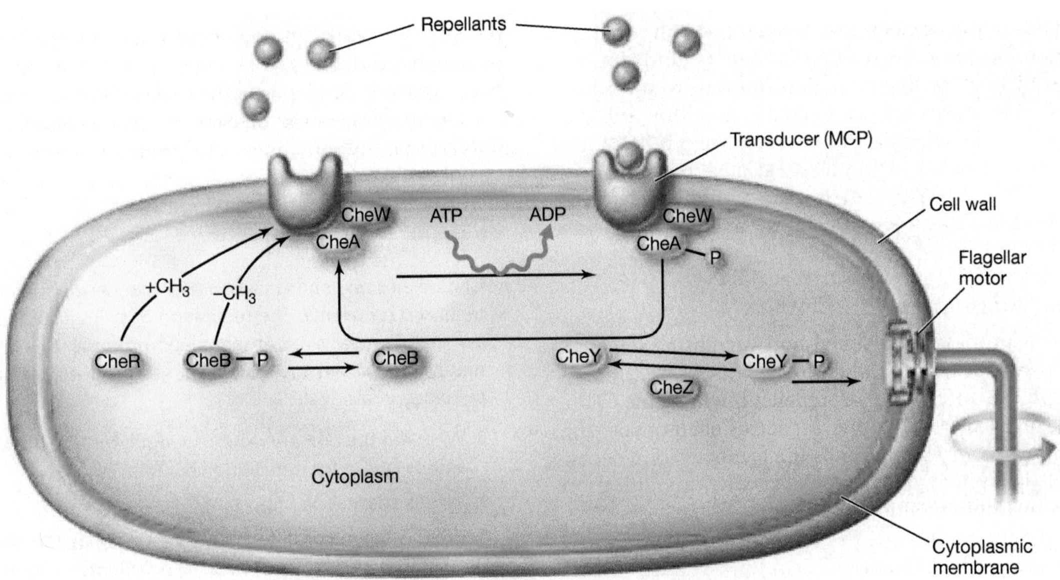

Figure 15 **Interactions of MCPs, Che proteins, and the flagellar motor in bacterial chemotaxis.** The MCP forms a complex with the sensor kinase CheA and the coupling protein CheW. This combination results in a signal-regulated autophosphorylation of CheA to CheA-P. CheA-P can then phosphorylate the response regulators CheB and CheY. Phosphorylated CheY (CheY-P) interacts directly with the flagellar motor switch. CheZ dephosphorylates CheY-P. CheR continually adds methyl groups to the transducer. CheB-P (but not CheB) removes them. The degree of methylation of the MCPs controls their ability to respond to attractants and repellents and leads to adaptation.

7 Regulation of Chemotaxis

We have previously seen how prokaryotes can move toward attractants or away from repellents, a process called *chemotaxis*. We noted that prokaryotes are too small to actually sense spatial gradients of a chemical, but they can respond to temporal gradients. That is, they can sense the *change* in concentration of a chemical over time rather than the absolute concentration of the chemical stimulus. Prokaryotes use a modified two-component system to sense temporal changes in attractants or repellents and process this information to regulate flagellar rotation. Note that in the case of chemotaxis we have a two-component system that directly regulates the activity of preexisting flagella not the transcription of the genes encoding the flagella.

Step One: Response to Signal

The mechanism of chemotaxis is complex and depends upon a variety of different proteins. Several sensory proteins reside in the cytoplasmic membrane and sense the presence of attractants and repellents. These sensor proteins are not themselves sensor kinases but interact with cytoplasmic sensor kinases. These sensory proteins allow the cell to monitor the concentration of various substances over time.

The sensory proteins are called *methyl-accepting chemotaxis proteins (MCPs)*. In *Escherichia coli*, five different MCPs have been identified, and each is a transmembrane protein (Figure 15). Each MCP can sense a variety of compounds. For example, the Tar MCP of *E. coli* can sense the attractants aspartate and maltose as well as repellents such as the heavy metals cobalt and nickel.

MCPs bind attractants or repellents directly or in some cases indirectly through interactions with periplasmic binding proteins. Binding of an attractant or repellent initiates a series of interactions with cytoplasmic proteins that eventually affects flagellar rotation. Recall that if rotation of the flagellum is counterclockwise, the cell will continue to move in a run, whereas if the flagellum rotates clockwise, the cell will tumble.

MCPs are in contact with the cytoplasmic proteins CheW and CheA (Figure 15). CheA is the sensor kinase in chemotaxis. When an MCP binds a chemical, it changes conformation and (with help from CheW) affects the autophosphorylation of CheA to form CheA-P. Attractants *decrease* the rate of autophosphorylation, whereas repellents *increase* this rate. CheA-P then passes the phosphate to CheY (forming CheY-P); this is the response regulator. CheA-P can also pass the phosphate to CheB, another response regulator, but this is a much slower reaction than the phosphorylation of CheY. We will discuss the activity of CheB-P later.

Step Two: Controlling Flagellar Rotation

CheY is a key protein in the system because it governs the direction of rotation of the flagellum. CheY-P interacts with the flagellar motor to induce clockwise flagellar rotation and tumbling. If nonphosphorylated, CheY cannot bind to the flagellar motor and the flagellum continues to rotate counterclockwise; this causes the cell to continue to run. Another protein, CheZ, dephosphorylates CheY, returning it to a form that allows runs instead of tumbles. Because repellents increase the level of CheY-P, they lead to tumbling, whereas attractants lead to a lower level of CheY-P and smooth swimming (runs).

Step Three: Adaptation

In addition to processing a signal and regulating flagellar rotation, the system must be able to detect a change in concentration of the attractant or repellent with time. This problem is solved by yet another aspect of chemotaxis, the process of *adaptation*. Adaptation is the feedback loop necessary to reset the system. This involves covalent modification of the MCPs by CheB, mentioned earlier.

As their name implies, MCPs can be methylated. The cytoplasmic protein, CheR (Figure 15), continually adds methyl groups to the MCPs at a slow rate using *S*-adenosylmethionine as a methyl donor. The response regulator CheB is a demethylase that removes methyl groups from the MCPs. Phosphorylation of CheB greatly increases its rate of activity. The changes in level of methylation of the MCPs results in conformational changes similar to those caused by binding of attractant or repellant. Methylation thus allows adaptation to sensory signals as outlined below.

If the level of an attractant remains *high*, the level of phosphorylation of CheA (and, therefore, of CheY and CheB) remains *low*, and the cell swims smoothly. The level of methylation of the MCPs increases during this period because CheB-P is not present to demethylate them rapidly. However, MCPs no longer respond to the attractant when they are fully methylated. Therefore, even if the level of attractant remains high, the level of CheA-P and CheB-P increases and the cell begins to tumble. However, now the MCPs can be demethylated by CheB-P, and when this happens, the receptors are "reset" and can once again respond to further increase or decrease in level of attractants.

The course of events is just the opposite for repellents. Fully methylated MCPs respond best to an increasing gradient of repellents and send a signal for cell tumbling to begin. The cell then moves off in a random direction while MCPs are slowly demethylated. With this mechanism for adaptation, chemotaxis successfully achieves the ability to monitor small changes in the concentrations of both attractants and repellents over time.

Other Taxes

In addition to chemotaxis, several other microbial taxes are known, for example, *phototaxis* (movement toward light), *aerotaxis* (movement toward oxygen), and other types of directed movements. Interestingly, many of the cytoplasmic Che proteins that function in chemotaxis also play a role in these other taxes. In phototaxis, for example, a light sensor protein replaces the MCPs of chemotaxis, and in aerotaxis, a redox protein monitors levels of oxygen. These sensors then interact with cytoplasmic Che proteins to direct runs or tumbles in response to these other signals. It thus appears that several different prokaryotic taxes can be driven by a common set of cytoplasmic proteins.

7 MiniReview

Chemotaxis responds in a complex manner to both attractants and repellents. The regulation of swimming affects the activity of proteins rather than their synthesis. Adaptation by methylation allows the system to reset itself to the continued presence of a signal.

- What are the primary response regulator and the primary sensor kinase for regulating chemotaxis?
- Why is adaptation important?
- What is the major difference in response by the chemotaxis system to an attractant versus a repellent?

8 Control of Transcription in *Archaea*

All organisms regulate expression of their genes. There are two alternative approaches to regulating the activity of RNA polymerase. One strategy, predominately used by *Bacteria* and *Archaea*, is to use DNA-binding proteins that either prevent RNA polymerase activity (repressor proteins) or promote RNA polymerase activity (activator proteins) (Section 3). The alternative, used most often by eukaryotes, is to transmit signals to the protein subunits of the RNA polymerase itself. It is perhaps surprising, then, that despite the greater overall similarity between the *mechanisms* of replication and transcription in *Archaea* and *Eukarya*, the *regulation* of transcription in *Archaea* more closely resembles that of *Bacteria*.

Few repressor or activator proteins from *Archaea* have yet been characterized in detail, but it is clear that both types of regulatory proteins exist. Archaeal repressor proteins function either by blocking the binding of RNA polymerase itself or by blocking binding of the TBP and TFB proteins required for promoter recognition and RNA polymerase binding in *Archaea*. At least some archaeal activator proteins function in just the opposite way, by recruiting TBP to the promotor, thereby facilitating transcription.

Repressor Proteins in *Archaea*

A good example of an archaeal repressor is the NrpR protein from the methanogen *Methanococcus maripaludis;* this protein represses genes involved in nitrogen metabolism (Figure 16) such as those involved in nitrogen fixation or glutamine synthesis. When levels of organic nitrogen are plentiful in the cell, NrpR represses genes involved in nitrogen fixation and glutamine biosynthesis. However, if the level of

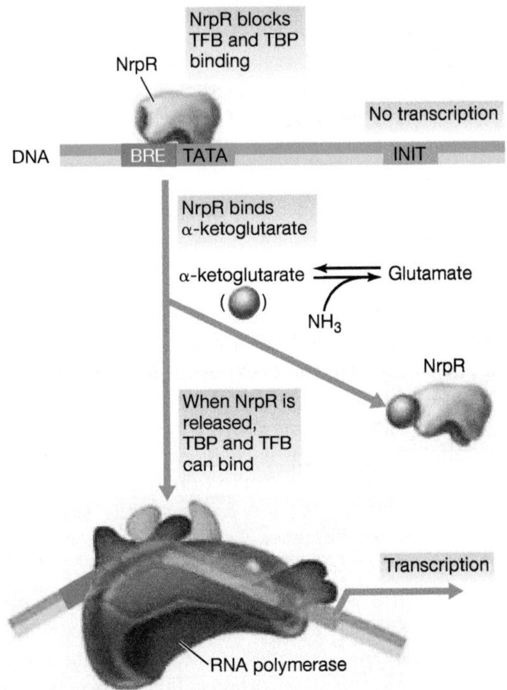

Figure 16 **Repression of genes for nitrogen metabolism in *Archaea*.** The NrpR protein of *Methanococcus maripaludis* acts as a repressor. It blocks the binding of the TFB and TBP proteins, which are required for promoter recognition, to the BRE site and TATA box, respectively. If there is a shortage of ammonia, α-ketoglutarate is not converted to glutamate. The α-ketoglutarate accumulates and binds to NrpR, releasing it from the DNA. Now TBP and TFB can bind. This in turn allows RNA polymerase to bind and transcribe the operon, starting from a point within the initiator box.

nitrogen compounds becomes limiting in the cell, this is a signal to the cell that more nitrogen is needed and that the repressor must be inactivated.

Interestingly, the signal that the level of nitrogen is limiting comes from elevated levels of α-ketoglutarate, a citric acid cycle intermediate, in the cell. This compound is converted to the amino acid glutamate by the addition of ammonia. When levels of α-ketoglutarate rise, this is a signal that ammonia is limiting and that additional means for obtaining ammonia, such as nitrogen fixation or the high-affinity nitrogen assimilation enzyme glutamine synthetase, need to be synthesized. Elevated levels of α-ketoglutarate function as an inducer by binding to the NrpR protein, which is then released from the DNA. This allows RNA polymerase to bind and transcribe the genes. Here the mechanism of inactivation of a repressor protein by a small molecule is analogous to the mechanism of induction considered earlier in *Bacteria,* where the presence of an inducer, such as lactose in the *lac* operon of *Escherichia coli,* triggered the transcription of genes involved in lactose catabolism (Section 3).

8 MiniReview

Archaea resemble *Bacteria* in using DNA-binding activator and repressor proteins to regulate gene expression at the level of transcription.

- What is the major difference between transcriptional regulation in *Archaea* versus eukaryotes?

IV GLOBAL REGULATORY MECHANISMS

An organism often needs to regulate many unrelated genes simultaneously in response to a change in its environment. Regulatory mechanisms that respond to environmental signals by regulating the expression of many different genes are called *global control systems*. Both the lactose operon and the maltose regulon respond to global controls in addition to their own specific regulation discussed in Sections 3 and 4. We begin our consideration of global regulation by revisiting the *lac* operon.

9 Global Control and the *lac* Operon

Our discussions of the lactose and maltose regulatory systems did not consider the possibility that the cell's environment might contain several different carbon sources that the bacteria could use. For example, *Escherichia coli* can use many different sugars. When faced with several sugars, including glucose, do cells of *E. coli* use them simultaneously or one at a time? The answer is that glucose is always used first. Indeed, it would be wasteful to induce enzymes for the metabolism of other sugars if glucose were available, because *E. coli* grows faster on glucose than on any other carbon source. Thus, one mechanism of global control, catabolite repression, ensures that glucose is used first if available.

Catabolite Repression

In **catabolite repression** the syntheses of unrelated, primarily catabolic enzymes are repressed when cells are grown in a medium that contains glucose. Catabolite repression is also called the "glucose effect" because glucose was the first substance shown to initiate this response. In some organisms, however, carbon sources other than glucose cause catabolite repression. The key point is that the substrate that represses the use of other substrates is a better carbon and energy source. In this way, catabolite repression ensures that the organism uses the *best* available carbon and energy source first.

One consequence of catabolite repression is that it leads to two exponential growth phases, a situation called *diauxic growth*. If two usable energy sources are available, the cells grow first on the better energy source. Then, following a lag period, growth resumes on the other energy source. Diauxic

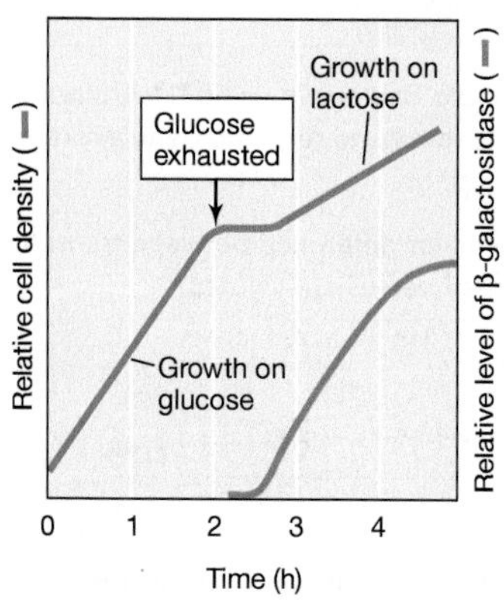

Figure 17 Diauxic growth of *Escherichia coli* on a mixture of glucose and lactose. Glucose represses the synthesis of β-galactosidase. After glucose is exhausted, a lag occurs until β-galactosidase is synthesized, and then growth resumes on lactose but at a slower rate.

growth is illustrated in Figure 17 for the growth of *E. coli* on a mixture of glucose and lactose.

As we have seen, the proteins of the *lac* operon, including the enzyme β-galactosidase, are required for using lactose and are induced in its presence (Figures 6 and 8). But, in addition, their synthesis is subject to catabolite repression. As long as glucose is present, the *lac* operon is not expressed and lactose is not used. However, when glucose is exhausted, catabolite repression is abolished, and after a brief lag period, the *lac* operon is expressed and the cells grow on lactose. As Figure 17 shows, the cells grow more rapidly on glucose than on lactose. Even though glucose and lactose are both excellent energy sources for *E. coli*, glucose is a better carbon source for this organism, and growth is faster on this substrate.

Cyclic AMP and CRP

Despite its name, in catabolite repression transcription is controlled by an activator protein and is actually a form of positive control (Section 4). The activator protein is called the *cyclic AMP receptor protein* (*CRP*) (also called the catabolite activator protein, or CAP). A gene that encodes a catabolite-repressible enzyme is expressed only if CRP protein binds to DNA in the promoter region. This then allows RNA polymerase to bind to the promoter. CRP is an allosteric protein and binds to DNA only if it has first bound a small molecule called *cyclic adenosine monophosphate* (*cyclic AMP* or *cAMP*) (Figure 18). As for most DNA-binding proteins (Section 2), CRP binds to DNA as a dimer.

Cyclic AMP is a key molecule in many metabolic control systems, both in prokaryotes and eukaryotes. Because it is derived from a nucleic acid precursor, it is a **regulatory nucleotide**. Other regulatory nucleotides include cyclic GMP (cyclic guanosine monophosphate; important mostly in eukaryotes), cyclic di-GMP, and ppGpp (Section 10). Cyclic AMP is synthesized from ATP by an enzyme called *adenylate*

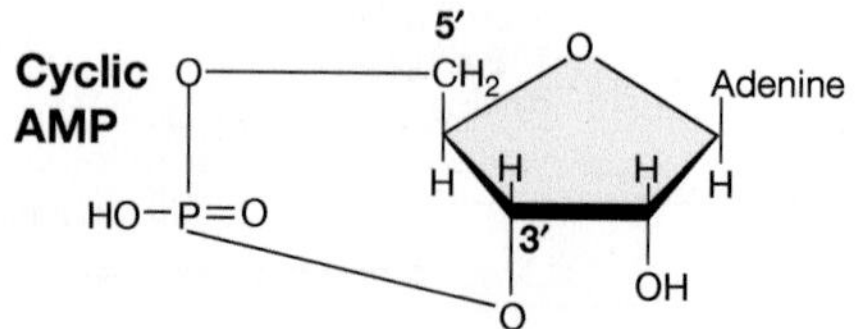

Figure 18 Cyclic AMP. Cyclic adenosine monophosphate is made from ATP by the enzyme adenylate cyclase.

cyclase. However, glucose inhibits the synthesis of cyclic AMP and also stimulates cyclic AMP transport out of the cell. When glucose enters the cell, the cyclic AMP level is lowered, CRP protein cannot bind DNA, and RNA polymerase fails to bind to the promoters of operons subject to catabolite repression. Thus, catabolite repression is really an indirect result of the presence of a better energy source (glucose). The direct cause of catabolite repression is a low level of cyclic AMP.

Global Aspects of Catabolite Repression

Why is catabolite repression considered a mechanism of *global* control? In *E. coli* and other organisms for which glucose is the preferred energy source, catabolite repression prevents expression of most other catabolic operons as long as glucose is present. Dozens of catabolic operons are affected, including those for lactose, maltose, a host of other sugars, and most of the other commonly used carbon and energy sources of *E. coli*. In addition, genes for the synthesis of flagella are controlled by catabolite repression—if bacteria have a good carbon source available, there is no need to swim around in search of nutrients.

Let us return to the *lac* operon to put catabolite repression into the context of the entire regulatory picture. To show this, the entire regulatory region of the *lac* operon is diagrammed in Figure 19. For *lac* genes to be transcribed, two requirements must be met: (1) the level of cyclic AMP must be high enough that the CRP protein binds to the CRP-binding site (positive control), and (2) lactose must be present so that the lactose repressor does not block transcription by binding to the operator (negative control). If these two conditions are met, the cell is signaled that glucose is absent and lactose is present; then and only then does transcription of the *lac* operon begin.

9 MiniReview

Global control systems regulate the expression of many genes simultaneously. Catabolite repression is a global control system that helps cells make the most efficient use of available carbon sources. The *lac* operon is under the control of catabolite repression as well as its own specific negative regulatory system.

- Explain how catabolite repression depends on an activator protein.
- Explain how the *lac* operon is both positively and negatively controlled.

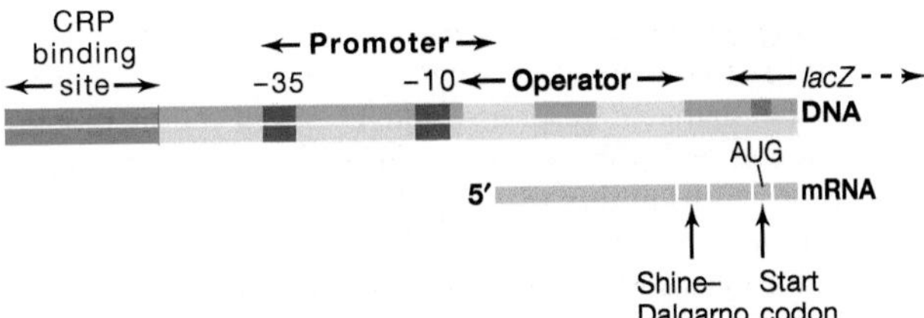

Figure 19 Overall regulation of the lactose operon. The first structural gene in this operon, *lacZ*, encodes the enzyme β-galactosidase, which breaks down lactose. The operon contains two other genes that also take part in lactose metabolism. The two halves of the operator (where the repressor binds) and the CRP-binding site are almost perfect inverted repeats. The transcriptional start site is located on the DNA exactly at the 5′-end of the mRNA. The location of the −35 sequence and the −10 sequence, which are part of the promoter, are also shown. In addition, the location of the Shine–Dalgarno sequence and the start codon are also given. These two sequences are critical for translation of the mRNA.

10 The Stringent Response

Nutrient levels in the natural environments of bacterial cells often change significantly, even if only briefly. Such conditions can easily be simulated in the laboratory, and much work has been done with *Escherichia coli* and other prokaryotes on the regulation of gene expression following a "shift down" or "shift up" in nutrient status. These include, in particular, the regulatory events triggered by starvation for amino acids or energy.

As a result of a shift down from amino acid excess to limitation—as would occur when a culture is transferred from a rich complex medium to a defined medium with a single carbon source—the synthesis of rRNA and tRNA ceases almost immediately. No new ribosomes are produced. Protein and DNA synthesis is curtailed, but the biosynthesis of new amino acids is activated (Figure 20a). Following such a shift, new proteins must be made to synthesize the amino acids no longer available in the environment; these are made by existing ribosomes. After a while, rRNA synthesis (and hence, the production of new ribosomes) begins again but at a new rate commensurate with the cell's reduced growth rate (Figure 20*a*). This course of events is called the **stringent response** (or stringent control) and is another example of global control.

ppGpp and the Mechanism of the Stringent Response

The stringent response is triggered by a mixture of two regulatory nucleotides, *guanosine tetraphosphate* (ppGpp) and *guanosine pentaphosphate* (pppGpp); this mixture is often written as (p)ppGpp (Figure 20*b*). In *E. coli,* these nucleotides, which are also called *alarmones*, rapidly accumulate during a shift down from amino acid excess to amino acid starvation. Alarmones are synthesized by a specific protein, called RelA, using ATP as a phosphate donor (Figure 20*b*,*c*). RelA adds two phosphate groups from ATP to GTP or GDP,

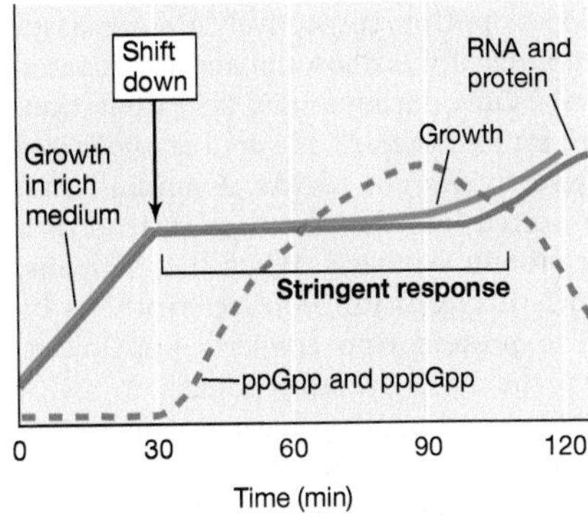

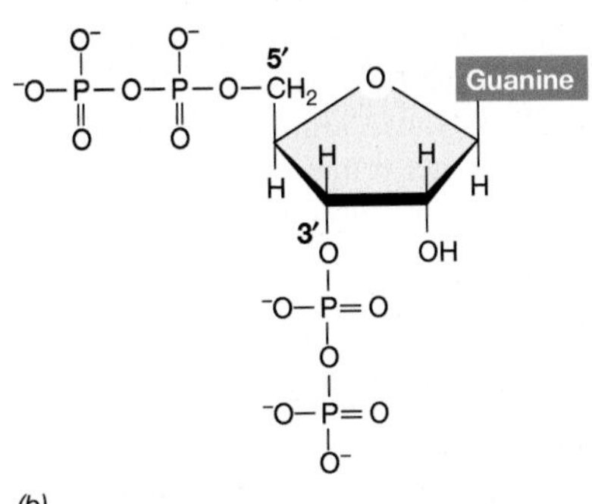

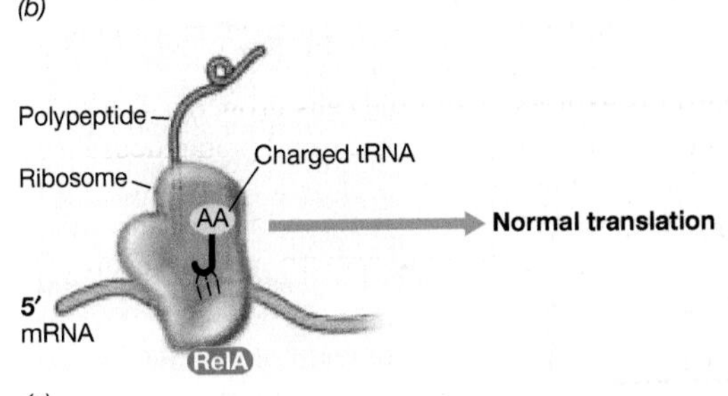

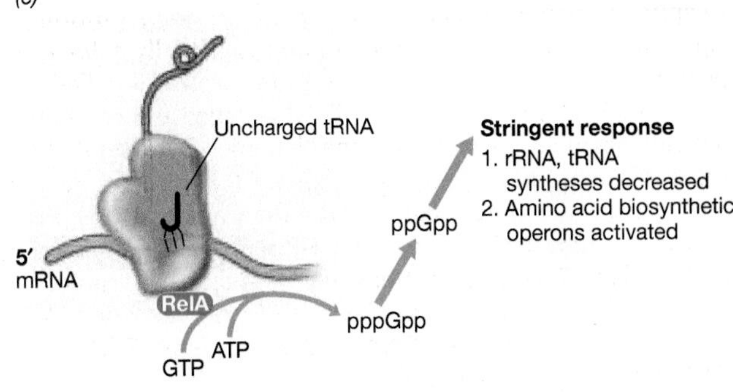

Figure 20 The stringent response. *(a)* Upon nutrient downshift, rRNA, tRNA, and protein syntheses temporarily cease. Some time later growth resumes at a new (decreased) rate. *(b)* Structure of guanosine tetraphosphate (ppGpp), a trigger of the stringent response. *(c)* Normal translation, which requires charged tRNAs. *(d)* Synthesis of ppGpp. When cells are starved for amino acids, an uncharged tRNA can bind to the ribosome, which stops ribosome activity. This event triggers the RelA protein to synthesize a mixture of pppGpp and ppGpp.

thus producing pppGpp or ppGpp, respectively. RelA is associated with the 50S subunit of the ribosome and is activated by a signal from the ribosome during amino acid limitation. When the cell is limited for amino acids, the pool of *uncharged* tRNAs increase relative to *charged* tRNAs. Eventually, an uncharged tRNA is inserted into the ribosome instead of a charged tRNA during protein synthesis. When this happens, the ribosome stalls, and this leads to (p)ppGpp synthesis by RelA (Figure 20*c*). The protein Gpp converts pppGpp to ppGpp so that ppGpp is the major overall product.

The alarmones ppGpp and pppGpp have global control effects. They strongly inhibit rRNA and tRNA synthesis by binding to RNA polymerase and preventing initiation of transcription of genes for these RNAs. On the other hand, alarmones activate the biosynthetic operons for certain amino acids as well as catabolic operons that yield precursors for amino acid synthesis. By contrast, operons that encode biosynthetic proteins whose amino acid products are present in sufficient amounts remain shut down. The stringent response also inhibits the initiation of new rounds of DNA synthesis and cell division and slows down the synthesis of cell envelope components, such as membrane lipids. Efficient binding of (p)ppGpp to RNA polymerase requires the protein DksA, which is needed to position the (p)ppGpp correctly in the channel that normally allows substrates (that is nucleoside triphosphates) into the RNA polymerase active site.

In addition to RelA, another protein, SpoT, helps trigger the stringent response. The SpoT protein can either make (p)ppGpp or degrade it. Under most conditions, SpoT is responsible for degrading (p)ppGpp; however, SpoT synthesizes (p)ppGpp in response to certain stresses or when there is a shortage of energy. Thus the stringent response is the result of not only the absence of precursors for protein synthesis but also the lack of energy for biosynthesis.

The stringent response can be thought of as a mechanism for adjusting the cell's biosynthetic machinery to the availability of the required precursors and energy. By so doing, the cell achieves a new balance between anabolism and catabolism. In many natural environments, nutrients appear suddenly and are consumed rapidly. Thus a global mechanism such as the stringent response that balances the metabolic state of a cell with the availability of precursors and energy likely improves its ability to compete in nature.

The RelA/(p)ppGpp system is found only in *Bacteria* and in the chloroplasts of plants. *Archaea* and eukaryotes do not make (p)ppGpp in response to resource shortages. Although *Archaea* display an overall response similar to the stringent response of *Bacteria* when faced with carbon and energy shortages, they use regulatory mechanisms other than those described here to deal with these nutritional situations.

10 MiniReview

The stringent response is a global control mechanism triggered by amino acid starvation. The alarmones ppGpp and pppGpp are produced by RelA, a protein that monitors ribosome activity. Within the cell the stringent response achieves balance between protein production and amino acid requirements.

- Which genes are activated during the stringent response, and why?
- Which genes are repressed during the stringent response, and why?
- How are the alarmones ppGpp and pppGpp synthesized?

11 Other Global Control Networks

In Section 9 we discussed catabolite repression in *Escherichia coli*, and in Section 10 we discussed the stringent response. Both are examples of global control. There are several other global control systems in *E. coli* (and probably in all prokaryotes), and a few of these are shown in Table 3.

Global control systems regulate more than one regulon (Section 4). Global control networks may include activators, repressors, signal molecules, two-component regulatory

Table 3 Examples of global control systems known in *Escherichia coli*[a]

System	*Signal*	*Primary activity of regulatory protein*	*Number of genes regulated*
Aerobic respiration	Presence of O_2	Repressor (ArcA)	>50
Anaerobic respiration	Lack of O_2	Activator (FNR)	>70
Catabolite repression	Cyclic AMP level	Activator (CRP)	>300
Heat shock	Temperature	Alternative sigmas (RpoH and RpoE)	36
Nitrogen utilization	NH_3 limitation	Activator (NR_I)/alternative sigma RpoN	>12
Oxidative stress	Oxidizing agents	Activator (OxyR)	>30
SOS response	Damaged DNA	Repressor (LexA)	>20

[a]For many of the global control systems, regulation is complex. A single regulatory protein can play more than one role. For instance, the regulatory protein for aerobic respiration is a repressor for many promoters but an activator for others, whereas the regulatory protein for anaerobic respiration is an activator protein for many promoters but a repressor for others. Regulation can also be indirect or require more than one regulatory protein. Some of the regulatory proteins involved are members of two-component systems (Section 5). Many genes are regulated by more than one global system.

systems (Section 5), regulatory RNA (Sections 13 and 14), and alternative sigma factors. An example of a global response that is widespread in *Bacteria* is the response to high temperature. In many bacteria, this **heat shock response** is largely controlled by alternative sigma factors.

Heat Shock Proteins

Most proteins are relatively stable. Once made, they continue to perform their functions and are passed along at cell division. However, some proteins are less stable at elevated temperatures and tend to unfold. Such improperly folded proteins are recognized by protease enzymes in the cell and are degraded. Consequently, cells that are heat stressed induce the synthesis of a set of proteins, the **heat shock proteins**, which help counteract the damage. Heat shock proteins assist the cell in recovering from stress. They are not only induced by heat, but by several other stress factors that the cell can encounter. These include exposure to high levels of certain chemicals—such as ethanol—and exposure to high doses of ultraviolet radiation.

In *E. coli* and in most prokaryotes examined, there are three major classes of heat shock protein, Hsp70, Hsp60, and Hsp10. We have encountered these proteins before, although not by these names. The Hsp70 protein of *E. coli* is DnaK, which prevents aggregation of newly synthesized proteins and stabilizes unfolded proteins. Major representatives of the Hsp60 and Hsp10 families in *E. coli* are the proteins GroEL and GroES, respectively. These are molecular chaperones that catalyze the correct refolding of misfolded proteins. Another class of heat shock proteins includes various proteases that function in the cell to remove denatured or irreversibly aggregated proteins.

The heat shock proteins are apparently very ancient and are highly conserved. Molecular sequencing of heat shock proteins, especially Hsp70, has been used to help unravel the phylogeny of eukaryotes. Heat shock proteins are present in all cells although the regulatory system that controls their expression varies greatly in different groups of organisms.

Heat Shock Response

In many bacteria, such as *E. coli*, the heat shock response is controlled by the alternative sigma factors RpoH (σ^{32}) and RpoE (Figure 21). The RpoH sigma factor controls expression of heat shock proteins in the cytoplasm, and RpoE (about which less is known) regulates the expression of a different set of heat shock proteins in the periplasm and cell envelope. RpoH is normally degraded within a minute or two of its synthesis. However, when cells suffer a heat shock, degradation of RpoH is inhibited and its level therefore increases. Consequently, transcription of those operons whose promoters are recognized by RpoH increases too. The rate of degradation of RpoH depends on the level of free DnaK protein, which inactivates RpoH. In unstressed cells the level of free DnaK is relatively high and the level of intact RpoH is correspondingly low. However, if heat stress unfolds proteins, DnaK binds preferentially to the unfolded proteins and so is no longer free to promote degradation of RpoH. Thus the more denatured proteins there are, the lower the level of free DnaK and the higher the level of RpoH; the result is heat shock gene expression.

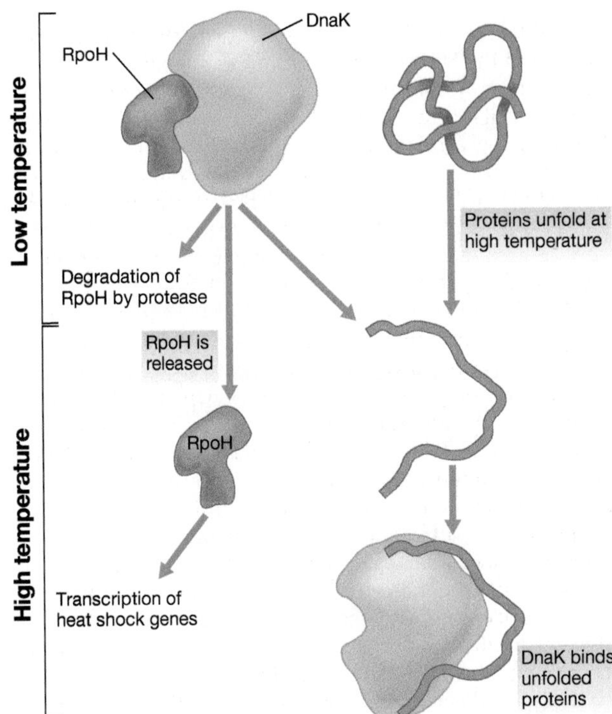

Figure 21 **Control of heat shock in *Escherichia coli*.** The RpoH alternative sigma factor is broken down rapidly by proteases at normal temperatures. This is stimulated by binding of the DnaK chaperonin to RpoH. At high temperatures, some proteins are denatured, and DnaK recognizes and binds to the unfolded polypeptide chains. This removes DnaK from RpoH, which slows the degradation rate. The level of RpoH rises, and the heat shock genes are transcribed.

When the stress situation has passed, for example, upon a temperature downshift, RpoH is rapidly inactivated by DnaK, and the synthesis of heat shock proteins is greatly reduced. Because heat shock proteins perform vital functions in the cell, there is always a low level of these proteins present, even when cells are growing under optimal conditions. However, the rapid synthesis of heat shock proteins in stressed cells emphasizes how important they are in surviving excessive heat, chemicals, or physical agents. Heat or other stresses can generate large amounts of inactive proteins that need to be refolded (and in the process, reactivated) or degraded to release free amino acids for the biosynthesis of new proteins.

A heat-shock response also occurs in *Archaea*, even in species that grow best at very high temperatures. An analog of the bacterial Hsp70 is found in many *Archaea* and is structurally quite similar to those found in gram-positive species of

Bacteria. Hsp70 is also present in eukaryotes. In addition, other types of heat shock proteins are present in *Archaea* that are unrelated to stress proteins of *Bacteria*.

11 MiniReview

Cells can control sets of genes by employing alternative sigma factors. These recognize only certain promoters and thus allow transcription of a select category of genes that is appropriate under certain environmental conditions. Cells respond to both heat and cold by expressing sets of genes whose products help the cell overcome stress.

- Why do cells have more than one type of sigma factor?
- Why might the proteins induced during a heat shock not be needed during a cold shock?

V REGULATION OF DEVELOPMENT IN MODEL BACTERIA

Differentiation and development are largely characteristics of multicellular organisms. Because most prokaryotic microorganisms grow as single cells, few show differentiation. Nonetheless, there are occasional examples among single-celled prokaryotes that illustrate the basic principle of differentiation, namely that one cell gives rise to two genetically identical descendents that perform different roles and must therefore express different sets of genes. Here we discuss two well-studied examples, the formation of endospores in the gram-positive bacterium *Bacillus* and the formation of two cell types, mobile and stationary, in the gram-negative bacterium *Caulobacter*.

Although forming just two different cell types may seem superficially simple, the regulatory systems that control these processes are highly complex. There are three major phases for the regulation of differentiation: (1) triggering the response, (2) asymmetric development of two sister cells and (3) reciprocal communication between the two differentiating cells.

12 Sporulation in *Bacillus*

Many microorganisms, both prokaryotic and eukaryotic, respond to adverse conditions by forming spores. Once good conditions return, the spore germinates and the microorganism returns to its normal lifestyle. Among the *Bacteria*, the genus *Bacillus* is well known for the formation of endospores, that is, spores formed inside a mother cell. Prior to endospore formation, the cell divides asymmetrically. The smaller cell develops into the endospore, which is surrounded by the larger mother cell. Once development is complete, the mother cell bursts, releasing the endospore.

Endospore formation in *Bacillus subtilis* is triggered by adverse external conditions, such as starvation, desiccation, or growth-inhibitory temperatures. In fact, multiple aspects of the environment are monitored by a group of five sensor kinases. These function via a phosphotransfer relay system whose mechanism resembles that of a two-component regulatory system (Section 5) but is considerably more complex (Figure 22). The net result of multiple adverse conditions is the successive phosphorylation of several proteins called *sporulation factors*, culminating with the sporulation factor Spo0A (Figure 22a). When Spo0A is highly phosphorylated, sporulation events proceed.

Development of the Endospore

Once triggered, endospore development is controlled by four different sigma factors, two of which (σF and σG) activate genes needed inside the developing endospore itself and two (σE and σK) of which activate genes needed in the mother cell that surrounds the endospore (Figure 22b). The sporulation signal, transmitted via Spo0A, activates σF in the smaller cell that is destined to become the endospore. σF is already present but is inactive, as it is bound by an anti-sigma factor. The signal from Spo0A activates a protein that binds to the anti-sigma factor. This inactivates the anti-sigma factor and liberates σF. Once free, σF binds to RNA polymerase and allows transcription (inside the spore) of genes whose products are needed for the next stage of sporulation. These include the gene for the sigma factor σG and the genes for proteins that cross into the mother cell and activate σE. Active σE is required for transcription inside the mother cell of yet more genes, including the gene for the sigma factor σK. The sigma factors σG (in the endospore) and σK (in the mother cell) are required for transcription of genes needed even later in the sporulation process.

One fascinating aspect of endospore formation is that it is preceded by what is in effect cellular cannibalism. Those cells in which Spo0A has already become activated secrete a protein that lyses nearby cells of the same species whose Spo0A protein has not yet become activated. This toxic protein is accompanied by a second protein that delays sporulation of neighboring cells. Cells committed to sporulation also make an antitoxin protein to protect themselves against the effects of their own toxin. Their sacrificed sister cells are used as a source of nutrients for developing endospores. Shortages of certain nutrients, such as phosphate, increase the expression level of the toxin-encoding gene.

12 MiniReview

Sporulation during adverse conditions is triggered via a complex phosphorelay system that monitors multiple aspects of the environment. The sporulation factor Spo0A then sets in motion a cascade of regulatory responses under the control of several alternative sigma factors.

- How are different sets of genes expressed in the developing endospore and the mother cell?
- What is an anti-sigma factor and how can its effect be overcome?

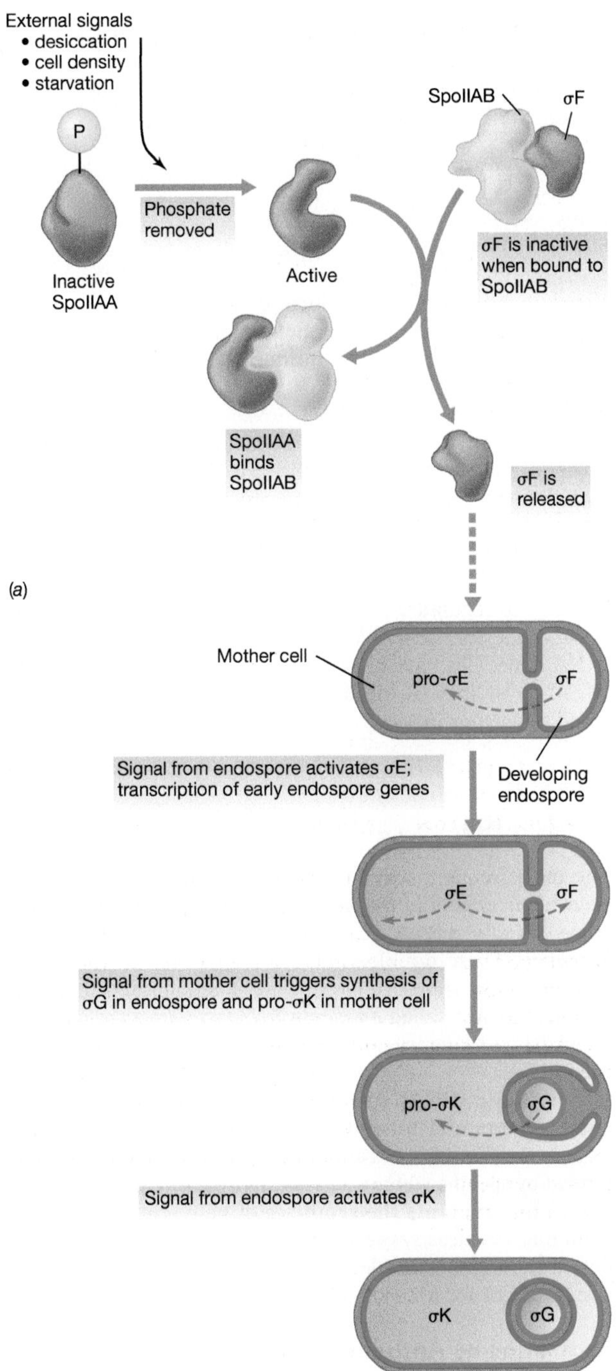

Figure 22 **Control of endospore formation in *Bacillus*.** After an external signal is received, a cascade of sigma factors controls differentiation. *(a)* Active SpoIIAA binds the anti-sigma factor SpoIIAB, thus liberating the first sigma factor, σF. *(b)* Sigma factor σF initiates a cascade of sigma factors, some of which already exist and need to be activated, others of which are not yet present and whose genes need to be expressed. These sigma factors then promote transcription of genes needed for endospore development.

13 *Caulobacter* Differentiation

Caulobacter provides another example in which a cell divides into two genetically identical daughter cells that perform different roles and express different sets of genes. *Caulobacter* is a species of *Proteobacteria* that is common in aquatic environments, typically in waters that are very nutrient poor (oligotrophic). In the *Caulobacter* life cycle, free-swimming (swarmer) cells alternate with cells that lack flagella and are attached to surfaces by a stalk with a holdfast at its end. The role of the swarmer cells is dispersal, as swarmers cannot divide or replicate their DNA. Conversely, the role of the stalked cell is reproduction.

The *Caulobacter* Life Cycle

The *Caulobacter* cell cycle is controlled by three major regulatory proteins whose concentrations oscillate in succession. Two of these are the transcriptional regulators, GcrA and CtrA. The third is DnaA, a protein that functions both in its normal role in DNA replication and also as a transcriptional regulator. Each of these regulators is active at a specific stage in the cell cycle, and each controls many other genes that are needed at that particular stage in the cycle (Figure 23).

CtrA is activated by phosphorylation in response to external signals. Once phosphorylated, CtrA-P activates genes needed for the synthesis of the flagella and other functions in swarmer cells. Conversely, CtrA-P represses the synthesis of GcrA and also inhibits the initiation of DNA replication by binding to and blocking the origin of replication (Figure 23). As the cell cycle proceeds, CtrA is degraded by a specific protease; as a consequence, levels of DnaA rise. The absence of CtrA-P allows access to the chromosomal origin of replication, and, as in all *Bacteria*, DnaA binds to the origin and triggers the initiation of DNA replication. In addition, in *Caulobacter*, DnaA activates several other genes needed for chromosomal replication. The level of DnaA then falls due to protease degradation, and the level of GcrA rises. The GcrA regulator promotes the elongation phase of chromosome replication, cell division, and the growth of the stalk on the immobile daughter cell. Eventually, GcrA levels fall and high levels of CtrA reappear (in the daughter cell destined to swim away) (Figure 23).

Many of the details of the regulation of the *Caulobacter* cell cycle are still uncertain. Both external stimuli and internal factors such as nutrient and metabolite pools are known to affect the cycle but how this information is integrated into the overall control system is only partly understood.

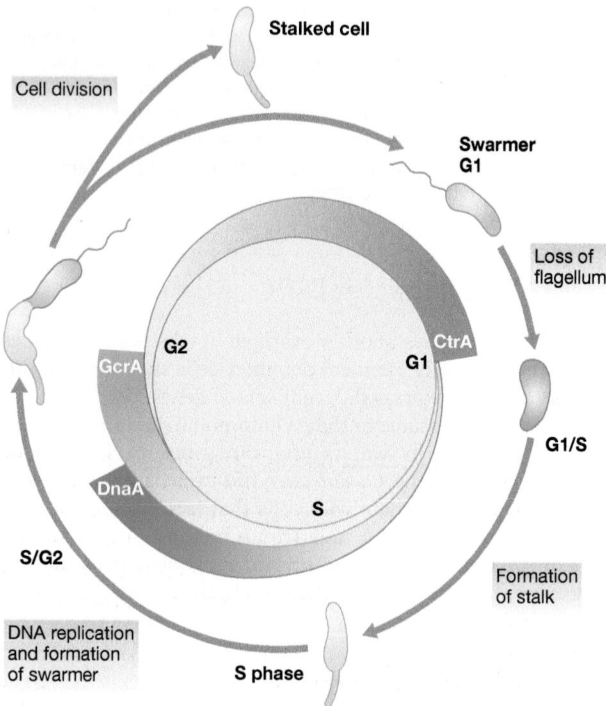

Figure 23 Cell cycle regulation in *Caulobacter*. Three global regulators CtrA, DnaA, and GcrA, oscillate in levels through the cycle as shown. In G1 swarmer cells, CtrA represses initiation of DNA replication and expression of GcrA. At the G1/S transition, CtrA is degraded and DnaA levels rise. DnaA binds to the origin of replication and initiates replication. GcrA also rises and activates genes for cell division and DNA synthesis. At the S/G2 transition, CtrA levels begin to rise again and shut down GcrA expression. GcrA levels slowly decline in the stalked cell but are rapidly degraded in the swarmer. CtrA is degraded in the stalked cell.

However, since its genome has been sequenced and good genetic systems are available, differentiation in *Caulobacter* has been used as a model system for studying cell developmental processes.

13 MiniReview

Differentiation in *Caulobacter* consists of the alternation between motile cells and those that are attached to surfaces. Three major regulatory proteins CtrA, GcrA, and DnaA, act in succession to control the three phases of the cell cycle. Each in turn controls many other genes needed at specific times in the cell cycle.

- Why are the levels of DnaA protein controlled during the *Caulobacter* cell cycle?
- When do the regulators CtrA and GcrA carry out their main roles during the *Caulobacter* life cycle?

VI RNA-BASED REGULATION

Thus far we have discussed several mechanisms that cells use to regulate the transcription of their genes. To this point we have focused on mechanisms in which regulatory proteins sense signals or bind to DNA. In some cases a single protein does both; in other cases separate proteins carry out these two activities. Nonetheless, all of these mechanisms rely on *regulatory proteins*. However, RNA itself may regulate gene expression, at both the level of transcription and the level of translation of mRNA to produce proteins.

RNA molecules that are not translated to give proteins are collectively known as **noncoding RNA**. This category includes the rRNA and tRNA molecules that take part in protein synthesis and the RNA present in the signal recognition particle, a structure that identifies newly synthesized proteins for secretion from the cell. Noncoding RNA also includes small RNA molecules necessary for RNA processing, especially the splicing of mRNA in eukaryotes. In addition, a variety of small RNA (sRNA) molecules are known. Small RNAs range from approximately 40–400 nucleotides long and function to regulate gene expression in both prokaryotes and eukaryotes. In *Escherichia coli,* for example, a number of sRNA molecules have been found to regulate various aspects of cell physiology by binding to other RNAs or even to other small molecules in some cases.

14 RNA Regulation and Antisense RNA

The most frequent way in which regulatory RNA molecules exert their effects is by base-pairing with other RNA molecules, usually mRNA, that have regions of complementary sequence. These double-stranded regions tie up the mRNA and prevent its translation (Figure 24). Small RNAs that show this activity are called *antisense RNA*, so named because the sRNA has a sequence complementary to the coding sense of the mRNA.

Antisense sRNAs survey the cytoplasm for their mRNA complements and form double-stranded RNAs with them. Double-stranded RNAs cannot be translated and are soon degraded by specific ribonucleases (Figure 24). This removes the mRNA and prevents the synthesis of new protein molecules from mRNAs already present in the cell but whose gene products are no longer needed because of a change in nutrional conditions or for a variety of other reasons.

Regulation by Antisense RNA

Theoretically, antisense RNA could be made by transcribing the non-template strand of the same gene that yielded a specific mRNA. Instead, a distinct "anti-gene" is used to form the antisense RNA. Only a relatively short piece of antisense RNA is needed to block transcription of a mRNA, and therefore the "anti-gene" that encodes the antisense RNA is much shorter

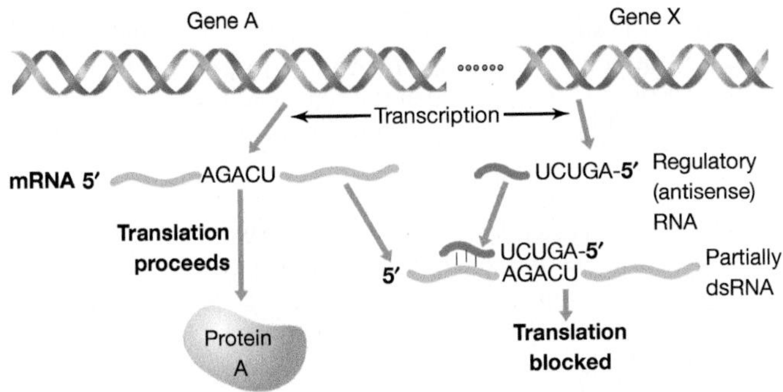

Figure 24 Regulation by Antisense RNA. Gene A is transcribed from its promoter to yield an mRNA that can be translated to form protein A. Gene X is a small gene with a sequence identical to that of part of Gene A but with its promoter at the opposite end. Therefore, if it is transcribed, the resulting RNA will be complementary to the mRNA of gene A. If these two RNAs base pair, translation will be blocked.

than the gene that encodes the original message. Typically, antisense RNAs are around 100 nucleotides long and bind to a target region approximately 30 nucleotides long. In addition, however, each antisense RNA can regulate several different mRNAs, all of which share the same target sequence for antisense RNA binding.

Transcription of antisense RNA is enhanced under conditions in which its target gene(s) needs to be turned off. For example, the RyhB antisense RNA of *E. coli* is transcribed when iron is limiting for growth. RyhB RNA binds to a dozen or more target mRNAs that encode proteins needed for iron metabolism or that use iron as cofactors. The base-paired RyhB/mRNA molecules are then degraded by ribonucleases, in particular, ribonuclease E. This forms part of the mechanism by which *E. coli* and related bacteria respond to a shortage of iron. Other responses to iron limitation in *E. coil* include transcriptional controls involving repressor and activator proteins (Sections 3 and 4) that function to increase the capacity of cells to take up iron and to tap into intracellular iron stores.

Although antisense RNA usually blocks translation of mRNA, occasional examples are known in which antisense RNA does just the opposite and actually enhances the translation of its target mRNA. It is hypothesized that in these cases the native mRNA attains a secondary structure that prevents translation. The antisense RNA is then thought to bind to a short region of the mRNA and unfold it, thereby allowing access to the ribosome.

14 MiniReview

Cells can control genes in several ways by employing regulatory RNA molecules. One way is to take advantage of base pairing and use antisense RNA to form a double-stranded RNA that cannot be translated.

- Why are antisense RNAs much shorter than the mRNA molecules to which they bind?
- How do cells synthesize antisense RNA molecules?
- What happens to mRNA molecules following binding of their antisense RNAs?

15 Riboswitches

One of the most interesting findings in molecular biology has been the discovery that RNA can carry out many roles once thought to be the purview of proteins only. In particular, RNA can specifically recognize and bind other molecules, including low-molecular-weight metabolites. It is important to emphasize that such binding does not involve complementary base pairing (as does antisense RNA described in the previous section) but occurs as a result of a folding of the RNA into a specific three-dimensional structure that recognizes the target molecule, much as a protein enzyme recognizes its substrate. Some of these RNA molecules are called *ribozymes* because they are catalytically active like enzymes. Other RNA molecules resemble repressors and activators in binding metabolites such as amino acids or vitamins and regulating gene expression; these are the **riboswitches**.

Certain mRNAs contain regions upstream of the coding sequences that can fold into specific three-dimensional structures that bind small molecules (Figure 25). These recognition domains are riboswitches and exist as two alternative structures, one with the small molecule bound and the other without. Alternation between the two forms of the riboswitch thus depends on the presence or absence of the small molecule and in turn controls expression of the mRNA. Riboswitches have been found that control the synthesis of enzymes in biosynthetic pathways for various enzymatic cofactors, such as the vitamins thiamine, riboflavin, and cobalamin (B_{12}), for a few amino acids, for the purine bases adenine and guanine, and for glucosamine 6-phosphate, a precursor in peptidoglycan synthesis.

Mechanism of Riboswitches

The riboswitch control mechanism is analogous to one we have seen before. Early in this chapter we discussed the regulation of enzyme synthesis by negative control of transcription (Section 3).

In this case, the presence of a specific metabolite shuts down the transcription of genes encoding enzymes for the corresponding biosynthetic pathway. This is achieved by use of a protein repressor, such as the arginine repressor in the case of the arginine biosynthetic operon (Figure 5). In the

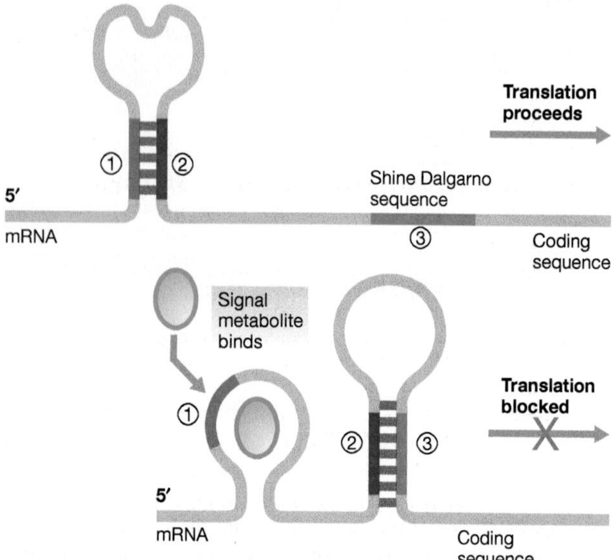

Figure 25 Regulation by a Riboswitch. Binding of a specific metabolite alters the secondary structure of the riboswitch domain, which is located in the 5′-untranslated region of the mRNA, preventing translation. The Shine–Dalgarno site is where the ribosome binds the RNA.

case of a riboswitch, there is no regulatory protein. Instead, the metabolite binds directly to the riboswitch domain at the 5′ end of the mRNA. Riboswitches usually exert their control after the mRNA has already been synthesized. Therefore, most riboswitches function to control *translation* of the mRNA, rather than its *transcription*.

The metabolite that is bound by the riboswitch is typically the product of a biosynthetic pathway whose constituent enzymes are encoded by the mRNAs that carry the corresponding riboswitches. For example, the thiamine riboswitch that binds thiamine pyrophosphate is upstream of the coding sequences for enzymes that participate in the thiamine biosynthetic pathway. When the pool of thiamine pyrophosphate is sufficient in the cell, this metabolite binds to its specific riboswitch mRNA. The new secondary structure of the riboswitch blocks the Shine–Dalgarno ribosome-binding sequence on the mRNA and prevents the message from binding to the ribosome; this prevents translation (Figure 25). If the concentration of thiamine pyro-phosphate drops sufficiently low, this molecule can dissociate from its riboswitch mRNA. This unfolds the message and exposes the Shine–Dalgarno site, allowing the mRNA to bind to the ribosome and become translated.

The thiamine analog pyrithiamine blocks the synthesis of thiamine and hence, inhibits bacterial growth. Until the discovery of riboswitches, the site of action of pyrithiamine remained mysterious. It now appears that pyrithiamine is converted by cells to pyrithiamine pyrophosphate, which then binds to the thiamine riboswitch. Thus the biosynthetic pathway is shut off even when no thiamine is available. Bacterial mutants selected for resistance to pyrithiamine have alterations in the sequence of the riboswitch that result in failure to bind both pyrithiamine pyrophosphate and thiamine pyrophosphate.

In *Bacillus subtilis*, where about 2% of the genes are under riboswitch control, the same riboswitch is present on several mRNAs that together encode the proteins for a particular pathway. For example, over a dozen genes in six operons are controlled by the thiamine riboswitch.

Despite being part of the mRNA, some riboswitches nevertheless do control transcription. The mechanism is similar to that seen in attenuation—a conformational change in the riboswitch causes premature termination of the synthesis of the mRNA that carries it (Section 16).

Riboswitches and Evolution

How widespread are riboswitches and how did they evolve? Thus far riboswitches have been found only in some bacteria and a few plants and fungi. Some scientists believe that riboswitches are remnants of the RNA world, a period eons ago before cells, DNA, and protein, when it is hypothesized that catalytic RNAs were the only self-replicating life forms. In such an environment, riboswitches may have been a primitive mechanism of metabolic control—a simple means by which RNA life forms could have controlled the synthesis of other RNAs. As proteins evolved, riboswitches might have been the first control mechanisms for their synthesis, as well. If true, the riboswitches that remain today may be the last vestiges of this simple form of control, because, as we have seen in this chapter, metabolic regulation is almost exclusively carried out by way of regulatory proteins.

15 MiniReview

Riboswitches are RNA domains at the 5′-ends of mRNA that recognize small molecules and respond by changing their three-dimensional structure. This in turn affects the translation of the mRNA or, sometimes, its premature termination. Riboswitches are mostly used to control biosynthetic pathways for amino acids, purines, and a few other metabolites.

- What happens when a riboswitch binds the small molecule it recognizes?
- What are the major differences between using a repressor protein versus a riboswitch to control gene expression?

16 Attenuation

Attenuation is a form of transcriptional control that functions by premature termination of mRNA synthesis. That is, in attenuation, control is exerted *after* the initiation of transcription but *before* its completion. Consequently, the number of completed transcripts from an operon is reduced, even though the number of initiated transcripts is not.

The basic principle of attenuation is that the first part of the mRNA to be made, called the *leader region*, can fold up into two alternative secondary structures. In this respect, the mechanism of attenuation resembles that of riboswitches. In attenuation, one mRNA secondary structure allows continued synthesis of the mRNA, whereas the other secondary structure causes premature termination. Folding of the mRNA depends on either events at the ribosome or the activity of regulatory proteins, depending on the organism. The best examples of attenuation involve regulation of genes controlling the biosynthesis of certain amino acids in gram-negative *Bacteria*. The first such system to be described was in the tryptophan operon in *Escherichia coli*, and we focus on it here. Attenuation control has been documented in several other species of *Bacteria*, and genomic analyses of *Archaea* suggest that the mechanism is present in this domain as well. However, because the processes of transcription and translation are spatially separated in eukaryotes, attenuation control is absent from *Eukarya*.

Attenuation and the Tryptophan Operon

The tryptophan operon contains structural genes for five proteins of the tryptophan biosynthetic pathway plus the usual promoter and regulatory sequences at the beginning of the operon (Figure 26). Like many operons, the tryptophan operon has more than one type of regulation. The first enzyme in the pathway, anthranilate synthase (a multisubunit enzyme encoded by *trpD* and *trpE*) is subject to feedback inhibition by tryptophan. Transcription of the entire tryptophan operon is also under negative control (Section 3). However, in addition to the promoter (P) and operator (O) regions needed for negative control, there is a sequence in the operon called the *leader sequence*. The leader encodes a short polypeptide, the *leader peptide*, that contains tandem tryptophan codons near its terminus and functions as an attenuator (Figure 26).

The basis of control of the tryptophan attenuator is as follows. If tryptophan is plentiful in the cell, there will be a sufficient pool of charged tryptophan tRNAs and the leader peptide will be synthesized. On the other hand, if tryptophan is in short supply, the tryptophan-rich leader peptide will not be synthesized. Synthesis of the leader peptide results in termination of transcription of the remainder of the *trp* operon, which includes the structural genes for the biosynthetic enzymes. By contrast, if synthesis of the leader peptide is blocked by tryptophan deficiency, the rest of the operon is transcribed. www.microbiologyplace.com **Online Tutorial 2: Attenuation and the Tryptophan Operon**

Mechanism of Attenuation

How does translation of the leader peptide regulate transcription of the tryptophan genes downstream? Consider that in prokaryotic cells transcription and translation are simultaneous processes; as mRNA is released from the DNA, the ribosome binds to it and translation begins. That is, while transcription of downstream DNA sequences is still proceeding, translation of sequences transcribed has already begun (Figure 27).

Attenuation occurs (transcription stops) because a portion of the newly formed mRNA folds into a unique stem-loop that causes cessation of RNA polymerase activity. The stem-loop structure forms in the mRNA because two stretches of nucleotides near each other are complementary and can thus base-pair. If tryptophan is plentiful, the ribosome will translate the leader sequence until it comes to the leader stop codon. The remainder of the leader RNA then assumes the stem-loop, a transcription pause site, which is followed by a uracil-rich sequence that actually causes termination (Figure 27).

If tryptophan is in short supply, transcription of genes encoding tryptophan biosynthetic enzymes is obviously desirable. During transcription of the leader, the ribosome pauses at a tryptophan codon because of a shortage of charged tryptophan tRNAs. The presence of the stalled ribosome at this position allows a stem-loop to form that differs from the terminator stem-loop (sites 2 and 3 in Figure 27). This alternative stem-loop is not a transcription termination signal. Instead, it prevents the terminator stem-loop (sites 3 and 4 in Figure 27) from forming. This allows RNA polymerase to move past the termination site and begin

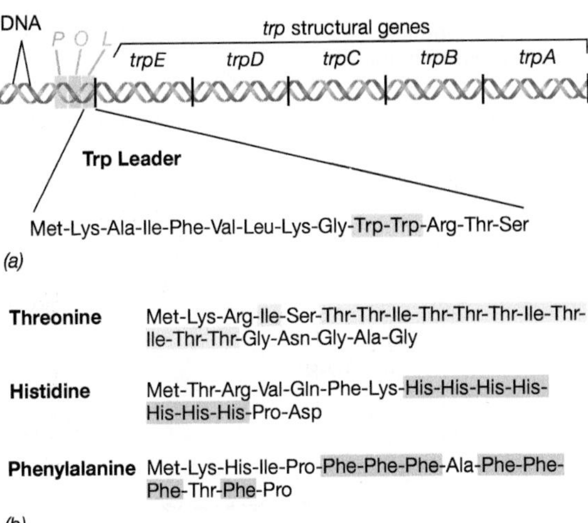

Figure 26 Attenuation and the leader peptide. Structure of the tryptophan operon and of tryptophan and other leader peptides in *Escherichia coli*. *(a)* Arrangement of the tryptophan operon. Note that the leader (*L*) encodes a short peptide containing two tryptophan residues near its terminus (there is a stop codon following the Ser codon). The promoter is labeled *P*, and the operator is labeled *O*. The genes labeled *trpE* through *trpA* encode the enzymes needed for tryptophan synthesis. *(b)* Amino acid sequences of leader peptides of some other amino acid synthetic operons. Because isoleucine is made from threonine, it is an important constituent of the threonine leader peptide.

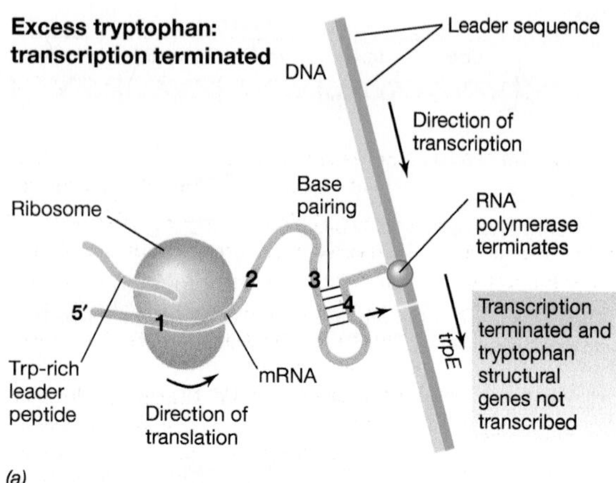

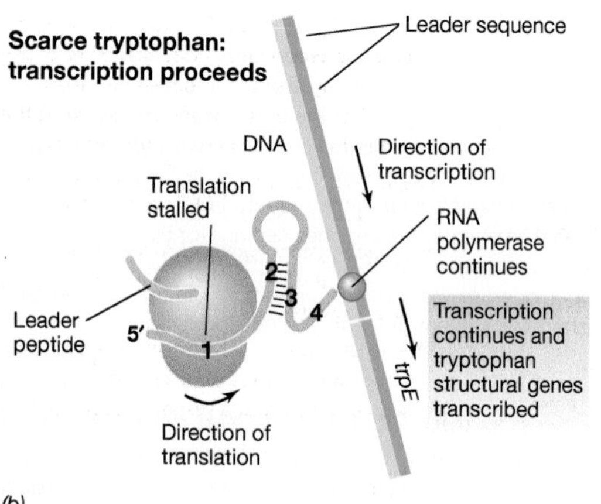

Figure 27 Mechanism of attenuation. Control of transcription of tryptophan operon structural genes by attenuation in *Escherichia coli*. The leader peptide is encoded by regions 1 and 2 of the mRNA. Two regions of the growing mRNA chain are able to form double-stranded loops, shown as 3:4 and 2:3. *(a)* When there is excess tryptophan, the ribosome translates the complete leader peptide, and so region 2 cannot pair with region 3. Regions 3 and 4 then pair to form a loop that terminates RNA polymerase. *(b)* If translation is stalled because of tryptophan starvation, a loop forms by pairing of region 2 with region 3, loop 3:4 does not form, and transcription proceeds past the leader sequence.

transcription of tryptophan structural genes. Thus, in attenuation control, the rate of transcription is influenced by the rate of translation.

Attenuation also occurs in *Escherichia coli* in the biosynthetic pathways for histidine, threonine-isoleucine, phenylalanine, and several other amino acids and essential metabolites. As shown in Figure 26*b*, the leader peptide for each of these amino acid biosynthetic operons is rich in that particular amino acid. The *his* operon is dramatic in this regard because its leader contains seven histidines in a row near the end of the peptide (Figure 26*b*). This longer stretch of regulatory codons gives attenuation a major effect in regulation, which may compensate for the fact that unlike the *trp* operon, the *his* operon in *E. coli* is not under negative control.

Translation-Independent Attenuation Mechanisms

Gram-positive *Bacteria*, such as *Bacillus*, also use attenuation of transcription to regulate certain amino acid biosynthetic operons. And, as in gram-negative *Bacteria*, the mechanism relies on alternative mRNA secondary structures, which in one configuration lead to termination. However, the mechanism is independent of translation and requires an RNA-binding protein.

In the *Bacillus subtilis* tryptophan operon, the binding protein is called the *trp* attenuation protein. In the presence of sufficient amounts of the amino acid tryptophan, this regulatory protein binds to the leader mRNA and causes transcription termination. By contrast, if tryptophan is limiting, the protein does not bind to the mRNA. This allows the favorable secondary structure to form and transcription proceeds.

Attenuation also occurs with genes unrelated to amino acid biosynthesis. These mechanisms obviously do not rely on amino acid levels. Some of the operons for pyrimidine biosynthesis (the *pyr* operons) in *E. coli* are regulated by attenuation, and the same is true for *Bacillus*. The mechanisms in the two organisms are, however, quite different, although each employs a system to assess the level of pyrimidines in the cell. In *E. coli* the mechanism monitors the rate of transcription, not translation. If pyrimidines are plentiful, RNA polymerase moves along and transcribes the leader DNA at a normal rate; this allows a stem-loop that signals termination to form in the mRNA. By contrast, if pyrimidines are scarce, the polymerase pauses at pyrimidine-rich sequences, which leads to formation of a nonterminator stem-loop that allows further transcription.

In *Bacillus*, a different mechanism is employed. For *pyr* attenuation, an RNA-binding protein controls the alternative stem-loop structures of the *pyr* mRNA, terminating transcription when pyrimidines are in excess. In this way the cell can maintain levels of pyrimidines—compounds that require significant cell resources to biosynthesize—at levels needed to balance biosynthetic needs.

16 MiniReview

Attenuation is a mechanism whereby gene expression is controlled after initiation of mRNA synthesis. Attenuation mechanisms depend upon alternative stem-loop structures in the mRNA.

- Explain how the formation of one stem-loop in the RNA can block the formation of another.
- How does attenuation of the tryptophan operon differ between *Escherichia coli* and *Bacillus subtilis*?

Review of Key Terms

Activator protein a regulatory protein that binds to specific sites on DNA and stimulates transcription; involved in positive control

Attenuation a mechanism for controlling gene expression; typically transcription is terminated after initiation but before a full-length mRNA is produced

Autoinducer small signal molecule that takes part in quorum sensing

Catabolite repression the suppression of alternative catabolic pathways by a preferred source of carbon and energy

Cyclic AMP a regulatory nucleotide that participates in catabolite repression

Gene expression transcription of a gene followed by translation of the resulting mRNA into protein(s)

Heat shock proteins proteins induced by high temperature (or certain other stresses) that protect against high temperature, especially by refolding partially denatured proteins or by degrading them

Heat shock response response to high temperature that includes the synthesis of heat shock proteins together with other changes in gene expression

Induction production of an enzyme in response to a signal (often the presence of the substrate for the enzyme)

Negative control a mechanism for regulating gene expression in which a repressor protein prevents transcription of genes

Noncoding RNA an RNA molecule that is not translated into protein

Operon one or more genes transcribed into a single RNA and under the control of a single regulatory site

Positive control a mechanism for regulating gene expression in which an activator protein functions to promote transcription of genes

Quorum sensing a regulatory system that monitors the population level and controls gene expression based on cell density

Regulatory nucleotide a nucleotide that functions as a signal rather than being incorporated into RNA or DNA

Regulon a series of operons controlled as a unit

Repression preventing the synthesis of an enzyme in response to a signal

Repressor protein a regulatory protein that binds to specific sites on DNA and blocks transcription; involved in negative control

Response regulator protein one of the members of a two-component system; a protein that is phosphorylated by a sensor kinase and then acts as a regulator, often by binding to DNA

Riboswitch an RNA domain, usually in an mRNA molecule, that can bind a specific small molecule and alter its secondary structure; this in turn controls translation of the mRNA

Sensor kinase protein one of the members of a two-component system; a protein that phosphorylates itself in response to an external signal and then transfers the phosphoryl group to a response regulator protein

Signal transduction *see* two-component regulatory system.

Stringent response a global regulatory control that is activated by amino acid starvation or energy deficiency

Two-component regulatory system a regulatory system consisting of two proteins: a sensor kinase and a response regulator

Review Questions

1. Describe why a protein that binds to a specific sequence of double-stranded DNA is unlikely to bind to the same sequence if the DNA is single-stranded (Section 2).
2. Most biosynthetic operons need only be under negative control for effective regulation, whereas most catabolic operons need to be under both negative and positive control. Why (Sections 4 and 5)?
3. What are the two components that give their name to a signal transduction system in prokaryotes? What is the function of each of the components (Section 5)?
4. How can quorum sensing be considered a regulatory mechanism for conserving cell resources (Section 6)?
5. Adaptation allows the mechanism controlling flagellar rotation to be reset. How is this achieved (Section 7)?
6. What is the difference between an operon and a regulon (Section 9)?
7. Describe the mechanism by which cAMP receptor protein (CRP), the regulatory protein for catabolite repression, functions using the lactose operon as an example (Section 9).
8. What events trigger the stringent response? Why are the events that occur in the stringent response a logical consequence of the trigger of the response (Section 10)?
9. Describe the proteins produced when cells of *Escherichia coli* experience a heat shock. Of what value are they to the cell (Section 11)?
10. How does regulation by antisense RNA differ from that of riboswitches (Section 14 and 15)?
11. Describe how transcriptional attenuation works. What is actually being "attenuated" (Section 16)?
12. Why hasn't the type of attenuation that controls several different amino acid biosynthetic pathways in *Escherichia coli* also been found in eukaryotes (Section 16)?

Application Questions

1. What would happen to regulation from a promoter under negative control if the region where the regulatory protein binds were deleted? What if the promoter were under positive control?
2. Promoters from *Escherichia coli* under positive control are not close matches to the DNA consensus sequence for *E. coli*. Why?
3. The attenuation control of some of the pyrimidine biosynthetic pathway genes in *Escherichia coli* actually involves coupled transcription and translation. Can you describe a mechanism whereby the cell could somehow make use of translation to help it measure the level of pyrimidine nucleotides?
4. Most of the regulatory systems described in this chapter involve regulatory proteins. However, regulatory RNA is also important. Describe how one could achieve negative control of the *lac* operon using either of two different types of regulatory RNA.
5. Many amino acid biosynthetic operons under attenuation control are also under negative control. Considering that the environment of a bacterium can be highly dynamic, what advantage could be conferred by having attenuation as a second layer of control?

Microbial Genomics

Genomics goes well beyond simply listing all of the genes in a particular genome; genomic analyses help unravel important features of an organism's biology. Analysis of the genome of Mycobacterium tuberculosis*, shown here, revealed important clues about how this pathogen establishes and maintains chronic infections.*

CAMR/A. Barry Dowsett / Photo Researchers, Inc.

An organism's **genome** is its entire complement of genetic information, including the genes themselves together with regulatory sequences and noncoding DNA. Genome analyses make up the field of genomics, the subject of this chapter. Knowledge of the genome sequence of an organism reveals not only its genes, but also yields important clues to how the organism functions and its evolutionary history. Genomic sequences also aid the study of gene expression, the transcription and translation of the genetic information in the genome. The traditional approach to studying gene expression was to focus on a single gene or group of related genes. Today, expression of the entire complement of an organism's genes can be examined in a single experiment.

It would have been impossible to sequence and analyze large and complex genomes without corresponding improvements in molecular technology. Major advances include shotgun cloning and the automation of DNA sequencing, and the development of powerful computational methods for DNA and protein sequences. The technology behind DNA analyses continues to improve as new advances drive down the cost and increase the speed at which genomes are sequenced. Here we focus on microbial genomes, some techniques used to analyze these genomes, and what microbial genomics has revealed thus far.

I MICROBIAL GENOMES

The word **genomics** refers to the discipline of mapping, sequencing, analyzing, and comparing genomes. Several hundred microbial genomes, mostly prokaryotic, have now been sequenced, and hundreds more projects are ongoing. Here we discuss only a few of them and explore what analysis of these genomes tells us.

1 A Short History of Genomics

The first genome to be sequenced was the 3569-nucleotide RNA genome of the *virus* MS2 in 1976. The first DNA genome to be sequenced was the 5386-nucleotide sequence of the small, single-stranded DNA virus, ϕX174 in 1977. This feat was accomplished by a group led by the British scientist Fred Sanger and debuted the dideoxynucleotide technique for DNA sequencing.

The First Cellular Genome

The first cellular genome to be sequenced was the 1,830,137-bp chromosome of *Haemophilus influenzae* described in 1995 by Hamilton O. Smith, J. Craig Venter, and their colleagues at The Institute for Genomic Research in Maryland. At present well over 2,000 genomes of prokaryotes have either been sequenced or are in progress. Because new advances in DNA sequencing are introduced quite frequently, it is likely that the number of sequenced prokaryotic genomes will grow rapidly.

In addition, we now have genome sequences of several higher animals, including the haploid human genome, which contains about 3 billion bp yet only around 25,000 genes. The largest genomes so far sequenced, in terms of the number of genes, are those of the higher plants, rice and black cottonwood (a species of poplar), and the protozoans, *Paramecium* and *Trichomonas*, all of which have significantly more genes than humans. Information from genome sequences has provided new insight on topics as diverse as clinical medicine and microbial evolution.

1 MiniReview

Small viruses were the first organisms subjected to genomic sequencing, but now many prokaryotic and eukaryotic genomes have been sequenced.

- Do humans have the largest genome?

2 Prokaryotic Genomes: Sizes and ORF Contents

The DNA sequences of several hundred prokaryotic genomes are now available in public databases (for an up-to-date list of genome sequencing projects search http://www.genomesonline.org/), and several thousand prokaryotic genome sequences have either been sequenced or are in progress. Table 1 lists some representative examples. These include many species of *Bacteria* and *Archaea* and representatives containing circular as well as linear genomes. Although rare, linear chromosomes are present in several *Bacteria*, including *Borrelia burgdorferi*, the causative agent of Lyme disease, and the important antibiotic-producing genus *Streptomyces*.

Note that the list of prokaryotic genomes in Table 1 contains several pathogens. Naturally, such organisms have high priority for sequencing. The hyperthermophiles on the list may have important uses in biotechnology because the enzymes in these organisms are heat-stable. Indeed, the needs of the biomedical and biotechnology industries have been important drivers for selecting organisms for genome sequencing. However, the list in Table 1 also includes organisms such as *Bacillus subtilis, Escherichia coli,* and *Pseudomonas aeruginosa*, all of which remain widely studied genetic model systems. Currently, however, genome sequencing has become so routine and inexpensive that sequencing projects are no longer driven by medical or biotechnological rationales. In some cases the genomes of several different *strains* of the same bacterium have been sequenced in order to reveal the extent of genetic variability within a species.

Size Range of Prokaryotic Genomes

Genomes of species in both prokaryotic domains, *Bacteria* and *Archaea*, show a strong correlation between genome size

Table 1 Select prokaryotic genomes[a]

Organism	Cell type[b]	Size (base pairs)	ORFs[c]	Comments
Bacteria				
Carsonella ruddii	E	159,662	182	Degenerate aphid endosymbiont
Buchnera aphidicola BCc	E	422,434	362	Primary aphid endosymbiont
Mycoplasma genitalium	P	580,070	470	Smallest nonsymbiotic bacterial genome
Borrelia burgdorferi	P	910,725	853	Spirochete, linear chromosome, causes Lyme disease
Chlamydia trachomatis	P	1,042,519	894	Obligate intracellular parasite, common human
Rickettsia prowazekii	P	1,111,523	834	Obligate intracellular parasite, causes epidemic typhus
Treponema pallidum	P	1,138,006	1041	Spirochete, causes syphilis
Pelagibacter ubique	FL	1,308,759	1354	Marine heterotroph
Aquifex aeolicus	FL	1,551,335	1544	Hyperthermophile, autotroph
Prochlorococcus marinus	FL	1,657,990	1716	Most abundant marine oxygenic phototroph
Streptococcus pyogenes	FL	1,852,442	1752	Causes strep throat and scarlet fever
Thermotoga maritima	FL	1,860,725	1877	Hyperthermophile
Chlorobaculum tepidum	FL	2,154,946	2288	Model green phototrophic bacterium
Deinococcus radiodurans	FL	3,284,156	2185	Radiation resistant, multiple chromosomes
Synechocystis sp.	FL	3,573,470	3168	Model cyanobacterium
Bdellovibrio bacteriovorus	FL	3,782,950	3584	Predator of other prokaryotes
Caulobacter crescentus	FL	4,016,942	3767	Complex life cycle
Bacillus subtilis	FL	4,214,810	4100	Gram-positive genetic model
Mycobacterium tuberculosis	P	4,411,529	3924	Causes tuberculosis
Escherichia coli K12	FL	4,639,221	4288	Gram-negative genetic model
Escherichia coli O157:H7	FL	5,594,477	5361	Enteropathogenic strain of *E. coli*
Bacillus anthracis	FL	5,227,293	5738	Pathogen, biowarfare agent
Rhodopseudomonas palustris	FL	5,459,213	4836	Metabolically versatile anoxygenic phototroph
Pseudomonas aeruginosa	FL	6,264,403	5570	Metabolically versatile opportunistic pathogen
Streptomyces coelicolor	FL	8,667,507	7825	Linear chromosome, produces antibiotics
Bradyrhizobium japonicum	FL	9,105,828	8317	Nitrogen fixation, nodulates soybeans
Archaea				
Nanoarchaeum equitans	P	490,885	552	Smallest nonsymbiotic cellular genome
Thermoplasma acidophilum	FL	1,564,905	1509	Thermophile, acidophile
Methanocaldococcus jannaschii	FL	1,664,976	1738	Methanogen, hyperthermophile
Aeropyrum pernix	FL	1,669,695	1841	Hyperthermophile
Pyrococcus horikoshii	FL	1,738,505	2061	Hyperthermophile
Methanothermobacter thermautotrophicus	FL	1,751,377	1855	Methanogen
Archaeoglobus fulgidus	FL	2,178,400	2436	Hyperthermophile
Halobacterium salinarum	FL	2,571,010	2630	Extreme halophile, bacteriorhodopsin
Sulfolobus solfataricus	FL	2,992,245	2977	Hyperthermophile, sulfur chemolithotroph
Haloarcula marismortui	FL	4,274,642	4242	Extreme halophile, bacteriorhodopsin
Methanosarcina acetivorans	FL	5,751,000	4252	Acetotrophic methanogen

[a]Information on these and hundreds of other prokaryotic genomes can be found in the TIGR Database (**www.tigr.org/tdb**), a web site maintained by The Institute for Genomic Research (TIGR), Rockville, MD, a not-for-profit research institute, and at **http://www.genomesonline.org**. Links are listed there to other relevant web sites.

[b]E, endosymbiont; P, parasite; FL, free-living.

[c]Open reading frames. The purpose of reporting ORFs is to predict the total number of proteins that an organism might encode. Of course, genes encoding known proteins are included, as are all ORFs that could encode a protein greater than 100 amino acid residues. Smaller ORFs are typically not included unless they show similarity to a gene from another organism or unless the codon usage is typical of the organism being studied.

and ORF content (Figure 1). Regardless of the organism, each megabase of prokaryotic DNA encodes about 1,000 open-reading frames (ORFs). As prokaryotic genomes increase in size, they also increase proportionally in gene number. This contrasts with eukaryotes, in which noncoding DNA can be a large fraction of the genome, especially in organisms with large genomes (see Table 4).

Analyzing genomic sequences can yield answers to fundamental biological questions. For example, how many genes are necessary for life to exist? For free-living cells, the smallest genomes found so far encode approximately 1,400 genes.

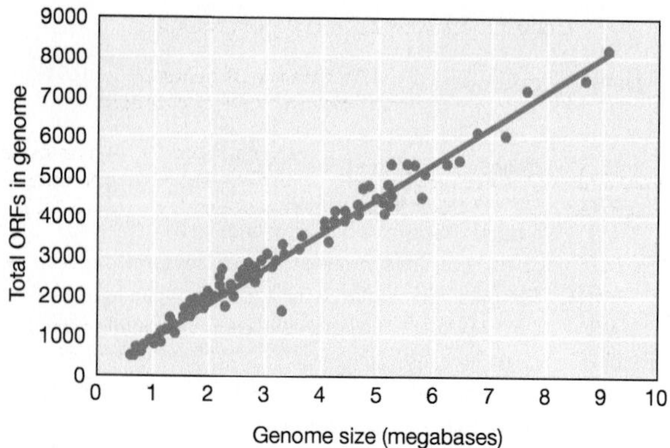

Figure 1 Correlation between genome size and ORF content in prokaryotes. These data are from analyses of 115 completed prokaryotic genomes and include species of both *Bacteria* and *Archaea*. Data from *Proc. Natl. Acad. Sci. (USA)* 101: 3160–3165 (2004).

Both free-living *Bacteria* and *Archaea* are known that have genomes in this range. The record at present is held by *Pelagibacter ubique*, a marine heterotroph that has approximately 1,350 genes. This organism is extremely efficient in its use of DNA; it has no introns, inteins, or transposons and has the shortest intergenic spaces yet recorded. The largest genomes of prokaryotes contain over 10,000 genes and are primarily from soil organisms, such as the myxobacteria, prokaryotes that undergo a complex life cycle.

Perhaps surprisingly, genomic analyses have shown that autotrophic organisms need only a few more genes than heterotrophs. For example, *Methanocaldococcus jannaschii* (*Archaea*) is an autotroph and contains only 1,738 **ORFs.** This enables it to be not only free living, but also to rely on carbon dioxide as its sole carbon source. *Aquifex aeolicus* (*Bacteria*) is also an autotroph and contains the smallest known genome of any autotroph at just 1.5 **Megabase pair (Mbp**, one million base pairs) (Table 1). Both *Methanocaldococcus* and *Aquifex* are also hyperthermophiles, growing optimally at temperatures above 80°C. Thus, a large genome is not necessary to support an extreme lifestyle, including that of autotrophs living in near-boiling water.

Small Genomes

The smallest cellular genomes belong to prokaryotes that are parasitic or endosymbiotic. A disproportionate number of such small genomes have been sequenced, partly because many are of medical importance and partly because smaller genomes are easier to sequence. Genome sizes for prokaryotes that are obligate parasites range from 490 kbp, for *Nanoarchaeum equitans* (*Archaea*), to 4,400 kbp, for *Mycobacterium tuberculosis* (*Bacteria*). The genomes of *N. equitans* and several other bacteria, including *Mycoplasma, Chlamydia,* and *Rickettsia,* are smaller than the largest known *viral* genome, that of Mimivirus with 1.2 Mbp.

Excluding endosymbionts, the smallest prokaryotic genome is that of the archaeon *N. equitans,* which is some 90 kbp smaller that that of *Mycoplasma genitalium* (Table 1). However, the genome of *N. equitans* actually contains more **ORFs** than the larger genome of *M. genitalium*. This is because the *N. equitans* genome is extremely compact and contains virtually no noncoding DNA. *N. equitans* is a hyperthermophile and a parasite of a second hyperthermophile, the archaeon *Ignicoccus*. Analyses of the gene content of *N. equitans* show it to be free of virtually all genes that encode proteins for anabolism or catabolism.

Using *Mycoplasma,* which has around 500 genes, as a starting point, several investigators have estimated that around 250–300 genes are the minimum for a viable cell. These estimates rely partly on comparisons with other small genomes. In addition, systematic mutagenesis has been performed to identify those *Mycoplasma* genes that are essential. However, these estimates are compromised by the fact that *Mycoplasma* is not a free-living organism and cannot make many vital components, such as purines and pyrimidines.

Smaller still than the genomes of prokaryotic parasites are those of some endosymbionts. Endosymbiotic bacteria live inside the cells of their hosts and are relatively common among insects. *Buchnera aphidicola,* for example, is an endosymbiont of aphids that supplies its host with essential amino acids in exchange for a protected habitat. Different strains of *B. aphidicola* that live in different species of aphids have genomes that vary considerably in size, from around 600 kbp down to 420 kbp. Even smaller is the remarkable genome of the insect endosymbiont *Carsonella ruddii*. This genome has a mere 160 kbp making it by far the smallest bacterial genome yet characterized. This genome has many genes of reduced length and many overlapping genes. Although *Carsonella* retains many genes for amino acid biosynthesis, it lacks many other genes previously regarded as essential for life. It has been suggested that *Carsonella* may be degenerating into an organelle-like status.

Large Genomes

Some prokaryotes have very large genomes that are comparable in size to those of eukaryotic microorganisms. Because eukaryotes tend to have significant amounts of noncoding DNA and prokaryotes do not, some prokaryotic genomes actually have more genes than microbial eukaryotes, despite having less DNA. For example, *Bradyrhizobium japonicum,* which forms nitrogen-fixing root nodules on soybeans, has 9.1 Mbp of DNA and 8,300 ORFs, whereas the yeast *Saccharomyces cerevisiae,* a eukaryote, has 12.1 Mbp of DNA but only 5,800 ORFs (see Table 4). *Myxococcus xanthus* also has 9.1 Mbp of DNA, whereas its relatives in the Delta proteobacteria have genomes approximately half this size. It has been suggested that there were multiple duplication events of substantial segments of DNA in the evolutionary history of *M. xanthus*.

The largest prokaryotic genome known at present is the 12.3-Mbp chromosome of *Sorangium cellulosum,* a gliding bacterium, which has not yet been completely sequenced and annotated. In contrast to *Bacteria,* the largest genomes found in *Archaea* thus far are around 5 Mbp (Table 1). Overall, prokaryotic genomes thus range in size from those of large viruses to those of eukaryotic microorganisms.

2 MiniReview

Sequenced prokaryotic genomes range in size from 0.16 Mbp to 9.1 Mbp, and even larger genomes are known. The smallest prokaryotic genomes are smaller than those of the largest viruses. The largest prokaryotic genomes have more genes than some eukaryotes. In prokaryotes, gene content is typically proportional to genome size.

- What is the lifestyle of prokaryotic organisms that have genomes smaller than that of certain viruses?
- Approximately how many protein-encoding genes will a bacterial genome of 4 Mbp contain?
- Which organism is likely to have more genes, a prokaryote with 8 Mbp of DNA or a eukaryote with 10 Mbp of DNA? Explain.

3 Prokaryotic Genomes: Bioinformatic Analyses and Gene Distributions

Following assembly and annotation of a genome, a typical genomic analysis proceeds to the gene comparison stage. The basic question here is how does the complement of genes in this organism compare with that of other organisms? Such analyses put the just-sequenced genome in perspective when considering the genomes of similar as well as more distantly related organisms. These activities are a major part of the field of **bioinformatics**, the science that applies powerful computational tools to DNA and protein sequences for the purpose of analyzing, storing, and accessing the sequences for comparative purposes.

Gene Content of Prokaryotic Genomes

The complement of genes in a particular organism defines its biology. Conversely, genomes are molded by an organism's lifestyle. One might imagine, for instance, that obligate parasites such as *Treponema pallidum* would require relatively few genes for amino acid biosynthesis because the amino acids they need can be supplied by their hosts. This is indeed the case, as the *T. pallidum* genome lacks recognizable genes for amino acid biosyntheses, although genes are found encoding several proteases, enzymes that can convert peptides taken up from the host into free amino acids. In contrast, the free-living bacterium *Escherichia coli* has 131 genes for amino acid biosynthesis and metabolism, and the soil bacterium *Bacillus subtilis* has over 200.

Comparative analyses are useful in the search for genes that encode enzymes that almost certainly must exist because of the known properties of an organism. *Thermotoga maritima* (*Bacteria*), for example, is a hyperthermophile found in hot marine sediments, and laboratory studies have shown it to be able to catabolize a large number of sugars. Figure 2 summarizes some of the metabolic pathways and transport systems of *T. maritima* that have been deduced from analysis of its genome. As expected, its genome is rich in genes for transport, particularly for carbohydrates and amino acids. In fact, a large portion of the *T. maritima* genome (7%) consists of genes that encode proteins for the metabolism of simple and complex sugars. All this suggests that *T. maritima* exists in an environment rich in organic material.

Table 2 Gene function in bacterial genomes

Functional categories	Percentage of genes on chromosome in that category: *Escherichia coli* (4.64 Mbp)[a]	*Haemophilus influenzae* (1.83 Mbp)[a]	*Mycoplasma genitalium* (0.58 Mbp)[a]
Metabolism	21.0	19.0	14.6
Structural	5.5	4.7	3.6
Transport	10.0	7.0	7.3
Regulation	8.5	6.6	6.0
Translation	4.5	8.0	21.6
Transcription	1.3	1.5	2.6
Replication	2.7	4.9	6.8
Other, known	8.5	5.2	5.8
Unknown	38.1	43.0	32.0

[a]Chromosome size, in megabase pairs. Each organism listed contains only a single circular chromosome.

A functional analysis of genes and their activities in several prokaryotes is given in Table 2. Similar data are assembled when each new genome is published. Thus far a distinct pattern has emerged of gene distribution in prokaryotes. Metabolic genes are typically the most abundant class of genes in prokaryotic genomes, although genes for protein synthesis overtake metabolic genes on a percentage basis as genome size decreases (Table 2, and see Figure 3). Interestingly, as vital as they are, genes for DNA replication and transcription make up only a minor fraction of the typical prokaryotic genome.

In addition to protein-encoding genes, most organisms have a substantial number of genes that encode nontranslated RNA. These include genes for ribosomal RNA, which are often present in multiple copies, tRNAs, and a variety of small regulatory RNAs.

Uncharacterized ORFs

Although there are differences from organism to organism, in most cases the number of genes whose role can be clearly identified in a given genome is 70% or less of the total number of ORFs detected. Uncharacterized ORFs are said to encode *hypothetical proteins*, proteins that likely exist although their function is unknown. An uncharacterized ORF shares with a known protein-encoding gene an uninterrupted reading frame of reasonable length and start and stop codons, but it encodes a protein lacking sufficient amino acid sequence homology with any known protein and thus cannot be readily identified as such.

Uncharacterized ORFs reveal that there is still much we don't know about the function of prokaryotic genes. On the

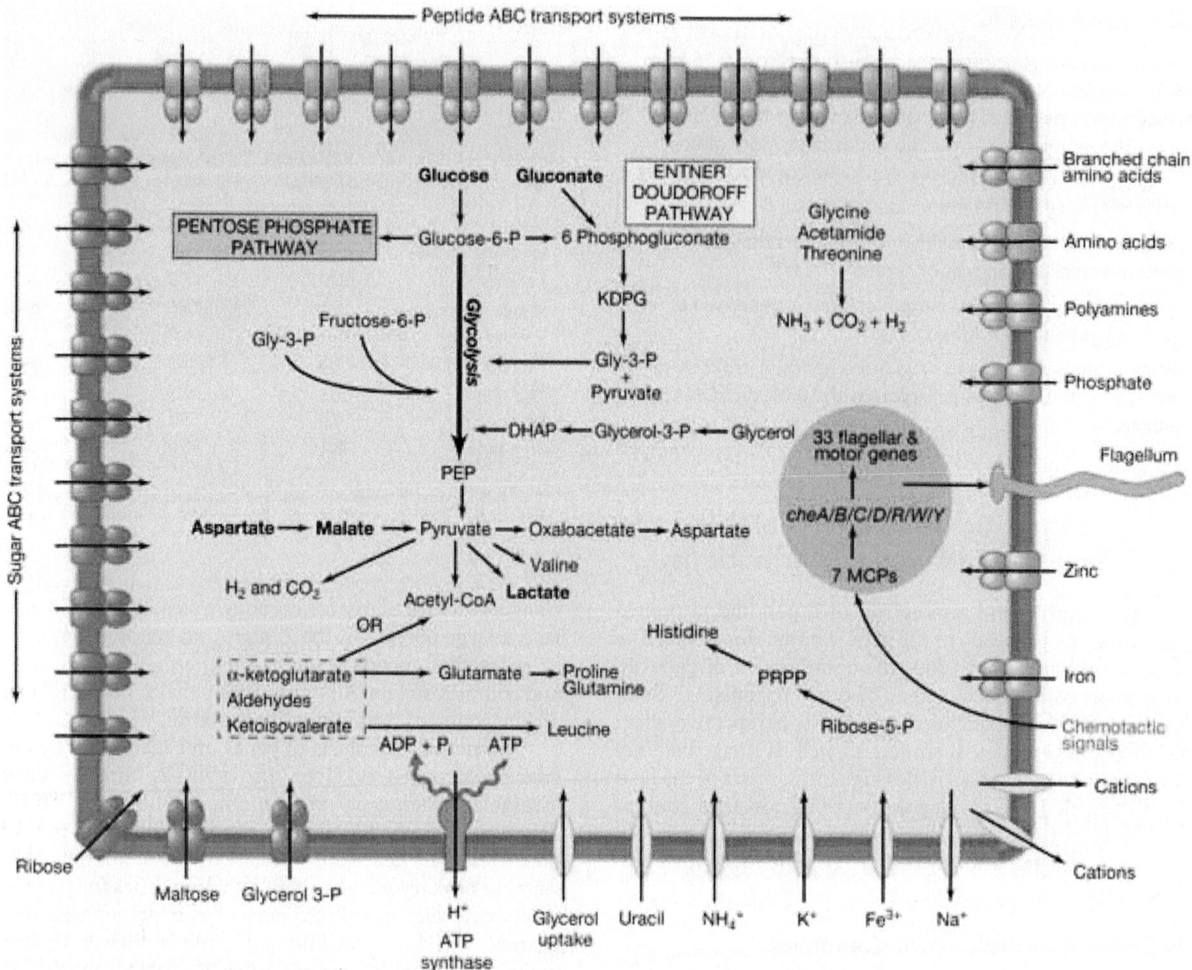

Figure 2 **Overview of metabolism and transport in *Thermotoga maritima.*** The figure shows a blueprint for the metabolic capabilities of this organism. These include some of the pathways for energy production and the metabolism of organic compounds, including transport proteins that were identified from analysis of the genomic sequence. Gene names are not shown. The genome contains several ABC-type transport systems, 12 for carbohydrates, 14 for peptides and amino acids, and still others for ions. These are shown as multisubunit structures in the figure. Other types of transport proteins have also been identified and are shown as simple ovals. The flagellum is shown, and this organism has seven transducers (MCPs) and several chemotaxis (*che*) genes and genes required for flagellar assembly. A few aspects of sugar metabolism are also shown. This figure is adapted from one published by The Institute for Genomic Research.

other hand, as gene functions are identified in one organism, homologous ORFs in other organisms can be assigned functions. Even in the world's best-understood organism, *E. coli,* functions still have not been assigned to over 1,000 of its almost 4,300 genes. However, most of the genes for macromolecular syntheses and central metabolism essential for growth of *E. coli* have been identified. Therefore, as the functions of the remaining ORFs are identified, it is likely that most of them will encode nonessential proteins.

As progress is made in identifying hypothetical proteins, the relative percentage of *E. coli* genes involved in macromolecular syntheses or central metabolism will probably decrease. Many of the unidentified genes in *E. coli* are predicted to encode regulatory or redundant proteins; these might include proteins needed only under special conditions or as "backup" systems for key enzymes. However, it must be remembered that the precise function of many genes, even in well-studied organisms such as *E. coli,* are often unpredictable. Some gene identifications merely assign a given gene to a family or to a general function (such as "transporter"). By contrast, other genes are completely unknown and have only been predicted using bioinformatics, whereas some are actually incorrect; it has been estimated that as many as 10% of genes in databases are incorrectly annotated.

Gene Categories as a Function of Genome Size

As the data of Table 2 show, the percentage of an organism's genes devoted to one or another cell function is to some degree a function of genome size. This is summarized for a large number of bacterial genomes in Figure 3. Core cellular processes, such as protein synthesis, DNA replication and energy production, show only minor variations in gene number with genome size (Figure 3). Consequently, the relative percentage of genes devoted to protein synthesis, for example, rises dramatically in small genome organisms. By contrast, genes devoted to regulation of transcription increase significantly in large genome organisms.

The data summarized in Figure 3 suggest that although many genes can be dispensed with, genes that encode the protein-synthesizing apparatus cannot. Thus, the smaller the genome, the greater the percentage of its genes encode translational processes (Table 2). Large genomes, on the other hand, contain more genes for regulation than small genomes. These additional regulatory systems allow the cell to be more flexible in diverse environmental situations by controlling gene expression accordingly. In small genome prokaryotes these regulatory processes are dispensable because such organisms are often parasitic and obtain much of what they need from their hosts.

Large genome organisms can afford to encode many regulatory and specialized metabolic genes. This likely makes these organisms more competitive in their habitats, which, for prokaryotes with very large genomes, is often soil. Soil is a habitat in which carbon and energy sources are often scarce or available only intermittently, and vary greatly. A large genome encoding multiple metabolic options would thus be strongly selected for in such a habitat. Interestingly, all of the prokaryotes listed in Table 1 whose genomes are in excess of 6 Mbp inhabit soil.

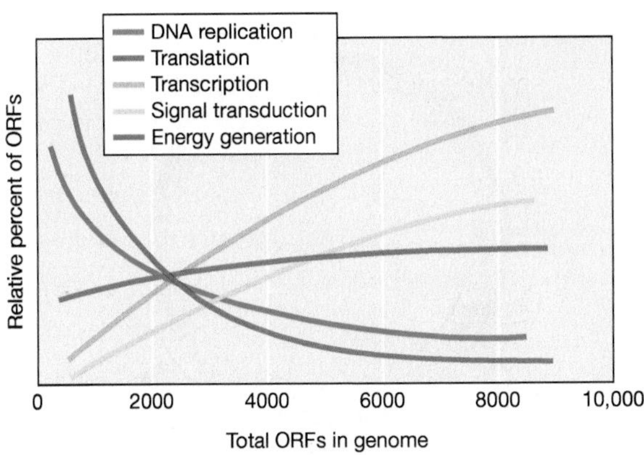

Figure 3 **Functional category of genes as a percentage of the genome.** Note how genes encoding products for translation or DNA replication increase in percentage in small genome organisms, whereas transcriptional regulatory genes increase in percentage in large genome organisms. Data from *Proc. Natl. Acad. Sci. (USA)* 101: 3160–3165 (2004).

Gene Distribution in *Bacteria* and *Archaea*

Analyses of gene categories have been done on several *Bacteria* and *Archaea* and the results are compared in Figure 4. Note that these data reflect the average gene content for several separate genomes. On average, species of *Archaea* devote a higher percentage of their genomes to energy and coenzyme production than do *Bacteria* (these results are undoubtedly skewed a bit due to the large number of novel coenzymes produced by methanogenic *Archaea*). On the other hand, *Archaea* appear to contain fewer genes for carbohydrate metabolism or cytoplasmic membrane functions, such as transport and membrane biosynthesis, than do *Bacteria*. However, this finding may be skewed because the corresponding pathways are less well studied in *Archaea* than in *Bacteria*, and

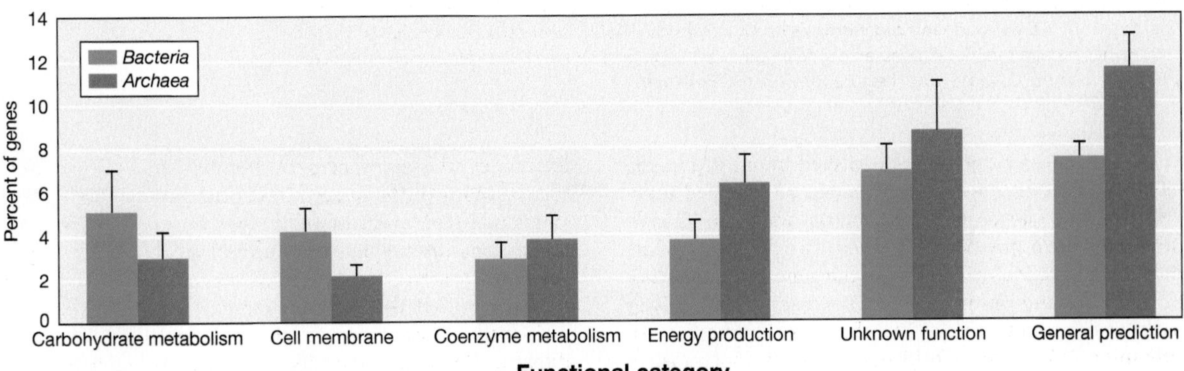

Figure 4 **Variations in gene category in *Bacteria* and *Archaea*.** Data are averages from 34 species of *Bacteria* and 12 species of *Archaea*. "Unknown function" represents genes known to encode proteins but whose functions are unknown. Genes labeled as "general prediction" encode hypothetical proteins that may or may not exist. Data from *Proc. Natl. Acad. Sci. (USA)* 101: 3160–3165 (2004).

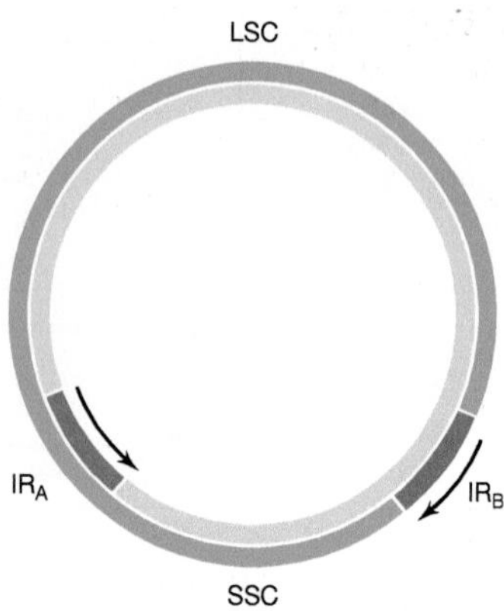

Figure 5 Map of a typical chloroplast genome. The genomes of chloroplasts are circular double-stranded DNA molecules. Most contain two inverted repeat regions (IR_A and IR_B), which form the borders of a small single copy region (SSC) and a large single copy region (LSC).

many of the corresponding archaeal genes are probably still unknown.

Both domains of prokaryotes have relatively large numbers of genes whose functions are either unknown or that encode only hypothetical proteins, although in both categories more uncertainty exists among the *Archaea* than the *Bacteria* (Figure 4). However, this may be an artifact due to the availability of fewer genome sequences from the *Archaea* than from the *Bacteria*.

3 MiniReview

Many genes can be identified by their sequence similarity to genes found in other organisms. However, a significant percentage of sequenced genes are of unknown function. On average, the gene complements of Bacteria and Archaea are related but distinct. Bioinformatics plays an important role in genomic analyses.

- Does every functional ORF encode a protein?
- What is a hypothetical protein?
- What category of genes do prokaryotes contain the most of on a percentage basis?

4 The Genomes of Eukaryotic Organelles

Eukaryotic cells contain a variety of membrane-bound organelles in addition to the nucleus. The mitochondrion and the chloroplast each contain a small genome. In addition, both organelles contain the machinery necessary for protein synthesis, including ribosomes, transfer RNAs, and all the other components necessary for translation and formation of functional proteins. Indeed, these organelles share many traits in common with prokaryotic cells, to which they are phylogenetically related.

The Chloroplast Genome

Green plant cells contain chloroplasts, the organelles responsible for photosynthesis. Known chloroplast genomes are all circular DNA molecules. Although there are several copies of the genome in each chloroplast, they are identical. The typical chloroplast genome is about 120–160 kbp and contains two inverted repeats of 6–76 kbp (Figure 5). Several chloroplast genomes have been completely sequenced, and a few of these are summarized in Table 3. The flagellated protozoan *Mesostigma viride* belongs to the earliest diverging green plant lineage. Its chloroplast contains more protein-encoding genes and tRNA genes than any other so far known and has the typical genome structure illustrated in Figure 5.

Many of the chloroplast genes encode proteins for photosynthesis and autotrophy. However, the chloroplast genome also encodes rRNA used in chloroplast ribosomes, tRNA used in translation, several proteins used in transcription and translation, as well as some other proteins. Some proteins that

Table 3 Some chloroplast genomes[a]

			Genes encoding			
Organism		***Size (bp)***	***Proteins[b]***	***tRNA***	***rRNA[c]***	***Inverted repeats[d]***
Chlorella vulgaris	Green alga	150,613	77	31	1	Absent
Euglena gracilis	Protozoan	143,170	67	27	3	Absent
Mesostigma viride	Protozoan	118,360	92	37	2	Present
Pinus thunbergii	Black pine	119,707	72	32	1	Present[e]
Oryza sativa	Rice	134,525	70	30	2	Present
Zea mays	Corn	140,387	70	30	2	Present

[a]All chloroplast genomes are circular, double-stranded DNA.
[b]These include genes encoding proteins of known function and ORFs that might be functional.
[c]Each unit is an rRNA operon, containing genes for each of the rRNAs.
[d]See Figure 5.
[e]Although the inverted repeats are present, they are greatly truncated.

function in the chloroplast are encoded by nuclear genes. These are thought to be genes that migrated to the nucleus as the chloroplast evolved from an endosymbiont into a photosynthetic organelle. Unlike free-living prokaryotes, introns are common in chloroplast genes, and they are primarily of the self-splicing type.

Analyses of chloroplast genomes firmly support the endosymbiotic hypothesis. For example, chloroplast genomes contain genes that are homologs of those in *Escherichia coli*, cyanobacteria, and other *Bacteria*. These include genes encoding proteins for cell division, suggesting that the mechanism of chloroplast division resembles that of bacterial cells. In addition, chloroplast genes for protein transport through membranes are highly related to those of *Bacteria*.

Mitochondrial Genomes

Mitochondria are responsible for energy production by respiration and are found in most eukaryotic organisms. Mitochondrial genomes primarily encode proteins for oxidative phosphorylation and, as do chloroplast genomes, also encode rRNAs, tRNAs, and proteins involved in protein synthesis. However, most mitochondrial genomes encode many fewer proteins than do those of chloroplasts.

Several hundred mitochondrial genomes have been sequenced. The largest mitochondrial genome has 62 protein-encoding genes, but others encode as few as 3 proteins. The mitochondria of almost all mammals, including humans, encode only 13 proteins plus 22 tRNAs and 2 rRNAs. Figure 6 shows a map of the 16,569-bp human mitochondrial genome. The mitochondrial genome of the yeast *Saccharomyces cerevisiae* is larger (85,779 bp), but has only 8 protein-encoding genes. Besides the genes encoding the RNA and proteins, the genome of yeast mitochondria contains large stretches of extremely AT-rich DNA that has no apparent function.

Whereas chloroplasts use the "universal" genetic code, mitochondria use slightly different, simplified genetic codes. These seem to have arisen from selection pressure for smaller genomes. For example, the 22 tRNAs produced in mitochondria are insufficient to read the entire genetic code, even with the "standard" wobble pairing taken into consideration. Therefore, base pairing between the anticodon and the codon is even more flexible in mitochondria than it is in cells.

Unlike chloroplast genomes, which are all single, circular DNA molecules, the genomes of mitochondria, are quite diverse. For example, some mitochondrial genomes are linear, including those of some species of algae, protozoans, and fungi. In other cases, such as in the bakers and brewer's yeast *S. cerevisiae*, although genetic analyses indicate that the mitochondrial genome is circular, it seems that the major *in vivo* form is linear. (Recall that bacteriophage T4 has a genetically circular genome but is physically linear).

Finally, it should be noted that small plasmids exist in the mitochondria of several organisms, complicating mitochondrial genome analysis. An additional problem in analyzing some organelle genomes is that it is sometimes difficult to find the gene for a particular protein even when the sequence of the protein and the organelle DNA are both known. This is because of **RNA editing** (see the Microbial Sidebar, "RNA Editing").

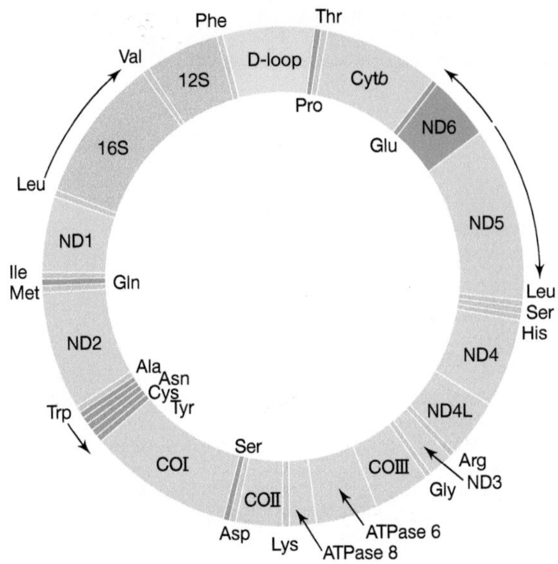

Figure 6 **Map of the human mitochondrial genome.** The circular genome of the human mitochondrion contains 16,569 bp. The genome encodes the 16S and 12S rRNA (corresponding to the prokaryotic 23S and 16S rRNAs) and 22 tRNAs. Genes that are transcribed counterclockwise (CCW) are in dark orange, and those transcribed clockwise (CW) in light orange. The amino acid designations for tRNA genes are on the outside for CCW-transcribed genes and on the inside of the map for CW genes. The 13 protein-encoding genes are shown in green (dark green, transcribed CCW; light green, transcribed CW). Cytb, cytochrome *b*; ND1-6, components of the NADH dehydrogenase complex; COI-III, subunits of the cytochrome oxidase complex; ATPase 6 and 8, polypeptides of the mitochondrial ATPase complex. The two promoters are in the region called the D-loop, a region also involved in DNA replication.

Organelles and the Nuclear Genome

Chloroplasts and mitochondria require many more proteins than they encode. For example, far more proteins are needed for translation in organelles than are encoded by the organelle genome. Thus, many organelle functions are encoded by nuclear genes.

It is estimated that the yeast mitochondrion contains over 400 different proteins; however, only 8 of them are encoded by the yeast mitochondrial genome, the remaining proteins being encoded by nuclear genes. Although one might predict that proteins that function in specific processes in the eukaryotic nucleus and cytoplasm could be put to the same use in organelles, this is not the case. Although the genes for many organelle proteins are present in the nucleus, transcribed there, and translated on the 80S ribosomes in the eukaryotic cytoplasm, the proteins are used specifically by the organelles and must be transported into them.

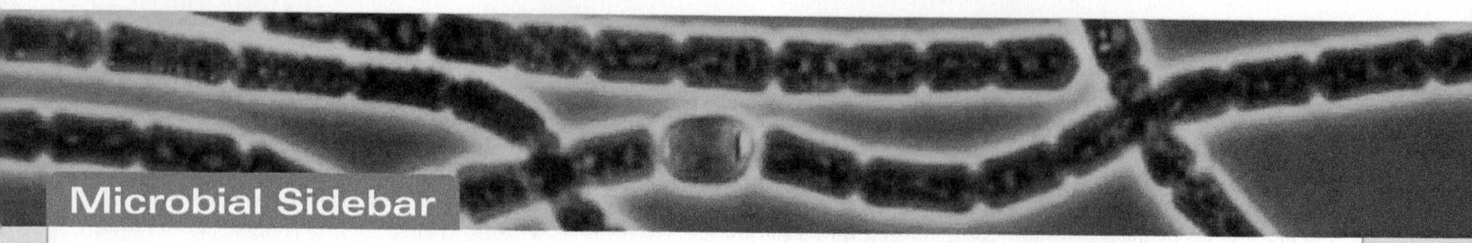

RNA Editing

RNA editing is the process of altering the base sequence of a messenger RNA *after* transcription. Consequently, the nucleotide sequence of the final mRNA does not correspond exactly to the sequence of the DNA from which it was transcribed. There are two forms of RNA editing. In one, nucleotides are either inserted or deleted in the mRNA. In the other, a base in the mRNA is chemically modified in a way that changes its identity. In either case, RNA editing can alter the coding sequence of a mRNA with the consequence that the amino acid sequence of the resulting polypeptide differs from that predicted from its gene sequence.

RNA editing is very rare in most organisms, especially higher animals. Mammals and plants only employ editing by chemical modification. One important human example is the adenosine to inosine editing of mRNA for some neurotransmitter receptor proteins in the nervous system. In this case, adenosine is converted into inosine by deamination and the inosine generated functions as a guanosine during translation. Defects in this editing can cause severe neurological symptoms.

RNA editing is more common in the mitochondria and chloroplasts of higher plants. At specific sites in some mRNAs, a C will be converted to a U by oxidative deamination (the opposite modification is more rare). There are at least 25 sites of C to U conversion in the maize chloroplast. Depending on the location of the editing, a new codon may be formed, leading to an altered protein sequence.

Protein	...Leu Cys Phe Trp Phe Arg Phe Phe Cys...
mRNA	...uuG uGu UUU UGG uuu AGG uuu uuu uGu...
DNA	... G G TTT TCC AGG G ...
	... C C AAA AGG TCC C ...

Figure 1 **RNA editing.** *The first row shows a portion of the amino acid sequence of subunit III of the enzyme cytochrome oxidase from the protozoan* Trypanosoma brucei. *This protein is encoded by the mitochondrial genome. The sequence of the mRNA for this region is shown beneath the amino acid sequence. The bases in uppercase letters are those transcribed from the gene, which is shown below in green. The bases in the mRNA (orange) in lowercase are inserted into the transcript by RNA editing. The spaces shown between the DNA base pairs are simply to aid in visualization; there are no actual gaps in the DNA molecule itself.*

Editing of mRNA by the insertion or deletion of nucleotides occurs in certain protozoa, notably the trypanosomes and their relatives, and more often in mitochondrial genes than in nuclear genes. Some mitochondrial transcripts are edited such that large numbers (hundreds in some cases) of uridines are added or, more rarely, deleted. An example of this type of RNA editing is shown in Figure 1. In such cases, the coding sequences in the DNA usually have incorrect reading frames. If the mRNA were not edited, the resulting proteins would be frame-shifted and defective.

RNA editing is precisely controlled by short sequences in the mRNA that "guide" editing enzymes. In the case of insertional editing, the sequences in the mRNA are recognized by short guide RNA molecules that are complementary to the mRNA except that they have an extra A. The U residues are inserted into the mRNA opposite the extra A on the guide RNA. Obviously, this process must be very precisely controlled. Inserting too many or too few bases would generate frameshift errors that would yield dysfunctional proteins.

RNA editing, although a curious phenomenon, was not a significant obstacle in analyzing organellar genomes. This is because the number of proteins they encode is small and the proteins highly conserved. By contrast, if RNA editing had been widespread in nuclear genomes or in the genomes of prokaryotic cells, comparative genomics would be an even more formidable task.

The function and origin of RNA editing is unknown. But some scientists have suggested that this process may be yet another remnant, along with ribozymes, of an era on Earth before the evolution of cells or DNA, the RNA world.

Those nuclear-encoded mitochondrial proteins involved in translation and energy generation are closely related to counterparts in the *Bacteria*, not to those that function in the eukaryotic cytoplasm. Thus, it initially appeared that most genes encoding mitochondrial proteins had been transferred from the mitochondrion to the nucleus during maturation of the endosymbiotic process. However, what was needed to confirm such a hypothesis was both the nuclear and mitochondrial genome sequences of a eukaryote, the genome sequence of a species of *Bacteria* phylogenetically closely related to the mitochondrial genome, and the genomes of other *Bacteria* for comparative purposes. All these requirements were met in the case of the yeast *S. cerevisiae* and the necessary *Bacteria*, and the analysis has been revealing.

Surprisingly, of the 400 nuclear genes encoding mitochondrial proteins, only about 50 were closely related to the phylogenetic lineage in *Bacteria* that led to mitochondria (the *Alpha proteobacteria*). Another 150 were clearly related to proteins of *Bacteria,* but not necessarily *Alpha proteobacteria*. These *Bacteria*-like proteins were mostly needed for energy conversions, translation, and biosynthesis. However, the remaining 200 or so mitochondrial proteins were encoded by genes that have no identifiable homologues among known genes of *Bacteria*. These proteins were mostly required for membranes, regulation, and transport. Thus, although the mitochondrion shows many of signs of having originated from endosymbiotic events, genomic analyses have shown that its genetic history is more complicated than previously thought.

4 MiniReview

All eukaryotic cells (except for a few parasites) contain mitochondria. In addition, plant cells contain chloroplasts. Both organelles contain circular DNA genomes that encode rRNAs, tRNAs, and a few proteins involved in energy metabolism. Although the genomes of the organelles are independent of the nuclear genome, the organelles themselves are not. Many genes in the nucleus encode proteins required for organelle function.

- What is unusual about the genes that encode mitochondrial functions in yeast?
- How are genome size and gene content correlated in yeast and human mitochondria?
- What is RNA editing? How does it differ from RNA processing?

5 Eukaryotic Microbial Genomes

A large number of eukaryotes are known, and the genomes of several microbial and higher eukaryotes have now been sequenced (Table 4). The genomes of mammals, including human, mouse, and rat, have around 25,000 genes—about

Table 4 Some eukaryotic nuclear genomes[a]

Organism	*Comments*	*Organism/ Cell type*[b]	*Genome size (Mbp)*	*Haploid chromosome number*	*Protein-encoding genes*[c]
Nucleomorph of *Bigelowiella natans*	Degenerate endosymbiotic nucleus	E	0.37	3	331
Encephalitozoon cuniculi	Smallest known eukaryotic genome; human pathogen	P	2.9	11	2,000
Cryptosporidium parvum	Parasitic protozoan	P	9.1	8	3,800
Plasmodium falciparum	Malignant malaria	P	23	14	5,300
Saccharomyces cerevisiae	Yeast, a model eukaryote	FL	13	16	5,800
Ostreococcus tauri	Marine green alga; smallest free-living eukaryote	FL	12.6	20	8,200
Aspergillus nidulans	Filamentous fungus	FL	30	8	9,500
Giardia lamblia	Flagellated protozoan; causes acute gastroenteritis	P	12	5	9,700
Dictyostelium discoideum	Social amoeba	FL	34	6	12,500
Drosophila melanogaster	Fruit fly; model organism for genetic studies	FL	180	4	13,600
Caenorhabditis elegans	Roundworm; model organism for animal development	FL	97	6	19,100
Arabidopsis thaliana	Model plant for genetic studies	FL	125	5	26,000
Mus musculus	Mouse, a model mammal	FL	2,500	23	25,000
Homo sapiens	Human	FL	2,850	23	25,000
Oryza sativa	Rice; the world's most important crop plant	FL	390	12	38,000
Paramecium tetraaurelia	Ciliate protozoan	FL	72	>50	40,000
Populus trichocarpa	Black poplar, a tree	FL	500	19	45,000
Trichomonas vaginalis	Flagellated protozoan; human pathogen	P	160	6	60,000

[a]All data are for the haploid nuclear genomes of these organisms.
[b]E, endosymbiont; P, parasite; FL, free-living.
[c]The number of protein-encoding genes is in all cases an estimate based on the number of known genes and sequences that seem likely to encode functional proteins.

twice the number found in insects and four times that of yeast. However, the genomes of higher plants, such as rice and black poplar, contain even more genes, approaching twice that of humans. It is thought that sequencing of corn (maize) and other large plant genomes presently in progress will reveal even higher gene numbers.

Interestingly, both single-celled protozoans *Paramecium* (40,000 genes) and *Trichomonas,* (60,000 genes) have significantly more genes than humans do (Table 4). Indeed, *Trichomonas* presently holds the record for gene number of any organism. This is puzzling because *Trichomonas* is a human parasite, and as we have seen, such organisms typically have small genomes relative to comparable free-living organisms.

Of single-celled eukaryotes, the yeast *Saccharomyces cerevisiae* is most widely used as a model organism as well as being extensively used in industry, and so we focus on it here.

The Yeast Genome

The haploid yeast genome contains 16 chromosomes ranging in size from 220 kbp to about 2,352 kbp. The total yeast nuclear genome (excluding the mitochondria and some plasmid and viruslike genetic elements) is approximately 13,392 kbp. Why are the words "about" and "approximately" used to describe this genome when it has been completely sequenced? Yeast, like many other eukaryotes, has a large amount of repetitive DNA. When the yeast genome was published in 1997, not all of the "identical" repeats had been sequenced. It is difficult to sequence a very long run of identical or nearly identical sequences and then assemble the data into a coherent framework. For example, yeast chromosome XII contains a stretch of approximately 1,260 kbp containing 100–200 repeats of yeast rRNA genes. Another repeated sequence follows this long series of rRNA gene repeats. Because of such identical repeats, the sizes of eukaryotic genomes are inevitably only close approximations.

In addition to having multiple copies of the rRNA genes, the yeast nuclear genome has around 300 genes for tRNAs (only a few are identical) and nearly 100 genes for other types of noncoding RNA. As with other eukaryotic genomes, the number of predicted ORFs in yeast has changed somewhat as sequence analysis is refined. As of 2006, approximately 5,800 ORFs plus another 800 possible ORFs have been identified in the yeast genome; this is fewer ORFs than in some prokaryotic genomes (Tables 1 and 4). Of the yeast ORFs, about 3,500 encode proteins whose functions are known. The wide variety of genetic and biochemical techniques available for studying this organism have resulted in significant advances in the understanding of the function of the remaining proteins as well (Section 7).

Minimal Gene Complement of Yeast

How many of the known yeast genes are actually essential? This question can be approached by systematically inactivating each gene in turn with knockout mutations (mutations that render a gene nonfunctional). Knockout mutations cannot normally be obtained in genes essential for cell viability in a haploid organism. However, yeast can be grown in both diploid and haploid states. By generating knockout mutations in diploid cells and then investigating whether they can also exist in haploid cells, it is possible to determine whether a particular gene is essential for cell viability.

Using knockout mutations, it has been shown that at least 877 yeast ORFs are essential, whereas 3,121 clearly are not. Note that this number of essential genes is much greater than the approximately 300 genes (or possibly fewer than 200 genes, Section 3) predicted to be the minimal number required in prokaryotes. However, because eukaryotes are more complex than prokaryotes, a larger minimal gene complement would be expected.

Yeast Introns

Yeast is a eukaryote and contains introns. However, the total number of introns in the protein-encoding genes of yeast is a mere 225. Most yeast genes with introns have a single small intron near the 5′ end of the gene. This situation differs greatly from that seen in higher eukaryotes (Table 4). In the worm *Caenorhabditis elegans,* for example, the average gene has 5 introns, and in the fruit fly *Drosophila,* the average gene has 4 introns. Introns are also very common in the genes of higher plants. Thus the plant *Arabidopsis* averages 5 introns per gene, and over 75% of *Arabidopsis* genes have introns. In humans almost all protein-encoding genes have introns, and it is not uncommon for a single gene to have 10 or more. Moreover, human introns are typically much larger than human exons. Indeed, exons make up only about 1% of the human genome, whereas introns account for 24%.

Other Eukaryotic Microorganisms

The genomes of several other eukaryotic microorganisms, mostly those of medical importance, have been sequenced. The smallest eukaryotic cellular genome known belongs to *Encephalitozoon cuniculi,* an intracellular pathogen of humans and other animals that causes lung infections. *E. cuniculi* lacks mitochondria, and although its haploid genome contains 11 chromosomes, the genome size is only 2.9 Mbp with approximately 2,000 genes (Table 4); this is smaller than many prokaryotic genomes (Table 1). As is also true in the prokaryotes, the smallest eukaryotic genome belongs to an endosymbiont (Table 4). Known as a *nucleomorph,* this is the degenerate remains of a eukaryotic endosymbiont found in certain green algae that have acquired photosynthesis by secondary endosymbioses. Nucleomorph genomes range from about 0.45 to 0.85 Mbp.

As previously mentioned, the largest eukaryotic genome belongs to *Trichomonas,* which has about 60,000 genes despite its parasitic existence (Table 4). The free-living ciliate *Paramecium* has about 40,000 genes, and the free-living social amoeba, *Dictyostelium,* has about 12,500 genes (but note that *Dictyostelium* has both single-celled and multicellular phases in its life cycle). For comparison, the pathogenic amoeba *Entamoeba histolytica,* the causative agent of amebic dysentery, has approximately 10,000 genes.

Apart from the strange case of *Trichomonas,* parasitic eukaryotic microorganisms have genomes containing 10–30 Mbp of DNA and between 4,000 and 11,000 genes. For example, the genome of the trypanosome *Trypanosoma brucei*, the agent of African sleeping sickness, has 11 chromosomes, 35 Mbp of DNA, and almost 11,000 genes. The most important eukaryotic parasite is *Plasmodium*, which causes malaria. The 25-Mbp genome of *Plasmodium falciparum* consists of 14 chromosomes ranging in size from 0.7 to 3.4 Mbp. The estimated number of genes for *P. falciparum*, which infects humans, is 5,300, and for the related species *Plasmodium yoelli*, which infects rodents, is 5,900.

5 MiniReview

The complete genomic sequence of the yeast *Saccharomyces cerevisiae* and that of many other microbial eukaryotes has been determined. Yeast may encode up to 5,800 proteins, of which only about 900 appear essential for viability. Relatively few of the protein-encoding genes of yeast contain introns. The number of genes in single-celled eukaryotes ranges from 2,000 (less than many bacteria) to 60,000 (more than twice as many as humans).

- How can you show whether a gene is essential?
- What is unusual about the genome of the eukaryote *Encephalitozoon*?

II GENOME FUNCTION AND REGULATION

Despite the major effort required to generate an annotated genome sequence, in some ways the net result is simply a "list of parts." To understand how a cell functions, we need to know more than which genes are present. It is also necessary to investigate both gene expression (transcription) and the function of the final gene product.

We focus here on gene expression. In analogy to the term "genome," the entire complement of RNA produced under a given set of conditions is known as the **transcriptome**.

6 Microarrays and the Transcriptome

Knowing the conditions under which a gene is transcribed may reveal a gene's function. We have already discussed how nucleic acid hybridization reveals the location of genes on specific fragments of DNA. Hybridization techniques can also be used in conjunction with genomic sequence data to measure gene expression by hybridizing mRNA to specific DNA fragments. This technique has been radically enhanced with the development of microarrays, or *gene chips* as they are also called.

Microarrays and the DNA Silica Chip

Microarrays are small solid-state supports to which genes or more often, portions of genes, are fixed and arrayed spatially in a known pattern. The gene segments are synthesized by the polymerase chain reaction (PCR), or, alternatively, oligonucleotides are designed for each gene based on the genomic sequence. Once attached to the solid support, these DNA segments can be hybridized with mRNA from cells grown under specific conditions and scanned and analyzed by computer. Hybridization between a specific mRNA and the corresponding DNA on the chip indicates that the gene has been transcribed.

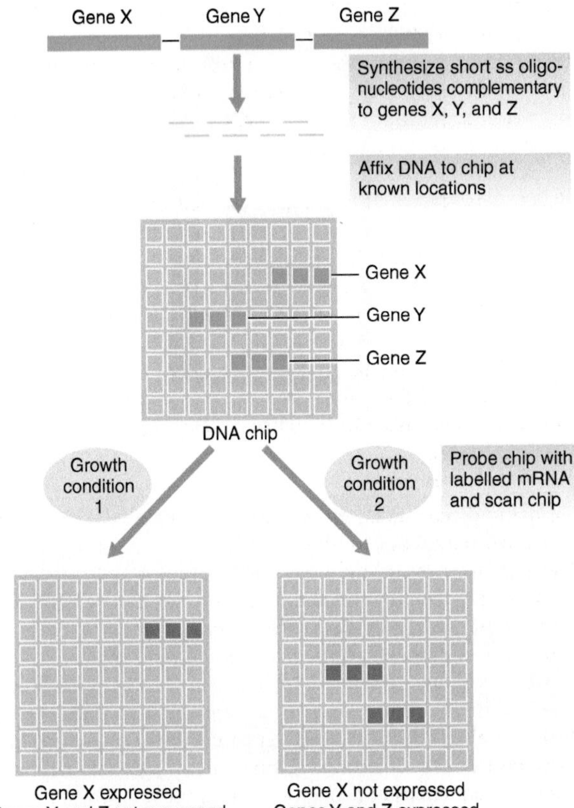

Figure 7 **Making and using DNA chips.** Short single-stranded oligonucleotides corresponding to all the genes of an organism are synthesized individually and affixed at known locations to make a DNA chip (microarray). The DNA chip is assayed by hybridizing fluorescently labeled mRNA obtained from cells grown under a specific condition to the DNA probes on the chip and then scanning the chip with a laser.

In practice, mRNA is present in amounts too low for direct use. Consequently, the mRNA sequences must first be amplified. Reverse transcriptase (RT) is used to generate complementary DNA (cDNA) from the mRNA. The cDNA may then be amplified by PCR (these two steps constitute the RT-PCR procedure). Alternatively, the cDNA may be used as a template by T7 RNA polymerase, which generates multiple RNA copies called *cRNA*. The cDNA or cRNA is then applied to the array.

A method for making and using microarrays is shown in Figure 7. Photolithography, a process used to produce computer chips, has been adapted to produce silica microarray

(a)

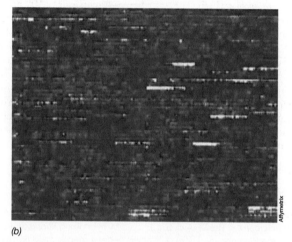

(b)

Figure 8 Using DNA chips to assay gene expression. (*a*) The human genome chip containing over 40,000 gene fragments. (*b*) A hybridized yeast chip. The photo shows fragments from one-fourth of the entire genome of baker's yeast, *Saccharomyces cerevisiae*, affixed to a gene chip. Each gene is present in several copies and has been probed with fluorescently labeled cDNA derived from the mRNA extracted from yeast cells grown under a specific condition. The background of the chip is blue. Locations where the cDNA has hybridized are indicated by a gradation of colors up to maximum hybridization, which shows as white. Because the location of each gene on the chip is known, when the chip is scanned, it reveals which genes were expressed.

chips of 1 to 2 cm in size, each of which can hold thousands of different DNA fragments. Whole genome arrays contain DNA segments representing the entire genome of an organism. In practice, each gene is often represented more than once in the array to provide increased reliability. For example, one company markets a human genome chip that contains the entire human genome (Figure 8*a*). This single chip can analyze over 47,000 human transcripts and has room for 6,500 additional oligonucleotides for use in clinical diagnostics.

Figure 8*b* shows a part of a chip used to assay expression of the *Saccharomyces cerevisiae* genome. This chip easily holds the 5,600 protein-encoding genes of *S. cerevisiae* (Section 5) so that global gene expression in this organism can be measured in a single experiment. To do this, the chip is hybridized with cRNA or cDNA derived from mRNA obtained from yeast cells grown under specific conditions. Any particular cRNA/cDNA binds only to the DNA on the chip that is complementary in sequence. To visualize binding, the cRNA/cDNA is tagged with a fluorescent dye, and the chip is scanned with a laser fluorescence detector. The signals are then analyzed by computer. A distinct pattern of hybridization is observed, depending upon which DNA sequences correspond to which mRNAs (Figures 7 and 8*b*). The intensity of the fluorescence gives a quantitative measure of gene expression (Figure 8*b*). This allows the computer to make a list of which genes were expressed and to what extent. Thus, using gene chips, the transcriptome of the organism of interest grown under specified conditions is revealed from the pattern and intensity of the fluorescent spots generated.

Applications of DNA Chips: Gene Expression

Gene chips may be used in several ways, depending on the genes attached to the chip. Global gene expression is monitored by affixing to the array an oligonucleotide complementary to each gene in the genome and then using the entire population of mRNA as the test sample (Figure 8*b*). Alternatively, one can compare expression of specific groups of genes under different growth conditions. The ability to analyze the simultaneous expression of thousands of genes has tremendous potential for unraveling the complexities of metabolism and regulation. This is true both for organisms as "simple" as bacteria or as complex as higher eukaryotes.

The *S. cerevisiae* gene chip (Figure 8*b*) has been used to study metabolic control in this important industrial organism. Yeast can grow by fermentation and by respiration. Transcriptome analysis can reveal which genes are shut down and which are turned on when yeast cells are switched from fermentative (anaerobic) to respiratory metabolism or vice versa. Transcriptome analyses of such gene expression show that yeast undergoes a major metabolic "reprogramming" during the switch from anaerobic to aerobic growth. A number of genes that control production of ethanol (a key fermentation product) are strongly repressed, whereas citric acid cycle functions (needed for aerobic growth) are strongly activated by the switch. Overall, over 700 genes are turned on and over 1,000 turned off during this metabolic transition. Moreover, by using a microarray, the expression pattern of genes of unknown function are also monitored during the fermentative to respiratory switch, yielding clues to their possible role. At present, no other available method can give as much information about gene expression as microarrays.

Another important use of DNA microarrays is the comparison of genes in closely related organisms. For example, this approach has been used to follow the evolution of pathogenic bacteria from their harmless relatives. In human medicine microarrays are used to monitor gene loss or duplication in cancer cells. In environmental microbiology microarrays have been used to assess microbial diversity. Phylochips, as they are called, contain oligonucleotides complementary to the 16S rRNA sequences of different bacterial species. After extracting bulk DNA or RNA from an environment, the presence or absence of each species can be assessed by the presence or absence of hybridization on the chip. www.microbiologyplace.com **Online Tutorial 1: DNA Chips**

Applications in Identification

Besides probing gene expression, microarrays can be used to specifically identify microorganisms. In this case the array contains a set of characteristic DNA sequences from each of a variety of organisms or viruses. Such an approach can be used to differentiate between closely related strains by differences in their hybridization patterns. This allows very rapid identification of pathogenic viruses or bacteria from clinical samples or detection of these organisms in various other substances, such as food. For example, identification (ID) chips have been used in the food industry to detect particular pathogens, for example *Escherichia coli* O157:H7.

DNA chips are also available to identify higher organisms as well. A commercially available chip called the FoodExpert-ID contains 88,000 gene fragments from vertebrate animals and is used in the food industry to ensure food purity. For example, the chip can confirm the presence of the meat listed on a food label and can also detect foreign animal meats that may have been added as supplements to or substitutes for the official ingredients. The eventual goal is to have each meat product receive an "identity card" listing all the animal species whose tissues were detected in it. This is intended to give consumers more confidence in the wholesomeness of their food products. The FoodExpert-ID can also be used to detect vertebrate by-products in animal feed, a growing concern with the advent of prion-mediated diseases such as mad cow disease.

6 MiniReview

Microarrays consist of genes or gene fragments attached to a solid support in a known pattern. These arrays are used to hybridize to mRNA and then analyzed to determine patterns of gene expression. The arrays are large enough and dense enough that the transcription pattern of an entire genome (the transcriptome) can be analyzed.

- What do microarrays tell you that studying gene expression by assaying a particular enzyme cannot?
- Why is it useful to know how gene expression of the entire genome responds to a particular condition?

7 Proteomics

A further aim of genomic studies is to determine which expressed genes actually yield protein products and then to determine the function of these proteins. The genomewide study of the structure, function, and regulation of an organism's proteins is called **proteomics**.

The number and types of proteins present in a cell are subject to change in response to an organism's environment or other factors, such as developmental cycles. As a result, the term **proteome** has unfortunately become ambiguous. In its wider sense, a proteome refers to *all* the proteins encoded by an organism's genome. In its narrower sense, however, it refers to those proteins present in a cell *at any given time*.

Methods in Proteomics

The first major approach to proteomics was developed decades ago with the advent of two-dimensional (2D) polyacrylamide gel electrophoresis. This technique can separate, identify, and measure all the proteins present in a cell sample. A 2D gel separation of proteins from *Escherichia coli* is shown in Figure 9. In the first dimension (the horizontal dimension in the figure), the proteins are separated by differences in their isoelectric points, the pH at which the net charge on each protein reaches zero. In the second dimension, the proteins are denatured in a way that gives each amino acid residue a fixed charge. The proteins are then separated by size (in much the same way as for DNA molecules).

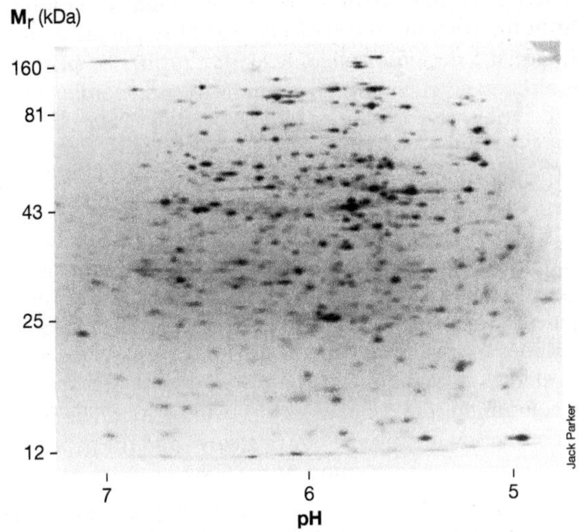

Figure 9 **Two-dimensional polyacrylamide gel electrophoresis of proteins.** Autoradiogram of the proteins of cells of *Escherichia coli*. Each spot on the gel is a different protein. The proteins are radioactively labeled to allow for visualization and quantification. The proteins were separated in the first dimension (X-direction) by isoelectric focusing under denaturing conditions. The second dimension (Y-direction) separates denatured proteins by their mass (M_r; in kilodaltons), with the largest proteins being toward the top of the gel.

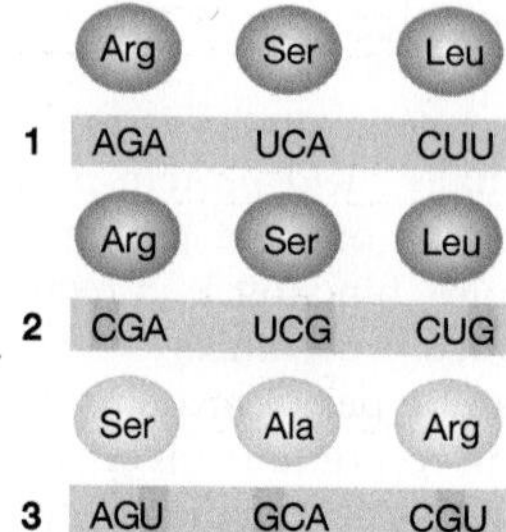

Figure 10 Comparison of nucleic acid and amino acid sequence similarities. Three different nucleotide sequences are shown (for convenience RNA is shown). Both sequence 2 and sequence 3 differ from sequence 1 in only three positions. However, the amino acid sequence encoded by 1 and 2 are identical, whereas that encoded by sequence 3 is unrelated to the other two.

In studies of *E. coli* and a few other organisms, hundreds of proteins separated in 2D gels have been identified by biochemical or genetic means, and their regulation has been studied under various conditions. Using 2D gels, the presence of a particular protein under different growth conditions can be measured and related to environmental signals. One method of connecting an unknown protein with a particular gene using the 2D gel system is to elute the protein from the gel and sequence a portion of it, usually from its N-terminal end. More recently, eluted proteins have been identified by a technique called *mass spectrometry* (Section 8), usually after preliminary digestion to give a characteristic set of peptides. This sequence information may be sufficient to completely identify the protein. Alternatively, partial sequence data may allow for the design of oligonucleotide probes or primers to locate the gene encoding the protein from genomic DNA by hybridization or polymerase chain reaction. Then, following sequencing of the DNA, the gene's identity may be determined.

Today, liquid chromatography is increasingly used to separate protein mixtures. In high-pressure liquid chromatography (HPLC), the sample is dissolved in a suitable liquid and forced under pressure through a column packed with a stationary phase material that separates proteins by variations in their chemical properties, such as size, ionic charge, or hydrophobicity. As the mixture travels through the column, it is separated by interaction of the proteins with the stationary phase. Fractions are collected at the column exit. The proteins in each fraction are digested by proteases and the peptides are identified by mass spectrometry.

Comparative Genomics and Proteomics

Although proteomics often requires intensive experimentation, *in silico* techniques can also be quite useful. Once the sequence of an organism's genome is obtained, it can be compared to that of other organisms to locate and identify genes that are similar to those already known. The sequence that is most important here is the amino acid sequence of the encoded proteins. Because the genetic code is degenerate, differences in DNA sequence may not necessarily lead to differences in the amino acid sequence (Figure 10).

Proteins with greater than 50% sequence identity frequently have similar functions. Proteins with identities above 70% are almost certain to have similar functions. Many proteins consist of distinct structural modules, called *protein domains,* each with characteristic functions. Such regions include metal-binding domains, nucleotide-binding domains, or domains for certain classes of enzyme activity, such as helicase or nuclease. Identification of domains of known function within a protein may reveal much about its role, even in the absence of complete sequence homology.

Structural proteomics refers to the proteome-wide determination of the three-dimensional (3D) structures of proteins. At present, it is not possible to directly predict the 3D structure of proteins from their amino acid sequences. However, structures of unknown proteins can often be modeled if the 3D structure is available for a protein with 30% or greater identity in amino acid sequence.

Coupling proteomics with genomics is yielding important clues to how gene expression in different organisms correlates with environmental stimuli. Not only does such information have important basic science benefits, but it also has potential applications. These include advances in medicine, the environment, and agriculture. In all of these areas, understanding the link between the genome and the proteome and how it is regulated could give humans unprecedented control in fighting disease and pollution, as well as unprecedented benefits for agricultural productivity.

7 MiniReview

Proteomics is the analysis of all the proteins present in an organism. The ultimate aim of proteomics is to understand the structure, function, and regulation of these proteins.

- Why is the term "proteome" ambiguous, whereas the term "genome" is not?
- What are the most common experimental methods used to survey the proteome?

8 Metabolomics

By analogy with the terms *genome* and *proteome,* the **metabolome** is the complete set of metabolic intermediates and other small molecules produced in an organism. Metabolomics has lagged behind other "omics" in large part due to the immense chemical diversity of small metabolites. This makes systematic screening technically challenging. Early attempts used nuclear magnetic resonance (NMR) analysis of extracts from cells labeled with ^{13}C-glucose. However, this method is limited in sensitivity, and the number of compounds that can be simultaneously identified in a mixture is too low for resolution of complete cell extracts.

Mass Spectrometric Analyses of the Metabolome

The most promising approach to metabolomics is the use of newly developed techniques of mass spectrometry. This approach is not limited to particular classes of molecules and can be extremely sensitive. The mass of carbon-12 is defined as exactly 12 molecular mass units (Daltons). However, the masses of other atoms, such as nitrogen-14 or oxygen-16 are not exact integers. Mass spectrometry using extremely high mass resolution, which is now possible in special instruments, allows the unambiguous determination of the molecular formula of any small molecule. Clearly, isomers will have the same molecular formula, but they may be distinguished by their different fragmentation patterns during mass spectrometry.

Metabolome analysis is especially useful in the study of plants, many of which produce several thousand different metabolites—more than most other types of organism. This is because plants make many *secondary metabolites,* such as scents, flavors, alkaloids, and pigments, many of which are commercially important. Metabolomic investigations have monitored the levels of several hundred metabolites in the model plant *Arabidopsis,* and significant changes were observed in the levels of many of these metabolites in response to changes in temperature. Future directions for metabolomics, presently under development, include assessing the effect of disease on the metabolome of various human organs and tissues. Such results should greatly improve our understanding of how the human body fights off infectious and noninfectious disease.

8 MiniReview

The metabolome is the complete set of metabolic intermediates produced by an organism.

- What techniques are used to monitor the metabolome?

III THE EVOLUTION OF GENOMES

In addition to understanding how genes function and organisms interact with the environment, comparative genomics can also reveal evolutionary relationships between organisms. Reconstructing evolutionary relationships from genome sequences helps to distinguish between primitive and derived characteristics and can resolve ambiguities in phylogenetic trees based on analyses of a single gene, such as small subunit rRNA. Genomics is also a link to understanding early life forms and, eventually, may answer the most fundamental of all questions in biology: How did life first arise?

9 Gene Families, Duplications, and Deletions

Genomes from both prokaryotic and eukaryotic sources often contain multiple copies of genes that are related in sequence due to shared evolutionary ancestry; such genes are called **homologous** genes. Groups of gene homologs are called **gene families**. Not surprisingly, larger genomes tend to contain more individual members from a particular gene family.

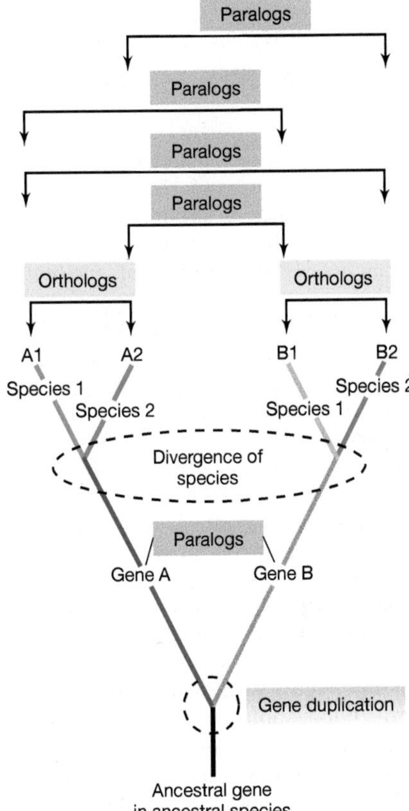

Figure 11 Orthologs and paralogs. This family tree depicts an ancestral gene that duplicated and diverged into two paralogous genes, A and B. Next, the ancestral species diverged into species 1 and species 2, both of which have genes for A and B (designated A1 and B1 and A2 and B2 respectively). Each such pair are paralogs. However, because species 1 and 2 are now separate species, A1 is an ortholog of A2 and B1 is an ortholog of B2.

Paralogs and Orthologs

Comparative genomics has shown that many genes have arisen by duplication of other genes. Such homologs may be subdivided, depending on their origins. Genes whose similarity is the result of gene duplication at some time in the evolution of an organism are called **paralogs**. Genes found in one organism that are similar to genes in another organism, but that differ because of speciation or more distant evolutionary events, are called **orthologs** (Figure 11). An example of paralogous genes are those encoding several different lactate dehydrogenase (LDH) isoenzymes in humans. These enzymes are structurally distinct yet are all highly related and carry out the same enzymatic reaction. By contrast, the corresponding LDH from *Lactobacillus* is orthologous to all of the human LDH isoenzymes. Thus, gene families contain both paralogs and orthologs.

Gene Duplication

It is widely thought that gene duplication is the mechanism for the evolution of most new genes. If a segment of duplicated DNA is long enough to include an entire gene or group of genes, the organism with the duplication contains multiple copies of these particular genes. After duplication, one of the duplicates is free to evolve while the other copy continues to supply the cell with the original function. In this way, evolution can "experiment" with one copy of the gene. Such gene-duplication events, followed by diversification of one copy, are thought to be the major events that fuel microbial evolution. Genomic analyses have revealed numerous examples of protein-encoding genes that were clearly derived from gene duplication.

Duplications that occur in genetic material may include just a handful of bases or even whole genomes. For example, comparison of the genomes of the yeast *Saccharomyces cerevisiae* and other fungi suggests that the ancestor of *Saccharomyces* duplicated its entire genome. This was followed by extensive deletions that eliminated much of the duplicated genetic material. Analysis of the genome of the model plant *Arabidopsis* suggests that there was one or more whole genome duplications in the ancestor of the flowering plants.

Did bacterial genomes evolve by whole genome duplication? The distribution of duplicated genes and gene families in the genomes of bacteria suggests that many frequent but relatively small duplications have occurred. For example, among the *Deltaproteobacteria*, the soil bacterium *Myxococcus* has a genome of 9.1 Mbp. This is approximately twice that of the genomes of other typical *Deltaproteobacteria*, which range from 4 to 5 Mbp. Among the *Alphaproteobacteria*, genome sizes range from 1.1 to 1.5 Mbp for parasitic members to 4 Mbp for free-living *Caulobacter*, and up to 7–9 Mbp for plant-associated bacteria. However, in all of these cases gene distribution analysis points to frequent small-scale duplications rather than whole genome duplications. Conversely, in bacteria that are parasitic, frequent successive deletions have eliminated genes no longer needed for a parasitic lifestyle, leading to their unusually small genomes (Section 2).

Gene Analysis in Different Domains

The comparison of genes and gene families is a major task in comparative genomics. Because chromosomes from many different microorganisms have already been sequenced, such comparisons can be easily done, and the results are often surprising. For instance, genes in *Archaea* involved in DNA replication, transcription, and translation are more similar to those in *Eukarya* than to those in *Bacteria*. Unexpectedly, however, many other genes in *Archaea*, for example, those encoding metabolic functions other than information processing, are more similar to those in *Bacteria* than those in *Eukarya*. The powerful analytical tools of bioinformatics allow genetic relationships between any organisms to be deduced very quickly and at the single gene, gene group, or entire genome level. The results obtained thus far lend further support to the phylogenetic picture of life deduced originally by comparative ribosomal RNA sequence analysis and suggest that many genes in all organisms have common evolutionary roots. However, such analyses have also revealed instances of horizontal gene flow, an important issue to which we now turn.

9 MiniReview

Genomics can be used to study the evolutionary history of an organism. Organisms contain gene families, genes with related sequences. If these arose because of gene duplication, the genes are said to be paralogs; if they arose by speciation, they are called orthologs.

- What is a gene family?
- Contrast gene paralogs with gene orthologs.

10 Mobile DNA: Transposons and Insertion Sequences

Evolution is based on the transfer of genetic traits from one generation to the next. However, in prokaryotes, **horizontal (lateral) gene transfer** also occurs, and it can complicate evolutionary studies, especially those of entire genomes. Horizontal gene transfer occurs whenever genes are transferred from one cell to another other than by the usual inheritance process, from mother cell to daughter cell. In prokaryotes, at least three mechanisms for horizontal gene transfer are known: *transformation, transduction,* and *conjugation*.

Horizontal gene flow may be extensive in nature and may sometimes cross even phylogenetic domain boundaries. However, to be detectable by comparative genomics, the difference between the organisms must be rather large. For example, several genes with eukaryotic origins have been found in *Chlamydia* and *Rickettsia*, both human pathogens. In particular, two genes encoding histone H1-like proteins have been found in the *Chlamydia trachomatis* genome, suggesting horizontal transfer from a eukaryotic source, possibly even its human host. Note that this is opposite the situation in which genes from the ancestor of the mitochondrion were transferred to the eukaryotic nucleus (Section 4).

Detecting Horizontal Gene Flow

Horizontal gene transfers can be spotted in genomes once the genes have been annotated. The presence of genes that encode proteins typically found only in distantly related species is one signal that the genes originated from horizontal transfer. However, another clue to horizontally transferred genes is the presence of a stretch of DNA whose GC content or codon bias differs significantly from the rest of the genome. Using these clues, many likely examples of horizontal transfer have been documented in the genomes of various prokaryotes. A classic example exists with the organism *Thermotoga maritime*, a species of *Bacteria*, which was shown to contain over 400 genes (greater than 20% of its genome) of archaeal origin. Of these genes, 81 were found in discrete clusters. This strongly suggests that they were obtained by horizontal gene transfer, presumably from thermophilic *Archaea* that share the hot environments inhabited by *Thermotoga*.

Horizontally transferred genes typically encode metabolic functions other than the core molecular processes of DNA replication, transcription, and translation, and may account for the previously mentioned similarities of metabolic genes in *Archaea* and *Bacteria* (Section 9). In addition, there are several examples of virulence genes of pathogens having been transferred by horizontal means. It is obvious that prokaryotes are exchanging genes in nature, and the process likely functions to "fine-tune" an organism's genome to a particular situation or habitat.

Caveat to Horizontal Flow

It is necessary to be cautious when invoking horizontal gene transfer to explain the distribution of genes. When the human genome was first sequenced, a couple hundred genes were identified as being horizontal transfers from prokaryotes. However, when more eukaryotic genomes became available for examination, homologs were found for most of these genes in many eukaryotic lineages. Consequently, it now seems that most of these genes are in fact of eukaryotic origin. Only about a dozen human genes are now accepted as strong candidates for having relatively recent prokaryotic origins. The phrase "relatively recent" here refers to genes transferred from prokaryotes after separation of the major eukaryotic lineages, not to genes of possible ancient prokaryotic origin that are shared by eukaryotes as a whole.

10 MiniReview

Organisms may acquire genes from other organisms in their environment by a process called horizontal gene transfer. Such transfer may cross the domain boundaries between *Bacteria*, *Archaea*, and *Eukarya*.

- Which class of genes is rarely transferred horizontally? Why?
- List the major mechanisms by which horizontal gene transfer occurs in prokaryotes.

11 Horizontal Gene Transfer and Genome Stability

Mobile DNA refers to segments of DNA that move from one location to another within host DNA molecules. Most mobile DNA consists of transposable elements, but integrated virus genomes and integrons are also found. All of these mobile elements play important roles in genome evolution.

Genome Evolution and Transposons

Transposons may move between different host DNA molecules, including chromosomes, plasmids, and viruses. In doing so they may pick up and horizontally transfer genes for a variety of characteristics, including resistance to antibiotics or production of toxins. However, transposons may also mediate a variety of large-scale chromosomal changes. Bacteria that are undergoing rapid evolutionary change often contain relatively large numbers of mobile elements, especially insertion sequences. Recombination among identical elements generates chromosomal rearrangements such as deletions, inversions, or translocations. This is thought to provide a source of genome diversity upon which selection can act. Thus, chromosomal rearrangements that accumulate in bacteria during stressful growth conditions are often flanked by repeats or insertion sequences.

Conversely, once a species settles into a stable evolutionary niche, most mobile elements are apparently lost. For example, genomes of species of *Sulfolobus* (*Archaea*) have unusually high numbers of insertion sequences and show a high frequency of gene translocations. By contrast, *Pyrococcus* (*Archaea*) shows an almost complete lack of insertion sequences and a correspondingly low number of gene translocations. This suggests that for whatever reason, perhaps because of fluctuations in conditions in their habitats, the genome of *Sulfolobus* is more dynamic than the more stable genome of *Pyrococcus*.

Insertion Sequences

Chromosomal rearrangements due to insertion sequences have apparently contributed to the evolution of several bacterial pathogens. In *Bordetella*, *Yersinia*, and *Shigella*, the more highly pathogenic species show a much greater frequency of insertion sequences. For example, *Bordetella bronchiseptica* has a genome of 5.34 Mbp but carries no known insertion sequences. Its more pathogenic relative, *Bordetella pertussis*, has a smaller genome (4.1 Mb) but has more than 260 insertion sequences. Comparison of these genomes suggests that the insertion sequences are responsible for substantial genome rearrangement, including deletions responsible for the reduction of genome size in *B. pertussis*.

Insertion sequences also play a role in assembling genetic modules to generate novel plasmids. Thus 46% of the 220-kbp virulence megaplasmid of *Shigella flexneri* consists of insertion sequence DNA! In addition to full-length insertion sequences, there are many fragments in this plasmid that imply multiple ancestral rearrangements.

Integrons and Super-Integrons

Integrons are genetic elements that collect and express genes carried on mobile segments of DNA, called *cassettes*. Gene cassettes suitable for integration consist of a coding sequence lacking a promoter, but containing an integrase recognition

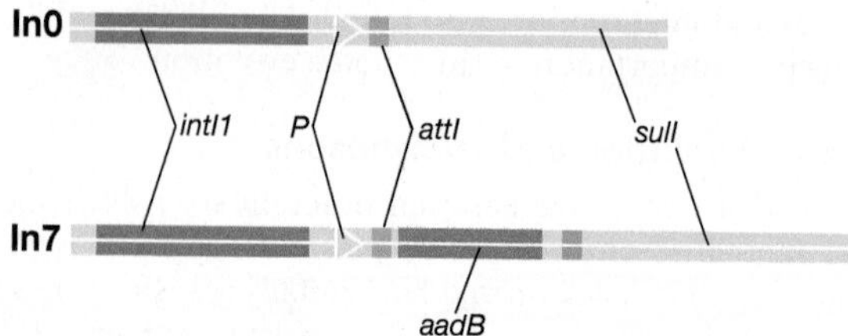

Figure 12 Structure of two naturally occurring integrons from *Pseudomonas*. Integron In0 has the basic set of genes: *intI1*, integrase; *attI*, the integration site; P, promoter; and *sulI*, a gene conferring sulfonamide resistance. Integron In7 contains all of these plus an integrated gene cassette. All cassettes contain a site (blue) for site-specific recombination. This cassette contains *aadB*, which confers resistance to certain aminoglycoside antibiotics.

site, the *attC* site. The integrons themselves contain a corresponding integration site, the *attI* site, into which gene cassettes may be integrated. The integron also possesses a gene encoding the **integrase**, the enzyme responsible for inserting cassettes. Integration occurs by recombination between the *attI* site and the *attC* site. Once a gene cassette has been inserted into an integron, the gene it carries may be expressed from a promoter that is provided by the integron.

Neither integrons nor gene cassettes are transposable elements (they do not have terminal inverted repeats, nor do they transpose). However, gene cassettes may exist transiently as free nonreplicating circular DNA incapable of gene expression, or they may be found integrated into the *attI* site of an integron. Thus the gene cassettes are a form of mobile DNA that may move from one integron to another. Most integrons are found on plasmids or in transposons and may collect multiple gene cassettes. A few integrons are found on bacterial chromosomes and may collect hundreds of gene cassettes, whereupon they are called *superintegrons*. For example, the second chromosome of *Vibrio cholerae* (causative agent of cholera) has a super-integron with approximately 200 genes, mostly of unknown function.

Most known integrons carry genes for antibiotic resistance. However, this is probably due to a bias in observation, since antibiotic resistance is of clinical importance. Over 40 different antibiotic resistance genes have been identified on integron gene cassettes, as have some genes associated with virulence in certain pathogenic bacteria. Figure 12 shows the structure of two integrons from *Pseudomonas aeruginosa,* a potentially serious pathogen. Integrons have been found in various species of *Bacteria,* often in clinical isolates, and their selection by horizontal gene transfer in such antibiotic-rich environments as hospitals and clinics is obvious. What is less obvious is the origin of the gene cassettes themselves. These are not simply random genes, as they must possess specific DNA sequences that are recognized by the integrase; they are incapable of expression until they become part of an integron and can be transcribed from the integron's promoter.

11 MiniReview

Mobile DNA elements, including transposons, integrons, and viruses are important in genome evolution. Mobile DNA often carries genes encoding antibiotic resistance or virulence factors. Integrons are genetic structures that collect and express promoterless genes carried on gene cassettes.

- Why are transposons especially important in the evolution of pathogenic bacteria?
- What are integrons and how do they differ from transposons?

12 Evolution of Virulence: Pathogenicity Islands

Comparison of the genomes of pathogenic bacteria with those of their harmless close relatives often reveals extra blocks of genetic material that contain genes that encode *virulence factors,* special proteins or other molecules or structures necessary to cause disease.

Some virulence genes are carried on plasmids or lysogenic bacteriophages. However, many others are clustered in chromosomal regions called **pathogenicity islands**. For example, the identity and chromosomal location of most genes of pathogenic strains of *Escherichia coli* correspond to those of the harmless laboratory strain *E. coli* K-12, as would be expected. However, most pathogenic strains contain pathogenicity islands of considerable size that are absent from *E. coli* K-12 (Figure 13). Consequently, two strains of the same bacterial species may show significant differences in genome size. For example, as shown in Table 1, the enterohemorrhagic strain *E. coli* O157:H7 contains 20% more DNA and genes than the *E. coli* strain K12.

Chromosomal Islands

Pathogenicity islands are merely the best-known case of **chromosomal islands**. Such islands are presumed to have a "foreign" origin based on several observations. First, these extra regions are often flanked by inverted repeats, implying that the whole region was inserted into the chromosome by transposition at some period in the recent evolutionary past. Second, the base composition and codon usage in chromosomal islands often differ significantly from that of the rest of the genome. Third, chromosomal islands are often found in some strains of a particular species but not in others.

Some chromosomal islands carry a gene for an integrase and are thought to move in a manner analogous to conjugative transposons. Chromosomal islands are typically inserted into a gene for a tRNA; however, because the target site is duplicated upon insertion, an intact tRNA gene is regenerated during the insertion process. In a few cases, transfer of a whole chromosomal island between related bacteria has been demonstrated in the laboratory; transfer can presumably

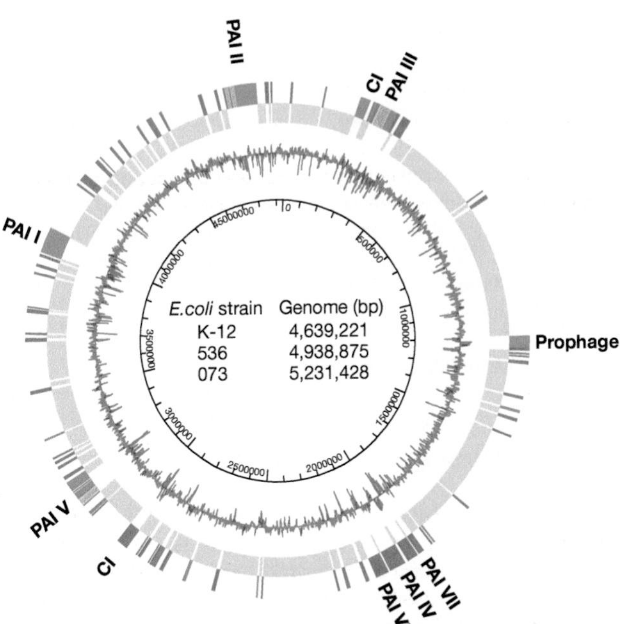

Figure 13 **Pathogenicity islands in *Escherichia coli*.** Genetic map of *E. coli* strain 536, a urinary tract pathogen, compared with a second pathogenic strain (073) and the wild-type strain K-12. The pathogenic strains contain pathogenicity islands, and thus their chromosomes are larger than that of K-12. Inner circle, nucleotide base pairs. Jagged circle, DNA GC distribution; regions where GC content varies dramatically from the genome average are in red. Outermost circle, three-way genomic comparison: green, genes common to all strains; red, genes present in the pathogenic strains only; blue, genes found only in strain 536; orange, genes of strain 536 present in a different location in strain 073. Some very small inserts deleted for clarity. PAI, pathogenicity islands; CI, chromosomal island. Prophage, DNA from a temperate bacteriophage. Note the correlation between genomic islands and skewed GC content. Data adapted from *Proc. Natl. Acad. Sci. (USA)* 103: 12879–12884 (2006).

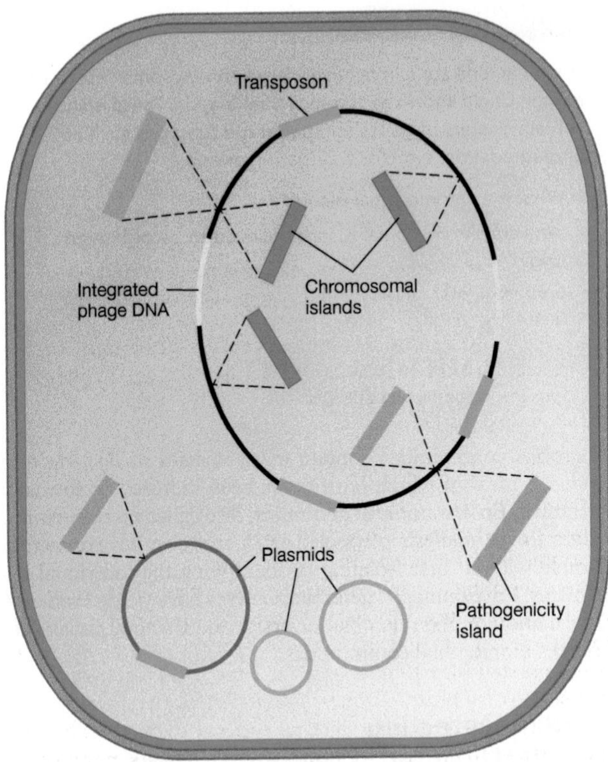

Figure 14 **Pan genome versus core genome.** The core genome is represented by the black regions of the chromosome and is present in all strains of a species. The pan genome includes elements that are present in one or more strains but not in all strains. Each colored wedge indicates a single insertion. Where two wedges emerge from the same location, they represent alternative islands that can insert at that site. However, only one insertion can be present at a given location.

occur by any of the mechanisms of lateral transfer previously discussed: transformation, transduction, and conjugation. It is thought that after insertion into the genome of a new host cell, chromosomal islands gradually accumulate mutations—both point mutations and small deletions. Thus, over many generations, chromosomal islands tend to lose their ability to move.

Chromosomal islands contribute specialized functions that are not needed for simple survival. Not surprisingly, pathogenicity islands with their clinical relevance have drawn the most interest. However, chromosomal islands are also known that carry genes for the biodegradation of various substrates derived from human activity, such as aromatic hydrocarbons and herbicides. In addition, many of the genes essential for the symbiotic relationship of rhizobia with plants in the root nodule symbiosis are carried in symbiosis islands inserted into the genome of these bacteria. Perhaps the most unique chromosomal island is the magnetosome island of the bacterium *Magnetospirillum*; this DNA fragment carries the genes needed for the formation of magnetosomes, intracellular magnetic particles used to orient the organism in a magnetic field and influence the direction of its motility.

The presence or absence of chromosomal islands, transposable elements, integrated virus genomes, and plasmids means that there may be major differences in the total amount of DNA and the suite of accessory capabilities (virulence, symbiosis, biodegradation) between strains of a single bacterial species. This has led to the concept that the genome of a bacterial species consists of two components, the *core* genome and the *pan* genome. The core genome is shared by all strains of the species, whereas the pan-genome includes all of the optional extras present in some but not all strains of the species (Figure 14). In other words, one could say that the core genome is typical of the species as a whole, whereas the pan genome is unique to particular strains within a species.

12 MiniReview

Many bacteria contain relatively large chromosomal inserts of foreign origin known as chromosomal islands. These islands contain clusters of genes for specialized functions such as biodegradation, symbiosis, or pathogenesis.

- What is a chromosomal island?
- Why are chromosomal islands believed to be of foreign origin?

IV ENVIRONMENTAL GENOMICS

Microbial communities contain many species of *Bacteria* and *Archaea*, most of which have never been cultured or formally identified. **Environmental genomics**, also called *metagenomics*, refers to the analysis of pooled DNA from an environmental sample without first isolating or identifying the individual organisms. Environmental genomic analyses have yielded valuable information on the microbial diversity and the total genetic resources of microbial communities.

13 Detecting Uncultured Microorganisms

Most microorganisms present in nature have never been brought into laboratory culture. Nevertheless, it is possible to obtain information on the organisms and their activities by carrying out analyses of DNA or RNA directly extracted from the environment. Just as the total gene content of an organism is its genome, so the total gene content of the organisms inhabiting an environment is known as its **metagenome**.

Several environments have been surveyed by large-scale metagenome sequencing projects. Extreme environments, such as acid mine run-off waters tend to have limited species diversity. In such environments it has been possible to isolate community DNA and assemble much of it into nearly complete genomes. Conversely, complex environments such as fertile soil yield too much sequence data to allow successful assembly at present.

In addition to metagenome analyses, microarrays (Section 6) have been used to explore the patterns of gene expression in natural microbial communities. These techniques have empowered microbiologists to ask new and very complex questions about the structure and function of microbial communities and to measure the contributions of specific members of a microbial community to overall ecosystem function.

One curious recent revelation is that most DNA in natural habitats does not belong to living cells. First, about 50–60% of the DNA in the oceans is extracellular DNA found in deep-sea sediments. This is deposited when dead organisms from the upper layers of the ocean sink to the bottom and disintegrate. Because nucleic acids are repositories of phosphate, this DNA is a major contributor to the global phosphorus cycle. Second, as discussed in the next section, virus particles greatly outnumber living cells in most environments.

13 MiniReview

Most microorganisms present in the environment have never been cultured. Nonetheless, analysis of DNA samples has revealed colossal sequence diversity in most habitats. The concept of the metagenome embraces the total genetic content of the organisms in a particular habitat.

- What is a metagenome?
- How is a metagenome analyzed?

14 Viral Genomes in Nature

The number of prokaryotic cells on Earth is far greater than the total number of eukaryotic cells; estimates of total prokaryotic cell numbers are on the order of 10^{30}. However, the number of viruses on Earth is even greater—an estimated 10^{31}. The best estimates of both cell and virus numbers in the environment come from the analysis of seawater, as this is much easier to analyze than soil or sediments.

Viral Metagenomics

There are millions of bacteria, and approximately ten times as many viruses, present in every milliliter of seawater (Figure 15). Not surprisingly, most of these viruses are bacteriophages, and these populations turn over rapidly. It has been

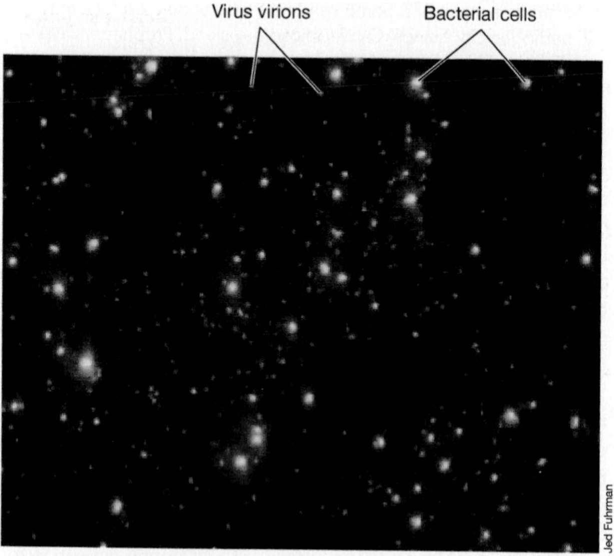

Figure 15 **Viruses and bacteria in seawater.** An epifluorescence photomicrograph of seawater stained with the dye SYBR Green to reveal prokaryotic cells and viruses. Although viruses are too small to be seen with the light microscope, fluorescence from a stained virus is visible.

estimated that every day from 5–50% of the bacteria in seawater are killed by bacteriophages, and most of the others are eaten by protozoa.

Overall, most of the genetic diversity on Earth is thought to reside in viruses, mostly bacteriophages. Many bacteriophages can integrate into the genomes of their bacterial hosts and can transfer bacterial genes from one bacterium to another. Thus, viruses have a massive influence on bacterial evolution, partly by culling the large bacterial populations on a daily basis and partly by catalyzing horizontal gene transfer.

The *viral metagenome* is the sum total of all the virus genes in a particular environment. Several viral metagenomic studies have been undertaken, and they invariably show that immense viral diversity exists on Earth. For example, approximately 75% of the gene sequences found in viral metagenomic studies show no similarity to any genes presently in viral or cellular gene databases. By comparison, surveys of bacterial metagenomes typically reveal approximately 10% unknown genes. Thus, most viruses await discovery and most viral genes have unknown functions.

14 MiniReview

Viruses outnumber cells about tenfold in most habitats. Consequently, most global genetic information is carried by virus genomes. Most virus genes are presently uncharacterized and many are unlike those found in cells of any of the domains of life.

- How do viruses affect the evolution of bacterial genomes?

Review of Key Terms

Bioinformatics the use of computational tools to acquire, analyze, store, and access DNA and protein sequences

Chromosomal island region of bacterial chromosome of foreign origin that contains clustered genes for some extra property such as virulence or symbiosis

Environmental genomics genomic analysis of pooled DNA from an environmental sample without first isolating or identifying the individual organisms

Gene family genes that are related in sequence to each other as the result of a common evolutionary origin

Genome the total complement of genetic information of a cell or a virus

Genomics the discipline that maps, sequences, analyzes, and compares genomes

Homologous related in sequence to an extent that implies common genetic ancestry; includes both orthologs and paralogs

Horizontal gene transfer the transfer of genetic information between organisms as opposed to its vertical inheritance from parental organism(s)

Integrase the enzyme that inserts cassettes into an integron

Integron a genetic element that accumulates and expresses genes carried by cassettes

Lateral gene transfer the same as horizontal gene transfer

Megabase pair (Mbp) one million base pairs

Metabolome the total complement of small molecules and metabolic intermediates of a cell or organism

Metagenome the total genetic complement of all the cells present in a particular environment

Microarray small solid-state supports to which genes or portions of genes are affixed and arrayed spatially in a known pattern (also called *gene chips*)

Ortholog a gene found in one organism that is similar to that in another organism but differs because of speciation (see also *Paralog*)

Paralog a gene whose similarity to one or more other genes in the same organism is the result of gene duplication (see also *Ortholog*)

Pathogenicity island region of bacterial chromosome of foreign origin that contains clustered genes for virulence

Proteome the total set of proteins encoded by a genome or the total protein complement of an organism

Proteomics the genomewide study of the structure, function, and regulation of the proteins of an organism

RNA editing changing the coding sequence of an RNA molecule by altering, adding, or removing bases

Transcriptome the complement of mRNAs produced in an organism under a specific set of conditions

Review Questions

1. What is the relationship between genome size and ORF content of prokaryotic genomes (Section 2)?
2. As a proportion of the total genome, which class of genes predominates in small genome organisms? In large genome organisms (Section 3)?
3. Whose genomes are larger, those of chloroplasts or those of mitochondria? Describe one unusual feature about a chloroplast and a mitochondrial genome (Section 4).
4. How much larger is your genome than that of yeast? How many more genes do you have than yeast (Section 5)?

5. In *Bacteria* and *Archaea* the acronym ORF is almost a synonym for the word "gene." However, in eukaryotes this is not, strictly speaking, true. Explain (Section 5).
6. Distinguish between the terms *genome, proteome,* and *transcriptome* (Sections 6 and 7).
7. Why is the term *proteome* ambiguous (Section 7)?
8. What does a 2D protein gel show? How can the results of such a gel be tied to protein function (Section 7)?
9. Why is investigation of the metabolome lagging behind that of the proteome (Section 8)?
10. What is the major difference in how duplications have contributed to the evolution of prokaryote versus eukaryote genomes (Section 9)?
11. Explain how horizontally transferred genes can be detected in a genome (Section 11).
12. Explain how chromosomal islands might be expected to move between different bacterial hosts (Section 12).
13. How can gene expression be measured in uncultured bacteria (Section 13)?
14. Most of the genetic information on our planet does not belong to cellular organisms. Discuss (Section 14).

Application Questions

1. Although the sequence of the yeast nuclear genome was published, the entire sequence was never actually completely determined. Describe the practical difficulties that were encountered in the sequencing.
2. Describe how one might determine which proteins in *Escherichia coli* are repressed when a culture is shifted from a minimal medium (which contains only a single carbon source) to a rich medium, containing a large number of amino acids, bases, and vitamins? Describe how one might study which genes are expressed during each growth condition.
3. The gene encoding the beta subunit of RNA polymerase from *Escherichia coli* is said to be orthologous to the *rpoB* gene of *Bacillus subtilis*. What does that mean about the relationship between the two genes? What protein do you suppose the *rpoB* gene of *Bacillus subtilis* encodes? The genes for the different sigma factors of *Escherichia coli* are paralogous. What does that say about the relationship between these genes?

Nutrition, Culture, and Metabolism of Microorganisms

An understanding of nutrition and bioenergetics is necessary to grow microorganisms in the laboratory and to understand how microbial cells "make a living" in their natural habitats.

James A. Shapiro, University of Chicago

I NUTRITION AND CULTURE OF MICROORGANISMS

Before a cell can replicate, it must coordinate many different chemical reactions and organize molecules into specific structures. Collectively, these reactions are called **metabolism.** Metabolic reactions are either energy *releasing,* called **catabolic reactions (catabolism),** or energy *requiring,* called **anabolic reactions (anabolism).** Several catabolic and anabolic reactions occur in cells, and we will examine some of the key ones in this and future chapters. However, before we do, we consider how microorganisms are grown in the laboratory and the nutrients they need for growth. Indeed, most of what we know about the metabolism of microorganisms has emerged from the study of laboratory cultures. Our focus here will be on chemoorganotrophic microorganisms, also called *heterotrophs;* these are organisms that use organic compounds for carbon and energy. Later in this chapter we will briefly consider energy-generating mechanisms other than chemoorganotrophy, including chemolithotrophy and phototrophy.

1 Microbial Nutrition

Recall that, besides water, cells consist mainly of macromolecules and that macromolecules are polymers of smaller units called monomers. Microbial nutrition is that aspect of microbial physiology that deals with the supply of monomers (or the precursors of monomers) that cells need for growth. Collectively, these required substances are called *nutrients.*

Different organisms need different complements of nutrients, and not all nutrients are required in the same amounts. Some nutrients, called *macronutrients,* are required in large amounts, while others, called *micronutrients,* are required in trace amounts. All microbial nutrients originate from the chemical elements; however, just a handful of elements dominate biology (Figure 1). Although cells consist mainly of H, O, C, N, P, and S, at least 50 of the chemical elements are metabolized in some way by microorganisms (Figure 1). We begin our study of microbial nutrition with the key macronutrient elements, *carbon* and *nitrogen* (Figure 1 and Table 1).

Carbon and Nitrogen

All cells require carbon, and most prokaryotes require organic compounds as their source of carbon. On a dry weight basis, a typical cell is about 50% carbon, and carbon is the major element in all classes of macromolecules. Bacteria can assimilate organic compounds and use them to make new cell material. Amino acids, fatty acids, organic acids, sugars, nitrogen bases, aromatic compounds, and countless other organic compounds can be used by one or another bacterium. By contrast, some microorganisms are *autotrophs* and able to build all of their cellular structures from carbon dioxide (CO_2). The energy needed to support autotrophy is obtained from either light or inorganic chemicals.

Following carbon, the next most abundant element in the cell is nitrogen. A bacterial cell is about 12% nitrogen (by dry weight), and nitrogen is a key element in proteins, nucleic acids, and several other cell constituents. In nature, nitrogen is available in both organic and inorganic forms (Table 1).

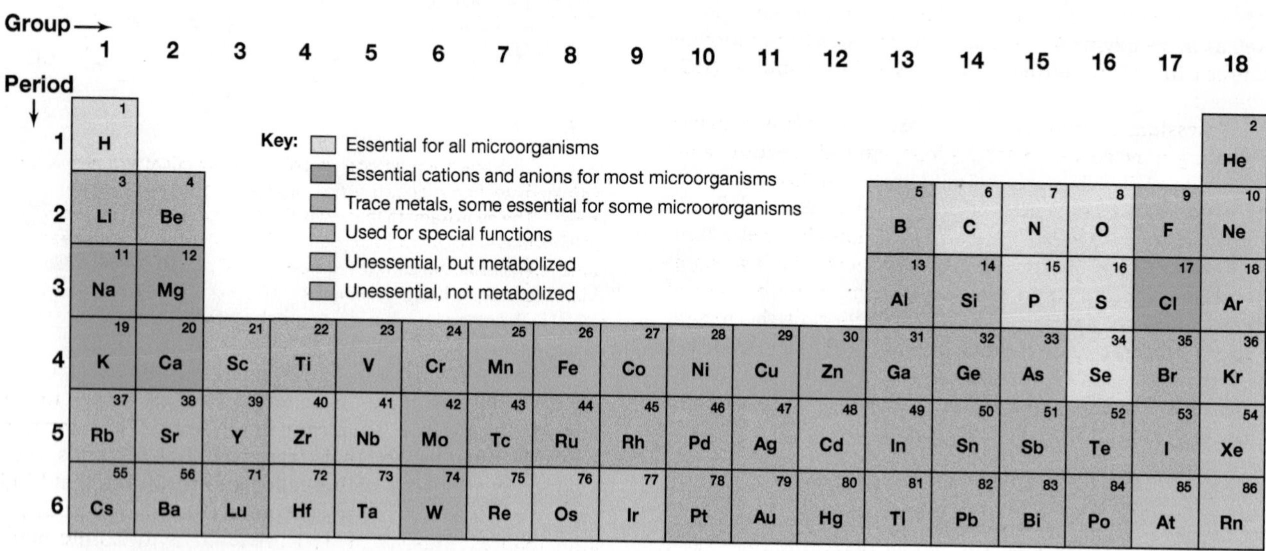

Figure 1 **A microbial periodic table of the elements.** With the exception of uranium, which can be metabolized by some prokaryotes, elements in period 7 or beyond in the complete periodic table of the elements are not metabolized. The atomic number of each element is shown in the upper right corner of each box.

Table 1 Macronutrients

Element	*Usual form found in the environment*
Carbon (C)	CO_2, organic compounds
Hydrogen (H)	H_2O, organic compounds
Oxygen (O)	H_2O, O_2, organic compounds
Nitrogen (N)	NH_3, NO_3^-, N_2, organic nitrogen compounds
Phosphorus (P)	PO_4^{3-}
Sulfur (S)	H_2S, SO_4^{2-}, organic S compounds, metal sulfides (FeS, CuS, ZnS, NiS, and so on)
Potassium (K)	K^+ in solution or as various K salts
Magnesium (Mg)	Mg^{2+} in solution or as various Mg salts
Sodium (Na)	Na^+ in solution or as NaCl or other Na salts
Calcium (Ca)	Ca^{2+} in solution or as $CaSO_4$ or other Ca salts
Iron (Fe)	Fe^{2+} or Fe^{3+} in solution or as FeS, $Fe(OH)_3$, or many other Fe salts

However, the bulk of available nitrogen is in inorganic form, either as ammonia (NH_3), nitrate (NO_3^-), or N_2. Virtually all bacteria can use ammonia as their nitrogen source, and many can also use nitrate. However, nitrogen gas (N_2) can satisfy the nitrogen needs of only a few bacteria, the nitrogen-fixing bacteria.

Other Macronutrients: P, S, K, Mg, Ca, Na

After C and N, other essential elements are needed in smaller amounts. Phosphorus occurs in nature in the form of organic and inorganic phosphates and is required by the cell primarily for synthesis of nucleic acids and phospholipids. Sulfur is required because of its structural role in the amino acids cysteine and methionine and because it is present in several vitamins, including thiamine, biotin, and lipoic acid, as well as in coenzyme A. Most sulfur originates from inorganic sources in nature, either sulfate (SO_4^{2-}) or sulfide (HS^-) (Table 1).

Potassium is required by all organisms. Many enzymes, including some necessary for protein synthesis, require potassium for activity. Magnesium functions to stabilize ribosomes, membranes, and nucleic acids and is also required for the activity of many enzymes. Calcium helps stabilize cell walls in many microorganisms and plays a key role in the heat stability of endospores. Sodium is required by some but not all microorganisms and is typically a reflection of the habitat. For example, seawater contains relatively high levels of Na^+, and marine microorganisms usually require sodium for growth. By contrast, freshwater species are usually able to grow in the absence of sodium.

Iron and Trace Metals

Microorganisms require various metals for growth (Figure 1). Chief among these is iron, which plays a major role in cellular respiration. Iron is a key component of cytochromes and iron–sulfur proteins involved in electron transport reactions. Under anoxic conditions, iron is generally in the ferrous (Fe^{2+}) form and soluble. However, under oxic conditions, iron is typically in the ferric (Fe^{3+}) form in insoluble minerals. To obtain iron from such minerals, cells produce iron-binding agents called **siderophores** that bind iron and transport it into the cell. One major group of siderophores consists of derivatives of hydroxamic acid, which chelate ferric iron strongly (Figure 2a). Once the iron–hydroxamate complex has passed into the cell, the iron

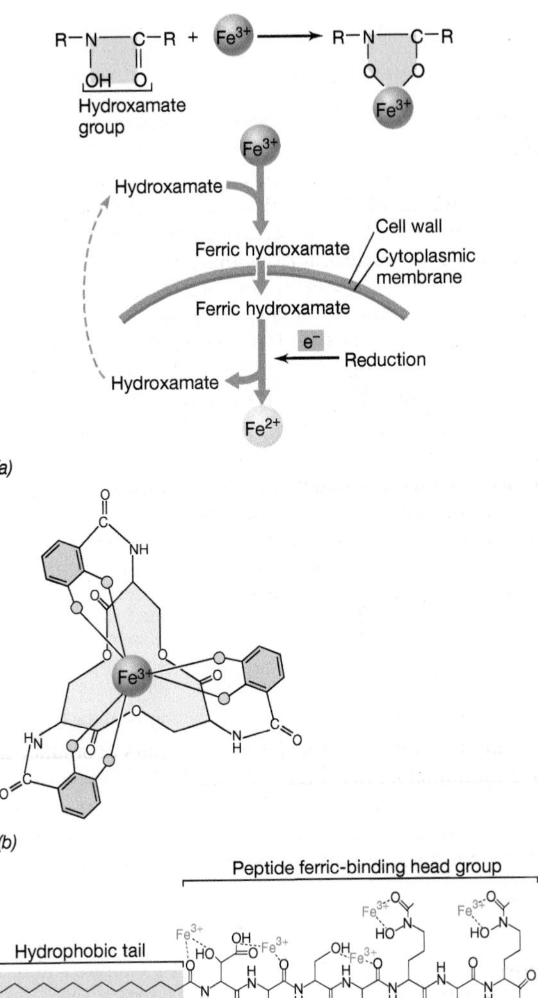

Figure 2 Iron-chelating agents produced by microorganisms. *(a)* Hydroxamate. Iron is bound as Fe^{3+} and released inside the cell as Fe^{2+}. The hydroxamate then exits the cell and repeats the cycle. *(b)* Ferric enterobactin of *Escherichia coli*. The oxygen atoms of each catechol molecule are shown in yellow. *(c)* The peptidic and tailed siderophore aquachelin, showing Fe^{3+} binding. The hydrophobic tail assists in threading aquachelin through the membrane into the cell.

Table 2 Micronutrients (trace elements) needed by microorganisms[a]

Element	*Cellular function*
Boron (B)	Present in an autoinducer for quorum sensing in bacteria; also found in some polyketide antibiotics
Chromium (Cr)	Required by mammals for glucose metabolism; microbial requirement possible but not proven
Cobalt (Co)	Vitamin B_{12}; transcarboxylase (propionic acid bacteria)
Copper (Cu)	Respiration, cytochrome *c* oxidase; photosynthesis, plastocyanin, some superoxide dismutases
Iron (Fe)[b]	Cytochromes; catalases; peroxidases; iron–sulfur proteins; oxygenases; all nitrogenases
Manganese (Mn)	Activator of many enzymes; present in certain superoxide dismutases and in the water-splitting enzyme in oxygenic phototrophs (photosystem II)
Molybdenum (Mo)	Certain flavin-containing enzymes; some nitrogenases, nitrate reductases, sulfite oxidases, DMSO-TMAO reductases; some formate dehydrogenases
Nickel (Ni)	Most hydrogenases; coenzyme F_{430} of methanogens; carbon monoxide dehydrogenase; urease
Selenium (Se)	Formate dehydrogenase; some hydrogenases; the amino acid selenocysteine
Tungsten (W)	Some formate dehydrogenases; oxotransferases of hyperthermophiles
Vanadium (V)	Vanadium nitrogenase; bromoperoxidase
Zinc (Zn)	Carbonic anhydrase; alcohol dehydrogenase; RNA and DNA polymerases; and many DNA-binding proteins

[a]Not every micronutrient listed is required by all cells; some metals listed are found in enzymes present in only specific microorganisms.
[b]Needed in greater amounts than other trace metals.

is released and the hydroxamate can be excreted and used again for iron transport.

Many other iron-binding agents are known. Some bacteria produce phenolic siderophores called *enterobactins* (Figure 2*b*). These siderophores are derivatives of the aromatic compound catechol and have an extremely high binding affinity for iron. Iron is present in the oceans at extremely low levels, often only a few picograms (1 picogram is 10^{-12} g) of iron per milliliter. To obtain this iron, many marine bacteria produce peptide siderophores such as aquachelin (Figure 2*c*) that can sequester iron present in these vanishingly small amounts. Peptide siderophores contain a peptide head group that complexes Fe^{3+} and a lipid tail that associates with the cytoplasmic membrane. Once aquachelin binds iron, the lipid tail helps transport it through the cytoplasmic membrane and into the cell.

As important as iron is for cells, some organisms can grow in the absence of iron. For example, the bacteria *Lactobacillus plantarum* and *Borrelia burgdorferii* (the latter is the causative agent of Lyme disease) do not contain detectable iron. In these bacteria, Mn^{2+} substitutes for iron as the metal component of enzymes that normally contain Fe^{2+}.

Table 3 Growth factors: Vitamins and their functions

Vitamin	*Function*
p-Aminobenzoic acid	Precursor of folic acid
Folic acid	One-carbon metabolism; methyl group transfer
Biotin	Fatty acid biosynthesis; β-decarboxylations; some CO_2 fixation reactions
Cobalamin (B_{12})	Reduction of and transfer of single carbon fragments; synthesis of deoxyribose
Lipoic acid	Transfer of acyl groups in decarboxylation of pyruvate and α-ketoglutarate
Nicotinic acid (niacin)	Precursor of NAD^+ (see Figure 11); electron transfer in oxidation-reduction reactions
Pantothenic acid	Precursor of coenzyme A; activation of acetyl and other acyl derivatives
Riboflavin	Precursor of FMN (see Figure 16), FAD in flavoproteins involved in electron transport
Thiamine (B_1)	α-Decarboxylations; transketolase
Vitamins B_6 (pyridoxal-pyridoxamine group)	Amino acid and keto acid transformations
Vitamin K group; quinones	Electron transport; synthesis of sphingolipids
Hydroxamates	Iron-binding compounds; solubilization of iron and transport into cell

Many other metals are required or otherwise metabolized by microorganisms (Figure 1). Like iron, these micronutrients are called *trace elements*. Micronutrients typically play a role as components of enzymes, the cells' catalysts (Section 5). Table 2 lists the major micronutrients and examples of enzymes in which each plays a role.

Growth Factors

Growth factors are organic compounds that share with trace metals the fact that they are required in only small amounts and then only by certain organisms. Growth factors include vitamins, amino acids, purines, and pyrimidines. Although most microorganisms are able to synthesize all of these compounds, some require one or more of them preformed from the environment and thus must be supplied with these compounds when cultured in the laboratory.

Vitamins are the most commonly required growth factors. Most vitamins function as coenzymes, and these are summarized in Table 3. Vitamin requirements vary among microorganisms, ranging from none to several. Lactic acid bacteria, which include the genera *Streptococcus*, *Lactobacillus*, and *Leuconostoc*, among others, are renowned for their many vitamin requirements, which are even more extensive than those of humans (see Table 4).

Table 4 Examples of culture media for microorganisms with simple and demanding nutritional requirements[a]

Defined culture medium for Escherichia coli	*Defined culture medium for* Leuconostoc mesenteroides	*Complex culture medium for either* E. coli *or* L. mesenteroides	*Defined culture medium for* Thiobacillus thioparus
K_2HPO_4 7 g	K_2HPO_4 0.6 g	Glucose 15 g	KH_2PO_4 0.5 g
KH_2PO_4 2 g	KH_2PO_4 0.6 g	Yeast extract 5 g	NH_4Cl 0.5 g
$(NH_4)_2SO_4$ 1 g	NH_4Cl 3 g	Peptone 5 g	$MgSO_4$ 0.1 g
$MgSO_4$ 0.1 g	$MgSO_4$ 0.1 g	KH_2PO_4 2 g	$CaCl_2$ 0.05 g
$CaCl_2$ 0.02 g	Glucose 25 g	Distilled water 1,000 ml	KCl 0.5 g
Glucose 4–10 g	Sodium acetate 25 g	pH 7	$Na_2S_2O_3$ 2 g
Trace elements (Fe, Co, Mn, Zn, Cu, Ni, Mo) 2–10 μg each	Amino acids (alanine, arginine, asparagine, aspartate, cysteine, glutamate, glutamine, glycine, histidine, isoleucine, leucine, lysine, methionine, phenylalanine, proline, serine, threonine, tryptophan, tyrosine, valine) 100–200 μg of each		Trace elements (same as *E. coli* recipe)
Distilled water 1,000 ml	Purines and pyrimidines (adenine, guanine, uracil, xanthine) 10 mg of each		Distilled water 1,000 ml
pH 7	Vitamins (biotin, folate, nicotinic acid, pyridoxal, pyridoxamine, pyridoxine, riboflavin, thiamine, pantothenate, *p*-aminobenzoic acid) 0.01–1 mg of each		pH 7
	Trace elements (see first column) 2–10 μg each		Carbon source CO_2 from air
	Distilled water 1,000 ml		
	pH 7		

[a]The photos are tubes of *(a)* the defined medium described, and *(b)* the complex medium described. Note how the complex medium is colored from the various organic extracts and digests that it contains. Photos courtesy of Cheryl L. Broadie and John Vercillo, Southern Illinois University at Carbondale.

1 MiniReview

Cells are made up primarily of H, O, C, N, P, and S; however, many other elements may be present as well. The hundreds of chemical compounds present inside a living cell are formed from available nutrients in the environment. Elements required in fairly large amounts are called macronutrients, whereas metals and organic compounds needed in very small amounts are called micronutrients (trace metals) and growth factors, respectively.

- What two classes of macromolecules contain the bulk of the nitrogen in a cell?
- Why is an element such as Co^{2+} considered a micronutrient whereas an element such as C is considered a macronutrient?
- What roles does iron play in cellular metabolism? How do cells sequester iron?

2 Culture Media

Culture media are the nutrient solutions used to grow microorganisms in the laboratory. Because laboratory culture is required for the detailed study of a microorganism, careful attention must be paid to both the selection and preparation of media for successful culture to take place.

Classes of Culture Media

Two broad classes of culture media are used in microbiology: **defined media** and **complex media** (Table 4). Defined media are prepared by adding precise amounts of highly purified inorganic or organic chemicals to distilled water. Therefore, the *exact* chemical composition of a defined medium is known. Of major importance in any culture medium is the carbon source, since all cells need large amounts of carbon to make new cell material. In a simple defined medium (Table 4), a single carbon source is usually present. The nature of the carbon source and its concentration depends on the organism to be cultured.

For growing many organisms, knowledge of the exact composition of a medium is not essential. In these instances complex media may suffice and may even be advantageous. Complex media employ digests of animal or plant products, such as casein (milk protein), beef (beef extract), soybeans (tryptic soy broth), yeast cells (yeast extract), or any of a number of other highly nutritious yet impure substances. These digests are commercially available in powdered form and can be quickly weighed and dissolved in distilled water to yield a medium. However, a major concession in using a complex medium is loss of control over its precise nutrient composition.

In particular situations, especially in clinical microbiology, culture media are often made to be selective or differential (or both). A *selective* medium contains compounds that selectively inhibit the growth of some microorganisms but not others. By contrast, a *differential* medium is one in which an indicator, typically a dye, is added that allows for the differentiation of particular chemical reactions that have occurred during growth. Differential media are quite useful for distinguishing between species of bacteria, some of which may carry out the particular reaction while others do not.

Nutritional Requirements and Biosynthetic Capacity

Table 4 lists four recipes for culture media, three defined and one complex. The complex medium is easiest to prepare and supports growth of both *Escherichia coli* and *Leuconostoc mesenteroides*. However, the simple defined medium shown in Table 4 supports growth of *E. coli* but not of *L. mesenteroides*. Growth of the latter organism, a nutritionally demanding bacterium, in defined medium requires the addition of several nutrients not needed by *E. coli* (Table 4). Which organism, *E. coli* or *L. mesenteroides*, has the greater biosynthetic capacity? Obviously, it is *E. coli*, because its ability to grow in a simple defined medium means that it can synthesize all of its organic constituents from a single carbon compound, in this case glucose (Table 4). By contrast, *L. mesenteroides* has multiple growth factor and other nutrient requirements, revealing its limited biosynthetic capacity. The nutritional needs of *L. mesenteroides* can be satisfied by preparing either a highly supplemented defined medium, a rather laborious undertaking because of all of the individual nutrients that need to be added (Table 4), or by preparing a complex medium, typically a much quicker operation.

Some pathogenic microorganisms have even more stringent nutritional requirements than those shown for *L. mesenteroides*. For culturing these organisms, an *enriched medium* may be needed. An enriched medium is a complex medium base to which additional nutrients, such as serum or whole blood, are added. These added nutrients better mimic conditions in the host and are required for the successful laboratory culture of some human pathogens such as *Streptococcus pyogenes* (strep throat) and *Neisseria gonorrhoeae* (gonorrhea).

The fourth medium shown in Table 4 is that for the sulfur chemolithotroph *Thiobacillus thioparus*. This organism is an autotroph and thus has no organic carbon requirements. *T. thioparus* derives all of its carbon from CO_2 and obtains its energy from the oxidation of the reduced sulfur compound thiosulfate ($Na_2S_2O_3$). Thus, *T. thioparus* has the greatest biosynthetic capacity of all of the organisms listed in Table 4, surpassing even *E. coli* in this regard.

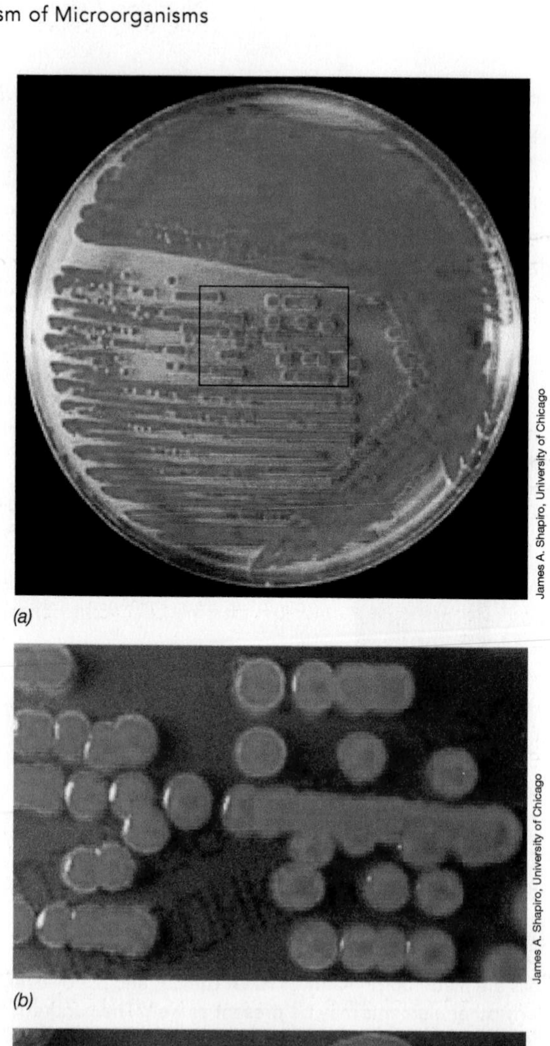

(a) James A. Shapiro, University of Chicago

(b) James A. Shapiro, University of Chicago

(c) James A. Shapiro, University of Chicago

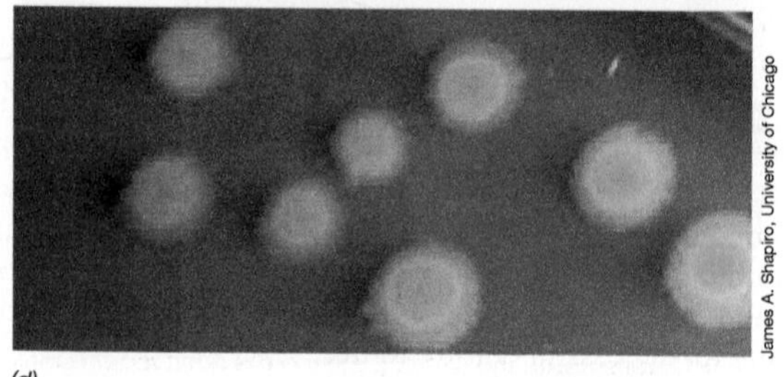

(d) James A. Shapiro, University of Chicago

Figure 3 Bacterial colonies. Colonies are visible masses of cells formed from the subsequent division of one or a few cells and can contain over a billion (10^9) individual cells. *(a) Serratia marcescens,* grown on MacConkey agar. *(b)* Close-up of colonies outlined in *(a)*. *(c) Pseudomonas aeruginosa*, grown on Trypticase soy agar. *(d) Shigella flexneri*, grown on MacConkey agar.

What does Table 4 tell us? Simply put, it tells us that different microorganisms can have vastly different nutritional requirements. Thus, for successful culture of any microorganism it is necessary to understand its nutritional requirements and then supply the nutrients in the proper form and in the proper proportions in a culture medium. If care is taken in preparing culture media, it is fairly easy to culture many different types of microorganisms in the laboratory. We discuss the procedures for culturing microorganisms next.

2 MiniReview

Culture media supply the nutritional needs of microorganisms and are either chemically defined or undefined (complex). "Selective," "differential," and "enriched" are the terms that describe media used for the isolation of particular species or for comparative studies of microorganisms.

- Why would the routine culture of *Leuconostoc mesenteroides* be easier in a complex medium than in a chemically defined medium?
- In which medium shown in Table 4, defined or complex, do you think *Escherichia coli* would grow the fastest? Why? Although they are both simple defined media, why wouldn't *E. coli* grow in the medium described for *Thiobacillus thioparus*?

3 Laboratory Culture of Microorganisms

Once a culture medium has been prepared and made **sterile** to render it free of all microorganisms, organisms can be inoculated (added to it) and the culture incubated under conditions that will support growth. In a laboratory, inoculation will typically be of a **pure culture,** a culture containing only a single kind of microorganism.

It is essential to prevent other organisms from entering a pure culture. Such unwanted organisms, called *contaminants,* are ubiquitous (as Pasteur discovered over 125 years ago), and microbiological techniques are designed to avoid contamination. A major method for obtaining pure cultures and for assessing the purity of a culture is the use of solid media, specifically, solid media prepared in the Petri plate, and we consider this now.

Solid versus Liquid Culture Media

Culture media are sometimes prepared in a semisolid form by the addition of a gelling agent to liquid media. Such solid culture media immobilize cells, allowing them to grow and form visible, isolated masses called *colonies* (Figure 3). Bacterial colonies can be of various shapes and sizes depending on the organism, the culture conditions, the nutrient supply, and several other physiological parameters. Some bacteria produce pigments that cause the colony to be colored (Figure 3). Colonies permit the microbiologist to visualize the purity of the culture. Plates that contain more than one colony type are indicative of a contaminated culture. The appearance and uniformity of colonies on a Petri plate has been used as one criterion of culture purity for over 100 years.

Solid media are prepared the same way as for liquid media except that before sterilization, agar is added as a gelling agent, usually at a concentration of about 1.5%. The agar melts during the sterilization process, and the molten medium is then poured into sterile glass or plastic plates and allowed to solidify before use (Figure 3). www.microbiologyplace.com **Online Tutorial 1: Aseptic Transfer and the Streak Plate Method**

Aseptic Technique

Because microorganisms are everywhere, culture media must be sterilized before use. Sterilization is typically achieved with moist heat in a large pressure cooker called an *autoclave*. We discuss the operation and principles of the autoclave later, along with other methods of sterilization.

Once a sterile culture medium has been prepared, it is ready to receive an inoculum from a previously grown pure culture to start the growth process once again. This manipulation requires the practice of **aseptic technique**, a series of steps to prevent contamination during manipulations of cultures and sterile culture media (Figures 4 and 5). A mastery of aseptic technique is required for success in the

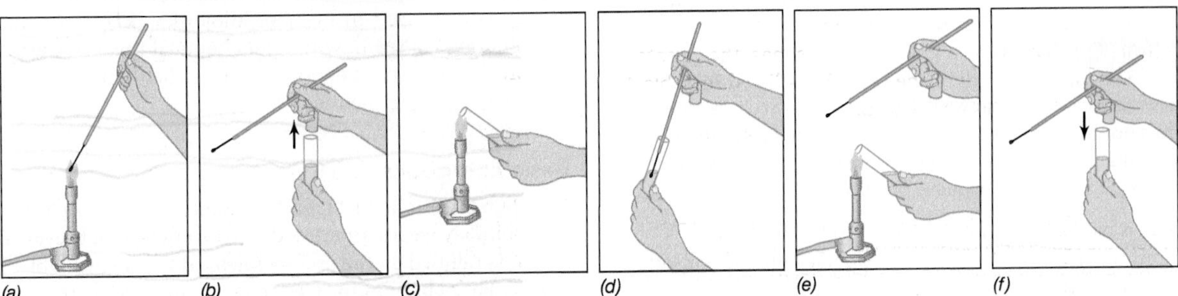

Figure 4 **Aseptic transfer.** *(a)* Loop is heated until red hot and cooled in air briefly. *(b)* Tube is uncapped. *(c)* Tip of tube is run through the flame. *(d)* Sample is removed on sterile loop and transferred to a sterile medium. *(e)* The tube is reflamed. *(f)* The tube is recapped. Loop is reheated before being taken out of service.

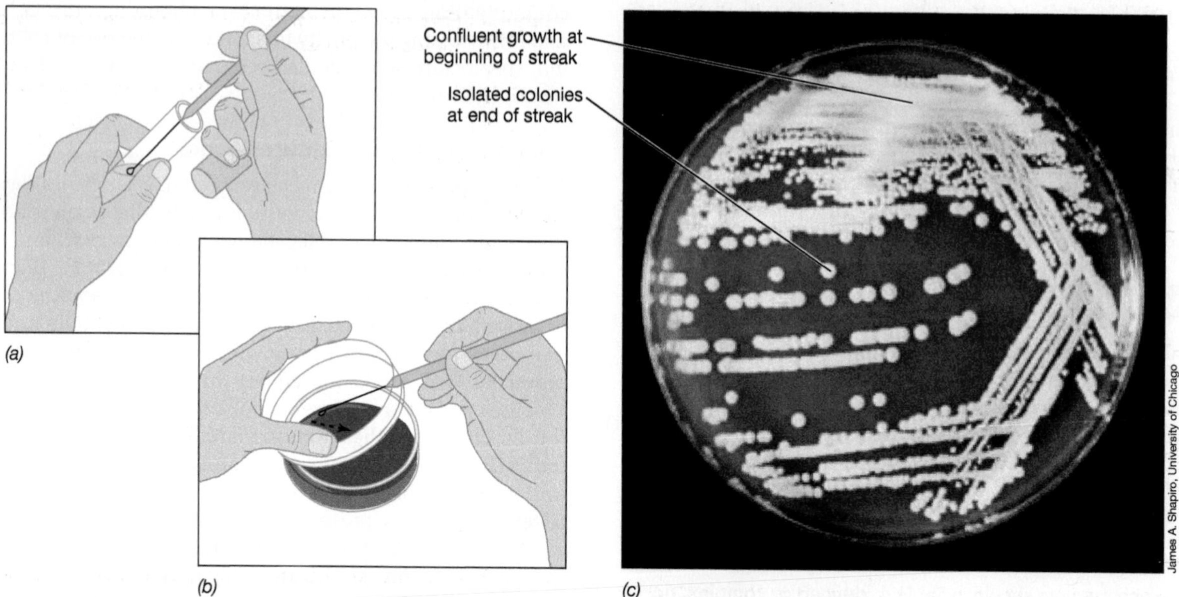

Figure 5 Method of making a streak plate to obtain pure cultures. *(a)* The loop is sterilized and a loopful of inoculum is removed from tube. *(b)* Streak is made and spread out on a sterile agar plate. Following the initial streak, subsequent streaks are made at angles to it, the loop being resterilized between streaks. *(c)* Appearance of a well-streaked plate after incubation. Colonies of the bacterium *Micrococcus luteus* on a blood agar plate. It is from such well-isolated colonies that pure cultures can usually be obtained.

microbiology laboratory, and it is one of the first methods learned by the novice microbiologist. Airborne contaminants are the most common problem because the dust in laboratory air contains microorganisms. When containers are opened, they must be handled in such a way that contaminant-laden air does not enter (Figures 4 and 5).

Aseptic transfer of a culture from one tube of medium to another is accomplished with an inoculating loop or needle that has previously been sterilized in a flame (Figure 4). Cells from liquid cultures can also be transferred to the surface of agar plates, where colonies develop from the growth and division of single cells (Figure 5). Picking an isolated colony and restreaking it is the main method for obtaining pure cultures from samples containing several different organisms.

3 MiniReview

Microorganisms can be grown in the laboratory in culture media containing the nutrients they require. Successful cultivation and maintenance of pure cultures of microorganisms can be done only if aseptic technique is practiced.

- What is meant by the word "sterile"? What would happen if freshly prepared culture media were not sterilized and left at room temperature?
- Why is aseptic technique necessary for successful cultivation of pure cultures in the laboratory?

II ENERGETICS AND ENZYMES

Regardless of how an organism makes a living, it must be able to conserve some of the energy released in its energy-yielding reactions. Here we discuss the principles of energy conservation, using some simple laws of chemistry and physics to guide our understanding. We then consider enzymes, the cell's biocatalysts.

4 Bioenergetics

Energy is defined as the ability to do work. In microbiology, energy is discussed in units of kilojoules (kJ), a measure of heat energy. We see now that all chemical reactions are associated with *changes* in energy, energy either being required for or released during the reaction.

Basic Energetics

Although in any chemical reaction some energy is lost as heat, in microbiology we are interested in **free energy** (abbreviated ***G***), which is defined as the energy released that is available to do work. The change in free energy during a reaction is expressed as $\Delta G^{0\prime}$, where the symbol Δ should be read "change in." The "0" and "prime" superscripts mean that the free-energy value is for standard conditions: pH 7, 25°C,

1 atmosphere of pressure, and all reactants and products at 1 M concentration.

Consider the reaction:

$$A + B \rightarrow C + D$$

If $\Delta G^{0\prime}$ for this reaction is *negative* in arithmetic sign, then the reaction will proceed with the release of free energy, energy that the cell may conserve as ATP. Such energy-yielding reactions are called **exergonic**. However, if $\Delta G^{0\prime}$ is *positive*, the reaction requires energy in order to proceed. Such reactions are called **endergonic**. Thus, exergonic reactions *yield* energy while endergonic reactions *require* energy.

Free Energy of Formation and Calculating $\Delta G^{0\prime}$

To calculate the free energy yield of a reaction, one first needs to know the free energy of its reactants and products. This is the free energy of formation (G_f^0), the energy released or required during the formation of a given molecule from the elements. Table 5 gives a few examples of G_f^0. By convention, the free energy of formation of the elements in their elemental and electrically neutral form (for instance, C, H_2, N_2) is zero. The free energies of formation of compounds, however, are not zero. If the formation of a compound from its elements proceeds exergonically, then the G_f^0 of the compound is negative (energy is released). If the reaction is endergonic, then the G_f^0 of the compound is positive (energy is required).

For most compounds G_f^0 is negative. This reflects the fact that compounds tend to form spontaneously (that is, with energy being released) from their elements. However, the positive G_f^0 for nitrous oxide (+104.2 kJ/mol, Table 5) indicates that this molecule will not form spontaneously. Instead, it will decompose spontaneously to nitrogen and oxygen. A more complete list can be found in physical chemistry handbooks.

Using free energies of formation, it is possible to calculate a very useful value: the *change* in free energy ($\Delta G^{0\prime}$) that occurs in a given reaction. For the reaction $A + B \rightarrow C + D$, $\Delta G^{0\prime}$ is calculated by subtracting the sum of the free energies of formation of the reactants (A + B) from that of the products (C + D). Thus:

$$\Delta G^{0\prime} = G_f^0[C + D] - G_f^0[A + B]$$

The $\Delta G^{0\prime}$ value obtained tells us whether the reaction is exergonic or endergonic. The phrase "products minus reactants" is a simple way to recall how to calculate changes in free energy during chemical reactions. However, it is first necessary to balance the reaction before free energy calculations can be made.

$\Delta G^{0\prime}$ versus ΔG

Although calculations of $\Delta G^{0\prime}$ are usually good estimates of actual free energy changes, under some circumstances they are not. We will see later that the actual concentrations of products and reactants in nature, which are rarely at 1 M levels, can alter the bioenergetics of reactions, sometimes in significant ways. Thus, what may be most relevant to a bioenergetic calculation is not $\Delta G^{0\prime}$, but ΔG, the free energy change that occurs under the actual conditions in which the organism is growing. ΔG is a form of the free energy equation that takes into account the actual concentrations of reactants and products in the reaction, and it is calculated as:

$$\Delta G = \Delta G^{0\prime} + RT \ln K$$

where R and T are physical constants and K is the equilibrium constant for the reaction in question. For now, we only need to focus on the expression $\Delta G^{0\prime}$ and what it tells us about a chemical reaction catalyzed by a particular microorganism. Only reactions that are exergonic are capable of yielding energy and thus supporting growth.

Table 5 Free energy of formation for a few compounds of biological interest

Compound	Free energy of formation[a]
Water (H_2O)	−237.2
Carbon dioxide (CO_2)	−394.4
Hydrogen gas (H_2)	0
Oxygen gas (O_2)	0
Ammonium (NH_4^+)	−79.4
Nitrous oxide (N_2O)	+104.2
Acetate ($C_2H_3O_2^-$)	−369.4
Glucose ($C_6H_{12}O_6$)	−917.3
Methane (CH_4)	−50.8
Methanol (CH_3OH)	−175.4

[a] The free energy of formation values (G_f^0) are in kJ/mol.

4 MiniReview

The chemical reactions of the cell are accompanied by changes in energy, expressed in kilojoules. A chemical reaction can occur with the release of free energy (exergonic) or with the consumption of free energy (endergonic).

- What is free energy?
- In general, are catabolic reactions exergonic or endergonic?
- Using the data in Table 5, calculate $\Delta G^{0\prime}$ for the reaction $CH_4 + \frac{1}{2}O_2 \rightarrow CH_3OH$. How does $\Delta G^{0\prime}$ differ from ΔG?
- Does glucose formation from the elements release or require energy?

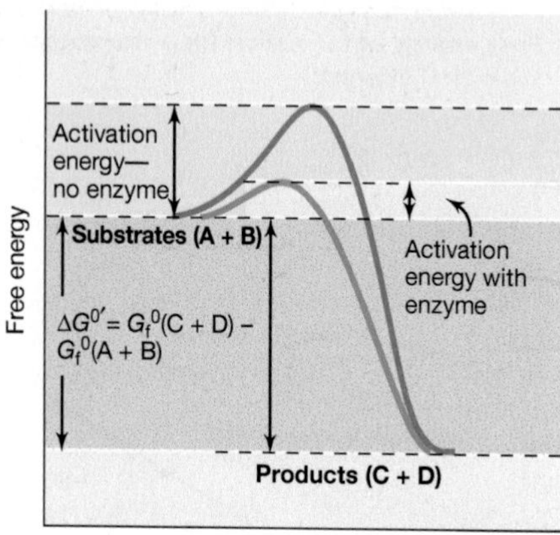

Figure 6 **Activation energy and catalysis.** Even chemical reactions that release energy may not proceed spontaneously because the reactants must first be activated. Once they are activated, the reaction proceeds spontaneously. Catalysts such as enzymes lower the required activation energy.

5 Catalysis and Enzymes

Free energy calculations only reveal whether energy is released or required in a given reaction. The value obtained says nothing about the *rate* of the reaction. Consider the formation of water from gaseous oxygen and hydrogen. The energetics of this reaction are quite favorable: $H_2 + \frac{1}{2}O_2 \rightarrow H_2O$ $\Delta G^{0\prime} = -237$ kJ. However, if we were to mix O_2 and H_2 together in a sealed bottle and leave it for years, no measurable formation of water would occur. This is because the bonding of oxygen and hydrogen atoms to form water requires that the chemical bonds of the reactants first be broken. The breaking of these bonds requires some energy, and this energy is called **activation energy**.

Activation energy is the energy required to bring all molecules in a chemical reaction into the reactive state. For a reaction that proceeds with a net release of free energy (that is, an exergonic reaction), the situation is as diagrammed in Figure 6. Although the activation energy barrier is virtually insurmountable in the absence of catalysis, in the presence of the proper catalyst it is much less formidable (Figure 6).

Enzymes

The concept of activation energy leads us to consider catalysis and enzymes. In biochemistry, a **catalyst** is a substance that lowers the activation energy of a reaction, thereby increasing the reaction rate. Catalysts facilitate reactions but are not consumed or transformed by them. Moreover, catalysts do not affect the energetics or the equilibrium of a reaction; catalysts affect only the rate at which reactions proceed.

Most cellular reactions would not proceed at appreciable rates without catalysis. Biological catalysts are called **enzymes**. Enzymes are proteins (or in a few cases, RNAs) that are highly specific in the reactions they catalyze. That is, each enzyme catalyzes only a single type of chemical reaction, or in the case of some enzymes, a single class of closely related reactions. This specificity is a function of the precise three-dimensional structure (as dictated by protein structure) of the enzyme molecule.

In an enzyme-catalyzed reaction, the enzyme combines with the reactant, called a *substrate* (S), forming an enzyme–substrate complex. Then, as the reaction proceeds, the *product* (P) is released and the enzyme (E) is returned to its original state:

$$E + S \leftrightarrow E\text{—}S \leftrightarrow E + P$$

The enzyme is generally much larger than the substrate(s), and binding of enzyme and substrate(s) typically relies on weak bonds, such as hydrogen bonds, van der Waals forces, and hydrophobic interactions. The portion of the enzyme to which substrate binds is called the *active site*, and the entire reaction from initial substrate binding to product release may take only a few milliseconds.

Enzyme Catalysis

The catalytic power of enzymes is remarkable. Enzymes increase the rate of chemical reactions anywhere from 10^8 to 10^{20} times the rate that would occur spontaneously. To catalyze a specific reaction, an enzyme must do two things: (1) bind its substrate and (2) position the substrate relative to the catalytically active amino acids in the enzyme's active site. The enzyme–substrate complex (Figure 7) aligns reactive groups and places strain on specific bonds in the substrate(s). The net result is a reduction in the activation energy required to make the reaction proceed from substrate(s) to product(s) (Figure 6). These steps are shown in Figure 7 for the glycolytic enzyme fructose bisphosphate aldolase (Section 10).

The particular reaction depicted in Figure 6 is exergonic because the free energy of formation of the substrates is greater than that of the products. However, enzymes can also catalyze reactions that require energy, converting energy-poor substrates into energy-rich products.

In these cases, however, not only must an activation energy barrier be overcome, but sufficient free energy must also be put into the reaction to raise the energy level of the substrates to that of the products. This is done by coupling the energy-*requiring* reaction to an energy-*yielding* one, such as the hydrolysis of ATP.

Theoretically, all enzymes are reversible in their activity. However, enzymes that catalyze highly exergonic or highly endergonic reactions are essentially unidirectional in their activity. If a particularly exergonic or endergonic reaction needs to be reversed, a different enzyme usually catalyzes the reverse reaction.

Structure and Nomenclature of Enzymes

Most enzymes are proteins, polymers of amino acids, and every protein has a specific three-dimensional shape. A given protein thus assumes specific binding and physical properties. The structure of an enzyme may be visualized in a space-fill-

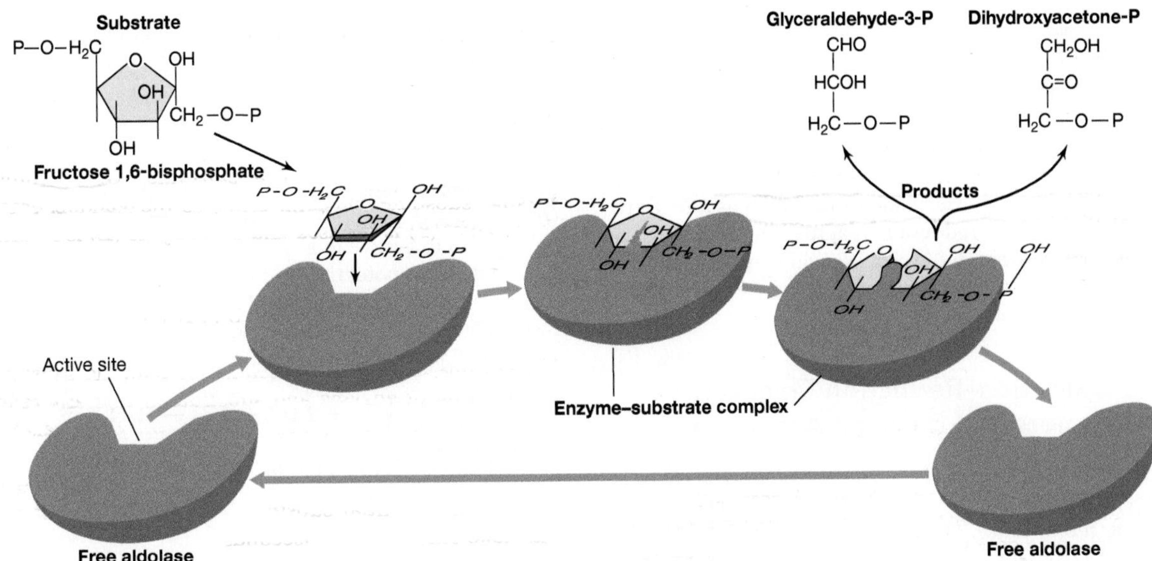

Figure 7 **The catalytic cycle of an enzyme.** The enzyme depicted here, fructose bisphosphate aldolase, catalyzes the reaction: fructose 1,6-bisphosphate → glyceraldehyde-3-phosphate + dihydroxyacetone phosphate in glycolysis. Following binding of fructose 1,6-bisphosphate in the formation of the enzyme–substrate complex, the conformation of the enzyme alters, placing strain on bonds of the substrate, which break and yield the two products.

ing model (Figure 8). In this example of the peptidoglycan-cleaving enzyme lysozyme, the large cleft is the site where the substrate binds (the active site). The active site of lysozyme binds peptidoglycan but does not bind other polysaccharides, even those whose structure may closely resemble peptidoglycan.

Many enzymes contain small nonprotein molecules that participate in catalysis but are not themselves substrates. These small molecules can be divided into two classes based on the way they associate with the enzyme: *prosthetic groups* and *coenzymes*. Prosthetic groups are bound very tightly to their enzymes, usually covalently and permanently. The heme group present in cytochromes (Section 11) is an example of a prosthetic group. **Coenzymes,** by contrast, are loosely bound to enzymes, and a single coenzyme molecule may associate with a number of different enzymes. Most coenzymes are derivatives of vitamins, and NAD^+/NADH is a good example, being a derivative of the vitamin niacin (Table 3).

Enzymes are named for either the substrate they bind or for the chemical reaction they catalyze, by addition of the suffix "-ase." Thus, cellulase is an enzyme that attacks cellulose, glucose oxidase is an enzyme that catalyzes the oxidation of glucose, and ribonuclease is an enzyme that decomposes ribonucleic acid. A more formal enzyme nomenclature system exists, in which a numbering system is used to classify enzymes according to the type of reaction they catalyze. However, for our purposes, enzyme names ending in "ase" are sufficient.

5 MiniReview

The reactants in a chemical reaction must first be activated before the reaction can take place, and this requires a catalyst. Enzymes are catalytic proteins that speed up the rate of biochemical reactions. Enzymes are highly specific in the reactions they catalyze, and this specificity resides in the three-dimensional structure of the polypeptide(s) in the protein.

- What is the function of a catalyst? What are enzymes made of?
- Where on an enzyme does the substrate bind?
- What is activation energy?

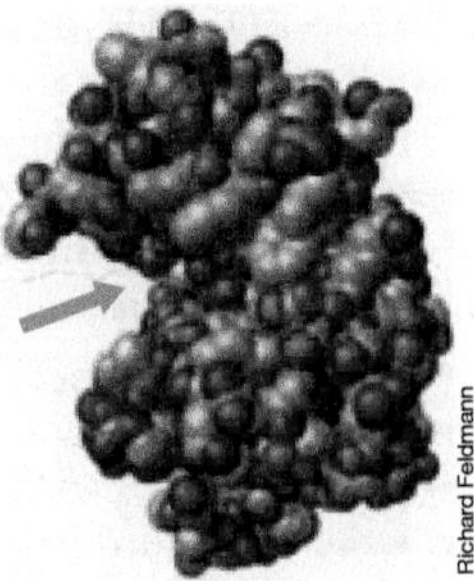

Figure 8 **Space-filling model of the enzyme lysozyme.** The substrate-binding site (the active site) is in the large cleft (arrow) on the left side of the model.

III OXIDATION–REDUCTION AND ENERGY-RICH COMPOUNDS

Energy is conserved in cells from oxidation–reduction (redox) reactions. The energy released in these reactions is conserved in the synthesis of energy-rich compounds, such as ATP. Here we consider oxidation–reduction reactions and the major electron carriers present in the cell. We will then examine the compounds that actually conserve the energy released in oxidation–reduction reactions.

6 Oxidation–Reduction Electron Donors and Electron Acceptors

An oxidation is the removal of an electron or electrons from a substance and a reduction is the addition of an electron or electrons to a substance. Oxidations and reductions can involve just electrons or an electron plus a proton (that is, a hydrogen atom).

Electron Donors and Electron Acceptors

Redox reactions occur in pairs. For example, hydrogen gas (H_2) can release electrons and protons and become oxidized:

$$H_2 \rightarrow 2\,e^- + 2\,H^+$$

However, electrons cannot exist alone in solution; they must be part of atoms or molecules. Thus, the equation as drawn does not itself represent an independent reaction. The reaction is only a *half reaction,* a term that implies the need for a second half reaction. This is because for any substance to be oxidized, another substance must be reduced. The oxidation of H_2 can be coupled to the reduction of many different substances, including O_2, in a second reaction:

$$\tfrac{1}{2}O_2 + 2\,e^- + 2\,H^+ \rightarrow H_2O$$

This half reaction, which is a reduction, when coupled to the oxidation of H_2, yields the following overall balanced reaction:

$$H_2 + \tfrac{1}{2}O_2 \rightarrow H_2O$$

In reactions of this type, we refer to the substance *oxidized,* in this case H_2, as the **electron donor,** and the substance *reduced,* in this case O_2, as the **electron acceptor** (Figure 9). The concept of electron donors and electron acceptors is very important in microbiology as it pervades all aspects of energy metabolism.

Reduction Potentials

Substances vary in their tendency to become oxidized or reduced. This tendency is expressed as the **reduction potential** (E_0', standard conditions) of the half reaction, measured in volts (V) in reference to a standard substance, H_2. By convention, reduction potentials are expressed for half reactions as *reductions* with reactions at pH 7, because the cytoplasm of most cells is neutral, or nearly so. Using these conventions, at pH 7 the E_0' of

$$\tfrac{1}{2}O_2 + 2\,H^+ + 2\,e^- \rightarrow H_2O$$

is +0.816 volt (V), and the E_0' of

$$2\,H^+ + 2\,e^- \rightarrow H_2$$

is −0.421 V. We will see shortly that these E_0' values mean that O_2 is an excellent electron acceptor and that H_2 is an excellent electron donor.

Oxidation–Reduction Couples

Substances can be either electron donors or electron acceptors under different circumstances, depending on the substances with which they react. The chemical constituents on each side of the arrow in half reactions can be thought of as representing a *redox couple,* such as $2\,H^+/H_2$ or $\tfrac{1}{2}O_2/H_2O$. By convention, when writing a redox couple, the oxidized form of the couple is always placed on the left, before the slash mark.

In constructing redox reactions from their constituent half reactions, the reduced substance of a redox couple whose E_0' is more negative donates electrons to the oxidized substance of a redox couple whose E_0' is more positive. Thus, in the couple $2\,H^+/H_2$ (E_0' – 0.42 V), H_2 has a greater tendency to donate electrons than do protons to accept them. On the other hand, in the couple $\tfrac{1}{2}O_2/H_2O$ (E_0' + 0.82 V), H_2O has a very weak tendency to donate electrons, whereas O_2 has a great tendency to accept them. It follows then that in a reaction of H_2 and O_2, H_2 will be the electron donor and become oxidized, and O_2 will be the electron acceptor and become reduced (Figure 9).

As previously mentioned, by convention in electrochemistry all half reactions are written as *reductions*. However, in an actual redox reaction, the half reaction with the more negative E_0' proceeds as an oxidation and is therefore written in the

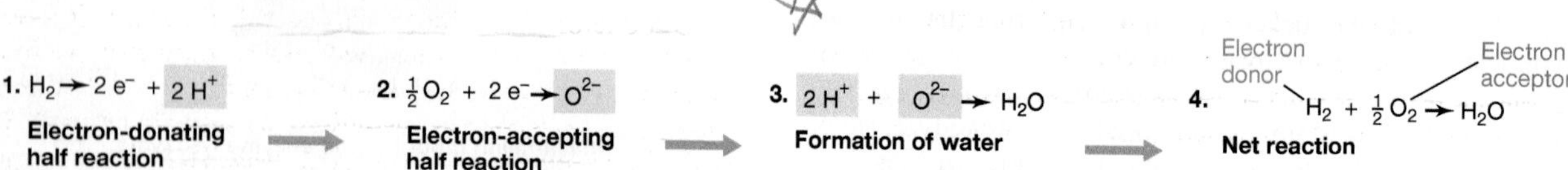

Figure 9 **Example of an oxidation–reduction reaction.** The formation of H_2O from the electron donor H_2 and the electron acceptor O_2.

opposite direction. Thus, in the reaction shown in Figure 9, the oxidation of H_2 to 2 H^+ + 2 e^- is reversed from its formal half reaction, written as a reduction.

The Redox Tower

A convenient way of viewing electron transfer reactions in biological systems and their importance to bioenergetics is to imagine a vertical tower (Figure 10). The tower represents the range of reduction potentials possible for redox couples in nature, from those with the most negative on the top to those with the most positive at the bottom; thus, we can call the tower a *redox tower*. The *reduced* substance in the redox couple at the top of the tower has the greatest tendency to donate electrons, whereas the *oxidized* substance in the redox couple at the bottom of the tower has the greatest tendency to accept electrons.

Using the tower analogy, imagine electrons from an electron donor near the top of the tower falling and being "caught" by electron acceptors at various levels. The difference in reduction potential between the donor and acceptor redox couples is expressed as $\Delta E_0'$. The farther the electrons drop from a donor before they are caught by an acceptor, the greater the amount of energy released. That is, $\Delta E_0'$ is proportional to $\Delta G^{0\prime}$ (Figure 10). Oxygen (O_2), at the bottom of the redox tower, is the strongest naturally occurring electron acceptor. In the middle of the redox tower, redox couples can be either electron donors or acceptors depending on which redox couples they react with. For instance, the 2 H^+/H_2 couple (−0.42 V) can react with the fumarate/succinate (+0.02 V), NO_3^-/NO_2^- (+0.42 V), or $\frac{1}{2}O_2/H_2O$ (+0.82 V) couples, with increasing amounts of energy being released, respectively (Figure 10).

Electron donors used in energy metabolism are also called *energy sources* because energy is released when they are oxidized (Figure 10). Many potential electron donors exist in nature, including a wide variety of organic and inorganic compounds. However, it should be understood that it is not the electron donor per se that contains energy but the chemical reaction in which the electron donor participates that actually releases energy. The presence of a suitable electron acceptor is just as important as the presence of a suitable electron donor. Lacking one or the other, the energy releasing reaction cannot proceed.

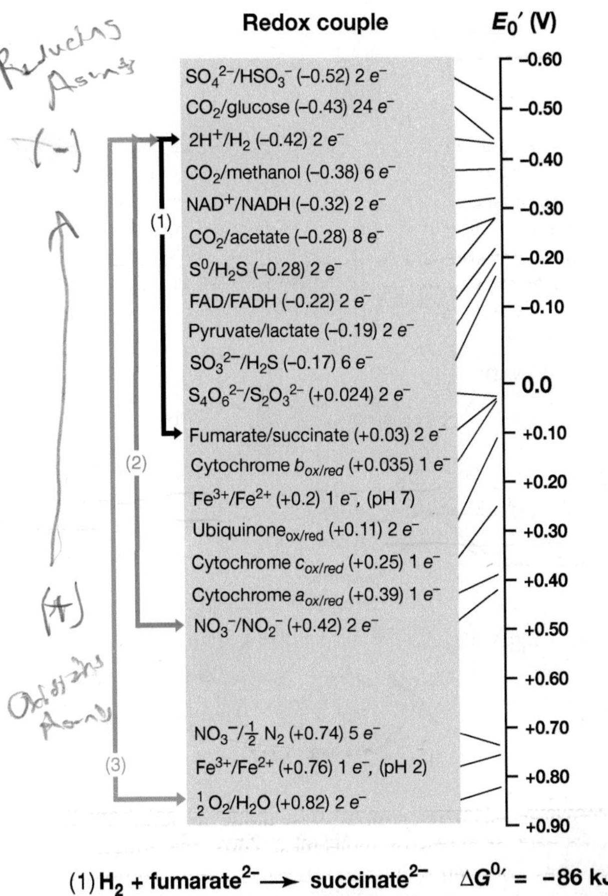

(1) H_2 + fumarate^{2-} → succinate^{2-} $\Delta G^{0\prime}$ = −86 kJ

(2) H_2 + NO_3^- → NO_2^- + H_2O $\Delta G^{0\prime}$ = −163 kJ

(3) H_2 + $\frac{1}{2}$ O_2 → H_2O $\Delta G^{0\prime}$ = −237 kJ

Figure 10 The redox tower. Redox couples are arranged from the strongest reductants (negative reduction potential) at the top to the strongest oxidants (positive reduction potentials) at the bottom. As electrons are donated from the top of the tower, they can be "caught" by acceptors at various levels. The farther the electrons fall before they are caught, the greater the difference in reduction potential between electron donor and electron acceptor and the more energy is released. As an example of this, the differences in energy released when a single electron donor, H_2, reacts with any of three different electron acceptors, fumarate, nitrate, and oxygen is shown.

6 MiniReview

Oxidation–reduction reactions require electron donors and electron acceptors. The tendency of a compound to accept or release electrons is expressed quantitatively by its reduction potential, E_0'.

- In the reaction $H_2 + \frac{1}{2}O_2 \rightarrow H_2O$, what is the electron donor and what is the electron acceptor?
- What is the E_0' of the 2 H^+/H_2 couple? Are protons good electron acceptors? Why or why not?
- Why is nitrate (NO_3^-) a better electron acceptor than fumarate?

7 NAD as a Redox Electron Carrier

Redox reactions in microbial cells typically involve reactions between one or more intermediates called *carriers*. Electron carriers can be divided into two classes: those that are freely diffusible (coenzymes) and those that are firmly attached to enzymes in the cytoplasmic membrane (prosthetic groups). The fixed carriers function in membrane-associated electron transport reactions and are discussed in Section 11. Common diffusible carriers include the coenzymes nicotinamide-adenine dinucleotide (NAD^+) and NAD-phosphate ($NADP^+$)

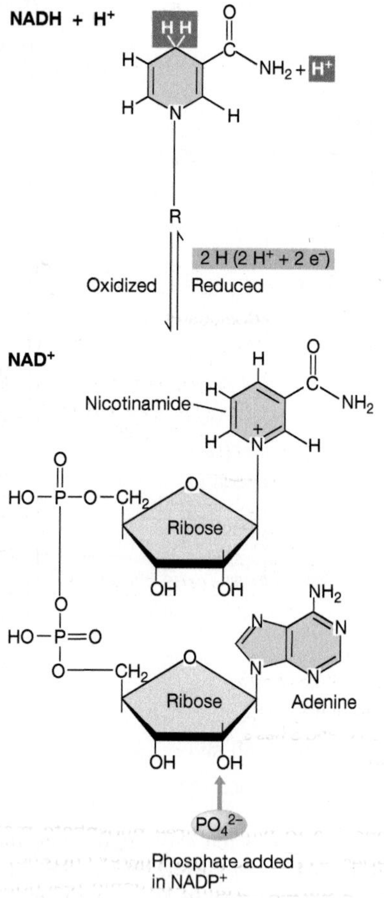

Figure 11 The oxidation–reduction coenzyme nicotinamide adenine dinucleotide (NAD^+). In $NADP^+$, a phosphate group is present, as indicated. Both NAD^+ and $NADP^+$ undergo oxidation–reduction as shown, are freely diffusible, and are $2e^- + 2H^+$ carriers. "R" in the top portion of the art is the adenine dinucleotide portion of NAD^+, shown in full in the bottom portion of the figure.

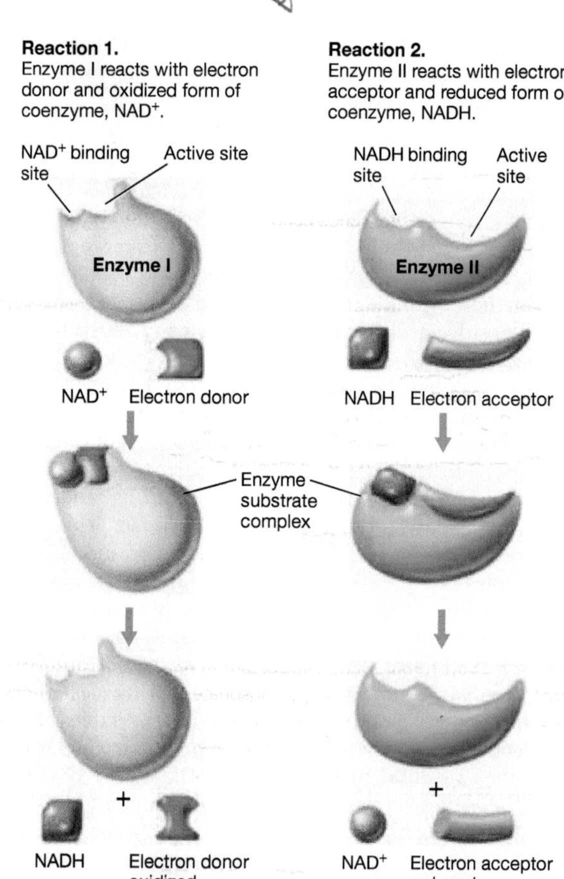

Figure 12 NAD^+/NADH cycling. A schematic example of a redox reaction requiring two different enzymes, linked by their use of a common coenzyme.

(Figure 11). NAD^+ and $NADP^+$ are electron plus proton carriers, transporting $2e^-$ and $2H^+$ at a time.

The reduction potential of the NAD^+/NADH (or $NADP^+$/NADPH) couple is –0.32 V, which places it fairly high on the electron tower; that is, NADH (or NADPH) is a good electron donor (Figure 10). However, although the NAD^+ and $NADP^+$ couples have the same reduction potentials, they typically function in different capacities in the cell. NAD^+/NADH play roles in energy-generating (catabolic) reactions, whereas $NADP^+$/NADPH play roles in biosynthetic (anabolic) reactions.

NAD/NADH Cycling

Coenzymes increase the diversity of redox reactions possible in a cell by allowing chemically dissimilar electron donors and acceptors to interact, the coenzyme acting as the intermediary. With NAD^+/NADH, for example, electrons removed from an electron donor can reduce NAD^+ to NADH, and the latter can be converted back to NAD^+ by donating electrons to the electron acceptor. Figure 12 shows an example of electron shuttling by NAD^+/NADH. In the reaction, NAD^+ and NADH facilitate the redox reaction without being consumed in the process. Thus, unlike the primary electron donor (the substance that was oxidized to yield NADH) or acceptor (such as O_2), where relatively large amounts of each are required, the cell needs only a tiny amount of NAD^+ and NADH because they are constantly being recycled. All that is needed is an amount sufficient to service the redox enzymes in the cell that use these coenzymes in their reaction mechanisms (Figure 12).

7 MiniReview

The transfer of electrons from donor to acceptor in a cell typically involves electron carriers. Some electron carriers are membrane-bound, whereas others, such as NAD^+/NADH, are freely diffusible coenzymes.

- Review Figure 10. Is NADH a better electron donor than H_2? Is NAD^+ a better acceptor than H^+? How do you determine this?

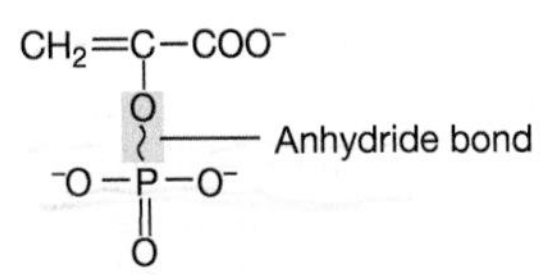

Compound	$G^{0'}$ kJ/mol
$\Delta G^{0'}$ > 30kJ	
Phosphoenolpyruvate	−51.6
1,3-Bisphosphoglycerate	−52.0
Acetyl phosphate	−44.8
ATP	−31.8
ADP	−31.8
Acetyl CoA	−31
$\Delta G^{0'}$ < 30kJ	
AMP	−14.2
Glucose 6-phosphate	−13.8

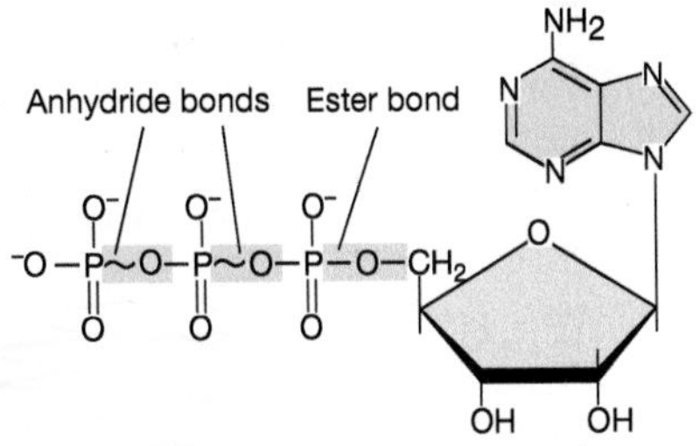

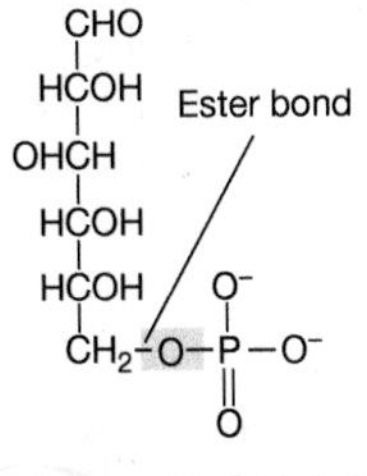

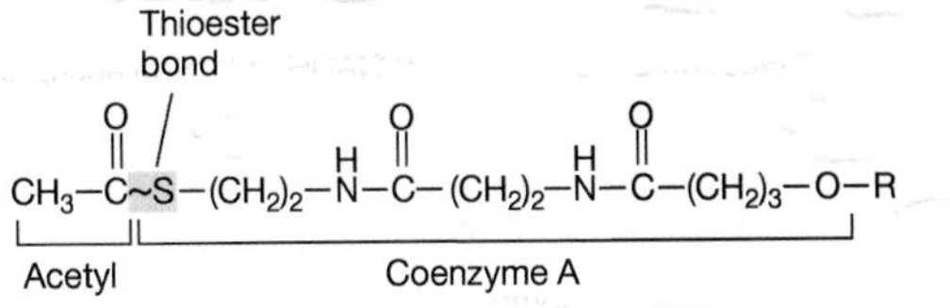

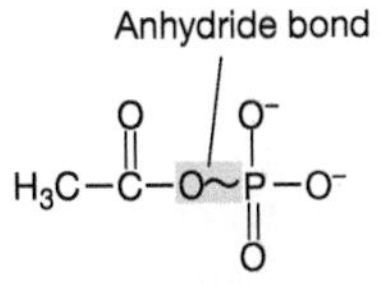

Figure 13 **Some compounds important in energy transformations in cells.** The table shows the free energy of hydrolysis of some of the key phosphate esters and anhydrides, indicating that some of the phosphate ester bonds are more energy-rich than others. Structures of four of the compounds show the position of ester and anhydride bonds. ATP contains three phosphates, but only two of them have free energies of hydrolysis >30 kJ. Also shown is the structure of the coenzyme acetyl-CoA. The thioester bond between C and S has a free energy of hydrolysis of >30 kJ. The "R" group of acetyl-CoA is a 3′ phospho ADP group.

8 Energy-Rich Compounds and Energy Storage

Energy released from redox reactions must be conserved by the cell if it is to be used to drive energy-requiring cell functions. In living organisms, chemical energy released in redox reactions is conserved primarily in the form of certain phosphorylated compounds that are energy rich. The free energy released upon hydrolysis of the phosphate in energy-rich compounds is significantly greater than that of the average covalent bond in the cell.

Phosphate can be bonded to organic compounds by either ester or anhydride bonds, as illustrated in Figure 13. However, not all phosphate bonds are energy-rich. As seen, the $\Delta G^{0'}$ of hydrolysis of the phosphate *ester* bond in glucose 6-phosphate is only −13.8 kJ/mol. By contrast, the $\Delta G^{0'}$ of hydrolysis of the phosphate *anhydride* bond in phosphoenolpyruvate is −51.6 kJ/mol, almost four times that of glucose 6-phosphate. Although either compound could be hydrolyzed to yield energy, cells typically use a small group of compounds whose $\Delta G^{0'}$ of hydrolysis is greater than −30 kJ/mol as energy "currencies" in the cell (Figure 13). Thus, phosphoenolpyruvate is energy-rich and glucose 6-phosphate is not (Figure 13).

Adenosine Triphosphate (ATP)

The most important energy-rich phosphate compound in cells is **adenosine triphosphate (ATP)**. ATP consists of the ribonucleoside adenosine to which three phosphate molecules are bonded in series. ATP is the prime energy currency in all cells, being generated during certain exergonic reactions and consumed in certain endergonic reactions. From the structure of ATP (Figure 13) it can be seen that two of the phosphate bonds are phosphoanhydrides and thus have free energies of hydrolysis greater than 30 kJ. Thus the reactions ATP → ADP + P_i and ADP → AMP + P_i each release roughly 32 kJ/mol of energy. By contrast, AMP is not energy-rich because its free energy of hydrolysis is only about half that of ADP or ATP (Figure 13).

Although the energy released in ATP hydrolysis is −32 kJ, a caveat must be introduced here to more precisely define the energy requirements for the synthesis of ATP. In an actively growing cell, the ratio of ATP to ADP is maintained near 1,000. This major deviation from equilibrium significantly affects the energy requirements for ATP synthesis. In such a cell, the actual energy expenditure (that is, the ΔG, Section 4) for the synthesis of one mole of ATP is on the order of −55 to −60 kJ. Nevertheless, for the purposes of learning and applying the basic principles of bioenergetics, we will consider reactions to conform to "standard conditions" ($\Delta G^{0'}$) and thus the energy required for synthesis or hydrolysis of ATP to be the same, 32 kJ/mol.

Coenzyme A

In addition to energy-rich phosphate compounds, cells can produce other energy-rich compounds. These include, in particular, derivatives of *coenzyme A* (for example, acetyl-CoA;

see structure in Figure 13). Coenzyme A derivatives contain thioester bonds. Upon hydrolysis, these yield sufficient free energy to drive the synthesis of an energy-rich phosphate bond. For example, in the reaction

$$\text{acetyl-S-CoA} + H_2O + ADP + P_i \rightarrow \text{acetate}^- + \text{HS-CoA} + ATP + H^+$$

the energy released in the hydrolysis of coenzyme A is conserved in the synthesis of ATP. Coenzyme A derivatives (acetyl-CoA is just one of many) are especially important to the energetics of anaerobic microorganisms, in particular those whose energy metabolism depends on fermentation.

Long-Term Energy Storage

ATP is a dynamic molecule in the cell; it is continuously being broken down to drive anabolic reactions and resynthesized at the expense of catabolic reactions. For longer-term energy storage, microorganisms typically produce insoluble polymers that can be oxidized later for the production of ATP.

Examples of energy storage polymers in prokaryotes include glycogen, poly-β-hydroxybutyrate and other polyhydroxyalkanoates, and elemental sulfur, stored from the oxidation of H_2S by sulfur chemolithotrophs. These polymers are deposited within the cell as large granules that can be seen with the light or electron microscope. In eukaryotic microorganisms, polyglucose in the form of starch or lipids in the form of simple fats are the major reserve materials. In the absence of an external energy source, cells can break down these polymers in order to make new cell material or to supply the very low amount of energy needed to maintain cell integrity, called *maintenance energy*, when in a nongrowing state.

8 MiniReview

The energy released in redox reactions is conserved in the formation of compounds that contain energy-rich phosphate or sulfur bonds. The most common of these compounds is ATP, the prime energy carrier in the cell. Longer-term storage of energy is linked to the formation of polymers, which can be consumed to yield ATP.

- How much energy is released per mole of ATP converted to ADP + P_i? Per mole of AMP converted to adenosine and P_i?
- During periods of nutrient abundance, how can cells prepare for periods of nutrient starvation?

IV ESSENTIALS OF CATABOLISM

We now consider some key catabolic reactions in the cell and how energy released in these reactions is conserved in microorganisms. We begin with fermentation and respiration and then examine how the proton motive force is generated. We end with a review of catabolic diversity, a major feature of microorganisms, in particular prokaryotes.

9 Energy Conservation

Two reaction series are linked to energy conservation in chemoorganotrophs: **fermentation** and **respiration**. In both forms of energy conservation, ATP synthesis is coupled to energy release in oxidation–reduction reactions. However, the redox reactions that occur in fermentation and respiration differ significantly. In fermentation the redox process occurs in the absence of exogenous electron acceptors. In respiration, on the other hand, molecular oxygen or some other exogenous electron acceptor serves as a terminal electron acceptor. As we will see, this lack of an exogenous electron acceptor in fermentation places severe constraints on the yield of energy obtained.

Substrate-Level Phosphorylation and Oxidative Phosphorylation

Fermentation and respiration differ in the mechanism by which ATP is synthesized. In fermentation, ATP is produced by **substrate-level phosphorylation**. In this process, ATP is synthesized directly from an energy-rich intermediate during steps in the catabolism of the fermentable compound (Figure 14a). This is in contrast to **oxidative phosphorylation**, in which ATP is produced at the expense of the proton motive force (Figure 14*b*). A third form of ATP synthesis, **photophosphorylation**, occurs in phototrophic organisms. We will see later that both photophosphorylation and oxidative phosphorylation rely on the proton motive force to drive ATP synthesis. In fermentation, by contrast, the proton motive force is not involved.

9 MiniReview

Fermentation and respiration are the two means by which chemoorganotrophs can conserve energy from the oxidation of organic compounds. During these catabolic reactions, ATP is synthesized by either substrate-level phosphorylation (fermentation) or oxidative phosphorylation (respiration).

- Which form(s) of ATP synthesis requires cytoplasmic membrane participation? Why?
- How does substrate-level phosphorylation differ from oxidative phosphorylation?

10 Glycolysis as an Example of Fermentation

The substance fermented in a fermentation is both the electron donor and electron acceptor. Not all substances can be fermented; fatty acids, for example, are too reduced to be fermentable. However, many compounds can be fermented, and sugars, especially hexoses such as glucose, are excellent examples. A common pathway for the fermentation

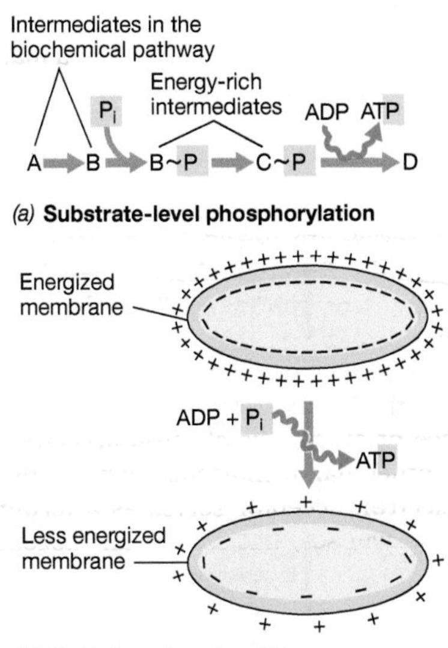

(a) **Substrate-level phosphorylation**

(b) **Oxidative phosphorylation**

Figure 14 **Energy conservation in fermentation and respiration.** *(a)* In fermentation, substrate-level phosphorylation produces ATP. *(b)* In respiration, the cytoplasmic membrane, energized by the proton motive force, dissipates some of that energy in the formation of ATP from ADP plus inorganic phosphate (P_i) by oxidative phosphorylation. The proton motive force is coupled to ATP synthesis by way of ATP synthase (ATPase, see Figure 21).

of glucose is **glycolysis**, also called the *Embden–Meyerhof pathway* for its major discoverers.

Glycolysis is an anaerobic process and can be divided into three stages, each involving a series of enzymatic reactions (Figure 15). Stage I comprises "preparatory" reactions; these are not redox reactions and do not release energy but lead to the production of two molecules of a key intermediate, glyceraldehyde 3-phosphate, from glucose. In Stage II, redox reactions occur, energy is conserved in the form of ATP, and two molecules of pyruvate are formed. In Stage III, redox reactions occur once again and *fermentation products* are formed (Figure 15).

Stage I: Preparatory Reactions

In Stage I, glucose is phosphorylated by ATP, yielding glucose 6-phosphate. The latter is then converted to fructose 6-phosphate. A second phosphorylation leads to the production of fructose 1,6-bisphosphate. The enzyme aldolase splits fructose 1,6-bisphosphate into two 3-carbon molecules, *glyceraldehyde 3-phosphate* and its isomer, *dihydroxyacetone phosphate,* which can be converted into glyceraldehyde 3-phosphate. Note that thus far, all of the reactions, including the consumption of ATP, have proceeded without redox reactions.

Stage II: The Production of NADH, ATP, and Pyruvate

The first redox reaction of glycolysis occurs in Stage II during the oxidation of glyceraldehyde 3-phosphate to 1,3-bisphosphoglyceric acid. In this reaction (which occurs twice, once for each of the two molecules of glyceraldehyde 3-phosphate produced from glucose), the enzyme glyceraldehyde-3-phosphate dehydrogenase reduces NAD^+ to NADH. Simultaneously, each glyceraldehyde-3-phosphate molecule is phosphorylated by the addition of a molecule of inorganic phosphate. This reaction, in which inorganic phosphate is converted to organic form, sets the stage for energy conservation. ATP formation is possible because 1,3-bisphosphoglyceric acid is an energy-rich compound (Figure 13). The synthesis of ATP occurs (1) when each molecule of 1,3-bisphosphoglyceric acid is converted to 3-phosphoglyceric acid, and (2) when each molecule of phosphoenolpyruvate is converted to pyruvate (Figure 15).

At this point in glycolysis, *two* ATP molecules have been consumed (in Stage I) and *four* ATP molecules have been synthesized in the reactions of Stage II (Figure 15). Thus, the net energy yield in glycolysis is *two* molecules of ATP per molecule of glucose fermented.

Stage III: Consumption of NADH and the Production of Fermentation Products

During the formation of two 1,3-bisphosphoglyceric acid, two NAD^+ are reduced to NADH (Figure 15). However, as previously discussed (Section 7 and Figure 12), NAD^+ is only an electron shuttle, not a terminal electron acceptor. Thus, the NADH produced from NAD^+ in glycolysis must be oxidized back to NAD^+ in order for glycolysis to continue, and this is accomplished by enzymes that reduce pyruvate to fermentation products (Figure 15). In the fermentation of yeast, pyruvate is reduced by NADH to ethanol with the subsequent production of CO_2. By contrast, in lactic acid bacteria pyruvate is reduced by NADH to lactate (Figure 15). Many other possibilities for pyruvate reduction in glycolysis are possible, but the net result is always the same: NADH is reoxidized to NAD^+ during the process.

In any energy-yielding process, oxidations must balance reductions, and there must be an electron acceptor for each electron removed. In this example, the reduction of NAD^+ at one enzymatic step in glycolysis is balanced by the oxidation of NADH at another. The final product(s) must also be in redox and atomic balance with the starting substrate, glucose. Hence, the fermentation products discussed here, ethanol plus CO_2, or lactate plus protons, are in both electrical and atomic balance with the starting substrate, glucose (Figure 15).

Glucose Fermentation: Net and Practical Results

During glycolysis glucose is consumed, two ATPs are made, and fermentation products are generated. For the organism the crucial product is ATP, which is used in a wide variety of energy-requiring reactions, and fermentation products are merely waste products. However, the latter substances are hardly considered waste products by the distiller, the brewer, the cheese maker, or the baker (see the Microbial Sidebar, "The Products of Yeast Fermentation and the Pasteur Effect"). Thus, fermentation is more than just an energy-yielding

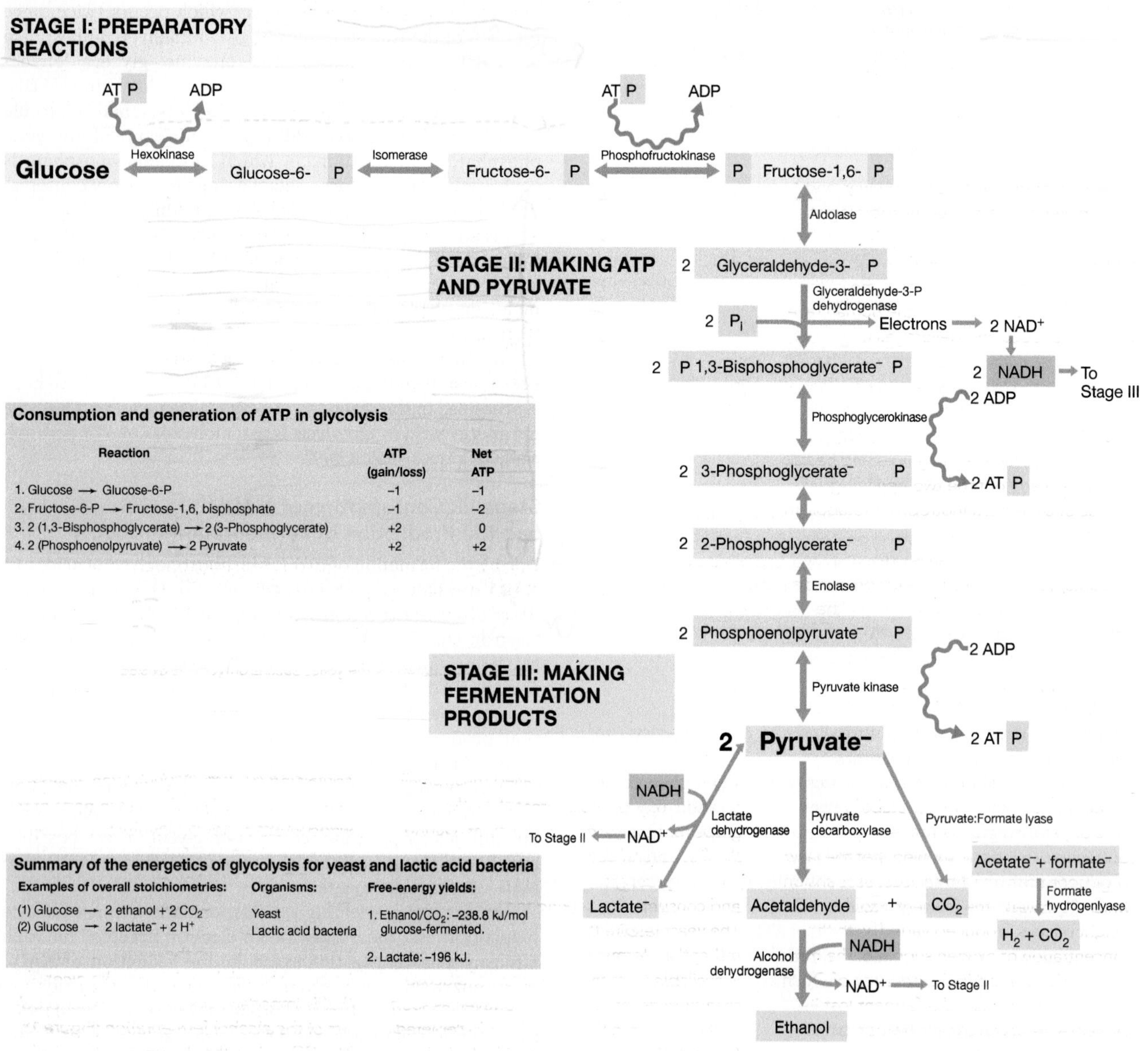

Consumption and generation of ATP in glycolysis

Reaction	ATP (gain/loss)	Net ATP
1. Glucose → Glucose-6-P	–1	–1
2. Fructose-6-P → Fructose-1,6, bisphosphate	–1	–2
3. 2 (1,3-Bisphosphoglycerate) → 2 (3-Phosphoglycerate)	+2	0
4. 2 (Phosphoenolpyruvate) → 2 Pyruvate	+2	+2

Summary of the energetics of glycolysis for yeast and lactic acid bacteria

Examples of overall stoichiometries:	Organisms:	Free-energy yields:
(1) Glucose → 2 ethanol + 2 CO_2	Yeast	1. Ethanol/CO_2: –238.8 kJ/mol glucose-fermented.
(2) Glucose → 2 lactate⁻ + 2 H^+	Lactic acid bacteria	2. Lactate: –196 kJ.

Figure 15 Embden–Meyerhof pathway (glycolysis). The sequence of reactions in the conversion of glucose to pyruvate and then to fermentation products (enzymes are shown in small type). The product of aldolase is actually glyceraldehyde 3-P and dihydroxyacetone P, but the latter is converted to glyceraldehyde 3-P. Note how pyruvate is the central "hub" of glycolysis—all fermentation products are made from pyruvate, and just a few common examples are given.

process. It is also a means of producing natural products useful to humans.

10 MiniReview

Glycolysis is a major pathway of fermentation and is a widespread means of anaerobic metabolism. The end result of glycolysis is the release of a small amount of energy that is conserved as ATP and the production of fermentation products. For each glucose consumed in glycolysis, two ATPs are produced.

- Which reaction(s) in glycolysis involve oxidations and reductions?
- What is the role of NAD^+/NADH in glycolysis?
- Why are fermentation products made during glycolysis?

Microbial Sidebar

The Products of Yeast Fermentation and the Pasteur Effect

Every home wine maker, brewer, and baker is an amateur microbiologist, perhaps without even realizing it. Indeed, the anaerobic processes of energy generation are at the heart of some of the most striking discoveries of the human race: fermented foods and beverages (**Figure 1**).

In the production of breads and most alcoholic beverages, the yeast *Saccharomyces cerevisiae* is exploited to produce ethanol plus CO_2. Found in various sugar-rich environments such as fruit juices and nectar, yeasts can carry out the two opposing modes of chemoorganotrophic metabolism discussed in this chapter, *fermentation* and *respiration*. When oxygen is present in high amounts, yeast grows efficiently on various sugars, making yeast cells and CO_2 (the latter from the citric acid cycle, Section 13) in the process. However, when conditions are anoxic, yeasts switch to fermentative metabolism. This results in a reduced cell yield but significant amounts of alcohol and CO_2.

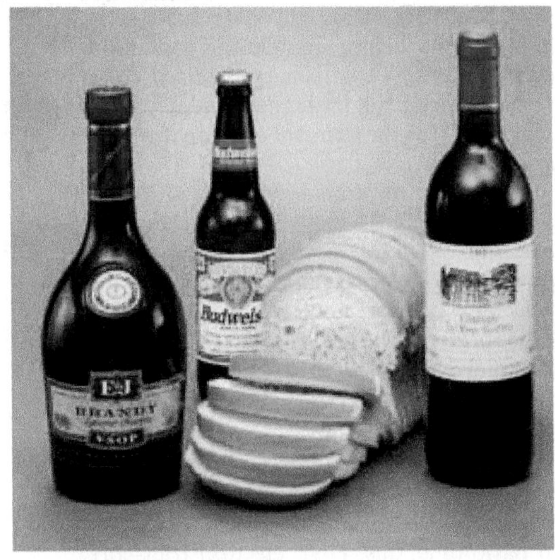

Figure 1 *Major products in which fermentation by the yeast* Saccharomyces cerevisiae *is critical.*

The early microbiologist Louis Pasteur recognized this change in metabolic patterns of yeast during his studies on fermentation. Pasteur showed that the ratio of glucose consumed by a yeast suspension (which he called "the ferment") to the weight of cells produced varied with the concentration of oxygen supplied; the maximum ratio occured in the absence of O_2. In Pasteur's own words, "the ferment lost its fermentative abilities in proportion to the concentration of this gas."

Pasteur describes what has come to be known as the "Pasteur effect," a phenomenon that occurs in any organism (even humans) that can both ferment and respire glucose. The fermentation of glucose occurs maximally under anoxic conditions and is inhibited by O_2 because respiration yields much more energy per glucose than does fermentation.

The Pasteur effect occurs in the alcoholic beverage fermentation. When grapes are squeezed to make juice, called *must,* small numbers of yeast cells present on the grapes are transferred to the must. During the first several days of the wine-making process, yeast grow primarily by respiration and consume O_2, making the juice anoxic. The yeast respire the glucose in the juice rather than ferment it because more energy is available from the respiration of glucose than from its fermentation. However, as soon as the oxygen in the grape juice is depleted, fermentation begins along with alcohol formation. This switch from aerobic to anaerobic metabolism is crucial in wine making, and care must be taken to ensure that air is kept out of the fermentation vessel.

Wine is only one of many alcoholic products made with yeast. Others include beer and distilled spirits such as brandy, whisky, vodka, and gin. In distilled spirits, the ethanol, produced in relatively low amounts (10–15% by volume) by the yeast, is concentrated by distilling to make a beverage containing 40–70% alcohol. Even alcohol for motor fuel is made with yeast in parts of the world where sugar is plentiful but petroleum is in short supply (such as Brazil). In the United States, ethyl alcohol for use as an industrial solvent and motor fuel is produced using corn starch as a source of glucose. Yeast also serves as the leavening agent in bread, although here it is not the alcohol that is important, but CO_2, the *other* product of the alcohol fermentation (Figure 15). The CO_2 raises the dough, and the alcohol produced along with it is volatilized during the baking process.

We should thus appreciate the impact that the yeast cell, forced to carry out a fermentative lifestyle because the oxygen it needs for respiration is absent, has had on the lives of humans. Substances that from a physiological standpoint are "waste products" of the glycolytic pathway—ethanol plus CO_2—are the basis of the alcoholic beverage and baking industries, respectively.

11 Respiration and Membrane-Associated Electron Carriers

Fermentation occurs anaerobically in the absence of usable external electron acceptors, and it releases only a relatively small amount of energy. Only a few ATP molecules are synthesized as a result. By contrast, if O_2 or some other usable terminal acceptor is present, the production of fermentation products is unnecessary and glucose can be oxidized completely to CO_2. When this occurs, a far higher yield of ATP is possible. Oxidation using O_2 as the terminal electron acceptor is called *aerobic respiration*.

Our discussion of aerobic respiration will deal with both the carbon transformations and the redox reactions, and will thus focus on two issues: (1) the way electrons are transferred from the organic compound to the terminal electron acceptor and (2) the pathway by which organic carbon is converted into CO_2. During the former, ATP synthesis occurs at the expense of the proton motive force (Figure 14*b*); thus we begin with a discussion of electron transport, the series of reactions that lead to the proton motive force.

Electron Transport Carriers

Electron transport systems are membrane associated. These systems have two basic functions. First, electron transport systems mediate the transfer of electrons from primary donor to terminal acceptor. And second, these systems conserve some of the energy released during this process and use it to synthesize ATP.

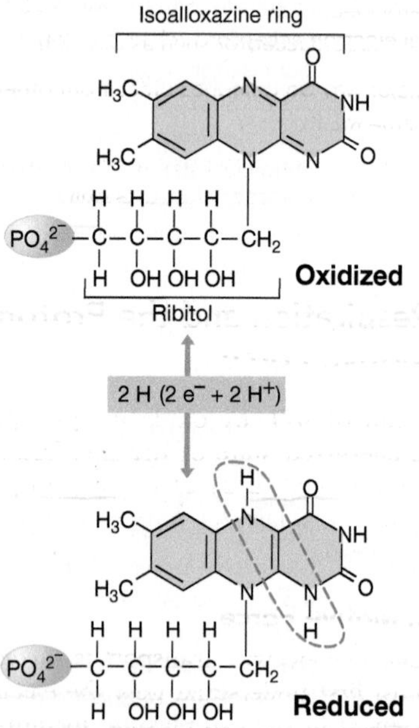

Figure 16 Flavin mononucleotide (FMN), a hydrogen atom carrier. The site of oxidation–reduction (dashed red circle) is the same in FMN and flavin-adenine dinucleotide (FAD).

Several types of oxidation–reduction enzymes participate in electron transport. These include *NADH dehydrogenases*, *flavoproteins*, *iron-sulfur proteins*, and *cytochromes*. In addition, a class of nonprotein electron carriers exists in the *quinones*. The carriers are arranged in the membrane in order of their increasingly positive reduction potentials, with NADH dehydrogenase first and the cytochromes last (see Figure 20).

NADH dehydrogenases are proteins bound to the inside surface of the cytoplasmic membrane. They have an active site that binds NADH and accepts 2 e^- + 2 H^+ when NADH is converted to NAD^+ (Figures 11 and 12). The 2 e^- + 2 H^+ are then passed on to flavoproteins, the next carrier in the chain.

Flavoproteins contain a derivative of the vitamin riboflavin (Figure 16). The flavin portion, which is bound to a protein, is a prosthetic group that is reduced as it accepts electrons plus protons and oxidized when electrons are passed on to the next carrier in the chain. Note that flavoproteins *accept* 2 e^- + 2 H^+ but *donate* only electrons. We will consider what happens to the two protons later. Two flavins are common in cells, flavin mononucleotide (FMN) (Figure 16) and flavin-adenine dinucleotide (FAD). In the latter, FMN is bonded to ribose and adenine through a second phosphate. Riboflavin, also called vitamin B_2, is a source of the parent flavin molecule in flavoproteins and is a required growth factor for some organisms.

The cytochromes are proteins that contain heme prosthetic groups (Figure 17). Cytochromes undergo oxidation and reduction through loss or gain of a single electron by the iron atom in the heme of the cytochrome:

$$\text{Cytochrome} - Fe^{2+} \longleftrightarrow \text{Cytochrome} - Fe^{3+} + e^-$$

Several classes of cytochromes are known, differing widely in their reduction potentials (Figure 10). Different classes of cytochromes are designated by letters, such as cytochrome *a*, cytochrome *b*, cytochrome *c*, and so on, depending upon the type of heme they contain. The cytochromes of a given class in one organism may differ slightly from those of another, and so there are designations such as cytochromes a_1, a_2, a_3, and so on among cytochromes of the same class. Occasionally, cytochromes form complexes with other cytochromes or with iron-sulfur proteins. An example is the cytochrome bc_1 complex, which contains two different *b*-type cytochromes and one *c*-type cytochrome. The cytochrome bc_1 complex plays an important role in energy metabolism, as we will see later.

In addition to the cytochromes, in which iron is bound to heme, one or more proteins with iron not bound to heme are typically present in electron transport chains. These proteins contain clusters of iron and sulfur atoms, with Fe_2S_2 and Fe_4S_4 clusters being the most common. The iron atoms are bonded to free sulfur and to the protein via sulfur atoms from cysteine residues (Figure 18). Ferredoxin, a common iron-sulfur protein, has an Fe_2S_2 configuration.

The reduction potentials of iron-sulfur proteins vary over a wide range depending on the number of iron and sulfur atoms present and how the iron centers are embedded in the

(a) Pyrrole

(b) Porphyrin (a tetrapyrrole, $C_{20}H_{14}N_4$)

(c) Heme (a porphyrin) — Protein — Histidine-N — Fe — N-Histidine — Cysteine-S — S-Cysteine — Amino acid—Amino acid — Cytochrome

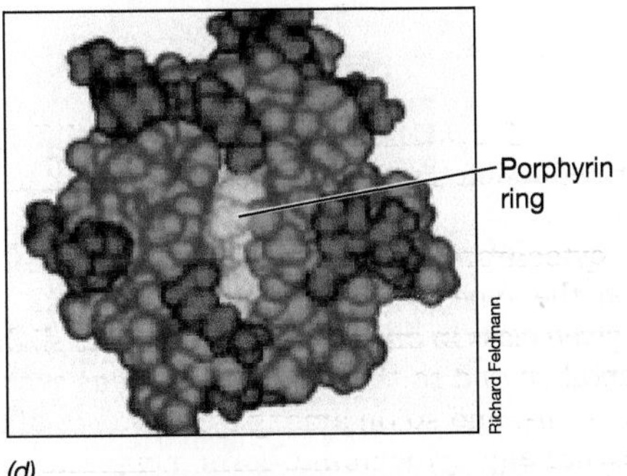

(d)

Figure 17 Cytochrome and its structure. *(a)* Structure of the pyrrole ring. *(b)* Four pyrrole rings are condensed to form the porphyrin ring. *(c)* In cytochrome *c* (shown), the porphyrin ring is covalently linked via disulfide bridges to cysteine molecules in the protein. *(d)* Computer-generated model of cytochrome *c*. The protein completely surrounds the porphyrin ring (light color) in the center. Cytochromes carry electrons only; the redox site is the iron atom, which can alternate between the Fe^{2+} and Fe^{3+} oxidation states.

protein. Thus, different iron-sulfur proteins can function at different locations in the electron transport process. Like cytochromes, iron-sulfur proteins carry electrons only.

Quinones (Figure 19) are hydrophobic nonprotein-containing molecules involved in electron transport. Some quinones found in bacteria are related to vitamin K, a growth factor for higher animals. Like flavoproteins, quinones accept 2 e$^-$ + 2 H$^+$, but transfer only electrons to the next carrier in the chain.

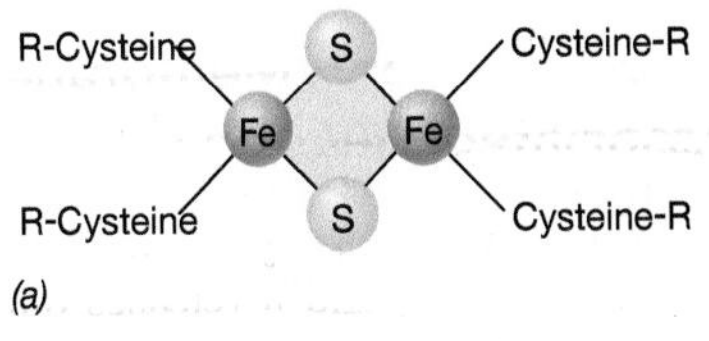

(a)

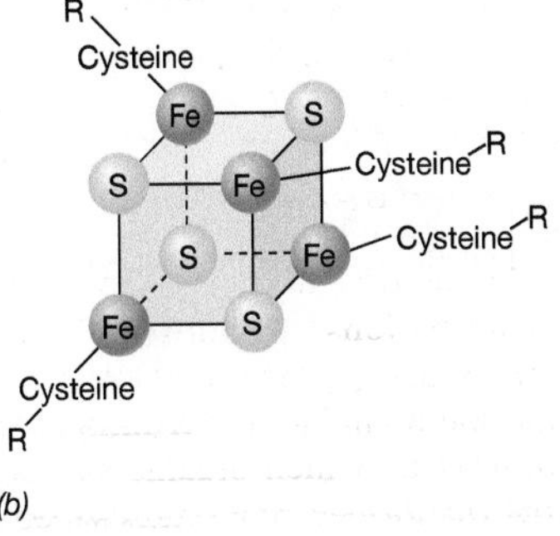

(b)

Figure 18 Arrangement of the iron-sulfur centers of nonheme iron-sulfur proteins. *(a)* Fe_2S_2 center. *(b)* Fe_4S_4 center. The cysteine linkages are from the protein portion of the molecule.

11 MiniReview

Electron transport systems consist of a series of membrane-associated electron carriers that function in an integrated fashion to carry electrons from the primary electron donor to a terminal electron acceptor such as oxygen.

- In what major way do quinones differ from other electron carriers in the membrane?
- Which electron carriers described in this section accept 2 e$^-$ + 2 H$^+$? Which accept electrons only?

12 Respiration and the Proton Motive Force

The production of ATP by oxidative phosphorylation is linked to an energized state of the membrane. This energized state is established by electron transport reactions with the electron carriers we have just discussed; we see how this occurs now.

The Proton Motive Force

To understand how electron transport is linked to ATP synthesis, we must first understand how the electron transport system is oriented in the cytoplasmic membrane. Electron transport carriers are oriented in the membrane in such a way that, as electrons are transported, protons are separated from electrons. Two electrons plus two protons enter the electron

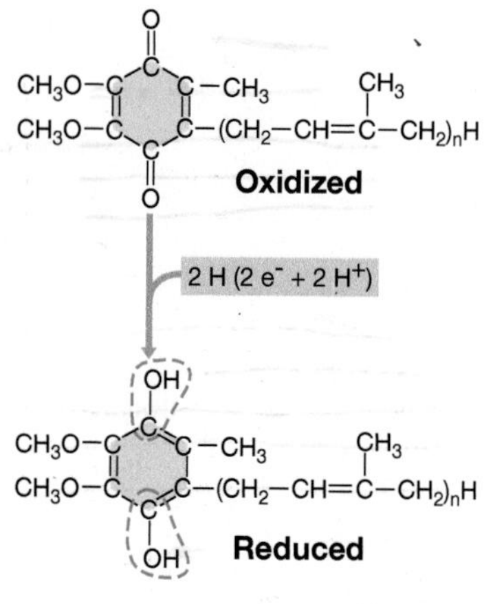

Figure 19 Structure of oxidized and reduced forms of coenzyme Q, a quinone. The five-carbon unit in the side chain (an isoprenoid) occurs in a number of multiples. In prokaryotes, the most common number is $n = 6$; in eukaryotes, $n = 10$. Note that oxidized quinone requires 2 e^- and 2 H^+ to become fully reduced (dashed red circles). An intermediate form, the semiquinone (one H more reduced than oxidized quinone), is formed during the reduction of a quinone.

transport chain from NADH to initiate the process. Carriers in the electron transport chain are arranged in the membrane in order of their increasingly positive reduction potential, with the final carrier in the chain donating the electrons plus protons to a terminal electron acceptor such as O_2 (Figure 20). During this process, several protons are released into the environment, causing a slight acidification of the external surface of the membrane. These protons originate from two sources: (1) NADH and (2) the dissociation of water into H^+ and OH^- in the cytoplasm. The extrusion of H^+ to the environment causes OH^- to accumulate on the inside of the membrane. Despite their small size, neither H^+ nor OH^- can diffuse through the membrane because they are charged. Thus, equilibrium cannot be spontaneously restored.

The result of electron transport is the generation of a pH gradient and an electrochemical potential across the membrane (Figure 20). The *inside* surface of the membrane becomes electrically negative and alkaline and the *outside* surface of the membrane electrically positive and acidic. This pH gradient and electrochemical potential, collectively called the **proton motive force**, causes the membrane to be energized, much like a battery. Some of this energy is then conserved in the formation of ATP. Besides driving ATP synthesis, the energized state of the membrane can also be used to do work, such as ion transport, flagellar rotation, and many other energy-requiring reactions in the cell.

We now consider the individual electron transport reactions that lead to formation of the proton motive force.

Generation of the Proton Motive Force: Complexes I and II

The proton motive force develops from the activities of flavin enzymes, quinones, the cytochrome bc_1 complex, and the

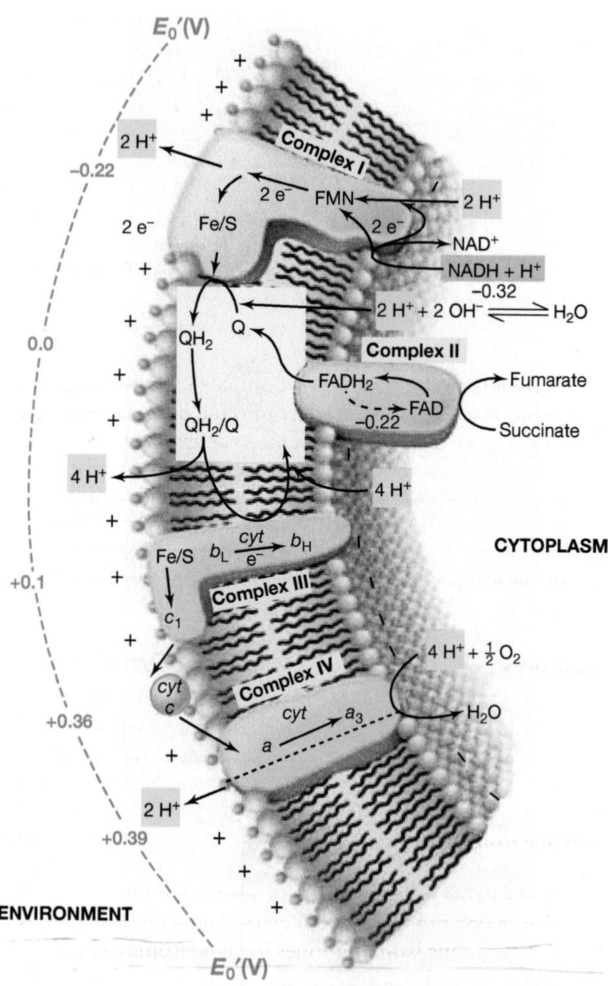

Figure 20 Generation of the proton motive force during aerobic respiration. The orientation of electron carriers in the membrane of *Paracoccus denitrificans*, a model for studies of respiration. The + and − charges at the edges of the membrane represent H^+ and OH^-, respectively. E_0' values for the major carriers are shown. Note how when a hydrogen atom carrier (for example, FMN in complex I) reduces an electron-accepting carrier (for example, the Fe/S protein in complex I) protons are extruded to the outer surface of the membrane. Abbreviations: FMN, flavoprotein; FAD, flavin adenine dinucleotide; Q, quinone; Fe/S, iron sulfur protein; cyt *a*, *b*, *c*, cytochromes (b_L and b_H, low and high potential *b*-type cytochromes, respectively). At the quinone site electrons are recycled during the "Q cycle." This is because electrons from QH_2 can be split in the bc_1 complex (Complex III) between the Fe/S protein and the *b*-type cytochromes. Electrons that travel through the cytochromes reduce Q (in two, one-electron steps) back to QH_2, thus increasing the number of protons pumped at the Q-bc_1 site. Electrons that travel to Fe/S proceed to reduce cytochrome c_1, then cytochrome *c*, and then *a*-type cytochromes in Complex IV, eventually reducing O_2 to H_2O (two electrons and two protons are required to reduce $\frac{1}{2}O_2$ to H_2O, and these come from electrons through cyt *c* and cytoplasmic protons, respectively). Complex II, the succinate dehydrogenase complex, bypasses Complex I and feeds electrons directly into the quinone pool.

terminal cytochrome oxidase. Following the donation of 2 e^- + 2 H^+ from NADH to FAD to form FADH, 2 H^+ are extruded to the outer surface of the membrane when FADH donates 2 e^- to a nonheme iron protein, part of membrane protein *Complex I,* shown in Figure 20. These electron carriers are referred to as complexes because each actually consists of several proteins. For example, Complex I in *Escherichia coli* contains 14 distinct proteins. Complex I is also called *NADH:quinone oxidoreductase,* because the reaction is one in which NADH is oxidized and quinone is reduced. Two protons are taken up from the dissociation of water in the cytoplasm when the iron protein of Complex I reduces coenzyme Q (Figure 20).

Complex II simply bypasses Complex I and feeds electrons and protons from FADH directly into the quinone pool. Complex II is also called the *succinate dehydrogenase complex* because of the specific substrate, succinate (a product of the citric acid cycle, Section 13), that it oxidizes. However, because Complex II bypasses Complex I, fewer protons are pumped per two electrons that enter the electron transport chain here than for two electrons that enter from NADH (Figure 20).

Complexes III and IV: bc_1 and *a*-Type Cytochromes

Reduced coenzyme Q passes electrons one at a time to the cytochrome bc_1 complex (*Complex III,* Figure 20. The cytochrome bc_1 complex is an association of several proteins containing hemes (Figure 17) or other metal centers. These include two *b* type hemes (b_L and b_H), one *c* type heme (c_1), and one iron-sulfur protein. The bc_1 complex is present in the electron transport chain of most organisms that can respire. It also plays a role in photosynthetic electron flow.

The major function of the cytochrome bc_1 complex is to transfer electrons from quinones to cytochrome *c* (Figure 20). Electrons travel from the bc_1 complex to a molecule of cytochrome *c*, located in the periplasm. Cytochrome *c* functions as a shuttle to transfer electrons to the high-potential cytochromes *a* and a_3 (*Complex IV,* Figure 20). Complex IV is the terminal oxidase and reduces O_2 to H_2O in the final step of the electron transport chain. Complex IV also pumps two H^+ to the outer surface of the membrane per each 2 e^- consumed in the reaction (Figure 20).

Besides transferring electrons to cytochrome *c*, the cytochrome bc_1 complex can also interact with the quinone pool in such a way that two additional protons are pumped at the Q-bc_1 site (Figure 20). This happens in a series of electron exchanges between cytochrome bc_1 and Q, called the *Q cycle*. Because quinone and bc_1 have roughly the same E_0' (near 0 V, Figure 20), different molecules of quinone can alternately oxidize and reduce one another using electrons fed back from the bc_1 complex. This mechanism allows on average a total of 4H^+ to be pumped to the outer surface of the membrane at the Q-bc_1 site for every 2 e^- that enter the chain in Complex I (Figure 20).

The electron transport chain shown in Figure 20 is one of many different sequences of electron carriers known from different organisms. However, three features are characteristic of all electron transport chains: (1) arrangement of membrane-associated electron carriers in order of increasingly more positive E_0', (2) alternation of electron-only and electron-plus-proton carriers in the chain, and (3) generation of a proton motive force (Figure 20).

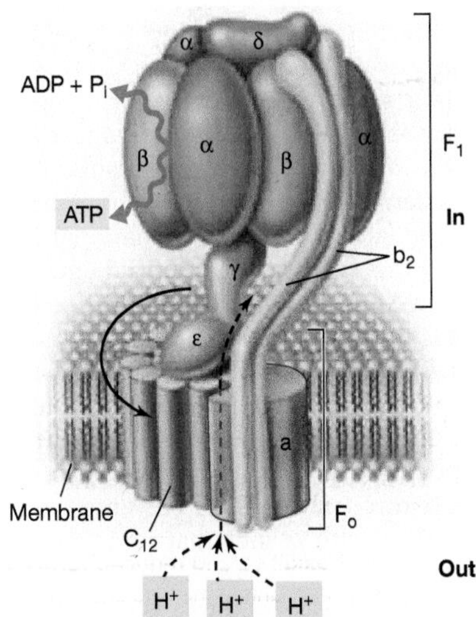

Figure 21 Structure and function of ATP synthase (ATPase). F_1 consists of five different polypeptides present as an $\alpha_3\beta_3\gamma\varepsilon\delta$ complex. F_1 is the catalytic complex responsible for the interconversion of ADP + P_i and ATP. F_o is integrated in the membrane and consists of three polypeptides in an ab_2c_{12} complex. Protons cross the membrane between the a and c_{12} subunits. Subunit b protrudes outside the membrane and forms, along with the b_2 and δ subunits, the stator. As protons enter, the dissipation of the proton motive force drives ATP synthesis. The ATPase is reversible in its action; that is, ATP hydrolysis can drive formation of a proton motive force.

As we will see now, it is this last characteristic, the proton motive force, that drives ATP synthesis.

ATPase

How does the proton motive force generated by electron transport (Figure 20) actually drive ATP synthesis? Interestingly, there is a strong parallel here between the mechanism of ATP synthesis and the mechanism of the motor that drives rotation of the bacterial flagellum. In a fashion similar to the way the proton motive force applies torque to the bacterial flagellum, it also applies force to a large protein complex that makes ATP. The complex that converts the proton motive force into ATP is called **ATP synthase,** or **ATPase** for short.

ATPases consist of two components, a multiprotein extramembrane complex called F_1 that faces into the cytoplasm and a proton-conducting intramembrane channel called F_o (Figure 21). ATPase catalyzes a reversible reaction between ATP and ADP + P_i as shown in Figure 21. The structure of ATPase proteins is highly conserved throughout all the domains of life, suggesting that this mechanism of energy conservation was a very early evolutionary invention.

ATPase is a small biological motor. Proton movement through F_o drives rotation of the *c* proteins; this generates a torque that is transmitted to F_1 by the $\gamma\varepsilon$ subunits (Figure 21). Energy is transferred to F_1 through the coupled rotation of the $\gamma\varepsilon$ subunits. The latter causes conformational changes in the β subunits, and this is a form of potential energy that can be tapped to make ATP. This is possible because the conformational changes in the β subunits allow for the sequential binding of ADP + P_i to each subunit. ATP is synthesized when the β subunits return to their original conformation, releasing the energy needed to drive the process. In analogy to the flagellar motor, the primary function of the $b_2\delta$ subunits of F_1 is to serve as a fixture (stator). This prevents the α and β subunits from rotating with $\gamma\varepsilon$ such that conformational changes in β can occur.

ATPase-catalyzed ATP synthesis is called oxidative phosphorylation if the proton motive force originates from respiration reactions and photophosphorylation if it originates from photosynthetic reactions. Measurements of the stoichiometry between the number of protons consumed by ATPase per ATP produced yield a number of 3–4.

Reversibility of the ATPase

ATPase is reversible. The hydrolysis of ATP supplies torque for γ to rotate in the opposite direction from that in ATP synthesis, and this catalyzes the pumping of protons from the inside to the outside of the cell. This generates instead of dissipates the proton motive force. Reversibility of the ATPase explains why strictly fermentative organisms that lack electron transport chains and are unable to carry out oxidative phosphorylation still have ATPases. As we have said, many important reactions in the cell, such as motility and transport, require energy from the proton motive force rather than from ATP. Thus, ATPase in nonrespiratory organisms such as the strictly fermentative lactic acid bacteria, for example, functions unidirectionally to generate the proton motive force necessary to drive these cell functions.

Inhibitors and Uncouplers

Electron transport reactions have long been studied with chemicals that affect electron flow or the proton motive force. Two classes of such chemicals are known: *inhibitors* and *uncouplers*. Inhibitors block electron flow and, thus, establishment of the proton motive force. Examples include carbon monoxide (CO) and cyanide (CN^-), both of which bind tightly to *a*-type cytochromes (Figure 20) and prevent their functioning. By contrast, uncouplers prevent ATP synthesis without affecting electron transport. Uncouplers are lipid-soluble substances, such as dinitrophenol and dicumarol. These substances make membranes leaky, thereby destroying the proton motive force and its ability to drive ATP synthesis (Figure 21). Thus inhibitors and uncouplers both block ATP synthesis but for distinctly different reasons.

12 MiniReview

When electrons are transported through an electron transport chain, protons are extruded to the outside of the membrane forming the proton motive force. Key electron carriers include flavins, quinones, the cytochrome bc_1 complex, and other cytochromes, depending on the organism. The cell uses the proton motive force to make ATP through the activity of ATPase.

- How do electron transport reactions generate the proton motive force?
- What is the ratio of protons extruded per NADH oxidized through the electron transport chain of *Paracoccus* shown in Figure 20? At which sites in the chain is the proton motive force being established?
- What structure in the cell converts the proton motive force to ATP? How does it operate?

13 Carbon Flow in Respiration: The Citric Acid Cycle

Now that we have a grasp of how ATP is made in respiration, we need to consider the important reactions in carbon metabolism associated with formation of ATP. Our focus here is on the citric acid cycle, a key pathway found in virtually all cells.

The Respiration of Glucose

The early steps in the respiration of glucose are the same biochemical steps as those of glycolysis; all steps from glucose to pyruvate (Figure 15) are the same. However, whereas in fermentation pyruvate is reduced and converted into fermentation products that are subsequently excreted, in respiration pyruvate is oxidized to CO_2. The pathway by which pyruvate is completely oxidized to CO_2 is called the **citric acid cycle** (CAC), summarized in Figure 22.

Pyruvate is first decarboxylated, leading to the production of CO_2, NADH, and the energy-rich substance, *acetyl-CoA* (Figure 13). The acetyl group of acetyl-CoA then combines with the four-carbon compound oxalacetate, forming citric acid (Figure 22). A series of hydration, decarboxylation, and oxidation reactions follow, and two additional CO_2 molecules, three more NADH, and one FADH are formed. Ultimately, oxalacetate is regenerated and returns as an acetyl acceptor, thus completing the cycle (Figure 22).

CO_2 Release and Fuel for Electron Transport

For each pyruvate molecule oxidized through the citric acid cycle, three CO_2 molecules are released (Figure 22). Electrons released during the enzymatic oxidation of intermediates in the CAC are transferred to NAD^+ to form NADH or FAD to form FADH. Here's where respiration and fermentation differ in a major way. Instead of being used in the reduction of pyruvate as in fermentation (Figure 15), in respiration electrons from NADH and FADH are transferred to oxygen by way of

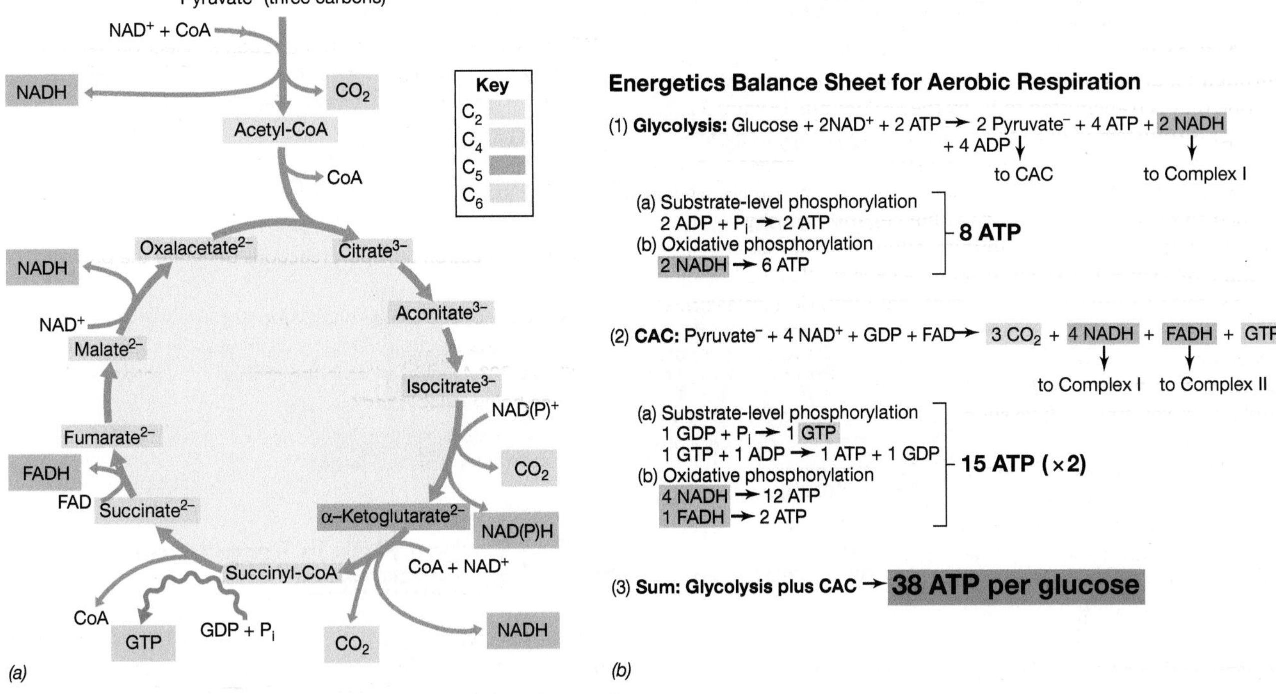

Figure 22 The citric acid cycle. *(a)* The citric acid cycle begins when the two-carbon compound acetyl-CoA condenses with the four-carbon compound oxalacetate to form the six-carbon compound citrate. Through a series of oxidations and transformations, this six-carbon compound is ultimately converted back to the four-carbon compound oxalacetate, which then begins another cycle with addition of the next molecule of acetyl-CoA. *(b)* The overall balance sheet of fuel (NADH/FADH) for the electron transport chain and CO_2 generated in the citric acid cycle. NADH and FADH feed into electron transport chain Complexes I and II, respectively (Figure 20).

the electron transport chain. Thus, unlike in fermentation, the presence of an electron acceptor (O_2) in respiration allows for the complete oxidation of glucose to CO_2 with a much greater yield of energy (Figure 22*b*). Thus while only *2 ATP* are produced per glucose fermented in the alcoholic or lactic acid fermentations (Figure 15), *38 ATP* can be made by respiring the same glucose molecule to CO_2 (Figure 22).

Biosynthesis and the Citric Acid Cycle

Besides playing a key role in catabolism, the citric acid cycle is vital to the cell for other reasons as well. This is because the cycle generates several key biochemical compounds that can be drawn off for biosynthetic purposes when needed. Particularly important in this regard are α-ketoglutarate and oxalacetate, which are precursors of a number of amino acids (Section 16), and succinyl-CoA, needed to form cytochromes, chlorophyll, and several other tetrapyrrole compounds (Figure 17). Oxalacetate is also important because it can be converted to phosphoenolpyruvate, a precursor of glucose. In addition, acetyl-CoA provides the starting material for fatty acid biosynthesis (Section 17). The citric acid cycle thus plays two major roles in the cell: *bioenergetic* and *biosynthetic*. Much the same can be said about the glycolytic pathway, as certain intermediates from this pathway are drawn off for various biosynthetic needs as well (Section 16).

13 MiniReview

Respiration results in the complete oxidation of an organic compound with much greater energy release than occurs during fermentation. The citric acid cycle plays a major role in the respiration of organic compounds.

- How many molecules of CO_2 and pairs of electrons are released per pyruvate oxidized in the citric acid cycle?
- What two major roles do the citric acid cycle and glycolysis have in common?

14 Catabolic Diversity

Thus far in this chapter we have dealt only with the reactions of chemoorganotrophs. We now briefly consider catabolic diversity, some of the alternatives to the use of organic

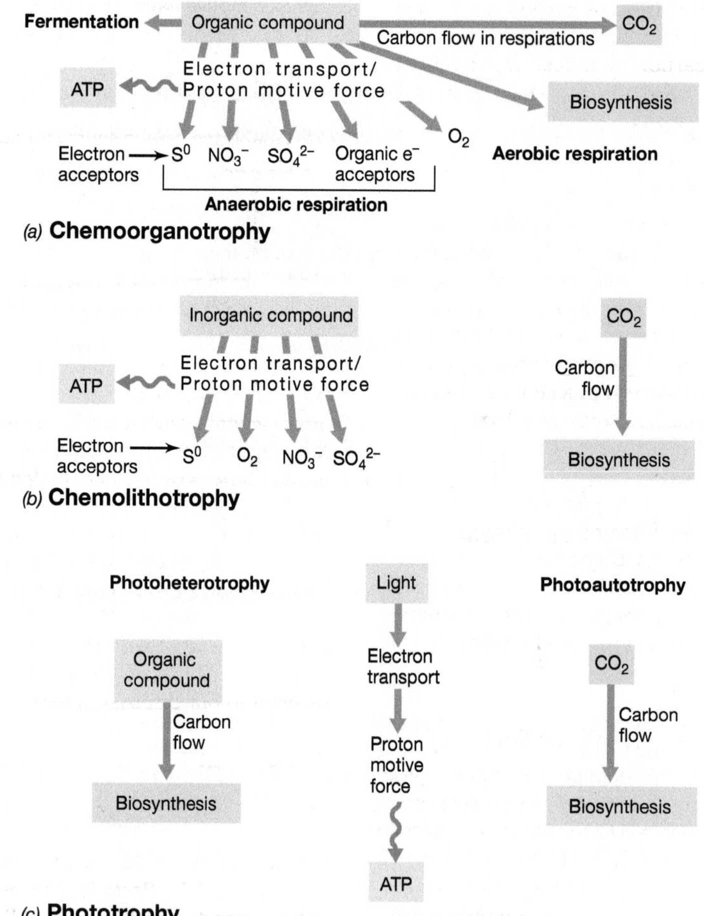

Figure 23 Catabolic diversity. *(a)* Chemoorganotrophic metabolism, *(b)* chemolithotrophic metabolism, and *(c)* phototrophic metabolism. Note how in phototrophic metabolism carbon for biosynthesis can come from CO_2 (photoautotrophy) or organic compounds (photoheterotrophy). Note also the importance of electron transport leading to proton motive force formation in each case.

compounds as energy sources, with an emphasis on electron and carbon flow. Figure 23 summarizes the mechanisms by which cells generate energy other than by fermentation and aerobic respiration. These include anaerobic respiration, chemolithotrophy, and phototrophy.

Anaerobic Respiration

Under anoxic conditions, electron acceptors other than oxygen can be used to support respiration. These processes are called **anaerobic respiration**. Some of the electron acceptors used in anaerobic respiration include nitrate (NO_3^-), ferric iron (Fe^{3+}), sulfate (SO_4^{2-}), carbonate (CO_3^{2-}), and even certain organic compounds. Because of their positions on the redox tower (none of these acceptors has an E_0' as positive as the O_2/H_2O couple; Figure 10), less energy is released when these electron acceptors are used instead of oxygen (recall that $\Delta G^{0\prime}$ is proportional to $\Delta E_0'$; Section 6). Nevertheless, because oxygen is often limiting in anoxic environments, anaerobic respirations can be very important for supporting the growth of prokaryotes in such habitats. Like aerobic respiration, anaerobic respirations depend on electron transport, generation of a proton motive force, and the activity of ATPase.

Chemolithotrophy

Organisms able to use inorganic chemicals as electron donors are called **chemolithotrophs**. Examples of relevant inorganic electron donors include hydrogen sulfide (H_2S), hydrogen gas (H_2), ferrous iron (Fe^{2+}), and ammonia (NH_3).

Chemolithotrophic metabolism is typically aerobic, but begins with the oxidation of an inorganic rather than an organic electron donor (Figure 23). However, like chemoorganotrophs, chemolithotrophs have electron transport chains and form a proton motive force. However, one important distinction between chemolithotrophs and chemoorganotrophs, besides their electron donors, is their sources of carbon for biosynthesis. Chemoorganotrophs use organic compounds (glucose, acetate, and the like) as carbon sources. By contrast, chemolithotrophs use carbon dioxide (CO_2) as a carbon source and are therefore **autotrophs**.

Phototrophy

Many microorganisms are **phototrophs**, using light as an energy source in the process of photosynthesis. The mechanisms by which light is used as an energy source are complex, but the end result is the same as in respiration: generation of a proton motive force that can be used in the synthesis of ATP. Light-mediated ATP synthesis is called **photophosphorylation**. Most phototrophs use energy conserved in ATP for the assimilation of carbon dioxide as the carbon source for biosynthesis; they are called *photoautotrophs*. However, some phototrophs use organic compounds as carbon sources with light as the energy source; these are the *photoheterotrophs* (Figure 23).

Photosynthesis can be of two different types: oxygenic and anoxygenic. Oxygenic photosynthesis, carried out by cyanobacteria and their relatives, is similar to that of higher plants and results in O_2 evolution. Anoxygenic photosynthesis is a simpler process found in purple and green bacteria and in which O_2 evolution does not occur.

The Proton Motive Force and Catabolic Diversity

Microorganisms show an amazing diversity of bioenergetic strategies. Thousands of organic compounds, many inorganic compounds, and light can be used by one or another microorganism as an energy source. However, with the exception of fermentations, where substrate-level phosphorylation occurs, ATP synthesis in respiration and photosynthesis requires generation of a proton motive force.

Whether electrons come from the oxidation of organic or inorganic chemicals or from phototrophic processes, in all forms of respiration and photosynthesis, electron transport occurs and energy conservation is linked to the proton motive force through ATPase (Figure 21). Considered in this way, respiration and anaerobic respiration are simply metabolic variations employing different electron acceptors. Likewise, chemoorganotrophy, chemolithotrophy, and photosynthesis are simply variations upon a theme of different electron donors. Electron transport and the proton motive force link all of these processes, bringing these seemingly quite different forms of metabolism into a common focus.

14 MiniReview

Electron acceptors other than O_2 can function as terminal electron acceptors for energy generation. Because O_2 is absent under these conditions, the process is called anaerobic respiration. Chemolithotrophs use inorganic compounds as electron donors, whereas phototrophs use light to form a proton motive force. The proton motive force operates in all forms of respiration and photosynthesis.

- In terms of their electron donor(s), how do chemoorganotrophs differ from chemolithotrophs?
- What is the carbon source for autotrophic organisms?
- How do photoautotrophs differ from photoheterotrophs?

V ESSENTIALS OF ANABOLISM

We close this chapter with a consideration of biosynthesis. Our focus here will be on biosynthesis of the individual units—sugars, amino acids, nucleotides, and fatty acids—that make up the four classes of macromolecules. Collectively, these biosynthetic processes are called **anabolism**.

Many detailed biochemical pathways lie behind the metabolic patterns we present here, but we will keep our focus on the essential principles. We finish this unit with a brief look at how the enzyme activities in these biosynthetic processes are controlled by the cell. For a cell to be competitive, it must regulate its metabolism. This happens in several ways and at several levels, one of which, the control of enzyme activity, is relevant to our discussion here.

15 Biosynthesis of Sugars and Polysaccharides

Polysaccharides are key constituents of the cell walls of many organisms, and in *Bacteria*, the peptidoglycan cell wall has a polysaccharide backbone. In addition, cells often store carbon and energy reserves in the form of the polysaccharides glycogen or starch. The monomeric units of these polysaccharides are six-carbon sugars called *hexoses*, in particular, glucose or glucose derivatives. In addition to hexoses, five-carbon sugars called *pentoses* are common in the cell. Most notably, these include ribose and deoxyribose, present in the backbone of RNA and DNA, respectively.

In prokaryotes, polysaccharides are synthesized from either uridine diphosphoglucose (UDPG; Figure 24a) or adenosine-diphosphoglucose (ADPG), both of which are activated forms of glucose. ADPG is the precursor for the biosynthesis of glycogen. UDPG is the precursor of various glucose derivatives needed for the biosynthesis of other polysaccharides in the cell, such as *N*-acetylglucosamine and *N*-acetylmuramic acid in peptidoglycan or the lipopolysaccharide component of the gram-negative outer membrane.

When a cell is growing on a hexose such as glucose, obtaining glucose for polysaccharide synthesis is obviously not a problem. But when the cell is growing on other carbon compounds, glucose must be synthesized. This process, called *gluconeogenesis*, uses phosphoenolpyruvate, one of the intermediates of glycolysis (Figure 15), as starting material.

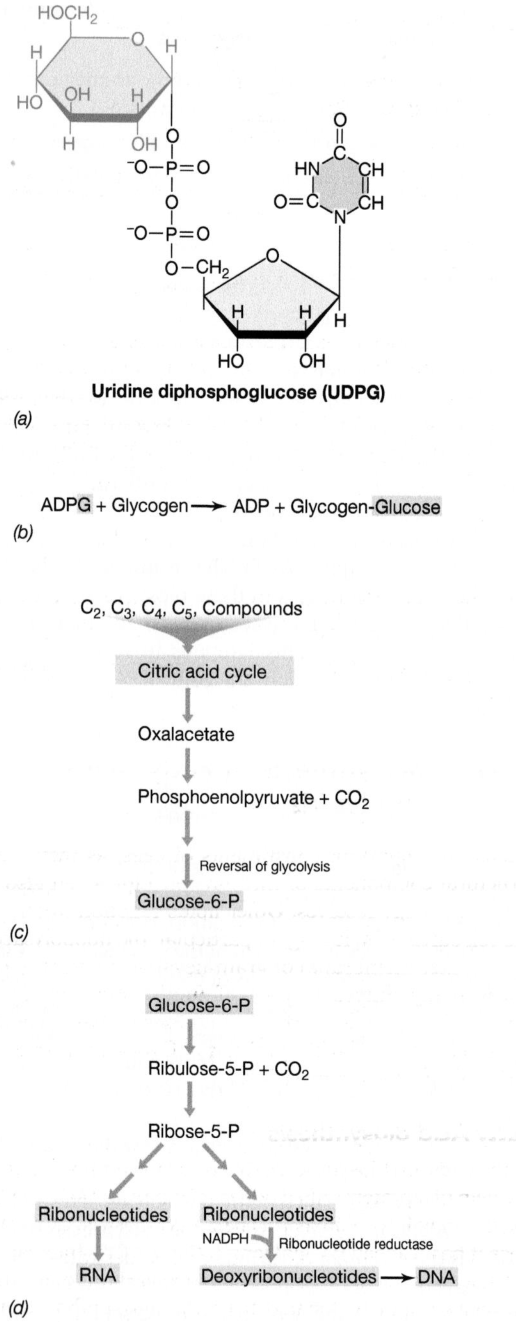

Figure 24 Sugar metabolism. *(a)* Polysaccharides are synthesized from activated forms of hexoses such as UDPG. Glucose is shown here in blue. *(b)* Glycogen is biosynthesized from adenosine-diphosphoglucose (ADPG) by the sequential addition of glucose. *(c)* Gluconeogenesis. When glucose is needed, it can be biosynthesized from other carbon compounds, generally by the reversal of steps in glycolysis. *(d)* Pentoses for nucleic acid synthesis are formed by decarboxylation of hexoses like glucose-6-phosphate. Note how the precursors of DNA are produced from the precursors of RNA by the enzyme ribonucleotide reductase.

Phosphoenolpyruvate can be synthesized from oxalacetate, a citric acid cycle intermediate (Figure 22). An overview of gluconeogenesis is shown in Figure 24*c*.

Biosynthesis of Pentoses

Pentoses are formed by the removal of one carbon atom from a hexose, typically as CO_2. The pentoses needed for nucleic acid synthesis, ribose and deoxyribose, are formed as shown in Figure 24*d*. The enzyme ribonucleotide reductase converts ribose into deoxyribose by reduction of the 2′ carbon on the ring. Interestingly, this reaction occurs after, not before, synthesis of nucleotides. Thus, ribonucleotides are biosynthesized, and some of them are later reduced to *deoxy*ribonucleotides for use as precursors of DNA.

15 MiniReview

Polysaccharides are important structural components of cells and are biosynthesized from activated forms of their monomers. Gluconeogenesis is the production of glucose from nonsugar precursors.

- What form of glucose is used in the biosynthesis of glycogen?

16 Biosynthesis of Amino Acids and Nucleotides

The monomeric constituents of proteins and nucleic acids are amino acids and nucleotides, respectively. Their biosyntheses are often long, multistep pathways requiring many individual enzymes to complete. We approach their biosyntheses here by identifying the carbon skeletons needed to begin the biosynthetic pathways.

Monomers of Proteins: Amino Acids

Organisms that cannot obtain some or all of their amino acids preformed from the environment must synthesize them from other sources. Amino acids can be grouped into structurally related families that share biosynthetic steps. The carbon skeletons for amino acids come almost exclusively from intermediates of glycolysis or the citric acid cycle (Figure 25).

The amino group of amino acids is typically derived from some inorganic nitrogen source in the environment, such as ammonia (NH_3). Ammonia is most often incorporated through formation of the amino acids glutamate or glutamine by the enzymes *glutamate dehydrogenase* and *glutamine synthetase,* respectively (Figure 26). When ammonia is present at high levels, glutamate dehydrogenase or other amino acid dehydrogenases are used. However, when ammonia is present at low levels, glutamine synthetase, with its energy-consuming reaction mechanism (Figure 26*b*) and high affinity for substrate, is employed. We discuss control of the activity of glutamine synthetase in Section 18.

Once ammonia is incorporated, it can be used to form other nitrogenous compounds. For example, glutamate can

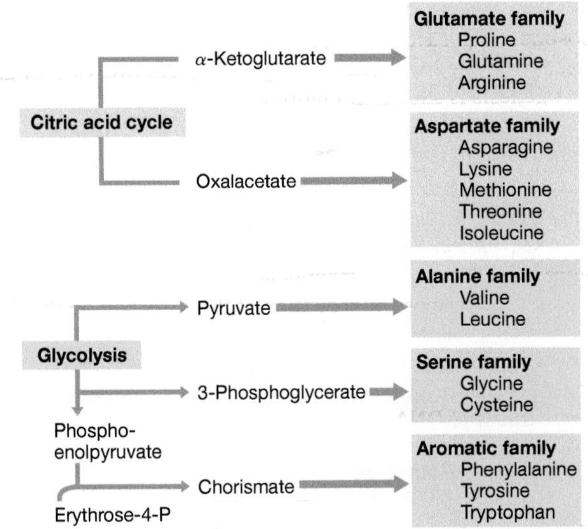

Figure 25 Amino acid families. Most amino acids are derived from either the citric acid cycle or from glycolysis. Synthesis of the various amino acids in a family frequently requires many separate enzymatically catalyzed steps starting with the parent amino acid (shown in bold).

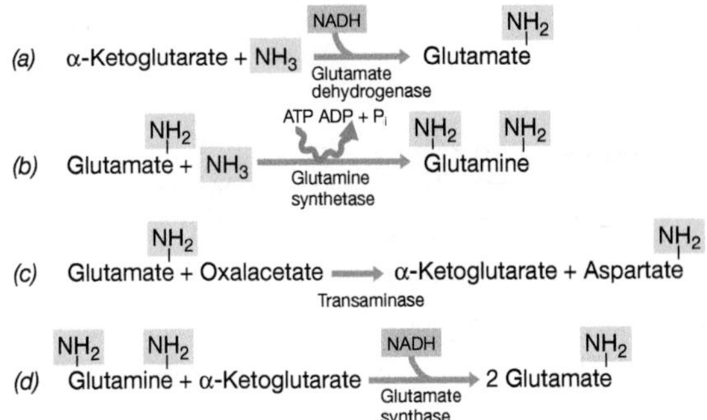

Figure 26 Ammonia incorporation in bacteria. To follow the flow of nitrogen, both free ammonia and the amino groups of all amino acids are shown in blue. Two major pathways for NH_3 assimilation in bacteria are those catalyzed by the enzymes *(a)* glutamate dehydrogenase and *(b)* glutamine synthetase. *(c)* Transaminase reactions transfer an amino group from an amino acid to an organic acid. *(d)* The enzyme glutamate synthase forms two glutamates from one glutamine and one α-ketoglutarate.

donate its amino group to oxalacetate in a transaminase reaction, producing α-ketoglutarate and aspartate (Figure 26*c*). Alternatively, glutamine can react with α-ketoglutarate to form two molecules of glutamate in an aminotransferase reaction (Figure 26*d*). The end result of these types of reactions is the shuttling of ammonia into various carbon skeletons from which further biosynthetic reactions can occur to form all the 22 amino acids needed to make proteins.

Monomers of Nucleic Acids: Nucleotides

The biochemistry behind purine and pyrimidine biosynthesis is quite complex. Purines are constructed literally atom by atom from several distinct carbon and nitrogen sources, including CO_2 (Figure 27*a*). The first key purine, inosinic acid (Figure 27*b*), is the precursor of the purine nucleotides adenine and guanine. Once these are synthesized (in their triphosphate forms) and have been attached to their correct pentose sugar, they are ready to be incorporated into DNA or RNA.

Like the purine ring, the pyrimidine ring is also constructed from several sources (Figure 27*c*). The first key pyrimidine is the compound uridylate, and from this the pyrimidines thymine, cytosine, and uracil are derived (Figure 27*d*).

16 MiniReview

Amino acids are formed from carbon skeletons generated during catabolism whereas nucleotides are biosynthesized using carbon from several sources.

- What form of nitrogen is commonly used to form the amino group of amino acids?
- Which nitrogen bases are purines and which are pyrimidines?

17 Biosynthesis of Fatty Acids and Lipids

Lipids are important constituents of cells, as they are major structural components of membranes. Lipids can also be carbon and energy reserves. Other lipids function in and around the cell surface, including, in particular, the lipopolysaccharide layer (outer membrane) of gram-negative bacteria. A cell produces many different types of lipids, some of which are produced only under certain conditions or have special functions in the cells. The biosynthesis of fatty acids is thus a major series of reactions in most cells.

Fatty Acid Biosynthesis

Fatty acids are biosynthesized two carbon atoms at a time with the help of a protein called *acyl carrier protein* (ACP). ACP holds the growing fatty acid as it is being synthesized and releases it once it has reached its final length (Figure 28). Interestingly, although fatty acids are constructed *two* carbons at a time, each two-carbon unit is donated from the *three*-carbon compound malonate, which is attached to the ACP to form malonyl-ACP. As each malonyl residue is donated, one molecule of CO_2 is released (Figure 28).

The fatty acid composition of cells varies from species to species and can also vary within a species due to differences in temperature (growth at low temperatures promotes the biosynthesis of shorter-chain fatty acids and growth at higher temperatures promotes longer-chain fatty acids). The most common fatty acids in lipids of *Bacteria* contain C_{12}–C_{20} fatty acids.

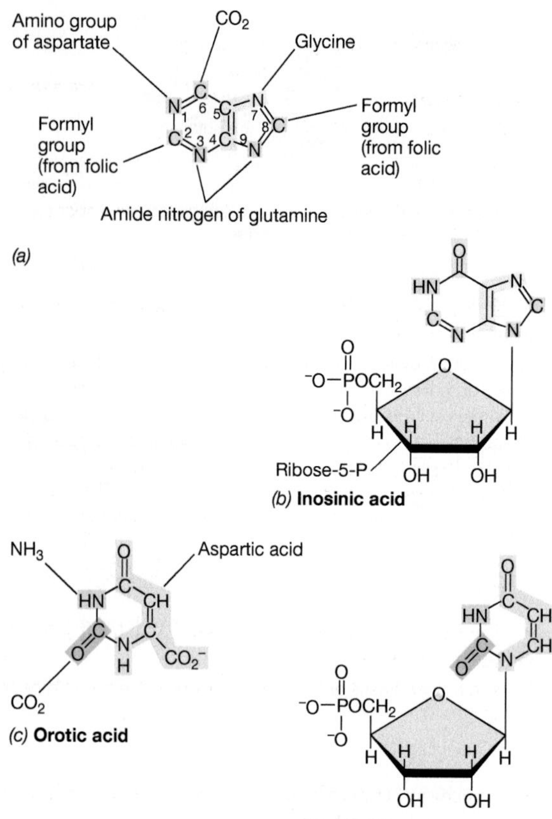

Figure 27 **Biosynthesis of purines and pyrimidines.** *(a)* The precursors of the purine skeleton. *(b)* Inosinic acid, the precursor of all purine nucleotides. *(c)* The precursor of the pyrimidine skeleton, orotic acid. *(d)* Uridylate, the precursor of all pyrimidine nucleotides. Uridylate is formed from orotate following a decarboxylation and the addition of ribose-5-phosphate.

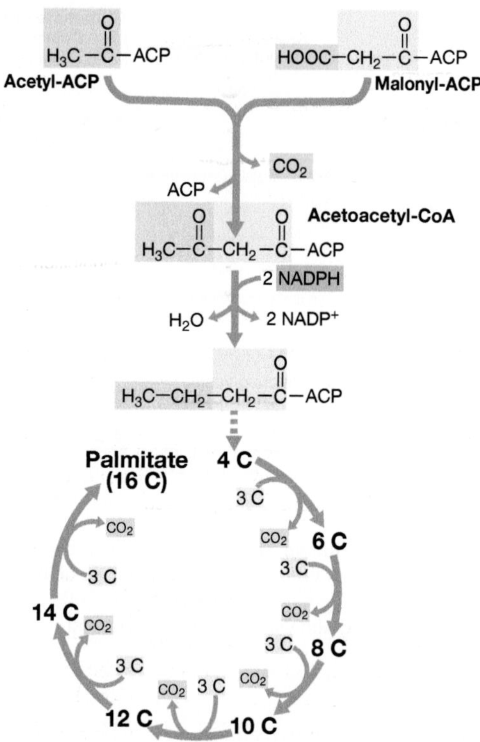

Figure 28 **The biosynthesis of fatty acids.** Shown is the biosynthesis of the C_{16} fatty acid palmitate. ACP, acyl carrier protein. The condensation of acetyl-ACP and malonyl-ACP forms acetoacetyl-CoA. Each successive addition of an acetyl unit comes from malonyl-ACP.

In addition to saturated, even-carbon-number fatty acids, fatty acids can also be unsaturated, branched, or have an odd number of carbon atoms. Unsaturated fatty acids contain one or more double bonds in the long hydrophobic portion of the molecule. The number and position of these double bonds is often species- or group-specific, and the double bonds are typically added by desaturating a saturated fatty acid. Branched chain and odd-carbon-number fatty acids are biosythesized using an initiating molecule that contains a branched chain fatty acid or a propionyl (C_3) group, respectively.

Lipids

In the final assembly of lipids in *Bacteria* and *Eukarya,* fatty acids are added to glycerol. For simple triglycerides (fats), all three glycerol carbons are esterified with fatty acids. In complex lipids, one of the glycerol carbon atoms contains a molecule of phosphate, ethanolamine, a sugar, or some other polar substance. In *Archaea,* lipids contain phytanyl side chains instead of fatty acid side chains, and the biosynthesis of phytanyl is distinct from that described here for fatty acids. However, as for the lipids of *Bacteria* or *Eukarya,* the third carbon of the glycerol backbone in archaeal membrane lipids contains a polar group of some sort to allow the typical membrane structure to form: a hydrophobic interior with hydrophilic surfaces.

17 MiniReview

Fatty acids are synthesized two carbons at a time and then attached to glycerol to form lipids. Only the lipids of *Bacteria* and *Eukarya* contain fatty acids.

- Explain why in fatty acid synthesis fatty acids are constructed two carbon atoms at a time even though the immediate donor for these carbons contains three carbon atoms.

18 Regulation of Activity of Biosynthetic Enzymes

We have just considered some of the key biosyntheses that occur in cells. There are hundreds of different enzymatic reactions that occur in these anabolic processes, and many of the en-

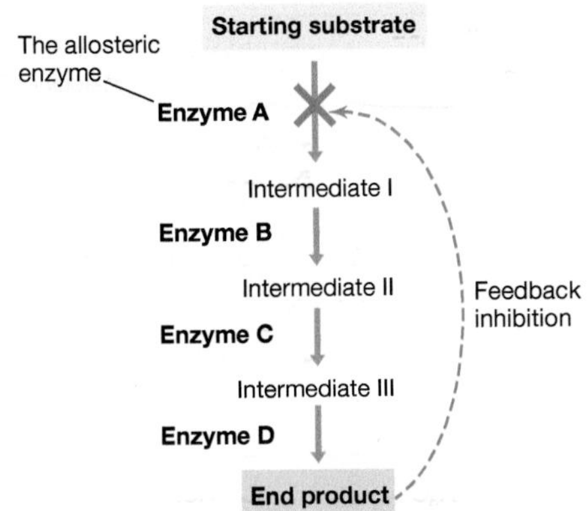

Figure 29 Feedback inhibition of enzyme activity. The activity of the first enzyme of the pathway is inhibited by the end product, thus shutting off the production of the end product.

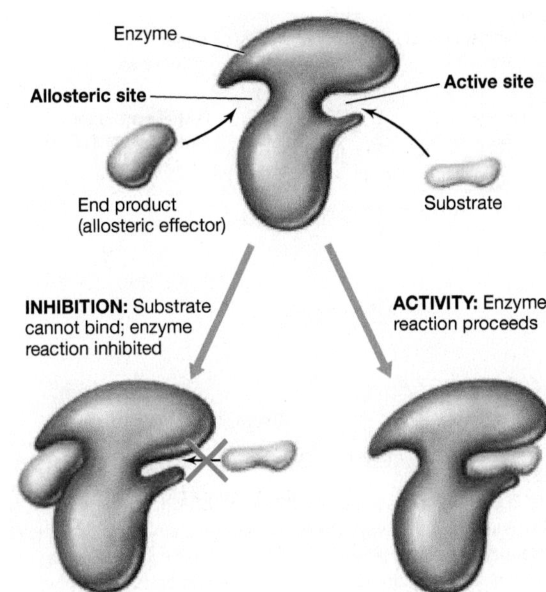

Figure 30 Allostery, the mechanism of enzyme inhibition by the end product of a pathway. When the end product combines with the allosteric site, the conformation of the enzyme is altered such that the substrate can no longer bind to the active site.

zymes that carry these out are highly regulated. The advantage to the cell of regulating enzymes of a biosynthetic pathway should be clear: Neither carbon nor energy is wasted as they would be if a metabolite already present in the environment in sufficient amount were instead biosynthesized by the cell.

There are two major modes of enzyme regulation, one that controls the *amount* (or even the complete presence or absence) of an enzyme in the cell and another that controls the *activity* of a preexisting enzyme by temporarily inactivating the protein. In prokaryotic cells, regulation of the number of copies (amount) of a given enzyme occurs at the gene level, and we reserve discussion of this until after we have considered the principles of molecular biology. Here we focus on what the cell can do to control the activity of enzymes that already exist in the cell.

Inhibition of an enzyme's activity is the result of either covalent or noncovalent changes in the enzyme structure. We begin with the simple case of feedback inhibition and isoenzymes, both examples of noncovalent interactions, and end with the classical case of covalent modification of the enzyme glutamine synthetase.

Feedback Inhibition

A major mechanism for the control of enzymatic activity is **feedback inhibition**. Feedback inhibition is a mechanism for turning off the reactions in an entire biosynthetic pathway, such as a biosynthetic pathway of an amino acid or nucleotide. The regulation in feedback inhibition occurs because an excess of the end product of the pathway inhibits activity of the *first* enzyme of the pathway. Inhibiting the first step effectively shuts down the entire pathway because no intermediates are generated for other enzymes further down the pathway (Figure 29). Feedback inhibition is reversible, however, because once levels of the end product become limiting, its synthesis resumes.

How can the end product of a pathway inhibit the activity of an enzyme whose substrate is quite unrelated to it? This is possible because the inhibited enzyme is an **allosteric enzyme**. Such enzymes have two binding sites, the *active site*, where the substrate binds (Section 5), and the *allosteric site*, where the end product of the pathway binds reversibly. When the end product binds at the allosteric site, the conformation of the enzyme changes such that the substrate can no longer bind at the active site (Figure 30). When the concentration of the end product begins to fall in the cytoplasm, the enzyme returns to its catalytic form and is once again active.

Isoenzymes

Some biosynthetic pathways controlled by feedback inhibition employ *isoenzymes* ("iso" means "same"). Isoenzymes are different enzymes that catalyze the same reaction but are subject to different regulatory controls. An example is the synthesis of the aromatic amino acids tyrosine, tryptophan, and phenylalanine in *Escherichia coli*.

The enzyme 3-deoxy-D-arabino-heptulosonate 7-phosphate (DAHP) synthase plays a central role in aromatic amino acid biosynthesis (Figure 31). In *E. coli*, three DAHP synthase isoenzymes catalyze the first reaction in this pathway, each regulated independently by only one of the end-product amino acids. However, unlike the example of feedback inhibition where an end product completely inhibited an enzyme activity, in the case of DAHP synthase enzyme activity is diminished in a stepwise fashion; enzyme activity falls to zero only when *all three* products are present in excess. Some organisms use only a single enzyme to accomplish the same thing. In these organisms *concerted* feedback inhibition occurs. Each end product feedback inhibits the enzyme's

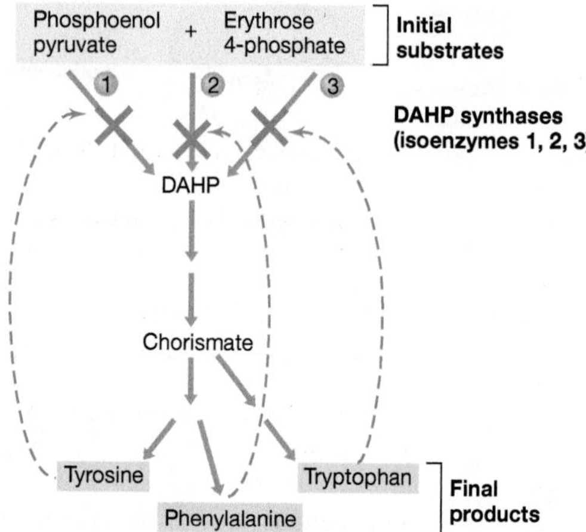

Figure 31 Isoenzymes and feedback inhibition. The common pathway leading to the synthesis of the aromatic amino acids contains three isoenzymes of DAHP synthase. Each of these enzymes is specifically feedback inhibited by one of the aromatic amino acids. Note how an excess of all three amino acids is required to completely shut off the synthesis of DAHP.

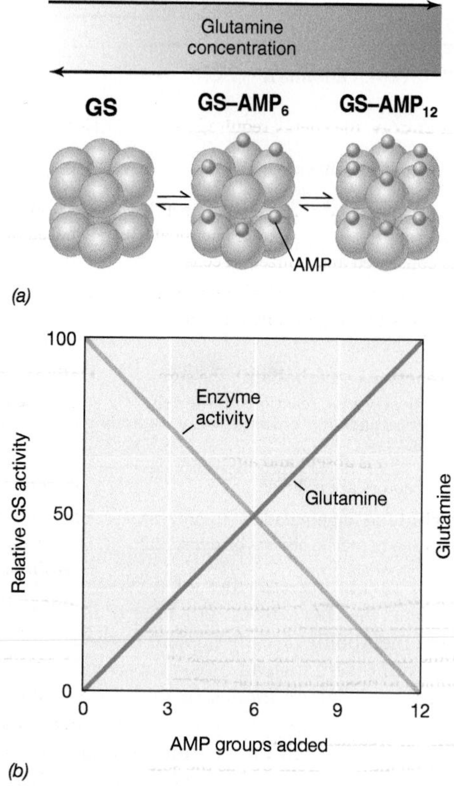

Figure 32 Regulation of glutamine synthetase by covalent modification. *(a)* When cells are grown in a medium rich in fixed nitrogen, glutamine synthetase (GS) is covalently modified by becoming progressively adenylylated; as many as 12 adenyl (AMP) groups can be added. When the medium becomes nitrogen poor, the groups are removed, forming ADP. *(b)* Adenylylated GS subunits are catalytically inactive, so the overall GS activity decreases as more subunits are adenylylated. See Figure 26*b* for the reaction carried out by glutamine synthetase.

activity only partially; complete inhibition occurs only when all three end products are present in excess.

Enzyme Regulation by Covalent Modification

Some biosynthetic enzymes are regulated by covalent modification, typically by attaching or removing some small molecule to the protein. As for allosteric proteins, binding of the small molecule changes the conformation of the protein, inhibiting its catalytic activity. Removal of the molecule then returns the enzyme to an active state. Common modifiers include the nucleotides adenosine monophosphate (AMP) and adenosine diphosphate (ADP), inorganic phosphate (PO_4^{2-}), and methyl (CH_3) groups. We consider here the well-studied case of glutamine synthetase (GS), a key enzyme in ammonia assimilation (Figure 32 and Figure 26*b*), whose activity is modulated by the addition of AMP, a process called *adenylylation*.

Each molecule of GS is composed of 12 identical subunits, and each subunit can be adenylylated. When the enzyme is fully adenylylated (that is, each molecule of GS contains 12 AMP groups), it is catalytically inactive. When it is partially adenylylated, it is partially active. As the glutamine pool in the cell increases, GS becomes more highly adenylylated and its activity diminishes. As glutamine levels diminish, GS becomes deadenylylated and its activity increases (Figure 32).

Other enzymes in the cell add and remove the AMP groups from GS, and these enzymes are themselves controlled, ultimately by levels of ammonia in the cell. Why should there be all of this elaborate regulation surrounding the enzyme GS? The activity of GS requires ATP (Figure 26*b*), and nitrogen assimilation is a major biosynthetic process in the cell. However, when ammonia is present at high levels in the cell, it can be assimilated into amino acids by enzymes that do not consume ATP (Figure 26*a*); under these conditions, GS remains inactive. When ammonia levels are very low, however, GS is needed, and it then becomes catalytically active. By using GS to assimilate ammonia present only at low levels, the cell conserves ATP that would be used unnecessarily if GS were active when ammonia was present in high amounts.

18 MiniReview

One mechanism for modulating an enzyme's activity is feedback inhibition, in which the final product of a biosynthetic pathway inhibits the first enzyme unique to that pathway. Employing isoenzymes is a second way of doing this, and reversible covalent modification is yet another way of doing this.

- What is feedback inhibition?
- What is an allosteric enzyme?
- In glutamine synthetase, what does adenylylation do to enzyme activity?

Review of Key Terms

Activation energy the energy required to bring the substrate of an enzyme to the reactive state

Adenosine triphosphate (ATP) a nucleotide that is the primary form in which chemical energy is conserved and utilized in cells

Allosteric enzyme an enzyme containing an active site plus an allosteric site for binding an effector molecule

Anabolic reactions (Anabolism) the sum total of all biosynthetic reactions in the cell

Anaerobic respiration a form of respiration in which oxygen is absent and alternative electron acceptors are reduced

Aseptic technique manipulations to prevent contamination of sterile objects or microbial cultures during handling

ATPase (ATP synthase) a multiprotein enzyme complex embedded in the cytoplasmic membrane that catalyzes the synthesis of ATP coupled to dissipation of the proton motive force

Autotroph an organism capable of biosynthesizing all cell material from CO_2 as the sole carbon source

Catabolic reactions (Catabolism) biochemical reactions leading to energy conservation (usually as ATP) by the cell

Catalyst a substance that accelerates a chemical reaction but is not consumed in the reaction

Chemolithotrophs organisms that can grow with inorganic compounds as electron donors in energy metabolism

Citric acid cycle a cyclical series of reactions resulting in the conversion of acetate to two CO_2

Coenzyme a small and loosely bound nonprotein molecule that participates in a reaction as part of an enzyme

Complex medium a culture medium composed of digests of chemically undefined substances such as yeast and meat extracts

Culture medium an aqueous solution of various nutrients suitable for the growth of microorganisms

Defined medium a culture medium whose precise chemical composition is known

Electron acceptor a substance that can accept electrons from an electron donor, becoming reduced in the process

Electron donor a substance that can donate electrons to an electron acceptor, becoming oxidized in the process

Endergonic energy requiring

Enzyme a protein that can speed up (catalyze) a specific chemical reaction

Exergonic energy releasing

Feedback inhibition a process in which an excess of the end product of a multistep pathway inhibits activity of the first enzyme in the pathway

Fermentation anaerobic catabolism in which an organic compound is both an electron donor and an electron acceptor, and ATP is produced by substrate-level phosphorylation

Free energy (G) energy available to do work; $G^{0\prime}$ is free energy under standard conditions

Glycolysis a biochemical pathway in which glucose is fermented yielding ATP and various fermentation products; also called the Embden–Meyerhof pathway

Metabolism the sum total of all the chemical reactions that occur in a cell

Oxidative phosphorylation the production of ATP from a proton motive force formed by electron transport of electrons from organic or inorganic electron donors

Photophosphorylation the production of ATP from a proton motive force formed from light-driven electron transport

Phototrophs organisms that use light as their source of energy

Proton motive force a source of potential energy resulting from the separation of charge and protons from hydroxyl ions across the cytoplasmic membrane

Pure culture a culture that contains a single kind of microorganism

Reduction potential ($E_0{}'$) the inherent tendency, measured in volts under standard conditions, of a compound to donate electrons

Respiration the process in which a compound is oxidized with O_2 (or an O_2 substitute) as the terminal electron acceptor, usually accompanied by ATP production by oxidative phosphorylation

Siderophore an iron chelator that can bind iron present at very low concentrations

Substrate-level phosphorylation production of ATP by the direct transfer of an energy-rich phosphate molecule from a phosphorylated organic compound to ADP

Sterile absence of all microorganisms, including viruses

Review Questions

1. Why are carbon and nitrogen macronutrients while cobalt is a micronutrient (Section 1)?
2. What are siderophores and why are they necessary (Section 1)?
3. Why would the following medium not be considered a chemically defined medium: glucose, 5 grams (g); NH_4Cl, 1 g; KH_2PO_4, 1 g; $MgSO_4$, 0.3 g; yeast extract, 5 g; distilled water, 1 liter (Section 2)?
4. What is aseptic technique and why is it necessary (Section 3)?
5. Describe how you would calculate $\Delta G^{0\prime}$ for the reaction: glucose + 6 $O_2 \rightarrow$ 6 CO_2 + 6 H_2O. If you were told that this reaction is highly *exergonic*, what would be the arithmetic sign (negative or positive) of the $\Delta G^{0\prime}$ you would expect for this reaction (Section 4)?
6. Distinguish between $\Delta G^{0\prime}$, ΔG, and G_f^0 (Section 4).
7. Why are enzymes needed by the cell (Section 5)?
8. Describe the difference between a coenzyme and a prosthetic group (Section 5).
9. The following is a series of coupled electron donors and electron acceptors (written as donor/acceptor). Using just the data given in Figure 10, order this series from most energy-yielding to least energy-yielding. H_2/Fe^{3+}, H_2S/O_2, methanol/NO_3^- (producing NO_2^-), H_2/O_2, Fe^{2+}/O_2, NO_2^-/Fe^{3+}, H_2S/NO_3^- (Section 6).

10. What is the reduction potential of the $NAD^+/NADH$ couple (Section 7)?
11. Why is acetyl phosphate considered an energy-rich compound while glucose 6-phosphate is not (Section 8)?
12. How is ATP made in fermentation and respiration (Section 9)?
13. Where in glycolysis is NADH produced? Where is NADH consumed (Section 10)?
14. What is needed to reduce NAD^+ to NADH? Cytochrome $bc_{1\text{-oxidized}}$ to $bc_{1\text{-reduced}}$ (Section 11)?
15. What is meant by the term proton motive force and why is this concept so important in biology (Section 12)?
16. How is rotational energy in the ATPase used to produce ATP (Section 12)?
17. The chemicals dinitrophenol and cyanide are both cellular poisons but act in quite different ways. Compare and contrast the modes of action of these two chemicals (Section 12).
18. Work through the energy balance sheets for fermentation and respiration, and account for all sites of ATP synthesis. Organisms can obtain nearly 20 times more ATP when growing aerobically on glucose than by fermenting it. Write one sentence that accounts for this difference (Section 13).
19. Why can it be said that the citric acid cycle plays two major roles in the cell (Section 13)?
20. What are the differences in electron donor and carbon source used by *Escherichia coli* and *Thiobacillus thioparus* (a sulfur chemolithotroph) (Section 14 and see Table 4)?
21. What two catabolic pathways supply carbon skeletons for sugar and amino acid biosyntheses (Sections 15 and 16)?
22. Describe the process by which a fatty acid such as palmitate (a C_{16} straight-chain saturated fatty acid) is synthesized in a cell (Section 17).
23. Contrast regulation of DAHP synthase and glutamine synthetase (Section 18).

Application Questions

1. Design a defined culture medium for an organism that can grow aerobically on acetate as a carbon and energy source. Make sure all the nutrient needs of the organism are accounted for and in the correct relative proportions.
2. Explain the following observation in light of the redox tower: cells of *Escherichia coli* fermenting glucose grow faster when NO_3^- is supplied to the culture (NO_2^- is produced) and then grow even faster (and stop producing NO_2^-) when the culture is highly aerated.

Nutrient Cycles, Bioremediation, and Symbioses

Nutrient Cycles, Bioremediation, and Symbioses

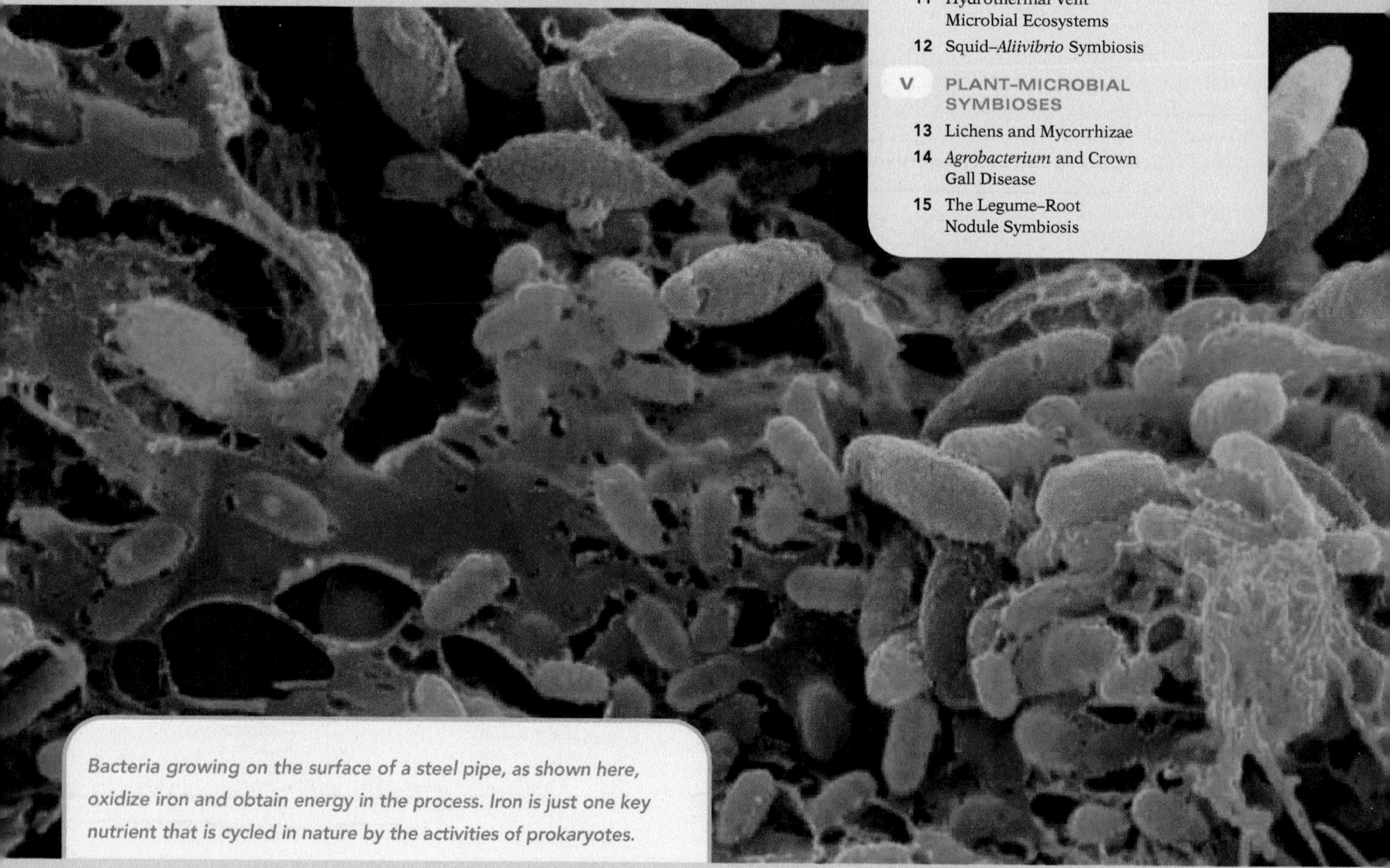

Bacteria growing on the surface of a steel pipe, as shown here, oxidize iron and obtain energy in the process. Iron is just one key nutrient that is cycled in nature by the activities of prokaryotes.

Dennis Kunkel/Dennis Kunkel Microscopy

I THE CARBON AND OXYGEN CYCLES

Global carbon cycling requires the activities of both microorganisms and macroorganisms. Major areas of interest in the carbon cycle are the magnitude of carbon reservoirs, the major sources and sinks for CO_2 and CH_4, and the rates of carbon cycling within and between compartments.

1 The Carbon Cycle

On a global basis, carbon is cycled through all of Earth's major carbon reservoirs: the atmosphere, the land, the oceans and other aquatic environments, sediments and rocks, and biomass (Figure 1). As we have already seen for freshwater environments, the carbon and oxygen cycles are intimately linked, and this is true of soil and all other environments on Earth as well.

Carbon Reservoirs

The largest carbon reservoir is in the sediments and rocks of Earth's crust (Table 1), but the turnover time is so long that flux out of this compartment is insignificant on a human time scale. From the viewpoint of living organisms, a large amount of organic carbon is found in land plants. This is the carbon of forests, grasslands, and crop agriculture, and constitutes major sites of photosynthetic CO_2 fixation. However, more carbon is present in dead organic material, called **humus**, than in living organisms. Humus is a complex mixture of organic materials that is derived from dead soil microorganisms that have resisted decomposition along with resistant plant organic materials. Some humic substances are fairly stable, with a global turnover time of several decades, but certain other humic components decompose much more rapidly than this.

The most rapid means of global transfer of carbon is via the CO_2 of the atmosphere. Carbon dioxide is removed from the atmosphere primarily by photosynthesis of land plants and marine microorganisms and is returned to the atmosphere by respiration of animals and chemoorganotrophic microorganisms. The single most important contribution of CO_2 to the atmosphere is microbial decomposition of dead organic material, including humus. In recent eras, however, human activities have added enormous amounts of new CO_2 to the atmosphere from previously buried carbon by the burning of fossil fuels. For example, in the past 40 years alone, CO_2 levels in the atmosphere have risen nearly 15%. This has in large part triggered a period of steadily increasing global temperatures called *global warming*.

Importance of Photosynthesis in the Carbon Cycle

The only major ways in which new organic carbon is synthesized on Earth are via phototrophic and chemolithotrophic CO_2 fixation; most organic carbon comes from photosynthesis. Phototrophic organisms are therefore the foundation of the carbon cycle (Figure 1). However, phototrophic organisms are abundant in nature only in habitats where light is available. Thus, the deep sea and other permanently dark habitats are devoid of indigenous phototrophs.

Oxygenic phototrophic organisms can be divided into two groups: *plants* and *microorganisms*. Plants are the dominant phototrophic organisms of terrestrial environments, whereas phototrophic microorganisms dominate aquatic environments.

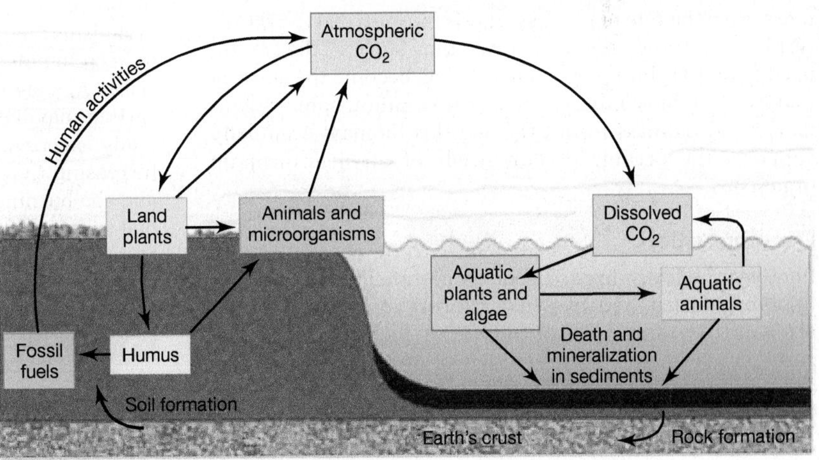

Figure 1 The carbon cycle. The carbon and oxygen cycles are closely connected, as oxygenic photosynthesis both removes CO_2 and produces O_2 and respiratory processes both produce CO_2 and remove O_2. By far the greatest reservoir of carbon on Earth is in rocks and sediments, and most of this is inorganic carbon (carbonates).

Table 1 Major carbon reservoirs on Earth

Reservoir	*Carbon (gigatons)*[a]	*Percent of total carbon on Earth*
Oceans	38×10^3 (>95% is inorganic C)	0.05
Rocks and sediments	75×10^6 (>80% is inorganic C)	>99.5[b]
Terrestrial biosphere	2×10^3	0.003
Aquatic biosphere	1–2	0.000002
Fossil fuels	4.2×10^3	0.006
Methane hydrates	10^4	0.014

[a]One gigaton is 10^9 tons. Data adapted from *Science* 290:291–295 (2000).
[b]Much of the organic carbon is in prokaryotic cells.

The redox cycle for carbon (Figure 2) begins with photosynthesis:

$$CO_2 + H_2O \xrightarrow[\text{light}]{} (CH_2O) + O_2$$

Here (CH_2O) represents organic matter at the oxidation state of cell material, such as polysaccharides (the main form in which photosynthesized organic matter is stored in the cell). Phototrophic organisms also carry out respiration, both in the light and the dark. The overall equation for respiration is the reverse of oxygenic photosynthesis:

$$(CH_2O) + O_2 \xrightarrow[\text{light or dark}]{} CO_2 + H_2O$$

where (CH_2O) again represents storage polysaccharides. If a phototrophic organism is to increase in cell number or mass, then the rate of photosynthesis must exceed the rate of respiration. If the organism grows, then some of the carbon fixed from CO_2 into polysaccharide has become the starting material for biosynthesis. In this way, autotrophic organisms build biomass from CO_2, and this biomass eventually supports the organic carbon needs of all heterotrophic organisms.

Decomposition

Photosynthetically fixed carbon is eventually degraded by microorganisms, and two major forms of carbon remain: *methane* (CH_4) and *carbon dioxide* (CO_2) (Figure 2). These two gases are formed from the activities of methanogens and chemoorganotrophs, respectively. In anoxic habitats CH_4 is produced from the reduction of CO_2 with H_2 and from certain organic compounds such as acetate. However, virtually any organic compound can eventually be converted to CH_4 from the combined activities of methanogens and other bacteria (syntrophs); H_2 generated from the fermentative degradation of organic compounds by syntrophs gets consumed by methanogens and converted to CH_4 as discussed in the next section. Methane produced in anoxic habitats is insoluble and

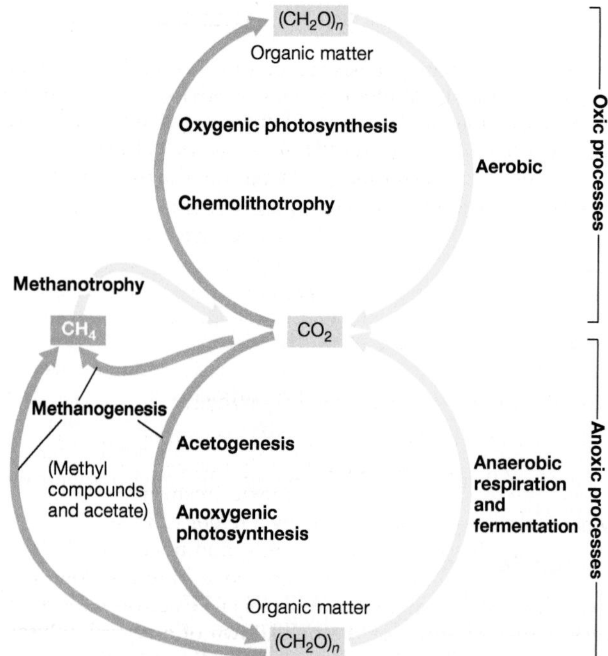

Figure 2 Redox cycle for carbon. The figure contrasts autotrophic ($CO_2 \rightarrow$ organic compounds) and heterotrophic (organic compounds $\rightarrow CO_2$) processes. Yellow arrows indicate oxidations; red arrows indicate reductions.

flows to oxic environments where it is oxidized to CO_2 by methanotrophs (Figure 2). Hence, all organic carbon eventually returns to CO_2, and the carbon cycle is complete.

The balance between the oxidative and reductive portions of the carbon cycle is critical: The metabolic products of some organisms are the substrates for others. Thus, the cycle needs to keep in balance if it is to continue as it has for billions of years. Any significant changes in levels of gaseous forms of carbon may have serious global consequences, as we are already experiencing in the form of global warming from the increasing CO_2 levels in the atmosphere from deforestation and the burning of fossil fuels. Total CO_2 released by microbial activities far exceeds that produced from decomposition by higher eukaryotes, and this is especially true of anoxic environments, which we consider next.

1 MiniReview

The oxygen and carbon cycles are interconnected through the complementary activities of autotrophic and heterotrophic organisms. Microbial decomposition is the single largest source of CO_2 released to the atmosphere.

- How is new organic matter made in nature?
- In what ways are oxygenic photosynthesis and respiration related?

2 Syntrophy and Methanogenesis

Biological methanogenesis is central to carbon cycling in anoxic habitats. Methanogenesis is carried out by a group of *Archaea*, the methanogens, which are strict anaerobes. Most methanogens can use CO_2 as a terminal electron acceptor in anaerobic respiration, reducing it to CH_4 with H_2 as electron donor. Only a very few other substrates, acetate being chief among them, are directly converted to CH_4 by methanogens. To convert most organic compounds to CH_4, methanogens must therefore team up with partner organisms that can supply them with methanogenic precursors. This is the job of the syntrophs.

Anoxic Decomposition and Syntrophy

Here we consider the interactions of syntrophic bacteria with their partner organisms and their significance for the anoxic carbon cycle. Our focus is on anoxic freshwater sediments, where methanogenesis is typically a major process.

Polysaccharides, proteins, lipids, and nucleic acids from dead organisms find their way into anoxic habitats. Following hydrolysis, the monomers are excellent electron donors for energy metabolism. For the breakdown of a typical polysaccharide such as cellulose (Figure 3 and Table 2), the process begins with *cellulolytic bacteria*; these organisms hydrolyze cellulose into cellobiose (glucose–glucose) and then into glucose. The glucose is fermented by *primary* fermenters to short-chain fatty acids (acetate, propionate, and butyrate) and to alcohols, H_2, and CO_2. H_2 is quickly removed by methanogens, along with the acetate, but the bulk of the organic carbon remains in the form of fatty acids and alcohols; these cannot be directly catabolized by methanogens. The catabolism of these compounds requires **syntrophy** and the important fermentative activities of syntrophic bacteria (Figure 3).

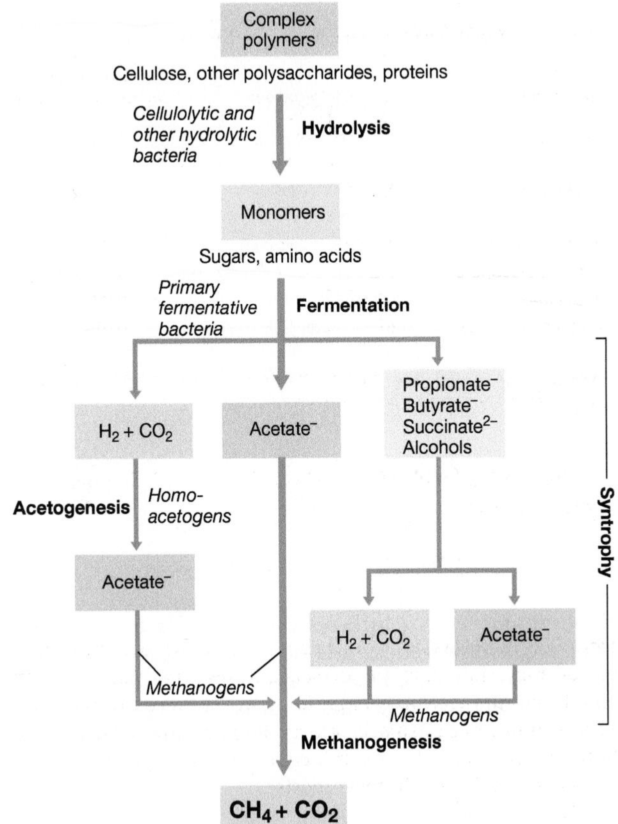

Figure 3 **Anoxic decomposition.** Shown is the overall process of anoxic decomposition, in which various groups of fermentative anaerobes cooperate in the conversion of complex organic materials to methane (CH_4) and CO_2. This picture holds for environments in which sulfate-reducing bacteria play only a minor role, for example, in freshwater lake sediments, sewage sludge bioreactors, or the rumen.

Role of the Syntrophs

Key bacteria in the conversion of organic materials to methane are the syntrophs. These organisms are *secondary* fermenters. Syntrophs ferment the products of primary fermenters, producing primarily H_2, CO_2, and acetate. For example, *Syntrophomonas wolfei* oxidizes C_4 to C_8 fatty acids yielding acetate, CO_2 (if the fatty acid contained an odd number of carbon atoms), and H_2 (Table 2). Other species of *Syntrophomonas* use fatty acids up to C_{18} in length, including some unsaturated fatty acids. *Syntrophobacter wolinii* specializes in propionate (C_3) fermentation, generating acetate, CO_2, and H_2, and *Syntrophus gentianae* degrades aromatic compounds such as benzoate to acetate, H_2, and CO_2 (Table 2). However, the syntrophs are unable to carry out these syntrophic reactions in pure culture; their growth requires a H_2-consuming partner organism. This requirement has to do with the energetics of syntrophic processes.

H_2 consumption by a partner organism is absolutely essential for growth of the syntrophs. When the reactions in Table 2 are written with all reactants at standard conditions (solutes, 1 M; gases, 1 atm, 25°C), the reactions yield free-energy changes that are positive in arithmetic sign. That is, the $\Delta G^{0\prime}$ of these reactions is endergonic (Table 2). But H_2 consumption dramatically affects the energetics, making the reaction exergonic and allowing energy to be conserved. This can be seen in Table 2, where the ΔG values (free-energy change measured under actual conditions in the habitat) are exergonic if H_2 concentrations are kept very low through consumption by a partner organism.

The final products of the syntrophic partnership are CO_2 plus CH_4 (Figure 3), and virtually any organic compound that enters a methanogenic habitat will eventually be converted to

Table 2 Major reactions occurring in the anoxic conversion of organic compounds to methane[a]

Reaction type	Reaction	Free-energy change (kJ/reaction) $\Delta G^{0\prime b}$	ΔG^{c}
Fermentation of glucose to acetate, H_2, and CO_2	Glucose + 4 $H_2O \rightarrow$ 2 Acetate$^-$ + 2 HCO_3^- + 4 H^+ + 4 H_2	−207	−319
Fermentation of glucose to butyrate, CO_2, and H_2	Glucose + 2 $H_2O \rightarrow$ Butyrate$^-$ + 2 HCO_3^- + 2 H_2 + 3 H^+	−135	−284
Fermentation of butyrate to acetate and H_2	Butyrate$^-$ + 2 $H_2O \rightarrow$ 2 Acetate$^-$ + H^+ + 2 H_2	+48.2	−17.6
Fermentation of propionate to acetate, CO_2, and H_2	Propionate$^-$ + 3 $H_2O \rightarrow$ Acetate$^-$ + HCO_3^- + H^+ + H_2	+76.2	−5.5
Fermentation of ethanol to acetate and H_2	2 Ethanol + 2 $H_2O \rightarrow$ 2 Acetate$^-$ + 4 H_2 + 2 H^+	+19.4	−37
Fermentation of benzoate to acetate, CO_2, and H_2	Benzoate$^-$ + 7 $H_2O \rightarrow$ 3 Acetate$^-$ + 3 H^+ + HCO_3 + 3 H_2	+70.1	−18
Methanogenesis from H_2 + CO_2	4 H_2 + HCO_3^- + $H^+ \rightarrow CH_4$ + 3 H_2O	−136	−3.2
Methanogenesis from acetate	Acetate$^-$ + $H_2O \rightarrow CH_4$ + HCO_3^-	−31	−24.7
Acetogenesis from H_2 + CO_2	4 H_2 + 2 HCO_3^- + $H^+ \rightarrow$ Acetate$^-$ 4 H_2O	−105	−7.1

[a]Data adapted from Zinder, S. 1984. Microbiology of anaerobic conversion of organic wastes to methane: Recent developments. *Am. Soc. Microbiol.* 50:294–298.

[b]Standard conditions: solutes, 1 M; gases, 1 atm, 25°C.

[c]Concentrations of reactants in typical anoxic freshwater ecosystem: fatty acids, 1 m*M*; HCO_3^-, 20 m*M*; glucose, 10 μ*M*; CH_4, 0.6 atm; H_2, 10^{-4} atm.

these products. This includes even complex aromatic and aliphatic hydrocarbons. Additional organisms other than those shown in Figure 3 may be involved in such degradations, but eventually fatty acids and alcohols will be generated, and they will be converted to methanogenic substrates by the syntrophs.

Methanogenic Symbionts

In addition to the great diversity of free-living methanogens, endosymbiotic methanogens have also been found in certain protists. Several protists, including free-living aquatic amoebas and flagellates present in certain insect guts, have been shown to harbor methanogens. In termites, for example, methanogens are present primarily within cells of trichomonal protists inhabiting the termite hindgut (Figure 4). Methanogenic symbionts of protists are rod-shaped species of the genus *Methanobacterium* or *Methanobrevibacter*, but their exact relationship to free-living methanogens is unclear. In the termite hindgut, endosymbiotic methanogens (along with acetogens, see later text) are thought to benefit their protist hosts by consuming H_2 generated from glucose fermentation by cellulolytic protists.

Global Methanogenesis

Although levels of methanogenesis are high only in anoxic environments such as swamps, lake sediments, and marshes, or in the rumen (Section 10), there is some production of methane in habitats that would otherwise be considered oxic, such as forest and grassland soils. In such habitats methane is produced in anoxic microenvironments, for example in the midst of soil crumbs. In addition, certain plants make methane as well, although the mechanism of methane formation and the global input from this source is uncertain.

Table 3 lists the methane outputs of different habitats. Note that biogenic production of methane far exceeds production from gas wells and other abiogenic sources. Eructation by ruminants and CH_4 released from termites, paddy fields, and natural wetlands are the largest sources of biogenic methane (Table 3).

Acetogenic Habitats

A competing H_2-consuming process to methanogenesis is *acetogenesis* (formation of acetate). In some habitats, for example the rumen, acetogens appear to compete only poorly with methanogens, and thus methanogenesis is the dominant H_2-consuming process. But in other habitats, such as the termite hindgut, where methane is released by methanogens living inside protists (Figure 4), acetogenesis is quantitatively a much more important process.

Based on simple energetic considerations, methanogenesis from H_2 is more favorable than acetogenesis (−131 kJ versus −105 kJ, respectively), and thus methanogens should have a competitive advantage in all habitats in which the two processes compete. However, in termites they do not. There are at least three reasons why this may be so. First, in some way acetogens may be able to position themselves in the termite gut nearer to the source of H_2 than methanogens and thus consume the majority of H_2 produced from cellulose fermentation before it arrives to the endosymbiotic methanogens (Figure 4*c*). Second, unlike methanogens, acetogens can ferment glucose (obtained from cellulose). And third, termites eat wood, which contains a high lignin content, and this type of material may be degraded in such a way that favors the production of methoxylated aromatic compounds, which are also substrates for acetogens. So, despite the fact that termites are methanogenic (Table 3), carbon and electron flow favor acetogenesis in this anoxic habitat. Other habitats in which acetogenesis is a major process include very cold environments, such as permafrost soils, where the

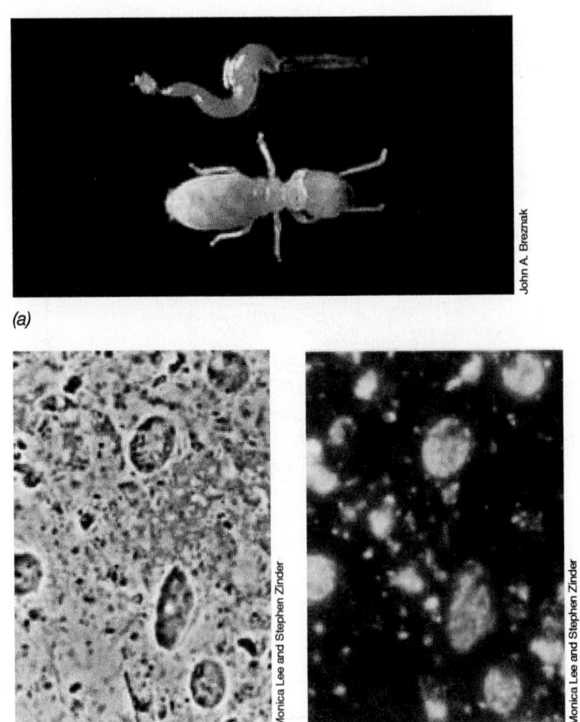

Figure 4 **Termites and their carbon metabolism.** *(a)* A common eastern (USA) subterranean termite worker larva shown beneath a hindgut extracted from a separate worker. The animal is about 0.5 cm long. Acetogenesis is the major form of anoxic carbon metabolism in these termites although methanogenesis also occurs. *(b, c)* Microorganisms from the hindgut of the termite, *Zootermopsis angusticolis*; a single microscope field was photographed by two different methods. *(b)* Phase contrast. *(c)* Epifluorescence, showing color typical of methanogens due to the high content of the fluorescent coenzyme F_{420}. The methanogens are inside cells of the protist *Tricercomitis* sp. Plant particles fluoresce yellow. The average diameter of a protist cell is 15–20 μm.

very cold temperatures seem to be better tolerated by acetogens than by methanogens.

Methanogenesis versus Sulfidogenesis

Methanogenesis and acetogenesis are extensive processes in anoxic freshwater sediments and terrestrial environments but not in marine sediments. This is because sulfate-reducing bacteria are abundant in marine sediments and outcompete methanogens and acetogens for H_2. The basis for this lies in the fact that the energetics of sulfate reduction with H_2 is better than the reduction of CO_2 with H_2 to either CH_4 or acetate; for biochemical reasons, this favors sulfate reduction. In freshwater, however, where sulfidogenesis is typically very low because sulfate is limiting, methanogenesis and acetogenesis dominate.

Table 3 Estimates of CH_4 released into the atmosphere[a]

Source	*CH_4 emission (10^{12} g/year)*	
Biogenic		
Ruminants	80–100	
Termites	25–150[b]	
Paddy fields	70–120	
Natural wetlands	120–200	
Landfills	5–70	
Oceans and lakes	1–20	
Tundra	1–5	
Abiogenic		
Coal mining	10–35	
Natural gas flaring and venting	10–30	
Industrial and pipeline losses	15–45	
Biomass burning	10–40	
Methane hydrates	2–4	
Volcanoes	0.5	
Automobiles	0.5	
Total	350–820	
Total biogenic	302–665	81–86% of total
Total abiogenic	48–155	13–19% of total

[a]Data adapted from estimates in Tyler, S. C. 1991. The global methane budget, pp. 7–58, in E. J. Rogers and W. B. Whitman (eds.), *Microbial Production and Consumption of Greenhouse Gases: Methane, Nitrogen Oxides, and Halomethanes*, American Society for Microbiology, Washington, DC.

[b]More recent estimates indicate that the lower value is probably the more accurate.

2 MiniReview

Under anoxic conditions, organic matter is degraded to CH_4 and CO_2. CH_4 is formed primarily from the reduction of CO_2 by H_2 and from acetate, both supplied by syntrophic bacteria; these organisms depend on H_2 consumption as the basis of their energetics. On a global basis, biogenic CH_4 is a much larger source than abiogenic CH_4.

- What kinds of organisms can grow in coculture with *Syntrophomonas*?
- What is the final product of acetogenesis? What anoxic habitat shows greater acetogenesis than methanogenesis?
- Why is methanogenesis from H_2 not a major process in marine sediments?

II NITROGEN, SULFUR, AND IRON CYCLES

In addition to carbon, many other key elements are metabolized by microorganisms. These include in particular *nitrogen*, *sulfur*, and *iron*, and we examine the cycling of these key nutrients now.

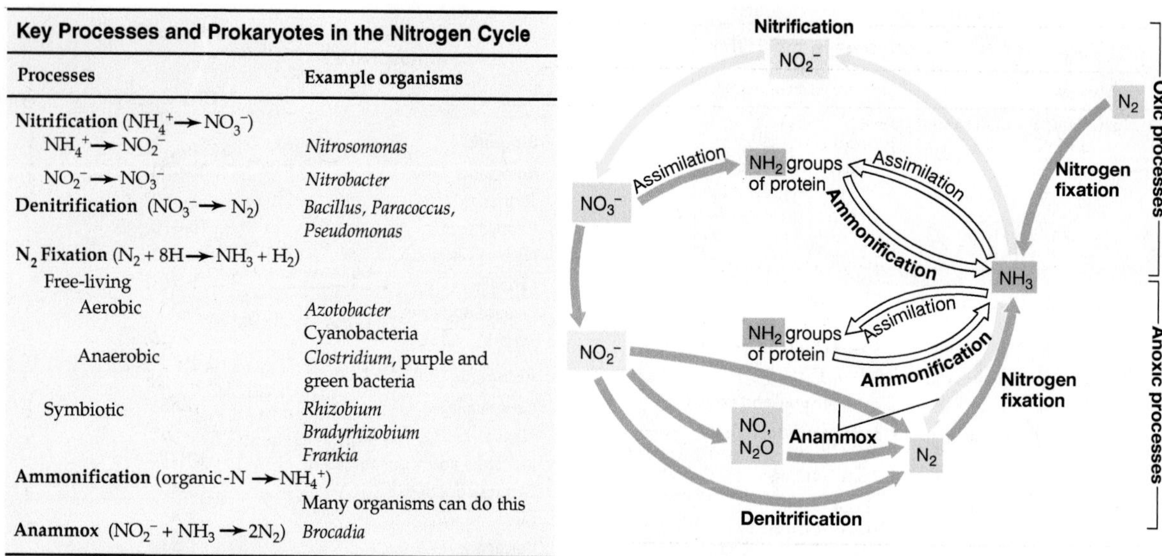

Key Processes and Prokaryotes in the Nitrogen Cycle

Processes	Example organisms
Nitrification ($NH_4^+ \rightarrow NO_3^-$)	
$NH_4^+ \rightarrow NO_2^-$	*Nitrosomonas*
$NO_2^- \rightarrow NO_3^-$	*Nitrobacter*
Denitrification ($NO_3^- \rightarrow N_2$)	*Bacillus, Paracoccus, Pseudomonas*
N_2 Fixation ($N_2 + 8H \rightarrow NH_3 + H_2$)	
Free-living	
Aerobic	*Azotobacter* Cyanobacteria
Anaerobic	*Clostridium*, purple and green bacteria
Symbiotic	*Rhizobium* *Bradyrhizobium* *Frankia*
Ammonification (organic-N $\rightarrow NH_4^+$)	Many organisms can do this
Anammox ($NO_2^- + NH_3 \rightarrow 2N_2$)	*Brocadia*

Figure 5 Redox cycle for nitrogen. Oxidation reactions are shown by yellow arrows and reductions by red arrows. Reactions without redox change are in white. The anammox reaction is $NH_3 + NO_2^- + H^+ \rightarrow N_2 + 2H_2O$.

3 The Nitrogen Cycle

The element nitrogen, N, a key constituent of cells, exists in a number of oxidation states. We have discussed four major microbial nitrogen transformations thus far: nitrification, denitrification, anammox, and nitrogen fixation. These and other key nitrogen transformations are summarized in the redox cycle shown in Figure 5.

Nitrogen Fixation

Nitrogen gas (N_2) is the most stable form of nitrogen and is a major reservoir for nitrogen on Earth. However, only a relatively small number of prokaryotes are able to use N_2 as a cellular nitrogen source by *nitrogen fixation* ($N_2 + 8\ H \rightarrow 2\ NH_3 + H_2$). The nitrogen recycled on Earth is mostly in fixed forms of nitrogen, such as ammonia (NH_3) and nitrate (NO_3^-). In many environments, however, the short supply of such compounds puts a premium on biological nitrogen fixation. We revisit this important process later in this chapter when we describe symbiotic N_2 fixation in Section 15.

Denitrification

Under most conditions, the end product of nitrate reduction is N_2, NO, or N_2O. The reduction of nitrate to gaseous nitrogen compounds, called *denitrification* (Figure 5), is the main means by which gaseous N_2 is formed biologically. On the one hand, denitrification is a detrimental process. For example, if fields fertilized with potassium nitrate fertilizer become waterlogged following heavy rains, anoxic conditions can develop and denitrification can be extensive; this removes fixed nitrogen from the soil. On the other hand, denitrification can aid in wastewater treatment. By removing nitrate, denitrification minimizes algal growth when the treated sewage is discharged into lakes and streams.

The production of N_2O and NO by denitrification can have other environmental consequences. N_2O can be photochemically oxidized to NO in the atmosphere. NO reacts with ozone (O_3) in the upper atmosphere to form nitrite (NO_2^-), and this returns to Earth as nitric acid (HNO_2). Thus, denitrification contributes to both ozone destruction and acid rain, leading to increased passage of ultraviolet radiation to the surface of Earth and acidic soils, respectively. Increases in soil acidity can change microbial community structure and function and, ultimately, soil fertility, impacting both plant diversity and agricultural yields of crop plants.

Ammonia Fluxes, Nitrification, and Anammox

Ammonia is released during the decomposition of organic nitrogen compounds such as amino acids and nucleotides, a process called *ammonification* (Figure 5). At neutral pH, ammonia exists as ammonium ion (NH_4^+). Much of the ammonium released by aerobic decomposition in soils is rapidly recycled and converted to amino acids in plants and microorganisms. However, because ammonia is volatile, some of it can be lost from alkaline soils by vaporization, and there are major losses of ammonia to the atmosphere in areas with dense animal populations (for example, cattle feedlots). On a global basis, however, ammonia constitutes only about 15% of

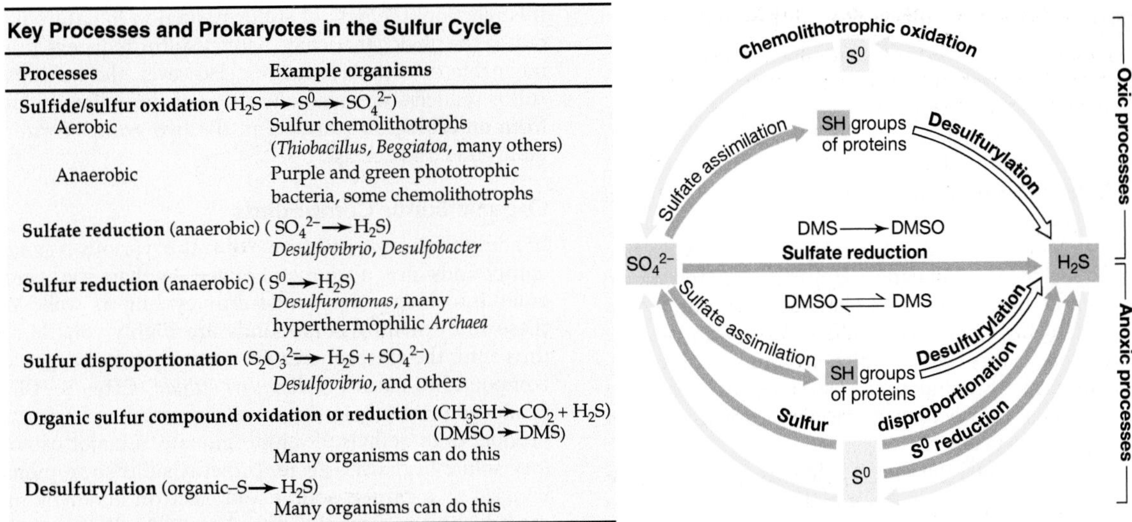

Key Processes and Prokaryotes in the Sulfur Cycle

Processes	Example organisms
Sulfide/sulfur oxidation ($H_2S \rightarrow S^0 \rightarrow SO_4^{2-}$)	
Aerobic	Sulfur chemolithotrophs (*Thiobacillus, Beggiatoa,* many others)
Anaerobic	Purple and green phototrophic bacteria, some chemolithotrophs
Sulfate reduction (anaerobic) ($SO_4^{2-} \rightarrow H_2S$)	*Desulfovibrio, Desulfobacter*
Sulfur reduction (anaerobic) ($S^0 \rightarrow H_2S$)	*Desulfuromonas,* many hyperthermophilic *Archaea*
Sulfur disproportionation ($S_2O_3^{2-} \rightarrow H_2S + SO_4^{2-}$)	*Desulfovibrio,* and others
Organic sulfur compound oxidation or reduction ($CH_3SH \rightarrow CO_2 + H_2S$) (DMSO → DMS)	Many organisms can do this
Desulfurylation (organic–S → H_2S)	Many organisms can do this

Figure 6 Redox cycle for sulfur. Oxidations are shown by yellow arrows and reductions by red arrows. Reactions without redox changes are in white. DMSO, dimethylsulfoxide; DMS, dimethylsulfide.

the nitrogen released to the atmosphere, the rest being primarily N_2 or N_2O from denitrification.

Nitrification, the oxidation of NH_3 to NO_3^-, occurs readily in well-drained soils at neutral pH through the activities of the nitrifying bacteria (Figure 5). Whereas denitrification *consumes* nitrate, nitrification *produces* nitrate. If materials high in protein, such as manure or sewage, are added to soils, the rate of nitrification increases. Although nitrate is readily assimilated by plants, it is very water-soluble and is rapidly leached or denitrified from soils receiving high rainfall. Consequently, nitrification is not beneficial to plant agriculture. Ammonia, on the other hand, is positively charged and strongly adsorbed to negatively charged clay-rich soils.

Anhydrous ammonia is used extensively as a nitrogen fertilizer, and chemicals are commonly added to the fertilizer to inhibit nitrification. One common inhibitor is a substituted pyridine called *nitrapyrin* (2-chloro-6-trichloromethylpyridine, also known as N-SERVE). Nitrapyrin specifically inhibits the first step in nitrification, the oxidation of NH_3 to NO_2^-. This effectively inhibits both steps in the nitrification process because the second step, $NO_2^- \rightarrow NO_3^-$, depends on the first. The addition of nitrification inhibitors to anhydrous ammonia has greatly increased the efficiency of crop fertilization and has helped prevent the pollution of waterways from nitrate leached from fertilized soils.

Ammonia can be catabolized anaerobically by *Brocadia* and related organisms in the process called *anammox.* In this reaction, ammonia is oxidized with nitrite (NO_2^-) as electron acceptor, forming N_2 as the final product (Figure 5), which is released to the atmosphere. Although a major process in sewage and sediments, anammox is not significant in well-drained soils.

3 MiniReview

The principal form of nitrogen on Earth is nitrogen gas (N_2), which can be used as a nitrogen source only by nitrogen-fixing bacteria. Ammonia produced by nitrogen fixation or by ammonification can be assimilated into organic matter or oxidized to nitrate. Denitrification and anammox cause losses of nitrogen from the biosphere.

- What is nitrogen fixation and why is it important to the nitrogen cycle?
- How do the processes of nitrification and denitrification differ? How do nitrification and anammox differ?
- How does the compound nitrapyrin benefit both agriculture and the environment?

4 The Sulfur Cycle

Sulfur transformations by microorganisms are even more complex than those of nitrogen because of the large number of oxidation states of sulfur and the fact that several transformations of sulfur occur abiotically. The redox cycle for microbial sulfur transformations is shown in Figure 6.

Although a number of oxidation states of sulfur are possible, only three are significant in nature, −2 (sulfhydryl, R—SH, and sulfide, HS^-), 0 (elemental sulfur, S^0), and +6 (sulfate, SO_4^{2-}). The bulk of the sulfur on Earth is in sediments and rocks in the form of sulfate minerals, primarily gypsum ($CaSO_4$) and sulfide minerals (pyrite, FeS_2), although the oceans constitute the most significant reservoir of sulfur (as sulfate) in the biosphere.

Hydrogen Sulfide and Sulfate Reduction

A major volatile sulfur gas is hydrogen sulfide (H_2S). Sulfide is produced from bacterial sulfate reduction ($SO_4^{2-} + 8\ H^+ \rightarrow H_2S + 2\ H_2O + 2\ OH^-$) (Figure 6) or is emitted from geochemical sources in sulfide springs and volcanoes. Although H_2S is volatile, the form of sulfide present in an environment is pH dependent: H_2S predominates below pH 7 and HS^- and S^{2-} predominate above pH 7.

Sulfate-reducing bacteria are a large and highly diverse group and are widespread in nature. However, in many anoxic habitats, such as freshwaters and many soils, sulfate reduction is limited by the low levels of sulfate. Moreover, because organic electron donors (or H_2, which is a product of the fermentation of organic compounds) are needed to support sulfate reduction, it only occurs where significant amounts of organic material are present.

In marine sediments, the rate of sulfate reduction is typically carbon-limited and can be greatly increased by the addition of organic matter. This is important because the disposal of sewage, sewage sludge, and garbage in the oceans can lead to marked increases in organic matter in the sediments and trigger sulfate reduction. Because H_2S is toxic to many plants and animals, formation of HS^- by sulfate reduction is potentially detrimental (sulfide is toxic because it combines with the iron of cytochromes and blocks respiration). Sulfide is commonly detoxified in the environment by combination with iron, forming the insoluble minerals FeS and FeS_2 (pyrite). The black color of sulfidic sediments is due to these metal sulfide minerals.

Sulfide and Elemental Sulfur Oxidation/Reduction

Under oxic conditions, sulfide rapidly oxidizes spontaneously at neutral pH. Sulfur-oxidizing chemolithotrophic bacteria, most of which are aerobes, can catalyze the oxidation of sulfide. However, because of the rapid chemical reaction, significant amounts of sulfide are oxidized by bacteria only in areas in which H_2S emerging from anoxic areas meets O_2 from oxic areas. In addition, if light is available, there can also be anoxic oxidation of sulfide, catalyzed by the phototrophic purple and green sulfur bacteria.

Elemental sulfur (S^0) is chemically stable but is readily oxidized by sulfur-oxidizing chemolithotrophic bacteria such as *Thiobacillus* and *Acidithiobacillus*. Elemental sulfur is insoluble, and thus the bacteria that oxidize it must attach to the sulfur crystals to obtain their substrate. The oxidation of elemental sulfur forms sulfuric acid (H_2SO_4), and thus sulfur oxidation characteristically lowers the pH in the environment. Elemental sulfur is sometimes added to alkaline soils to lower the pH, reliance being placed on the ubiquitous thiobacilli to carry out the acidification process.

Elemental sulfur can be reduced as well as oxidized. Sulfur reduction to sulfide (a form of anaerobic respiration) is a major ecological process, especially among hyperthermophilic *Archaea*. Although sulfate-reducing bacteria can also carry out this reaction, the bulk of sulfur reduction in nature is carried out by the phylogenetically distinct sulfur reducers, organisms incapable of sulfate reduction. However, the habitats of the sulfur reducers are generally those of the sulfate reducers, so from an ecological standpoint, the two groups form a metabolic guild and coexist.

Organic Sulfur Compounds

In addition to *inorganic* forms of sulfur, various *organic* sulfur compounds are also metabolized by bacteria, and these enter into biogeochemical sulfur cycling as well. Many of these foul-smelling compounds are highly volatile and can thus enter the atmosphere. The most abundant organic sulfur compound in nature is *dimethyl sulfide* ($CH_3—S—CH_3$); it is produced primarily in marine environments as a degradation product of dimethylsulfoniopropionate, a major osmoregulatory solute in marine algae. Dimethylsulfoniopropionate can be used as a carbon source and electron donor by microorganisms and is catabolized to dimethyl sulfide and acrylate. The latter, a derivative of the fatty acid propionate, is used to support growth.

Dimethyl sulfide released to the atmosphere undergoes photochemical oxidation to methane sulfonate ($CH_3SO_3^-$), SO_2, and SO_4^{2-}. By contrast, dimethyl sulfide produced in anoxic habitats can be transformed microbially in at least three ways: (1) by methanogenesis (yielding CH_4 and H_2S), (2) as an electron donor for photosynthetic CO_2 fixation in phototrophic purple bacteria (yielding dimethyl sulfoxide, DMSO), and (3) as an electron donor in energy metabolism in certain chemoorganotrophs and chemolithotrophs (also yielding DMSO). DMSO can be an electron acceptor for anaerobic respiration, producing dimethyl sulfide. Many other organic sulfur compounds affect the global sulfur cycle, including methanethiol (CH_3SH), dimethyl disulfide ($H_3C—S—S—CH_3$), and carbon disulfide (CS_2), but on a global basis, dimethyl sulfide is the most significant.

4 MiniReview

Bacteria play major roles in both the oxidative and reductive sides of the sulfur cycle. Sulfur- and sulfide-oxidizing bacteria produce sulfate, whereas sulfate-reducing bacteria consume sulfate, producing hydrogen sulfide. Because sulfide is toxic and reacts with various metals, sulfate reduction is an important biogeochemical process. Dimethyl sulfide is the major organic sulfur compound of ecological significance in nature.

- Is H_2S a substrate or a product of the sulfate-reducing bacteria? Of the chemolithotrophic sulfur bacteria?
- Why does the bacterial oxidation of sulfur result in a pH drop?
- What organic sulfur compound is most abundant in nature?

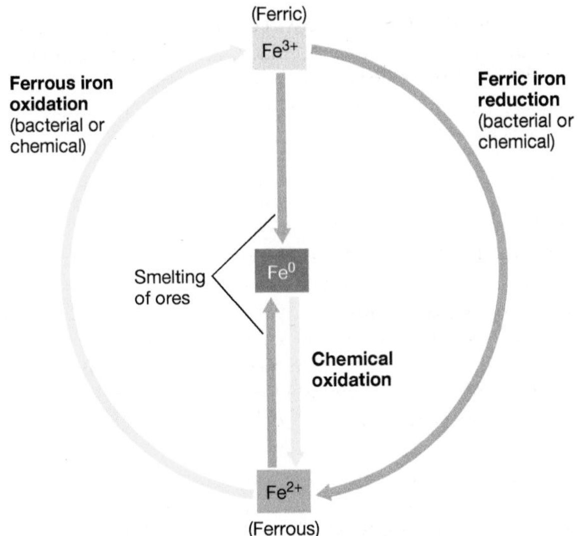

Figure 7 **Redox cycle for iron.** The major forms of iron in nature are Fe^{2+} and Fe^{3+}; Fe^0 is primarily a product of human activities in the smelting of iron ores. Oxidations are shown by yellow arrows and reductions by red arrows.

5 The Iron Cycle

Iron is one of the most abundant elements in Earth's crust. On the surface of Earth, iron exists naturally in two oxidation states, ferrous (Fe^{2+}) and ferric (Fe^{3+}). A third oxidation state, Fe^0, is a major product of human activities only, from the smelting of iron ores to form cast iron. In nature, iron cycles primarily between the ferrous and ferric forms. The redox reactions in the iron cycle include both oxidations and reductions. Fe^{3+} is reduced both chemically and as a form of anaerobic respiration, and Fe^{2+} is oxidized both chemically and as a form of chemolithotrophic metabolism (Figure 7).

Bacterial Iron Reduction

Some organisms can use ferric iron as an electron acceptor in anaerobic respiration. Ferric iron reduction is common in waterlogged soils, bogs, and anoxic lake sediments. Movement of iron-rich groundwater from anoxic bogs or waterlogged soils can result in the transport of large amounts of ferrous iron. When this iron-laden water reaches oxic regions, the ferrous iron is oxidized chemically or by iron bacteria. Ferric compounds then precipitate, leading to the formation of brown iron deposits:

$$Fe^{2+} + \tfrac{1}{4}O_2 + 2\tfrac{1}{2}H_2O \longrightarrow Fe(OH)_3 + 2\ H^+$$

The ferric hydroxide precipitate can interact with other nonbiological substances, such as humics (Section 1), to reduce Fe^{3+} back to Fe^{2+} (Figure 7). Ferric iron can also form complexes with various organic constituents. In this way it becomes solubilized and once again available to ferric iron-reducing bacteria as an electron acceptor.

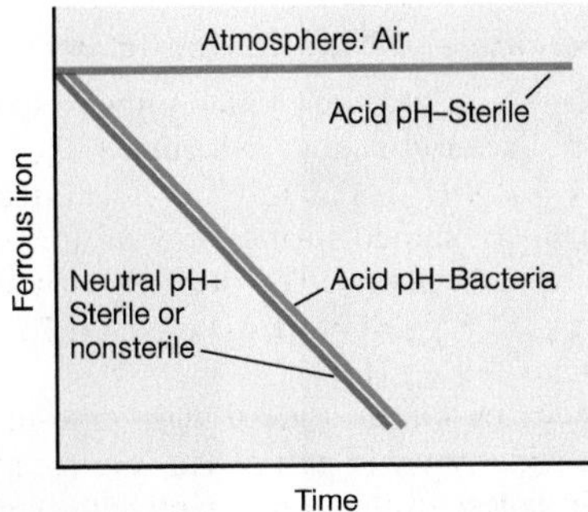

(a)

(b)

Figure 8 **Oxidation of ferrous iron (Fe^{2+}).** *(a)* Oxidation of ferrous iron as a function of pH and the presence of the bacterium *Acidithiobacillus ferrooxidans.* Note how Fe^{2+} is stable under acidic conditions in the absence of bacterial cells. *(b)* A microbial mat containing acidophilic green algae and various iron-oxidizing prokaryotes in the Rio Tinto, Spain. The river is highly acidic and contains high levels of dissolved metals, in particular Fe^{2+}. The red-brown precipitates contain $Fe(OH)_3$.

Ferrous Iron and Pyrite Oxidation at Acid pH

The only electron acceptor able to oxidize Fe^{2+} abiotically is O_2. In neutral pH habitats Fe^{2+} can be oxidized by iron bacteria such as *Gallionella* and *Leptothrix*. However, this occurs primarily at interfaces between anoxic ferrous-rich groundwaters and air. The most extensive bacterial iron oxidation occurs at acidic pH, where Fe^{2+} is stable to spontaneous oxidation. In extremely acidic habitats, the acidophilic chemolithotroph *Acidithiobacillus ferrooxidans* and related acidophilic iron oxidizers oxidize Fe^{2+} to Fe^{3+} (Figure 8). Very little energy is generated in the oxidation of ferrous to ferric iron, and so these bacteria must oxidize large amounts of iron in order to grow; consequently, even a small population can precipitate a

(a)

(b)

Figure 9 Pyrite and coal. *(a)* Pyrite in coal that can be oxidized by sulfur- and iron-oxidizing bacteria. Shown is a section through a piece of coal from the Black Mesa formation in northern Arizona (USA). The gold-colored spherical discs (about 1 mm in diameter) are particles of pyrite, FeS_2. *(b)* A coal seam in a surface coal-mining operation. Exposing the coal to oxygen and moisture stimulates the activities of iron-oxidizing bacteria growing on the pyrite in the coal.

FeS_2 (pyrite) + $3\frac{1}{2}$ O_2 + H_2O → Fe^{2+} + 2 SO_4^{2-} + 2 H^+

(a) **Initiator reaction** Spontaneous (bacteria may also catalyze)

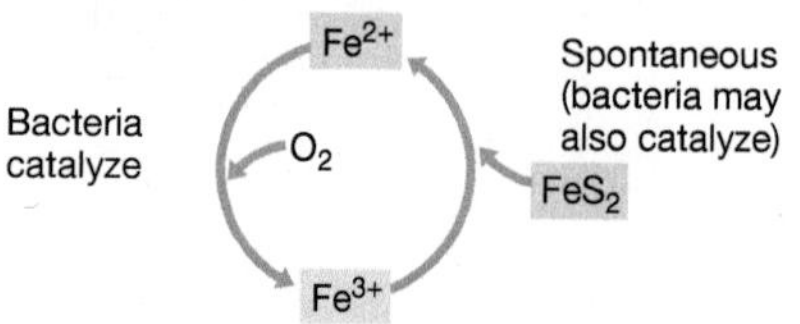

(b) **Propagation cycle**

Figure 10 Role of iron-oxidizing bacteria in oxidation of the mineral pyrite. *(a)* The primarily nonbiological initiator reaction *(b)* The propagation cycle, which includes biotic and abiotic components.

large amount of iron. *A. ferrooxidans* is a strict acidophile and is very common in acid mine drainages and in acidic springs; it is responsible for most of the ferric iron precipitated under moderately acidic (pH 2–4) conditions.

A. ferrooxidans and *Leptospirillum ferrooxidans* live in environments in which sulfuric acid is the dominant acid and large amounts of sulfate are present. At 20–30°C and moderately acidic pH, *A. ferrooxidans* dominates; at 30–50°C and more acidic pH (1–2), *L. ferrooxidans* is the dominant organism. Under these conditions, ferric iron does not precipitate as the hydroxide but as a complex sulfate mineral called *jarosite* $[HFe_3(SO_4)_2(OH)_6]$. Jarosite is a yellowish or brownish precipitate and is one of the major pollutants in acid mine drainage, an unsightly yellow solution called "yellow boy" by U.S. coal miners (Figure 8). *A. ferrooxidans* and *L. ferrooxidans* are phylogenetically and morphologically distinct, but are also distinct in their metabolism. Whereas *L. ferrooxidans* can grow only on Fe^{2+}, *A. ferrooxidans* grows chemolithotrophically on either Fe^{2+} or S^0 as electron donors.

One of the most common forms of iron in nature is **pyrite** (FeS_2). Pyrite forms from the reaction of sulfur with ferrous sulfide (FeS) as an insoluble crystalline mineral; pyrite is very common in bituminous coals and in many ore bodies (Figure 9). The bacterial oxidation of pyrite is of great significance in the development of acidic conditions in coal-mining operations (Figure 9*b*). Additionally, oxidation of pyrite by bacteria is of considerable importance in the microbial leaching of ores described in the next section.

The oxidation of pyrite is a combination of chemically and bacterially catalyzed reactions. Two electron acceptors are involved in this process: molecular oxygen (O_2) and ferric ions (Fe^{3+}). When pyrite is first exposed, as in a mining operation (Figure 9*b*), a slow chemical reaction with O_2 occurs, as shown in Figure 10*a*. This reaction, called the *initiator reaction,* leads to the oxidation of sulfide to sulfate and the development of acidic conditions under which the ferrous iron released is stable in the presence of oxygen. *A. ferrooxidans* and *L. ferrooxidans* then catalyze the oxidation of ferrous iron to ferric iron. The Fe^{3+} formed under these acidic conditions, being soluble, reacts spontaneously with more pyrite and oxidizes it to ferrous ions plus sulfuric acid:

$$FeS_2 + 14\,Fe^{3+} + 8\,H_2O \longrightarrow 15\,Fe^{2+} + 2\,SO_4^{2-} + 16\,H^+$$

The ferrous ions formed are again oxidized to ferric ions by the bacteria, and these ferric ions again react with more pyrite. Thus, there is a progressive, rapidly increasing rate at which pyrite is oxidized, called the *propagation cycle* (Figure 10*b*). Under natural conditions some of the ferrous iron generated by the bacteria leaches away, being carried by groundwater into surrounding streams. However, because oxygen is present in the aerated drainage, bacterial oxidation of the ferrous iron takes place in these outflows and an insoluble ferric precipitate is formed.

Acid Mine Drainage

Bacterial oxidation of sulfide minerals is the major factor in **acid mine drainage**, an environmental problem in coal-mining regions (Figure 11). Mixing of acidic mine waters into natural waters in rivers and lakes seriously degrades water quality because both the acid and the dissolved metals are toxic to aquatic organisms. In addition, such polluted waters are unsuitable for human consumption and industrial use. The breakdown of pyrite ultimately leads to the formation of sulfuric acid and ferrous iron, and pH values can be lower than 1. The acid formed attacks other minerals associated with the coal and pyrite, causing breakdown of the rock fabric. A major rock-forming element, aluminum, is soluble only at low pH, and often high levels of Al^{3+}, which

Figure 11 Acid mine drainage from a bituminous coal region. Note the yellowish-red color ("yellow boy") due to precipitated iron oxides.

can be highly toxic to aquatic organisms, are present in acid mine waters.

The oxygen requirement for the oxidation of ferrous to ferric iron explains how acid mine drainage develops. As long as the coal is unmined, pyrite cannot be oxidized because air, water, and the bacteria cannot reach it. However, when the coal seam is exposed (Figure 9*b*), it quickly becomes contaminated with *A. ferrooxidans,* and O_2 and water are introduced, making oxidation of pyrite possible. The acid formed can then leach into the surrounding streams (Figure 11).

Where acid mine drainage is extensive, a strongly acidophilic species of *Archaea, Ferroplasma,* is typically present. This aerobic iron-oxidizing prokaryote is capable of growth at pH 0 and at temperatures to 50°C. *Ferroplasma acidarmanus* forms slimy cell masses attached to pyrite surfaces in iron ore deposits. At Iron Mountain, California (Figure 12), a particularly well-studied acid mine drainage site, the thick biofilm of *F. acidarmanus* maintains the pH near 0. With iron concentrations of nearly 30 g/l at this site, the *F. acidarmanus* mat is constantly bathed in fresh substrate (Fe^{2+}) from which more acid is generated by the reactions described previously. *Ferroplasma* is a cell wall–less prokaryote and is phylogenetically related to *Thermoplasma* (Figure 12*b*).

5 MiniReview

Iron exists naturally in two oxidation states, ferrous (Fe^{2+}) and ferric (Fe^{3+}). Bacteria reduce ferric iron in anoxic environments and oxidize ferrous iron aerobically at acidic pH. Ferrous iron oxidation is common in coal-mining regions where it causes a type of pollution called acid mine drainage.

- What oxidation state is iron in the mineral $Fe(OH)_3$? FeS? How is $Fe(OH)_3$ formed?
- Why does biological Fe^{2+} oxidation under oxic conditions occur mainly at acidic pH?

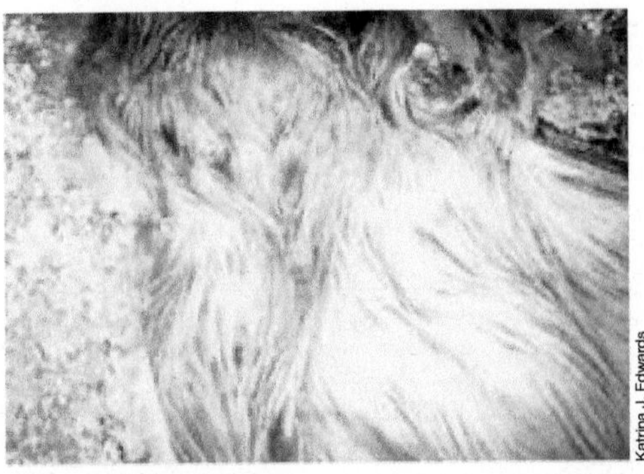

(a)

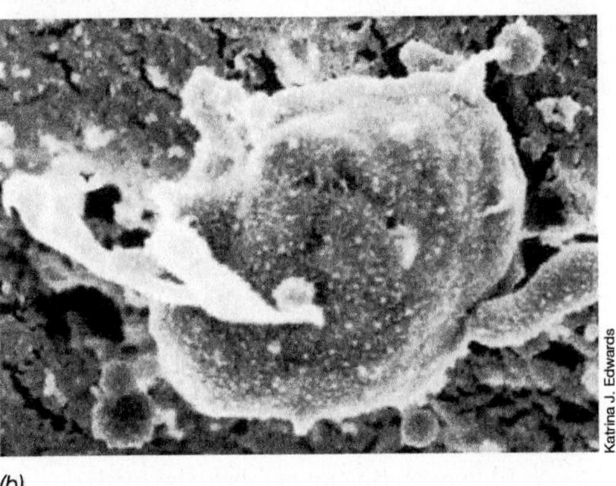

(b)

Figure 12 ***Ferroplasma acidarmanus.*** An extremely acidophilic iron-oxidizing archaeon responsible for severe acid mine drainage. *(a)* Streamers of *F. acidarmanus* cells growing in an acid (pH near 0) mine drainage stream, Iron Mountain, CA. *(b)* Scanning electron micrograph of a cell of *F. acidarmanus* among mineral matter.

III MICROBIAL BIOREMEDIATION

The biogeochemical capacities of microorganisms seem almost limitless, and it has often been said that microorganisms are Earth's greatest chemists. As such, microorganisms have been used to extract valuable metals from low-grade ores (microbial leaching) and as agents for cleaning up the environment. The term **bioremediation** refers to the cleanup of oil, toxic chemicals, or other pollutants from the environment by microorganisms. Bioremediation is a cost-effective way of cleaning up pollutants, and in some cases, is the only practical way to get the job done.

6 Microbial Leaching of Ores

The acid production and mineral dissolution by acidophilic bacteria discussed in the previous section can be put to use in the mining of metal ores. Sulfide forms insoluble minerals with many metals, and many ores mined as sources of these metals are sulfides. If the concentration of metal in the ore is

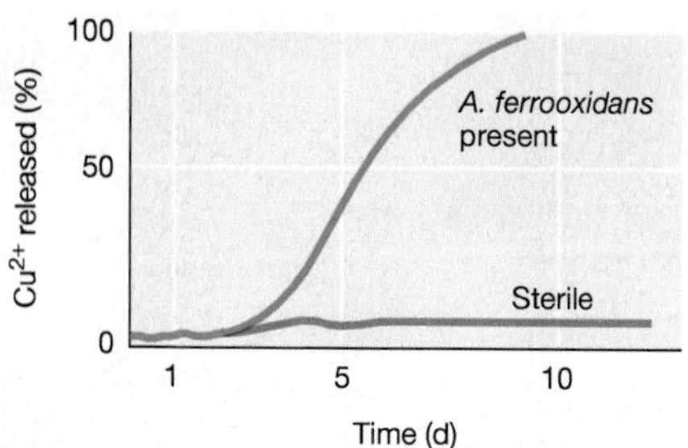

Figure 13 Effect of the bacterium *Acidithiobacillus ferrooxidans* on the leaching of copper from the mineral covellite (CuS). The leaching was done in a laboratory column and the acidic leach solution contained inorganic nutrients necessary for growth of the bacterium. The leaching activity was monitored by assaying for soluble copper in the leach solution at the bottom of the column. The leach solution was continuously recirculated, maintaining an essentially closed system.

low, it may not be economically feasible to concentrate the mineral by conventional means. Under these conditions, **microbial leaching** is practiced. Leaching is especially useful for copper ores because copper sulfate, formed during the oxidation of copper sulfide ores, is very water-soluble. Indeed, approximately one-fourth of all of the copper mined worldwide is obtained by leaching.

Acidithiobacillus ferrooxidans and other metal-oxidizing chemolithotrophic bacteria can catalyze the oxidation of sulfide minerals, thus aiding in solubilization of the metal. The relative oxidation rates of a copper mineral in the presence and absence of bacteria are illustrated in Figure 13. The susceptibility to oxidation varies among minerals, and those minerals that are most readily oxidized are most amenable to microbial leaching. Thus, iron and copper sulfide ores such as pyrrhotite (FeS) and covellite (CuS) are readily leached, whereas lead and molybdenum ores are much less so.

The Leaching Process

In microbial leaching, low-grade ore is dumped in a large pile (the leach dump) and a dilute sulfuric acid solution (pH 2) is percolated down through the pile (Figure 14). The liquid emerging from the bottom of the pile (Figure 14*b*) is rich in dissolved metals and is transported to a precipitation plant (Figure 14*c*) where the desired metal is precipitated and purified (Figure 14*d*). The liquid is then pumped back to the top of the pile and the cycle repeated. As needed, acid is added to maintain the low pH.

We illustrate copper ore leaching with the example of covellite (CuS), in which copper has a valence of +2. As shown in Figure 15, *A. ferrooxidans* oxidizes the sulfide in CuS to SO_4^{2-}, thus releasing copper as Cu^{2+}. However, this reaction can also occur spontaneously. Indeed, the key reaction in copper leaching is the chemical oxidation of CuS with ferric ions generated by the bacterial oxidation of ferrous ions (Figure 15). In any copper ore, pyrite (FeS_2) is also present,

Figure 14 The leaching of low-grade copper ores using iron-oxidizing bacteria. *(a)* A typical leaching dump. The low-grade ore has been crushed and dumped in a large pile in such a way that the surface area exposed is as high as possible. Pipes distribute the acidic leach water over the surface of the pile. The acidic water slowly percolates through the pile and exits at the bottom. *(b)* Effluent from a copper leaching dump. The acidic water is very rich in Cu^{2+}. *(c)* Recovery of copper as metallic copper (Cu^0) by passage of the Cu^{2+}-rich water over metallic iron in a long flume. *(d)* A small pile of metallic copper removed from the flume, ready for further purification.

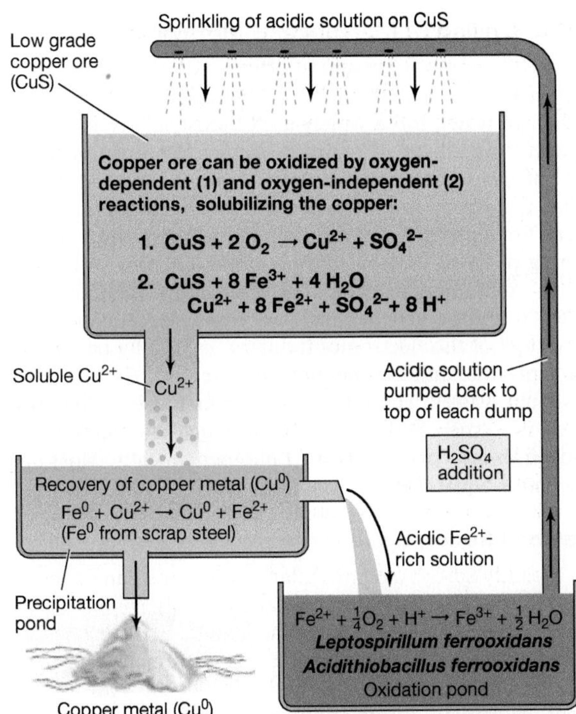

Figure 15 Arrangement of a leaching pile and reactions in the microbial leaching of copper sulfide minerals to yield metallic copper. Reaction 1 occurs both biologically and chemically. Reaction 2 is strictly chemical and is the most important reaction in copper-leaching processes. For Reaction 2 to proceed, it is essential that the Fe^{2+} produced from the oxidation of sulfide in CuS to sulfate be oxidized back to Fe^{3+} by iron chemolithotrophs.

Figure 16 Gold bioleaching. Gold leaching tanks in Ghana (Africa). Within the tanks, a mixture of *Acidithiobacillus ferrooxidans*, *Acidithiobacillus thiooxidans*, and *Leptospirillum ferrooxidans* solubilizes the pyrite/arsenic mineral containing trapped gold and releases the gold.

and its oxidation by bacteria leads to the formation of Fe^{3+} (Figure 15). The spontaneous reaction of CuS with Fe^{3+} forms Cu^{2+} plus Fe^{2+}. Importantly, this reaction can take place deep in the leach dump where conditions are anoxic.

Metal Recovery

The precipitation plant is where the Cu^{2+} from the leaching solution is recovered (Figure 14*c*, *d*). Shredded scrap iron, Fe^0, is added to the precipitation pond to recover copper from the leach liquid by the reaction shown in the lower part of Figure 15, and this once again results in the formation of Fe^{2+}. This Fe^{2+}-rich liquid is transferred to a shallow oxidation pond where *A. ferrooxidans* grows and oxidizes the Fe^{2+} to Fe^{3+}. This now ferric-rich liquid is pumped to the top of the pile and the Fe^{3+} used to oxidize more CuS (Figure 15). The entire leaching operation is thus maintained by the oxidation of Fe^{2+} to Fe^{3+} by the iron-oxidizing bacteria.

High temperature can be a problem with leaching operations. *A. ferrooxidans* is a mesophile, but temperatures inside a leach dump often rise spontaneously as a result of heat generated by microbial activities. Thus, thermophilic iron-oxidizing chemolithotrophs such as thermophilic *Thiobacillus* species, *Leptospirillum ferrooxidans*, and *Sulfobacillus* or, at higher temperatures (60–80°C), the organism *Sulfolobus*, are also important in the leaching of ores.

Other Microbial Leaching Processes: Uranium and Gold

Microorganisms are also used in the leaching of uranium and gold ores. *A. ferrooxidans* can oxidize U^{4+} to U^{6+} with O_2 as an electron acceptor. However, uranium leaching probably depends more on the abiotic oxidation of U^{4+} by Fe^{3+}, with *A. ferrooxidans* contributing mainly through the reoxidation of Fe^{2+} to Fe^{3+} as in copper leaching (Figure 15). The reaction observed is

$$\underset{(U^{4+})}{UO_2} + \underset{(Fe^{3+})}{Fe_2(SO_4)_3} \longrightarrow \underset{(U^{6+})}{UO_2SO_4} + 2\ \underset{(Fe^{2+})}{FeSO_4}$$

Unlike UO_2, the oxidized uranium mineral is soluble and is recovered by other processes.

Gold is typically found in deposits associated with minerals containing arsenic and pyrite. *A. ferrooxidans* and its relatives can attack and solubilize the arsenopyrite minerals, releasing the trapped gold (Au):

$$2\ FeAsS[Au] + 7\ O_2 + 2\ H_2O + H_2SO_4 \longrightarrow Fe_2(SO_4)_3 + 2\ H_3AsO_4 + [Au]$$

The gold is then complexed with cyanide by traditional gold-mining methods. Unlike copper, where leaching occurs in a huge leach dump (Figure 14*a*), gold leaching takes place in relatively small and enclosed bioreactor tanks (Figure 16), where more than 95% of the trapped gold is released. Moreover, although arsenic and cyanide are toxic residues from the mining process, both are removed in the gold-leaching bioreactor. Arsenic is removed as a ferric precipitate, and cyanide (CN^-) is removed by its microbial oxidation to CO_2 plus urea in later stages of the gold recovery process. Small-scale microbial gold leaching has thus

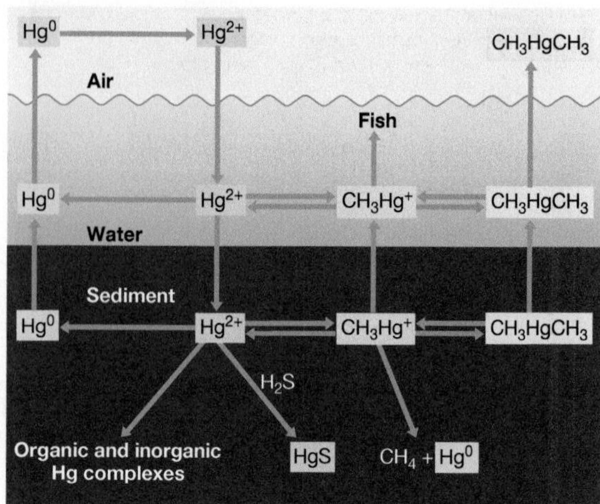

Figure 17 **Biogeochemical cycling of mercury.** The major reservoirs of mercury are in water and in sediments where it can be concentrated in animal tissues or precipitated out as HgS, respectively. The forms of mercury commonly found in aquatic environments are each shown in a different color.

become popular as an alternative to the more costly and environmentally devastating conventional gold-mining techniques. Pilot processes are also being developed for the bioleaching of zinc, lead, and nickel using bioreactor methods.

6 MiniReview

Bacterial solubilization of copper is a process called microbial leaching. Leaching is important in the recovery of copper, uranium, and gold from low-grade ores. Bacterial oxidation of ferrous iron is the key reaction in the microbial leaching process because the ferric iron itself can oxidize metals in the ores.

- How can CuS be oxidized under anoxic conditions?
- Why is it important to keep the sprinkling solution in the copper ore leaching process acidic?
- From the standpoint of metal oxidation, how does the copper leaching process differ from the gold leaching process?

7 Mercury and Heavy Metal Transformations

Metals are typically present in low concentrations in rocks, soils, waters, and the atmosphere. Some of these are trace metals needed by cells (for example, cobalt, copper, zinc, nickel, molybdenum). In high concentrations, however, these same metals can be toxic. Of these, several are sufficiently volatile to contaminate air as well. These include mercury, lead, arsenic, cadmium, and selenium. Because of environmental concern and significant microbial involvement, we focus our discussion on the biogeochemistry of the element mercury.

Global Cycling of Mercury and Methylmercury

Although mercury is present in extremely low concentrations in most natural environments, averaging about 1 nanogram per liter of water, it is a widely used industrial product and is an active ingredient of many pesticides. Because of its unusual propensity to concentrate in living tissues and its high toxicity, mercury is of considerable environmental importance. For example, the mining of mercury ores and the burning of fossil fuels release about 40,000 *tons* of mercury into the environment each year; even more mercury is released in abiotic geochemical processes. Mercury is also a by-product of the electronics industry (especially battery and wiring production), the chemical industry, and the burning of municipal wastes. The major form of mercury in the atmosphere is elemental mercury (Hg^0), which is volatile and is oxidized to mercuric ion (Hg^{2+}) photochemically. Most mercury enters aquatic environments as Hg^{2+} (Figure 17).

Microbial Redox Cycle for Mercury

Hg^{2+} readily adsorbs to particulate matter and can be metabolized from there by microorganisms. Microbial activity results in the methylation of mercury, yielding *methylmercury*, CH_3Hg^+ (Figure 17). Methylmercury is extremely toxic to animals because it can be absorbed through the skin and is a potent neurotoxin. But in addition, methylmercury is soluble and can be concentrated in the food chain, primarily in fish, or can be further methylated by microorganisms to yield the volatile compound dimethylmercury, $CH_3{-}Hg{-}CH_3$.

Both methylmercury and dimethylmercury accumulate in animals, especially in muscle tissues. Methylmercury is about 100 times more toxic than Hg^0 or Hg^{2+}, and its accumulation seems to be a particular problem in freshwater lakes and marine coastal waters where enhanced levels have been observed in recent years in fish caught for human consumption. Mercury can also cause liver and kidney damage in humans and other animals.

Several other mercury transformations occur on a global scale, including reactions carried out by sulfate-reducing bacteria ($H_2S + Hg^{2+} \rightarrow HgS$) and methanogens ($CH_3Hg^+ \rightarrow CH_4 + Hg^0$) (Figure 17). The solubility of HgS is very low, so in anoxic sulfate-reducing sediments, most mercury is present as HgS. But upon aeration, HgS is oxidized, primarily by thiobacilli, leading to the formation of Hg^{2+} and SO_4^{2-}, and eventually, methylmercury.

Mercuric Resistance

At sufficiently high concentrations, Hg^{2+} and CH_3Hg^+ can be toxic not only to higher organisms but also to microorganisms. However, several bacteria can carry out the biotransformation of toxic mercury to nontoxic forms. In mercury-resistant gram-negative bacteria the NADPH-linked enzyme mercuric reductase reduces Hg^{2+} to Hg^0. The Hg^0 produced in this reaction is volatile but is nontoxic to humans and microorganisms. Bacterial conversion of Hg^{2+} to Hg^0 then allows for more CH_3Hg^+ to be converted to Hg^{2+}.

In the gram-negative bacterium *Pseudomonas aeruginosa*, genes for mercury resistance reside on a plasmid. These genes, called *mer* genes, are arranged in an operon and are under control of the regulatory protein MerR (Figure 18). MerR functions as both a repressor and an activator of transcription. In the absence of Hg^{2+}, MerR functions as a repressor and binds to the operator region of the *mer* operon, thus preventing transcription of *merTPCAD*. However, when Hg^{2+} is present, it forms a complex with MerR, which then activates transcription of the *mer* operon.

The protein MerP is a periplasmic Hg^{2+}-binding protein. MerP binds Hg^{2+} and transfers it to a membrane protein MerT, which transports Hg^{2+} into the cell for reduction by mercuric reductase (Figure 18*b*). The final result is reduction of Hg^{2+} to Hg^0 (which, as discussed, is volatile and nontoxic) and release of the Hg^0 from the cell (Figure 18*b*).

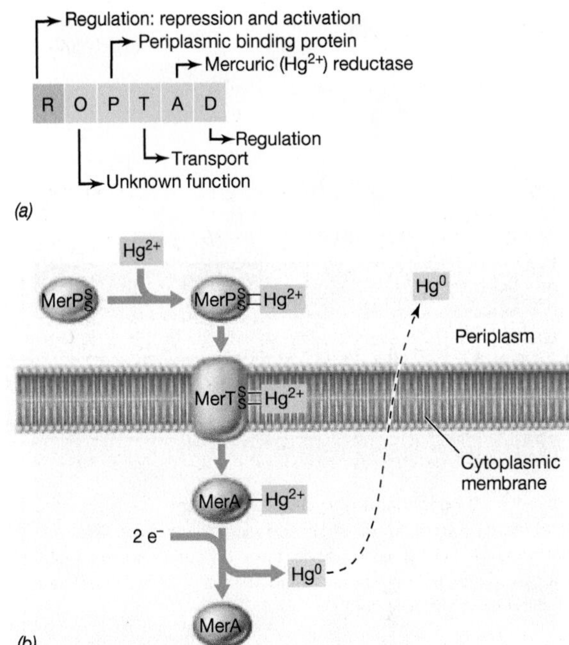

Figure 18 Mechanism of Hg^{2+} reduction to Hg^0 in *Pseudomonas aeruginosa*. *(a)* The *mer* operon. MerR can function as either a repressor (absence of Hg^{2+}) or transcriptional activator (presence of Hg^{2+}). *(b)* Transport and reduction of Hg^{2+}. Hg^{2+} is bound by cysteine residues in both proteins MerP and MerT.

Microbial Resistance to Other Heavy Metals

Plasmids isolated from diverse gram-positive and gram-negative *Bacteria* encode resistance to heavy metals. Certain antibiotic resistance plasmids also have genes for resistance to mercury and arsenic. The mechanism of resistance to any specific metal varies. For example, arsenate and cadmium resistances are due to the activity of enzymes that pump out any arsenate or cadmium that enters the cell, thus preventing the metals from accumulating and denaturing proteins. Other resistances involve redox changes in the metal. Bacteria naturally resistant to high levels of several different metals often contain multiple plasmids encoding the resistances. Such multiple-resistant organisms are common in wastewater effluents of the metal-processing industry or in mining operations, where heavy metals are typically leached out along with iron or copper (Section 6).

7 MiniReview

A major toxic form of mercury is methylmercury, which can yield Hg^{2+}, which is reduced by bacteria to Hg^0. The ability of bacteria to resist the toxicity of heavy metals is often due to the presence of specific plasmids that encode enzymes capable of detoxifying or pumping out the metals.

- What forms of mercury are most toxic to organisms?
- How is mercury detoxified by bacteria?

8 Petroleum Biodegradation

Petroleum is a rich source of organic matter, and because of this, microorganisms readily attack hydrocarbons when petroleum is brought into contact with air and moisture. Under some circumstances, such as in bulk storage tanks, microbial growth is undesirable. However, in oil spills, bioremediation is desirable and can be promoted by the addition of inorganic nutrients. Indeed, the importance of prokaryotes to petroleum bioremediation has been demonstrated in several major crude oil spills in recent years (Figure 19).

Both anoxic and oxic biodegradation is possible. Under oxic conditions we emphasized the important role that oxygenase enzymes play in introducing oxygen atoms into the hydrocarbon. Our discussion here will thus focus on aerobic processes, because it is only when oxygen is present that oxygenase enzymes are active and hydrocarbon oxidation a rapid process.

Hydrocarbon Decomposition

Diverse bacteria, fungi, and a few cyanobacteria and green algae can oxidize petroleum products aerobically. Small-scale oil pollution of aquatic and terrestrial ecosystems from human as well as natural activities is common. Oil-oxidizing microorganisms develop rapidly on oil films and slicks.

Oil-oxidizing activity is most extensive if temperature and inorganic nutrient (primarily nitrogen and phosphorous) concentrations are optimal. Because oil is insoluble in water and is less dense, it floats to the surface and forms slicks. There, hydrocarbon-degrading bacteria attach to the oil droplets (Figure 20) and eventually decompose the oil and disperse the slick. Certain oil-degrading specialist species, such as *Alcanivorax borkumensis*, a bacterium that grows only on hydrocarbons, fatty acids, or pyruvate, produce glycolipid surfactants that help break up the oil and solubilize it. Once solubilized, the oil can be taken up more readily and catabolized as an energy source.

(a)

(b)

(c)

Figure 19 **Environmental consequences of large oil spills and the effect of bioremediation.** *(a)* A contaminated beach along the coast of Alaska containing oil from the *Exxon Valdez* spill of 1989. *(b)* The center rectangular plot (arrow) was treated with inorganic nutrients to stimulate bioremediation of spilled oil by microorganisms, whereas areas to the left and right were untreated. *(c)* Oil spilled into the Mediterranean Sea from the Jiyyeh (Lebanon) power plant that flowed to the port of Byblos during the 2006 war in Lebanon.

In large oil spills, volatile hydrocarbon fractions evaporate quickly, leaving medium- to longer-chain aliphatic and aromatic components for cleanup crews and microorganisms to tackle. Microorganisms consume oil by oxidizing it to CO_2. When bioremediation activities have been promoted by inorganic nutrient application, oil-oxidizing bacteria can grow quickly after an oil spill (Figure 20*b*). Under ideal bioremediation conditions, up to 80% of the nonvolatile components in oil can be oxidized within a year of a spill. However, certain oil fractions, such as those containing branched-chain and polycyclic hydrocarbons, remain in the environment much longer. Spilled oil that travels to marine sediments is more slowly degraded, and it can have a significant long-term impact on fisheries and related activities that depend on unpolluted waters for productive yields.

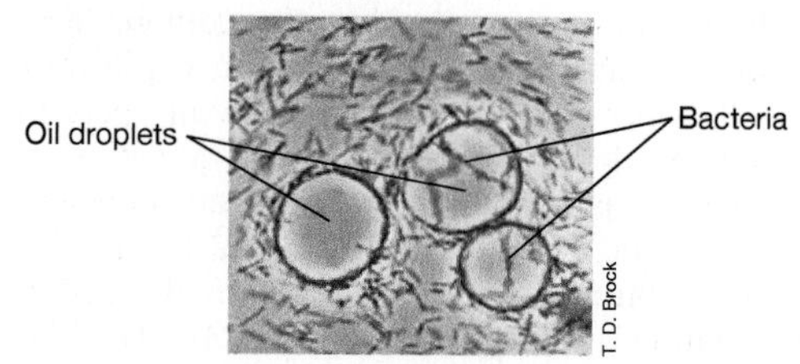

Figure 20 **Hydrocarbon-oxidizing bacteria in association with oil droplets.** The bacteria are concentrated in large numbers at the oil–water interface but are actually not within the droplet itself.

Interfaces where oil and water meet often form on a large scale. For example, it is virtually impossible to keep moisture from accumulating inside bulk-fuel storage tanks because water forms in a layer beneath the petroleum. Gasoline and crude oil storage tanks (Figure 21) are thus potential habitats for hydrocarbon-oxidizing microorganisms. If sufficient sulfate is present in the water, sulfate-reducing bacteria can grow in the tanks, consuming hydrocarbons under anoxic conditions. The sulfide (H_2S) produced is highly corrosive and causes pitting and subsequent leakage of the tanks along with souring of the fuel.

Petroleum Production

In addition to microbial *degradation* of petroleum, some microorganisms can also *produce* petroleum, particularly certain green algae. For example, as the colonial alga *Botryococcus braunii* grows, it excretes long-chain (C_{30}–C_{36})

Figure 21 **Oil biodegradation.** Bulk fuel-storage tanks often support massive microbial growth at oil–water interfaces.

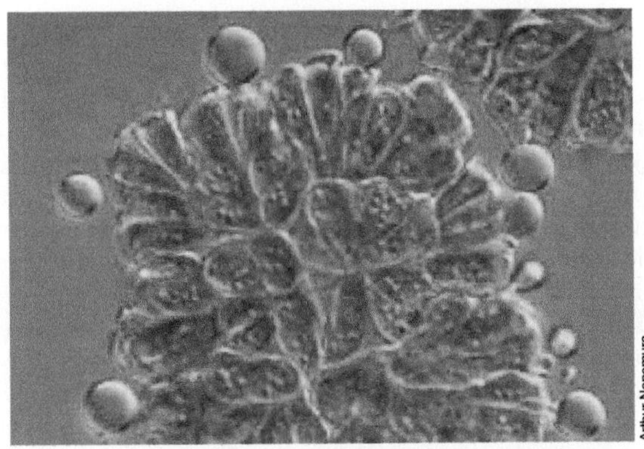

Figure 22 **Phototrophic oil production.** Photomicrograph by Nomarski interference contrast of cells of the green alga *Botryococcus braunii*. Note excreted oil droplets at the margin of the cells.

hydrocarbons that have the consistency of crude oil (Figure 22). In *B. braunii* about 30% of the cell dry weight is petroleum, and there has been some interest in using this and other oil-producing algae as renewable sources of petroleum. There is even evidence that oil in certain types of oil shale formations originated from green algae like *B. braunii* that grew in lakebeds in ancient times.

8 MiniReview

Hydrocarbons are subject to microbial oxidation. Hydrocarbon-oxidizing bacteria bioremediate spilled oil, and their activities are assisted by addition of inorganic nutrients. Some algae can produce hydrocarbons.

- What is bioremediation?
- Why would the addition of inorganic nutrients stimulate oil degradation whereas the addition of glucose would not?

9 Biodegradation of Xenobiotics

A **xenobiotic** compound is a synthetic chemical that is not naturally occurring. Xenobiotics include pesticides, polychlorinated biphenyls (PCBs), munitions, dyes, and chlorinated solvents, among other things. Some xenobiotics are structurally related to natural compounds and can sometimes be degraded slowly by enzymes that degrade the structurally related natural compounds. However, many xenobiotics differ chemically in such a major way from anything organisms have naturally experienced that they degrade extremely slowly, if at all. We focus here on pesticides as an example of the potential of microbial xenobiotics degradation.

Pesticide Catabolism

Some of the most widely distributed xenobiotics are pesticides, which are common components of toxic wastes. Over

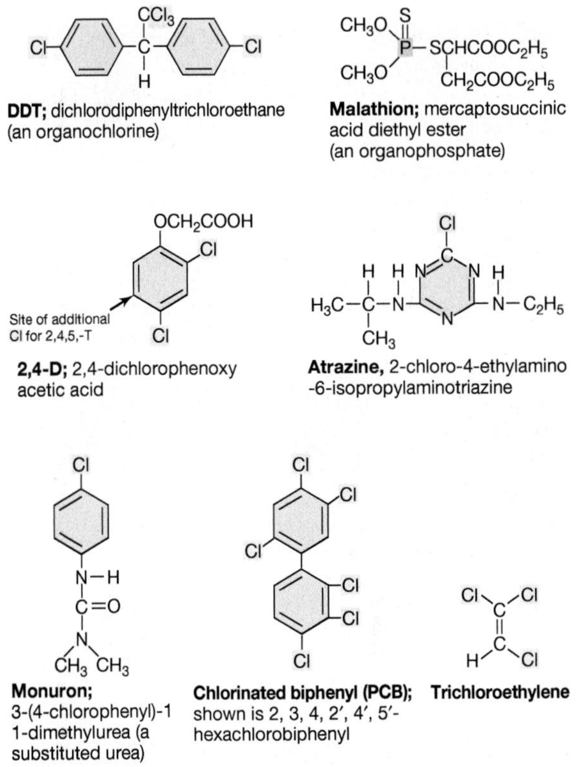

DDT; dichlorodiphenyltrichloroethane (an organochlorine)

Malathion; mercaptosuccinic acid diethyl ester (an organophosphate)

Site of additional Cl for 2,4,5,-T

2,4-D; 2,4-dichlorophenoxy acetic acid

Atrazine, 2-chloro-4-ethylamino -6-isopropylaminotriazine

Monuron; 3-(4-chlorophenyl)-1 1-dimethylurea (a substituted urea)

Chlorinated biphenyl (PCB); shown is 2, 3, 4, 2′, 4′, 5′-hexachlorobiphenyl

Trichloroethylene

Figure 23 **Examples of xenobiotic compounds.** Although none of these compounds exist naturally, microorganisms exist that can break them down.

1000 pesticides have been marketed for chemical pest control purposes. Pesticides include *herbicides, insecticides,* and *fungicides*. Pesticides display a wide variety of chemistries, including chlorinated, aromatic, and nitrogen- and phosphorus-containing compounds (Figure 23). Some of these substances can be used as carbon sources and electron donors by microorganisms, whereas others cannot.

If a xenobiotic substance can be biodegraded, it will eventually disappear from a habitat. Such degradation in the soil is desirable because toxic accumulations of the compound are avoided. However, even closely related compounds may differ remarkably in their degradability, as shown in Table 4. Some compounds persist relatively unaltered for years in soils whereas others are significantly degraded in only weeks or months. For example, some of the chlorinated insecticides (Figure 23) are so recalcitrant that they can persist for several years in soil (Table 4).

The relative persistence rates of xenobiotics are only approximate because environmental factors—temperature, pH, aeration, and organic matter content of the soil—also influence decomposition. Moreover, disappearance of a pesticide from an ecosystem does not necessarily mean that it was degraded by microorganisms; pesticides can also be removed by volatilization, leaching, or spontaneous chemical breakdown.

Table 4 Persistence of herbicides and insecticides in soils

Substance	*Time for 75–100% disappearance*
Chlorinated insecticides	
DDT [1,1,1-trichloro-2,2-bis-(p-chlorophenyl)ethanne][a]	4 years
Aldrin	3 years
Chlordane	5 years
Heptachlor	2 years
Lindane (hexachlorocyclohexane)	3 years
Organophosphate insecticides	
Diazinon	12 weeks
Malathion[a]	1 week
Parathion	1 week
Herbicides	
2,4-D (2,4-dichlorophenoxyacetic acid)[a]	4 weeks
2,4,5-T (2,4,5-trichlorophenoxyacetic acid)	20 weeks
Dalapon	8 weeks
Atrazine[a]	40 weeks
Simazine	48 weeks
Propazine	1.5 years

[a]Structure shown in Figure 23.

Substrate availability also governs microbial attack of xenobiotic compounds. Many xenobiotics are quite hydrophobic and poorly soluble in water. Adsorption of these compounds to organic matter and clay in soils and sediments prevents access by organisms. Thus the addition of surfactants or emulsifiers often increases bioavailability, and ultimately biodegradation, of the xenobiotic compound.

Many bacteria and fungi metabolize pesticides and herbicides. Some pesticides can be both carbon and energy sources and are oxidized completely to CO_2; however, other compounds are attacked only slightly, if at all. Some compounds may be degraded either partially or totally provided that some other organic material is present as primary energy source. This is a phenomenon called **cometabolism**. However, if the breakdown is only partial, the microbial degradation product may be even more toxic than the original compound. Thus, from an environmental standpoint, cometabolism of xenobiotics is not always a good thing.

Reductive Dechlorination

We previously described a form of anaerobic respiration called **reductive dechlorination**. In this process, chlorinated organic compounds are used as terminal electron acceptors under anoxic conditions. A laboratory model for studying reductive dechlorination is the reduction of chlorobenzoate to benzoate by the bacterium *Desulfomonile*:

$$C_7H_4O_2Cl^- + 2\,H \longrightarrow C_7H_5O_2^- + HCl$$

However, from a bioremediation standpoint, other chlorinated compounds are ecologically much more important than chlorobenzoate. For example, reductive dechlorination of the compounds dichloro-, trichloro-, and tetrachloro- (perchloro-) ethylene, chloroform, dichloromethane, and polychlorinated bi-phenyls (Figure 23) is observed, as well as the dehalogenation of several brominated and fluorinated compounds. These toxic compounds, some of which have been linked to cancer (particularly trichloroethylene, Figure 23), are widely used as industrial solvents, degreasing agents, and insulators in electrical transformers. They enter anoxic environments through accidental spills or from slow leakage of storage containers or abandoned electrical transformers. Eventually these compounds migrate into groundwater, where they are the most frequently detected groundwater contaminants in the United States. There is currently great interest in stimulating the bioremediation activities of reductive dechlorinators as a strategy for the removal of these highly toxic compounds from anoxic environments.

Aerobic Dechlorination

Aerobic dechlorination of chlorinated xenobiotics is also possible. For example, the pseudomonad *Burkholderia* will grow on the pesticide 2,4,5-T (Figure 23), dechlorinating the molecule and releasing Cl^- (Figure 24). The aerobic biodegradation of chlorinated aromatic compounds occurs by way of oxygenase enzymes. In the aerobic catabolism of 2,4,5-T, following dechlorination, a dioxygenase enzyme breaks down the aromatic ring. This generates compounds that can be metabolized by the citric acid cycle (Figure 24*b*).

Although the aerobic breakdown of chlorinated xenobiotics is undoubtedly of ecological importance, reductive dechlorination is of particular importance because of the rapidity with which anoxic conditions develop in polluted microbial habitats and the biochemical constraints (oxygen requirement, Figure 24*b*) this puts on aerobic organisms that could otherwise degrade the compound.

Biodegradable Plastics

A major area of environmental concern besides the biodegradation of toxic wastes such as pesticides and other chlorinated hydrocarbons is the biodegradation of solid wastes—in particular, plastics. The plastics industry currently produces over 40 *billion* kilograms of plastic per year, almost half of which is discarded in landfills. Plastics are xenobiotic polymers of various types; polyethylene, polypropylene, and polystyrene are typical examples (Figure 25). Many of these synthetic polymers remain essentially unaltered for decades in landfills and refuse dumps. This problem has fueled the search for biodegradable alternatives—called **biopolymers**—as replacements for some of the synthetic polymers now in use.

Several biopolymers with plastic-like properties are known. Photobiodegradable plastics are polymers whose structure is altered by exposure to ultraviolet radiation (from

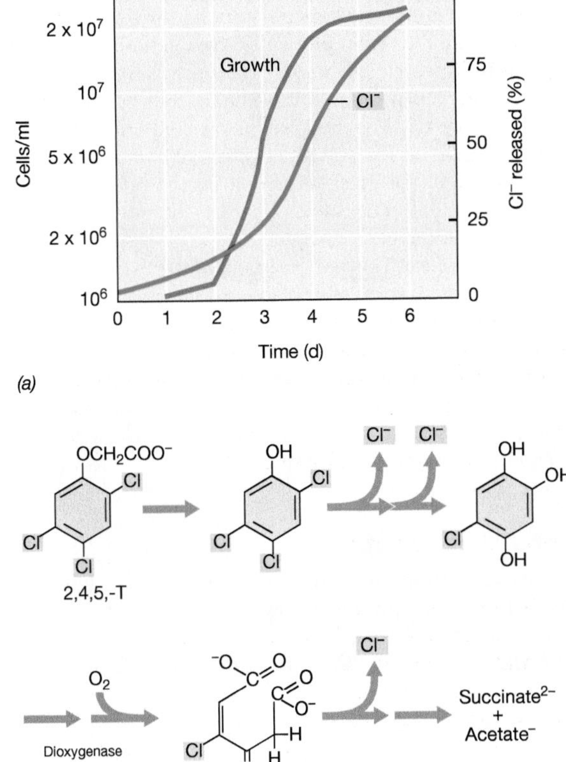

Figure 24 Biodegradation of the herbicide 2,4,5-T. *(a)* Growth of *Burkholderia cepacia* on 2,4,5-T as sole source of carbon and energy. The strain was enriched from nature using a chemostat to keep the concentration of herbicide low. Growth here is aerobic on 1.5 g/l of 2,4,5,-T. The release of chloride from the molecule is indicative of biodegradation. *(b)* Pathway of aerobic 2,4,5-T biodegradation.

sunlight), generating modified polymers more amenable to microbial attack. Starch-based plastics incorporate starch (a glucose polymer) as a link to short fragments of a second biodegradable polymer. This design accelerates biodegradation, because starch-digesting bacteria in soil attack the starch, releasing polymer fragments that are then degraded by other microorganisms. The glucose released from starch biodegradation can also be used as a carbon and energy source, thus supporting cometabolism of the polymer.

Microbial plastics are based on the carbon storage polymer poly-β-hydroxybutyrate and related compounds (∞ PHAs). These storage polymers have many of the desirable properties of synthetic plastics and can be biosynthesized in various chemical forms. A *copolymer* containing approximately equal amounts of poly-β-hydroxybutryate and poly- β-hydroxyvalerate (Figure 26*a*) has had the greatest market success thus far. However, because they are more cost effective, petroleum-based plastics make up virtually the entire plastics market today.

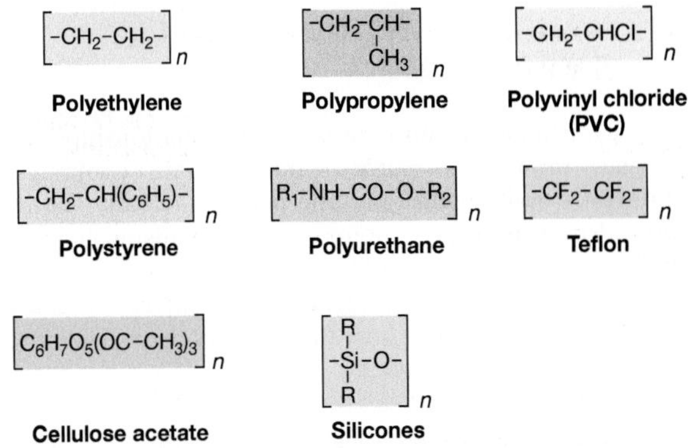

Figure 25 Chemistry of synthetic polymers. Shown is the monomeric structure of common synthetic polymers.

9 MiniReview

Many chemically synthesized compounds such as insecticides, herbicides, and plastics are called xenobiotics but can often be degraded by a bacterium. Both aerobic and anaerobic mechanisms are known.

- Which chemical class of pesticides are the most recalcitrant to microbial attack?
- What is reductive dechlorination and how does it differ from the reactions shown in Figure 24?
- What advantages do biopolymers have over synthetic polymers for the plastics industry?

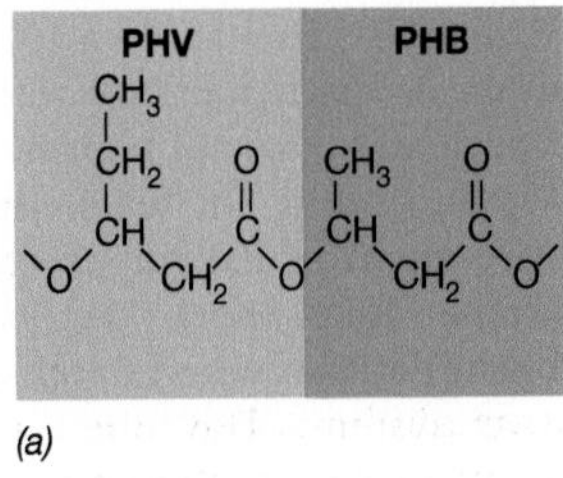

Figure 26 Bacterial plastics. *(a)* Copolymer of poly-β-hydroxybutyrate (PHB) and poly-β-hydroxyvalerate (PHV). *(b)* A brand of shampoo previously marketed in Germany and packaged in a bottle made of the PHB/PHV copolymer. Because this material is a natural product, the bottle readily degrades both aerobically and anaerobically.

IV ANIMAL–MICROBIAL SYMBIOSES

Microorganisms form intimate symbiotic relationships with all higher organisms. Some symbioses are commensal relationships that benefit only one partner, usually the microorganism. But other symbioses are mutualisms, in which both the higher organism and the microorganism benefit. We examine here three well-studied animal–microbial mutualisms, focusing in each on how the partners in the symbioses interact to each other's benefit.

10 The Rumen and Ruminant Animals

Ruminants are herbivorous mammals that possess a special digestive organ, the **rumen**, within which cellulose and other plant polysaccharides are digested with the help of microorganisms. Some of the most important domestic animals—cows, sheep, and goats—are ruminants. Microbial fermentation of sugars released from these polysaccharides produces fatty acids that feed the ruminants. Because the human food economy depends to a great extent on these animals, rumen microbiology is of considerable economic significance and importance.

Rumen Anatomy and Activity

The bulk of the organic matter in terrestrial plants is present in insoluble polysaccharides, of which cellulose is the most important. Mammals—and indeed almost all animals—lack the enzymes necessary to digest cellulose. But ruminants can metabolize cellulose by using microorganisms as digestive agents. Unique features of the rumen as a site of cellulose digestion are its relatively large size (100–150 liters in a cow, 6 liters in a sheep) and its position in the alimentary tract before the acidic stomach. The warm and constant temperature (39°C), constant pH (5.5–7, depending on when the animal last fed), and anoxic environment of the rumen are also important factors in overall rumen function.

Figure 27a shows the relationship of the rumen to other parts of the ruminant digestive system. The digestive processes and microbiology of the rumen have been well studied, in part because it is possible to create a sampling port, called a *fistula,* into the rumen of a cow (Figure 27*b*) or a sheep and remove samples for analysis. Food first enters the reticulum and is quickly pumped into the rumen. There it is mixed with saliva containing bicarbonate (HCO_3^-) and churned in a rotary motion. This peristaltic action grinds the cellulose into a fine suspension that assists in microbial attachment. The food mass is then transferred back into the reticulum, where it is formed into small clumps called *cuds;* these are regurgitated into the mouth and chewed again. The now finely divided solids, well mixed with saliva, are swallowed again, but this time the material passes mainly to the omasum and from there to the abomasum, an organ more like a true (acidic) stomach. In the abomasum, chemical digestive processes begin that continue in the small and large intestine.

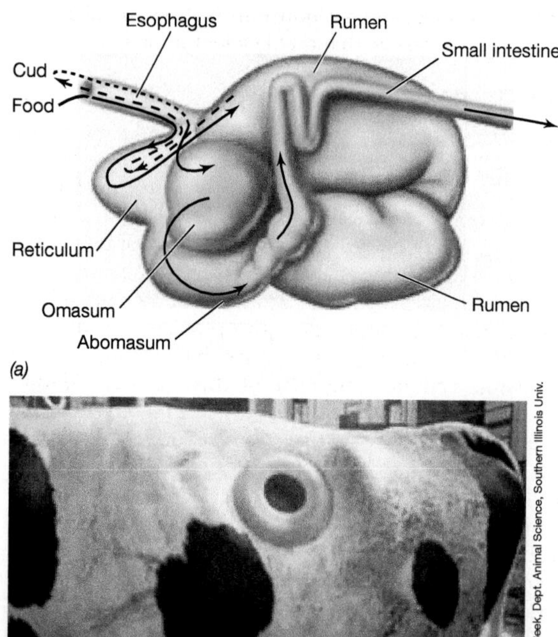

Figure 27 **The rumen.** *(a)* Schematic diagram of the rumen and gastrointestinal system of a cow. Food travels from the esophagus to the rumen and is then regurgitated and travels to the reticulum, omasum, abomasum, and intestines, in that order. The abomasum is an acidic vessel, analogous to the stomach of monogastric animals like pigs and humans. *(b)* Photo of a fistulated Holstein cow. The fistula, shown unplugged, is a sampling port that allows access to the rumen.

Microbial Fermentation in the Rumen

Food remains in the rumen about 9–12 hours. During this period cellulolytic microorganisms hydrolyze cellulose to free glucose. The glucose then undergoes bacterial fermentation with the production of **volatile fatty acids** (VFAs), primarily *acetic, propionic,* and *butyric,* and the gases CO_2 and CH_4 (Figure 28). These fatty acids pass through the rumen wall into the bloodstream and are oxidized by the animal as its main source of energy.

The rumen contains enormous numbers of prokaryotes (10^{10}–10^{11}/g of rumen contents). In addition to their digestive functions, rumen microorganisms synthesize amino acids and vitamins that are the main source of these essential nutrients for the animal. Most of the bacteria are adhered tightly to plant materials and feed particles. These materials proceed through the gastrointestinal tract of the animal where they undergo further digestive processes similar to those of nonruminant animals. Microbial cells from the rumen are digested in the acidic abomasum and thus are a major source of protein and vitamins for the animal. Because this microbial protein is recovered and used by the animal, a ruminant is nutritionally superior to a nonruminant when subsisting on foods, such as grasses, that are deficient in protein.

Rumen Bacteria

Because the rumen is anoxic, anaerobic bacteria naturally dominate. Furthermore, because cellulose is converted to CO_2 and CH_4 in a multistep microbial food chain, various anaerobes participate in the process (Table 5). Several different rumen bacteria hydrolyze cellulose to sugars and ferment the sugars to volatile fatty acids. *Fibrobacter succinogenes* and *Ruminococcus albus* are the two most abundant cellulolytic rumen anaerobes. Although both organisms produce cellulases, *Fibrobacter,* a gram-negative bacterium, contains a periplasmic cellulase. Because of this, cells of *Fibrobacter* must remain attached to the cellulose fibril while digesting it. *Ruminococcus,* by contrast, excretes cellulase into the rumen (thus cellulase is an *exoenzyme*), where it degrades cellulose outside the bacterial cell.

If a ruminant is gradually switched from cellulose to a diet high in starch (grain, for instance), the starch-digesting bacteria *Ruminobacter amylophilus* and *Succinomonas amylolytica* grow to high numbers in the rumen. On a low-starch diet these organisms are typically minor constituents. If an animal is fed legume hay, which is high in pectin, then the pectin-digesting bacterium *Lachnospira multiparus* (Table 5) becomes an abundant member of the rumen microbial community.

Some of the fermentation products of the saccharolytic rumen microflora are used as energy sources by secondary fermenters in the rumen. Thus, succinate is fermented to propionate plus CO_2 (Figure 28) by the bacterium *Schwartzia,* and lactate is fermented to acetic and other acids by *Selenomonas* and *Megasphaera* (Table 5). Hydrogen (H_2) produced in the rumen by fermentative processes never accumulates because it is quickly consumed by methanogens. Despite the high VFA content of the rumen, syntrophs (Section 2) do not play a role there because the animal itself is the sink for fatty acids (Figure 28). That is, with propionate and butyrate being consumed by the animal, syntrophic metabolisms are unnecessary in the rumen.

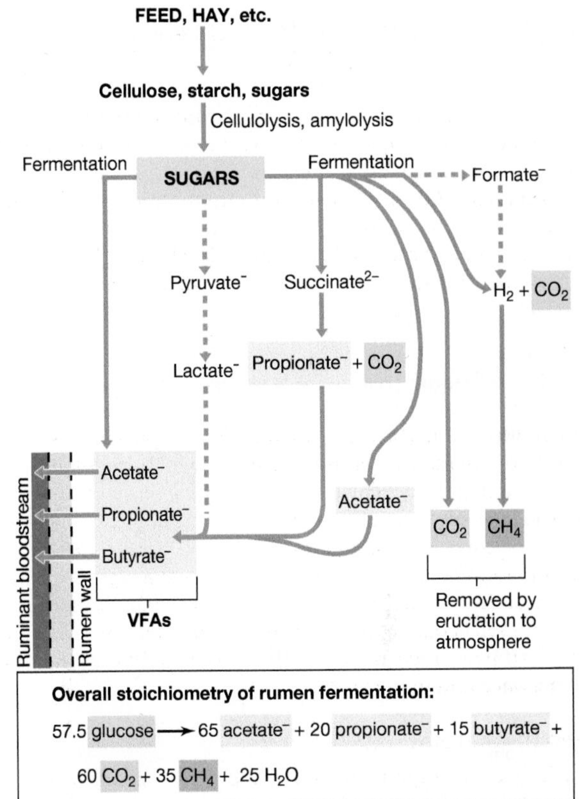

Figure 28 Biochemical reactions in the rumen. The major starting substrate, glucose, and end products are highlighted; dashed lines indicate minor pathways. Approximate steady-state rumen levels of volatile fatty acids (VFAs) are acetate, 60 mM; propionate, 20 mM; butyrate, 10 mM. VFAs are consumed by the ruminant and converted into animal proteins.

Dangerous Changes in the Rumen Microflora

Changes in the microbial composition of the rumen can cause illness or even death of the animal. For example, if a cow is changed abruptly from forage to a grain diet, the gram-positive bacterium *Streptococcus bovis* grows rapidly in the rumen. The normal level of *S. bovis,* about 10^7 cells/g, is insignificant in terms of total rumen bacterial numbers. But if large amounts of grain are fed abruptly, numbers of *S. bovis* can quickly rise to dominate the rumen microflora at over 10^{10} cells/g. This occurs because *S. bovis* grows rapidly on starch but is not cellulolytic; grain contains high levels of starch, whereas grasses contain mainly cellulose.

Because *S. bovis* is a lactic acid bacterium, when its populations are large its starch-fermenting metabolism elevates levels of lactic acid in the rumen. Lactic acid is a much stronger acid than the VFAs produced during normal rumen function. Lactate production thus acidifies the rumen below its lower functional limit of about pH 5.5, and this disrupts rumen activities. Rumen acidification, a condition called *acidosis,* causes inflammation of the rumen epithelium, and severe acidosis can cause hemorrhaging (bleeding) in the rumen followed by infections of other organs from rumen microflora that escape from the rumen.

Despite problems with *S. bovis,* ruminants such as cattle can be fed a diet exclusively of grain. However, to avoid acidosis, animals are switched from forage to grain gradually over a period of a few days. The slow introduction of starch selects for VFA-producing, starch-degrading bacteria (Table 5) instead of *S. bovis,* and thus normal rumen functions continue and the animal remains healthy. Animals suffering from acidosis can be treated by removing the source of starch and forcing strong buffering agents, such as calcium carbonate, into the rumen to help return rumen pH back to normal levels.

Table 5 Characteristics of some rumen prokaryotes

Organism	Gram stain	Phylogenetic domain[a]	Morphology	Motility	Fermentation products
Cellulose decomposers					
Fibrobacter succinogenes[b]	Negative	B	Rod	–	Succinate, acetate, formate
Butyrivibrio fibrisolvens[c]	Negative	B	Curved rod	+	Acetate, formate, lactate, butyrate, H_2, CO_2
Ruminococcus albus[b]	Positive	B	Coccus	–	Acetate, formate, H_2, CO_2
Clostridium lochheadii	Positive	B	Rod (endospores)	+	Acetate, formate, butyrate, H_2, CO_2
Starch decomposers					
Prevotella ruminicola	Negative	B	Rod	–	Formate, acetate, succinate
Ruminobacter amylophilus	Negative	B	Rod	–	Formate, acetate, succinate
Selenomonas ruminantium	Negative	B	Curved rod	+	Acetate, propionate, lactate
Succinomonas amylolytica	Negative	B	Oval	+	Acetate, propionate, succinate
Streptococcus bovis	Positive	B	Coccus	–	Lactate
Lactate decomposers					
Selenomonas lactilytica	Negative	B	Curved rod	+	Acetate, succinate
Megasphaera elsdenii	Positive	B	Coccus	–	Acetate, propionate, butyrate, valerate, caproate, H_2, CO_2
Succinate decomposer					
Schwartzia succinovorans	Negative	B	Rod	+	Propionate, CO_2
Pectin decomposer					
Lachnospira multiparus	Positive	B	Curved rod	+	Acetate, formate, lactate, H_2, CO_2
Methanogens					
Methanobrevibacter ruminantium	Positive	A	Rod	–	CH_4 (from H_2 + CO_2 or formate)
Methanomicrobium mobile	Negative	A	Rod	+	CH_4 (from H_2 + CO_2 or formate)

[a] *B, Bacteria; A, Archaea*
[b] These species also degrade xylan, a major plant cell wall polysaccharide.
[c] Also degrades starch

Rumen Protists and Fungi

The rumen has, in addition to prokaryotes, a characteristic fauna (about 10^6/ml), composed almost exclusively of ciliated protists. Many of these protists are obligate anaerobes, a property that is rare among eukaryotes. Although these protists are not essential for the rumen fermentation, they contribute to the overall process. In fact, some protists are able to hydrolyze cellulose and starch and ferment glucose with the production of the same VFAs formed by the bacteria (Figure 28 and Table 5). Rumen protists also ingest rumen bacteria as food sources and are thought to play a role in controlling bacterial densities in the rumen.

Anaerobic fungi also inhabit the rumen and play a role in ruminal digestive processes. Rumen fungi are typically species that alternate between a flagellated and a thallus form, and studies with pure cultures of them show that they can ferment cellulose to VFAs. *Neocallimastix,* for example, is an obligately anaerobic fungus that ferments glucose to formate, acetate, lactate, ethanol, CO_2, and H_2. Although a eukaryote, this fungus lacks mitochondria and cytochromes and thus lives an obligately fermentative existence. However, *Neocallimastix* cells contain a redox organelle called the *hydrogenosome*; this mitochondrial analogue evolves H_2 and has thus far been found only in certain protists. Rumen fungi play an important role in the degradation of polysaccharides other than cellulose as well, including a partial degradation of lignin (the strengthening agent in the cell walls of woody plants), hemicellulose (a derivative of cellulose that contains pentoses and other sugars), and pectins (a polysaccharide containing a mixture of C_6 and C_5 uronic acids).

Other Herbivorous Animals: Cecal Animals

The familiar ruminants are cows and sheep. Goats, camels, buffalo, deer, reindeer, caribou, and elk are also ruminants. However, although horses and rabbits are herbivorous mammals, they are not ruminants. Instead, these animals have only one stomach but use an organ called the *cecum,* a digestive organ located posterior to the small intestine and anterior to the large intestine, as their cellulolytic fermentation vessel. The cecum contains cellulolytic microorganisms, and cellulose is digested there. Nutritionally, ruminants are superior to cecal animals in that the cellulolytic microflora of the ruminant eventually passes through a true (acidic) stomach. As it does, it is killed and becomes a protein source for the animal. By contrast, in horses and rabbits the cellulolytic microflora is passed out of the animal in the feces because the cecum is located in the digestive tract posterior to the acidic stomach.

10 MiniReview

Ruminants have a digestive organ called the rumen that specializes in cellulose digestion. Bacteria, protists, and fungi in the rumen produce volatile fatty acids that are used by the ruminant. In addition to their role in the digestive process, rumen microorganisms synthesize vitamins and amino acids and are also a major source of protein for the ruminant.

- What physical and chemical conditions prevail in the rumen?
- What are VFAs and of what value are they to the ruminant?
- Why is the metabolism of *Streptococcus bovis* of special concern to ruminant nutrition?
- How do cecal animals differ from ruminants in their digestive tract anatomy?

11 Hydrothermal Vent Microbial Ecosystems

Although we have previously painted a picture of the deep sea as a remote, low-temperature, high-pressure environment suitable only for slow-growing barotolerant and barophilic bacteria, there are some amazing exceptions. Thriving animal communities have been found clustered about thermal springs in deep-sea waters throughout the world. These springs are located about 2500 m from the ocean surface in regions of the seafloor where volcanic magma has caused the floor to drift apart. Seawater seeping into these cracked regions mixes with hot minerals and is emitted from the springs. These underwater hot springs are called **hydrothermal vents** (Figure 29).

Two major types of hydrothermal vents have been discovered. Warm vents emit hydrothermal fluid at temperatures of 6–23°C. Hot vents, called **black smokers** because the mineral-rich hot water forms a dark cloud of precipitated material upon mixing with cold seawater, emit hydrothermal fluid at 270–380°C. As we will now see, an amazing diversity of prokaryotes lives in and about these undersea hot springs.

Animals Living at Hydrothermal Vents

Diverse invertebrate communities develop near hydrothermal vents, including tube worms over 2 m in length and large clams and mussels (Figure 30). Photosynthesis cannot support these animal communities because they exist below the photic zone. However, hydrothermal fluids contain large amounts of reduced inorganic materials, including H_2S, Mn^{2+}, H_2, and CO; some vents contain high levels of NH_4^+ instead of H_2S. All of these are good electron donors for

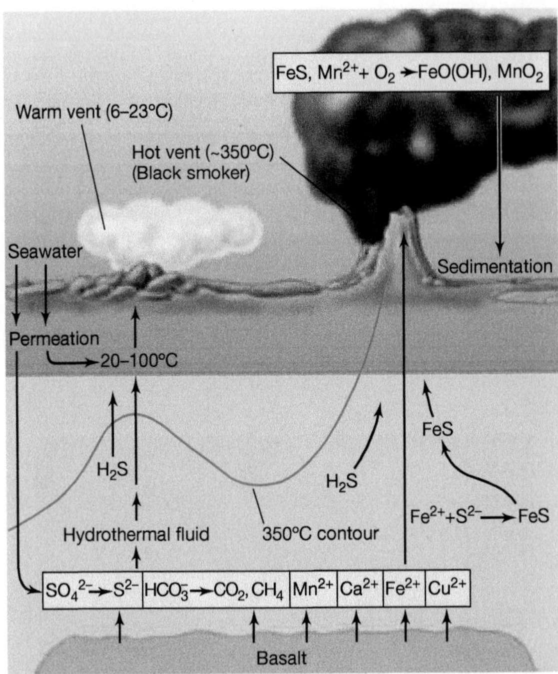

Figure 29 **Hydrothermal vents.** Schematic diagram showing geological formations and major chemical species at warm vents and black smokers. In warm vents, the hot hydrothermal fluid is cooled by cold 2–3°C seawater permeating the sediments. In black smokers, hot hydrothermal fluid near 350°C reaches the seafloor directly.

chemolithotrophic prokaryotes, and hydrothermal vent animals can exist in permanent darkness because they are nourished through a symbiotic association with these autotrophic bacteria. The bacteria actually live within the animal tissues and supply organic carbon to the animals in exchange for a safe residence and ready access to the electron donors needed for their energy metabolism.

Prokaryotes in Hydrothermal Vents

Large numbers of sulfur-oxidizing chemolithotrophs such as *Thiobacillus*, *Thiomicrospira*, *Thiothrix*, and *Beggiatoa* live near sulfide-emitting hydrothermal vents. Some vents support nitrifying, hydrogen-oxidizing, iron- and manganese-oxidizing bacteria, or methylotrophic bacteria, the latter presumably growing on the methane and carbon monoxide (CO) emitted from the vents. Table 6 summarizes the inorganic electron donors and electron acceptors that are thought to play a role in hydrothermal vent chemolithotrophic metabolisms.

Using the powerful tools of environmental genomics, studies of prokaryotic diversity near hydrothermal vents have revealed an enormous number of different *Bacteria*. These communities are dominated by species of *Proteobacteria*, in particular, *Epsilonproteobacteria*. *Alpha-*, *Delta-*, and *Gammaproteobacteria* are also abundant, whereas *Betaproteobacteria* are

(a)

(b)

(c)

Figure 30 **Invertebrates living near deep-sea thermal vents.** *(a)* Tube worms (family *Pogonophora*), showing the sheath (white) and plume (red) of the worm bodies. *(b)* Close-up photograph showing worm plume. *(c)* Mussel bed in vicinity of a warm vent. Note yellow deposition of elemental sulfur. See Table 6 for a list of chemolithotrophic prokaryotes found near hydrothermal vents.

all but absent. Many *Epsilon-* and *Gammaproteobacteria* oxidize sulfide and sulfur as electron donors, with either oxygen or nitrate as elctron acceptors. By contrast, most *Deltaproteobacteria* specialize in anaerobic metabolisms using sulfur compounds as electron acceptors.

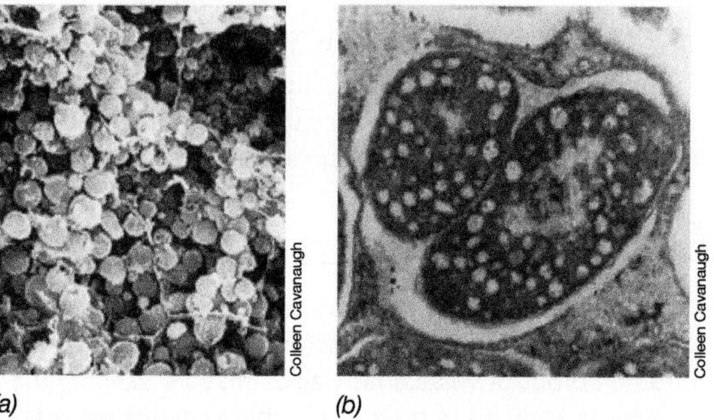

(a) (b)

Figure 31 **Chemolithotrophic sulfur-oxidizing bacteria associated with the trophosome tissue of tube worms from hydrothermal vents.** *(a)* Scanning electron microscopy of trophosome tissue showing spherical chemolithotrophic sulfur-oxidizing bacteria. Cells are 3–5 μm in diameter. *(b)* Transmission electron micrograph of bacteria in sectioned trophosome tissue. The cells are frequently enclosed in pairs by an outer membrane of unknown origin. Reprinted with permission from *Science* 213:340–342 (1981), © AAAS.

In contrast to *Bacteria,* the diversity of *Archaea* near hydrothermal vents is quite limited. Estimates of the number of unique phylotypes (a phylotype is a 16S rRNA sequence that differs from all other sequences by at least 3%) indicate that the diversity of *Bacteria* near hydrothermal vents is about ten times that of *Archaea*. Most of the *Archaea* detected near hydrothermal vents are either methanogens or representatives of the marine *Crenarchaeota* and *Euryarchaeota* groups.

Nutrition of Animals Living at Hydrothermal Vents

As mentioned, some chemolithotrophs, rather than living free in the vicinity of vents, have evolved associations with hydrothermal vent animals. For example, the 2-m-long tube worms (Figure 30) lack a mouth, gut, or anus, but contain an organ consisting primarily of spongy tissue called the *trophosome*. This structure, which constitutes half the worm's weight, is filled with sulfur granules and large populations of spherical sulfur-oxidizing prokaryotes (Figure 31). Bacterial cells taken from trophosome tissue show activity of enzymes of the Calvin cycle, a major pathway for autotrophy, but interestingly, contain enzymes of the reverse citric acid cycle, a second autotrophic pathway, as well, and also show a suite of sulfur-oxidizing enzymes necessary to obtain energy from reduced sulfur compounds. The tube worms are thus nourished by organic compounds produced from CO_2 and excreted by the sulfur chemolithotrophs.

Along with tube worms, giant mussels (Figure 30*c*) are also common inhabitants of warm vents, and sulfur-oxidizing bacterial symbionts have been found in the gill tissues of these animals. Phylogenetic analyses have shown that each vent animal harbors a single species of bacterial symbiont and that different bacterial symbionts inhabit different species of vent

Table 6 Chemolithotrophic prokaryotes present in the vicinity of deep-sea hydrothermal vents

Chemolithotroph	*Electron donor*	*Electron acceptor*	*Product from donor*
Sulfur-oxidizing	HS^-, S^0, $S_2O_3^{2-}$	O_2, NO_3^-	S^0, SO_4^-
Nitrifying	NH_4^+, NO_2	O_2	NO_2^-, NO_3^-
Sulfate-reducing	H_2	S^0, SO_4^{2-}	H_2S
Methanogenic	H_2	CO_2	CH_4
Hydrogen-oxidizing	H_2	O_2, NO_3^-	H_2O
Iron and manganese-oxidizing	Fe^{2+}, Mn^{2+}	O_2	Fe^{3+}, Mn^{4+}
Methylotrophic	CH_4, CO	O_2	CO_2

animal. Although fairly closely related to free-living sulfur chemolithotrophs, no animal symbionts have yet been obtained in laboratory culture.

The red plume of the tube worm (Figure 30*b*) is rich in blood vessels and is used to trap and transport inorganic substrates to the bacterial symbionts. The tube worms contain unusual hemoglobins that bind H_2S as well as O_2; these carry both substrates to the trophosome where they are released to the bacterial symbiont. The CO_2 content of tube worm blood is also high, about 25 mM, and presumably this is released in the trophosome as a carbon source for the symbionts. In addition, stable isotope analyses of elemental sulfur from the trophosome have shown that its $^{34}S/^{32}S$ composition is the same as that of the sulfide emitted from the vent. This ratio is distinct from that of seawater sulfate and is further proof that geothermal sulfide is actually entering the worm in large amounts.

Other marine animals have established bacterial symbioses for their nutrition, as well. For example, methanotrophic symbionts are present in giant clams that live near natural gas seeps at relatively shallow depths in the Gulf of Mexico. Although not autotrophs (CH_4 is an organic compound), the clam methanotrophs do provide nutrition to the animals; the symbionts use CH_4 as their electron donor and carbon source and excrete organic carbon to the clams.

Superheated Water: Black Smokers

Because of the huge hydrostatic pressure, water does not boil at the depths of hydrothermal vents until it reaches a temperature greater than 450°C. At some vent sites superheated hydrothermal fluid is emitted at temperatures as high as 350°C. These fluids contain metal sulfides, especially iron sulfides, and cool quickly as they mix with cold seawater. The precipitated metal sulfides form a tower called a "chimney" above the source (Figure 32), from which prokaryotes can be isolated.

Although it is clear that prokaryotes do not live in the superheated hydrothermal fluid itself, thermophilic and hyperthermophilic organisms live in the *gradients* that form as the hot water cools by mixing with cold seawater. For example, the walls of smoker chimneys are teeming with hyperthermophiles such as *Methanopyrus*, a species of *Archaea* that oxidizes H_2 and makes methane up to 110°C. Phylogenetic FISH staining has detected cells of both *Bacteria* and *Archaea* in smoker chimney walls (Figure 33). The most thermophilic of all known prokaryotes, species of *Pyrolobus* and *Pyrodictium*, were isolated from black smoker chimney walls.

When smokers plug up from mineral debris, hyperthermophiles presumably drift away to colonize active smokers and somehow become integrated into the growing chimney wall. Surprisingly, although requiring very high temperatures for growth, hyperthermophiles are remarkably tolerant of cold temperatures and oxygen. Thus, transport of cells from one vent site to another in cold oxic seawater apparently is not a problem.

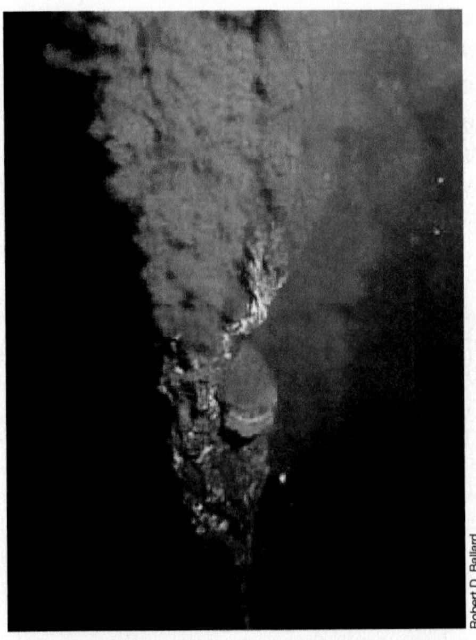

Figure 32 A hydrothermal vent black smoker emitting sulfide- and mineral-rich water at temperatures of 350°C. The walls of the black smoker chimneys display a steep temperature gradient and contain several types of prokaryotes.

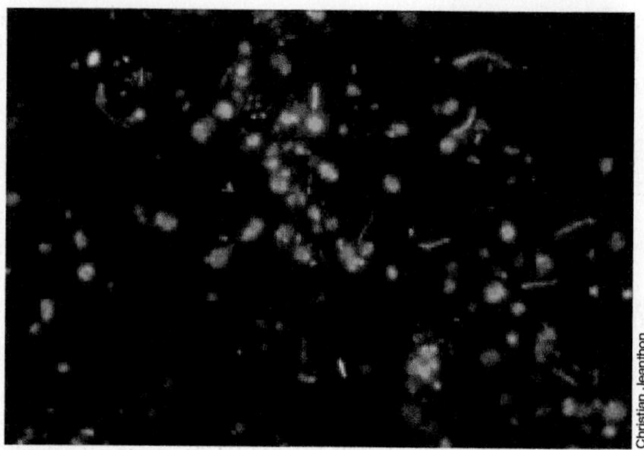

Figure 33 Phylogenetic FISH staining of black smoker chimney material. Snake Pit vent field, Mid-Atlantic Ridge (3500 m deep). A green fluorescing dye was conjugated to a probe that reacts with the 16S rRNA of all *Bacteria* and a red dye to a 16S rRNA probe for *Archaea*. The hydrothermal fluid going through the center of this chimney was 300°C.

Hydrothermal vents are deep-sea hot springs where volcanic activity generates fluids containing large amounts of inorganic electron donors that can be used by chemolithotrophic bacteria. Some of these organisms establish intimate mutualistic relationships with unusual marine invertebrates.

- How does a warm hydrothermal vent differ from a black smoker, both chemically and physically?
- How do giant tube worms receive their nutrition?
- Why is 350°C water emitting from a black smoker not boiling water?

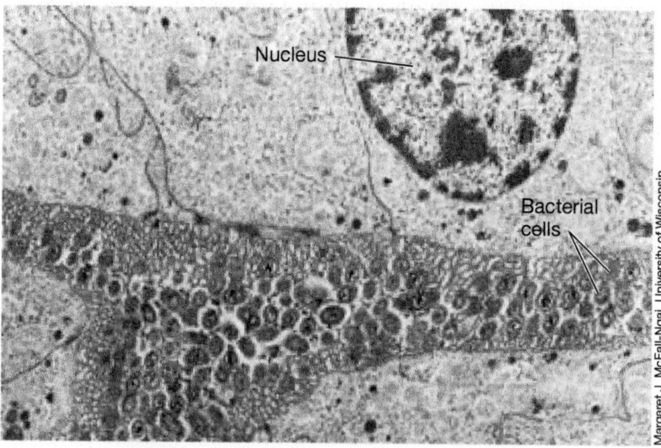

Figure 34 Squid–*Aliivibrio* symbiosis. *(a)* The Hawaiian bobtail squid, *Euprymna scolopes*. An animal is about 4 cm long. *(b)* Thin-sectioned transmission electron micrograph through the *E. scolopes* light organ showing the dense population of bioluminescent *Aliivibrio fischeri* cells.

12 Squid–*Aliivibrio* Symbiosis

A fascinating mutualistic symbiosis has evolved between the marine gram-negative bacterium *Aliivibrio fischeri* and the Hawaiian bobtail squid, *Euprymna scolopes*, a small marine invertebrate (an adult is about 4 cm long, Figure 34a). The bobtail squid sequesters large populations of the bioluminescent *A. fischeri* in a light organ located on its ventral side. The bacteria emit light that resembles moonlight penetrating marine waters, and this is thought to camouflage the squid from predators that strike from beneath, thus conferring a survival advantage on the squid. Several other species of *Euprymna* inhabit marine waters near Japan, Australia, and in the Mediterranean, and these contain *Aliivibrio* symbionts as well.

The Squid–*Aliivibrio* System as a Model Symbiosis

Many features of the *E. scolopes–Aliivibrio* symbiosis have made it an important model for how animal–bacterial symbioses are established. These features include in particular the fact that the animals can be grown in the laboratory and that there is only a single bacterial species in the symbiosis rather than the huge number inhabiting the mammalian large intestine or the rumen (Section 10). In addition, the symbiosis is not an essential one; both the squid and its bacterial partner can be cultured apart from each other in the laboratory. This allows juvenile squid to be grown without bacterial symbionts and then experimentally colonized. Using colonization assays, experiments can be done to study specificity in the symbiosis, the number of bacterial cells needed to initiate an infection, the capacity of genetically defined mutants of *A. fischeri* to initiate infection of the squid, and many other aspects of the relationship. Moreover, because the genome of *A. fischeri* has been sequenced, this also allows the powerful techniques of microbial genomics to be employed in studies of the symbiosis.

Establishing the Squid–*Aliivibrio* Symbiosis

Juvenile squid hatched from eggs do not contain cells of *A. fischeri*. Thus, transmission of bacterial cells to juvenile squid is a horizontal (environmental) rather than a vertical (transovarian) event. Cells of *A. fischeri* from surrounding seawater begin to colonize tissues in the juveniles almost immediately after they emerge from the eggs by entering an animal through ciliated ducts that end in the immature light organ. Amazingly, the light organ becomes colonized specifically with *A. fischeri* and not with any of the many other species of gram-negative bacteria present in seawater. Even if large numbers of other species of bioluminescent bacteria are offered to juvenile squid along with low numbers of *A. fischeri*, only *A. fischeri* establishes residence in the light organ. This implies that the animal in some way recognizes *A. fischeri* cells to the exclusion of other species.

The squid–*Aliivibrio* symbiosis develops in several stages. Contact of the squid with any bacterial cells triggers recognition in a very general way. Upon contact with peptidoglycan (a component of the cell wall of *Bacteria*), the young squid secretes mucus from its developing light organ. The mucus is the first layer of specificity in the symbiosis, as it makes gram-negative but not gram-positive bacteria aggregate. Within the aggregates of gram-negative cells that may contain only low numbers of *A. fischeri*, this bacterium somehow outcompetes the other gram-negative bacteria to eventually form a monoculture. All of these events occur within 2 h of a juvenile's hatching from an egg. The highly motile *A. fischeri* cells present in the aggregate then migrate into ducts that lead to the light organ tissues. Once there, they lose their flagella and become nonmotile and divide to form dense populations (Figure 34*b*). The light organ in a mature animal contains between 10^8 and 10^9 *A. fischeri* cells. Following colonization, the bacterial cells trigger a series of developmental events that lead to maturation of the host light organ.

Specific colonization of *A. fischeri* in the squid is also assisted by nitric oxide (NO). Nitric oxide is a well-known defense response of animal cells to attack by bacterial pathogens; the gas is a strong oxidant and causes oxidative damage to bacterial cells sufficient to kill them. Nitric oxide produced by the squid is incorporated into the mucus aggregates and is present in the light organ itself. As *A. fischeri* colonizes the light organ, NO levels diminish rapidly. It appears that cells of *A. fischeri* can tolerate exposure to NO and consume it through the activity of NO-inactivating enzymes. The inability of other gram-negative bacteria in the mucus aggregates to detoxify NO would help explain the sudden enrichment of *A. fischeri* prior to actual colonization of the light organ. Then, continued production of NO in the light organ would help perpetuate *A. fischeri* and prevent colonization by other bacterial species.

Propagating the Symbiosis

The squid matures into an adult in about 2 months and then lives a strictly nocturnal existence in which it feeds on small crustaceans and other seafood. During the day, the animal buries itself and remains quiescent in the sand. Each morning the squid nearly empties its light organ of *A. fischeri* cells and proceeds to grow a new population of the bacterium before beginning its nighttime feeding routine. The bacterial cells grow rapidly in the light organ; by midafternoon, the structure contains the dense populations of *A. fischeri* cells required for the production of visible light. The actual emission of light requires a certain density of cells and is controlled by the regulatory mechanism called *quorum sensing*. The diurnal expulsion of bacterial cells is thought to be a mechanism for seeding the environment with cells of the bacterial symbionts. This, of course, increases the chances for colonization of the next generation of juvenile squid.

A. fischeri grows much faster in the light organ than in the open ocean, presumably because it is supplied with nutrients by the squid. Thus *A. fischeri* benefits from the symbiosis by having an alternative habitat to seawater and one in which rapid growth to high populations is possible. Upon expulsion of *A. fischeri* cells from the light organ, numbers of the organism become enriched among the prokaryotic community. Isolation studies have shown that *A. fischeri* is not a particularly abundant marine bacterium. Thus, enrichment of *A. fischeri* through its symbiotic relationship with the squid probably helps this organism maintain larger populations in seawater than it would be capable of in the free-living state. Because the competitive success of a microbial species is to some degree a function of population size, this boost in cell numbers may confer an important ecological advantage on *A. fischeri* in its marine habitat.

12 MiniReview

The Hawaiian bobtail squid contains a light-emitting organ on its underside that is filled with cells of a single prokaryote, the bioluminescent marine bacterium *Aliivibrio fischeri*. This symbiotic relationship is highly specific and benefits both the animal and the bacterium.

- Of what value is the squid–*Aliivibrio* symbiosis to the squid? To the bacterium?
- What features of the squid–*Aliivibrio* symbiosis make it an ideal model for studying animal–bacterial symbioses?

V PLANT–MICROBIAL SYMBIOSES

We close this chapter with four examples of interactions among organisms: two will deal with plants and bacteria, one with fungi and plants, and the third is an exclusively microbial symbiosis. Many beneficial symbiotic associations exist; lichens, mycorrhizae, and the root nodules of leguminous plants are examples. However, there are also associations between plants and microorganisms that cause plant diseases. As an example of this, we consider crown gall, which is interesting because of the unique features of the disease and the microbial mode of transmission.

(a)

(b)

Figure 35 Lichens. *(a)* A lichen growing on a branch of a dead tree. *(b)* Lichens coating the surface of a large rock.

13 Lichens and Mycorrhizae

Lichens are leafy or encrusting microbial symbioses often found growing on bare rocks, tree trunks, house roofs, and the surfaces of bare soils (Figure 35). Lichens consist of a mutualistic relationship between two microorganisms, a fungus and an alga (or cyanobacterium), rather than between a microorganism and a macroorganism. The alga is the phototrophic partner and produces organic matter, which is then used for nutrition of the fungus. The fungus, unable to carry out photosynthesis, provides a firm anchor within which the phototrophic component can grow protected from erosion by rain or wind. Lichens are typically found on surfaces where other organisms do not grow, and their success in colonizing such environments is due to the mutualistic relationship.

Lichen Structure and Ecology

Lichens consist of a tight association of fungal cells within which cells of the phototroph are embedded (Figure 36). The morphology of a lichen is primarily determined by the fungus, and many fungi are able to form lichen associations. Diversity among the phototrophs is much lower, and many different kinds of lichens may have the same phototrophic component. Lichens that contain cyanobacteria frequently harbor N_2-fixing species, organisms such as *Anabaena* or *Nostoc*. The phototrophic cells are typically present in defined layers or clumps within the lichen structure (Figure 36).

The fungus clearly benefits from associating with the alga, but how does the phototroph benefit? Lichen acids, complex organic compounds excreted by the fungus, promote the dissolution and chelation of inorganic nutrients needed by the phototroph. Another role of the fungus is to protect the phototroph from drying; most of the habitats in which lichens live are dry (rock, bare soil, roof tops), and fungi are, in general, much better able to tolerate dry conditions than are algae. The fungus actually facilitates the uptake of water for the phototroph.

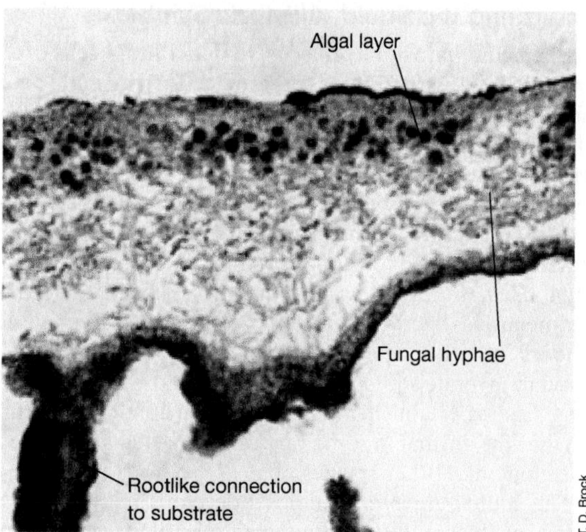

Figure 36 Lichen structure. Photomicrograph of a cross section through a lichen. The algal layer is positioned within the lichen structure so as to receive the most sunlight.

Lichens grow extremely slowly. For example, a lichen 2 cm in diameter growing on the surface of a rock may actually be several years old. Measurements of lichen growth vary from 1 mm or less per year to over 3 cm per year, depending on the organisms composing the symbiosis and the amount of rainfall and sunlight received.

Mycorrhizae

Mycorrhizae are mutualistic associations of plant roots and fungi. There are two classes of mycorrhizae. In *ectomycorrhizae,* fungal cells form an extensive sheath around the outside of the root with only a little penetration into the root tissue itself (Figure 37). In *endomycorrhizae,* the fungal mycelium becomes deeply embedded within the root tissue.

Ectomycorrhizae are found mainly in forest trees, especially conifers, beeches, and oaks, and are most highly developed in boreal and temperate forests. In such forests, almost every root of every tree is mycorrhizal. The root system of a mycorrhizal tree such as a pine (genus *Pinus*) is composed of both long and short roots. The short roots, which are characteristically dichotomously branched in *Pinus* (Figure 37*a*), show typical fungal colonization, and long roots are also frequently colonized. Endomycorrhizae are even more common than ectomycorrhizae. Arbuscular mycorrhizae, a type of endomycorrhizae, are found in the roots of over 80% of all terrestrial plant species so far examined.

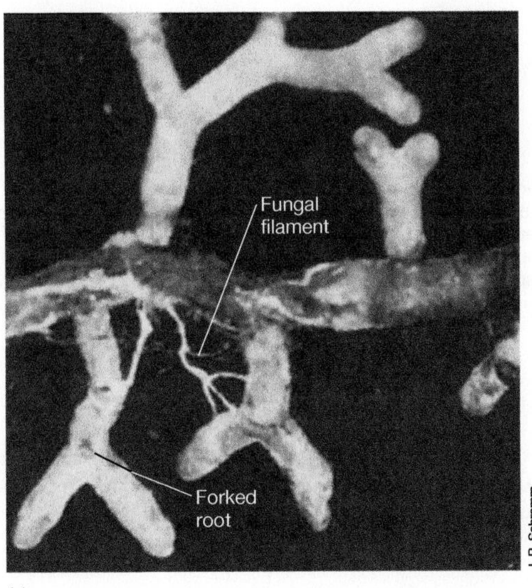

(a) (b)

Figure 37 **Mycorrhizae.** *(a)* Typical ectomycorrhizal root of the pine, *Pinus rigida*, with filaments of the fungus *Thelophora terrestris*. *(b)* Seedling of *Pinus contorta* (lodgepole pine), showing extensive development of the absorptive mycelium of its fungal associate *Suillus bovinus*. This grows in a fanlike formation from the ectomycorrhizal roots to capture nutrients from the soil. The seedling is about 12 cm high.

Most mycorrhizal fungi do not catabolize cellulose and other leaf litter polymers. Instead, they catabolize simple carbohydrates and typically have one or more vitamin requirements. They obtain their carbon from root secretions and get inorganic minerals from the soil. Mycorrhizal fungi are rarely found in nature except in association with roots, and many are probably obligate symbionts. Mycorrhizal fungi produce plant growth substances that induce morphological alterations in the roots, stimulating formation of the mycorrhizal state. However, despite the close relationship between fungus and root, a single species of pine can form a mycorrhizal association with over 40 species of fungi.

The beneficial effect of the mycorrhizal fungus on the plant is best observed in poor soils, where trees that are mycorrhizal thrive but nonmycorrhizal ones do not. For example, if trees planted in prairie soils, which ordinarily lack a suitable fungal inoculum, are artificially inoculated at the time of planting, they grow much more rapidly than uninoculated trees (Figure 38). The mycorrhizal plant can absorb nutrients from its environment more efficiently and thus has a competitive advantage. This improved nutrient absorption is due to the greater surface area provided by the fungal mycelium. For example, in the pine seedling shown in Figure 37*b*, the ectomycorrhizal fungal mycelium makes up the overwhelming part of the absorptive capacity of the plant root system.

In addition to helping plants absorb nutrients, mycorrhizae also play a significant role in supporting plant diversity. Field experiments have clearly shown a positive correlation between the abundance and diversity of mycorrhizae in a soil and the extent of the plant diversity that develops in it. Thus, mycorrhizae are a true mutualistic symbiosis: The mycorrhizal plant is better able to function physiologically and compete successfully in a species-rich plant community, and the fungus benefits from a steady supply of organic nutrients.

Figure 38 **Effect of mycorrhizal fungi on plant growth.** Six-month-old seedlings of Monterey pine (*Pinus radiata*) growing in pots containing prairie soil: left, nonmycorrhizal; right, mycorrhizal.

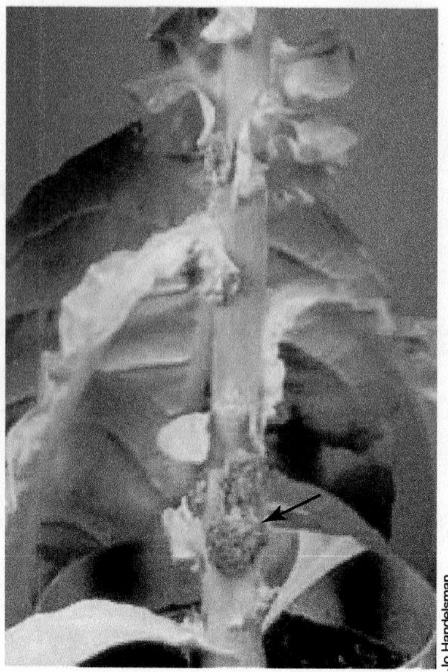

Figure 39 **Crown gall.** Photograph of a crown gall tumor (arrow) on a tobacco plant caused by the crown gall bacterium *Agrobacterium tumefaciens.* The disease usually does not kill the plant but may weaken it and make it more susceptible to drought and other diseases.

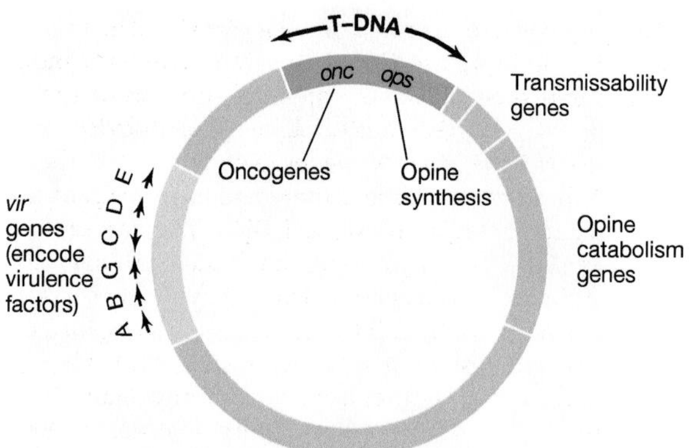

Figure 40 **Structure of the Ti plasmid of *Agrobacterium tumefaciens.*** T-DNA is the region transferred to the plant. Arrows indicate the direction of transcription of each gene. The entire Ti plasmid is about 200 kbp of DNA, and the T-DNA is about 20 kbp.

13 MiniReview

Lichens are a symbiotic association between a fungus and an oxygenic phototroph. Mycorrhizae are formed from fungi that associate with plant roots and improve their ability to absorb nutrients. Mycorrhizae have a great beneficial effect on plant health and competitiveness.

- How do endomycorrhizae differ from ectomycorrhizae?
- Why are mycorrhizal associations with plants considered a type of symbiosis?

14 *Agrobacterium* and Crown Gall Disease

Some microorganisms develop parasitic symbioses with plants. The genus *Agrobacterium,* a close relative of the root nodule bacterium *Rhizobium* (Section 15), is such an organism, causing the formation of tumorous growths on diverse plants. The two species of *Agrobacterium* most widely studied are *Agrobacterium tumefaciens,* which causes *crown gall* disease, and *Agrobacterium rhizogenes,* which causes *hairy root* disease.

The Ti Plasmid

Although plants often form a benign accumulation of tissue called a *callus* when wounded, the growth in crown gall (Figure 39) is different in that it is uncontrolled growth, resembling a tumor in animals. *A. tumefaciens* cells induce tumor formation only when a large plasmid called the **Ti** (*t*umor *i*nduction) **plasmid** (Figure 40) is present in *Agrobacterium*. In *A. rhizogenes,* a similar plasmid called the *Ri plasmid* is necessary for induction of hairy root disease.

Following infection, a part of the Ti plasmid called the *transferred DNA* (T-DNA), is integrated into the plant's genome. T-DNA carries the genes for tumor formation and also for the production of a number of modified amino acids called *opines*. Octopine [N^2-(1,3-dicarboxyethyl)-L-arginine] and nopaline [N^2-(1,3-dicarboxypropyl)-L-arginine] are two common opines. Opines are produced by plant cells transformed by T-DNA and are a source of carbon and nitrogen, and sometimes phosphate, for the parasitic *Agrobacterium* cells. These nutrients are the beneficial side of the symbiosis for the bacterium.

Recognition and T-DNA Transfer

To initiate the tumorous state, cells of *Agrobacterium* must first attach to a wound site on the plant, but little is known about any specificity that may be required. However, following attachment, the synthesis of cellulose microfibrils by the bacteria helps anchor them to the wound site and forms bacterial aggregates on the plant cell surface. This sets the stage for plasmid transfer from bacterium to plant.

The general structure of the Ti plasmid is shown in Figure 40. Although a number of genes are needed for infectivity, only a small region of the Ti plasmid, the *T-DNA,* is actually transferred to the plant. The T-DNA contains genes that induce tumorigenesis. The *vir* genes on the Ti plasmid encode proteins that are essential for T-DNA transfer. Transcription of *vir* is induced by metabolites synthesized by wounded plant tissues. Examples of inducers include the phenolic compounds acetosyringone, *p*-hydroxybenzoic acid, and vanillin. The transmissibility genes on the Ti plasmid (Figure 40) allow the plasmid to be transferred by conjugation from one bacterial cell to another.

The *vir* genes are the key to T-DNA transfer. The *virA* gene encodes a protein kinase (VirA) that interacts with inducer molecules and then phosphorylates the product of the *virG* gene (Figure 41). VirG is activated by phosphorylation and functions to activate other *vir* genes. The product of the *virD* gene (VirD) has endonuclease activity and nicks DNA in the Ti plasmid in a region adjacent to the T-DNA. The product of the *virE* gene is a DNA-binding protein that binds the single strand of T-DNA generated from endonuclease activity and transports this small fragment of DNA into the plant cell. VirB, located in the bacterial cytoplasmic membrane, mediates transfer of the single strand of DNA between bacterium and plant. T-DNA transfer from bacterium to plant (Figure 41) thus resembles bacterial conjugation.

The T-DNA then becomes inserted into the genome of the plant. Tumorigenesis (*onc*) genes on the Ti plasmid (Figure 40) encode enzymes for plant hormone production and at least one key enzyme of opine biosynthesis. Expression of these genes leads to tumor formation and opine production. The Ri plasmid responsible for hairy root disease also contains *onc* genes. However, in this case the genes confer increased auxin responsiveness to the plant, and this may promote overproduction of root tissue and the symptoms of the disease. The Ri plasmid also encodes several opine biosynthetic enzymes.

Genetic Engineering with the Ti Plasmid

From the standpoint of microbiology and plant pathology, in both crown gall and hairy root disease there are intimate interactions between the plant and the bacterium that lead to genetic exchange from bacterium to plant. That is, Ti is a natural plant transformation system. Thus, in recent years the interest in the Ti–crown gall system has shifted away from the disease itself to applications of this natural genetic exchange process in plant biotechnology.

Several modified Ti plasmids that lack disease genes but that can still transfer DNA to plants have been developed by genetic engineering. These have been used for the construction of genetically modified (transgenic) plants. Many transgenic plants have been constructed thus far, including crop plants carrying genes for resistance to herbicides, insect attack, and drought.

14 MiniReview

The crown gall bacterium *Agrobacterium* enters into a unique relationship with plants. Part of a plasmid (the Ti plasmid) in the bacterium can be transferred into the genome of the plant, initiating crown gall disease. The Ti plasmid has also been used for the genetic engineering of crop plants.

- What are opines and why are they produced?
- How do the *vir* genes differ from *T-DNA* in the Ti plasmid?
- How has an understanding of crown gall disease benefited the area of plant molecular biology?

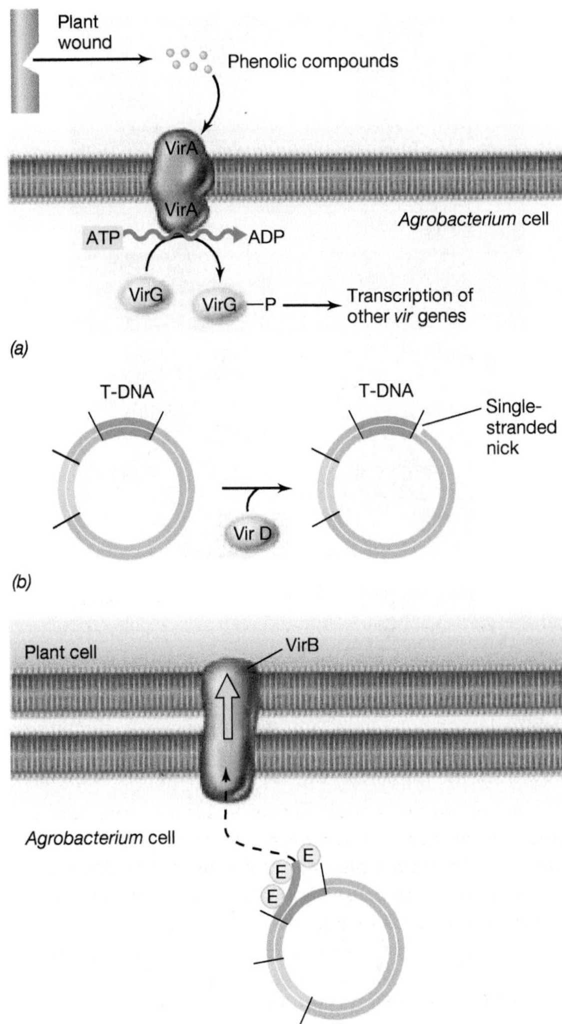

Figure 41 Mechanism of transfer of T-DNA to the plant cell by *Agrobacterium tumefaciens*. *(a)* VirA activates VirG by phosphorylation, and VirG activates transcription of other *vir* genes. *(b)* VirD is an endonuclease. *(c)* VirB functions as a conjugation bridge between the *Agrobacterium* cell and the plant cell, and VirE is a single-strand binding protein that assists in T-DNA transfer. Plant DNA polymerase produces the complementary strand to the transferred single strand of T-DNA.

15 The Legume–Root Nodule Symbiosis

One of the most important plant bacterial mutualisms is that between leguminous plants and nitrogen-fixing bacteria. Legumes are plants that bear their seeds in pods and are the third largest family of flowering plants. This large group includes such agriculturally important plants as soybeans, clover, alfalfa, beans, and peas. These plants are key commodities for the food and agricultural industries, and the

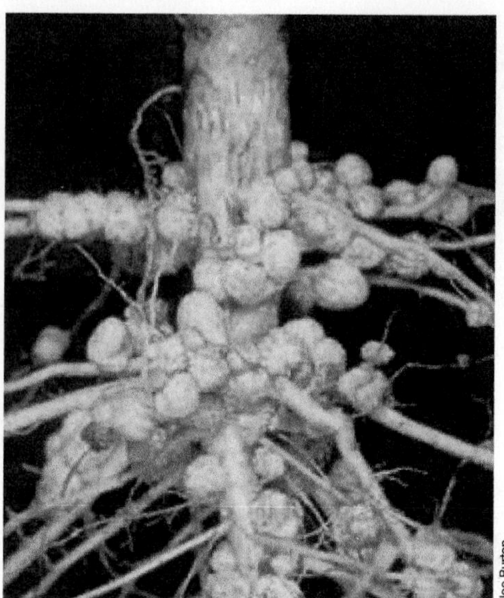

Figure 42 **Soybean root nodules.** The nodules develop from infection by *Bradyrhizobium japonicum*. The main stem of this soybean plant is about 0.5 cm in diameter.

ability of legumes to grow without nitrogen fertilizer saves farmers millions of dollars in fertilizer costs yearly.

Rhizobium, Bradyrhizobium, Sinorhizobium, Mesorhizobium, Azorhizobium, and *Photorhizobium* are genera of gram-negative *Alphaproteobacteria* that can grow in soil or can infect leguminous plants and establish a symbiotic relationship; these organisms are collectively called *rhizobia*. Infection of the roots of a legume by these bacteria leads to the formation of **root nodules** (Figure 42) that fix nitrogen. Nitrogen fixation in root nodules is of enormous agricultural importance as it leads to significant increases in combined

Figure 43 **Effect of nodulation on plant growth.** A field of unnodulated (left) and nodulated (right) soybean plants growing in nitrogen-poor soil.

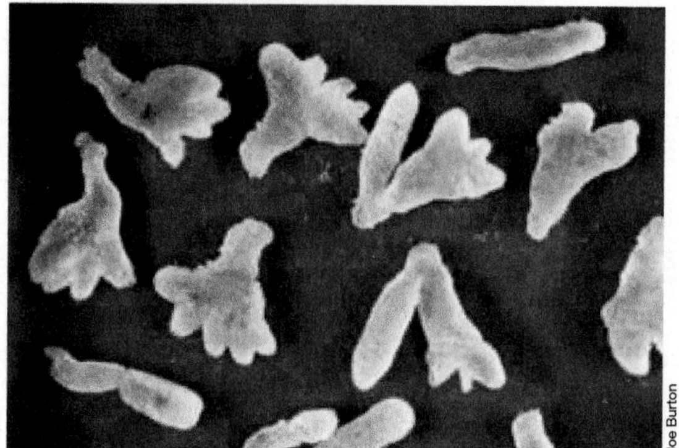

Figure 44 **Root nodule structure.** Sections of root nodules from the legume *Coronilla varia*, showing the reddish pigment leghemoglobin.

nitrogen in the soil. Because unfertilized bare soils are often nitrogen-deficient, nodulated legumes grow well in areas where other plants grow poorly (Figure 43).

Leghemoglobin and Cross-Inoculation Groups

In the absence of the correct symbiotic bacterium, a legume cannot fix nitrogen. In pure culture, rhizobia are able to fix N_2 alone when grown under microaerophilic conditions. The rhizobia need some O_2 to generate energy for N_2 fixation, but their nitrogenases, like those of other nitrogen-fixing organisms, are inactivated by O_2. In the nodule, precise O_2 levels are controlled by the O_2-binding protein **leghemoglobin**. This iron-containing protein is present in healthy N_2-fixing nodules (Figure 44) and is induced through the interaction of the plant host and the bacterial symbiont. Leghemoglobin functions as an "oxygen buffer," cycling between the oxidized (Fe^{3+}) and reduced (Fe^{2+}) forms to keep unbound O_2 within the nodule low. The ratio of leghemoglobin-bound O_2 to free O_2 in the root nodule is on the order of 10,000:1.

There is a marked specificity between the species of legume and rhizobial species in establishing the symbiotic state. A single rhizobial species is able to infect certain species of legumes and not others. A group of related legumes that may be infected by a particular species of rhizobia is called a *cross-inoculation group* (Table 7). For example, there is a clover group, bean group, alfalfa group, and so on. If the correct strain is used, leghemoglobin-rich, nitrogen-fixing root nodules result (Figure 44).

Steps in Root Nodule Formation

How root nodules form is now fairly well understood (Figure 45). The steps are as follows:

1. Recognition of the correct partner by both plant and bacterium and attachment of the bacterium to the root hairs;
2. Excretion of nod factors by the bacterium;
3. Bacterial invasion of the root hair;
4. Travel to the main root via the infection thread;

Table 7 Major cross-inoculation groups of leguminous plants

Host plant	*Nodulated by*
Pea	*Rhizobium leguminosarum* biovar *viciae*[a]
Bean	*Rhizobium leguminosarum* biovar *phaseoli*[a]
Bean	*Rhizobium tropici*
Lotus	*Mesorhizobium loti*
Clover	*Rhizobium leguminosarum* biovar *trifolii*[a]
Alfalfa	*Sinorhizobium meliloti*
Soybean	*Bradyrhizobium japonicum*
Soybean	*Bradyrhizobium elkanii*
Soybean	*Sinorhizobium fredii*
Sesbania rostrata (a trophical legume)	*Azorhizobium caulinodans*

[a]Several varieties (biovars) of *Rhizobium leguminosarum* exist, each capable of nodulating a different legume.

5. Formation of modified bacterial cells, bacteroids, within the plant cells and development of the nitrogen-fixing state; and
6. Continued plant and bacterial division, forming the mature root nodule.

Attachment and Infection

The roots of leguminous plants secrete organic compounds that stimulate the growth of a diverse rhizosphere microflora. If rhizobia of the correct cross-inoculation group are in the soil, they will form large populations and eventually attach to root hairs extending from the roots of the plant (Figure 45). A specific adhesion protein called *rhicadhesin* is present on the cell surfaces of rhizobia. Other substances, such as carbohydrate-containing proteins called *lectins* and specific receptors in the plant cytoplasmic membrane, also play roles in plant–bacterium attachment.

If attachment occurs, rhizobial cells penetrate into the root hairs. Following the initial binding of bacterium to root hair, the root hair curls as a result of substances excreted by the bacterium. Following curling, the bacterium enters the root hair and induces formation by the plant of a cellulosic tube, called the **infection thread** (Figure 45 and see Figure 46*a*), which spreads down the root hair. Root cells adjacent to the root hairs subsequently become infected by rhizobia, and plant cell division occurs. Continued plant cell division leads to formation of a tumor-like nodule (Figure 46; Figures 42 and 44).

Bacteroids

The rhizobia multiply rapidly within the plant cells and become transformed into swollen, misshapen, and branched cells called **bacteroids**. Bacteroids become surrounded by portions of the plant cytoplasmic membrane to form a structure called the *symbiosome* (Figure 46*e*), and only after the symbiosome forms does nitrogen fixation begin. Nitrogen-fixing nodules can be detected by acetylene reduction to ethylene.

When the plant dies, the nodule deteriorates, releasing bacteria into the soil. Bacteroids are incapable of division, but a small number of dormant rhizobial cells are always present in the nodule. These now proliferate, using some of the products of the deteriorating nodule as nutrients. The bacteria can then initiate the infection the next growing season or maintain a free-living existence in the soil.

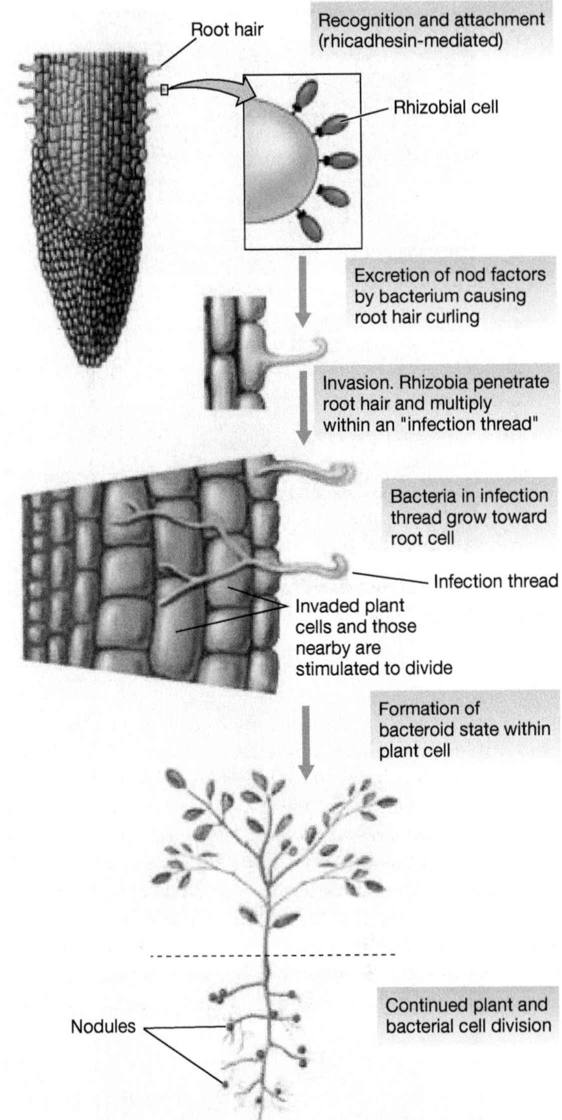

Figure 45 Steps in the formation of a root nodule in a legume infected by *Rhizobium*. Formation of the bacteroid state is a prerequisite for nitrogen fixation.

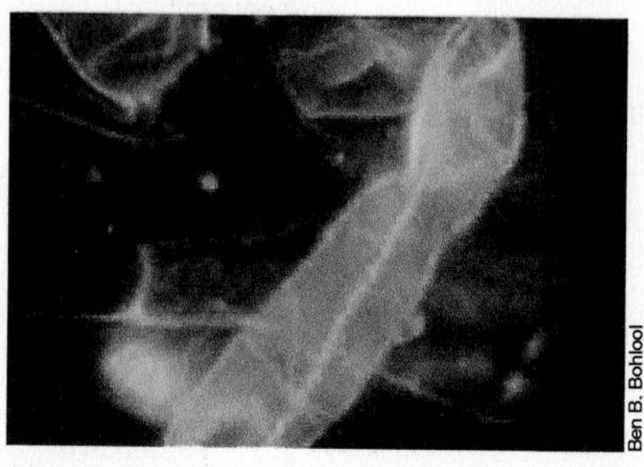

(a)

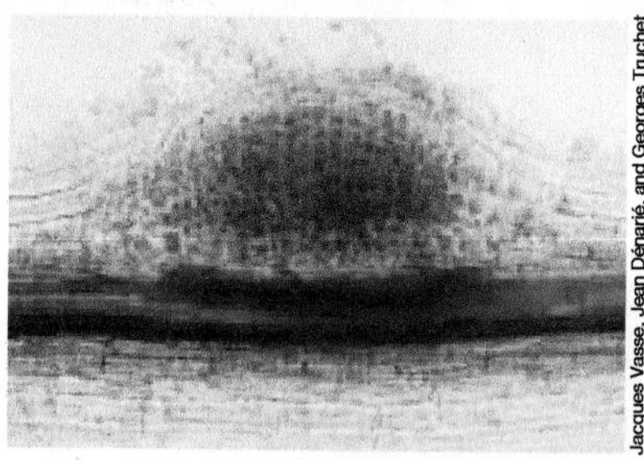

(b)

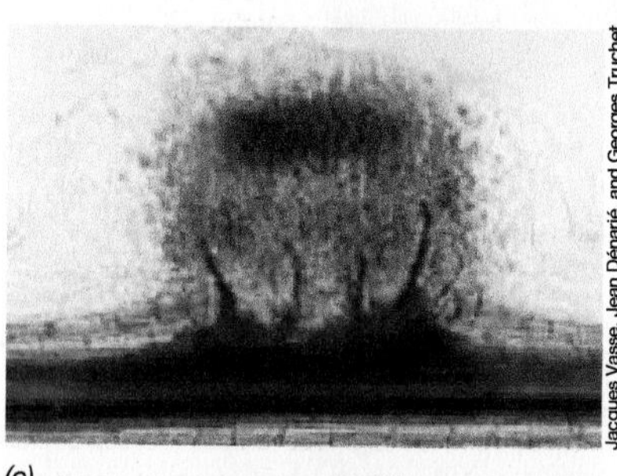

(c)

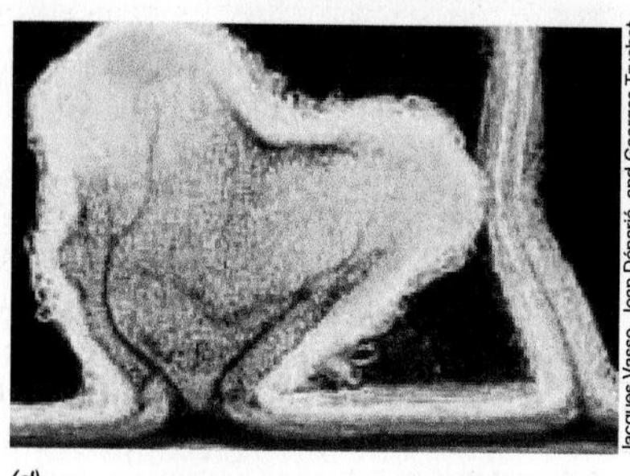

(d)

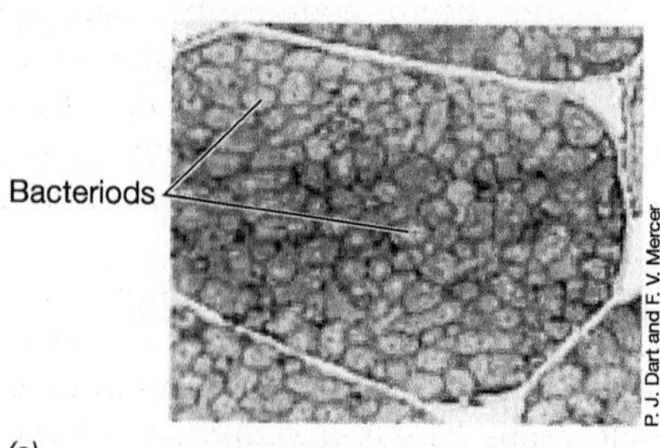

(e)

Figure 46 The infection thread and formation of root nodules. *(a)* An infection thread formed by cells of *Rhizobium leguminosarum* biovar *trifolii* on a root hair of white clover (*Trifolium repens*). The infection thread consists of a cellulosic tube through which bacteria move to root cells. *(b–d)* Nodules from alfalfa roots infected with cells of *Sinorhizobium meliloti* shown at different stages of development. Cells of both *R. leguminosarum* biovar *trifolii* and *S. meliloti* are about 2 μm long. The time course of nodulation events from infection to effective nodule is about 1 month in both soybean and alfalfa. *(e)* Cross-section through a root nodule of white clover showing the bacteroid form of *R. leguminosarum* biovar *trifolii* in the symbiosome. Bacteroids are about 2 μm long. Photos *(b–d)* reprinted with permission from *Nature* 351:670–673 (1991), © Macmillan Magazines Ltd.

Nodule Formation: Nod Genes, Nod Proteins, and Nod Factors

Bacterial genes that direct the steps in nodulation of a legume are called *nod genes*. In *Rhizobium leguminosarum* biovar *viciae*, ten nod genes have been identified. The *nodABC* genes encode proteins that produce oligosaccharides called **nod factors**; these induce root hair curling and trigger plant cell division, eventually leading to formation of the nodule.

Nod factors consist of a backbone of *N*-acetylglucosamine to which various substituents are linked (Figure 47). Host specificity is in part determined by the structure of the nod factor produced by a given species of *Rhizobium*. Besides the *nodABC* genes, which are universal and whose products synthesize the nod backbone, each cross-inoculation group contains nod genes that encode proteins that chemically modify the nod factor backbone to form the species-specific nod factor (Figure 47).

In *R. leguminosarum* biovar *viciae*, *nodD* encodes the regulatory protein NodD, and it controls transcription of other

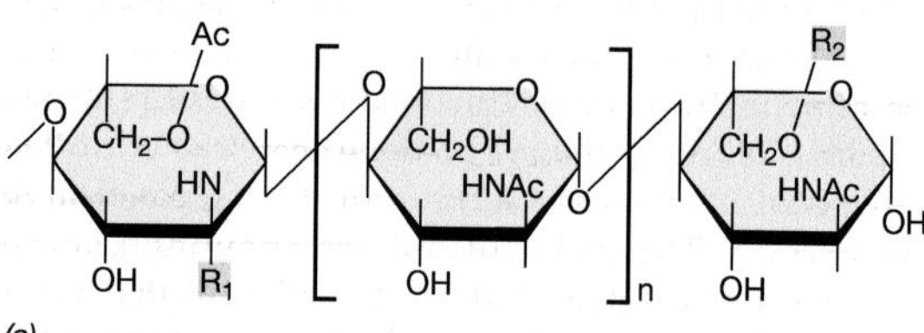

(a)

Species	R_1	R_2
Sinorhizobium meliloti	C16:2 or C16:3	SO_4^{2-}
Rhizobium leguminosarum biovar *viciae*	C18:1 or C18:4	H or Ac

(b)

Figure 47 Nod factors. *(a)* General structure of the nod factors produced by *Sinorhizobium meliloti* and *Rhizobium leguminosarum* biovar *viciae* and *(b)* a table of the structural differences (R_1, R_2) that define the precise nod factor of each species. The central hexose unit can repeat up to three times. C16:2, palmitic acid with two double bonds; C16:3, palmitic acid with three double bonds; C18:1, oleic acid with one double bond; C18:4, oleic acid with four double bonds; Ac, acetyl.

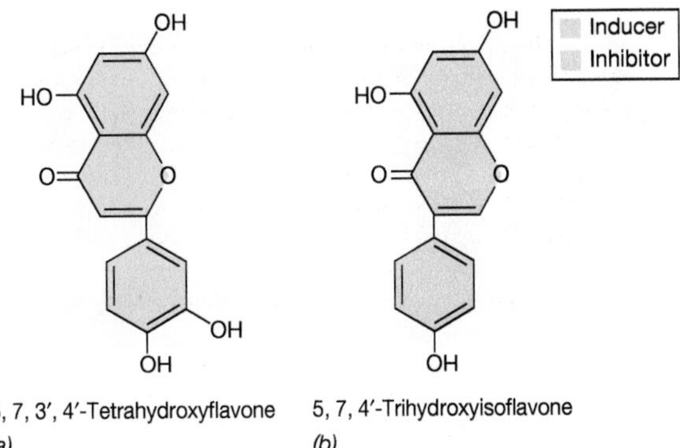

Figure 48 Plant flavonoids and nodulation. Structures of flavonoid molecules that are *(a)* an inducer of *nod* gene expression and *(b)* an inhibitor of *nod* gene expression in *Rhizobium leguminosarum* biovar *viciae*, the species that nodulates peas. Note the similarities in the structures of the two molecules. The common name of the structure shown in *(a)* is *luteolin*, and it is a flavone derivative. The structure in *(b)* is called *genistein*, and it is an isoflavone derivative.

nod genes. After interacting with inducer molecules, NodD promotes transcription and is thus a type of positive regulatory protein. NodD inducers are plant flavonoids, organic molecules that are widely excreted by plants (Figure 48). Interestingly, some flavonoids that are structurally very closely related to *nodD* inducers in *R. leguminosarum* biovar *viciae*, inhibit induction of nod genes in other rhizobial species (Figure 48). This indicates that part of the specificity observed between plant and bacterium in the *Rhizobium*–legume symbiosis lies in the chemistry of the flavonoids excreted by each species of legume.

Biochemistry of Root Nodules

Nitrogen fixation requires the enzyme nitrogenase. Nitrogenase from bacteroids shows the same biochemical properties as the enzyme from free-living N_2-fixing bacteria, including O_2 sensitivity and the ability to reduce acetylene as well as N_2. Bacteroids are dependent on the plant for the electron donor for N_2 fixation. The major organic compounds transported across the symbiosome membrane and into the bacteroid proper are citric acid cycle intermediates—in particular, the C_4 organic acids *succinate, malate,* and *fumarate* (Figure 49). These are used as electron donors for ATP production and, following conversion to pyruvate, as the ultimate source of electrons for the reduction of N_2.

The product of N_2 fixation is ammonia, and the plant assimilates most of this ammonia by forming organic nitrogen compounds. The ammonia-assimilating enzyme glutamine synthetase is present in high levels in the plant cell cytoplasm and can convert glutamate and ammonia into glutamine. This and a few other organic nitrogen compounds transport fixed nitrogen throughout the plant. www.microbiologyplace.com **Online Tutorial 1: Root Nodule Bacteria and Symbiosis with Legumes**

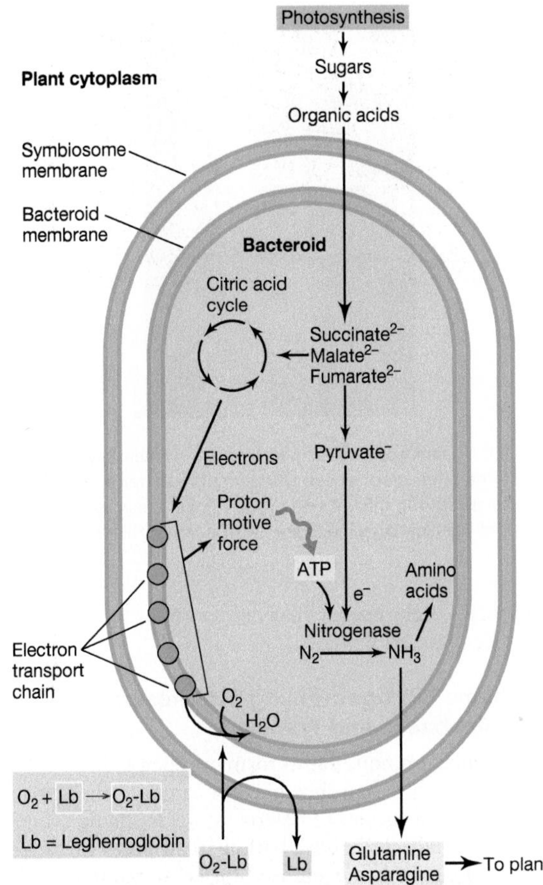

Figure 49 The root nodule bacteroid. Schematic diagram of major metabolic reactions and nutrient exchanges in the bacteroid. The symbiosome is a collection of bacteroids surrounded by a single membrane originating from the plant (Figure 46e).

Stem-Nodulating Rhizobia

Although most leguminous plants form nitrogen-fixing nodules on their *roots*, a few legume species bear nodules on their *stems*. Stem-nodulated leguminous plants are widespread in tropical regions where soils are often nitrogen-deficient because of leaching and intense biological activity. The best-studied system is the tropical aquatic legume *Sesbania*, which is nodulated by the bacterium *Azorhizobium caulinodans* (Figure 50). Stem nodules typically form in the submerged portion of the stems or just above the water level (Figure 50). The general sequence of events by which stem nodules form in *Sesbania* resembles that of root nodules: attachment, formation of an infection thread, and bacteroid formation.

Some stem-nodulating rhizobia produce bacteriochlorophyll *a* and thus have the potential to carry out anoxygenic photosynthesis. Bacteriochlorophyll-containing rhizobia, grouped in the genus *Photorhizobium*, are widespread in nature, particularly in association with tropical legumes. In

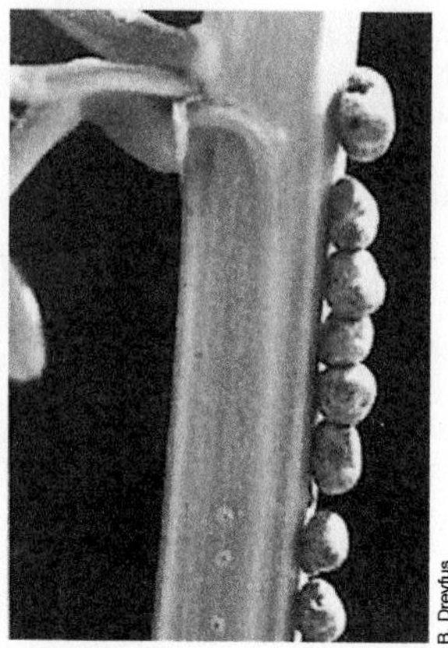

Figure 50 Stem nodules formed by stem-nodulating *Azorhizobium*. The photograph shows the stem of the tropical legume *Sesbania rostrata*. On the left side of the stem are uninoculated sites, on the right identical sites inoculated with stem-nodulating rhizobia.

these species, light energy likely supports at least part of the energy needs for N_2 fixation.

Nonlegume Nitrogen–Fixing Symbioses: *Azolla–Anabaena* and *Frankia*

Various nonleguminous plants form nitrogen-fixing symbioses with bacteria other than rhizobia. For example, the water fern *Azolla* contains a species of heterocystous N_2-fixing cyanobacteria called *Anabaena azollae* within small pores of its fronds (Figure 51). *Azolla* has been used for centuries to enrich rice paddies with fixed nitrogen. Before planting rice, the farmer allows the surface of the rice paddy to become densely covered with *Azolla*. As the rice plants grow, they eventually crowd out the *Azolla,* leading to death of the fern and release of its nitrogen, which is assimilated by the rice plants. By repeating this process each growing season, the farmer can obtain high yields of rice without applying nitrogenous fertilizers.

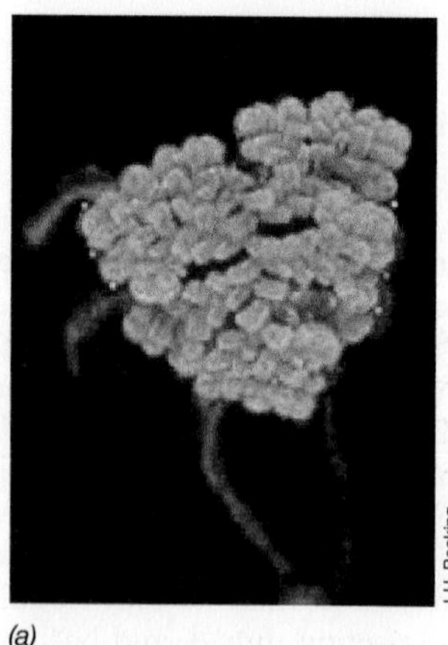

(a)

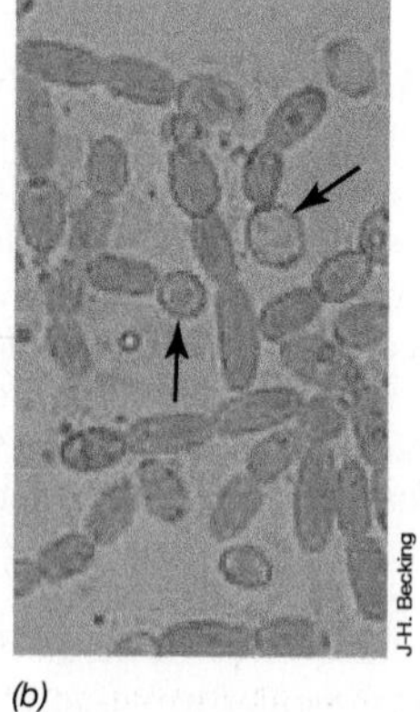

(b)

Figure 51 *Azolla–Anabaena* symbiosis. *(a)* Intact association showing a single plant of *Azolla pinnata*. The diameter of the plant is approximately 1 cm. *(b)* Cyanobacterial symbiont *Anabaena azollae* as observed in crushed leaves of *A. pinnata*. Single cells of *A. azollae* are about 5 μm wide. Note the spherical-shaped heterocysts (lighter color, arrows), the site of nitrogen fixation in the cyanobacterium.

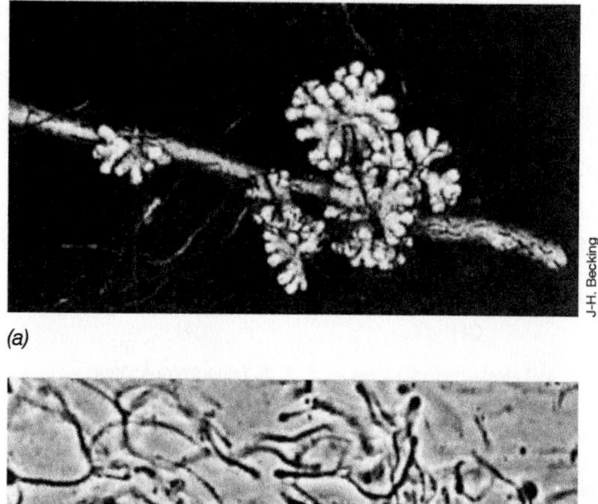

(a)

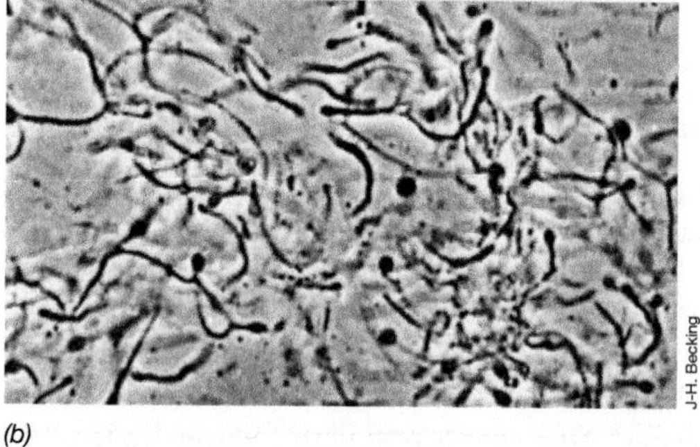

(b)

Figure 52 *Frankia* nodules and *Frankia* cells. *(a)* Root nodules of the common alder *Alnus glutinosa*. *(b) Frankia* culture purified from nodules of *Comptonia peregrina*. Note vesicles (black spherical structures) on the tips of hyphal filaments.

The alder tree (genus *Alnus*) has nitrogen-fixing root nodules (Figure 52a) that harbor a filamentous,streptomycete-like, nitrogen-fixing organism called *Frankia*. Although when assayed in cell extracts the nitrogenase of *Frankia* is sensitive to molecular oxygen, like cells of *Azotobacter,* cells of *Frankia* fix N_2 at full oxygen tensions. This is because *Frankia* protects its nitrogenase from O_2 by localizing the enzyme in terminal swellings on the cells called *vesicles* (Fig- ure 52*b*). The vesicles contain thick walls that retard O_2 diffusion, thus maintaining the O_2 tension within vesicles at levels compatible with nitrogenase activity. In this regard, *Frankia* vesicles resemble the heterocysts produced by some filamentous cyanobacteria as localized sites of N_2 fixation.

Alder is a characteristic pioneer tree able to colonize nutrient-poor soils, probably because of its ability to enter into a symbiotic nitrogen-fixing relationship with *Frankia*. A number of other small or bushy, woody plants are nodulated by *Frankia*. However, unlike the *Rhizobium*–legume relationship, a single strain of *Frankia* can form nodules on several different species of plants, suggesting that the *Frankia*–root nodule symbiosis is less specific than that of leguminous plants.

15 MiniReview

One of the most agriculturally important plant–microbial symbioses is that between legumes and nitrogen-fixing bacteria. The bacteria induce the formation of root nodules within which nitrogen fixation occurs. The plant provides the energy source needed by the root nodule bacteria, and the bacteria provide fixed nitrogen for the plant. Other nitrogen-fixing symbioses include the water fern *Azolla* and the nodule-forming *Frankia*.

- What is leghemoglobin and what is its function?
- What is a bacteroid and what occurs within it?
- What are the major similarities and differences between *Rhizobium* and *Frankia*?

Review of Key Terms

Acid mine drainage acidic water containing H_2SO_4 derived from the microbial oxidation of iron sulfide minerals

Bacteroid morphologically misshapen cells of rhizobia, inside a leguminous plant root nodule; can fix N_2

Biopolymers polymeric materials consisting of biologically produced (and thus biodegradable) substances

Bioremediation the cleanup of oil, toxic chemicals, and other pollutants by microorganisms

Black smoker an extremely hot (250–350°C) deep-sea hot spring emitting both hot water and various minerals

Cometabolism metabolism of a compound in the presence of a second organic compound, which is used as the primary energy source

Humus dead organic matter

Hydrothermal vent a deep-sea warm or hot spring

Infection thread in the formation of root nodules, a cellulosic tube through which *Rhizobium* cells can travel to reach and infect root cells

Leghemoglobin an O_2-binding protein found in root nodules

Lichen a fungus and an alga (or cyanobacterium) living in symbiotic association

Microbial leaching the removal of valuable metals such as copper from sulfide ores by microbial activities

Mycorrhizae a symbiotic association between a fungus and the roots of a plant

Nod factors oligosaccharides produced by root nodule bacteria that help initiate the plant–bacterial symbiosis

Pyrite a common iron-containing ore, FeS_2

Reductive dechlorination removal of Cl as Cl^- from an organic compound by reducing the carbon atom from C—Cl to C—H

Root nodule a tumorlike growth on plant roots that contains symbiotic nitrogen-fixing bacteria

Rumen the first vessel in the multichambered stomach of ruminant animals in which cellulose digestion occurs

Syntrophy a process whereby two or more microorganisms cooperate to degrade a substance neither can degrade alone

Ti plasmid a conjugative plasmid present in the bacterium *Agrobacterium tumefaciens* that can transfer genes into plants

Volatile fatty acids (VFAs) the major fatty acids (acetate, propionate, and butyrate) produced during fermentation in the rumen

Xenobiotic a synthetic compound not naturally occurring in nature

Review Questions

1. Why can it be said that the oxygen and carbon cycles are interconnected (Section 1)?
2. How can organisms such as *Syntrophobacter* and *Syntrophomonas* grow when their metabolism is based on thermodynamically unfavorable reactions? How does coculture of these syntrophs with certain other bacteria allow them to grow (Section 2)?
3. Compare and contrast the processes of nitrification and denitrification in terms of the organisms involved, the environmental conditions that favor each process, and the changes in nutrient availability that accompany each process (Section 3).
4. What organisms are involved in cycling sulfur compounds anoxically? If sulfur chemolithotrophs had never evolved, would there be a problem in the microbial cycling of sulfur compounds? What organic sulfur compounds are of interest in nature (Section 4)?
5. Why are most iron-oxidizing chemolithotrophs obligate aerobes, and why are most iron oxidizers acidophilic (Section 5)?
6. How is *Acidithiobacillus ferrooxidans* useful in the mining of copper ores? What crucial step in the indirect oxidation of copper ores is carried out by *A. ferrooxidans*? How is copper recovered from copper solutions produced by leaching (Section 6)?
7. How is mercury detoxified by the *mer* system (Section 7)?
8. What physical and chemical conditions are necessary for the rapid microbial degradation of oil in aquatic environments? Design an experiment that would allow you to test which conditions optimized the oil oxidation process (Section 8).
9. What are xenobiotic compounds and why might microorganisms have difficulty catabolizing them (Section 9)?

10. What is a rumen and how do the digestive processes operate in the ruminant digestive tract? What are the major benefits and the disadvantages of a rumen system? How does a cecal animal compare with a ruminant (Section 10)?
11. What evidence from hydrothermal vents exists to support the idea that prokaryotes are growing at extremely high temperatures (Section 11)?
12. How is the correct bacterial symbionts selected in the squid–*Aliivibrio* symbiosis (Section 12)?
13. How do mycorrhizae improve the growth of trees (Section 13)?
14. Compare and contrast the production of a plant tumor by *Agrobacterium tumefaciens* and a root nodule by a *Rhizobium* species. In what ways are these structures similar? In what ways are they different? Of what importance are plasmids to the development of both structures (Sections 14 and 15)?
15. Describe the steps in the development of root nodules on a leguminous plant. What is the nature of the recognition between plant and bacterium and how do nod factors help control this? How does this compare with recognition in the *Agrobacterium*–plant system (Section 15)?

Application Questions

1. Compare and contrast a lake ecosystem with a hydrothermal vent ecosystem. How does energy enter each ecosystem? What is the basis of primary production in each ecosystem? What nutritional classes of organisms exist in each ecosystem, and how do they feed themselves?
2. ^{14}C-Labeled cellulose is added to a vial containing a small amount of sewage sludge and sealed under anoxic conditions. A few hours later $^{14}CH_4$ appears in the vial. Discuss what has happened to yield such a result.
3. Imagine that you have discovered a new animal that consumes only grass in its diet. You suspect it to be a ruminant and have available a specimen for anatomical inspection. If this animal is a ruminant, describe the position and basic components of the digestive tract you would expect to find and any key microorganisms and substances you might look for.
4. Acid mine drainage is in part a chemical process and in part a biological process. Discuss the chemistry and microbiology that lead up to acid mine drainage and point out the key reaction(s) that are biological. How many ways can you think of to prevent acid mine drainage?

Characterizing and Classifying Viruses, Viroids, and Prions

Characterizing and Classifying Viruses, Viroids, and Prions

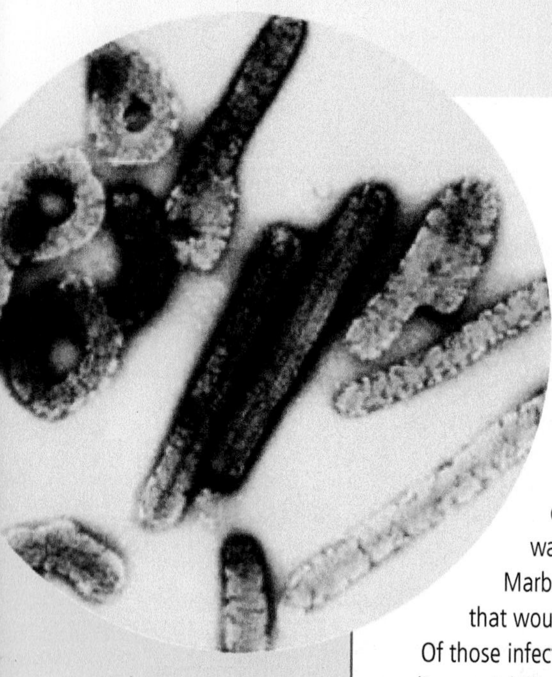

Marburg viruses

In the spring of 2005, children began dying with alarming frequency in a pediatric ward in Angola. The culprit: Marburg virus, which causes symptoms of fever, vomiting, and hemorrhaging. Extremely contagious, it is spread by contact with the bodily fluids of those infected, killing many of its victims within a week of the onset of symptoms. The cases in the pediatric ward were the first confirmed cases of a Marburg outbreak in Angola—an epidemic that would become the largest ever on record. Of those infected, 9 out of 10 succumbed to the disease; it killed 329 Angolans.

Hemorraghic fevers, smallpox, AIDS, SARS, influenza, common colds—many of the world's deadliest, most feared, and common diseases are caused by viruses. However, not all viruses are harmful to humans. Some, such as bacteriophages, attack bacteria and have clinical use. This chapter is an introduction to viruses and other pathogenic particles called viroids and prions: how they infect cells, how they multiply, and how they differ from cellular pathogens.

CHAPTER OUTLINE

Microprep Pre-Test: *Take the pre-test for this chapter on the web. Visit* ***www.microbiologyplace.com***

Not all pathogens are cellular. Many infections of humans, animals, and plants, and even of bacteria, are caused by **acellular** (noncellular) agents, including viruses and other pathogenic particles called viroids and prions. Although these agents are like some eukaryotic and prokaryotic microbes in that they cause disease when they invade susceptible cells, they are simple compared to a cell—lacking cell membranes and being composed of only a few organic molecules. In addition to lacking a cellular structure, they lack most of the characteristics of life: they cannot carry out any metabolic pathway, they can neither grow nor respond to the environment, and they cannot reproduce independently but instead must utilize the chemical and structural components of the cells they infect. They must recruit the cell's metabolic pathways in order to increase their numbers.

In this chapter we will first examine a range of topics concerning viruses: what their characteristics are, how they are classified, how they replicate, what role they play in some kinds of cancers, and how they are maintained in the laboratory. Then we consider the nature of viroids and prions before concluding with further discussion concerning whether or not viruses are alive.

Characteristics of Viruses

Viruses cause most of the diseases that still plague the industrialized world: the common cold, influenza, herpes, SARS, and AIDS, to name a few. Although we have immunizations against many viral diseases and are adept at treating the symptoms of others, the characteristics of viruses and the means by which they attack their hosts make cures for viral diseases elusive. Throughout this section, consider the clinical implications of the viral characteristics we discuss.

We begin by looking at the characteristics viruses have in common. A **virus** is a minuscule, acellular, infectious agent having one or several pieces of nucleic acid—either DNA or RNA. The nucleic acid is the genetic material (genome) of the virus. Being acellular, viruses have no cytoplasmic membrane (though, as we will see, some viruses possess a membrane-like *envelope*). Viruses also lack cytosol and functional organelles. They are not capable of metabolic activity on their own; instead, once viruses have invaded a cell, they take control of the cell's metabolic machinery to produce more molecules of viral nucleic acid and viral proteins, which then assemble into new viruses via a process we will examine shortly.

Viruses have an extracellular and an intracellular state. Outside of a cell, in the extracellular state, a virus is called a **virion** (vir'ē-on). Basically, a virion consists of a protein coat, called a **capsid,** surrounding a nucleic acid core **(Figure 1a).** Together the nucleic acid and its capsid are also called a *nucleocapsid,* which in many cases can crystallize

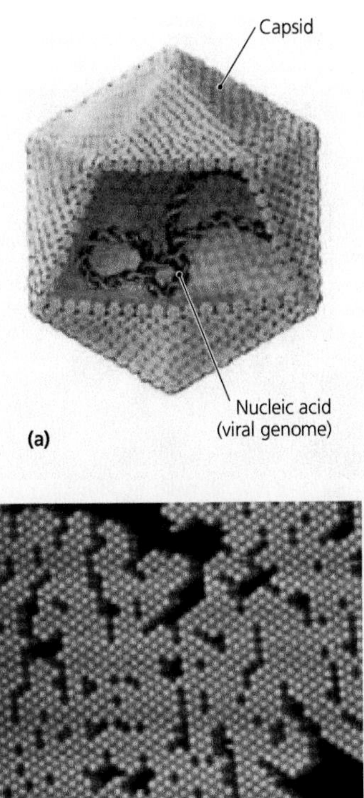

▲ *Figure 1*

Virions, complete virus particles, include a nucleic acid, a capsid, and in some cases an envelope. (a) A drawing of a nonenveloped polyhedral virus containing DNA. **(b)** An atomic force microscope image of crystallized tobacco mosaic virus. Like many chemicals and unlike cells, some viruses can form crystals.

like crystalline chemicals **(Figure 1b).** Some virions have a phospholipid membrane called an envelope surrounding the nucleocapsid. The outermost layer of a virion (capsid or envelope) provides the virus both protection and recognition sites that bind to complementary chemicals on the surfaces of cells. These are involved when the virus penetrates a cell. Envelopes typically fuse with a cell's membrane and the virus moves into the cell. Once the virus is inside, the intracellular state is initiated, and the capsid is removed. A virus without its capsid exists solely as nucleic acid, but is still referred to as a virus.

Now that we have examined ways in which viruses are alike, we will consider the characteristics that are used to distinguish different viral groups. Viruses differ in the type

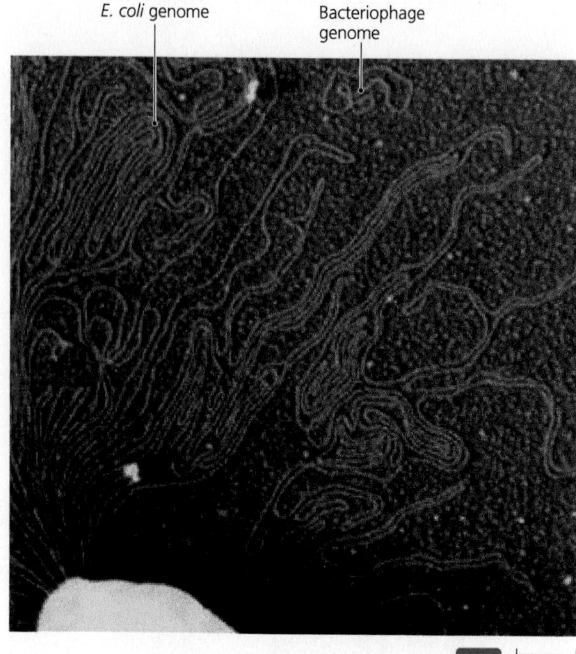

▲ *Figure 2*

The relative sizes of genomes. *E. coli* was ruptured to release the DNA.

of genetic material they contain, the kinds of cells they attack, their size, the nature of their capsid coat, their shapes, and the presence or absence of an envelope.

Genetic Material of Viruses

Learning Objective

✓ Discuss viral genomes in terms of dsDNA, ssDNA, ssRNA, dsRNA, and number of segments of nucleic acid.

Viruses show more variety in the nature of their genomes than do cells. Whereas the genome of every cell is double-stranded DNA, the genome of a virus may be either DNA or RNA. The primary way in which scientists categorize and classify viruses is based on the type of genetic material that makes up the viral genome.

Some viral genomes, such as those of herpesvirus and chickenpox virus, are double-stranded DNA (dsDNA), like the genomes of cells. Other viruses use either single-stranded RNA (ssRNA), single-stranded DNA (ssDNA), or double-stranded RNA (dsRNA) as their genomes. These molecules never function as a genome in any cell—in fact, ssDNA and dsRNA are almost nonexistent in cells. Further, the genome of any particular virus may be either linear and composed of several molecules of nucleic acid, as in eukaryotic cells, or circular and singular, as in most prokaryotic cells. For example, the genome of an influenzavirus is composed of eight linear segments of single-stranded RNA, whereas the genome of poliovirus is one molecule of single-stranded RNA.

Viral genomes are usually much smaller than the genomes of cells. For example, the genome of the smallest chlamydial bacterium has almost 1000 genes, whereas the genome of bacteriophage MS2 has only three genes. **Figure 2** compares the genome of a bacteriophage with the genome of the bacterium *Escherichia coli* (esh-ĕ-rik′ē-ă kō′lē), which contains over 4000 genes.

CRITICAL THINKING

Some viral genomes, composed of single-stranded RNA, act as mRNA. What advantage might these viruses have over other kinds of viruses?

Hosts of Viruses

Learning Objectives

✓ Explain how viruses are specific for their host cells.
✓ Compare and contrast viruses of fungi, plants, animals, and bacteria.

Most viruses infect only a particular host's cells. This specificity is due to the precise affinity of viral surface proteins or glycoproteins for complementary proteins or glycoproteins on the surface of the host cell. Viruses may be so specific they infect not only a particular host, but a particular kind of cell in that host. For example, HIV (human immunodeficiency virus, the agent that causes AIDS) specifically attacks helper T lymphocytes (a type of white blood cell) in humans and has no effect on, say, human muscle or bone cells. By contrast, some viruses are *generalists;* they infect many kinds of cells in many different hosts. An example of a generalist virus is rabies virus, which can infect most mammals, from humans to bats.

All types of organisms are susceptible to viral attack. There are viruses that infect archaeal, bacterial, plant, fungal, and animal cells **(Figure 3).** Most viral research and scientific study has focused on bacterial and animal viruses. A virus that infects bacteria is referred to as a **bacteriophage** (bak-tēr′ē-ō-fāj), or simply a **phage** (fāj). Scientists have determined that bacteriophages outnumber all bacteria, archaea, and eukaryotes put together; one survey found 50 million phages in one milliliter of seawater! We will return our attention to bacteriophages and animal viruses later in this chapter.

Viruses of plants are less well known than bacterial and animal viruses, even though viruses were first identified and isolated from tobacco plants. Plant viruses infect many food crops, including corn, beans, sugar cane, tobacco, and potatoes, resulting in billions of dollars in losses each year. Viruses of plants are introduced into plant cells either through abrasions of the cell wall or by plant parasites such as nematodes and aphids. After entry, plant viruses follow the replication cycle discussed below for animal viruses.

Fungal viruses have been little studied and are not well known. We do know that fungal viruses are different from animal and bacterial viruses in that fungal viruses exist

The Beneficial Microbe *Viruses That Change the World*

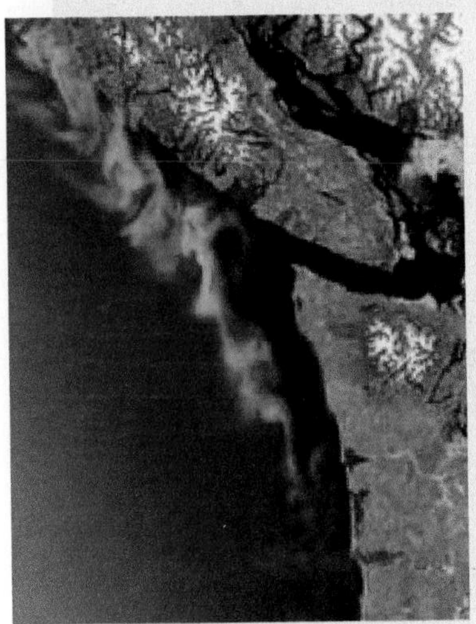

An algal bloom off the coast of Seattle, Washington

Viruses, though normally pathogenic to their host cells, do have positive influences, including what appear to be extensive roles in the environment. Two recent discoveries by the United Kingdom's Marine and Freshwater Microbial Biodiversity program demonstrate important ways viruses impact our world.

First: Scientists found that a previously unknown virus attacks a tiny marine alga that multiplies to form algal blooms consisting of hundreds of thousands to millions of algal cells per milliliter of water (see photo). Algal blooms like these can deplete the water of oxygen, potentially harming fish and other marine life. The newly discovered virus stops blooms by killing the algae, which is good for animal life. But the story continues: When the algae die by this means, they release an airborne sulfate compound that acts to seed clouds. The resulting increased cloudiness noticeably shades the ocean, measurably lowering water temperature. Thus, a marine virus helps to reduce global warming!

Second: The researchers also discovered a bacteriophage of oceanic cyanobacteria that transfers genes for photosynthetic machinery into its hosts' cells, so that the cells' photosynthetic rate increases. There are up to 10 million of these viruses in a single milliliter of seawater, so researchers estimate that much of the oxygen we breathe may be attributable to the action of these viruses on the blue-green bacteria.

only within cells; that is, they have no extracellular state. Presumably, fungal viruses cannot penetrate a thick fungal cell wall. However, because fusion of cells is typically a part of a fungal life cycle, viral infections can easily be propagated by the fusion of an infected fungal cell with an uninfected one.

Not all viruses are deleterious. **The Beneficial Microbe: Viruses That Change the World** illustrates some useful aspects of viruses in the environment.

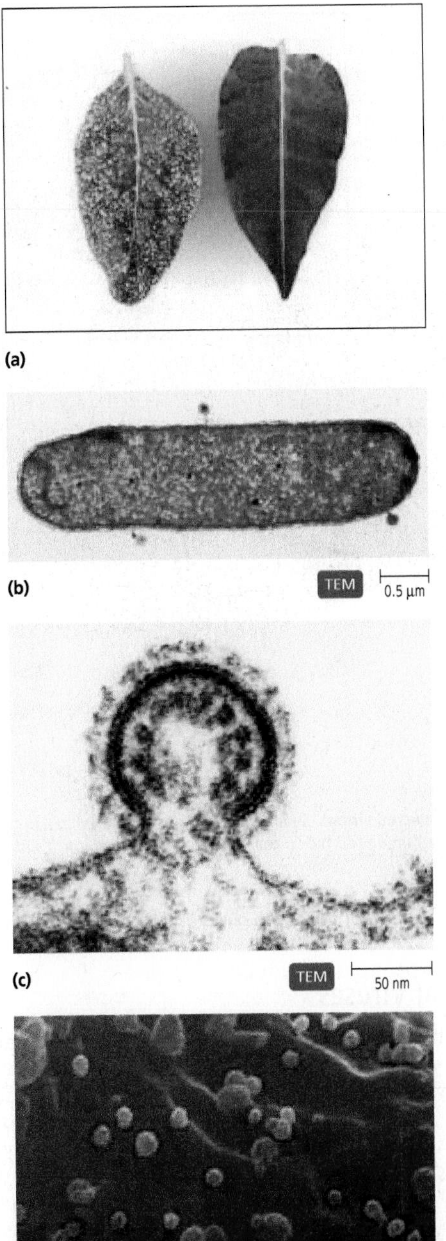

Figure 3 ➤

Some examples of plant, bacterial, and human hosts of viral infections. (a) Left, a tobacco leaf infected with tobacco mosaic virus, the first virus discovered. **(b)** A bacterial cell under attack by bacteriophages. **(c)** Human immunodeficiency viruses (HIV) budding from an infected cell. **(d)** A human white blood cell's cytoplasmic membrane, to which HIV is attached.

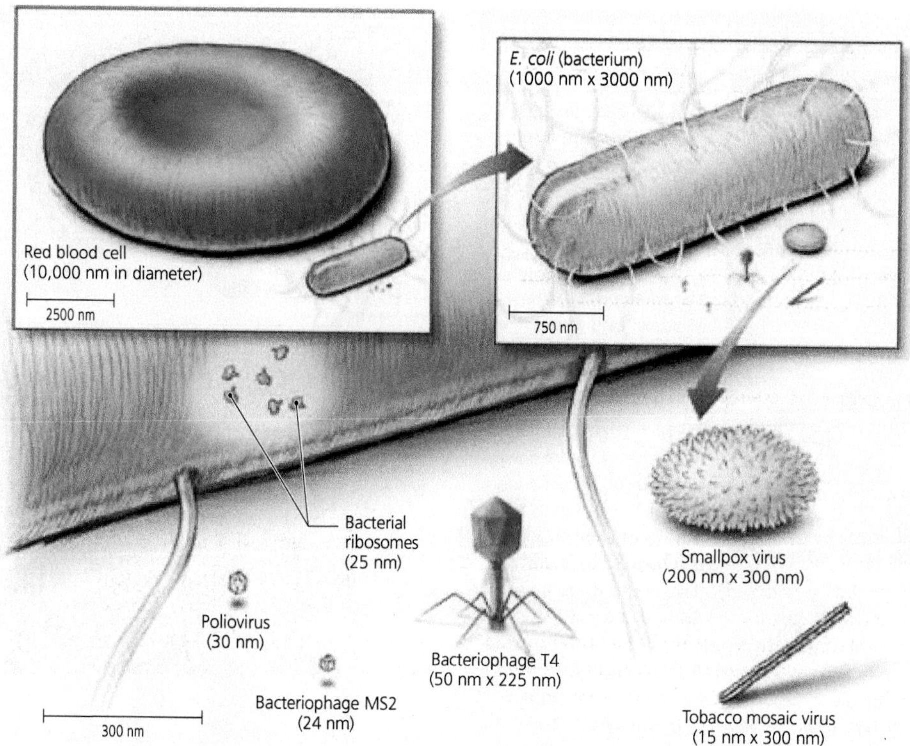

▲ *Figure 4*

Sizes of selected virions. Selected viruses are compared in size to a bacterium, *Escherichia coli*, and a human red blood cell. *How can viruses be so small and yet still be pathogenic?*

Figure 4 Viruses utilize a host cell's enzymes, organelles, and membranes to complete their replication cycle.

Sizes of Viruses

In the late 1800s, scientists hypothesized that the cause of many diseases, including polio and smallpox, was an agent smaller than a bacterium. They named these tiny agents "viruses," from the Latin word for "poison." Viruses are so small that most cannot be seen by light microscopy. One hundred million polioviruses could fit side by side on the period at the end of this sentence. The smallest viruses have a diameter of 10 nm, whereas the largest are approximately 400 nm in diameter, which is about the size of the smallest bacterial cells. **Figure 4** compares the sizes of selected viruses to *E. coli* and a human red blood cell.

In 1892, Russian microbiologist Dmitri Ivanowsky (1864–1920) first demonstrated that viruses are acellular with an experiment designed to elucidate the cause of tobacco mosaic disease. He filtered the sap of infected tobacco plants through a porcelain filter fine enough to trap even the smallest of bacterial cells. Viruses, however, were not trapped but instead passed though the filter with the liquid, which remained infectious to tobacco plants. This experiment proved the existence of an acellular disease-causing entity smaller than a bacterium. Tobacco mosaic virus (TMV) was isolated and characterized in 1935 by an American chemist, Wendell Stanley (1904–1971). The invention of electron microscopy allowed scientists to finally see TMV and other viruses.

Capsid Morphology

Learning Objective

✓ Discuss the structure and function of the viral capsid.

As we have seen, viruses have capsids—protein coats that provide both protection for viral nucleic acid and a means by which many viruses attach to their hosts' cells. The capsid of a virus is composed of proteinaceous subunits called **capsomeres** (or *capsomers*). Some capsomeres (and therefore some capsids) are composed of only a single

Figure 5 ➤

The shapes of virions. (a) A helical virus, tobacco mosaic virus. The tubular shape of the capsid results from the tight arrangement of several rows of helical capsomeres. **(b)** Polyhedral virions of a virus that causes common colds. **(c)** Complex virions of smallpox virus. **(d)** The complex shape of rabies virus, which results from the shapes of the capsid and bullet-shaped envelope.

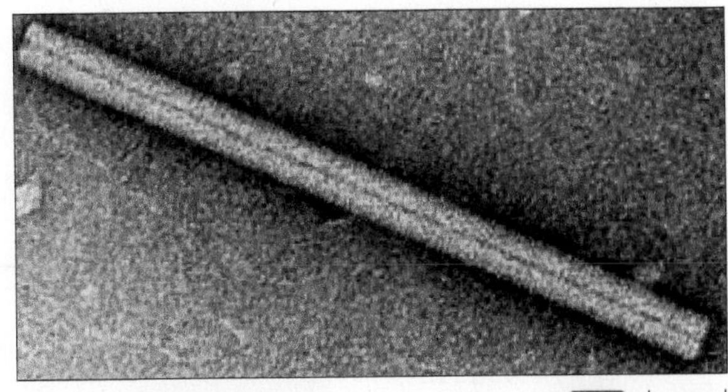

(a)

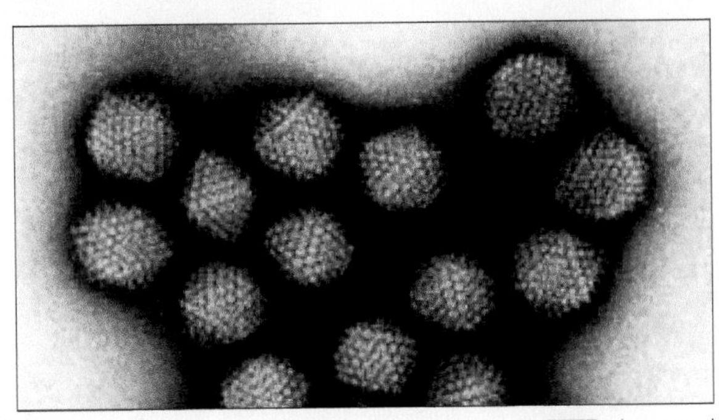

(b)

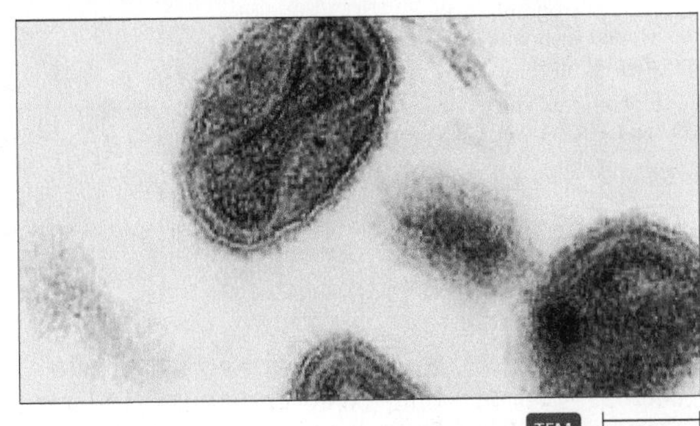

(c)

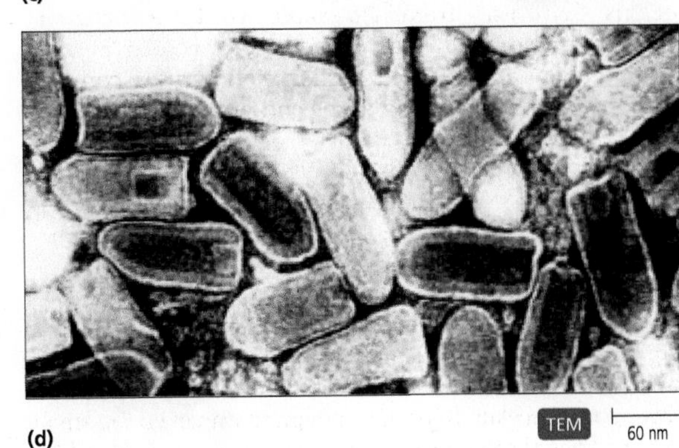

(d)

type of protein, whereas others are composed of several different protein molecules. Recall that viral nucleic acid surrounded by its capsid is termed a *nucleocapsid.*

CRITICAL THINKING

In some viruses, the capsomeres act enzymatically as well as structurally. What advantage might this provide the virus?

Viral Shapes

The shapes of virions are also used to classify viruses. There are three basic types of viral shapes: helical, polyhedral, and complex **(Figure 5).** The capsid of a helical virus is composed of capsomeres that bond together in a spiral fashion to form a tube around the nucleic acid. The capsid of a polyhedral virus is roughly spherical, with a shape similar to a geodesic dome. The most common type of polyhedral capsid is an icosahedron, which has 20 sides.

Complex viruses have capsids of many different shapes that do not readily fit into either of the other two categories. An example of a complex virus is smallpox virus, which has several covering layers (including lipid) and no easily identifiable capsid. The complex shapes of many bacteriophages include icosahedral heads, which contain the genome, attached to helical tails with tail fibers. The complex capsids of such bacteriophages somewhat resemble NASA's lunar lander **(Figure 6).**

The Viral Envelope

Learning Objective

✓ Discuss the origin, structure, and function of the viral envelope.

All viruses lack cell membranes (after all, they are not cells), but some, particularly animal viruses, have a membrane similar in composition to a cytoplasmic membrane surrounding their capsids. Other viral proteins called *matrix proteins* fill the region between capsid and membrane. The viral membrane is called an **envelope,** and a virus with a membrane is an *enveloped virion* **(Figure 7);** a virion without an envelope is called a *nonenveloped* or *naked virion.*

An enveloped virus acquires its envelope from its host cell during viral replication or release (discussed shortly). Indeed, the envelope of a virus is a portion of the membrane system of a host cell. Like a cytoplasmic membrane,

Figure 6 ➤

The complex shape of bacteriophage T4. It includes an icosahedral head and an ornate tail that enables viral attachment and penetration.

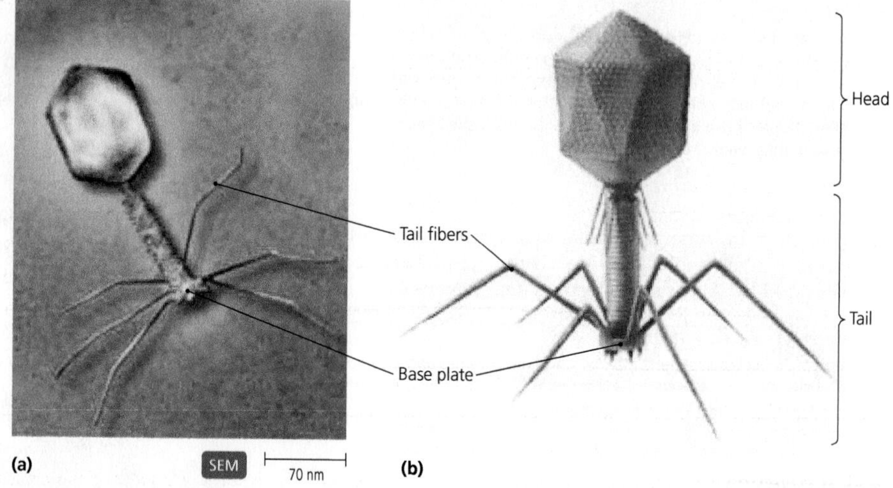

Figure 7 ➤

Enveloped virions. (a) Artist's rendition and electron micrograph of an enveloped virus with a helical capsid. **(b)** Artist's rendition and electron micrograph of an enveloped virus with a polyhedral capsid.

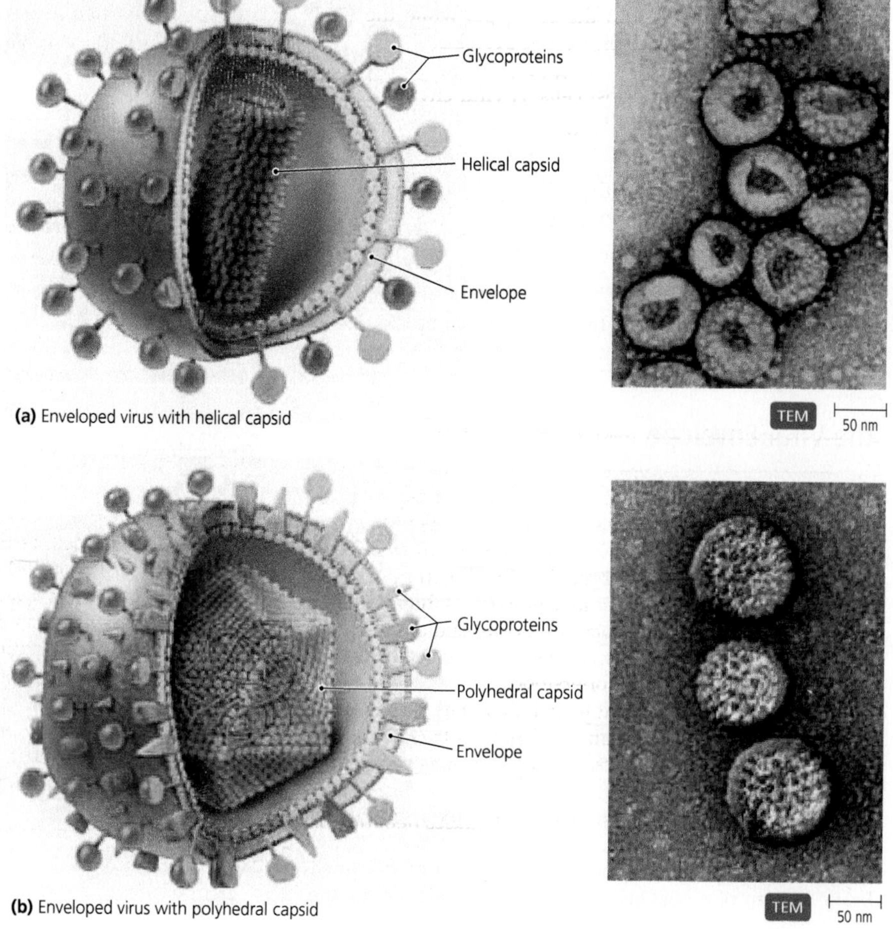

(a) Enveloped virus with helical capsid

(b) Enveloped virus with polyhedral capsid

Table 1 The Novel Properties of Viruses

Viruses	Cells
Inert macromolecules outside of a cell, but become active inside a cell	Metabolize on their own
Do not divide or grow	Divide and grow
Acellular	Cellular
Obligate intracellular parasites	Most free-living
Contain either DNA or RNA	Contain both DNA and RNA
Genome can be dsDNA, ssDNA, dsRNA, or ssRNA	Genome is dsDNA
Ultramicroscopic in size, ranging from 10 nm to 400 nm	200 nm to 12 cm in diameter
Have a proteinaceous capsid around genome; some have an envelope around the capsid	Surrounded by a phospholipid membrane and often a cell wall
Replicate in an assembly-line manner using the enzymes and organelles of a host cell	Self-replicating by asexual and/or sexual means

a viral envelope is composed of a phospholipid bilayer and proteins. Some of the proteins are virally coded glycoproteins, which appear as spikes protruding outward from the envelope's surface (see Figure 7b). Host DNA carries the genetic code required for the assembly of the phospholipids and some of the proteins in the envelope, while the viral genome specifies the other membrane proteins.

An envelope's proteins and glycoproteins often play a role in the recognition of host cells. A viral envelope does not perform the other physiological roles of a cytoplasmic membrane such as endocytosis or active transport.

Table 1 summarizes the novel properties of viruses, and how those properties differ from the corresponding characteristics of cells. Next we turn our attention to the criteria by which virologists classify viruses.

Classification of Viruses

Learning Objective

✓ List the characteristics by which viruses are classified.

The International Committee on Taxonomy of Viruses (ICTV) was established in 1966 to provide a single taxonomic scheme for viral classification and identification. Virologists classify viruses by their type of nucleic acid, presence of an envelope, shape, and size. So far, they have established families for all viral genera, but only three viral orders are described. Kingdoms, divisions, and classes have not been determined for viruses because the relationships among viruses are not well understood.

Family names are typically derived either from special characteristics of viruses within the family or from the name of an important member of the family. For example, family *Picornaviridae* contains very small[1] RNA viruses, and *Hepadnaviridae* contains a DNA virus that causes hepatitis B.

[1]Pico means one-trillionth, 10^{-12}.

Family *Herpesviridae* is named for herpes simplex, a virus that can cause genital herpes. **Table 2** lists the major families of human viruses, grouped according to the type of nucleic acid each contains.

Specific epithets for viruses are their common English designations written in italics. Accordingly, the nomenclature for two important viral pathogens, HIV and rabies virus, is as follows:

	HIV	Rabies virus
Order	Not yet established	Mononegavirales
Family	*Retroviridae*	*Rhabdoviridae*
Genus	*Lentivirus* (len'ti-vī-rŭs)	*Lyssavirus* (lis'ä-vī-rŭs)
Specific epithet	*human immunodeficiency virus*	*rabies virus*

CRITICAL THINKING

Why has it been difficult to develop a complete taxonomy for viruses?

Viral Replication

As previously noted, viruses cannot reproduce themselves because they have neither the genes for all enzymes necessary for replication, nor do they possess functional ribosomes for protein synthesis. Instead, viruses are dependent on their hosts' organelles and enzymes to produce new virions. Once a host cell falls under control of a viral genome, it is forced to replicate viral genetic material and translate new proteins, including viral capsomeres and viral enzymes.

The replication cycle of a virus usually results in the death and lysis of the host cell. Because the cell undergoes lysis near the end of the cycle, this type of replication is

Table 2 Families of Human Viruses

Family	Strand Type	Representative Genera (Diseases)
DNA Viruses		
Poxviridae	Double	*Orthopoxvirus* (smallpox)
Herpesviridae	Double	*Simplexvirus,* Herpes type 1 (fever blisters, respiratory infections), Herpes type 2 (genital infections); *Varicellovirus* (chickenpox); *Lymphocryptovirus,* Epstein-Barr virus (infectious mononucleosis, Burkitt's lymphoma); *Cytomegalovirus* (birth defects); *Roseolavirus* (roseola)
Papillomaviridae	Double	*Papillomavirus* (benign tumors, warts, cervical and penile cancers)
Polyomaviridae	Double	*Polyomavirus* (progressive multifocal leukoencephalopathy)
Adenoviridae	Double	*Mastadenovirus* (conjunctivitis, respiratory infections)
Hepadnaviridae	Partial single and partial double	*Orthohepadnavirus* (hepatitis B)
Parvoviridae	Single	*Erythrovirus* (erythema infectiosum)
RNA Viruses		
Picornaviridae	Single, +[a]	*Enterovirus* (polio); *Hepatovirus* (hepatitis A); *Rhinovirus* (common cold)
Caliciviridae	Single, +	*Norovirus* (gastroenteritis)
Astroviridae	Single, +	*Astrovirus* (gastroenteritis)
Hepeviridae	Single, +	*Hepevirus* (hepatitis E)
Togaviridae	Single, +	*Alphavirus* (encephalitis); *Rubivirus* (rubella)
Flaviviridae	Single, +	*Flavivirus* (yellow fever); Japanese encephalitis virus (encephalitis); *Hepacivirus* (hepatitis C)
Coronaviridae	Single, +	*Coronavirus* (common cold, severe acute respiratory syndrome)
Retroviridae	Single, +, segmented	Human T cell leukemia virus (leukemia); *Lentivirus* (AIDS)
Orthomyxoviridae	Single, −[b], segmented	*Influenzavirus* (flu)
Paramyxoviridae	Single, −	*Paramyxovirus* (common cold, respiratory infections); *Pneumovirus* (pneumonia, common cold); *Morbillivirus* (measles); *Rubulavirus* (mumps)
Rhabdoviridae	Single, −	*Lyssavirus* (rabies)
Bunyaviridae	Single, −, segmented	*Bunyavirus* (California encephalitis virus); *Hantavirus* (pneumonia)
Filoviridae	Single, −	*Filovirus* (Ebola hemorrhagic fever); Marburg virus (hemorrhagic fever)
Arenaviridae	Single, −, segmented	*Lassavirus* (hemorrhagic fever)
Reoviridae	Double, segmented	*Orbivirus* (encephalitis); *Rotavirus* (diarrhea); *Coltivirus* (Colorado tick fever)

[a]Positive-sense (+RNA) is equivalent to mRNA; i.e., it instructs ribosomes in protein translations.
[b]Negative-sense (−RNA) is complementary to mRNA; it cannot be directly translated.

termed **lytic replication**. In general, a lytic replication cycle consists of the following five stages:

- **Attachment** of the virion to the host cell
- **Entry** of the virion or its genome into the host cell
- **Synthesis** of new nucleic acids and viral proteins by the host cell's enzymes and ribosomes
- **Assembly** of new virions within the host cell
- **Release** of the new virions from the host cell

www.microbiologyplace.com **Animations: *Viral Replication: Overview***

In the following sections we will examine the events that occur in the replication of bacteriophages and animal viruses. We begin with lytic replication in bacteriophages, turn to a modification of replication (called lysogenic replication) in bacteriophages, and then consider the replication of animal viruses.

Lytic Replication of Bacteriophages

Learning Objective

✓ Sketch and describe the five stages of the lytic replication cycle as it typically occurs in bacteriophages.

Bacteriophages make excellent tools for the general study of viruses because they are easier and less expensive to culture than animal or human viruses. Studies of bacteriophages revealed the basics of viral biology. **The Beneficial Microbe: Prescription Bacteriophages?** is an interesting side note on the potential use of bacteriophages as an alternative to antibiotics.

Here we examine the replication of a much-studied dsDNA bacteriophage of *E. coli* called *type 4* or *T4.* T4 virions are complex, having the polyhedral heads and helical tails

The Beneficial Microbe *Prescription Bacteriophages?*

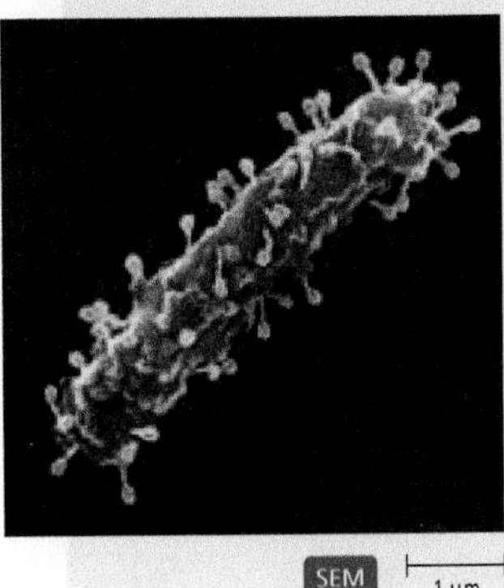

Escherichia coli infected with bacteriophages

In 1917, Canadian biologist Felix d'Herelle published a paper announcing the discovery of the *bacteriophage*, a virus that preyed on bacteria. D'Herelle felt that the bacteriophage (or *phage*, for short) could be a living, natural weapon against bacterial pathogens.

Phage therapy was used in the early 1900s to combat dysentery, typhus, and cholera, but was largely abandoned in the 1940s in the United States, eclipsed by the development of antibiotics such as penicillin. Phage therapy continued in the USSR and Eastern Europe, where research is still centered. Today, motivated by the growing problem of antibiotic-resistant bacteria, scientists in the U.S. and Western Europe have renewed interest in investigating phage therapy.

A phage reproduces by inserting genetic material into a bacterium, causing the bacterium to build copies of the virus that burst out of the cell to infect other bacteria. Each type of phage attacks a specific strain of bacteria. This means that phage treatment is effective only if the phages are carefully matched to the disease-causing bacterium. It also means that phage treatment, unlike the use of antibiotics, can be effective without killing the body's helpful bacteria.

Introducing an active microbe into a patient does present some dangers, however. Phages can kill bacteria, but they can also make bacteria more lethal. A strain of *Escherichia coli* that is responsible for a deadly form of food poisoning, for example, has been observed to gain the ability to produce a toxic chemical from a phage genome that integrates itself into the bacterium's DNA. If a phage being used in therapy picked up a toxin-coding gene, the attempted cure could become lethal.

seen in many bacteriophages. We begin with the first stage of replication: attachment.

Attachment 

Because virions are nonmotile, contact with a bacterium occurs by purely random collision, brought about as molecular bombardment and currents move virions through the environment. The structures responsible for the attachment of T4 to its host bacterium are its tail fibers **(Figure 8)**. Attachment is dependent on the chemical attraction and precise fit between attachment proteins on the phage's tail fibers and complementary receptor proteins on the surface of the host's cell wall. The specificity of the attachment proteins for the receptors ensures that the virus will attach only to *E. coli*. Bacteriophages may attach to receptor proteins on bacterial cells' walls, flagella, or pili.

Entry 

Now that phage T4 has attached to the bacterium's cell wall, it must still overcome the formidable barrier posed by the cell wall and cytoplasmic membrane if it is to enter the cell. T4 overcomes this obstacle in an elegant way. Upon contact with *E. coli*, T4 releases *lysozyme* (lī'sō-zīm), a protein enzyme carried within the capsid that weakens the peptidoglycan of the cell wall. The phage's tail sheath then contracts, which forces an internal hollow tube within the tail through the cell wall and membrane, much as a hypodermic needle penetrates the skin. The phage genome then moves through the tube and into the bacterium. The empty capsid, having performed its task, is left on the outside of the cell looking like an abandoned spacecraft.

Synthesis 3–4

After entry, viral enzymes (either carried within the capsid or coded by viral genes and made by the bacterium) degrade the bacterial DNA into its constituent nucleotides. As a result, the bacterium stops synthesizing its own molecules and begins synthesizing new viruses under control of the viral genome.

For dsDNA viruses like T4, protein synthesis is straightforward and similar to cellular transcription and translation, except that mRNA is transcribed from viral DNA instead of cellular DNA. Translation by the host cell's ribosomes results in viral proteins, including head capsomeres, components of the tail, viral DNA polymerase (which replicates viral DNA), and lysozyme (which weakens the bacterial cell wall from within, enabling the virions to leave the cell once they have been assembled).

Assembly 5

Scientists do not understand completely how phages are assembled inside a host cell, but it appears that as capsomeres accumulate within the cell, they spontaneously attach to one another to form new capsid heads. Likewise, tails assemble and attach to heads, and tail fibers attach to tails, forming mature virions. Such capsid assembly is a spontaneous process, requiring little or no enzymatic activity. For many years it was assumed that all capsids formed around a genome in just such a spontaneous manner. However, recent research has shown that for some viruses, enzymes pump the genome into the assembled capsid under high pressure—five times that used in a paintball gun. This process resembles stuffing a strand of cooked spaghetti into a matchbox through a single small hole.

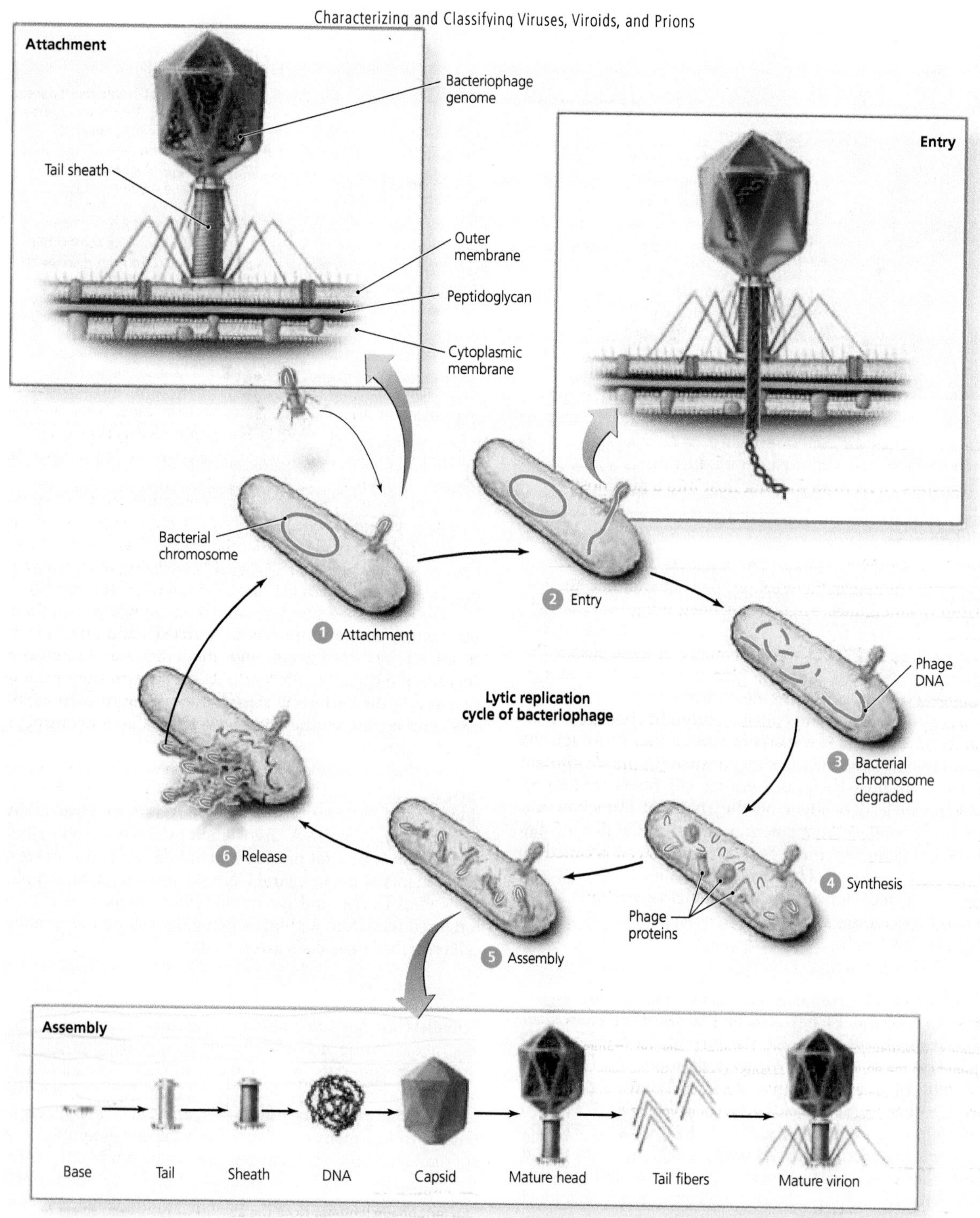

▲ *Figure 8*

The lytic replication cycle in bacteriophages. The phage shown in this illustration is T4, and the bacterium shown is *E. coli*. The circular bacterial chromosome is represented diagrammatically; in reality it would be much longer.

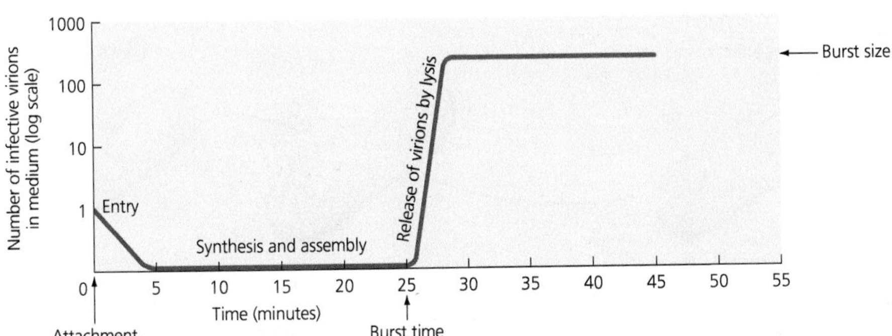

Figure 9
Pattern of virion abundance in lytic cycle. Virion abundance over time for single lytic replication cycle. New virions are not observed in the culture medium until synthesis, assembly, and release (lysis) are complete, at which time (the burst time) the new virions are released all at once. Burst size is the number of new virions released per lysed host cell.

Sometimes a capsid assembles around leftover pieces of host DNA instead of viral DNA. A virion formed in this manner is still able to attach to a new host by means of its tail fibers, but instead of inserting phage DNA it transfers DNA from the first host into a new host.

Release 6

Newly assembled virions are released from the cell as lysozyme completes its work on the cell wall and the bacterium disintegrates. Areas of disintegrating bacterial cells in a lawn of bacteria in a Petri plate look as if the lawn were being eaten, and it was the appearance of these *plaques* that prompted early scientists to give the name *bacteriophage,* "bacterial eater," to these viruses.

For phage T4, the process of lytic replication takes about 25 minutes and can produce as many as 100–200 new virions for each bacterial cell lysed **(Figure 9)**. For any phage undergoing lytic replication, the period of time required to complete the entire process, from attachment to release, is called the *burst time,* and the number of new virions released from each lysed bacterial cell is called the *burst size.*

www.microbiologyplace.com **Animations: *Viral Replication: Virulent Bacteriophages***

CRITICAL THINKING

If a colony of 1.5 billion *E. coli* cells were infected with a single phage T4, and each lytic replication cycle of the phage produced 200 new phages, how many replication cycles would it take for T4 phages to overwhelm the entire bacterial colony? (Assume for the sake of simplicity that every phage completes its replication cycle in a different cell and that the bacteria themselves do not reproduce.)

Lysogeny

Learning Objective

✓ Compare and contrast the lysogenic replication cycle of viruses with the lytic cycle and with latency.

Not all viruses follow the lytic pattern of phage T4 we just examined. Some bacteriophages have a modified replication cycle in which infected host cells grow and reproduce normally for many generations before they lyse. Such a replication cycle is called a **lysogenic replication cycle** or **lysogeny** (lī-soj'ĕ-nē), and the phages are called **temperate phages** or *lysogenic phages.*

Here we examine lysogenic replication as it occurs in a much-studied temperate phage, *lambda phage,* which is another parasite of *E. coli.* A lambda phage has a linear molecule of dsDNA in a complex capsid consisting of an icosahedral head attached to a tail that lacks tail fibers **(Figure 10)**.

Figure 11 illustrates lysogeny with lambda phage. First, the virion randomly contacts an *E. coli* cell and attaches via its tail 1. The viral DNA enters the cell, just as occurs with phage T4, but the host cell's DNA is not destroyed, and the phage's genome does not immediately assume control of the cell. Instead, the virus remains inactive. Such an inactive

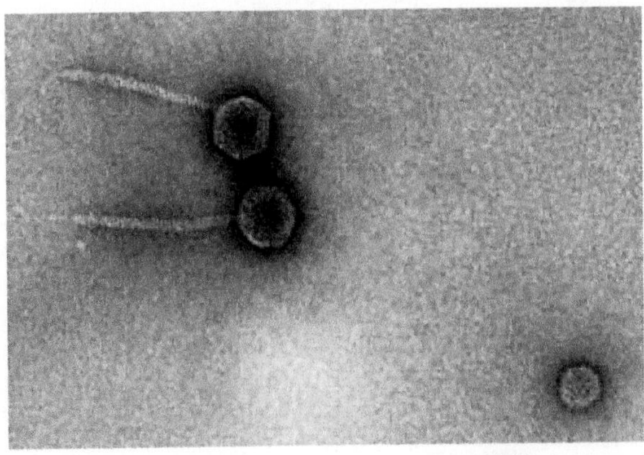

Figure 10
Bacteriophage lambda. Note the absence of tail fibers. *Phage T4 attaches by means of molecules on its tail fibers. How does lambda phage, which lacks fibers, attach?*

Figure 10 *Lambda has attachment molecules at the end of its tail rather than on its tail fibers.*

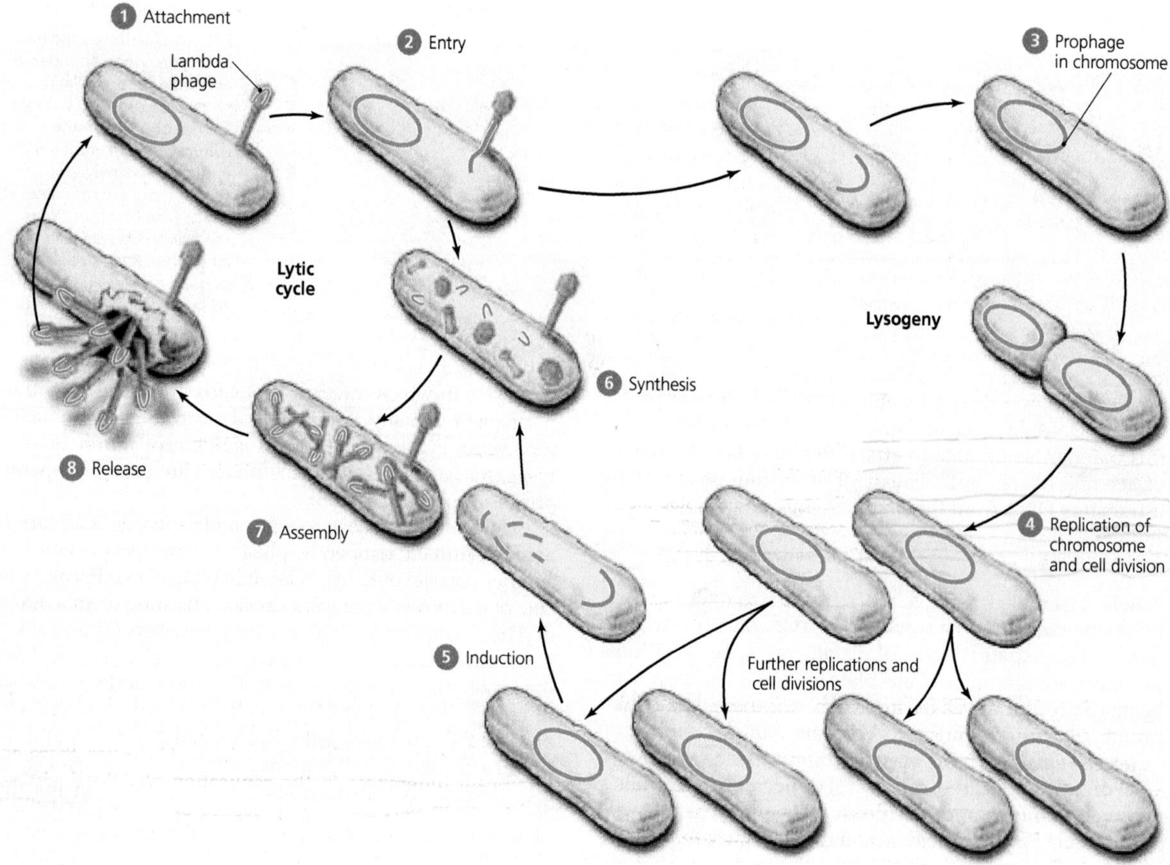

▲ *Figure 11*

The lysogenic replication cycle in bacteriophages. The phage shown in this illustration is phage lambda, and the bacterium shown is *E. coli.* The circular bacterial chromosome is represented diagrammatically; in reality it would be much longer. *How is a lysogenic cycle different from a lytic cycle?*

Figure 11 In a lysogenic cycle, the virus is inserted into the bacterial chromosome, and it is replicated and passed on to all daughter cells until it is induced to leave the chromosome; a lytic cycle is a replication cycle that results in cell death.

bacteriophage is called a **prophage** (prō′fāj) 2. A prophage remains inactive by coding for a protein that suppresses prophage genes. A side effect of this repressor protein is that it renders the bacterium resistant to additional infection by other viruses of the same type.

Another difference between a lysogenic cycle and a lytic cycle is that the prophage is inserted into the DNA of the bacterium, becoming a physical part of the bacterial chromosome 3. For DNA viruses like lambda phage, this is a simple process of fusing two pieces of DNA: one piece of DNA, the virus, is fused to another piece of DNA, the chromosome of the cell. Every time the cell replicates its infected chromosome, the prophage is also replicated 4. All daughter cells of a lysogenic cell are thus infected with the quiescent virus. A prophage and its descendants may remain a part of bacterial chromosomes for generations.

Lysogenic phages can change the phenotype of a bacterium, for example from a harmless form into a pathogen—a process called **lysogenic conversion.** Bacteriophage genes are responsible for toxins and other disease-evoking proteins found in the bacterial agents of diphtheria, cholera, rheumatic fever, and certain severe cases of diarrhea caused by *E. coli.*

At some later time a prophage may be excised from the chromosome by recombination or some other genetic event; it then reenters the lytic phase. The process whereby a prophage is excised from the host chromosome is called **induction** 5. Inductive agents are typically the same physical and chemical

Highlight *The Threat of Avian Influenza*

In 1997, 18 people in Hong Kong contracted avian influenza, caused by the H5N1 strain of influenzavirus that spreads easily among chickens and other birds. At least half of these people caught the disease directly from birds, something that scientists had previously thought improbable. When people began dying of the illness, Hong Kong officials slaughtered all 1.5 million chickens within three days. That stopped a potential epidemic in Hong Kong, but it didn't stop the spread of the avian flu. Today, the virus infects domesticated poultry in countries of Asia and Africa, including China, Thailand, Vietnam, Cambodia, Indonesia, Malaysia, Côte d'Ivoire, Niger, Nigeria, and Egypt. Human cases have had a 60% death rate.

Avian flu virus very rarely spreads from one person to another. However, the possibility that this may change is of great concern to health officials worldwide. Avian flu viruses mutate quickly and can pick up genes from other flu viruses. If an avian flu virus picks up genes from a human flu virus, it could become a strain that spreads easily from person to person. In a worst-case scenario such a strain of avian/human flu, in this age of jet travel, could cause a pandemic killing 2–50 million people worldwide, according to the World Health Organization.

What should be done? In Asia, more than 200 million chickens and other domesticated fowl have been slaughtered to prevent avian flu from spreading. But while governments concentrated on culling domestic poultry, the virus spread to wild birds, such as geese, gray herons, and feral pigeons, and via wild birds it has spread throughout Asia, Europe, and central Africa.

Scientists have developed a vaccine that they believe could protect against the H5N1 strain of the virus. Unfortunately, a government could stockpile vaccine for one strain of avian flu only to have the virus mutate into a new form against which the vaccine is ineffective.

agents that damage DNA molecules, including ultraviolet light, X rays, and carcinogenic chemicals.

After induction, the lytic steps of synthesis ❻, assembly ❼, and release ❽ resume from the point at which they stopped. The cell becomes filled with virions and breaks open.

Bacteriophages T4 and lambda demonstrate two replication strategies that are typical for many DNA viruses. RNA viruses and enveloped viruses present variations on the lytic and lysogenic cycles we have examined. We will next examine some of these variations as they occur with animal viruses.

www.microbiologyplace.com **Animations: *Viral Replication: Temperate Bacteriophages***

CRITICAL THINKING

What differences would you expect in the replication cycles of RNA phages from those of DNA phages? (Hints: Think about the processes of transcription, translation, and replication of nucleic acids. Also, note that RNA is not normally inserted into a DNA molecule.)

Replication of Animal Viruses

Learning Objectives

- ✓ Explain the differences between bacteriophage replication and animal viral replication.
- ✓ Compare and contrast the replication and synthesis of DNA, −RNA, and +RNA viruses.
- ✓ Compare and contrast the release of viral particles by lysis and budding.

Animal viruses have the same five basic steps in their replication pathways as bacteriophages—that is, attachment, entry, synthesis, assembly, and release. However, there are significant differences in the replication of animal viruses that result in part from the presence of envelopes around some of the viruses, and in part from the eukaryotic nature of animal cells as well as their lack of a cell wall. **Highlight: The Threat of Avian Influenza** highlights an animal virus that is of great concern to health officials worldwide.

In this section we examine the replication processes that are shared by DNA and RNA animal viruses, compare these processes with those of bacteriophages, and discuss how the synthesis of DNA and RNA viruses differ.

Attachment of Animal Viruses

As with bacteriophages, attachment of an animal virus is dependent on the chemical attraction and exact fit between proteins or glycoproteins on the virion and complementary protein or glycoprotein receptors on the animal cell's cytoplasmic membrane. Unlike the bacteriophages we have examined, animal viruses lack both tails and tail fibers. Instead, animal viruses typically have glycoprotein spikes or other attachment molecules on their capsids or envelopes.

Entry and Uncoating of Animal Viruses

Animal viruses enter a host cell shortly after attachment. Even though entry of animal viruses is not as well understood as entry of bacteriophages, there appear to be at least

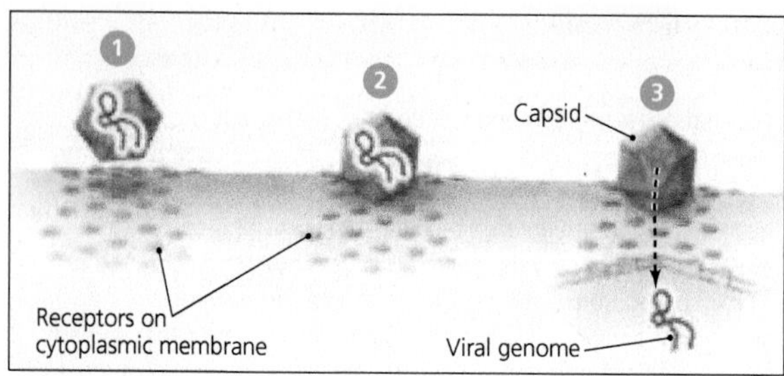

(a) Direct penetration

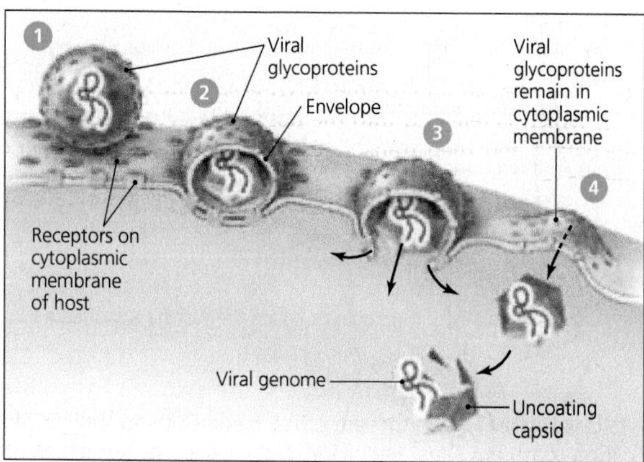

(b) Membrane fusion

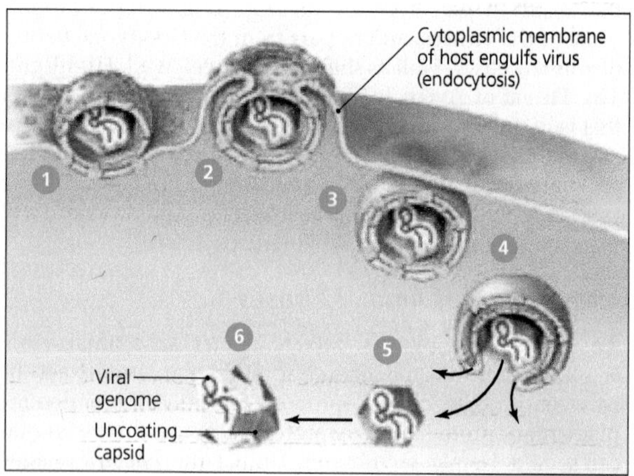

(c) Endocytosis

Figure 12

Three mechanisms of entry of animal viruses. (a) Direct penetration, a process whereby naked virions inject their genomes into their animal cell hosts. **(b)** Membrane fusion, in which fusion of the viral envelope and cell membrane dumps the capsid into the cell. **(c)** Endocytosis, in which attachment of a virus stimulates the host cell to engulf the entire virus. *After penetration, many animal viruses must be uncoated, but bacteriophages need not be. Why is this so?*

Figure 12 Generally bacteriophages inject their DNA during penetration, so the capsid does not enter the cell.

three different mechanisms: direct penetration, membrane fusion, and endocytosis.

At least some naked viruses enter their hosts' cells by direct penetration—a process in which the viral capsid attaches and sinks into the cytoplasmic membrane, creating a pore through which the genome alone enters the cell **(Figure 12a)**. Poliovirus and dengue fever virus are examples of virions that infect host cells via direct penetration.

In enveloped viruses, by contrast, the entire capsid and its contents (including the genome) enter the host cell by one of two methods: membrane fusion or endocytosis. With viruses using membrane fusion, including the measles and mumps viruses, the viral envelope and the host cell membrane fuse, releasing the capsid into the cell's cytoplasm and leaving the envelope glycoproteins as part of the cell membrane **(Figure 12b)**. Most enveloped viruses and some naked viruses enter host cells by triggering endocytosis. Attachment of the virus to receptor molecules on the cell's surface stimulates the cell to endocytize the entire virus **(Figure 12c)**. Adenoviruses (naked) and herpesviruses (enveloped) enter human host cells via endocytosis.

For those enveloped viruses that penetrate a host cell with their capsids intact, the capsids must be removed to release their genomes before the viruses can continue to replicate. The removal of a viral capsid within a host cell is called **uncoating**, a process that remains poorly understood. It apparently occurs via different means in different viruses; some viruses are uncoated within vesicles by cellular enzymes, whereas others are uncoated by enzymes within the cell's cytosol.

Synthesis of Animal Viruses

Synthesis of animal viruses also differs from synthesis of bacteriophages. Each type of animal virus requires a different strategy for synthesis that depends on the kind of nucleic acid involved—whether it is DNA or RNA, and whether it is double stranded or single stranded. DNA viruses typically enter the nucleus, whereas most RNA viruses are replicated in the cytoplasm. As we discuss the synthesis and assembly of each type of animal virus, consider the following two questions:

- How is mRNA—needed for the translation of viral proteins—synthesized?
- What molecule serves as a template for nucleic acid replication?

dsDNA Viruses Synthesis of new double-stranded DNA (dsDNA) virions is similar to the normal replication of cellular DNA and translation of proteins. The genomes of most dsDNA viruses enter the nucleus of the cell, where cellular enzymes replicate the viral genome in the same manner as host dsDNA is replicated—using each strand of viral DNA as a template for its complement. After messenger RNA is transcribed from viral DNA in the nucleus and capsomere proteins are made in the cytoplasm by host ribosomes, capsomeres enter the cell's nucleus, where new virions spontaneously assemble. This method of replication is seen with herpes and papilloma (wart) viruses.

There are two well-known exceptions to this regimen of dsDNA viruses:

- Every part of a poxvirus is synthesized and assembled in the cytoplasm of the host's cell; the nucleus is not involved.
- The genome of hepatitis B viruses is replicated using an RNA intermediary instead of replicating DNA from a DNA template. In other words, the genome of hepatitis B virus is transcribed into RNA, which is then used as a template to make multiple copies of viral DNA genome. The latter process, which is the reverse of normal transcription, is mediated by a viral enzyme, *reverse transcriptase.*

ssDNA Viruses A human virus with a genome composed of single-stranded DNA (ssDNA) is a parvovirus (see Table 2). When a parvovirus enters the nucleus of a host cell, host enzymes produce a new strand of DNA complementary to the viral genome. This complementary strand binds to the ssDNA of the virus to form a dsDNA molecule. Transcription of mRNA, replication of new ssDNA, and viral assembly then follow the DNA virus pattern just described.

As previously noted, RNA is not used as genetic material in cells, so it follows that the synthesis of RNA viruses must differ significantly from typical cellular processes, and from the replication of DNA viruses as well. There are four types of RNA viruses: positive-sense, single-stranded RNA (designated +ssRNA); retroviruses (a kind of +ssRNA virus); negative-sense, single-stranded RNA (−ssRNA); and double-stranded (dsRNA). The synthesis process for these RNA viruses is varied and sometimes rather complex. We start with the synthesis of +ssRNA viruses.

Positive-Sense ssRNA Viruses Single-stranded viral RNA that can act directly as mRNA is called **positive-strand RNA (+RNA).** Ribosomes translate polypeptides using the codons of such RNA. An example of a +ssRNA virus is poliovirus. In many +ssRNA viruses, a complementary **negative-strand RNA (−RNA)** is transcribed from the +ssRNA genome by viral RNA polymerase; −RNA then serves as the template for the transcription of multiple +ssRNA genomes. Such transcription of RNA from RNA is unique to viruses; no cell transcribes RNA from RNA.

Retroviruses Unlike other +ssRNA viruses, the +ssRNA viruses called **retroviruses** do not use their genome as mRNA. Instead, retroviruses use a DNA intermediary that is transcribed from +RNA by reverse transcriptase carried within the capsid. This DNA intermediary then serves as the template for the synthesis of additional +RNA molecules, which act both as mRNA for protein synthesis and as genomes for new virions. Human immunodeficiency virus (HIV) is a prominent retrovirus.

Negative-Sense ssRNA Viruses Other single-stranded RNA virions are −ssRNA viruses, which must overcome a unique problem. In order to synthesize a protein, a ribosome can use only mRNA (i.e., +RNA), because −RNA is not recognized by ribosomes. The virus overcomes this problem by carrying within its capsid an enzyme, *RNA-dependent RNA transcriptase,* which is released into the host cell's cytoplasm during uncoating and then transcribes +RNA molecules from the virus's −RNA genome. Translation of proteins can then occur as usual. The newly transcribed +RNA also serves as a template for transcription of additional copies of −RNA. Diseases caused by −ssRNA viruses include rabies and flu.

dsRNA Viruses Viruses that have double-stranded RNA use yet another method of synthesis. The positive strand of the molecule serves as mRNA for the translation of proteins, one of which is an RNA polymerase that transcribes dsRNA. Each strand of RNA acts as a template for transcription of its opposite, which is reminiscent of DNA replication in cells. Double-stranded RNA rotaviruses cause most cases of diarrhea in infants.

Figure 13 illustrates and **Table 3** summarizes the various strategies by which animal viruses are synthesized.

CRITICAL THINKING

Although many +ssRNA viruses use their genome directly as mRNA, retroviruses do not. Instead, their +RNA is transcribed into DNA by reverse transcriptase. What advantage do retroviruses gain by using reverse transcriptase?

Assembly and Release of Animal Viruses

As with bacteriophages, once the components of animal viruses are synthesized, they assemble into virions that are then released from the host cell. Most DNA viruses assemble in and are released from the nucleus into the cytosol, whereas most RNA viruses develop solely in the cytoplasm. The number of viruses produced and released depends on both the type of virus and the size and initial health of the host cell.

Replication of animal viruses takes more time than replication of bacteriophages. Herpesviruses, for example, require almost 24 hours to replicate, as compared to 25 minutes for hundreds of copies of bacteriophage T4.

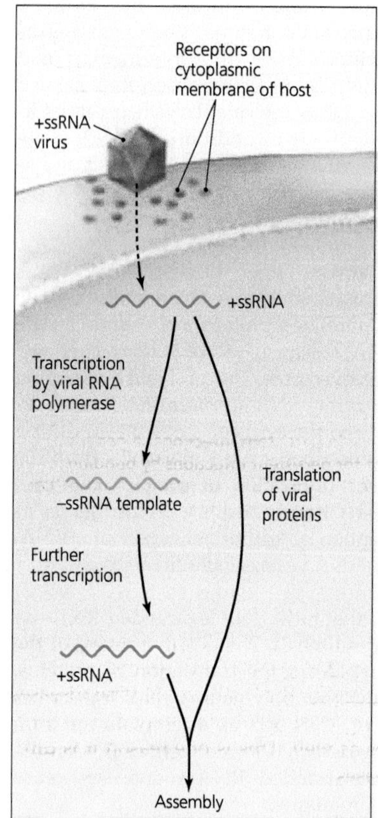

(a) Positive-sense ssRNA virus

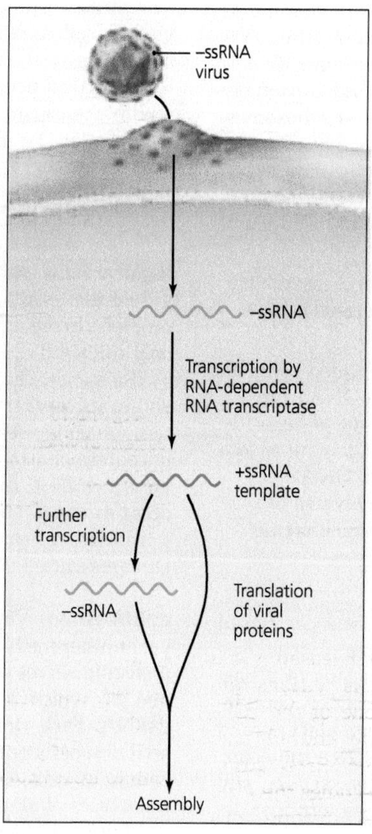

(b) Negative-sense ssRNA virus

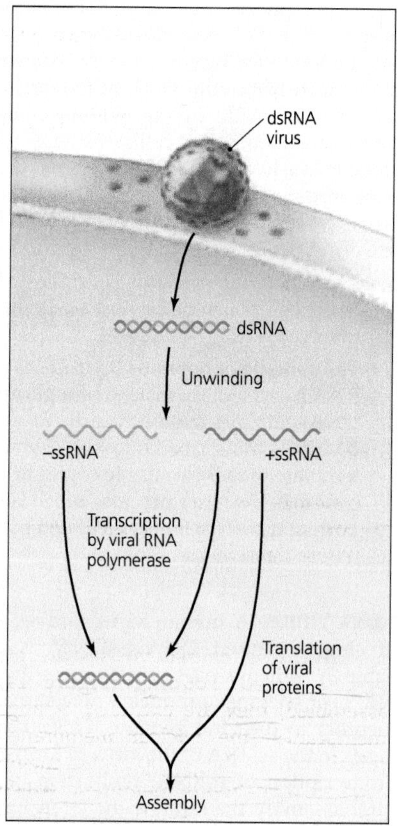

(c) Double-stranded RNA virus

▲ *Figure 13*

Synthesis of proteins and genomes in animal RNA viruses. (a) Positive-sense ssRNA virus, in which +ssRNA acts as mRNA and −ssRNA is the genome template. (b) Negative-sense ssRNA virus: transcription forms +ssRNA to serve both as mRNA and template. (c) dsRNA virus genome unwinds so that the positive-sense strand serves as mRNA, and each strand serves as a template for its complement.

Table 3 Synthesis Strategies of Animal Viruses

Genome	How Is mRNA Synthesized?	What Molecule Is the Template for Genome Replication?
dsDNA	By RNA polymerase (in nucleus or cytoplasm of cell)	Each strand of DNA serves as template for its complement (except for hepatitis B, which synthesizes RNA to act as the template for new DNA)
ssDNA	By RNA polymerase (in nucleus of cell)	Complementary strand of DNA is synthesized to act as template
+ssRNA	Genome acts as mRNA	−RNA is synthesized to act as template
+ssRNA (*Retroviridae*)	DNA is synthesized from RNA by reverse transcriptase; mRNA is transcribed from DNA by RNA polymerase	DNA
−ssRNA	By RNA-dependent RNA transcriptase	+RNA (mRNA)
dsRNA	Positive strand of genome acts as mRNA	Each strand of genome acts as template for its complement

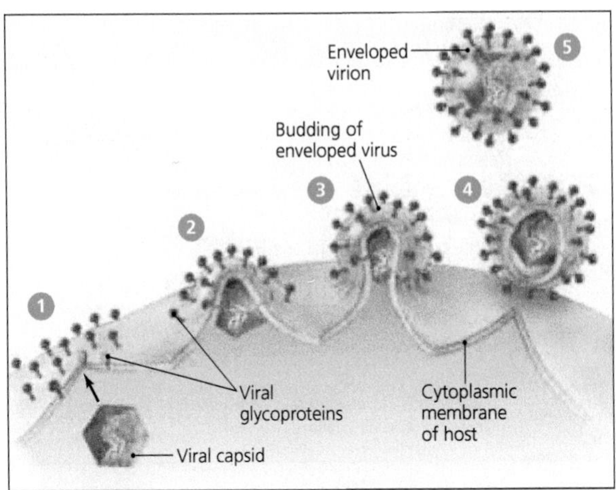

▲ *Figure 14*

The process of budding in enveloped viruses. *What term describes a nonenveloped virus?*

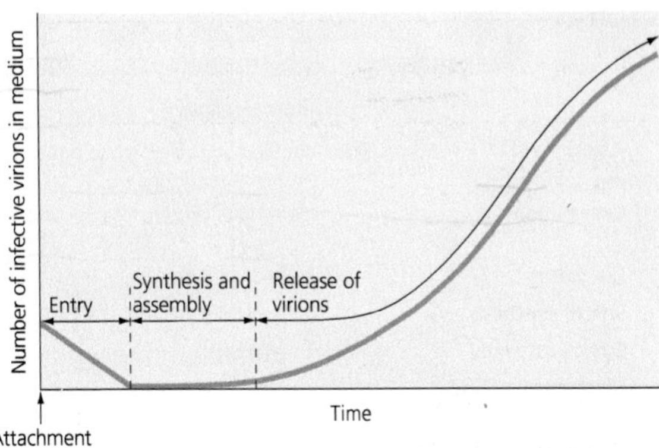

▲ *Figure 15*

Pattern of virion abundance in persistent infections. A generalized curve of virion abundance for persistent infections by budding enveloped viruses. Because the curve does not represent any actual infection, units for the graph's axes are omitted.

Figure 14 Naked.

Enveloped animal viruses are often released via a process called **budding (Figure 14).** As virions are assembled, they are extruded through one of the cell's membranes—the nuclear membrane, the endoplasmic reticulum, or the cytoplasmic membrane. Each virion acquires a portion of membrane, which becomes the viral envelope. During synthesis, some viral glycoproteins are inserted into cellular membranes, and these proteins become the glycoprotein spikes on the surface of the viral envelope.

Because the host cell is not quickly lysed, as occurs in bacteriophage replication, budding allows an infected cell to remain alive for some time. Infections with enveloped viruses in which host cells shed viruses slowly and relatively steadily are called *persistent infections;* a curve showing virus abundance over time during a persistent infection lacks the burst of new virions seen in lytic replication cycles **(Figure 15).**

Naked animal viruses may be released in one of two ways: They may either be extruded from the cell by exocytosis, in a manner similar to budding, but without the acquisition of an envelope, or they may cause lysis and death of the cell, reminiscent of bacteriophage release.

www.microbiologyplace.com **Animations: *Viral Replication: Animal Viruses***

CRITICAL THINKING

If an enveloped virus were somehow released from a cell without budding, it would not have an envelope. What effect would this have on the virulence of the virus? Why?

Because viral replication uses cellular structures and pathways involved in the growth and maintenance of healthy cells, any strategy for the treatment of viral diseases that involves disrupting viral replication may disrupt normal cellular processes as well. This is one reason it is difficult to treat viral diseases.

Latency of Animal Viruses

Some animal viruses, including chickenpox and herpesviruses, may remain dormant in cells in a process known as **latency;** the viruses involved in latency are called **latent viruses** or **proviruses.** Latency may be prolonged for years with no viral activity, signs, or symptoms. Though latency is similar to lysogeny as seen with bacteriophages, there are differences. Some latent viruses do not become incorporated into the chromosomes of their host cells, whereas lysogenic phages always do.

On the other hand, some animal viruses (e.g., HIV) are more like lysogenic phages in that they do become integrated into a host chromosome as a provirus. However, when a provirus is incorporated into its host DNA, the condition is permanent; induction never occurs, as it can in lysogeny. Thus an incorporated provirus becomes a permanent, physical part of the host's chromosome, and all descendants of the infected cell will carry the provirus.

An important feature of HIV infections is that proviruses become a permanent part of the DNA of the host's white blood cells. But given that RNA cannot be incorporated directly into a DNA molecule, how does the ssRNA of HIV become a provirus incorporated into the DNA of its host cell?

Table 4 A Comparison of Bacteriophage and Animal Virus Replication

	Bacteriophage	Animal Virus
Attachment	Proteins on tails attach to proteins on cell wall	Spikes, capsids, or envelope proteins attach to proteins or glycoproteins on cell membrane
Penetration	Genome is injected into cell or diffuses into cell	Capsid enters cell by direct penetration, fusion, or endocytosis
Uncoating	None	Removal of capsid by cell enzymes
Site of synthesis	In cytoplasm	RNA viruses in cytoplasm; most DNA viruses in nucleus
Site of assembly	In cytoplasm	RNA viruses in cytoplasm; most DNA viruses in nucleus
Mechanism of release	Lysis	Naked virions: exocytosis or lysis; enveloped virions: budding
Nature of chronic infection	Lysogeny, always incorporated into host chromosome, may leave host chromosome	Latency, with or without incorporation into host DNA; incorporation is permanent

HIV can become a permanent part of a host's DNA because it, like all retroviruses, carries reverse transcriptase, which transcribes the genetic information of the +RNA molecule to a DNA molecule—which *can* become incorporated into the host cell's genome.

CRITICAL THINKING

A latent virus that is incorporated into a host cell's chromosome is never induced; that is, it never emerges from the host cell's chromosome to become a free virus. Given that it cannot emerge from the host cell's chromosome, can such a latent virus be considered "safe"? Why or why not?

Table 4 compares the features of the replication of bacteriophages and animal viruses. Next we turn our attention to the part viruses can play in cancer, beginning with a brief consideration of the terminology needed to understand the basic nature of cancer.

The Role of Viruses in Cancer

Learning Objectives

- ✓ Define the terms *neoplasia, tumor, benign, malignant, cancer,* and *metastasis.*
- ✓ Explain in simple terms how a cell may become cancerous, with special reference to the role of viruses.

Under normal conditions, the division of cells in a mature multicellular animal is under strict genetic control; that is, the animal's genes dictate that some types of cells can no longer divide at all, and that those that can divide are prevented from unlimited division. In this genetic control, either genes for cell division are "turned off," or genes that inhibit division are "turned on," or some combination of both these genetic events occur. However, if something upsets the genetic control, cells begin to divide uncontrollably. This phenomenon of uncontrolled cell division in a multicellular animal is called **neoplasia**[2] (nē-ō-plā'zē-ă). Cells undergoing neoplasia are said to be neoplastic, and a mass of neoplastic cells is a **tumor.**

Some tumors are **benign;** that is, they remain in one place and are not generally harmful, although occasionally such noninvasive tumors are painful and rob adjacent normal cells of space and nutrients. Other tumors are **malignant,** invading neighboring tissues and even traveling throughout the body to invade other organs and tissues to produce new tumors—a process called **metastasis** (mĕ-tas'tă-sis). Malignant tumors are also called **cancers.** Cancers rob normal cells of space and nutrients and cause pain; in some kinds of cancer, malignant cells derange the function of the affected tissues, until eventually the body can no longer withstand the loss of normal function and dies.

Several theories have been proposed to explain the development of cancers and the role viruses play. These theories revolve around the presence of *protooncogenes* (prō-tō-ong'kō-jēnz)—genes that play a role in cell division. So long as the protooncogenes are repressed, no cancer results. However, activity of oncogenes (their name when they are active) or inactivation of oncogene repressors can cause cancer to develop. In most cases, several genetic changes must occur before cancer develops. Put another way, "multiple hits" to the genome must occur for cancer to result **(Figure 16).**

A variety of environmental factors contribute to the inhibition of oncogene repressors and the activation of oncogenes. Ultraviolet light, radiation, certain chemicals called *carcinogens* (kar-si'nō-jenz), and viruses have all been implicated in the development of cancer.

Viruses cause 20–25% of human cancers in several ways. Some viruses carry copies of oncogenes as part of their genomes; other viruses promote oncogenes already present in the host; still other viruses interfere with normal

[2]From Greek *neo,* meaning new, and *plassein,* meaning to mold.

tumor repression when they insert (as proviruses) into repressor genes.

That viruses cause some animal cancers is well established. In the first decade of the 1900s, virologist F. Peyton Rous (1879–1970) proved that viruses induce cancer in chickens. Though several DNA and RNA viruses are known to cause about 15% of human cancers, the link between viruses and most human cancers has been difficult to document. Among the virally induced cancers in humans are Burkitt's lymphoma, Hodgkin's disease, Kaposi's sarcoma, and cervical cancer. DNA viruses in the families *Adenoviridae, Herpesviridae, Hepadnaviridae, Papillomaviridae,* and *Polyomaviridae,* and two RNA viruses in the family *Retroviridae,* cause these and other human cancers.

CRITICAL THINKING

Why are DNA viruses more likely to cause neoplasias than are RNA viruses?

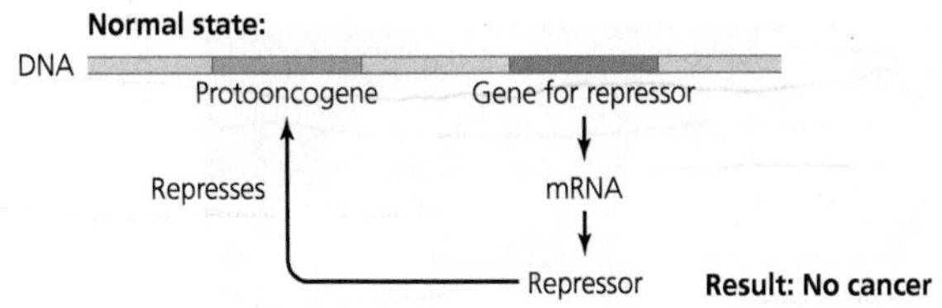

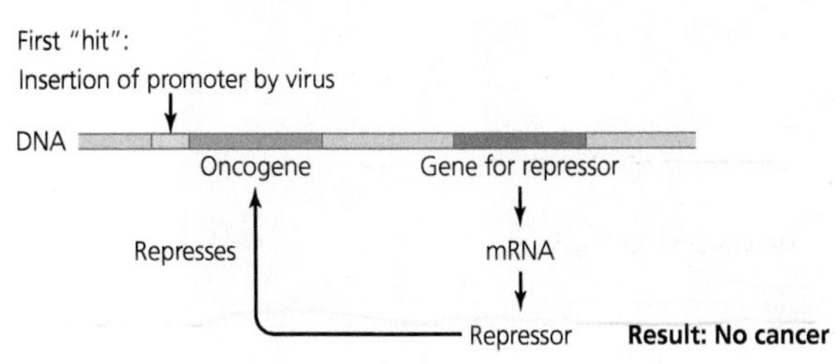

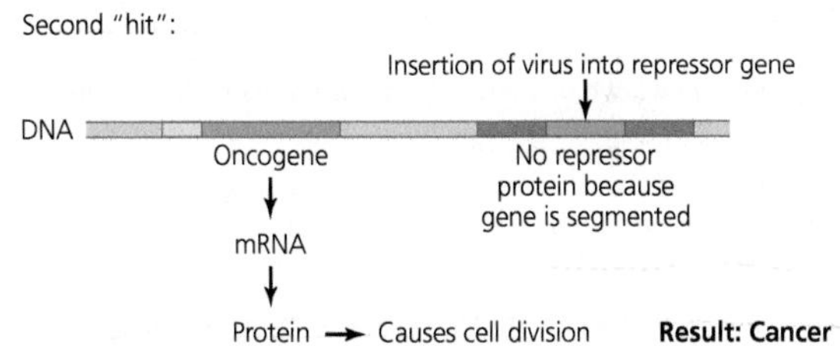

▲ *Figure 16*

The oncogene theory of the induction of cancer in humans. The theory suggests that more than one "hit" to the DNA (that is, any change or mutation), whether caused by a virus (as shown here) or various physical or chemical agents, is required to induce cancer.

Culturing Viruses in the Laboratory

Learning Objectives

✓ Describe some ethical and practical difficulties to overcome in culturing viruses.

✓ Describe three types of media used for culturing viruses.

Scientists must culture viruses in order to conduct research and develop vaccines and treatments, but because viruses cannot metabolize or replicate by themselves, they cannot be grown in standard microbiological broths or on agar plates. Instead, they must be cultured inside suitable host cells, a requirement that complicates the detection, identification, and characterization of viruses. Virologists have developed three types of media for culturing viruses: media consisting of whole organisms (bacteria, plants, or animals), embryonated (fertilized) eggs, and cell cultures. We begin by considering the culture of viruses in whole organisms.

Culturing Viruses in Whole Organisms

Learning Objective

✓ Explain the use of a plaque assay in culturing viruses in bacteria.

In the following sections we consider the use of bacterial cells as a virus culture medium before considering the issues involved in growing viruses in living animals.

Culturing Viruses in Bacteria

Most of our knowledge of viral replication has been derived from research on bacteriophages, which are relatively easy to culture because some bacteria are easily grown and maintained. Phages can be grown in bacteria maintained in either liquid cultures or on agar plates. In the latter case, bacteria and phages are mixed with warm (liquid) nutrient agar and poured in a thin layer across the surface of an agar plate. During incubation, bacteria infected by phages lyse and release new phages that infect nearby bacteria, while uninfected bacteria grow and reproduce normally. After incubation, the appearance of the plate includes a uniform bacterial lawn interrupted by clear zones called **plaques,** which are areas where phages have lysed the bacteria **(Figure 17).** Such plates enable the estimation of phage numbers via a technique called plaque assay, in which virologists assume that each plaque corresponds to a single phage in the original bacterium-virus mixture.

Culturing Viruses in Plants and Animals

Plant and animal viruses can be grown in laboratory plants and animals. Recall that the first discovery and isolation of a virus was the discovery of tobacco mosaic virus in tobacco plants. Rats, mice, guinea pigs, rabbits, pigs, and primates have been used to culture and study animal viruses.

However, maintaining laboratory animals can be difficult and expensive, and this practice raises ethical issues for

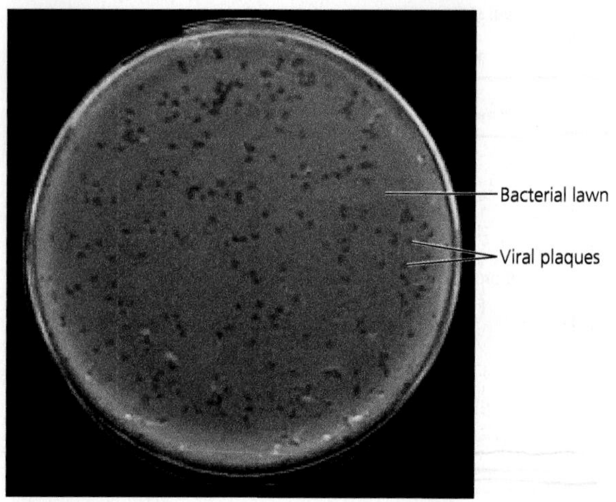

▲ *Figure 17*

Viral plaques in a lawn of bacterial growth on the surface of an agar plate. *What is the cause of viral plaques?*

Figure 17 Each plaque is an area in a bacterial lawn where bacteria have succumbed to phage infections.

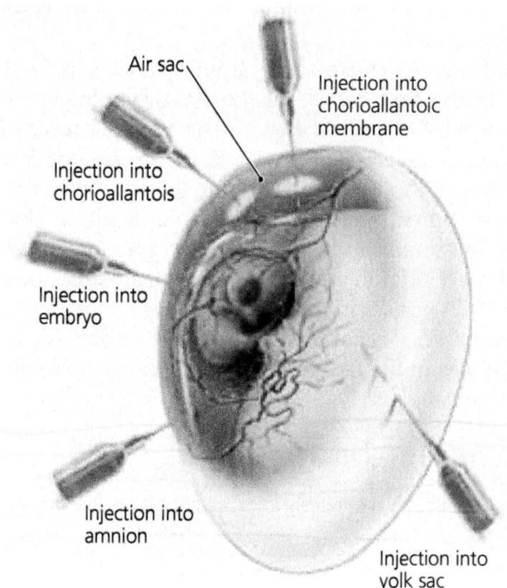

▲ *Figure 18*

Inoculation sites for the culture of viruses in embryonated chicken eggs. *Why are eggs often used to grow animal viruses?*

Figure 18 Eggs are large, sterile, self-sufficient cells that contain a number of different sites suitable for viral replication.

some. Growing viruses that infect only humans raises additional ethical complications. Therefore, scientists have developed alternative ways of culturing animal and human viruses using fertilized chicken eggs or cell cultures.

Culturing Viruses in Embryonated Chicken Eggs

Chicken eggs are a useful culture medium for viruses because they are inexpensive, are among the largest of cells, are free of contaminating microbes, and contain a nourishing yolk (which makes them self-sufficient). Most suitable for culturing viruses are chicken eggs that have been fertilized and thus contain a developing embryo, the tissues of which (called membranes, which should not be confused with cellular membranes) provide ideal inoculation sites for growing viruses **(Figure 18).** Researchers inject samples of virus into embryonated eggs at the sites that are best suited for the virus's maintenance and replication.

Vaccines against some viruses can also be prepared in egg cultures. You may have been asked if you are allergic to eggs before you received such a vaccine, because egg protein may remain as a contaminant in the vaccine.

Culturing Viruses in Cell (Tissue) Culture

Learning Objective

✓ Compare and contrast diploid **cell culture** and continuous cell culture.

Viruses can also be grown in **cell culture,** which consists of cells isolated from an organism and grown on the surface of a medium or in broth **(Figure 19).** Such cultures became practical when antibiotics provided a way to limit the growth of contaminating bacteria. Cell culture can be less expensive than maintaining research animals, plants, or eggs, and it avoids some of the moral problems associated with experiments performed on animals and humans. Cell cultures are sometimes called *tissue cultures,* but the term *cell culture* is more accurate because only a single type of cell is used in the culture. (By definition, a tissue is composed of at least two kinds of cells.)

Cell cultures are of two types. The first type, **diploid cell cultures,** are created from embryonic animal, plant, or human cells that have been isolated and provided appropriate growth conditions. The cells in diploid cell culture generally last no more than about 100 generations (cell divisions) before they die.

The second type of culture, **continuous cell cultures,** are longer lasting because they are derived from tumor cells. Recall that a characteristic of neoplastic cells is that they divide relentlessly, providing a never-ending supply of new cells. One of the more famous continuous cell cultures is of HeLa cells, derived from a woman named *He*nrietta *La*cks who died of cervical cancer in 1951. Though she is dead, Mrs. Lacks's cells live on in laboratories throughout the world.

It is interesting that HeLa cells have lost some of their original characteristics. For example, they are no longer diploid because they have lost many chromosomes.

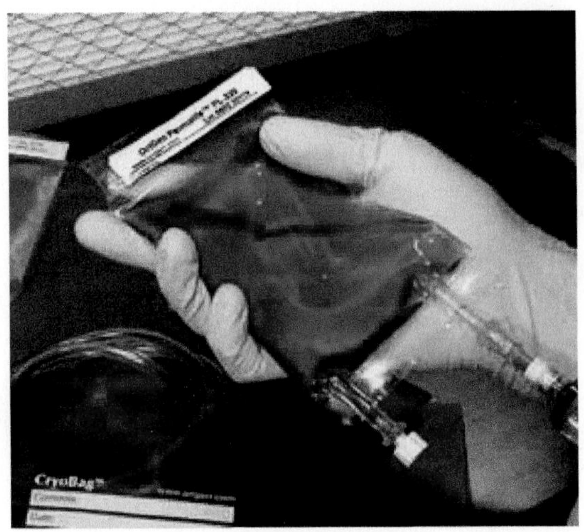

▲ *Figure 19*

An example of cell culture. The bag contains a colored nutrient medium for growing cells in which viruses can be cultured.

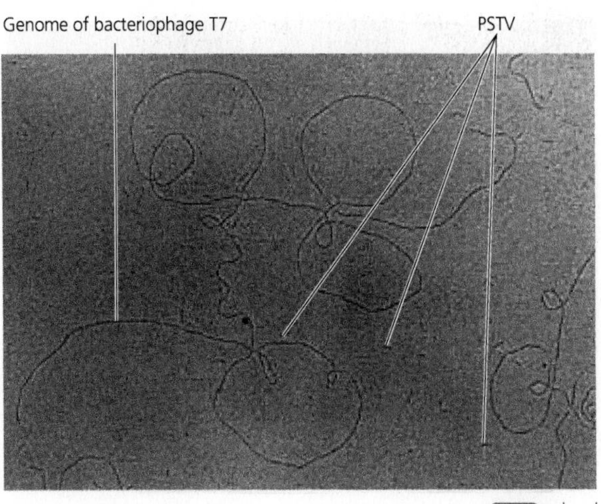

▲ *Figure 20*

The RNA strand of the small potato spindle tuber viroid (PSTV). Also shown for comparison is the longer DNA genome of bacteriophage T7. *How are viroids similar to and different from viruses?*

Figure 20 *Viroids are similar to certain viruses in that they are infectious and contain a single strand of RNA; they are different from viruses in that they lack a proteinaceous capsid.*

HeLa cells provide a semistandard[3] human tissue culture medium for studies on cell metabolism, aging, and (of course) viral infection.

CRITICAL THINKING

HIV replicates only in certain types of human cells, and one early problem in AIDS research was culturing those cells. How do you think scientists are now able to culture HIV?

Other Parasitic Particles: Viroids and Prions

Viruses are not the only submicroscopic entities capable of causing disorders within cells. In this section we will consider the characteristics of two molecular particles that infect cells: viroids and prions.

Characteristics of Viroids

Learning Objectives

✓ Define and describe viroids.
✓ Compare and contrast viroids and viruses.

Viroids are extremely small, circular pieces of RNA that are infectious and pathogenic in plants **(Figure 20).** Viroids are similar to RNA viruses except that they lack capsids. Even though they are circular, viroids may appear linear because of hydrogen bonding within the molecule. Several plant diseases, including some of coconut palm, chrysanthemum, potato, cucumber, and avocado, are caused by viroids, including the stunting shown in **Figure 21.**

Viroidlike agents—infectious, pathogenic RNA particles that lack capsids but do not infect plants—affect some fungi. (They are not called viroids because they do not infect plants.) No animal diseases are known to be caused by viroidlike molecules, though the possibility exists that infectious RNA may be responsible for some diseases in humans.

Characteristics of Prions

Learning Objectives

✓ Define and describe prions, including their replication process.
✓ Compare and contrast prions and viruses.
✓ List four diseases caused by prions.

In 1982, Stanley Prusiner (1942–) described a proteinaceous infectious agent that was different from any other known infectious agent in that it lacked nucleic acid. Prusiner named such agents of disease **prions** (prē′onz), for *pro*teinaceous *in*fective particles. Before his discovery, the diseases now known to be caused by prions were thought

[3]HeLa cells are "semistandard" because different strains have lost different chromosomes, and mutations have occurred over the years. Thus, HeLa cells in one laboratory may be slightly different from HeLa cells in another laboratory.

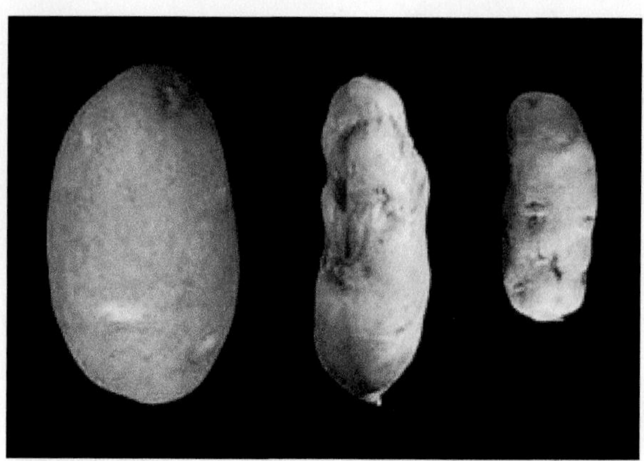

▲ *Figure 21*

One effect of viroids on plants. The potatoes at right are stunted as the result of infection with PSTV viroids.

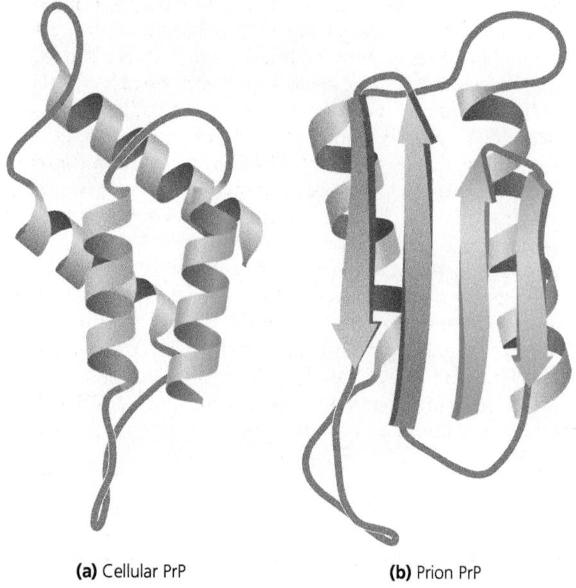

▲ *Figure 22*

The two stable, three-dimensional forms of prion protein (PrP). **(a)** Cellular prion protein found in normal functional cells has a preponderance of alpha-helices. **(b)** Prion PrP, which has the same amino acid sequence, is folded to produce a preponderance of beta-pleated sheets.

to be caused by what were known as "slow viruses," which were so named because of the long delay between infection and the onset of signs and symptoms. Through experiments, Prusiner and his colleagues showed that prions are not viruses because they lack any nucleic acid.

www.microbiologyplace.com **Animations: *Prions: Overview***

Some scientists resisted the concept of prions because particles that lack any nucleic acid violate the "universal" rule of protein synthesis—that proteins are translated from a molecule of mRNA, which is a copy of a portion of a DNA molecule. So, argued these detractors, if "infectious proteins" lack nucleic acid, how can they carry the information required to replicate themselves?

Prions are composed of a single protein, called PrP, and all mammals contain a gene that codes for the primary sequence of amino acids in PrP. Moreover, the sequence of amino acids in PrP is such that the protein can fold into at least two stable tertiary structures: a normal, functional structure that folds with several α-helices, called *cellular PrP,* and the disease-causing form having β-pleated sheets, called *prion PrP* **(Figure 22).**

Prusiner determined that prion PrP acts enzymatically to convert cellular PrP into prion PrP by inducing a conformational change in the shape of cellular PrP. In other words, prion PrP refolds cellular PrP into a prion shape. As cellular ribosomes synthesize more cellular PrP, prions already present cause these new molecules to refold, becoming more prions. Thus, the rule of protein synthesis is maintained, because prions do not code for new prions but instead convert extant cellular PrP into prions. For his work, Prusiner was awarded a Nobel Prize in 1997.

www.microbiologyplace.com **Animations: *Prions: Characteristics***

Why don't prions develop in all mammals, given that all mammals have PrP? Under normal circumstances, it appears that other nearby proteins and polysaccharides force PrP into the correct (cellular) shape. Only excess PrP production or mutations in the PrP gene result in the initial formation of prion PrP. For instance, it has been determined that human cellular PrP can misfold only if it contains methionine as the 129th amino acid. About 40% of humans have this type of cellular PrP and are thus susceptible to prion disease.

All known prion diseases involve fatal neurological degeneration, the deposition of fibrils in the brain, and the loss of brain matter such that eventually large vacuoles form. The latter process results in a characteristic spongy appearance **(Figure 23),** which is why as a group, prion diseases are called *spongiform encephalopathies* (spŭn′ji-fōrm en-sef′ă-lop′ă-thēz). The way in which prion PrP causes these changes in the brain is not totally understood, but it appears prions interupt signaling events that cellular PrP controls.

Prions are associated with several spongiform encephalopathies of animals and of humans, including *bovine spongiform encephalitis* (*BSE,* so-called mad cow disease), *scrapie* in sheep, *kuru* (a disease that afflicted Papua New Guinea in the 1950s but has since been eliminated), *chronic wasting disease (CWD)* in deer and elk, and *Creutzfeldt-Jakob disease (CJD)* in humans. All these diseases are transmitted through either the ingestion of infected tissue, including brain, spinal cord, eyes, and, at least in the case of CWD, skeletal muscle tissue; transplants of infected tissue, including nervous tissue and blood; or contact of mucous membranes or skin abrasions with infected tissue. www.microbiologyplace.com **Animations: *Prions: Diseases***

Normal cooking or sterilization procedures do not deactivate prions, though they are destroyed by incineration or autoclaving in 1 N NaOH. The European Union recently approved the use of special enzymes developed using biotechnology to remove infectious prions from medical equipment.

There is no treatment for any prion disease, though scientists have determined that the antimalarial drug quinacrine and the antipsychotic drug chlorpromazine forestall spongiform encephalopathy in prion-infected mice. Human trials of these drugs are ongoing.

PrP proteins of different species are slightly different in primary structure, and at one time it was thought unlikely that prions of one species could cross over into another species to cause disease. However, an epidemic of BSE in Great Britain in the late 1980s and in France in the 2000s resulted in the spread of prions not only to other cattle, but also to humans who ingested infected beef. To prevent further infection, most countries ban the use of animal-derived protein supplements in animal feed. Unfortunately, this step was too late to prevent the spread of bovine prions to more than 100 Europeans who have developed fatal *variant Creutzfeldt-Jakob disease.*[4] (See **Clinical Case Study: Invasion from Within or Without?**)

Prions composed of different proteins may lie behind other muscular and neuronal degenerative diseases, such as Alzheimer's disease, Parkinson's disease, and amyotrophic lateral sclerosis (ALS, or "Lou Gehrig's disease").

[4]"Variant" because it is derived from BSE prions in cattle, as opposed to the regular form of CJD, which is a genetic disease.

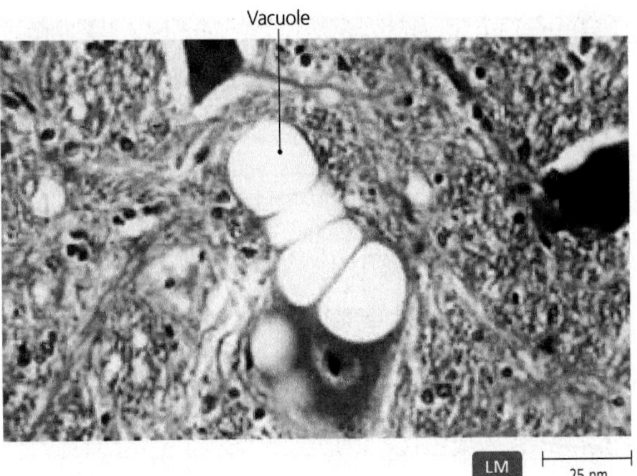

▲ *Figure 23*

A brain showing the large vacuoles and spongy appearance typical in prion-induced diseases. Shown here is the brain of a sheep with the prion disease called scrapie.

CRITICAL THINKING

Why did most scientists initially resist the idea of an infectious, replicating protein?

In this chapter we have seen that humans, animals, plants, fungi, bacteria, and archaea are susceptible to infection by acellular pathogens: viruses, viroids, and prions. **Table 5**

Table 5 Comparison of Viruses, Viroids, and Prions to Bacterial Cells

	Bacteria	Viruses	Viroids	Prions
Width	200–2000 nm	10–400 nm	2 nm	5 nm
Length	200–550,000 nm	20–800 nm	40–130 nm	5 nm
Nucleic acid?	Both DNA and RNA	Either DNA or RNA, never both	RNA only	None
Protein?	Present	Present	Absent	Present (PrP)
Cellular?	Yes	No	No	No
Cytoplasmic membrane?	Present	Absent (though some viruses do have a membranous envelope)	Absent	Absent
Functional ribosomes?	Present	Absent	Absent	Absent
Growth?	Present	Absent	Absent	Absent
Self-replicating?	Yes	No	No	Yes; transform PrP protein already present in cell
Responsiveness?	Present	Some bacteriophages respond to a host cell by injecting their genomes	Absent	Absent
Metabolism?	Present	Absent	Absent	Absent

Clinical Case Study *Invasion from Within or Without?*

A 32-year-old husband and father of two small children lived in the midwestern United States. An avid hunter and hearty meat eater since childhood, the man visited annually with family and friends in Colorado for elk hunting. His job required frequent international travel (including Europe) where he enjoyed exotic foods.

Early in the spring of 1988, his wife recalls that he began having problems. Frequently he forgot to pick up things from the store or even that his wife had called him. Later that summer, he was unable to complete his paperwork at his business and had great difficulty performing even basic math. In England on business, he had forgotten his home phone number in the U.S. and couldn't remember how to spell his last name to ask for directory assistance.

By September he could not perform his job and his wife insisted he seek medical care. All the standard blood tests came back normal. A psychologist diagnosed depression, but after a brain biopsy, the man was found to have spongiform changes in his brain. He was given 6–8 weeks to live as there is no treatment for this condition.

1. What is the likely diagnosis?
2. The man's wife was concerned for her children's welfare and asked, "Can we catch this disease from my husband?" How would you respond?

Reference: Adapted from http://mad-cow.org/99_tracie.html.

summarizes the differences and similarities between these pathogenic agents and bacterial pathogens.

Are Viruses Alive?

Now that we have studied the characteristics and replication processes of viruses, let's ask the question: Are viruses alive?

To be able to wrestle with the answer, we must first recall the characteristics of life: growth, self-reproduction, responsiveness, and the ability to metabolize, all within structures called cells. According to these criteria, viruses seem to lack the qualities of living things, prompting some scientists to consider them nothing more than complex pathogenic chemicals. For other scientists, however, at least three observations—that viruses use sophisticated methods to invade cells, have the means of taking control of their host cells, and possess genomes containing instructions for replicating themselves—indicate that viruses are the ultimate parasites, because they use cells to make more viruses. According to this viewpoint, viruses are the least complex living entities.

In any case, viruses are right on the threshold of life—outside of cells they do not appear to be alive, but within cells they direct the synthesis and assembly required to make copies of themselves.

What do you think? Are viruses alive?

CHAPTER SUMMARY

1. **Acellular** disease-causing agents, which lack cell structure and cannot metabolize, grow, reproduce, or respond to their environment, include viruses, viroids, and prions.

Characteristics of Viruses

1. A **virus** is a tiny infectious agent with nucleic acid surrounded by proteinaceous **capsomeres** that form a coat called a **capsid.** A virus exists in an extracellular state and an intracellular state. A **virion** is a complete viral particle, including a nucleic acid and a capsid, outside of a cell.
2. The genomes of viruses include either DNA or RNA. Viral genomes may be dsDNA, ssDNA, dsRNA, or ssRNA. They may exist as linear or circular and singular or multiple molecules of nucleic acid, depending on the type of virus.
3. A **bacteriophage** (or **phage**) is a virus that infects a bacterial cell.
4. Virions can have a membranous **envelope** or be naked—that is, without an envelope.

Classification of Viruses

1. Viruses are classified based on type of nucleic acid, presence of an envelope, shape, and size.
2. The International Committee on Taxonomy of Viruses (ICTV) has recognized viral family and genus names. With the exception of three orders, higher taxa are not established.

Viral Replication

1. Viruses depend on random contact with a specific host cell type for replication. Typically a virus in a cell proceeds with a lytic replication cycle with five stages: **attachment, entry, synthesis, assembly,** and **release.**
   www.microbiologyplace.com **Animations: *Viral Replication: Overview***
2. Once attachment has been made between virion and host cell, the nucleic acid enters the cell. With phages, only the nucleic acid enters the host cell. With animal viruses, the entire virion often enters the cell, where the capsid is then removed in a process called **uncoating.**
   www.microbiologyplace.com **Animations: *Viral Replication: Animal Viruses***
3. Within the host cell, the viral nucleic acid directs synthesis of more viruses using metabolic enzymes and ribosomes of the host cell.

4. Assembly of synthesized virions occurs in the host cell, typically as capsomeres surround replicated or transcribed nucleic acids to form new virions.
5. Virions are released from the host cell either by lysis of the host cell (seen with phages and animal viruses) or by the extrusion of enveloped virions through the host's cytoplasmic membrane (called **budding**), a process seen only with certain animal viruses. If budding continues over time, the infection is persistent. An envelope is derived from a cell membrane.
   www.microbiologyplace.com **Animations: *Viral Replication: Virulent Bacteriophages***
6. **Temperate (lysogenic)** bacteriophages enter a bacterial cell and remain inactive, in a process called **lysogeny** or a **lysogenic cycle.** Such inactive phages are called **prophages** and are inserted into the chromosome of the cell and passed to its daughter cells. **Lysogenic** conversion results when phages carry genes that alter the phenotype of a bacterium. At some point in the generations that follow, a prophage may be excised from the chromosome in a process known as induction. At that point the prophage again becomes a lytic virus.
   www.microbiologyplace.com **Animations: *Viral Replication: Temperate Bacteriophages***
7. In a similar process called **latency,** an animal virus remains inactive in a cell, possibly for years. A **latent** virus is also known as a **provirus.** A provirus that has become incorporated into a host's chromosome remains there.
8. With the exception of hepatitis B virus, dsDNA viruses act like cellular DNA in transcription and replication.
9. Some ssRNA viruses have **positive-strand RNA (+RNA),** which can be directly translated by ribosomes to synthesize protein. From the +RNA, complementary **negative-strand RNA (−RNA)** is transcribed to serve as a template for more +RNA.
10. **Retroviruses,** such as HIV, are +ssRNA viruses that carry an enzyme, reverse transcriptase, to transcribe DNA from their RNA. This reverse process (DNA transcribed from RNA) is reflected in the name retrovirus.
11. −ssRNA viruses carry an RNA-dependent RNA transcriptase for transcribing mRNA from the −RNA genome so that protein can then be translated. Transcription of RNA from RNA is not found in cells.
12. When double-stranded RNA (dsRNA) functions as the genome, one strand of the RNA molecule functions as the genome, and the other strand functions as a template for RNA replication.

The Role of Viruses in Cancer

1. **Neoplasia** is uncontrolled cellular reproduction in a multicellular animal. A mass of neoplastic cells, called a tumor, may be relatively harmless **(benign)** or invasive **(malignant).** Malignant tumors are also called **cancer. Metastasis** describes the spreading of malignant tumors. Environmental factors or oncogenic viruses may cause neoplasia.

Culturing Viruses in the Laboratory

1. In the laboratory, viruses must be cultured inside whole organisms, in embryonated chicken eggs, or in cell cultures because viruses cannot metabolize or replicate alone.
2. When a mixture of bacteria and phages is grown on an agar plate, bacteria infected with phages lyse, producing clear areas called **plaques** on the bacterial lawn. A technique called **plaque assay** enables the estimation of phage numbers.
3. Viruses can be grown in two types of **cell cultures.** Whereas **diploid cell cultures** last about 100 generations, continuous **cell cultures,** derived from cancer cells, last longer.

Other Parasitic Particles: Viroids and Prions

1. **Viroids** are small circular pieces of RNA with no capsid that infect and cause disease in plants. Similar pathogenic RNA molecules are known from fungi.
2. **Prions** are infectious protein particles that lack nucleic acids and replicate by converting similar normal proteins into new prions. Diseases caused by prions are spongiform encephalopathies, which involve fatal neurological degeneration.
   www.microbiologyplace.com **Animations: *Prions: Overview, Characteristics* and *Diseases***

Are Viruses Alive?

1. Outside of cells, viruses do not appear to be alive, but within cells, they exhibit lifelike qualities such as the ability to replicate themselves.

QUESTIONS FOR REVIEW

Access more review material (including animations and practice tests) online at www.microbiologyplace.com.

Multiple Choice

1. Which of the following is *not* an acellular agent?
   a. viroid
   b. virus
   c. rickettsia
   d. prion
2. Which of the following statements is true?
   a. Viruses contain both DNA and RNA in specific proportions.
   b. Viruses are capable of metabolism.
   c. Viruses lack a cell membrane.
   d. Viruses grow in response to their environmental conditions.
3. A virus that is specific for a bacterial host is called a
   a. phage.
   b. prion.
   c. virion.
   d. viroid.
4. A naked virus
   a. has no membranous envelope.
   b. has injected its DNA or RNA into a host cell.
   c. is devoid of capsomeres.
   d. is one that is unattached to a host cell.

5. Which of the following statements is *false*?
   a. Viruses may have circular DNA.
   b. dsRNA is found in bacteria more often than in viruses.
   c. Viral DNA may be linear.
   d. Viruses may have DNA or RNA, but not both.
6. When a eukaryotic cell is infected with an enveloped virus and sheds viruses slowly over time, this infection is
   a. called a lytic infection.
   b. a prophage cycle.
   c. called a persistent infection.
   d. caused by a quiescent virus.
7. Another name for a complete virus is
   a. virion.
   b. viroid.
   c. prion.
   d. capsid.
8. Which of the following viruses can be latent?
   a. HIV
   b. chickenpox
   c. herpes
   d. all of the above
9. Which of the following is *not* a criterion for specific family classification of viruses?
   a. the type of nucleic acid present
   b. envelope structure
   c. capsid type
   d. lipid composition
10. A clear zone of phage infection in a bacterial lawn is a
   a. prophage.
   b. plaque.
   c. naked area.
   d. capsomere.

Matching

Match each numbered term with its description.

____	1. uncoating	A. dormant virus in a eukaryotic cell
____	2. prophage	B. a virus that infects a bacterium
____	3. retrovirus	C. DNA transcribed from RNA
____	4. bacteriophage	D. protein coat of virus
____	5. capsid	E. a membrane outside a viral capsid
____	6. envelope	F. complete viral particle
____	7. virion	G. inactive virus within bacterial cell
____	8. provirus	H. removal of capsomeres from a virion
____	9. benign tumor	I. invasive neoplastic cells
____	10. cancer	J. harmless neoplastic cells

Short Answer

1. Compare and contrast a bacterium and a virus by writing either "Present" or "Absent" for each of the following structures.

Structure	Bacterium	Virus
Cell membrane	________	________
Functional ribosome	________	________
Cytoplasm	________	________
Nucleic acid	________	________
Nuclear membrane	________	________

2. Describe the five phases of a generalized lytic replication cycle.
3. Why is it difficult to treat viral infections?
4. Describe four different ways that viral nucleic acid can enter a host cell.
5. Contrast lysis and budding as means of release of virions from a host cell.
6. What is the difference between a virion and a virus particle?
7. How is a provirus like a prophage? How is it different?
8. Describe lysogeny.
9. How are viruses specific for their host's cells?
10. Compare and contrast diploid cell culture and continuous cell culture.

CRITICAL THINKING

1. Many viruses have a single-stranded genome, but it has been observed that larger viruses usually have a double-stranded genome. What reasonable explanation can you offer for this observation?
2. What are the advantages and disadvantages to bacteriophages of the lytic and lysogenic reproductive strategies?
3. How are computer viruses similar to biological viruses? Are computer viruses alive? Why or why not?
4. Compare and contrast lysogeny by a prophage and latency by a provirus.
5. An agricultural microbiologist wants to stop the spread of a viral infection of a crop. Is stopping viral attachment a viable option? Why or why not?

ANSWERS TO QUESTIONS FOR REVIEW

Multiple Choice

1. c; 2. c; 3. a; 4. a; 5. b; 6. c; 7. a; 8. d; 9. d; 10. b

Matching

1. H; 2. G; 3. C; 4. B; 5. D; 6. E; 7. F; 8. A; 9. J; 10. I

CREDITS

Illustration Credits

13.1, 13.4, 13.6–13.8, 13.11, 13.12, 13.14, 13.18: Kenneth Probst. 13.9, 13.13, 13.15, 13.16, 13.22: Precision Graphics.

Photo Credits

Opener: Erskine Palmer and Russell Regnery, CDC. 13.1b: Yu. G. Kuznetsov and A. McPherson, University of California, Irvine. 13.2: Huntington Potter, Byrd Alzheimers Institute and University of South Florida and David Dressler, Oxford University and Balliol College. 13.3a: Lam E, Kato N, Lawton M. Programmed cell death, mitochondria and the plant hypersensitive response. *Nature*. 2001 June; 411: 848–853, Fig.1. Reprinted with permission from Nature Publishing Group. 13.3b: George Chapman/Visuals Unlimited. 13.3c: NIBSC/Photo Researchers. 13.3d: Eye of Science/Photo Researchers. 13.5a: Robley C. Williams. 13.5b: Hans Gelderblom/Visuals Unlimited. 13.5c: CDC. 13.5d: Frederick A. Murphy, University of Texas Medical Branch, Galveston. 13.6a: Harold Fisher/Visuals Unlimited. 13.7a: G. Murti/Photo Researchers. 13.7b: Hans Gelderblom/Visuals Unlimited. 13.10: M. Wurtz, Biozentrum, University of Basil/Science Photo Library/Photo Researchers. 13.17: Wikimedia Commons. 13.19: Origen Biomedical. 13.19: Theodor O. Diener, Agricultural Research Service, U.S. Department of Agriculture. 13.21: Barry Fitzgerald and Peggy Greb, Agricultural Research Service, USDA. 13.23: James King-Holmes/SPL/Photo Researchers. Beneficial Microbe 13.1: NASA. Beneficial Microbe 13.2: Eye of Science/Photo Researchers. Highlight 13.1: AP Images.

Microbial Interactions with Humans

Large numbers of bacterial cells are present in many parts of the human body, including on the surface of the tongue, as shown here.

Steve Gschmeissner/Photo Researchers, Inc.

The human body has an extensive population of microorganisms, primarily bacteria, on the skin and the mucous membranes lining the mouth, gut, and excretory and reproductive systems. These microorganisms are often beneficial and sometimes necessary to maintain good health. However, other microorganisms called *pathogens* colonize, invade, and damage the human body through direct and indirect means. This is the process of infectious disease. Pathogens use several strategies to gain access to nutrients in a host. These strategies include the production of specialized attachment structures, unique growth factors, invasive enzymes, and potent biological toxins. These factors often lead to damage and occasionally death of the host.

Here we introduce the nonspecific defenses developed by our bodies to suppress or destroy most microbial invaders. Nonspecific physical, anatomical, and biochemical defense mechanisms make microbial infectious disease a relatively infrequent event.

I BENEFICIAL MICROBIAL INTERACTIONS WITH HUMANS

After a brief overview of human–microbial interactions, we discuss microorganisms that inhabit the healthy human body and contribute to overall good health under normal circumstances.

1 Overview of Human–Microbial Interactions

Through normal everyday activities, the human body is exposed to countless microorganisms in the environment. In addition, hundreds of species and countless individual microbial cells, collectively referred to as the **normal microbial flora**, grow on or in the human body. Most, but not all, microorganisms are benign; a few contribute directly to our health, and even fewer pose direct threats to health.

Colonization by Microorganisms

Mammals *in utero* develop in a sterile environment and have no exposure to microorganisms. Starting with the birth process, **colonization**, growth of a microorganism after it has gained access to host tissues, begins as animals are exposed to microorganisms. The skin surfaces are readily colonized by many species. Likewise, the oral cavity and gastrointestinal tract acquire microorganisms through feeding and exposure to the mother's body, which, along with other environmental sources, initiates colonization of the skin, oral cavity, upper respiratory tract, and gastrointestinal tract. Different populations of microorganisms colonize individuals in different localities and at different times. For example, *Escherichia coli*, a normal inhabitant of the human and animal gut, colonizes the guts of infants in developing countries within several days after birth. Infants in developed countries, however, typically do not acquire *E. coli* for several months; the first microorganisms to colonize the gut of these infants would more typically be *Staphylococcus aureus* and other microorganisms associated with the skin. Genetic factors also play a role. Thus, the normal microbial flora is highly dependent on the conditions to which an individual is exposed. The normal flora is highly diverse in each individual and may differ significantly between individuals, even in a given population.

Pathogens

A **host** is an organism that harbors a **parasite**, another organism that lives on or in the host and causes damage. Microbial parasites are called **pathogens**. The outcome of a host–parasite relationship depends on **pathogenicity**, the ability of a parasite to inflict damage on the host. Pathogenicity differs considerably among potential pathogens, as does the resistance or susceptibility of the host to the pathogen. An **opportunistic pathogen** causes disease only in the absence of normal host resistance.

Pathogenicity varies markedly for individual pathogens. The quantitative measure of pathogenicity is called **virulence**. Virulence can be expressed quantitatively as the cell number that elicits disease in a host within a given time period. Neither the virulence of the pathogen nor the relative resistance of the host is a constant factor. The host–parasite interaction is a dynamic relationship between the two organisms, influenced by changing conditions in the pathogen, the host, and the environment.

Infection and Disease

Infection refers to any situation in which a microorganism is established and growing in a host, whether or not the host is harmed. **Disease** is damage or injury to the host that impairs host function. Infection is not synonymous with disease because growth of a microorganism on a host does not always cause host damage. Thus, species of the normal microbial flora have infected the host, but seldom cause disease. However, the normal flora sometimes cause disease if host resistance is compromised, as happens in diseases such as cancer and acquired immune deficiency syndrome (AIDS).

Host–Parasite Interactions

Animal hosts provide favorable environments for the growth of many microorganisms. They are rich in the organic nutrients and growth factors required by chemoorganotrophs, and provide conditions of controlled pH, osmotic pressure, and temperature. However, the animal body is not a uniform environment. Each region or organ differs chemically and physically from others and thus provides a selective environment where the growth of certain microorganisms is favored. For example, the skin, respiratory tract, and gastrointestinal tract provide selective chemical and physical environments that support the growth of a highly diverse microflora. The

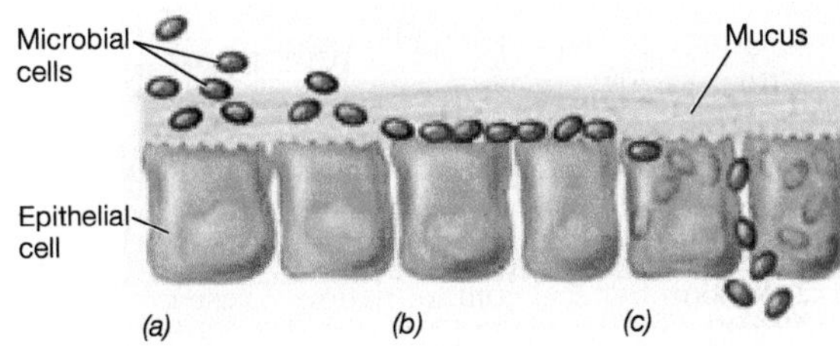

Figure 1 **Bacterial interactions with mucous membranes.** *(a)* Loose association. *(b)* Adhesion. *(c)* Invasion into submucosal epithelial cells.

relatively dry environment of the skin favors the growth of organisms that resist dehydration, such as the gram-positive bacterium *Staphylococcus aureus*; the highly oxygenated environment of the lungs favors the growth of the obligately aerobic *Mycobacterium tuberculosis*; and the anoxic environment of the large intestine supports growth of obligately anaerobic bacteria such as *Clostridium* and *Bacteroides*. Animals also possess defense mechanisms that collectively prevent or inhibit microbial invasion and growth. The microorganisms that successfully colonize the host have circumvented these defense mechanisms.

The Infection Process

Infections frequently begin at sites in the animal's **mucous membranes**. Mucous membranes consist of single or multiple layers of *epithelial cells*, tightly packed cells that interface with the external environment. They are found throughout the body, lining the urogenital, respiratory, and gastrointestinal tracts. Mucous membranes are frequently coated with a protective layer of viscous soluble glycoproteins called **mucus**. Microorganisms that contact host tissues at mucous membranes may associate loosely with the mucosal surface and are usually swept away by physical processes. Microorganisms may also adhere more strongly to the epithelial surface as a result of specific cell–cell recognition between pathogen and host. Tissue infection may follow, breaching the mucosal barrier and allowing the microorganism to invade deeper into submucosal tissues (Figure 1).

Microorganisms are almost always found on surfaces of the body exposed to the environment, such as the skin, and even on the mucosal surfaces of the oral cavity, respiratory tract, intestinal tract, and urogenital tract. They are not normally found on or in the internal organs or in the blood, lymph, or nervous systems of the body. The growth of microorganisms in these normally sterile environments indicates serious infectious disease.

Table 1 shows some of the major types of microorganisms normally found in association with body surfaces. Mucosal surfaces have a diverse microflora because they offer a sheltered, moist environment and a large overall surface area. For example, the specialized function of a mucosal organ such as the small intestine has a surface area of about 400 m^2 available for nutrient transport, and this entire surface is a potential site for microbial growth.

Table 1 Representative genera of microorganisms in the normal flora of humans

Anatomical site	*Genera or major groups*[a]
Skin	*Acinetobacter, Corynebacterium, Enterobacter, Klebsiella, Malassezia (f), Micrococcus, Pityrosporum (f), Propionibacterium, Proteus, Pseudomonas, Staphylococcus, Streptococcus*
Mouth	*Streptococcus, Lactobacillus, Fusobacterium, Veillonella, Corynebacterium, Neisseria, Actinomyces, Geotrichum (f), Candida (f), Capnocytophaga, Eikenella, Prevotella,* Spirochetes (several genera)
Respiratory tract	*Streptococcus, Staphylococcus, Corynebacterium, Neisseria, Haemophilus*
Gastrointestinal tract	*Lactobacillus, Streptococcus, Bacteroides, Bifidobacterium, Eubacterium, Peptococcus, Peptostreptococcus, Ruminococcus, Clostridium, Escherichia, Klebsiella, Proteus, Enterococcus, Staphylococcus Methanobrevibacter,* Gram-positive bacteria, Proteobacteria, Actinobacteria, Fusobacteria
Urogenital tract	*Escherichia, Klebsiella, Proteus, Neisseria, Lactobacillus, Corynebacterium, Staphylococcus, Candida (f), Prevotella, Clostridium, Peptostreptococcus, Ureaplasma, Mycoplasma, Mycobacterium, Streptococcus, Torulopsis (f)*

[a]This list is not meant to be exhaustive, and not all of these organisms are found in every individual. Some organisms are more prevalent at certain ages (adults vs. children). Distribution may also vary between sexes. Most of these organisms can be opportunistic pathogens under certain conditions. Several genera can be found in more than one body area. (f), fungi.

1 MiniReview

The animal body is a favorable environment for the growth of microorganisms, most of which do no harm. Microorganisms that cause harm are called pathogens. Pathogen growth initiated on host surfaces such as mucous membranes may result in infection and disease. The ability of a microorganism to cause or prevent disease is influenced by complex interactions between the microorganism and the host.

- Distinguish between infection and disease.
- Why might one area of the body be more suitable for microbial growth than another?

2 Normal Microbial Flora of the Skin

An average adult human has about 2 m^2 of skin surface that varies greatly in chemical composition and moisture content. Figure 2 shows the anatomy of the skin and regions in which microorganisms may live. The skin surface (epidermis) is not a favorable place for abundant microbial growth, as it is subject to periodic drying.

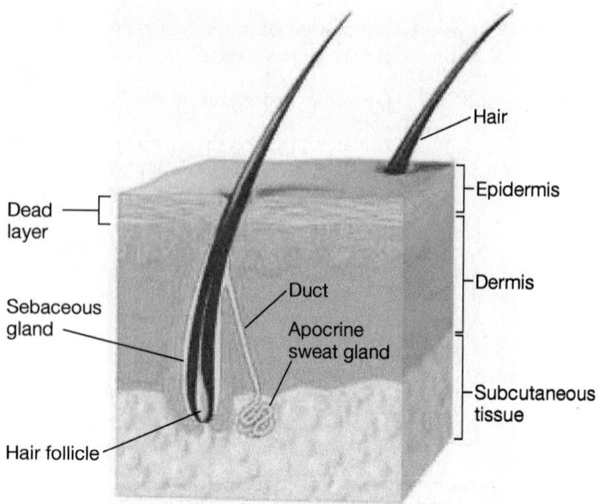

Figure 2 **The human skin.** Microorganisms are associated primarily with the sweat ducts and the hair follicles.

Most skin microorganisms are associated directly or indirectly with the apocrine (sweat) glands. These are secretory glands found mainly in the underarms, genital regions, the nipples, and the umbilicus. Inactive in childhood, they become fully functional at puberty. Microbial populations thrive on the surface of the skin in these warm, humid places in contrast to the poor growth observed on smooth, dry skin surfaces. Underarm odor develops as a result of bacterial activity in the apocrine secretions; aseptically collected apocrine secretions are odorless, but develop odor on inoculation with bacteria. Similarly, each hair follicle is associated with a sebaceous gland, a gland that secretes a lubricant fluid. Hair follicles provide an attractive habitat for microorganisms in the area just below the surface of the skin. The secretions of the skin glands are rich in microbial nutrients such as urea, amino acids, salts, lactic acid, and lipids. The pH of human secretions is almost always acidic, the usual range being between pH 4 and 6.

The Skin Microflora

The normal flora of the skin consist of either resident or transient populations of bacteria and fungi, mainly yeasts. Certain genera are highly conserved in healthy individuals, while others change over time. In all, over 180 species of *Bacteria* and several species of fungi are found on the skin when samples from many individuals are gathered. Samplings of individuals done several months apart indicate that certain members of the normal flora are extremely stable. The most common and stable resident microorganisms are gram-positive *Bacteria*, generally restricted to a few genera, including species of *Streptococcus* and *Staphylococcus*; various species of *Corynebacterium*; and *Propionibacterium*, including *Propionibacterium acnes*, which contributes to a skin condition called *acne* (Table 1). These four genera account for over one-half of all species found. The remaining groups of bacteria found on skin are much more transient, with over 70% changing with time and conditions on the individuals sampled.

Gram-negative *Bacteria* are occasional constituents of the normal skin flora because such intestinal organisms as *Escherichia coli* are continually being inoculated onto the surface of the skin by fecal contamination. These gram-negative *Bacteria* seldom grow on skin due to their inability to compete with gram-positive organisms that are better adapted to the dry conditions. The gram-negative rod *Acinetobacter*, however, is an exception and commonly colonizes skin.

Malassezia spp. are the most common fungi found on skin. At least five species of this yeast are typically found in healthy individuals. The lipophilic yeast *Pityrosporum ovalis* is occasionally found on the scalp. In the absence of host resistance, as in patients with AIDS or in the absence of normal bacterial flora, other yeasts such as *Candida* and other fungi sometimes grow and cause serious skin infections.

Although the resident microflora remains more or less constant, various environmental and host factors may influence its composition. (1) The *weather* may cause an increase in skin temperature and moisture, which increases the density of the skin microflora. (2) The *age* of the host has an effect; young children have a more varied microflora and carry more potentially pathogenic gram-negative *Bacteria* than do adults. (3) *Personal hygiene* influences the resident microflora; individuals with poor hygiene usually have higher microbial population densities on their skin. Organisms that cannot survive on the skin generally succumb from either the skin's low moisture content or low pH (due to organic acid content).

2 MiniReview

The skin is a generally dry, acidic environment that does not support the growth of most microorganisms. However, moist areas, especially around sweat glands, are colonized by gram-positive *Bacteria* and other skin normal flora. Environmental and host factors influence the quantity and makeup of the normal skin microflora.

- Compare the surface area of the skin to that of the mucosal tissues.
- Describe the properties of microorganisms that grow well on the skin.

3 Normal Microbial Flora of the Oral Cavity

The oral cavity is a complex, heterogeneous microbial habitat. Saliva contains microbial nutrients, but it is not an especially good growth medium because the nutrients are present in low concentration and saliva contains antibacterial substances. For example, saliva contains lysozyme, an enzyme that cleaves glycosidic linkages in peptidoglycan present in the bacterial cell wall, weakening the wall and causing cell lysis.

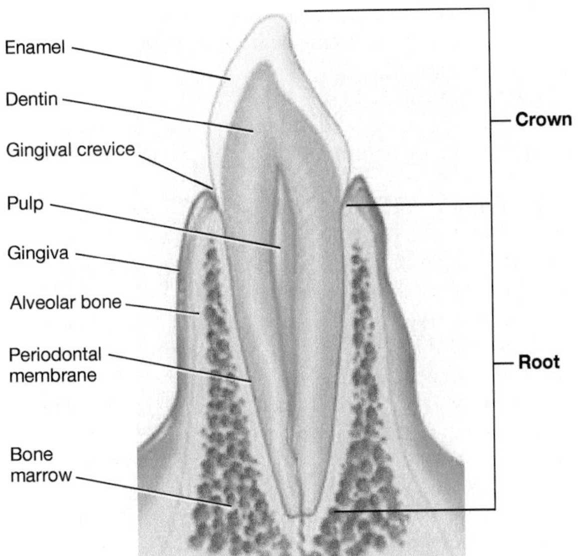

Figure 3 **Section through a tooth.** The diagram shows the tooth architecture and the surrounding tissues that anchor the tooth in the gum.

Figure 4 **Microcolonies of bacteria.** *(a)* The colonies are growing on a model tooth surface inserted into the mouth for 6 h. *(b)* Higher magnification of the preparation in *(a)*. Note the diverse morphology of the organisms present and the slime layer (arrows) holding the organisms together.

Lactoperoxidase, an enzyme in both milk and saliva, kills bacteria by a reaction in which singlet oxygen is generated. Despite the activity of these antibacterial substances, food particles and cell debris provide high concentrations of nutrients near surfaces such as teeth and gums, creating favorable conditions for extensive local microbial growth, tissue damage, and disease.

The Teeth and Dental Plaque

The tooth consists of a mineral matrix of calcium phosphate crystals (enamel) surrounding living tooth tissue (dentin and pulp) (Figure 3). Bacteria found in the mouth during the first year of life (when teeth are absent) are predominantly aerotolerant anaerobes such as streptococci and lactobacilli. However, other bacteria, including some aerobes, occur in small numbers. When the teeth appear, the balance of the microflora shift toward anaerobes that are specifically adapted to growth on surfaces of the teeth and in the gingival crevices.

Bacterial colonization of tooth surfaces begins with the attachment of single bacterial cells. Even on a freshly cleaned tooth surface, acidic glycoproteins from the saliva form a thin organic film several micrometers thick. This film provides an attachment site for bacterial microcolonies (Figure 4). Streptococci (primarily *Streptococcus sanguis, S. sobrinus, S. mutans*, and *S. mitis*) can then colonize the glycoprotein film. Extensive growth of these organisms results in a thick bacterial layer called **dental plaque** (Figures 5 and 6).

If plaque continues to form, filamentous anaerobes such as *Fusobacterium* species begin to grow. The filamentous bacteria embed in the matrix formed by the streptococci and extend perpendicular to the tooth surface, making an ever-thicker bacterial layer. Associated with the filamentous bacteria are spirochetes such as *Borrelia* species, gram-positive rods, and gram-negative cocci. In heavy plaque, filamentous obligately anaerobic organisms such as *Actinomyces* may predominate. Thus, dental plaque can be considered a mixed-culture biofilm, consisting of a relatively thick layer of bacteria from several different genera as well as accumulated bacterial products.

The anaerobic nature of the oral flora may seem surprising considering the intake of oxygen through the mouth. However, anoxia develops due to the metabolic activities of facultative bacteria growing on organic materials at the tooth surface. The plaque buildup produces a dense matrix that decreases oxygen diffusion to the tooth surface, forming an anoxic microenvironment. The microbial populations within

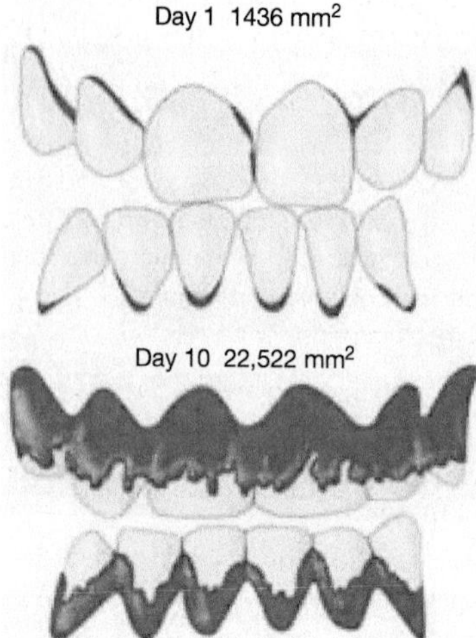

Figure 5 **Distribution of dental plaque.** Plaque is revealed by use of a disclosing agent on unbrushed teeth after 1 day (top) and 10 days (bottom). The stained areas indicate plaque. Plaque buildup starts near the gum line, beginning directly adjacent to the mucous membranes of the gingiva.

dental plaque exist in a microenvironment of their own making and maintain themselves in the face of wide variations in the conditions in the macroenvironment of the oral cavity.

Dental Caries

As dental plaque accumulates, the resident microflora produce locally high concentrations of organic acids that cause decalcification of the tooth enamel (Figure 3), resulting in **dental caries** (tooth decay). Thus, dental caries is an infectious disease. The smooth surfaces of the teeth are relatively easy to clean and resist decay. The tooth surfaces in and near the gingival crevice, however, can retain food particles and are the sites where dental caries typically begins.

Diets high in sucrose (table sugar) promote dental caries. Lactic acid bacteria ferment sugars to lactic acid. The lactic acid dissolves some of the calcium phosphate in localized areas, and proteolysis of the supporting matrix occurs through the action of bacterial proteolytic enzymes. Bacterial cells slowly penetrate further into the decomposing matrix. The structure of the calcified tooth tissue also plays a role in the extent of dental caries. For example, incorporation of fluoride into the calcium phosphate crystal tooth matrix increases resistance to acid decalcification. Consequently, fluorides in drinking water and dentifrices inhibit tooth decay.

Two bacteria implicated in dental caries are *Streptococcus sobrinus* and *Streptococcus mutans,* both lactic acid bacteria. *S. sobrinus* is probably the primary organism causing decay of smooth surfaces because of its specific affinity for salivary glycoproteins found on smooth tooth surfaces (Figure 6). *S. mutans,* found predominantly in crevices and small fissures, produces dextran, a strongly adhesive polysaccharide that it uses to attach to tooth surfaces (Figure 7). *S. mutans* produces

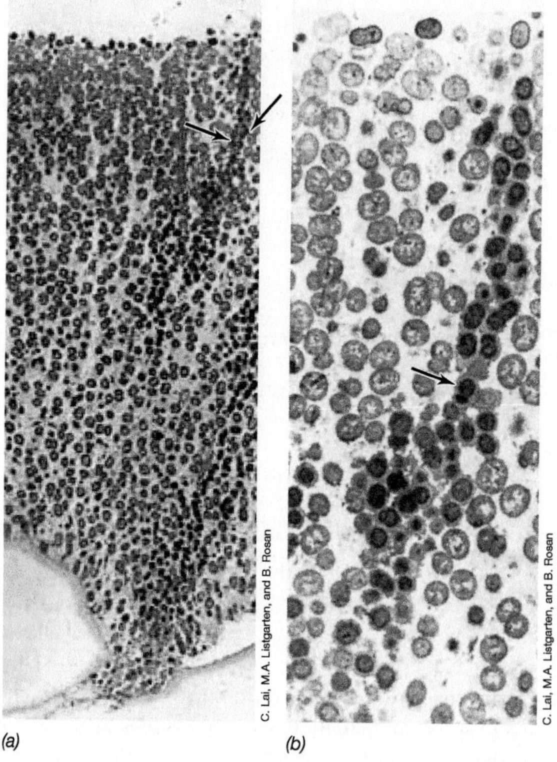

Figure 6 **Electron micrographs of thin sections of dental plaque.** The bottom of the photograph is the base of the plaque; the top is the portion exposed to the oral cavity. The total thickness of the plaque layer shown is about 50 μm. (*a*) Low-magnification electron micrograph. Organisms are predominantly streptococci. *Streptococcus sobrinus,* labeled by an antibody-microchemical technique, appears darker than the rest. *S. sobrinus* cells are seen as two distinct chains (arrows). (*b*) Higher-magnification electron micrograph showing the region with *S. sobrinus* cells (dark, arrow). Note the extensive slime layer surrounding the *S. sobrinus* cells. Individual cells are about 1 μm in diameter.

dextran only when sucrose is present by activity of the enzyme dextransucrase:

$$n \text{ Sucrose} \xrightarrow{\text{Dextransucrase}} \text{Dextran } (n \text{ Glucose}) + n \text{ Fructose}$$

Susceptibility to tooth decay varies and is affected by genetic traits in the individual as well as by diet and other extraneous factors. For example, sucrose, highly cariogenic because it is a substrate for dextransucrase, is part of the diet of most individuals in developed countries. Studies of the distribution of the cariogenic oral streptococci show a direct correlation between the presence of *S. mutans* and *S. sobrinus* and the extent of dental caries. In the United States and Western Europe, 80–90% of all individuals are infected by *S. mutans,* and dental caries is nearly universal. By contrast, *S. mutans* is absent from the plaque of Tanzanian children,

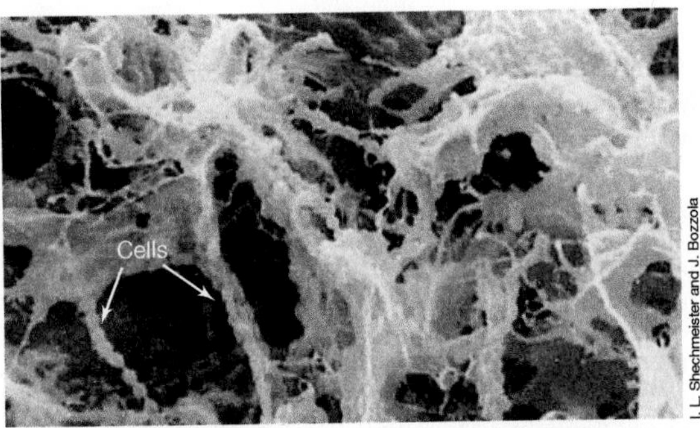

Figure 7 **Scanning electron micrograph of the cariogenic bacterium *Streptococcus mutans*.** The sticky dextran material holds the cells together as filaments. Individual cells are about 1 μm in diameter.

and dental caries does not occur, presumably because sucrose is almost completely absent from their diets.

Microorganisms in the mouth can also cause other infections. The areas along the periodontal membrane at or below the gingival crevice (periodontal pockets) (Figure 3) can be infected with microorganisms, causing inflammation of the gum tissues (gingivitis) leading to tissue and bone-destroying periodontal disease. Some of the genera involved include fusiform bacteria (long, thin, gram-negative rods with tapering ends) such as the facultative aerobe *Capnocytophaga*. The aerobe *Rothia*, and even strictly anaerobic methanogens, such as *Methanobrevibacter* (*Archaea*), may also be present.

3 MiniReview

Bacteria can produce adherent substances and growth on tooth surfaces, typically resulting in mixed-culture biofilms called plaque. Acid produced by microorganisms in plaque damages tooth surfaces, resulting in dental caries. Further infection can result in periodontal disease.

- How do anaerobic microorganisms become established in the mouth?
- Is dental caries an infectious disease? Give at least one reason for your answer.
- Identify the contribution of the lactic acid bacteria to tooth decay.

4 Normal Microbial Flora of the Gastrointestinal Tract

The human gastrointestinal tract consists of the stomach, small intestine, and large intestine (Figure 8). The gastrointestinal tract is responsible for digestion of food, absorption of nutrients, and the production of nutrients by the indigenous

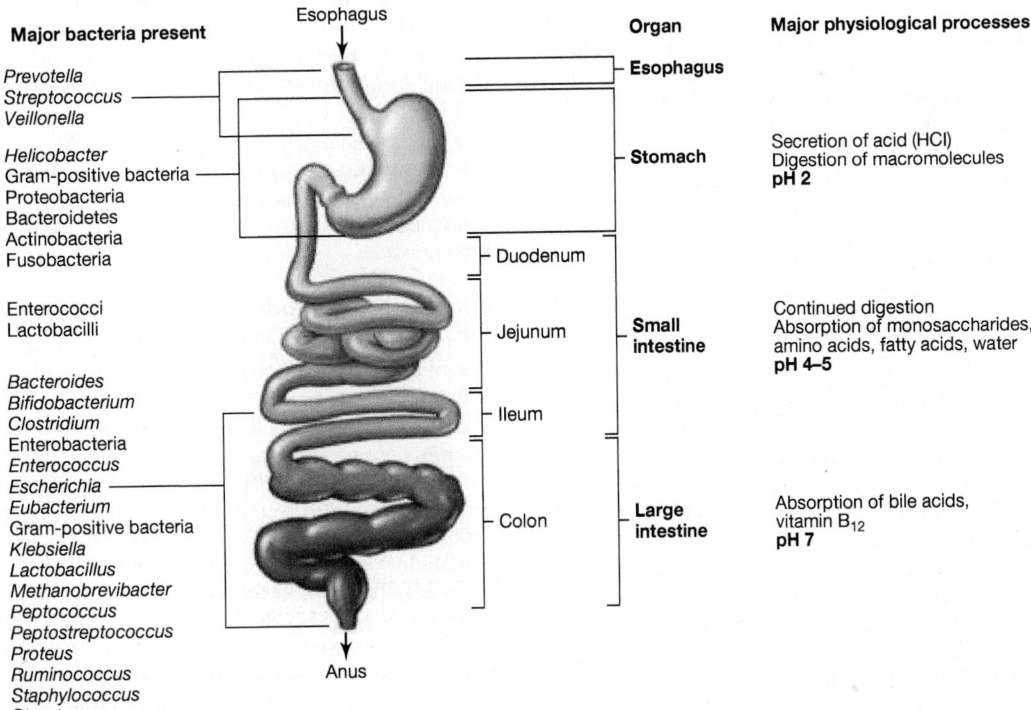

Figure 8 **The human gastrointestinal tract.** The distribution of representative nonpathogenic microorganisms often found in healthy adults.

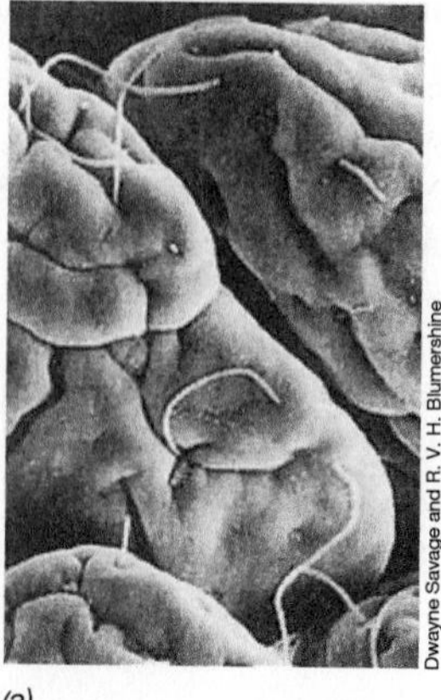

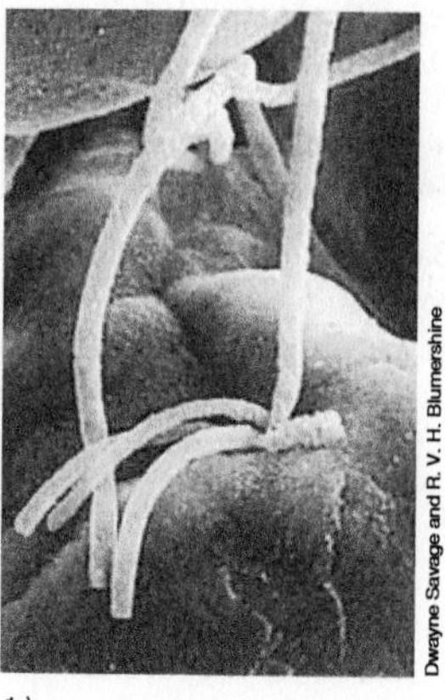

(a) (b)

Figure 9 Scanning electron micrographs of the microbial community on the surface of the epithelial cells in the mouse ileum. *(a)* An overview at low magnification. Note the long, filamentous fusiform bacteria lying on the surface. *(b)* Higher magnification, showing several filaments attached at a single depression. Note that the attachment is at the end of the filaments only. Individual cells are 10–15 μm long.

microbial flora. Starting with the stomach, the digestive tract is a column of nutrients mixed with microorganisms. The nutrients move one way through the column, encountering ever-changing populations of microorganisms. Here we examine the organisms as well as their functions and special properties.

Overall, about 10^{13} to 10^{14} microbial cells are present in the entire gastrointestinal tract. Our current view of the diversity and numbers of microorganisms that reside here has come from both standard culture methods and culture-independent molecular methods, such as microbial community analyses.

The Stomach

Because stomach fluids are highly acidic (about pH 2), the stomach is a chemical barrier to the entry of microorganisms into the gastrointestinal tract. However, microorganisms do populate this seemingly hostile environment. Studies using 16S rRNA sequences obtained from human stomach biopsies indicate that the stomach microbial population consists of several different phyla and a large number of bacterial taxa. Individuals clearly have very different populations, but all contain species of Gram-positive bacteria, *Proteobacteria, Bacteroidetes, Actinobacteria,* and *Fusobacteria* (Figure 8). *Helicobacter pylori,* the most common single organism found, colonizes the stomach wall in many, but not all, individuals and can cause ulcers in susceptible hosts. Some of the bacteria that populate the stomach consist of organisms found in the oral cavity, introduced with the passage of food.

Distal to the stomach, the intestinal tract consists of the *small* intestine and the *large* intestine, each of which is divided into different anatomical structures. The composition of the intestinal flora in humans varies considerably and is somewhat dependent on diet. For example, persons who consume a considerable amount of meat show higher numbers of *Bacteroides* and lower numbers of coliforms and lactic acid bacteria than do individuals with a vegetarian diet. Representative microorganisms found in the gastrointestinal tract are shown in Figure 8.

The Small Intestine

The small intestine is separated into two parts, the *duodenum* and the *ileum,* with the *jejunum* connecting them. The duodenum, adjacent to the stomach, is fairly acidic and resembles the stomach in its microbial flora. From the duodenum to the ileum, the pH gradually becomes less acidic, and bacterial numbers increase. In the lower ileum, cell numbers of 10^5–10^7/gram of intestinal contents are common, even though the environment becomes progressively more anoxic. Fusiform anaerobic bacteria are typically present here, attached to the intestinal wall at one end (Figure 9).

The Large Intestine

The ileum empties into the *cecum,* the connecting portion of the large intestine. The *colon* makes up the rest of the large intestine. In the colon, bacteria are present in enormous numbers. The colon is a fermentation vessel, and many bacteria live here, using nutrients derived from the digestion of food (Table 1). Facultative aerobes such as *Escherichia coli* are present but in smaller numbers than other bacteria; total counts of facultative aerobes are less than 10^7/gram of intestinal contents. The facultative aerobes consume any remaining oxygen, making the large intestine strictly anoxic. This condition promotes growth of obligate anaerobes, including species of *Clostridium* and *Bacteroides*. The total number of obligate anaerobes in the colon is enormous. Bacterial counts of 10^{10} to 10^{11} cells/gram in distal gut and fecal contents are normal, with *Bacteroidetes* and gram-positive species accounting for greater than 99% of all bacteria. The methanogen *Methanobrevibacter smithii* can also be present in significant numbers. Protists are not found in the gastrointestinal tract of healthy humans although various protists can cause opportunistic infections if ingested in contaminated food or water.

Functions and Products of Intestinal Flora

Intestinal microorganisms carry out a wide variety of essential metabolic reactions that produce various compounds (Table 2). The composition of the intestinal flora and the diet influence the type and amount of compounds produced. Among these products are vitamins B_{12} and K. These essential vitamins are not synthesized by humans, but are made by the intestinal microflora and absorbed from the gut. Steroids, produced in the liver and released into the intestine from the gall bladder as bile acids, are modified in the intestine by the microbial flora; modified and now activated steroid compounds are then absorbed from the gut.

Other products generated by the activities of fermentative bacteria and methanogens include gas (flatus) and the odor-producing substances listed in Table 2. Normal adults expel several hundred milliliters of gas, of which about half is N_2 from swallowed air, from the intestines every day. Some foods metabolized by fermentative bacteria in the intestines

Table 2 Biochemical/metabolic contributions of intestinal microorganisms

Process	Product
Vitamin synthesis	Thiamine, riboflavin, pyridoxine, B_{12}, K
Gas production	CO_2, CH_4, H_2
Odor production	H_2S, NH_3, amines, indole, skatole, butyric acid
Organic acid production	Acetic, propionic, butyric acids
Glycosidase reactions	β-glucuronidase, β-galactosidase, β-glucosidase, α-glucosidase, α-galactosidase
Steroid metabolism (bile acids)	Esterified, dehydroxylated, oxidized, or reduced steroids

result in the production of hydrogen (H_2) and carbon dioxide (CO_2). Methanogens, found in the intestines of over one-third of normal adults, convert H_2 and CO_2 produced by fermentative bacteria to methane (CH_4). The methanogens in the rumen of cattle produce significant amounts of methane, up to a quarter of the total global production.

During the passage of food through the gastrointestinal tract, water is absorbed from the digested material, which gradually becomes more concentrated and is converted to feces. Bacteria make up about one-third of the weight of fecal matter. Organisms living in the lumen of the large intestine are continuously displaced downward by the flow of material, and bacteria that are lost are continuously replaced by new growth. Thus, the large intestine resembles a chemostat in its action. The time needed for passage of material through the complete gastrointestinal tract is about 24 h in humans; the growth rate of bacteria in the lumen is one to two doublings per day. The total number of bacterial cells shed per day in human feces is on the order of 10^{13}.

Changing the Normal Flora

When an antibiotic is taken orally, it inhibits the growth of the normal flora as well as pathogens, leading to the loss of antibiotic-susceptible bacteria in the intestinal tract. This is often signaled by loose feces or diarrhea. In the absence of the full complement of normal flora, opportunistic microorganisms such as antibiotic-resistant *Staphylococcus, Proteus, Clostridium difficile,* or the yeast *Candida albicans* can become established. The retention of opportunistic pathogens can lead to a harmful alteration in digestive function or even to disease. For example, antibiotic treatment allows less susceptible microorganisms such as *C. difficile* to flourish, causing infection and colitis. After antibiotic therapy, however, the normal intestinal flora is typically reestablished quite quickly in adults. More rapid recolonization of the gut by desired species can be accomplished by administration of **probiotics,** live cultures of intestinal bacteria that, when administered to a host, may confer a health benefit. This is because a rapid recolonization of the gut may reestablish a competitive local flora and provide desirable microbial metabolic products (see the Microbial Sidebar, "Probiotics").

4 MiniReview

The stomach and the intestinal tract support a diverse population of microorganisms in a variety of nutritional and environmental conditions. The populations of microorganisms are influenced by the diet of the individual and by the unique physical conditions in each distinct anatomical area.

- Why might the small intestine be more suitable for growth of facultative aerobes than the large intestine?
- Identify several essential compounds made by indigenous intestinal microorganisms. What would happen if all microorganisms were completely eliminated from the body by the use of antibiotics?

5 Normal Microbial Flora of Other Body Regions

Each individual mucous membrane supports the growth of a specialized group of microorganisms. These organisms are part of the normal local environment and are characteristic of healthy tissue. In many cases, pathogenic microorganisms cannot colonize mucous membranes because of the competitive effects of the normal flora. Here we discuss two mucosal environments and their resident microorganisms.

Respiratory Tract

The anatomy of the respiratory tract is shown in Figure 10. In the **upper respiratory tract** (nasopharynx, oral cavity, larynx,

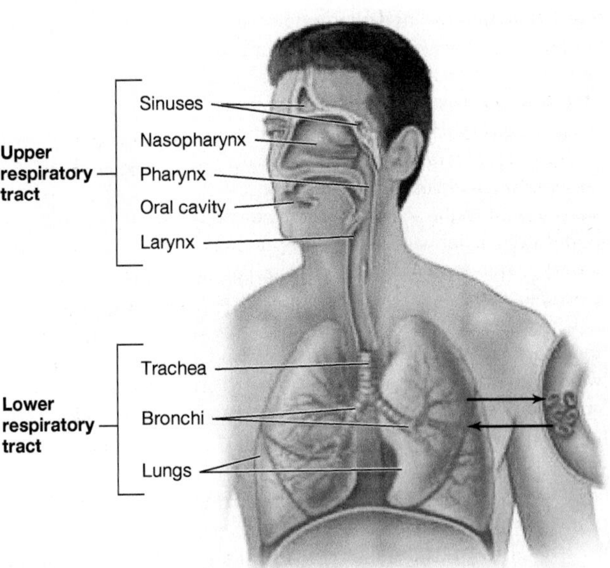

Figure 10 **The respiratory tract.** In healthy individuals the upper respiratory tract has a large variety and number of microorganisms. By contrast, the lower respiratory tract in a healthy person has few if any microorganisms.

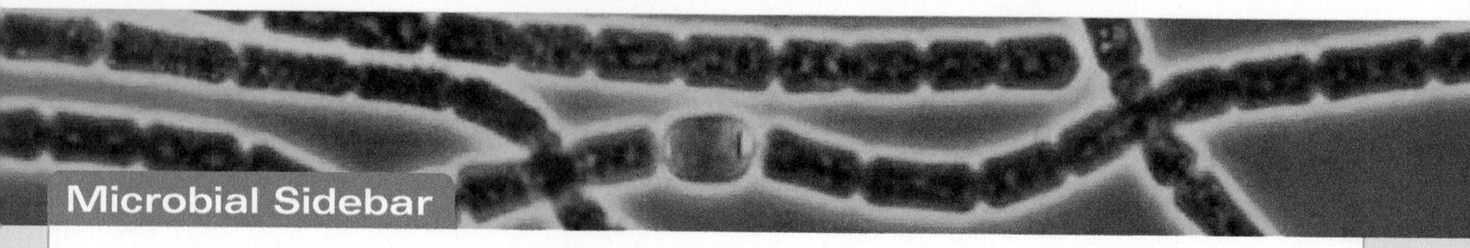

Probiotics[1]

The growth of microorganisms in and on the body is important for normal human development. These organisms, called *commensals*, grow on and in the body and are likely essential to the well-being of all macroorganisms.

The microorganisms we acquire and retain constitute our normal flora and compete at various sites in the body with pathogens, preventing colonization by these organisms. Commensals that reside in the gut are active participants in the digestion of food and manufacture essential nutrients. In theory, the ingestion of selected microorganisms might be used to change or reestablish our gastrointestinal microbial flora to promote health, especially in individuals who experience major changes in their normal microflora due to disease, surgery, or other medical treatments, or whose normal flora changes for other reasons, such as poor diet. Intentionally ingested microorganisms used for this purpose are called *probiotics* (**Figure 1**).

As defined by the United Nations Food and Agricultural Organization and the World Health Organization and adopted by the American Academy of Microbiology, probiotics are suspensions of live microorganisms that, when administered in adequate amounts, confer a perceived health benefit on the host.

Are probiotics really useful? There is no reproducible scientific evidence that conclusively shows that the alteration of commensal populations in normal healthy adults has major, long-lasting, positive health effects. For example, the products shown in Figure 1 are directed toward replacing or reconstituting the intestinal flora of humans by ingesting what amounts to concentrated microbial cultures. As with the animal applications we discuss below, the products are directed at prevention or correction of digestive problems. While these products may confer short-term benefits, conclusive evidence for long-lasting establishment or reestablishment of an altered microbial flora is lacking.

Probiotics, however, are routinely used in production farm animals to prevent digestive problems. For example, strains of *Lactobacillus, Propionibacterium, Bacillus,* and *Saccharomyces* have been successfully used for this purpose. Conceivably, similar treatments in humans could have similar effects.

A number of human ailments have been shown to respond positively to probiotics administration, although the mechanisms are unknown. For example, the period of watery diarrhea from rotavirus infection in children can be shortened by administration of several different probiotics preparations. *Saccharomcyes* (yeast) may reduce the recurrence of diarrhea and shorten infections due to *Clostridium difficile*. Probiotic lactobacilli have also been used to treat urogenital infections in humans.

Evidence thus far suggests that the composition of the gut microflora can change rapidly when probiotics are administered. However, over the long term the gut microflora returns to its original state, indicating that the effects of probiotics are likely only short term. Thus, while probiotics may offer several benefits, especially for reestablishing the gut's normal flora following catastrophic changes, evidence for positive and lasting benefits is not well-established. In this regard there is considerable need for carefully designed and scientifically controlled studies to document the outcomes of probiotic treatment using standardized probiotic preparations containing known organisms administered in precise doses.

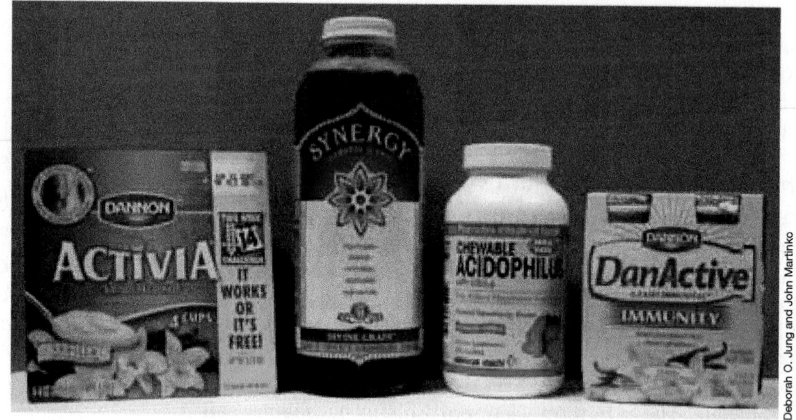

Figure 1 Some commercially available probiotics preparations. *The examples shown are marketed for use in humans.*

[1]Source: Walker, R., and M. Buckley. 2006. Probiotic Microbes: The Scientific Basis. American Academy of Microbiology.

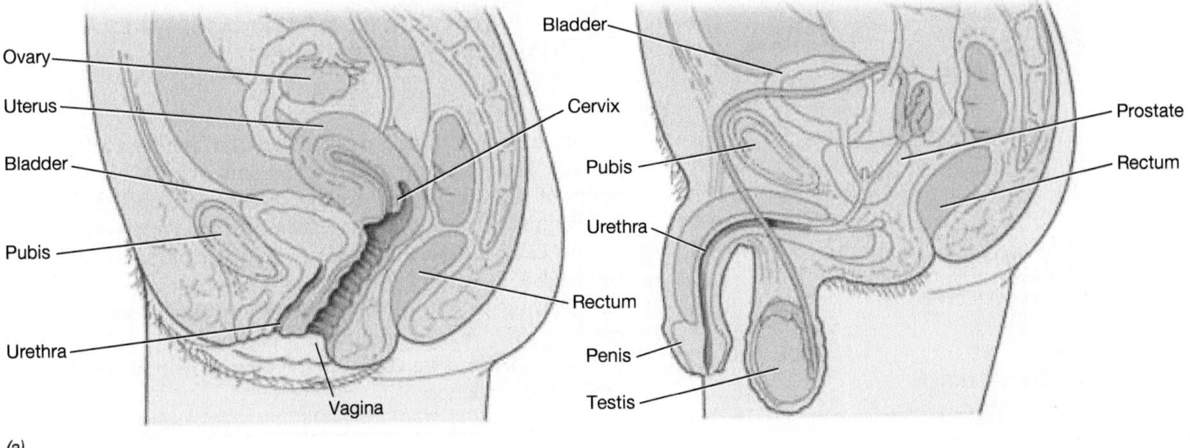

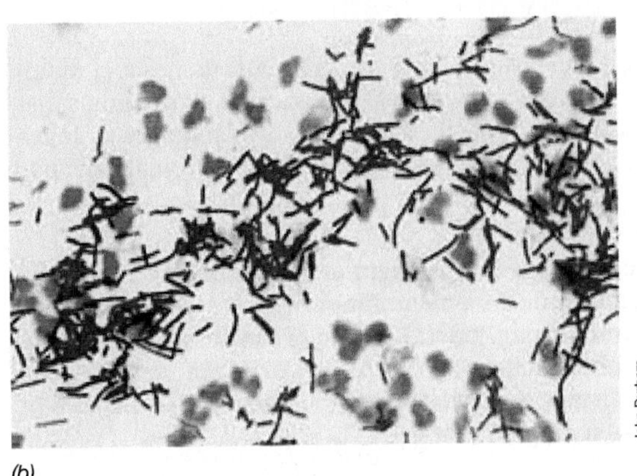

Figure 11 **Microbial growth in the genitourinary tract.** *(a)* The genitourinary tracts of the human female and male, showing regions (red) where microorganisms often grow. The upper regions of the genitourinary tracts of both males and females are sterile in healthy individuals. *(b)* Gram stain of *Lactobacillus acidophilus*, the predominant organism in the vagina of women between the onset of puberty and the end of menopause. Individual rod-shaped cells are 3–4 μm long.

and pharynx), microorganisms live in areas bathed with the secretions of the mucous membranes. Bacteria continually enter the upper respiratory tract from the air during breathing, but most are trapped in the nasal passages and expelled with the nasal secretions. A restricted group of microorganisms, however, colonizes respiratory mucosal surfaces in all individuals. The microorganisms most commonly found are staphylococci, streptococci, diphtheroid bacilli, and gram-negative cocci. Even potential pathogens such as *Staphylococcus aureus* and *Streptococcus pneumoniae* are often part of the normal flora of the nasopharynx of healthy individuals (Table 1). These individuals are *carriers* of the pathogens but do not normally develop disease, presumably because the other resident microorganisms compete successfully for resources and limit pathogen activities. The innate immune system and components of the adaptive immune system such as IgA are particularly active at mucosal surfaces and may also inhibit the growth of pathogens.

The **lower respiratory tract** (trachea, bronchi, and lungs) has no resident microflora in healthy adults, despite the large number of organisms potentially able to reach this region during breathing. Dust particles, which are fairly large, settle out in the upper respiratory tract. As the air passes into the lower respiratory tract, the flow rate decreases markedly, and organisms settle onto the walls of the passages. The walls of the entire respiratory tract are lined with ciliated epithelium, and the cilia, beating upward, push bacteria and other particulate matter toward the upper respiratory tract where they are then expelled in the saliva and nasal secretions. Only particles smaller than about 10 μm in diameter reach the lungs. Nevertheless, some pathogens can reach these locations and cause disease, most notably pneumonias caused by certain bacteria or viruses.

Urogenital Tract

In the male and female urogenital tracts (Figure 11), the bladder itself is typically sterile, but the epithelial cells lining the downstream urethra are colonized by facultatively aerobic gram-negative rods and cocci (Table 1). Potential pathogens such as *Escherichia coli* and *Proteus mirabilis*, normally present in small numbers in the body or local environment, can multiply in the urethra and become pathogenic under altered conditions such as changes in pH. Such organisms are a frequent cause of urinary tract infections, especially in women.

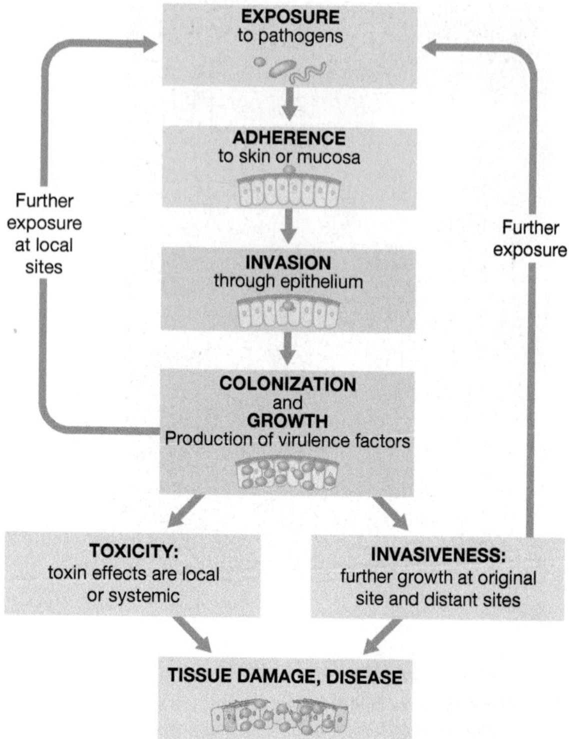

Figure 12 Microorganisms and mechanisms of pathogenesis. Following exposure to a pathogen, events in pathogenesis begin with specific adherence.

The vagina of the adult female is weakly acidic and contains significant amounts of glycogen. *Lactobacillus acidophilus,* a resident organism in the vagina, ferments the polysaccharide glycogen, producing lactic acid that maintains a local acidic environment (Figure 11*b*). Other organisms, such as yeasts (*Torulopsis* and *Candida* species), streptococci, and *E. coli,* may also be present. Before puberty, the female vagina is alkaline and does not produce glycogen, *L. acidophilus* is absent, and the flora consists predominantly of staphylococci, streptococci, diphtheroids, and *E. coli.* After menopause, glycogen production ceases, the pH rises, and the flora again resembles that found before puberty.

5 MiniReview

The presence of a population of normal nonpathogenic microorganisms in the respiratory and urogenital tracts is essential for normal organ function and often prevents the colonization of pathogens.

- Potential pathogens are often found in the normal flora of the upper respiratory tract. Why do they not cause disease in most cases?
- What is the importance of *Lactobacillus* found in the urogenital tract of normal adult women?

II HARMFUL MICROBIAL INTERACTIONS WITH HUMANS

Microbial interactions may be harmful to the host and cause disease. Here we examine mechanisms of *pathogenesis,* the ability of microorganisms to cause disease. Microbial pathogenesis begins with exposure and adherence of the microorganisms to host cells, followed by invasion, colonization, and growth. Unchecked growth of the pathogen then results in host damage. Pathogens use several different strategies to establish *virulence,* the relative ability of a pathogen to cause disease (Figure 12). Here we consider the factors responsible for establishing virulence.

6 Entry of the Pathogen into the Host

A pathogen must usually gain access to host tissues and multiply before damage can be done. In most cases, this requires that the organisms penetrate the skin, mucous membranes, or intestinal epithelium, surfaces that are normally microbial barriers.

Specific Adherence

Most microbial infections begin at breaks or wounds in the skin or on the mucous membranes of the respiratory, digestive, or genitourinary tract. Bacteria or viruses able to initiate infection often adhere specifically to epithelial cells (Figure 13) through macromolecular interactions on the surfaces of the pathogen and the host cell.

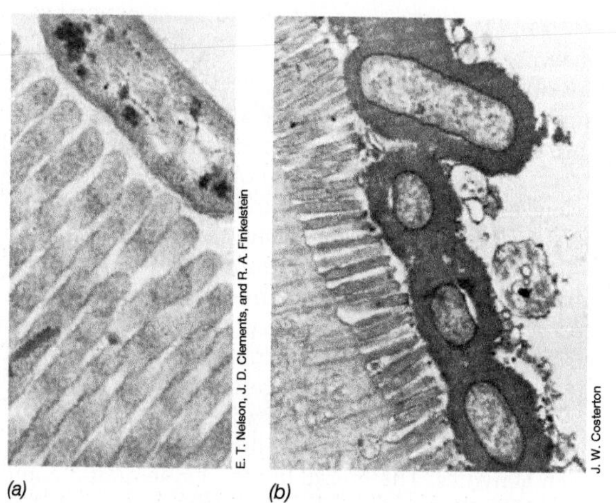

Figure 13 Adherence of pathogens to animal tissues. *(a)* Transmission electron micrograph of a thin section of *Vibrio cholerae* adhering to the brush border of rabbit villi in the intestine. Note the absence of a capsule. *(b)* Enteropathogenic *Escherichia coli* in a fatal model of infection in the newborn calf. The bacterial cells are attached to the brush border of calf intestinal villi through their distinct capsule. The rods are about 0.5 μm in diameter.

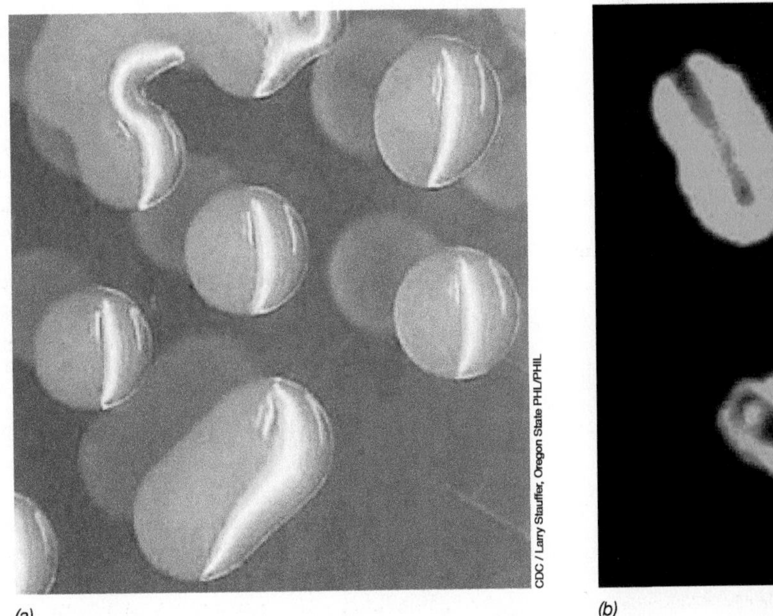

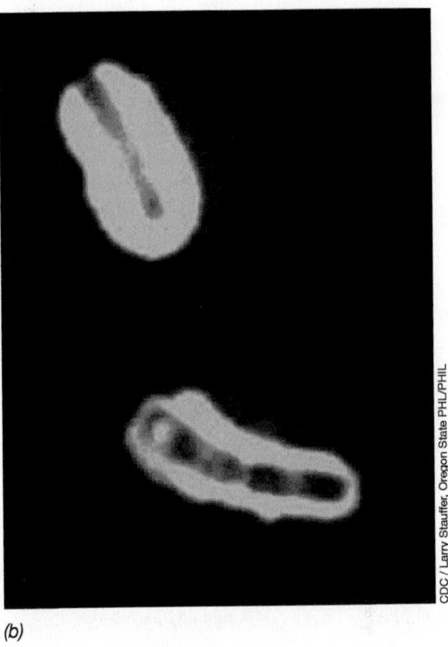

Figure 14 **Bacillus anthracis capsules.** *(a)* Capsules of *B. anthracis* on bicarbonate agar media. Encapsulated colonies are typically very large and mucoid in appearance. The individual encapsulated colonies are 0.5 cm in diameter. *(b)* Direct immunofluorescent stain of *B. anthracis* capsules. Antibodies coupled to fluorescein isothiocyanate (FITC) stain the capsule bright green, indicating that the capsule extends up to 1 μm from the cell, which is about 0.5 μm in diameter.

Most pathogens do not adhere to all epithelial cells equally, but selectively adhere to cells in a particular region of the body. For example, *Neisseria gonorrhoeae,* the pathogen that causes the sexually transmitted disease gonorrhea, adheres more strongly to urogenital epithelia. *N. gonorrhoeae* has a surface protein called Opa (*o*pacity *a*ssociated *p*rotein) that binds specifically to a host protein called CD66 found only on the surface of human epithelial cells. Thus *N. gonorrhoeae* interacts exclusively with host cells by binding a specific cell surface protein. The species of the host also influences specificity. In many cases, a bacterial strain that normally infects humans adheres more strongly to the appropriate human cells than to similar cells in another animal (for example, the rat) and vice versa.

Some macromolecules responsible for bacterial adherence are not covalently attached to the bacteria. These are usually polysaccharides, proteins, or protein–carbohydrate mixtures synthesized and secreted by the bacteria. A loose network of polymer fibers extending outward from a cell is called a **slime layer** (Figure 4*b*). A polymer coat consisting of a dense, well-defined layer surrounding the cell is called a **capsule** (Figures 13 and 14). These structures may be important for adherence to other bacteria as well as to host tissues. In some cases, these structures can protect bacteria from host defense mechanisms such as phagocytosis.

Fimbriae and pili are bacterial cell surface protein structures that may also function in the attachment process. For instance, the pili of *Neisseria gonorrhoeae* play a key role in attachment to urogenital epithelium, and fimbriated strains of *Escherichia coli* (Figure 15) are more frequent causes of urinary tract infections than strains lacking fimbriae. Among the best-characterized fimbriae are the type I fimbriae of enteric bacteria (*Escherichia, Klebsiella, Salmonella,* and *Shigella*). Type I fimbriae are uniformly distributed on the surface of cells. Pili are typically longer than fimbriae, with fewer pili found on the cell surface. Both pili and fimbriae function by

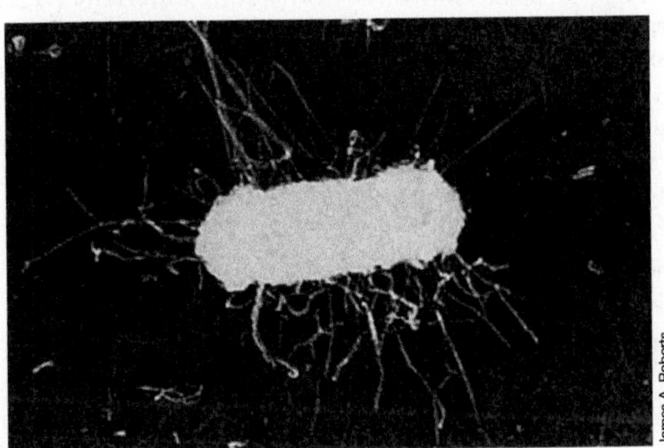

Figure 15 **Fimbriae.** Shadow-cast electron micrograph of the bacterium *Escherichia coli* showing type P fimbriae, which resemble type I fimbriae but are somewhat longer. The cell shown is about 0.5 μm wide.

Table 3 Major adherence factors used to facilitate attachment of microbial pathogens to host tissues[a]

Factor	*Example*
Capsule/slime layer Figure 4, Figure 13, Figure 14	Pathogenic *Escherichia coli*—capsule promotes adherence to the brush border of intestinal villi
	Streptococcus mutans—dextran slime layer promotes binding to tooth surfaces
Adherence proteins	*Streptococcus pyogenes*—M protein on the cell binds to receptors on respiratory mucosa
	Neisseria gonorrhoeae—Opa protein on the cell binds to receptors on epithelium
Lipoteichoic acid	*Streptococcus pyogenes*—facilitates binding to respiratory mucosal receptor (along with M protein)
Fimbriae (pili) (Figure 15)	*Neisseria gonorrhoeae*—pili facilitate binding to epithelium
	Salmonella species—type I fimbriae facilitate binding to epithelium of small intestine
	Pathogenic *Escherichia coli*—colonization factor antigens (CFAs) facilitate binding to epithelium of small intestine

[a]Most receptor sites on host tissues are glycoproteins or complex lipids such as gangliosides or globosides.

binding host cell surface glycoproteins, initiating attachment. Flagella can also increase adherence to host cells (see Figure 17).

Studies of diarrhea caused by enterotoxic strains of *E. coli* provide evidence for specific interactions between the mucosal epithelium and pathogens. Most strains of *E. coli* are normal nonpathogenic inhabitants of the cecum, the first part of the large intestine, and the colon (Figure 8). Several strains of *E. coli* are usually present in the body at the same time, and large numbers of these nonpathogens routinely pass through the body and are eliminated in feces. However, enterotoxic strains of *E. coli* contain genes encoding fimbrial CFA (colonization factor antigens); these are proteins that adhere specifically to cells in the small intestine. From here, they can colonize and produce enterotoxins that cause diarrhea as well as other illnesses (Section 11). Nonpathogenic strains of *E. coli* seldom express CFA proteins. Some major factors important in microbial adherence are shown in Table 3.

Invasion

A few microorganisms are pathogenic solely because of the toxins they produce. These organisms do not need to gain access to host tissues, and we will discuss them separately in Sections 10 and 11. However, most pathogens must penetrate the epithelium to initiate pathogenicity, a process called *invasion*. At the point of entry, usually at small breaks or lesions in the skin or in mucosal surfaces, growth is established. Growth may also begin on intact mucosal surfaces, especially if the normal flora is altered or eliminated, for example, by antibiotic therapy. Pathogens may then more readily colonize the tissue and begin the invasion process. Pathogen growth may also be established at sites distant from the original point of entry. Access to distant, usually interior, sites is through the blood or lymphatic circulatory system.

6 MiniReview

Pathogens gain access to host tissues by adherence at mucosal surfaces through interactions between pathogen and host macromolecules. Pathogen invasion starts at the site of adherence and may spread throughout the host via the circulatory or lymphatic systems.

- How do CFA molecules on *Escherichia coli* and Opa proteins on *Neisseria gonorrhoeae* influence adherence to mucosal tissues?
- How does adherence initiate invasion?

7 Colonization and Growth

If a pathogen gains access to tissues, it may multiply and colonize the tissue. Because the initial inoculum of a pathogen is usually too small to cause host damage, the pathogen must find appropriate nutrients and environmental conditions to grow in the host. Temperature, pH, and the presence or absence of oxygen affect pathogen growth, but the availability of microbial nutrients is most important.

Not all vitamins and growth factors are in adequate supply in all tissues at all times, even on a vertebrate host. Soluble nutrients such as sugars, amino acids, organic acids, and growth factors are limited, favoring organisms able to use host-specific nutrients. *Brucella abortus*, for example, grows very slowly in most tissues of infected cattle, but grows very rapidly in the placenta. The placenta is the only tissue that contains high concentrations of erythritol, a sugar that is readily metabolized by *B. abortus*. The erythritol enhances *B. abortus* growth, causing abortion in cattle (see Table 6).

Trace elements may also be in short supply and can influence establishment of the pathogen. For example, the concentration of iron greatly influences microbial growth. Specific host proteins called *transferrin* and *lactoferrin* bind iron tightly and transfer it through the body. These proteins have such high affinity for iron that microbial iron deficiency may limit infection by many pathogens; an iron solution given to an infected animal greatly increases the virulence of some pathogens.

Many bacteria produce iron-chelating compounds called *siderophores* that help them obtain iron, a growth-limiting micronutrient, from the environment. Siderophores from some pathogens are so efficient that they remove iron from animal iron-binding proteins. For example, *aerobactin*, a plasmid-encoded siderophore produced by certain strains of *Escherichia coli,* readily removes iron bound to transferrin. Likewise, *Neisseria* species produce a transferrin-specific receptor that binds to and removes iron from transferrin.

Localization in the Body

After initial entry, some pathogens remain localized, multiplying and producing a discrete focus of infection such as the boil that may arise from *Staphylococcus* skin infections. Other pathogens may enter the lymphatic vessels and move to the lymph nodes, where they may be contained by the immune system. If a pathogen reaches the blood, either by direct infection or through the lymphatic vessels, it will be distributed to distant parts of the body, usually concentrating in the liver or spleen. Spread of the pathogen through the blood and lymph systems can result in a generalized (systemic) infection of the body, with the organism growing in a variety of tissues. If extensive bacterial growth in tissues occurs, some of the organisms are usually shed into the bloodstream in large numbers, a condition called **bacteremia**. Widespread infections of this type almost always start as a local infection in a specific organ such as the kidney, intestine, or lung.

7 MiniReview

A pathogen must gain access to nutrients and appropriate growth conditions before it can colonize and grow in substantial numbers in host tissue. Pathogens may grow locally at the site of invasion or may spread through the body.

- Why are colonization and growth necessary for the success of most pathogens?
- Identify host factors that limit or accelerate colonization and growth of a microorganism at selected local sites.

8 Virulence

Virulence is the relative ability of a pathogen to cause disease, and here we discuss some basic methods used to measure it. We then provide specific examples of particularly virulent organisms, highlighting properties that enhance their virulence.

Measuring Virulence

The virulence of a pathogen can be estimated from experimental studies of the LD_{50} (lethal dose$_{50}$), the dose of an agent that kills 50% of the animals in a test group. Highly virulent pathogens frequently show little difference in the number of cells required to kill 100% of the population as compared with the number required to kill 50% of the population. This is illustrated in Figure 16 for experimental *Streptococcus* and *Salmonella* infections in mice. Only a few cells of virulent strains of *Streptococcus pneumoniae* are required to establish a fatal infection and kill all animals in a test population of mice. In fact, the LD_{50} for *S. pneumoniae* is hard to determine in mice because so few organisms are needed to produce a lethal infection. By contrast, the LD_{50} for *Salmonella typhimurium,* a much less virulent pathogen, is much higher. The number of cells of *S. typhimurium* required to kill 100% of the population is more than 100 times greater than the number of cells needed to reach the LD_{50}.

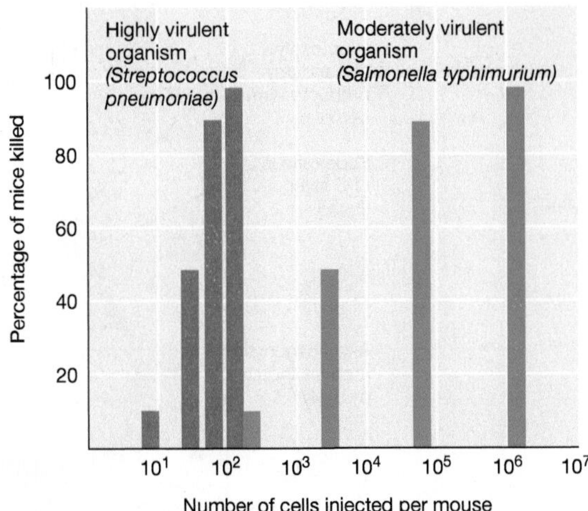

Figure 16 **Microbial virulence.** Differences in microbial virulence demonstrated by the number of cells of *Streptococcus pneumoniae* and *Salmonella typhimurium* required to kill mice.

When pathogens are kept in laboratory culture rather than isolated from diseased animals, their virulence is often decreased or even lost completely. Such organisms are said to be *attenuated.* **Attenuation** probably occurs because non-virulent or weakly virulent mutants grow faster and, after successive transfers to fresh media, such mutants are selectively favored. Attenuation often occurs more readily when culture conditions are not optimal for the species. If an attenuated culture is reinoculated into an animal, the organism can regain its original virulence, but in many cases loss of virulence is permanent. Attenuated strains are often used for production of vaccines, especially viral vaccines. Measles, mumps, and rubella vaccines, for example, consist of attenuated viruses.

Toxicity and Invasiveness

Virulence is due to the ability of a pathogen to cause host damage through toxicity and invasiveness. Each pathogen uses these properties to cause disease.

Toxicity is the ability of an organism to cause disease by means of a preformed toxin that inhibits host cell function or kills host cells. For example, the disease tetanus is caused by an exotoxin produced by *Clostridium tetani* (Section 10). *C. tetani* cells rarely leave the wound where they were first introduced, growing relatively slowly at the wound site. Yet

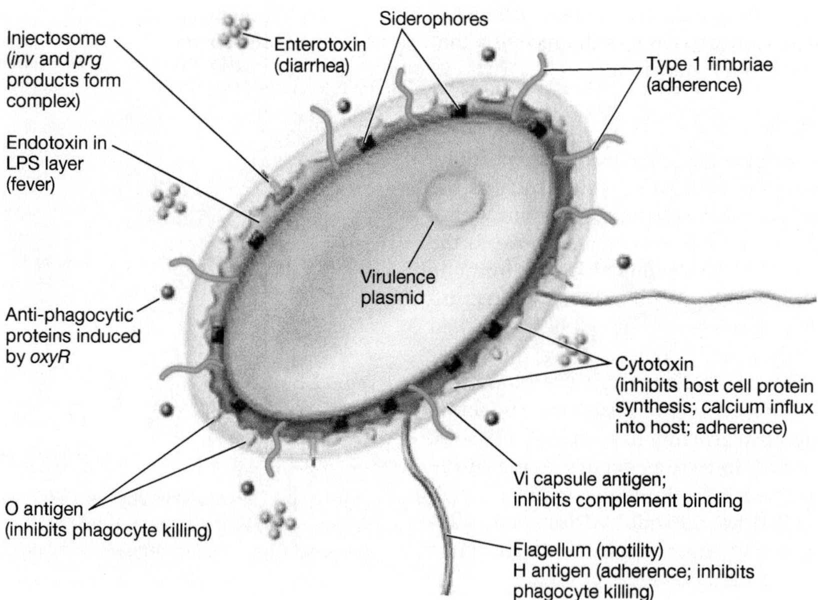

Figure 17 **Virulence factors in *Salmonella* pathogenesis.** Structural elements known to be important in pathogenesis are shown.

C. tetani is able to bring about disease because it produces tetanus toxin that moves to distant parts of the body, initiating irreversible muscle contraction and often death of the host.

Invasiveness is the ability of a pathogen to grow in host tissue in such large numbers that it inhibits host function. A microorganism may be able to produce disease through invasiveness even if it produces no toxin. For example, the major virulence factor for *Streptococcus pneumoniae* is the polysaccharide capsule that prevents the phagocytosis of pathogenic strains, defeating a major defense mechanism used by the host to prevent invasion. Encapsulated strains of *S. pneumoniae* grow in lung tissues in enormous numbers, where they initiate host responses that lead to pneumonia, interfere with lung function, and cause extensive host damage. Nonencapsulated strains are less invasive; they are quickly and efficiently ingested and destroyed by phagocytes, white blood cells that ingest and kill bacteria by a process called *phagocytosis*.

Clostridium tetani and *Streptococcus pneumoniae* exemplify the extremes of toxicity and invasiveness, respectively. Most pathogens fall between these extremes and their virulence results from a combination of toxicity and invasiveness.

Virulence in *Salmonella*

Salmonella species employ a mixture of toxins, invasiveness, and other virulence factors to enhance pathogenicity (Figure 17). First, at least three toxins, *enterotoxin, endotoxin,* and *cytotoxin* contribute to their virulence (Table 4). We discuss enterotoxins and endotoxins in detail later in this chapter. *Salmonella* cytotoxin inhibits host cell protein synthesis and allows Ca^{2+} to escape from host cells, killing the cells.

Several virulence factors contribute to invasiveness in *Salmonella*. As we mentioned above, many pathogens including *Salmonella* produce iron-chelating siderophores, sequestering iron to aid in growth. The cell surface polysaccharide O antigen, the flagellar H antigen, and fimbriae enhance adherence. The capsular Vi polysaccharide inhibits complement binding and antibody-mediated killing. The *inv* (invasion) genes of *Salmonella* encode at least ten different proteins that promote invasion. For example, *invH* encodes a surface adhesion protein. Other *inv* genes encode proteins important for trafficking of virulence proteins. The InvJ regulator protein controls assembly of structural proteins InvG, PrgH, PrgI, PrgJ, and PrgK that form an injection complex, called the *injectosome*, an organelle in the bacterial envelope that allows transfer of virulence proteins into host cells through a needlelike assembly.

Salmonella species readily establish infections through intracellular parasitism. *Salmonella* infections start with ingestion and passage of the bacterial cells through the stomach to the intestine. From here, *Salmonella* invades and replicates inside the cells that line the intestine as well as in phagocytes called *macrophages*. The genes that initiate the invasion process are contained on the chromosomal *Salmonella* pathogenicity island-1 (SPI-1). As with other pathogenicity islands, SPI-1 is a collection of virulence genes flanked by sequences suggesting a transposable genetic element. Another *Salmonella* pathogenicity island, SPI-2, contains genes that are responsible for systemic disease.

Pathogenic *Salmonella* species also have other virulence factors. For example, the toxic oxygen products produced by host macrophages as an antibacterial defense can be neutralized by proteins encoded by the *Salmonella oxyR* gene. In addition, macrophage-produced antibacterial molecules

Table 4 Exotoxins and extracellular virulence factors produced by human pathogens

Organism	Disease	Toxin or factor[a]	Action
Bacillus anthracis	Anthrax	Lethal factor (LF) Edema factor (EF) Protective antigen (PA) (AB)	PA is the cell-binding B component, EF causes edema, LF causes cell death
Bacillus cereus	Food poisoning	Enterotoxin complex	Induces fluid loss from intestinal cells
Bordetella pertussis	Whooping cough	Pertussis toxin (AB)	Blocks G protein signal transduction, kills cells
Clostridium botulinum	Botulism	Neurotoxin (AB)	Flaccid paralysis (Figure 21)
Clostridium tetani	Tetanus	Neurotoxin (AB)	Spastic paralysis (Figure 22)
Clostridium perfringens	Gas gangrene, food poisoning	α-Toxin (CT)	Hemolysis (lecithinase, Figure 18b)
		β-Toxin (CT)	Hemolysis
		γ-Toxin (CT)	Hemolysis
		δ-Toxin (CT)	Hemolysis (cardiotoxin)
		κ-Toxin (E)	Collagenase
		λ-Toxin (E)	Protease
		Enterotoxin (CT)	Alters permeability of intestinal epithelium
Corynebacterium diphtheriae	Diphtheria	Diphtheria toxin (AB)	Inhibits protein synthesis in eukaryotes (Figure 20)
Escherichia coli (enterotoxigenic strains only)	Gastroenteritis	Enterotoxin (Shiga-like toxin) (AB)	Induces fluid loss from intestinal cells
Haemophilus ducreyi	Chancroid	Cytolethal distending toxin[b] (CDT) (AB)	Genotoxin (DNA lesions cause apoptosis in host cells)
Pseudomonas aeruginosa	*P. aeruginosa* infections	Exotoxin A (AB)	Inhibits protein synthesis
Salmonella spp.	Salmonellosis, typhoid fever, paratyphoid fever	Enterotoxin (AB)	Inhibits protein synthesis, lyses host cells
		Cytotoxin (CT)	Induces fluid loss from intestinal cells
Shigella dysenteriae	Bacterial dysentery	Shiga toxin (AB)	Inhibits protein synthesis
Staphylococcus aureus	Pyogenic (pus-forming) infections (boils, and so on), respiratory infections, food poisoning, toxic shock syndrome, scalded skin syndrome	α-Toxin (CT)	Hemolysis
		Toxic shock syndrome toxin (SA)	Systemic shock
		Exfoliating toxin A and B (SA)	Peeling of skin, shock
		Leukocidin (CT)	Destroys leukocytes
		β-Toxin (CT)	Hemolysis
		γ-Toxin (CT)	Kills cells
		δ-Toxin (CT)	Hemolysis, leukolysis
		Enterotoxin A, B, C, D, and E (SA)	Induce vomiting, diarrhea, shock
		Coagulase (E)	Induces fibrin clotting
Streptococcus pyogenes	Pyogenic infections, tonsillitis, scarlet fever	Streptolysin O (CT)	Hemolysin
		Streptolysin S (CT)	Hemolysin (Figure 18a)
		Erythrogenic toxin (SA)	Causes scarlet fever
		Streptokinase (E)	Dissolves fibrin clots
		Hyaluronidase (E)	Dissolves hyaluronic acid in connective tissue
Vibrio cholerae	Cholera	Enterotoxin (AB)	Induces fluid loss from intestinal cells (Figure 23)

[a]AB, A-B toxin; CT, cytolytic toxin; E, enzymatic virulence factor; SA, superantigen toxin.

[b]Cytolethal distending toxin is found in other gram-negative pathogens including *Actinobacillus actinomycetemocomitans*, *Campylobacter* sp., *Escherichia coli*, *Helicobacter* sp., *Salmonella typhi*, and *Shigella dysenteriae*.

called *defensins* can be neutralized by the products of the *Salmonella phoP* and *phoQ* genes. Thus, the oxy and pho gene products of *Salmonella* enhance pathogenicity by promoting intracellular invasion and neutralizing host defenses that normally inhibit intracellular bacterial growth.

Finally, several plasmidborne virulence factors can be spread between most *Salmonella* species as well as other enteric bacteria. For example, antibiotic resistance is encoded on a R plasmid. Thus *Salmonella,* and most other pathogens, use a variety of factors and mechanisms to establish virulence and pathogenesis.

8 MiniReview

Virulence is determined by the invasiveness and toxicity of a pathogen. In most pathogens, a number of mechanisms and factors contribute to virulence. Attenuation is loss of virulence. *Salmonella* has many traits that enhance virulence.

- Distinguish between *toxicity* and *invasiveness.* Give examples of organisms that rely almost exclusively on toxicity or invasiveness to promote virulence.
- For *Salmonella,* identify structural genes involved in virulence and relate them to the toxic or invasive properties of the pathogen.

III VIRULENCE FACTORS AND TOXINS

Extracellular capsules and slime layers, cell wall and envelope material, and fimbriae and pili are all integral macromolecular components of microorganisms that may aid in pathogenesis and act as virulence factors. However, in addition to these, a number of microbial intracellular and extracellular components function solely as virulence factors. These specialized virulence factors are produced by different pathogens, but many share molecular characteristics and modes of action. Here we examine some key factors.

9 Virulence Factors

Many pathogens produce toxins, which we discuss in the following three sections. Many other virulence factors are enzymes that enhance pathogen colonization and growth. For example, streptococci, staphylococci, and certain clostridia produce hyaluronidase (Table 4), an enzyme that promotes spreading of organisms in tissues by breaking down the polysaccharide hyaluronic acid, a material that functions in animals as an intercellular cement. Hyaluronidase digests the intercellular matrix, enabling these organisms to spread from an initial infection site. Streptococci and staphylococci also produce proteases, nucleases, and lipases that degrade host proteins, nucleic acids, and lipids. Similarly, clostridia that cause gas gangrene produce collagenase, or κ-toxin (Table 4), which breaks down the tissue-supporting collagen network, enabling these organisms to spread through the body.

Fibrin, Clots, and Virulence

Fibrin is a protein that functions in the clotting of blood, and thus fibrin clots are often formed by the host at a site of microbial invasion. The clotting mechanism, triggered by tissue injury, isolates the pathogens, limiting infection to a local region. Some pathogens counter this process by producing fibrinolytic enzymes that dissolve the clots and make further invasion possible. One fibrinolytic substance produced by *Streptococcus pyogenes* is called *streptokinase* (Table 4).

By contrast, other pathogens produce enzymes that promote the formation of fibrin clots. These clots localize and protect the organism. The best-studied fibrin-clotting enzyme is *coagulase* (Table 4), produced by pathogenic *Staphylococcus aureus*. Coagulase causes fibrin to be deposited on *S. aureus* cells, protecting them from attack by host cells. The fibrin matrix produced as a result of coagulase activity probably accounts for the extremely localized nature of many staphylococcal infections, as in boils and pimples. Coagulase-positive *S. aureus* strains are typically more virulent than coagulase-negative strains.

9 MiniReview

Pathogens produce enzymes that enhance virulence by breaking down or altering host tissue to provide access and nutrients. Other pathogen-produced virulence factors protect the pathogen by interfering with normal host defense mechanisms. These factors enhance colonization and growth of the pathogen.

- What advantage does the pathogen gain by producing enzymes that affect structural components of host tissues?
- How does streptokinase enhance the virulence of *Streptococcus pyogenes*? How does coagulase enhance the virulence of *Staphylococcus aureus*?

10 Exotoxins

Exotoxins are toxic proteins released from the pathogen cell as it grows. These toxins travel from a site of infection and cause damage at distant sites. Table 4 provides a summary of the properties and actions of some of the known exotoxins as well as other extracellular virulence factors.

Exotoxins fall into one of three categories: the *cytolytic toxins,* the *AB toxins,* and the *superantigen toxins*. The cytolytic toxins work by degrading cytoplasmic membrane integrity, causing lysis. The AB toxins consist of two subunits, A and B. The B component generally binds to a host cell surface receptor, allowing the transfer of the A subunit across the targeted cell membrane, where it damages the cell. The

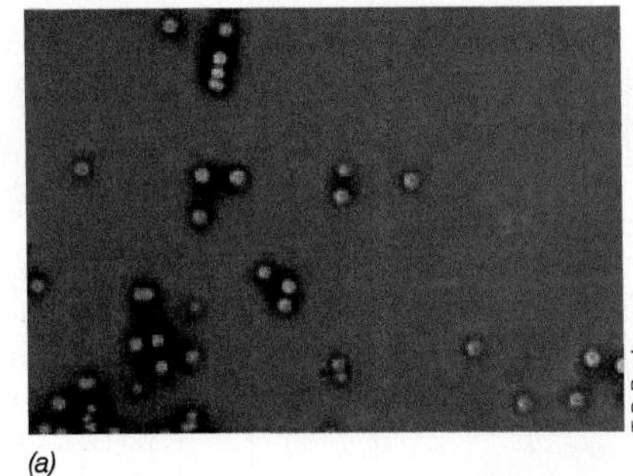

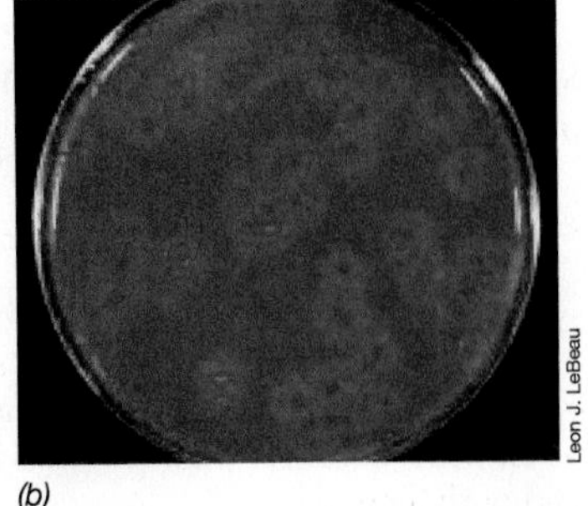

Figure 18 **Hemolysis.** *(a)* Zones of hemolysis around colonies of *Streptococcus pyogenes* growing on a blood agar plate. *(b)* Action of lecithinase, a phospholipase, around colonies of *Clostridium perfringens* growing on an agar medium containing egg yolk, a source of lecithin. Lecithinase dissolves the membranes of red blood cells, producing the cloudy zones of hemolysis around each colony.

superantigens work by stimulating large numbers of immune cells, resulting in extensive inflammation and tissue damage, as we will discuss later.

Cytolytic Toxins

Various pathogens produce proteins that damage the host cytoplasmic membrane, causing cell lysis and death. Because the activity of these toxins is most easily observed with assays involving the lysis of red blood cells (erythrocytes), the toxins are called *hemolysins* (Table 4). However, they also lyse cells other than erythrocytes. The production of hemolysin is demonstrated in the laboratory by streaking the pathogen on a blood agar plate (a rich medium containing 5% whole blood). During growth of the colonies, hemolysin is released and lyses the surrounding red blood cells, releasing hemoglobin and creating a clearing, called *hemolysis* (Figure 18).

Some hemolysins attack the phospholipid of the host cytoplasmic membrane. Because the phospholipid lecithin (phosphatidylcholine) is often used as a substrate, these enzymes are called *lecithinases* or *phospholipases*. An example is the α-toxin of *Clostridium perfringens*, a lecithinase that dissolves membrane lipids, resulting in cell lysis (Table 4, Figure 18*b*). Because the cytoplasmic membranes of all organisms contain phospholipids, phospholipases sometimes destroy bacterial as well as animal cytoplasmic membranes.

Some hemolysins, however, are not phospholipases. Streptolysin O, a hemolysin produced by streptococci, affects the sterols of the host cytoplasmic membrane. *Leukocidins* (Table 4) lyse white blood cells and may decrease host resistance.

Staphylococcal α-toxin (Figure 19 and Table 4) kills nucleated cells and lyses erythrocytes. Toxin subunits first bind to the lipid bilayer. The subunits then oligomerize into nonlytic heptamers, now associated with the membrane. Following oligomerization, each heptamer undergoes conformational changes to produce a membrane-spanning pore, releasing the cell contents and allowing influx of extracellular material, disrupting cell function and causing cell death.

Protein Synthesis Inhibitor Toxins

Several pathogens produce AB exotoxins that inhibit protein synthesis. Diphtheria toxin, produced by *Corynebacterium diphtheriae*, is a good example of an AB toxin and is an important virulence factor. Rats and mice are relatively resistant to diphtheria toxin, but human, rabbit, guinea pig, and bird cells are very susceptible, with only a single toxin molecule required to kill each cell. Diphtheria toxin is secreted by cells of *C. diphtheriae* as a single polypeptide. Fragment B specifically binds to a host cell receptor (Figure 20). After binding, proteolytic cleavage between fragment A and B allows entry of fragment A into the host cytoplasm. Here fragment A disrupts protein synthesis by blocking transfer of an amino acid from a tRNA to the growing polypeptide chain. The toxin specifically inactivates elongation factor 2, a protein involved in growth of the polypeptide chain, by catalyzing the attachment of adenosine diphosphate (ADP) ribose from NAD^+. Follow-

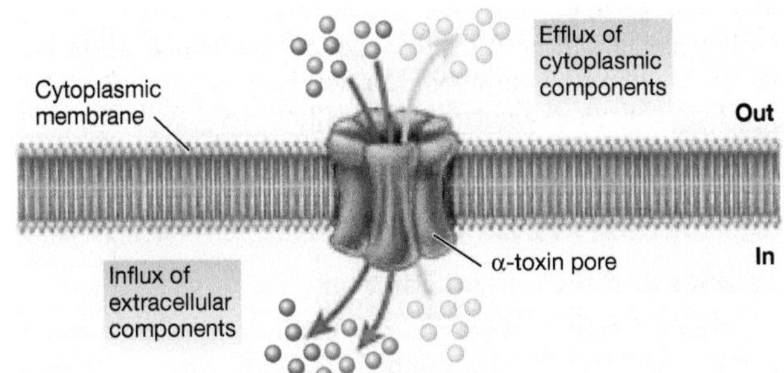

Figure 19 **Staphylococcal α-toxin.** Staphylococcal α-toxin is a pore-forming cytotoxin that is produced by growing *Staphylococcus* cells. Released as a monomer, seven identical protein subunits oligomerize in the cytoplasmic membrane of target cells. The oligomer forms a pore, releasing the contents of the cell and allowing the influx of extracellular material and the efflux of intracellular material. Eukaryotic cells swell and lyse. In erythrocytes, hemolysis occurs, visually indicating cell lysis.

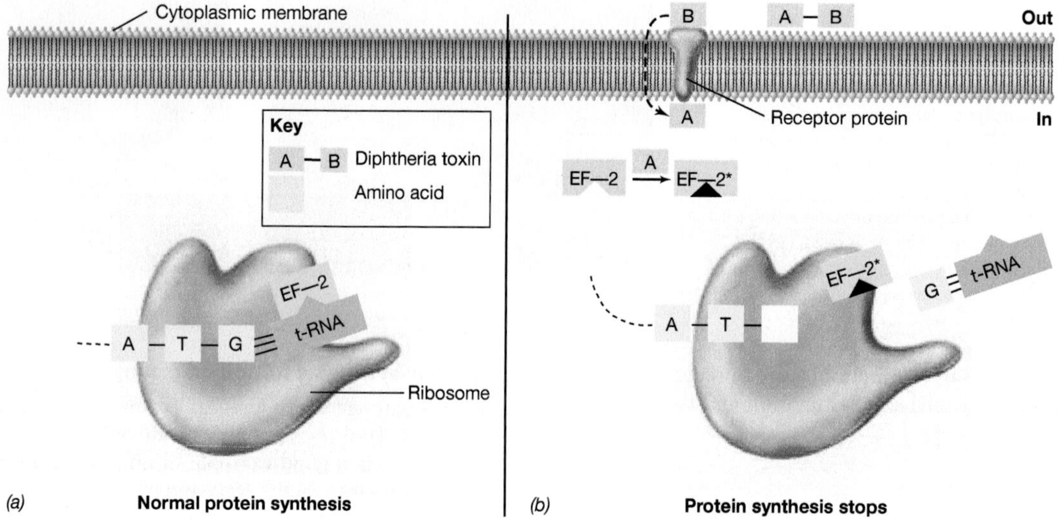

Figure 20 **The action of diphtheria toxin from *Corynebacterium diphtheriae*.** In a normal eukaryotic cell *(a)* elongation factor 2 (EF-2) binds to the ribosome, bringing an amino acid-charged t-RNA to the ribosome, causing protein elongation. In a cell affected by the diphtheria AB toxin *(b)*, the toxin binds to the cytoplasmic membrane receptor protein via the B portion. Cleavage between the A and B toxin components occurs, and the A peptide is internalized. The A peptide catalyzes the ADP-ribosylation of elongation factor 2 (EF—2*). This modified elongation factor no longer binds the ribosome and cannot aid transfer of amino acids to the growing polypeptide chain, resulting in shutdown of protein synthesis and death of the cell.

ing ADP-ribosylation, the activity of the modified elongation factor 2 decreases dramatically and protein synthesis stops.

Diphtheria toxin is formed only by strains of *C. diphtheriae* that are lysogenized by a bacteriophage called phage β; the *tox* gene in the phage genome encodes the toxin. Nontoxigenic, nonpathogenic strains of *C. diphtheriae* can be converted to pathogenic strains by infection with phage β (this is a process called *phage conversion*).

Exotoxin A of *Pseudomonas aeruginosa* functions similarly to diphtheria toxin, also modifying elongation factor 2 by ADP-ribosylation (Table 4). www.microbiologyplace.com **Online Tutorial 28.1: Diphtheria and Cholera Toxin**

Tetanus and Botulinum Toxins

Clostridium tetani and *Clostridium botulinum*, soil endospore-forming bacteria that occasionally cause disease in animals, produce potent AB exotoxins that affect nervous tissue. Neither species is very invasive, and virtually all pathogenic effects are due to neurotoxicity. *C. botulinum* sometimes grows directly in the body, causing infant or wound botulism, and also grows and produces toxin in improperly preserved foods. Death from botulism is usually from respiratory failure due to flaccid muscle paralysis. *C. tetani* grows in the body in deep wound punctures that become anoxic, and although *C. tetani* does not invade the body from the initial site of infection, the toxin can spread via the neural cells and cause spastic paralysis, the hallmark of tetanus, often leading to death.

Botulinum toxin consists of seven related AB toxins that are the most potent biological toxins known. One milligram of botulinum toxin is enough to kill more than 1 million guinea pigs. Of the seven distinct botulinum toxins known, at least two are encoded on lysogenic bacteriophages specific for *C. botulinum*. The major toxin is a protein that forms complexes with nontoxic botulinum proteins to yield a bioactive protein complex. The complex then binds to presynaptic membranes on the termini of the stimulatory motor neurons at the neuromuscular junction, blocking the release of acetylcholine. Transmission of the nerve impulse to the muscle requires acetylcholine interaction with a muscle receptor and botulinum toxin prevents the poisoned muscle from receiving the excitatory signal (Figure 21). This prevents muscle contraction and leads to flaccid paralysis and death by suffocation, the outcome of botulism.

Tetanus toxin is also an AB protein neurotoxin. On contact with the central nervous system, this toxin is transported through the motor neurons to the spinal cord, where it binds specifically to ganglioside lipids at the termini of the inhibitory interneurons. The inhibitory interneurons normally work by releasing an inhibitory neurotransmitter, typically the amino acid glycine, which binds to receptors on the motor neurons. Normally, glycine from the inhibitory interneurons stops the release of acetylcholine by the motor neurons and inhibits muscle contraction, allowing relaxation of the muscle fibers. However, if tetanus toxin blocks glycine release, the motor neurons cannot be inhibited, resulting in tetanus,

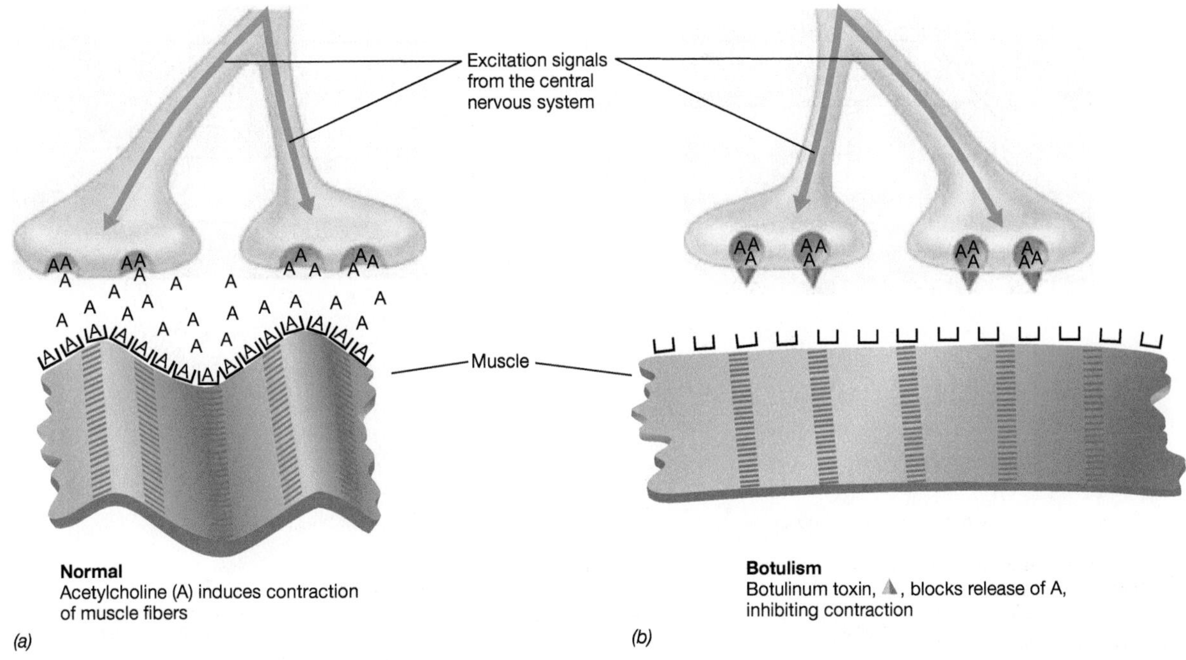
Excitation signals from the central nervous system
Muscle
Normal
Acetylcholine (A) induces contraction of muscle fibers
(a)
Botulism
Botulinum toxin, ▲, blocks release of A, inhibiting contraction
(b)

Figure 21 The action of botulinum toxin from *Clostridium botulinum*. *(a)* Upon stimulation of peripheral and cranial nerves, acetylcholine (A) is normally released from vesicles at the neural side of the motor end plate. Acetylcholine then binds to specific receptors on the muscle, inducing contraction. *(b)* Botulinum toxin acts at the motor end plate to prevent release of acetylcholine (A) from vesicles, resulting in a lack of stimulus to the muscle fibers, irreversible relaxation of the muscles, and flaccid paralysis.

continual release of acetylcholine, and uncontrolled contraction of the poisoned muscles (Figure 22). The outcome is a spastic, twitching paralysis, and affected muscles are constantly contracted. If the muscles of the mouth are involved, the prolonged contractions restrict the mouth's movement, resulting in the condition called *lockjaw* (trismus). If respiratory muscles are involved, prolonged contraction may result in death due to asphyxiation.

Tetanus toxin and botulinum toxin both block release of neurotransmitters involved in muscle control, but the symptoms are quite different and depend on the particular neurotransmitters involved.

10 MiniReview

Exotoxins contribute to the virulence of pathogens. Cytotoxins and AB toxins are potent exotoxins produced by microorganisms. Each exotoxin affects a specific host cell function. Bacterial exotoxins include some of the most potent biological toxins known.

- What key features are shared by all exotoxins? What features are unique to the AB exotoxins?
- Are bacterial growth and infection in the host necessary for the production of toxins? Explain and cite examples for your answer.

11 Enterotoxins

Enterotoxins are exotoxins whose activity affects the small intestine, generally causing massive secretion of fluid into the intestinal lumen resulting in vomiting and diarrhea. Generally acquired by ingestion of contaminated food or water, enterotoxins are produced by a variety of bacteria, including the food-poisoning organisms *Staphylococcus aureus, Clostridium perfringens,* and *Bacillus cereus,* and the intestinal pathogens *Vibrio cholerae, Escherichia coli,* and *Salmonella enteritidis*.

Cholera Toxin

The enterotoxin produced by *V. cholerae,* the organism that causes cholera, is the best understood enterotoxin. Cholera is characterized by massive fluid loss through the intestines, resulting in severe diarrhea characterized by life-threatening dehydration and electrolyte depletion. The disease starts by ingestion of *V. cholerae* in contaminated food or water. The organism travels to the intestine, where it colonizes and secretes the cholera toxin. Cholera toxin is an AB toxin consisting of an A subunit and five B subunits. In the gut, the B subunit binds specifically to GM1 ganglioside, a complex glycolipid found in the cytoplasmic membrane of intestinal epithelial

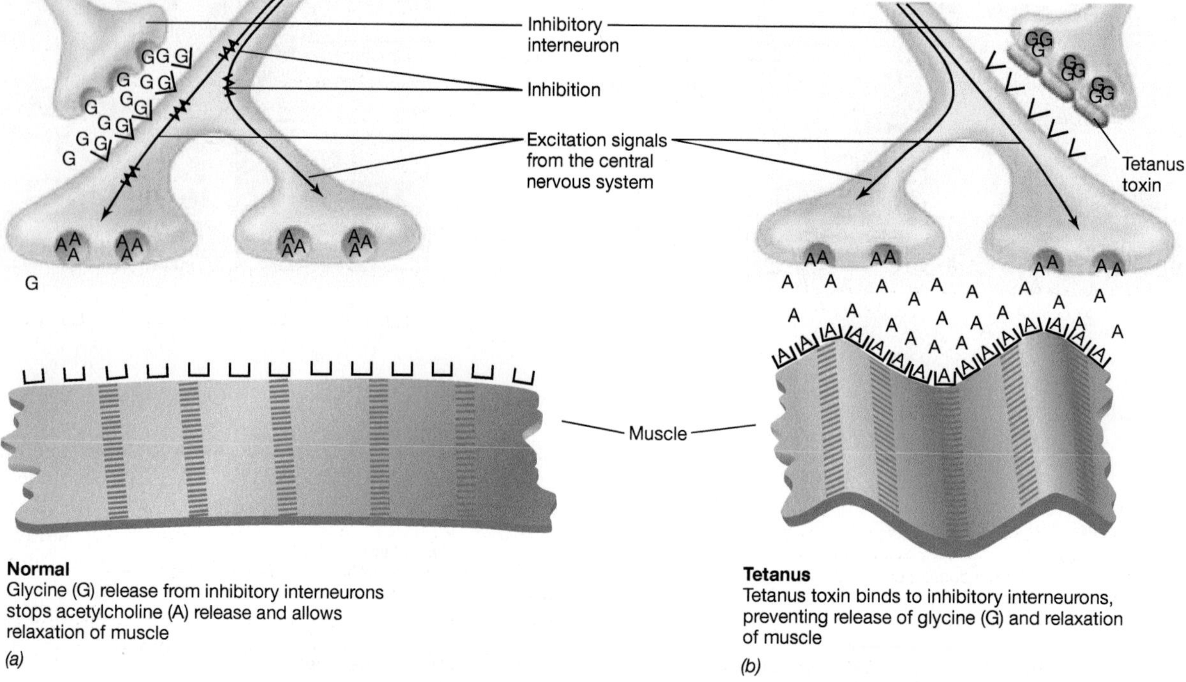

Figure 22 **The action of tetanus toxin from *Clostridium tetani*.** *(a)* Muscle relaxation is normally induced by glycine (G) release from inhibitory interneurons. Glycine acts on the motor neurons to block excitation and release of acetylcholine (A) at the motor end plate. *(b)* Tetanus toxin binds to the interneuron to prevent release of glycine from vesicles, resulting in a lack of inhibitory signals to the motor neurons, constant release of acetylcholine to the muscle fibers, irreversible contraction of the muscles, and spastic paralysis.

cells (Figure 23). The B subunit targets the toxin specifically to the intestinal epithelium but has no role in alteration of membrane permeability; the toxic action is a function of the A chain, which crosses the cytoplasmic membrane and activates adenyl cyclase, the enzyme that converts ATP to cyclic adenosine monophosphate (cAMP).

cAMP is a mediator of many different regulatory systems in cells, including ion balance. The increased cAMP levels induced by the cholera enterotoxin induce secretion of chloride and bicarbonate ions from the mucosal cells into the intestinal lumen. This change in ion concentrations leads to the secretion of large amounts of water into the intestinal lumen (Figure 23). In acute cholera, the rate of water loss into the small intestine is greater than the possible reabsorption of water by the large intestine, resulting in massive net fluid loss. Cholera treatment is by oral fluid replacement with solutions containing electrolytes and other solutes to offset the dehydration-coupled ion imbalance.

Expression of cholera enterotoxin genes *ctxA* and *ctxB* is controlled by *toxR*. The *toxR* gene product is a transmembrane protein that controls cholera A and B chain production as well as other virulence factors, such as the outer membrane proteins and pili required for successful attachment and colonization of *V. cholerae* in the small intestine.

Other Enterotoxins

Enterotoxins produced by enterotoxigenic *Escherichia* and *Salmonella* are functionally, structurally, and evolutionarily related to cholera toxin. These toxins are also produced in the gut by colonizing bacteria. However, enterotoxins produced by some of the food-poisoning bacteria (*Staphylococcus aureus*, *Clostridium perfringens*, and *Bacillus cereus*) have quite different modes of action and are often ingested as preformed toxins produced from bacterial growth in contaminated food; growth of the pathogen in the host is unnecessary. *C. perfringens* enterotoxin is a cytotoxin and *S. aureus* enterotoxin is a superantigen (Table 4). Superantigens have a completely different mode of action, stimulating large numbers of immune lymphocytes and causing systemic as well as intestinal inflammatory responses.

The toxin produced by *Shigella dysenteriae*, called *Shiga toxin*, and the Shiga-like toxin produced by enteropathogenic *E. coli* O157:H7 are protein synthesis-inhibiting AB toxins. The mode of action for this class of toxins is different, however, from that of the AB-type diphtheria toxin, as they specifically kill small intestine cells, leading to bloody diarrhea and related intestinal symptoms.

1. Normal ion movement, Na^+ from lumen to blood, no net Cl^- movement

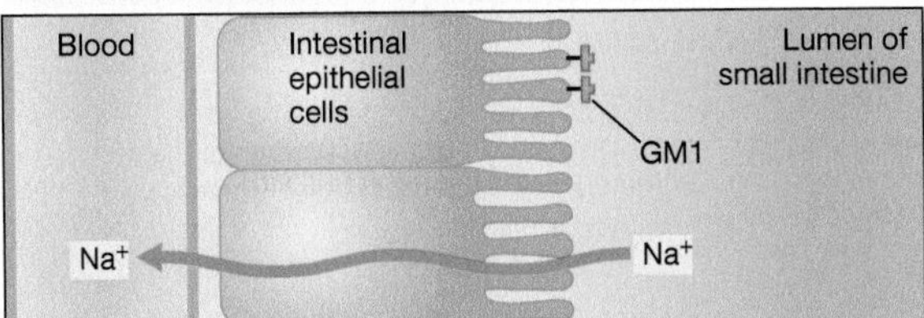

2. Colonization and toxin production

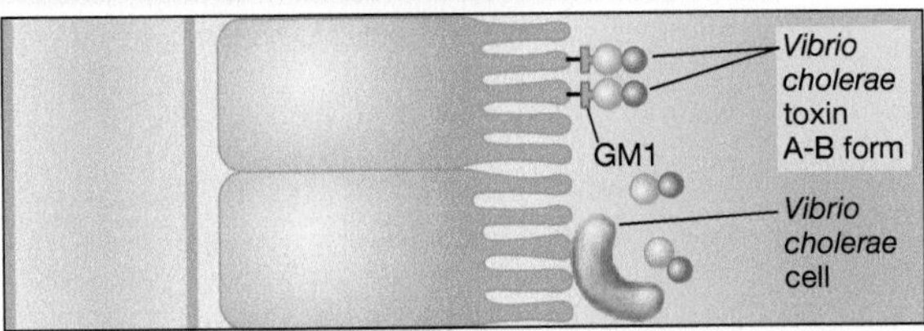

3. Activation of epithelial adenyl cyclase by cholera toxin

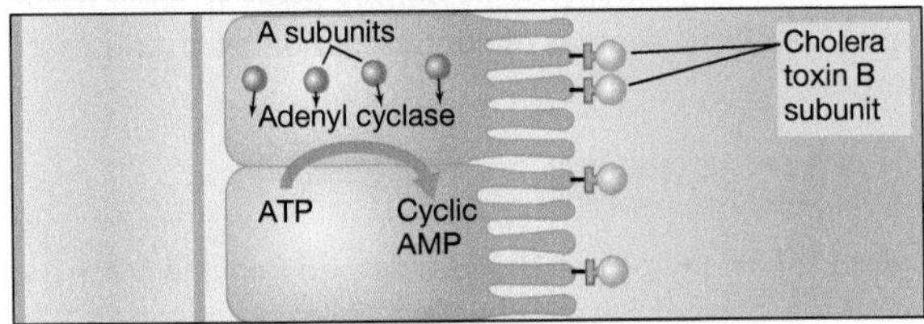

4. Na^+ movement blocked, net Cl^- movement to lumen

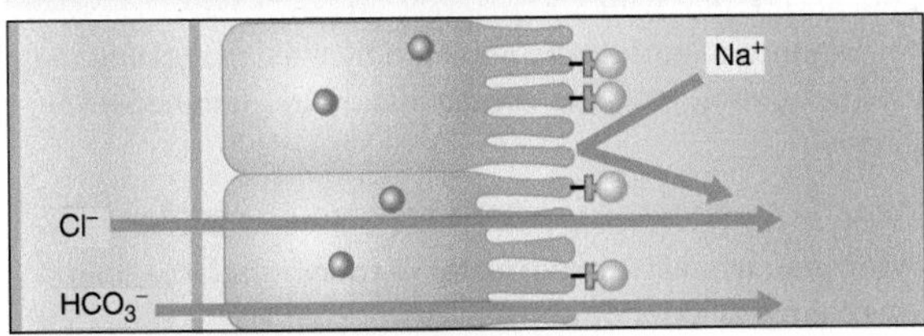

5. Massive water movement to the lumen

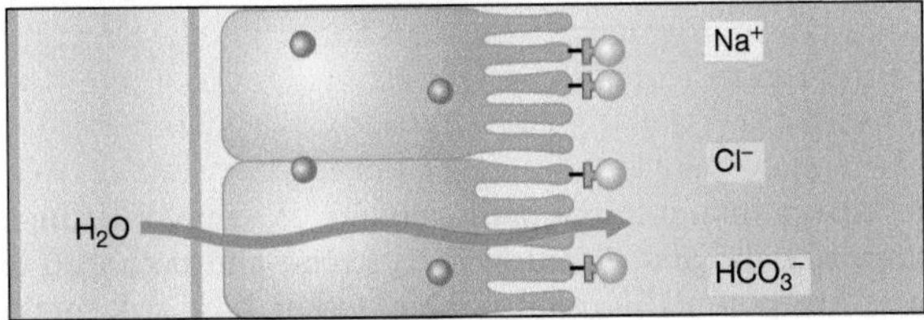

Figure 23 **The action of cholera enterotoxin.** Cholera toxin is a heat-stable AB enterotoxin that activates a second messenger pathway, disrupting normal ion flow in the intestine. (1) Ion movement in the normal intestine. (2) Adherence and colonization of the intestinal microvilli by *Vibrio cholerae*, followed by production and binding of the AB enterotoxin by interaction with the GM1 ganglioside on host cells. The B subunits (green) of AB toxin bind GM1, allowing the release of the A subunit (red) across the cell membrane. (3) The internalized A subunit activates adenyl cyclase, (4) blocking normal sodium (Na^+) influx, (5) causing massive loss of H_2O into the lumen, resulting in profuse diarrhea. Treatment for cholera is by ion replacement and rehydration. Antibiotic treatment may shorten the course of the disease by limiting *V. cholerae* growth, but does not affect the action of toxin that has already been produced.

11 MiniReview

Enterotoxins are exotoxins that affect the small intestine, causing changes in intestinal permeability that lead to diarrhea. Many enteric pathogens colonize the small intestine and produce AB enterotoxins. Food-poisoning bacteria often produce cytotoxins or superantigens.

- What key features are shared by all enterotoxins? By the AB enterotoxins?
- Describe the action of *Vibrio cholerae* toxin on the small intestine. Why does this lead to massive fluid loss?

12 Endotoxins

Many gram-negative *Bacteria* produce toxic lipopolysaccharides as part of the outer layer of their cell envelope. These lipopolysaccharides are called **endotoxins**. In contrast to exotoxins, which are the secreted products of living cells, endotoxins are cell bound and released in large amounts only when the cells lyse. Endotoxins have been studied primarily in *Escherichia, Shigella,* and especially *Salmonella*. The properties of exotoxins and endotoxins are compared in Table 5.

Endotoxin Structure and Function

Lipopolysaccharide (LPS) consists of three covalently linked subunits; the membrane-distal *O*-polysaccharide, lipid A, and a membrane-proximal core polysaccharide.

Endotoxins cause a variety of physiological effects. Fever is an almost universal result of endotoxin exposure because endotoxin stimulates host cells to release proteins called *endogenous pyrogens*, which affect the temperature-controlling center of the brain. In addition, endotoxins can cause diarrhea; rapid decrease in lymphocyte, leukocyte, and platelet numbers; release of cytokines; and generalized inflammation. Large doses of endotoxin can cause death from hemorrhagic shock and tissue necrosis. The toxicity of endotoxins is, however, much lower than that of exotoxins. For instance, in mice the LD_{50} for endotoxin is 200–400 μg per animal, whereas the LD_{50} for botulinum toxin is about 25 picograms (pg), about 10 million times less!

Studies indicate that the lipid A portion of LPS is responsible for toxicity, and the polysaccharide fraction makes the complex water-soluble and immunogenic. Animal studies indicate that both the lipid and polysaccharide fractions are necessary for toxic effects to be observed.

Limulus Amebocyte Lysate Assay for Endotoxin

Because endotoxins are pyrogens, pharmaceuticals such as antibiotics and intravenous solutions must be free of endotoxin. An endotoxin assay of very high sensitivity has been developed using lysates of amebocytes from the horseshoe crab, *Limulus polyphemus*. Endotoxin specifically causes lysis

Table 5 Properties of exotoxins and endotoxins

Property	*Exotoxins*	*Endotoxins*
Chemical properties	Proteins, excreted by certain gram-positive or gram-negative *Bacteria;* generally heat-labile	Lipopolysaccharide–lipoprotein complexes, released on cell lysis as part of the outer membrane of gram-negative *Bacteria;* extremely heat-stable
Mode of action; symptoms	Specific; usually binds to specific cell receptors or structures; either cytotoxin, enterotoxin, or neurotoxin with defined specific action on cells or tissues	General; fever, diarrhea, vomiting
Toxicity	Often highly toxic, sometimes fatal	Weakly toxic, rarely fatal
Immunogenicity response	Highly immunogenic; stimulate the production of neutralizing antibody (antitoxin)	Relatively poor immunogen; immune response not sufficient to neutralize toxin
Toxoid potential	Treatment of toxin with formaldehyde will destroy toxicity, but treated toxin (toxoid) remains immunogenic	None
Fever potential	Does not produce fever in host	Pyrogenic, often induces fever in host

of the amebocytes (Figure 24). In the standard *Limulus* amebocyte lysate (LAL) assay, *Limulus* amebocyte extracts are mixed with the solution to be tested. If endotoxin is present, the amebocyte extract forms a gel and precipitates, causing a change in turbidity. This reaction is measured quantitatively with a spectrophotometer and can detect as little as 10 pg/ml of LPS. The *Limulus* assay is used to detect endotoxin in clinical samples such as serum or cerebrospinal fluid. A positive test is presumptive evidence for infection by a gram-negative bacterium. Drinking water, water used for formulation of injectable drugs, and injectable aqueous solutions are routinely tested using the *Limulus* assay to identify and eliminate potential sources of contamination by gram-negative pathogens.

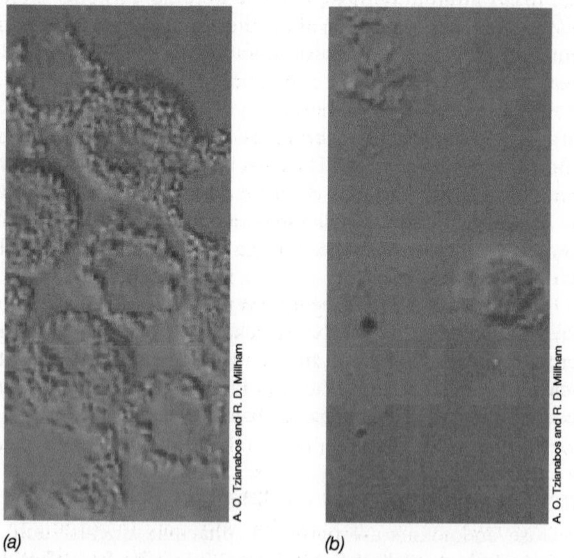

(a) A. O. Tzianabos and R. D. Millham

(b) A. O. Tzianabos and R. D. Millham

Figure 24 ***Limulus* amebocytes.** *(a)* Normal amebocytes from the horseshoe crab, *Limulus polyphemus. (b)* Amebocytes following exposure to bacterial lipopolysaccharide (LPS). LPS contained in test samples induces degranulation and lysis of the cells.

12 MiniReview

Endotoxins are lipopolysaccharides derived from the outer membrane of gram-negative bacteria. Released upon cell lysis, endotoxins cause fever and other systemic toxic effects in the host. Endotoxins are generally less toxic than exotoxins. The presence of endotoxin, detected by the *Limulus* amebocyte lysate assay, indicates contamination by gram-negative bacteria.

- Why do gram-positive bacteria not produce endotoxins?
- Why is it necessary to test water used for injectable drug preparations for endotoxin?

IV HOST FACTORS IN INFECTION

Host factors influence the pathogenicity of a microorganism. Certain risk factors related to diet, stress, and pathogen exposure are potentially controllable. Other host risk factors defined by, for example, age or genetics cannot be controlled. We conclude this chapter with a discussion of the passive physical and chemical barriers in human anatomy that limit infection and colonization. In the following chapter we deal with active host responses to pathogen contact.

13 Host Risk Factors for Infection

A number of factors contribute to the susceptibility of the host to infection and disease. Here we introduce some of the factors that provide passive resistance to infectious diseases. The failure of any of these mechanisms may result in invasion by pathogens and the onset of infectious disease.

Age as a Risk Factor

Age is an important factor for determining susceptibility to infectious disease. Infectious diseases are more common in the very young and in the very old. In the infant, for example, an intestinal microflora develops quickly, but the normal flora of an infant is not the same as that of an adult. Before the development of an adult flora, and especially in the days immediately following birth, pathogens have a greater opportunity to become established and produce disease. Thus, infants under the age of 1 year often acquire diarrhea caused by enteropathogenic strains of *Escherichia coli* or viruses such as Rotavirus.

Infant botulism results from an intestinal infection with *Clostridium botulinum*. As the pathogen colonizes and grows, it secretes botulinum toxin, leading to flaccid paralysis (Section 10). Infant botulism, contracted after ingestion of *C. botulinum* from soil, air, or foods such as raw honey, is found almost exclusively in infants under 1 year of age, presumably because establishment of the normal intestinal flora in older children and adults prevents colonization by *C. botulinum*.

In individuals over 65 years of age, infectious diseases are much more common than in younger adults. For example, the elderly are much more susceptible to respiratory infections, particularly influenza, probably because of a declining ability to make an effective immune response to respiratory pathogens.

Anatomical changes associated with age may also encourage infection. Enlargement of the prostate gland, a common condition in men over the age of 50, frequently leads to a decreased urinary flow rate, allowing pathogens to colonize the male urinary tract more readily, leading to an increase in urinary tract infections (Figure 11).

Stress and Diet as Risk Factors

Stress can predispose a healthy individual to disease. In studies with rats and mice, physiological stressors such as fatigue, exertion, poor diet, dehydration, or drastic climate changes increase the incidence and severity of infectious diseases. For example, rats subjected to intense physical activity for long periods of time show a higher mortality rate from experimental *Salmonella* infections compared with rested control animals. Hormones that are produced under stress can inhibit normal immune responses and may play a role in stress-mediated disease. For example, cortisol, a hormone produced at high levels in the body in times of stress, is an anti-inflammatory agent that inhibits the activation of the immune response.

Diet plays a role in host susceptibility to infection. Inadequate diets low in protein and calories alter the normal flora, allowing opportunistic pathogens a better chance to multiply and increasing susceptibility of the host to known pathogens. For example, the number of *Vibrio cholerae* cells necessary to produce cholera in an exposed individual is drastically reduced if the individual is malnourished. The consumption of pathogen-contaminated food is an obvious way to acquire infections, and ingestion of pathogens with food can sometimes enhance the ability of the pathogen to cause disease. The number of organisms necessary to induce cholera, for example, is greatly reduced when the *V. cholerae* is ingested in food, presumably because the food neutralizes stomach acids that would normally destroy the pathogen on its way to colonizing the small intestine.

In some cases, absence of a particular dietary substance may prevent disease by depriving a pathogen of critical nutrients. The best example here is the effect sucrose has on the development of dental caries. As we saw in Section 3, dietary restriction of sucrose, along with good oral hygiene, can virtually eliminate tooth decay. Without dietary sucrose, the highly cariogenic *Streptococcus mutans* and *Streptococcus sobrinus* are unable to synthesize the dextran layer needed to keep the bacterial cells attached to the teeth.

The Compromised Host

A compromised host is one in whom one or more resistance mechanisms are inactive and in whom the probability of infection is therefore increased. Many hospital patients with noninfectious diseases (for example, cancer and heart disease) acquire microbial infections because they are compromised hosts. Such healthcare-associated infections are called **nosocomial infections** and affect up to 2 million individuals each year in the United States, causing up to 100,000 deaths. Healthcare procedures such as catheterization, hypodermic injection, spinal puncture, biopsy, and surgery may unintentionally introduce microorganisms into the patient. The stress of surgery may also lower patient resistance. Anti-inflammatory drugs given to reduce pain and swelling may also reduce host resistance. Organ transplant patients are treated with immunosuppressive drugs to suppress immune rejection of the transplant, but suppressed immunity also reduces the ability of the patient to resist infection.

Some factors can compromise host resistance even outside the hospital. Smoking, excess consumption of alcohol, intravenous drug use, lack of sleep, poor nutrition, and acute or chronic infection with another agent are conditions that can reduce host resistance. For example, infection with the human immunodeficiency virus (HIV) predisposes a patient to infections from microorganisms that are not pathogens in uninfected individuals. HIV causes AIDS by destroying one type of immune cell, the CD4 T lymphocytes, involved in the immune response. The reduction in CD4 T cells reduces immunity, and an opportunistic pathogen, a microorganism that does not cause disease in a normal host, can then cause serious disease or even death.

Finally, certain genetic conditions compromise the host. For example, genetic diseases that eliminate important parts of the immune system predispose individuals to infections. Individuals with such conditions frequently die at an early age, not from the genetic condition itself, but from microbial infection.

13 MiniReview

Age, general health, prior or concurrent disease, genetic makeup, and lifestyle factors such as stress and diet contribute to susceptibility to infectious disease.

- Identify factors that control susceptibility to botulism in infants as compared to adults.
- Identify factors that influence susceptibility to infection and can be controlled by the host.

14 Innate Resistance to Infection

Hosts have innate resistance to most pathogens. Many pathogens are adapted to infect only certain hosts, and even closely related hosts with alterations in pathogen receptors or host metabolism can resist infection by individual pathogens. In addition, physical and chemical factors common to vertebrate hosts nonspecifically inhibit invasion by most pathogens (Figure 25 and Table 6).

Natural Host Resistance

Under certain circumstances, closely related species, or even members of the same species, may have different susceptibilities to a particular pathogen. The ability of a particular pathogen to cause disease in an individual animal species is highly variable. In rabies, for instance, death usually occurs in all species of mammals once symptoms of the disease develop. Nevertheless, certain animal species are much more susceptible to rabies than others. Raccoons and skunks, for example, are extremely susceptible to rabies infection as compared with opossums, which rarely acquire the disease. Anthrax infects a variety of animals, causing disease symptoms varying from mild pustules in cutaneous anthrax in humans to fatal blood poisoning in cattle. However, pulmonary, or airborne anthrax, such as that induced by weaponized strains used for bioterrorism, is almost universally fatal in humans. As another example of innate host resistance, diseases of warm-blooded animals are rarely transmitted to cold-blooded species, and vice versa. Presumably, the metabolic features of one group are not compatible with pathogens that infect the other.

Tissue Specificity

Most pathogens must first adhere and colonize at the site of exposure. Even if pathogens adhere to an exposure site, if the site is not compatible with their nutritional and metabolic needs, the organisms cannot colonize. Thus, if *Clostridium tetani* was ingested, tetanus would not result because the pathogen is either killed by the acidity of the stomach or cannot compete with the well-developed intestinal flora. If, on the other hand, *C. tetani* cells or endospores were introduced into a deep wound, the organism would grow and produce tetanus toxin in the anoxic zones created by local tissue death.

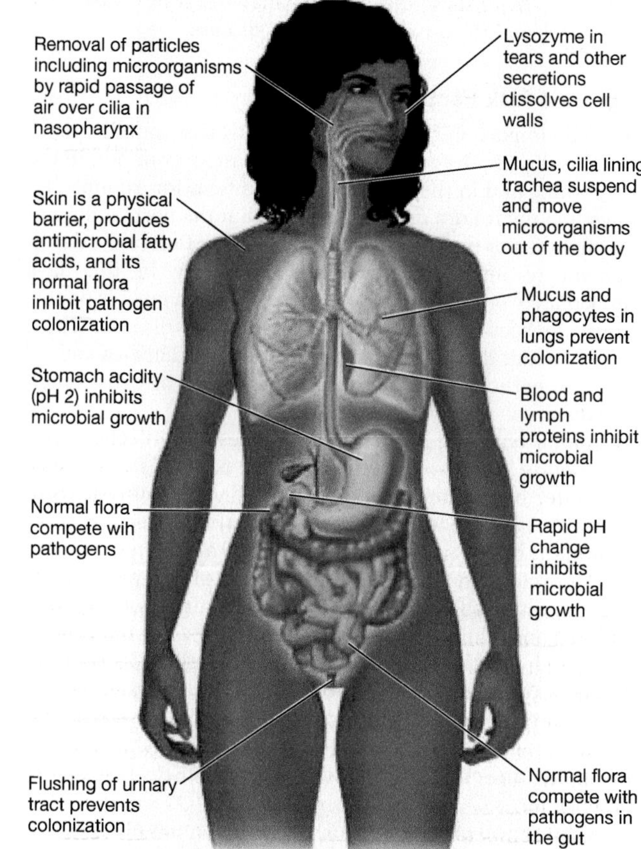

Figure 25 Physical, chemical, and anatomical barriers to infection. These barriers provide natural resistance to colonization and infection by pathogens.

Conversely, enteric bacteria such as *Salmonella* and *Shigella* do not cause wound infections but can successfully colonize the intestinal tract.

In some cases, pathogens interact exclusively with members of a few closely related host species because the hosts share tissue-specific receptors. HIV, for instance, infects only higher primates, including the great apes and humans. This is because the CXCR4 protein on human T cells and the CCR5 protein on human macrophages are also expressed in great apes. These proteins, the only cell surface receptors for HIV, bind the gp120 protein of HIV. Other animals lack these receptors, cannot bind HIV, and are thus protected from HIV infection. Table 6 presents examples of tissue specificity.

Physical and Chemical Barriers

The structural integrity of tissue surfaces poses a barrier to penetration by microorganisms. In the skin and mucosal

Table 6 Tissue specificity in infectious disease

Disease	*Tissue infected*	*Organism*
Acquired immunodeficiency syndrome (AIDS)	T helper lymphocytes	Human immunodeficiency virus (HIV)
Botulism	Motor end plate	*Clostridium botulinum*
Cholera	Small intestine epithelium	*Vibrio cholerae*
Dental caries	Oral epithelium	*Streptococcus mutans, S. sobrinus, S. sanguis, S. mitis*
Diphtheria	Throat epithelium	*Corynebacterium diphtheriae*
Gonorrhea	Epithelium	*Neisseria gonorrhoeae*
Malaria	Blood (erythrocytes)	*Plasmodium* spp.
Pyelonephritis	Kidney medulla	*Proteus* spp.
Spontaneous abortion (cattle)	Placenta	*Brucella abortus*
Tetanus	Inhibitory interneuron	*Clostridium tetani*

tissues, potential pathogens must first adhere to tissue surfaces and then grow at these sites before traveling elsewhere in the body. Resistance to colonization and invasion is due to the production of host defense substances and to various anatomical mechanisms.

The skin is an effective barrier to the penetration of microorganisms. Sebaceous glands in the skin (Figure 2) secrete fatty acids and lactic acid, lowering the acidity of the skin to pH 5 and inhibiting colonization of many pathogenic bacteria (blood and internal organs are about pH 7.4). Micro- organisms inhaled through the nose or mouth are removed by ciliated epithelial cells on the mucosal surfaces of the nasopharynx and trachea. Potential pathogens entering the stomach must survive its strong acidity (pH 2) and then successfully compete with the increasingly abundant resident microflora present in the small and large intestines. Finally, the lumen of the kidney, the surface of the eye, and some other tissues are constantly bathed with secretions containing lysozyme, an enzyme that can kill bacteria.

14 MiniReview

Innate resistance factors, as well as physical, anatomical, and chemical barriers, prevent colonization of the host by most pathogens. Breakdown of these passive defenses may result in susceptibility to infection and disease.

- Identify physical and chemical barriers to pathogens. How might these barriers be compromised?
- How might preexisting infection compromise an otherwise healthy host?

Review of Key Terms

Attenuation decrease or loss of virulence

Bacteremia the presence of microorganisms in the blood

Capsule dense, well-defined polysaccharide or protein layer closely surrounding a cell

Colonization growth of a microorganism after it has gained access to host tissues

Dental caries tooth decay resulting from bacterial infection

Dental plaque bacterial cells encased in a matrix of extracellular polymers and salivary products, found on the teeth

Disease injury to the host that impairs host function

Endotoxin the lipopolysaccharide portion of the cell envelope of certain gram-negative *Bacteria*, which is a toxin when solubilized

Enterotoxin protein released extracellularly by a microorganism as it grows that produces immediate damage to the small intestine of the host

Exotoxin protein released extracellularly by a microorganism as it grows that produces immediate host cell damage

Host an organism that harbors a parasite

Infection growth of organisms in the host

Invasiveness pathogenicity caused by the ability of a pathogen to enter the body and spread

Lower respiratory tract trachea, bronchi, and lungs

Mucous membrane layers of epithelial cells that interact with the external environment

Mucus soluble glycoproteins secreted by epithelial cells that coat the mucous membranes

Normal microbial flora microorganisms that are usually found associated with healthy body tissue

Nosocomial infection infection contracted in a healthcare-associated setting

Opportunistic pathogen an organism that causes disease in the absence of normal host resistance

Parasite an organism that grows in or on a host and causes disease

Pathogen an organism, usually a microorganism, that causes disease

Pathogenicity the ability of a pathogen to cause disease

Probiotic a live microorganism that, when administered to a host, may confer a health benefit

Slime layer a diffuse layer of polymer fibers, typically polysaccharides, that forms an outer surface layer on the cell

Toxicity pathogenicity caused by toxins produced by a pathogen

Upper respiratory tract the nasopharynx, oral cavity, and throat

Virulence the degree of pathogenicity displayed by a pathogen

Review Questions

1. Distinguish between a parasite and a pathogen. Distinguish between infection and disease. Identify organs in the human body that are normally colonized by microorganisms. Which organs are normally devoid of microorganisms? What do these organs have in common (Section 1)?
2. Distinguish between resident and transient microorganisms on the skin. How could you distinguish between resident and transient microorganisms experimentally (Section 2)?
3. Why are members of the genus *Streptococcus* instrumental in forming dental caries? Why are they more capable of causing caries than other organisms (Section 3)?
4. How do pH and oxygen affect the types of microorganisms that grow in each different region of the gastrointestinal tract (Section 4)?
5. Describe the relationship between *Lactobacillus acidophilus* and glycogen in the vaginal tract. What factors influence the differences between the normal vaginal flora of adult females as compared to that of prepubescent juvenile females (Section 5)?
6. Identify the role of the capsule and the fimbriae of bacteria in microbial adherence (Section 6).
7. Identify nutritional factors that may limit or accelerate growth of microorganisms in the body (Section 7).
8. Give an example of a microorganism that is pathogenic almost solely because of its toxin-producing ability. Define the toxin and its mode of action. Give an example of a microorganism that is pathogenic almost solely because of its invasive characteristics. What factors confer invasive qualities on this microorganism (Section 8)?
9. Identify the role of coagulase and streptokinase in virulence (Section 9).
10. Distinguish between AB toxins, cytotoxins, and superantigens. Give an example of each category of toxin. How does each toxin category promote disease (Section 10)?
11. Review the mode of action of cholera enterotoxin (Figure 23). What is the appropriate therapy for this disease, and why is antibiotic treatment generally not effective (Section 11)?
12. Describe the structure of a typical endotoxin. How does endotoxin induce fever? What microorganisms produce endotoxin (Section 12)?
13. Identify common factors that lead to host compromise. Indicate which factors are controllable by the host. Indicate which factors are not controllable by the host (Section 13).
14. In which body locations might pH values differ from standard body conditions? Which organisms might benefit or be inhibited by differences in body pH (Section 14)?

Application Questions

1. Mucous membranes are barriers against colonization and growth of microorganisms. However, mucous membranes, for example in the throat and the gut, are colonized with a variety of different microorganisms, some of which are potential pathogens. Explain how these potential pathogens are controlled under normal circumstances. Then describe at least one set of circumstances that might encourage pathogenicity.
2. Antibiotic therapy can significantly reduce the number of microorganisms residing in the gastrointestinal tract. What physiological symptoms might the reduction of normal flora produce in the host? Infection by opportunistic pathogens often follows long-term antimicrobial therapy. Many of these post-therapeutic infections are caused by the same microorganisms that produce opportunistic infections in individuals with AIDS. What pathogens might be involved? Why are individuals who have undergone antibiotic therapy particularly susceptible to these pathogens?
3. Design an experiment to increase the virulence and pathogenicity of *Streptococcus pneumoniae* (Hint: *S. pneumoniae* that is transferred for several passages in vitro loses its capsule and virulence for mice). Would an increase in virulence confer a selective advantage for the organism? Be sure to consider the natural habitat.
4. Coagulase is a virulence factor for *Staphylococcus aureus* that acts by causing clot formation at the site of *S. aureus* growth. Streptokinase is a virulence factor for *Streptococcus pyogenes* that acts by dissolving clots at the site of *S. pyogenes* growth. Reconcile these opposing strategies for enhancing pathogenicity.
5. Although mutants incapable of producing exotoxins are relatively easy to isolate, mutants incapable of producing endotoxins are much harder to isolate. From what you know of the structure and function of these types of toxins, explain the differences in mutant recovery.
6. Identify the potential for infectious disease problems in the case of burns to the body. What microorganisms are likely to be involved in burn infections? Why does the normal local microbial flora fail to protect burn victims from microbial infections?

Innate Immunity

CHAPTER OUTLINE

MicroPrep Pre-Test: *Take the pre-test for this chapter on the web. Visit* ***www.microbiologyplace.com.***

Each day the equivalent of a small room full of air enters your respiratory tract through your nose. With that air come dust, smoke, bacteria, viruses, fungi, pollen, soot, fuzz, sand, and more. Acting as a first line of defense, your respiratory mucous membrane uses nose hairs, ciliated epithelium, and mucus to cleanse the inhaled air of pathogens and certain harmful pollutants. Each day you swallow and subsequently digest about a liter of mucus, along with the trapped pathogens and pollutants it contains. Still more nasal mucus clumps around microbes and pollutants to form masses of mucus that may dry out or remain slimy, depending on how rapidly you're breathing and the humidity of the air. Yellowish or greenish mucus contains a large population of trapped bacteria and their waste products.

Mucus is just one example of the body's general defenses against pathogens. The skin, and certain protective cells, chemicals, and processes within the body, are other ways the body limits early stages of infection by microbes. In this chapter we will focus on each of these aspects of the body's defenses.

Cilia line the upper respiratory tracts

A pathogen can cause a disease only if it can (1) gain access, either by penetrating the surface of the skin or by entering through some other portal of entry; (2) attach itself to host cells; and (3) evade the body's defense mechanisms long enough to produce harmful changes. In this chapter we will examine the structures, processes, and chemicals that respond in a general way to protect the body from all types of pathogens.

An Overview of the Body's Defenses

Learning Objectives

- ✓ List and briefly describe the three lines of defense in the human body.
- ✓ Explain the phrase *innate immunity.*

Because the cells and certain basic physiological processes of humans are incompatible with those of most plant and animal pathogens, humans have what is termed **species resistance** to these pathogens. In many cases the chemical receptors these pathogens require for attachment to a host cell do not exist in the human body; in other cases the pH or temperature of the human body are incompatible with the conditions under which these pathogens can survive. Thus, for example, all humans have species resistance to both tobacco mosaic virus and to the virus that causes feline immunodeficiency syndrome in members of the cat family.

Nevertheless, we are confronted every day with pathogens that can cause disease in humans. Bacteria, viruses, fungi, protozoa, and parasitic worms come in contact with your body in the air you breathe, in the water you drink, in the food you eat, and during the contacts you have with other people. Your body must defend itself from these potential pathogens, and in some cases from members of the normal microbiota, which may become opportunistic pathogens.

It is convenient to cluster the structures, cells, and chemicals that act against pathogens into three main lines of defense, each of which overlaps and reinforces the other two. The first line of defense is chiefly composed of external physical barriers to pathogens, especially the skin and mucous membranes. The second line of defense is internal and is composed of protective cells, bloodborne chemicals, and processes that inactivate or kill invaders. Together, the first two lines of defense are called **innate immunity** because they are present at birth prior to contact with infectious agents or their products. Innate immunity is rapid and works against a wide variety of pathogens, including parasitic worms, protozoa, fungi, bacteria, and viruses.

By contrast, the third line of defense, **adaptive immunity,** responds against unique species or strains of pathogens and alters the body's defenses such that they act more effectively upon subsequent infection with the specific strain. Here we turn our attention to the two lines of innate immunity.

www.microbiologyplace.com **Animations: *Host Defenses: Overview***

The Body's First Line of Defense

The body's initial line of defense is made up of structures, chemicals, and processes that work together to prevent pathogens from entering the body in the first place. Here we discuss the main components of the first line of defense: the skin and the mucous membranes of the respiratory, digestive, urinary, and reproductive systems. These structures provide a formidable barrier to the entrance of microorganisms. If these barriers are pierced, broken, or otherwise damaged, they become portals of entry for pathogens. In this section we examine aspects of the first line of defense, including the role of the normal microbiota.

The Role of Skin in Innate Immunity

Learning Objective

- ✓ Identify the physical and chemical aspects of skin that enable it to prevent the entrance of pathogens.

The skin—the organ of the body with the greatest surface area—is composed of two major layers: an outer **epidermis,** and a deeper **dermis,** which contains hair follicles, glands, and nerve endings. Both the physical structure and the chemical components of skin enable it to act as an effective defense.

The epidermis is composed of multiple layers of tightly packed cells. It constitutes a physical barrier to most bacteria, fungi, and viruses. Very few pathogens can penetrate the layers of epidermal cells unless the skin has been burned, broken, or cut.

The deepest cells of the epidermis continually divide, pushing their daughter cells toward the surface. As the daughter cells are pushed toward the surface, they flatten and die and are eventually shed in flakes **(Figure 1).** Microorganisms that attach to the skin's surface are sloughed off with the flakes of dead cells. **The Beneficial Microbe: What Happens to All That Skin?** describes the fate of lost epidermal cells.

The epidermis also contains phagocytic cells called **dendritic**[1] **cells.** The slender, fingerlike processes of dendritic cells extend among the surrounding cells, forming an almost continuous network to intercept invaders. Dendritic cells both phagocytize pathogens nonspecifically and play a role in adaptive immunity.

The combination of the barrier function of the epidermis, its continual replacement, and the presence of phagocytic dendritic cells provides significant nonspecific defense against colonization and infection by pathogens.

[1]Form Greek *dendron,* meaning tree, referring to their branched appearance.

The Beneficial Microbe *What Happens to All That Skin?*

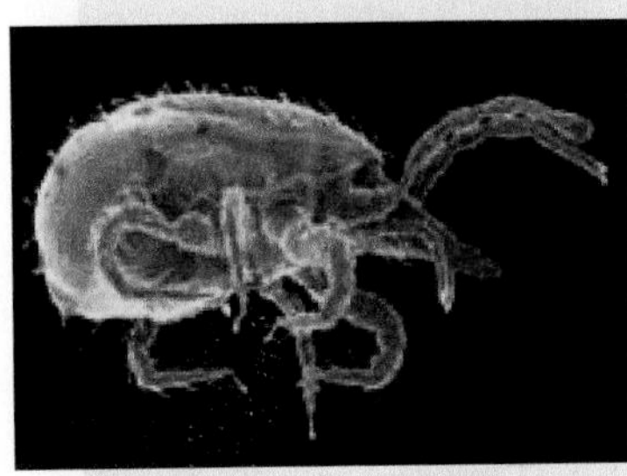

Dust mite

Your body sheds tens of thousands of skin flakes every time you walk or move, and you shed at only a slightly lower rate when you stand still. That comes to about 10 billion skin cells per day, or 250 grams (about half a pound) of skin every year! What happens to all that skin?

Much of household dust is skin that you and your housemates have shed as you go about your lives. The skin flakes fall to the rug and upholstery, where they become food for microscopic mites that live sedentary and harmless lives waiting patiently for meals to rain down on them from above. They dwell not only in the rug, but also in your mattress and pillow, and even in the hair follicles of your eyebrows, benefiting you by catching skin cells cascading down your forehead before they can irritate your eyes.

By the way, house dust also contains mite feces and mite skeletons, which can trigger allergies. So after reading this chapter, you just might want to clean your carpet.

The dermis also defends nonspecifically. It contains tough fibers of a protein called collagen. These give the skin strength and pliability to prevent jabs and scrapes from penetrating the dermis and introducing microorganisms. Blood vessels in the dermis deliver defensive cells and chemicals, which will be discussed shortly.

In addition to its physical structure, the skin has a number of chemical substances that nonspecifically defend against pathogens. Dermal cells secrete antimicrobial peptides and sweat glands secrete perspiration, which contains salt, antimicrobial peptides, and lysozyme. Salt draws water osmotically from invading cells, which inhibits their growth and kills them.

Antimicrobial peptides (also called *defensins*) are chains of about 40 amino acids that act against microorganisms. Sweat glands secrete a class of antimicrobial peptides called *dermicidins*. Dermicidins are broad-spectrum antimicrobials that are active against many Gram-negative and Gram-positive bacteria and fungi. As expected of a peptide active on the surface of the skin, dermicidins are insensitive to low pH and salt. The exact mechanism of dermicidin action is not known.

Lysozyme (lī'sō-zīm) is an enzyme that destroys the cell walls of bacteria by cleaving the bonds between the sugar subunits of the walls. Bacteria without cell walls are more susceptible to osmotic shock and digestion by other enzymes within phagocytes (discussed with respect to the second line of defense).

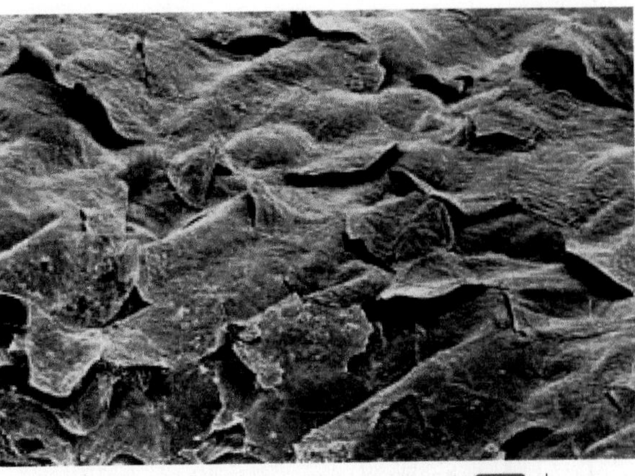

▲ *Figure 1*

A scanning electron micrograph of a section of skin. Epidermal cells are dead, dry, and slough off, providing an effective barrier to most microorganisms.

The skin also contains sebaceous (oil) glands that secrete **sebum** (sē'bŭm), an oily substance that not only helps keep the skin pliable and less sensitive to breaking or tearing but also contains fatty acids that lower the pH of the skin's surface to about pH 5, which is inhibitory to many bacteria.

Although salt, defensins, lysozyme, and acidity make the surface of the skin an inhospitable environment for most microorganisms, some bacteria, such as *Staphylococcus epidermidis* (staf'i-lō-kok'ŭs ep-i-der-mid'is), find the skin a suitable environment for growth and reproduction. Bacteria are particularly abundant in crevices around hairs and in the ducts of glands; usually they are nonpathogenic. In summary, the skin is a complex barrier that limits access by microbes.

CRITICAL THINKING

Some strains of *Staphylococcus aureus* produce exfoliative toxin, a chemical that causes portions of the entire outer layer of the skin to be sloughed off in a disease called scalded skin syndrome. Given that cells of the outer layer are going to fall off anyway, why is this disease dangerous?

The Role of Mucous Membranes and the Lacrimal Apparatus in Innate Immunity

Learning Objectives

- ✓ Identify the locations of the body's mucous membranes.
- ✓ Explain how mucous membranes protect the body both physically and chemically.
- ✓ Describe the lacrimal apparatus and the role of tears in combating infection.

Mucus-secreting (mucous) membranes, a second part of the first line of defense, cover all body cavities that are

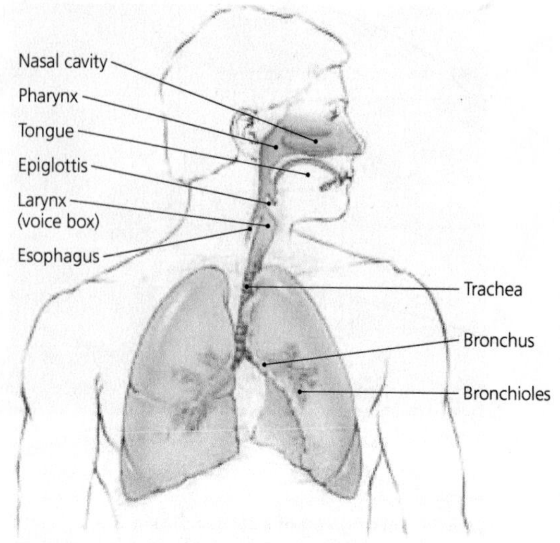

▲ *Figure 2*

The structure of the respiratory system, which is lined with a mucous membrane. The epithelium of the trachea contains mucus-secreting goblet cells and ciliated cells whose cilia propel the mucus (and the microbes trapped within it) up to the larynx for removal. *What is the function of stem cells within the respiratory epithelium?*

Figure 2 Stem cells in the respiratory epithelium undergo cytokinesis to form both ciliated cells and goblet cells to replace those lost during normal shedding.

open to the outside environment. Thus mucous membranes line the lumens[2] of the respiratory, urinary, digestive, and reproductive tracts. Like the skin, mucous membranes act nonspecifically to limit infection both physically and chemically.

Mucous membranes are moist and have two distinct layers: an outer covering of superficial (closest to the surface, in this case the lumen) cells called the *epithelium,* and a deeper connective tissue layer that provides mechanical and nutritive support for the epithelium. Epithelial cells of mucous membranes are packed closely together, like those of the epidermis, but they form only a thin tissue. Indeed, in some mucous membranes, the epithelium is only a single cell thick. Unlike surface epidermal cells, surface cells of mucous membranes are alive and play roles in the diffusion of nutrients and oxygen (in the digestive, respiratory, and female reproductive systems) and in the elimination of wastes (in the urinary, respiratory, and female reproductive systems).

The thin epithelium on the surface of a mucous membrane provides a less efficient barrier to the entrance of pathogens than the multiple layers of dead cells found at the skin's surface. So how are microorganisms kept from invading through these thin mucous membranes? In some cases they are not, which is why some mucous membranes, especially those of the respiratory and reproductive systems, are common portals of entry for pathogens. Nevertheless, the epithelial cells of mucous membranes are tightly packed to prevent the entry of many pathogens. Moreover, epithelial cells are continually shed and then replaced via the cytokinesis of **stem cells,** which are generative cells capable of dividing to form daughter cells of a variety of types; one effect of such shedding is that it carries attached microorganisms away.

Dendritic cells reside below the mucus epithelium to phagocytize invaders. These cells are also able to extend pseudopodia between epithelial cells to "sample" the contents of the lumen, which helps prepare adaptive immune responses against particular pathogens that might breach the mucosal barrier.

In addition, the epithelia of some mucous membranes have still other means of removing pathogens. In the mucous membrane of the trachea, for example, the stem cells produce both **goblet cells,** which secrete an extremely sticky mucus that traps bacteria and other pathogens, and ciliated columnar cells, whose cilia propel the mucus (and the particles and pathogens trapped within it) up from the lungs **(Figure 2).** The effect of the action of the cilia is often likened to that of an escalator. Mucus carried into the throat is coughed up and either swallowed or expelled. Because the poisons and tars in tobacco smoke damage cilia, the lungs of smokers are not properly cleared of mucus, so smokers may develop severe coughs as their respiratory tracts attempt to expel excess mucus from the lungs. Smokers also typically succumb to more respiratory pathogens, because they are unable to effectively clear pathogens from their lungs.

In addition to these physical actions, mucous membranes produce chemicals that defend against pathogens. Nasal mucus contains lysozyme, which chemically destroys bacterial cell walls. Mucus contains antimicrobial peptides (defensins). **Table 1** compares the physical and chemical actions of the skin and mucous membranes in the body's first line of defense.

Lacrimal Apparatus

The lacrimal apparatus is a group of structures that produce and drain away tears **(Figure 3).** Lacrimal glands, located above and to the sides of the eyes, secrete tears into lacrimal gland ducts and onto the surface of the eyes. The tears either evaporate or drain into small lacrimal canals, which carry them into nasolacrimal ducts that empty into the nose. There, the tears join the nasal mucus and flow into the pharynx, where they are swallowed. The blinking action of eyelids spreads the tears and washes the surfaces of the eyes. Normally, evaporation

[2] A lumen is a cavity or channel within any tubular structure or organ.

Table 1 The First Line of Defense: A Comparison of the Skin and Mucous Membranes

	Skin	Mucous Membrane
Number of cell layers	Many	One to a few
Cells tightly packed?	Yes	Yes
Cells dead or alive?	Outer layers: dead; inner layers: alive	Alive
Mucus present?	No	Yes
Relative water content	Dry	Moist
Defensins present?	Yes	With some
Lysozyme present?	Yes	With some
Sebum present?	Yes	No
Cilia present?	No	Trachea, uterine tubes
Constant shedding and replacement of cells?	Yes	Yes

and flow into the nose balance the flow of tears onto the eye. However, if the eyes are irritated, increased tear production floods the eyes, carrying the irritant away. In addition to their washing action, tears contain lysozyme, which destroys bacteria.

The Role of Normal Microbiota in Innate Immunity

Learning Objective

✓ Define *normal microbiota* and explain how they help provide protection against disease.

The skin and mucous membranes of the body are normally home to a variety of protozoa, fungi, bacteria, and viruses. This **normal microbiota** plays a role in protecting the body by competing with potential pathogens in a variety of ways, a situation called **microbial antagonism.**

A variety of activities of the normal microbiota make it less likely that a pathogen can compete with them and produce disease. Microbiota consume nutrients, making them unavailable to pathogens. Additionally, normal microbiota can change the pH, creating an environment that is favorable for themselves but unfavorable to other microorganisms.

Further, the presence of microbiota stimulates the body's second line of defense (discussed shortly). Researchers have observed that animals raised in an *axenic* (ā-zēn'ik) environment—that is, one free of all other organisms or viruses—are slower to defend themselves when exposed to a pathogen. Recent studies have shown that members of the normal microbiota in the intestines boost the production of antimicrobial substances by the body.

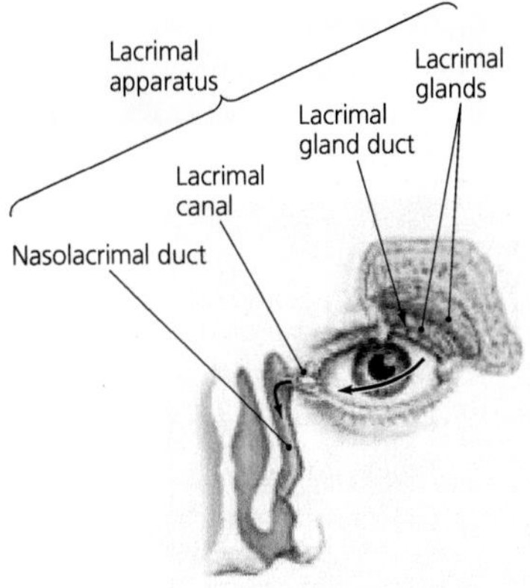

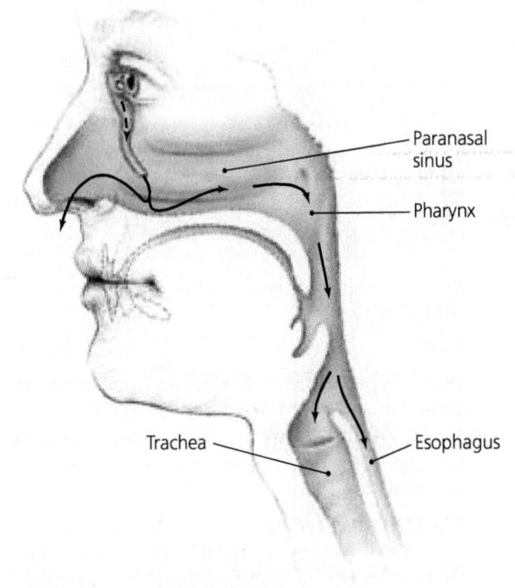

▲ *Figure 3*

The lacrimal apparatus. These structures function in the body's first line of defense by bathing the eye with tears. Arrows indicate the route tears take across the eye and into the throat. *What antimicrobial protein is found in tears?*

Figure 3 Tears contain lysozyme, an antimicrobial protein that acts against the peptidoglycan of bacterial cell walls.

Finally, the resident microbiota of the intestines improve overall health by providing several vitamins, including biotin and pantothenic acid (vitamin B_5), which are important in glucose metabolism; folic acid, which is essential for the production of the purine and pyrimidine bases of nucleic acids; and the precursor of vitamin K, which has an important role in blood clotting.

Table 2 Toll-Like Receptors and Their Natural Microbial Binding Partners

TLR	Microbial Molecule
TLR-1	Bacterial lipopeptides and certain proteins in multicellular parasites
TLR-2 (with TLR-6)	Bacterial lipopeptides, lipoteichoic acid (found in Gram-positive cell wall), and cell wall of yeast
TLR-3	Double-stranded RNA (found only in viruses)
TLR-4	Lipid A (found in Gram-negative cell wall)
TLR-5	Flagellin (bacterial flagella)
TLR-6 (with TLR-2)	Bacterial lipopeptides, lipoteichoic acid (found in Gram-positive cell wall), and cell wall of yeast
TLR-7	Single-stranded viral RNA
TLR-8	Single-stranded viral RNA
TLR-9	Unmethylated cytosine-guanine pairs of viral and bacterial DNA
TLR-10	Unknown

Other First-Line Defenses

Learning Objectives

✓ Describe antimicrobial peptides and Toll-like receptors as part of the body's defenses.

✓ Decribe the location and two possible functions of NOD proteins.

Besides the physical barrier of the skin and mucous membranes, there are other hindrances to microbial invasion. Among these are additional antimicrobial peptides and other processes and chemicals.

Antimicrobial Peptides

As we saw in our examination of skin and mucous membranes, antimicrobial peptides (sometimes called defensins) act against microorganisms. Scientists have discovered hundreds of these antimicrobial peptides in organisms as diverse as silkworms, frogs, and humans. Besides being secreted onto the surface of the skin, antimicrobial peptides are found in mucous membranes and in neutrophils. These peptides act against a variety of potential pathogens, being triggered by sugar and protein molecules on the external surfaces of microbes. Some antimicrobial peptides act only against Gram-positive bacteria or Gram-negative bacteria, others act against both, and still others act against protozoa, enveloped viruses, or fungi.

Researchers have elucidated several ways in which antimicrobial peptides work. Some punch holes in the cytoplasmic membranes of the pathogens, while others interrupt internal signaling or enzymatic action. Some antimicrobial peptides are chemotactic factors that recruit leukocytes to the site.

Toll-Like Receptors (TLRs)

Cells produce antimicrobial peptides when microbial chemicals bind to **Toll-like receptors (TLRs)**[3] on host cells' cytoplasmic or internal membranes. Scientists have discovered at least 10 different TLRs, each of which recognizes a particular microbial chemical. For example, lipoteichoic acid, which is a component of the cell walls of Gram-positive bacteria, adheres to TLR2, and lipid A (endotoxin) of Gram-negative bacteria binds to TLR4. **Table 2** lists the human Toll-like receptors and their microbial binding partners.

NOD Proteins

NOD[4] proteins are intracellular receptors for microbial components, particularly components of bacterial cell walls. Since they function in a cell's cytoplasm, they differ from TLRs, which bind extracellular chemicals. NOD proteins appear to regulate genes to mediate inflammation, apoptosis (cell suicide), and possibly other innate immune responses. Scientists are still elucidating exact details of the functions of NOD proteins, but they have determined that mutations in NOD genes are associated with several inflammatory bowel diseases, including Crohn's disease.

Other Processes and Chemicals

Many other body organs contribute to the first line of defense by secreting chemicals with antimicrobial properties that are secondary to their prime function. For example, whereas stomach acid is primarily present to aid digestion of proteins, it also prevents the growth of many potential pathogens. Likewise, saliva not only contains a digestive enzyme and provides lubrication for swallowing, it also contains lysozyme and physically washes microbes from the teeth. The contributions of these and other processes and chemicals to the first line of defense are listed in **Table 3.**

The Body's Second Line of Defense

Learning Objective

✓ Compare and contrast the body's first and second lines of defense against disease.

When pathogens succeed in penetrating the skin or mucous membranes, the body's second line of innate defense comes into play. Like the first line of defense, the second line operates against a wide variety of pathogens, from parasitic worms to viruses. But unlike the first line of defense, the second line includes no barriers; instead, it is composed of cells (especially phagocytes), antimicrobial chemicals (peptides, complement, interferons), and processes (inflammation, fever). Some cells and chemicals from the first line of defense

[3]Toll is an integral membrane protein of fruit flies. Toll-like proteins are similar to Toll in their amino acid sequence, though not necessarily in function.

[4]Nucleotide-oligomerization domains, referring to their ability to bind a region of a finite number (oligomer) of nucleotides in DNA.

Table 3 Secretions and Activities That Contribute to the First Line of Defense

Secretion/Activity	Function
Digestive System	
Saliva	Washes microbes from teeth, gums, tongue, and palate; contains lysozyme, an antibacterial enzyme
Stomach acid	Digests and/or inhibits microorganisms
Gastroferritin	Sequesters iron during its absorption, making it unavailable for microbial use
Bile	Inhibitory to most microorganisms
Intestinal secretions	Digests and/or inhibits microorganisms
Peristalsis	Moves gastrointestinal contents through GI tract, constantly eliminating potential pathogens
Defecation	Eliminates microorganisms
Vomiting	Eliminates microorganisms
Urinary System	
Urine	Contains lysozyme; urine's acidity inhibits microorganisms; may wash microbes from ureters and urethra during urination
Reproductive System	
Vaginal secretions	Acidity inhibits microorganisms; contains iron-binding proteins that sequester iron, making it unavailable for microbial use
Menstrual flow	Cleanses uterus and vagina
Prostate secretion	Contains iron-binding proteins that sequester iron, making it unavailable for microbial use
Cardiovascular System	
Blood flow	Removes microorganisms from wounds
Coagulation	Prevents entrance of many pathogens
Transferrin	Binds iron for transport, making it unavailable for microbial use

play additional roles in the second line of defense. We will consider each component of the second line of defense in some detail shortly, but because many of them are either contained in or originate in the blood, we first consider the components of blood.

Defense Components of Blood

Learning Objectives

- ✓ Discuss the components of blood and their functions in the body's defense.
- ✓ Explain how macrophages are named.

Blood is a complex liquid tissue composed of cells and portions of cells within a fluid called *plasma*. We begin our discussion of the defense functions of blood by briefly considering plasma.

Plasma

Plasma is mostly water containing electrolytes (ions), dissolved gases, nutrients, and—most relevant to the body's defenses—a variety of proteins. Some plasma proteins are involved in inflammation (discussed later) and in blood clotting, a defense mechanism that reduces both blood loss and the risk of infection. When clotting factors have been removed from the plasma, as for instance when blood clots, the remaining liquid is called *serum*.

Most cells require iron for metabolism: it is a component of cytochromes of electron transport chains, functions as an enzyme cofactor, and is an essential part of the hemoglobin—the oxygen-carrying protein of erythrocytes. Because iron is relatively insoluble, in humans it is transported in plasma to cells by a transport protein called *transferrin*. When transferrin-iron complexes reach cells with receptors for transferrin, the binding of the protein to the receptor stimulates the cell to take up the iron via endocytosis. Excess iron is stored in the liver bound to another protein called *ferritin*.

Though the main function of iron-binding proteins is transporting and storing iron, they play a secondary, defensive role—sequestering iron so that it is unavailable to microorganisms.

Some bacteria, such as *Staphylococcus aureus* (staf'i-lō-kok'ŭs o'rē-ŭs), respond to a shortage of iron by secreting their own iron-binding proteins called *siderophores*. Because siderophores have a greater affinity for iron than does transferrin, bacteria that produce them can in effect steal iron from the body. In response, the body produces *lactoferrin*, which retakes the iron from the bacteria by its even greater affinity. Thus, the body and the pathogens engage in a kind of chemical "tug-of-war" for the possession of iron.

Some pathogens bypass this contest altogether. For example, *Neisseria meningitidis* (nī-se'rē-ă me-nin-ji'ti-dis), a pathogen that causes often fatal meningitis, produces receptors for transferrin and plucks iron from the bloodstream as it flows by. *S. aureus* and related pathogens can secrete the protein *hemolysin*, which punches holes in the cytoplasmic membranes of red blood cells, releasing hemoglobin. Other bacterial proteins then bind hemoglobin to the bacterial membrane and strip it of its iron.

Another group of plasma proteins, called *complement proteins*, is an important part of the second line of defense and is discussed shortly. Still other plasma proteins, called *antibodies* or *immunoglobulins*, are a part of adaptive immunity, the body's third line of defense.

Defensive Blood Cells: Leukocytes

Cells and cell fragments suspended in the plasma are called **formed elements.** In a process called *hematopoiesis*,[5] blood stem cells located principally in the bone marrow within the hollow cavities of the large bones produce three types of formed

[5]From Greek *haima*, meaning blood, and *poiein*, meaning to make.

Figure 4 ➤

A schematic representation of hematopoiesis. In this process the division of stem cells in the bone marrow produces three types of formed (cellular) elements: erythrocytes, platelets, and leukocytes.

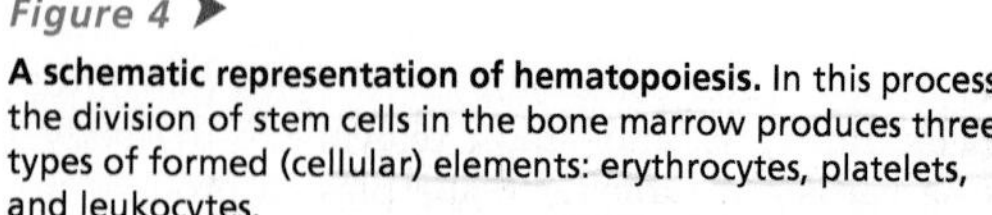

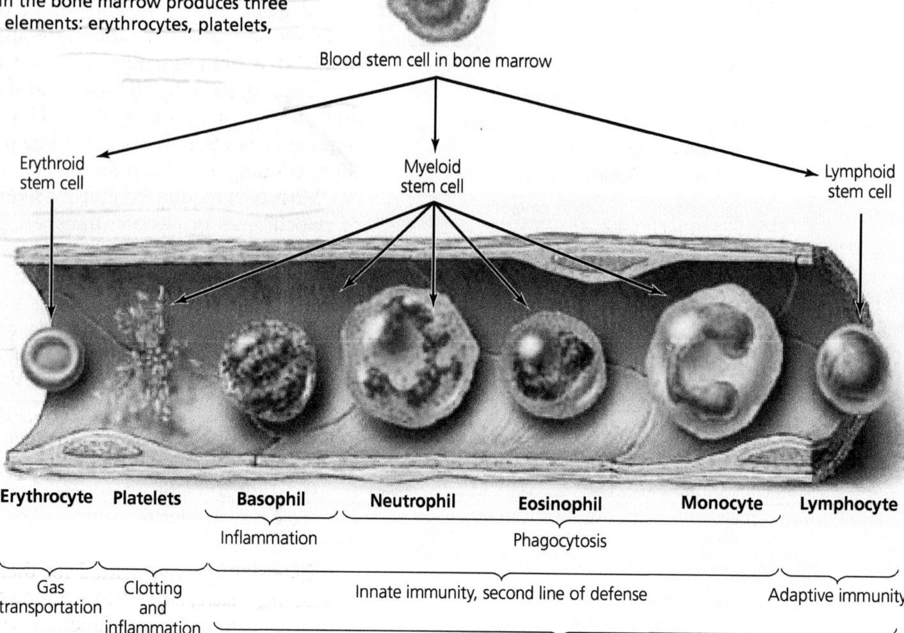

elements: **erythrocytes**[6] (ĕ-rith'rō-sītz), **platelets**[7] (plāt'letz), and **leukocytes**[8] (loo'kō-sīts) **(Figure 4).** Erythrocytes, the most numerous of the formed elements, carry oxygen and carbon dioxide in the blood. Platelets, which are pieces of large cells called *megakaryocytes* that have split into small portions of cytoplasm surrounded by cytoplasmic membranes, are involved in blood clotting. Leukocytes, the formed elements that are directly involved in defending the body against invaders, are commonly called white blood cells because they form a whitish layer when the components of blood are separated within a test tube.

Based on their appearance in stained blood smears when viewed under the microscope, leukocytes are divided into two groups: *granulocytes* (gran'ū-lō-sītz) and *agranulocytes* (ă-gran'ū-lō-sītz) **(Figure 5).**

Granulocytes have large granules in their cytoplasm that stain different colors depending on the type of granulocyte and the dyes used: **basophils** (bā'sō-fils) stain blue with the basic dye methylene blue; **eosinophils** (ē-ō-sin'ō-fils) stain red to orange with the acidic dye eosin; and **neutrophils** (noo'trō-fils), also known as *polymorphonuclear leukocytes* (PMNs), stain lilac with a mixture of acidic and basic dyes. Both neutrophils and eosinophils phagocytize pathogens, and both can exit the blood to attack invading microbes in the tissues by squeezing between the cells lining capillaries (the smallest blood vessels). This process is called **diapedesis**[9] (dī'ă-pĕ-dē'sis) or *emigration* **(Figure 6).** As we will see later in the chapter, eosinophils are also involved in defending the body against parasitic worms and are present in large number during many allergic reactions, though their exact function in allergies is disputed. Basophils can also leave the blood, though they are not phagocytic; instead, they release inflammatory chemicals, an aspect of the second line of defense that will be discussed shortly.

The cytoplasm of agranulocytes appears uniform when viewed via light microscopy, though granules do become visible with an electron microscope. Agranulocytes are of two types: **lymphocytes** (lim'fō-sītz), which are the smallest leukocytes and have nuclei that nearly fill the cells, and **monocytes** (mon'ō-sītz), which are large agranulocytes with slightly lobed nuclei. Although most lymphocytes are involved in adaptive immunity, *natural killer (NK) lymphocytes* function in innate defense and thus are discussed later in this chapter. Monocytes leave the blood and mature into **macrophages** (mak'rō-fāj-ĕz), which are phagocytic cells of the second line of defense. Their initial function is to devour foreign objects, including bacteria, fungi, spores, and dust, as well as dead body cells.

[6]From Greek *erythro,* meaning red, and *cytos,* meaning cell.

[7]French for small plates. Platelets are also called thrombocytes, from Greek *thrombos,* meaning lump, and *cytos,* meaning cell, though they are technically not cells, but instead pieces of cells.

[8]From Greek *leuko,* meaning white, and *cytos,* meaning cell.

[9]From Greek *dia,* meaning through, and *pedan,* meaning to leap.

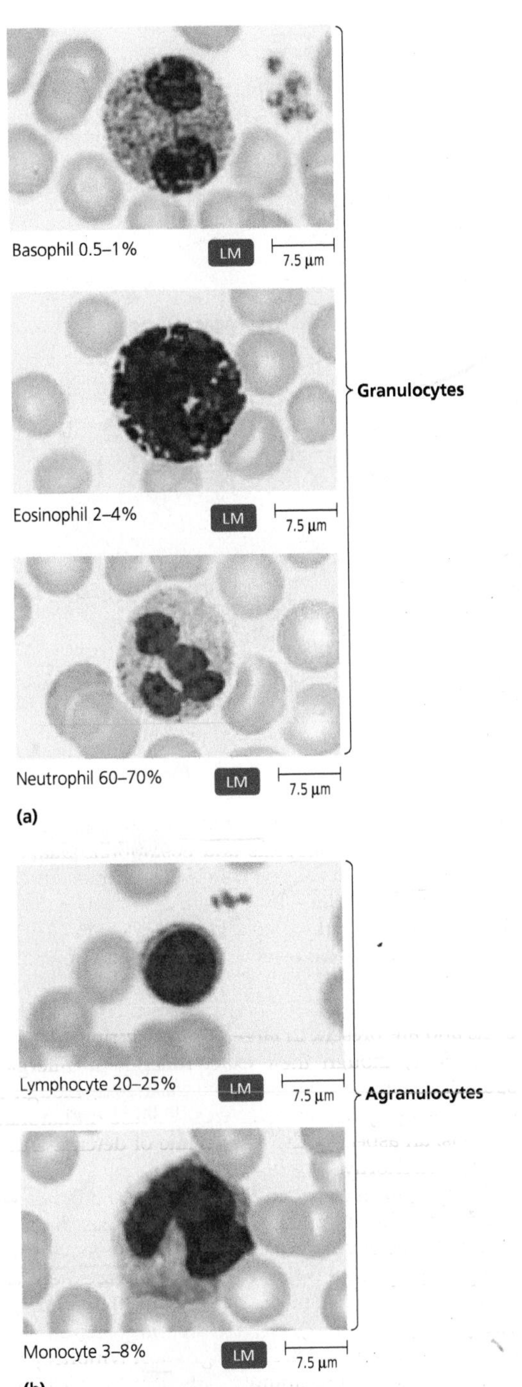

▲ *Figure 5*

Leukocytes as seen in stained blood smears. (a) Granulocytes: basophil, eosinophil, and neutrophil. **(b)** Agranulocytes: lymphocyte and monocyte. The numbers are the normal percentages of each cell type among all leukocytes.

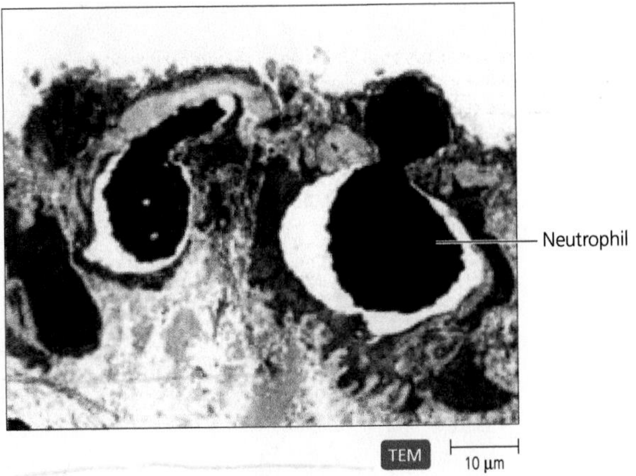

▲ *Figure 6*

Diapedesis. In this process leukocytes leave intact blood vessels. Shown here is a neutrophil squeezing between the cells lining a capillary on its way to fight an infection in the tissues.

Macrophages are named for their location in the body. *Wandering macrophages* leave the blood via diapedesis and perform their scavenger function while traveling throughout the body, including extracellular spaces. Other macrophages are fixed and do not wander. These include, *alveolar* (al-vē′ō-lăr) *macrophages*[10] of the lungs, *microglia* (mī-krog′lē-ă) of the central nervous system, and *Kupffer*[11] (kyūp′fer) *cells* of the liver. Fixed macrophages generally phagocytize within specific organs, such as the heart chambers, blood vessels, and lymphatic vessels.

A special group of phagocytes are dendritic cells. These multibranched cells are plentiful throughout the body, particularly in the skin and mucous membrances, where they await microbial invaders. **Figure 7** illustrates some of the body's phagocytes.

Lab Analysis of Leukocytes Analysis of blood for diagnostic purposes, including white blood cell counts, is one task of medical lab technologists. The proportions of leukocytes, as determined in a **differential white blood cell count,** can serve as a sign of disease. For example, an increase in the percentage of eosinophils can indicate allergies or infection with parasitic worms; bacterial diseases typically result in an increase in the number of leukocytes and an increase in the percentage of neutrophils, while viral infections are associated with an increase in the relative number of lymphocytes. The ranges for the normal values for each kind of white blood cell, expressed as a percentage of the total leukocyte population, are shown in Figure 5.

[10]Alveoli are small pockets at the end of respiratory passages where oxygen and carbon dioxide exchange occurs between the lungs and the blood.
[11]Named for German anatomist Karl von Kupffer.

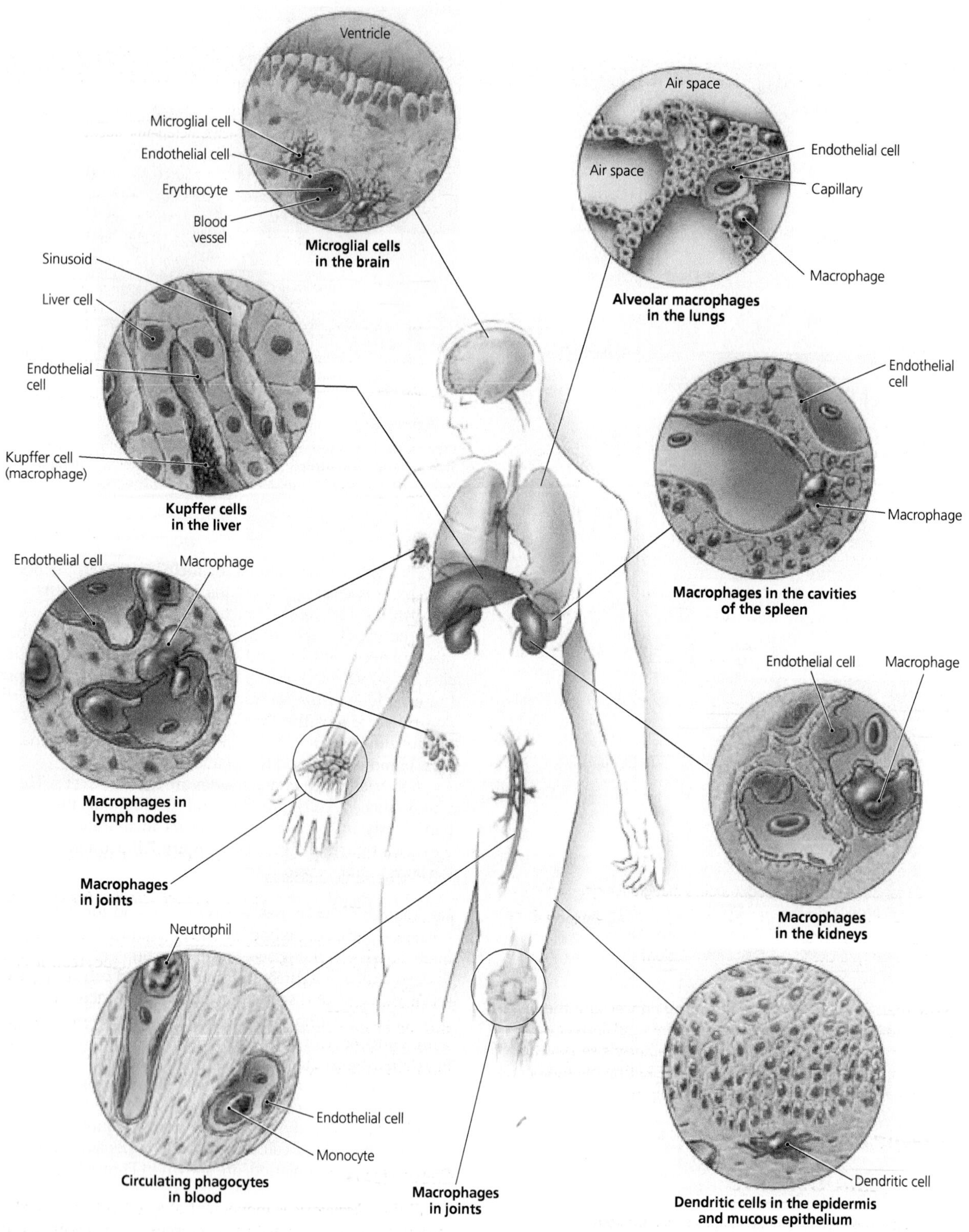

Ventricle
Microglial cell
Endothelial cell
Erythrocyte
Blood vessel
Microglial cells in the brain
Air space
Air space
Endothelial cell
Capillary
Macrophage
Alveolar macrophages in the lungs
Sinusoid
Liver cell
Endothelial cell
Kupffer cell (macrophage)
Kupffer cells in the liver
Endothelial cell
Macrophage
Macrophages in the cavities of the spleen
Endothelial cell
Macrophage
Macrophages in lymph nodes
Endothelial cell
Macrophage
Macrophages in joints
Macrophages in the kidneys
Neutrophil
Endothelial cell
Monocyte
Circulating phagocytes in blood
Macrophages in joints
Dendritic cell
Dendritic cells in the epidermis and mucous epithelium

▲ *Figure 7*

Some phagocytes of the body.

Clinical Case Study *Evaluating an Abnormal CBC*

CBC Profile

Name: Brown, Roger Age/Sex: 61/M Attend Dr: Kevin, Larry
Acct#: 04797747 Status: ADM IN
Reg: 12/27/07

SPEC #: 0303:AS:H00102T COLL: 12 / 03 / 07-0620 STATUS: COMP REQ #: 01797367
RECD: 12 / 03 / 07-0647 SUBM DR: Kevin, Larry

ENTERED: 12 / 03 / 07-0002 OTHER DR: NONE, PER PT
ORDERED: CBC W/ MAN DIFF

Test	Result	Flag	Reference	Site
CBC				
WBC (white blood cells)	0.8	*L*	4.8–10.8 K/mm3	ML
RBC (red blood cells)	3.09	*L*	4.20–5.40 M/mm3	ML
HGB (hemoglobin)	9.6	*L*	12.0–16.0 g/dL	ML
HCT (hematocrit)	28.2	*L*	37.0–47.0 %	ML
MCV	91.3		81.0–99.0 fL	ML
MCH	31.1	*H*	27.0–31.0 pg	ML
MCHC	34.1		32.0–36.0 g/dl	ML
RDW	17.1	*H*	11.5–14.5 %	ML
PLT (platelets)	21	*L*	150–450 K/mm3	ML
MPV	8.7		7.4–10.4 fL	ML
DIFF				
CELLS COUNTED	100		#CELLS	ML
SEGS	39		%	ML
BAND	4		%	ML
LYMPH (lymphocytes)	41		%	ML
MONO (monocytes)	15		%	ML
EOS (eosinophils)	1		%	ML
NEUT# (# neutrophils)	0.3	*L*	1.9–8.0 K/mm3	ML
LYMPH#	0.3	*L*	0.9–5.2 K/mm3	ML
MONO#	0.1		0.1–1.2 K/mm3	ML
EOS#	0.0		0–0.8 K/mm3	ML
PLATELET EST	DECREASED	*		ML
RBC MORPHOLOGY	ABNORMAL	*		ML
CELL MORPHOLOGY				
ANISOCYTOSIS	MODERATE	*		ML
POIKILOCYTOSIS	MODERATE			ML
TEAR DROP CELLS	PRESENT	*		ML

ML - MAIN LABORATORY

Roger Brown, an African American cancer patient, received a chemotherapeutic agent as a treatment for his disease. The drug used to destroy the cancer also produced an undesirable condition known as bone marrow depression. The complete blood count (CBC) profile shown here indicates that this patient is in trouble. Review the lab values and answer the following questions.

1. Note that the platelet count is very low. How does this affect the patient? Discuss measures to protect him.
2. Note that the white blood cell count is abnormally low. With the second line of defense impaired, how should the first line of defense be protected?

CRITICAL THINKING

A medical laboratory technologist argues that granulocytes are a natural group, whereas agranulocytes are an artificial grouping. Based on Figure 4, do you agree or disagree with the lab tech? What evidence can you cite to justify your conclusion?

Now that we have some background concerning the defensive properties of plasma components and leukocytes, we turn our attention to the details of the body's second line of defense: phagocytosis, nonphagocytic killing by leukocytes, nonspecific chemical defenses, inflammation, and fever.

Phagocytosis

Learning Objective

✓ Name and describe the five stages of phagocytosis.

Here we consider how those cells of the body that are capable of phagocytosis—collectively known as **phagocytes** (fag'ō-sītz)—play a role against pathogens that get past the body's first line of defense.

www.microbiologyplace.com **Animations: *Host Defenses: Phagocytosis: Overview***

Although phagocytosis was discovered over a century ago (see **Highlight: The Discovery of Phagocytes**), it is a complex process that is still not completely understood. For the purposes of our discussion, we will divide the continuous process of phagocytosis into five steps: (1) chemotaxis, (2) adherence, (3) ingestion, (4) killing, and (5) elimination **(Figure 8)**.

Chemotaxis

Recall that *chemotaxis* is movement of a cell either toward a chemical stimulus (positive chemotaxis) or away from a chemical stimulus (negative chemotaxis). In the case of phagocytes, positive chemotaxis involves the use of

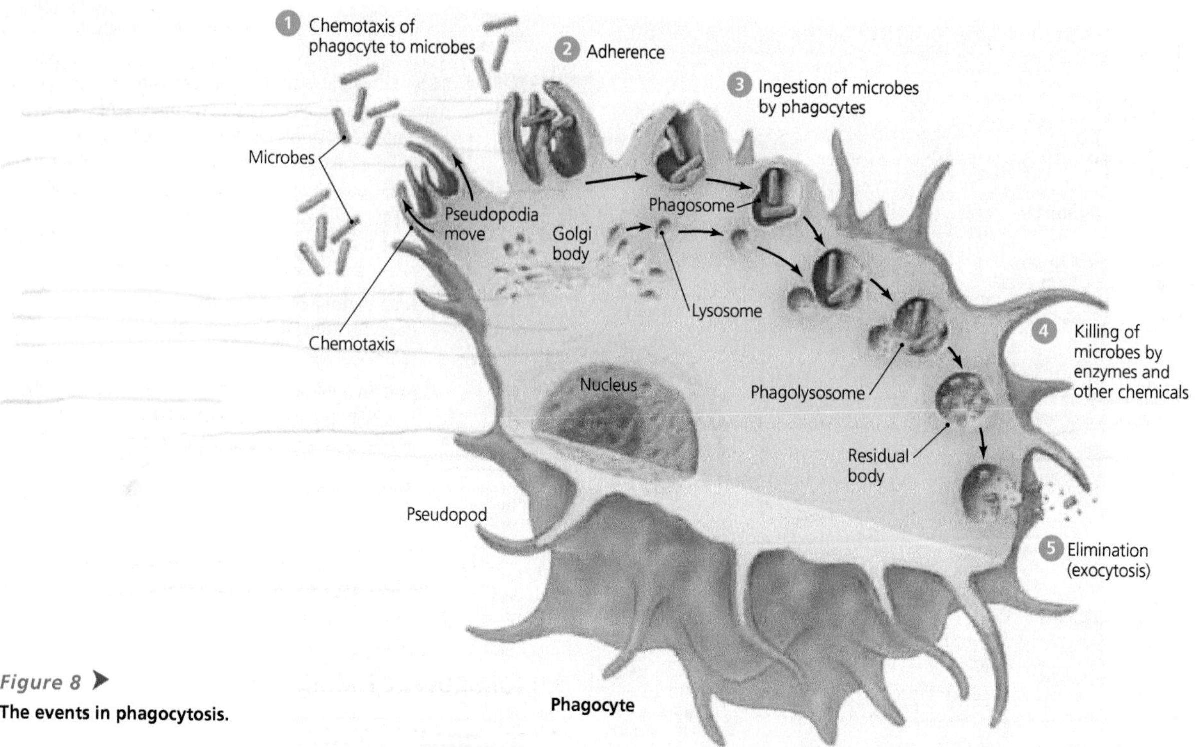

Figure 8 ➤
The events in phagocytosis.

pseudopodia (sū-dō-pō′dē-ă) to crawl toward microorganisms at the site of an infection (1). Chemicals that attract phagocytic leukocytes include microbial components and secretions, components of damaged tissues and white blood cells, and **chemotactic** (kem-ō-tak′tik) **factors.** Chemotactic factors include defensins, peptides derived from complement (discussed later in this chapter), and chemicals called **chemokines** (kē′mō-kīnz), which are released by leukocytes already at a site of infection.

Adherence

After arriving at the site of an infection, phagocytes attach to microorganisms through the binding of complementary chemicals such as glycoproteins found on the membranes of cells (2). This process is called **adherence.**

Some bacteria have virulence factors, such as M protein of *Streptococcus pyogenes* (strep-tō-kok′ŭs pī-oj′en-ēz), or slippery capsules that hinder adherence of phagocytes and thereby increase the virulence of the bacteria. Such bacteria are more readily phagocytized if they are pushed up against a surface such as connective tissue, the wall of a blood vessel, or a blood clot.

All pathogens are more readily phagocytized if they are first covered with antimicrobial proteins such as complement proteins (discussed later) or the specific antimicrobial proteins called antibodies. This coating process is called **opsonization,**[12] and the proteins are called **opsonins.** Generally, opsonins increase the number and kinds of binding sites on a microbe's surface.

Ingestion

After phagocytes adhere to pathogens, they extend *pseudopodia* to surround the microbe (3) in Figure 8 and **Figure 9.** The encompassed microbe is internalized as the pseudopodia fuse to form a food vesicle called a **phagosome.**

Killing

Lysosomes within the phagocyte fuse with newly formed phagosomes to form **phagolysosomes** (fag-ŏ-lī′sō-sōmz), or digestive vesicles (4). Phagolysosomes contain digestive enzymes and other antimicrobial substances such as highly reactive, toxic forms of oxygen, in an environment with a pH of about 5.5 due to the active pumping of H^+ from the cytosol. Among the 30 or so different enzymes within lysosomes are lipases, proteases, nucleases, and a variety of others that destroy the engulfed microbes. All of these substances damage proteins and lipids in cell membranes, allowing lethal enzymes access to microbial cells, which die.

---

[12]From Greek *opsonein*, meaning to supply food, and *izein*, meaning to cause; thus, loosely, "to prepare for dinner."

Highlight The Discovery of Phagocytes

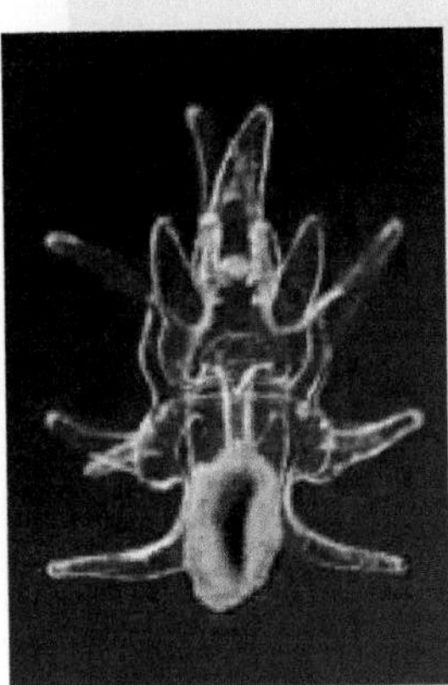

Starfish larva

During the latter part of the 19th century, when microbiology was coming of age in the labs of Louis Pasteur and Robert Koch, a Russian microbiologist named Ilya Metchnikoff (1845–1916) surprised the scientific world with the announcement that animals were protected from pathogens by the action of wandering cells he called *phagocytes*. Metchnikoff had observed these cells moving in the bodies of starfish larvae by means of pseudopodia, and he hypothesized that because they moved like free-living amoebae, they might also eat like amoebae, phagocytizing invasive pathogens.

He tested his hypothesis by stabbing a starfish larva with a rose thorn from his garden. The next morning he observed that thousands of phagocytes had migrated to the site of infection and were actively devouring germs. He subsequently demonstrated the same phenomenon in other animals and with these discoveries pointed the way toward understanding what we now call innate immunity and adaptive immunity.

In 1908, Metchnikoff received a Nobel Prize in Medicine or Physiology for his discoveries.

Most pathogens are dead within 30 minutes, though some bacteria contain virulence factors (such as M protein or waxy cell walls) that resist a lysosome's action. In the end, a phagolysosome is known as a *residual body*.

Elimination

Digestion is not always complete, and phagocytes eliminate remnants of microorganisms via *exocytosis*, a process that is essentially the reverse of ingestion 5. Some microbial components are specially processed and remain attached to the cytoplasmic membrane of some phagocytes, particularly dendritic cells, a phenomenon that plays a role in the adaptive immune response.

www.microbiologyplace.com **Animations: *Host Defenses: Phagocytosis: Mechanism***

How is it that phagocytes destroy invading pathogens, and leave the body's own healthy cells unharmed? At least two mechanisms are responsible for this:

- Some phagocytes have cytoplasmic membrane receptors for various microbial surface components lacking on the body's cells, such as cell wall components or flagellar proteins.
- Opsonins such as complement and antibody provide a signal to the phagocyte.

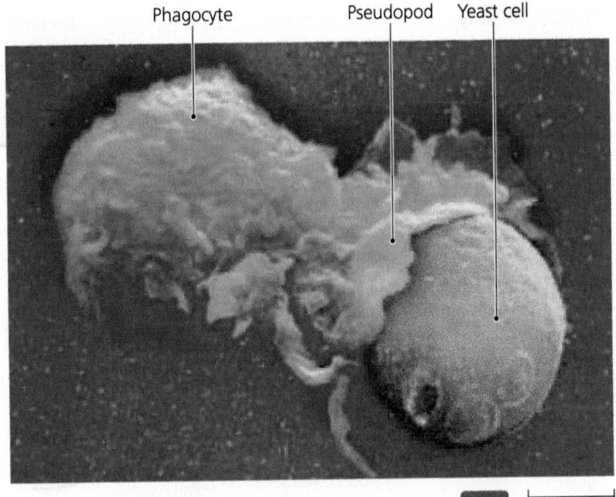

▲ *Figure 9*

A phagocyte at work. This macrophage is ingesting a yeast cell by surrounding it with pseudopodia to form a phagosome.

Nonphagocytic Killing

Learning Objective

✓ Describe the role of eosinophils, NK cells, and neutrophils in nonphagocytic killing of microorganisms and parasitic helminths.

Phagocytosis involves killing a pathogen once it has been ingested—that is, once it is inside the phagocyte. In contrast, eosinophils, natural killer cells, and neutrophils can accomplish killing without phagocytosis.

Killing by Eosinophils

As discussed earlier, eosinophils can phagocytize; however, this is not their usual mode of attack. Instead, they primarily attack parasitic helminths (worms) by attaching to the worm's surface. Once bound, eosinophils secrete extracellular protein toxins onto the surface of the parasite. These weaken the helminth and may even kill it. **Eosinophilia** (ē-ō-sin'ō-fil-e-ă), an abnormally high number of eosinophils in the blood, is often indicative of helminth infestation.

Killing by Natural Killer Lymphocytes

Natural killer lymphocytes (or **NK cells**) are another type of defensive leukocyte of innate immunity that works by secreting toxins onto the surfaces of virally infected cells and neoplasms (tumors). NK cells identify and spare normal body cells because the latter express membrane proteins similar to those on the NK cells.

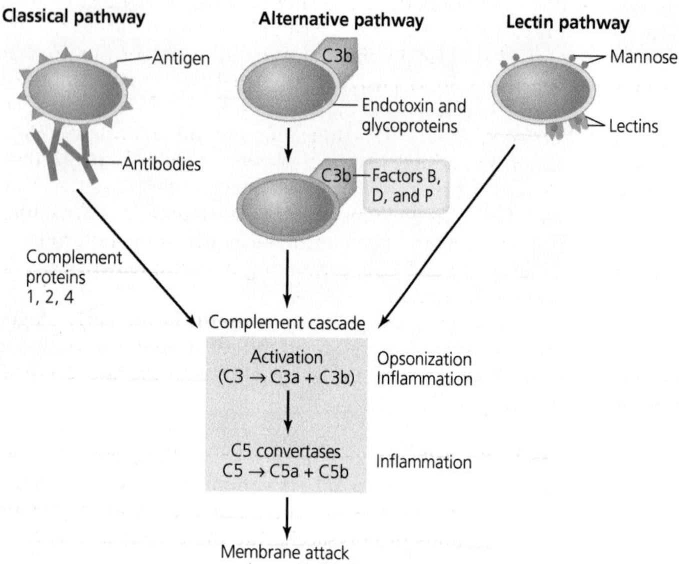

◀ *Figure 10*

Pathways by which complement is activated. In the classical pathway, the binding of antibodies to antigens activates complement. In the alternative pathway the binding of factors B, D, and P to endotoxin or glycoproteins in the cell walls of bacteria or fungi activates complement. The lectin pathway activates when lectins bind to microbial carbohydrates. *How did complement get that name?*

Figure 10 Complement proteins add to—or complement—the action of antibodies.

Killing by Neutrophils

Neutrophils do not always devour pathogens; they can destroy nearby microbial cells without phagocytosis. They can do this in at least two ways. Enzymes in a neutrophil's cytoplasmic membrane add electrons to oxygen, creating highly reactive superoxide radical O_2^- and hydrogen peroxide (H_2O_2). Another enzyme converts these into hypochlorite, the active antimicrobial ingredient in household bleach. These chemicals can kill nearby invaders. Yet another enzyme in the membrane makes nitric oxide, which is a powerful inducer of inflammation.

Scientists have recently discovered another way that neutrophils disable microorganisms in their vicinity. They generate webs of extracellular fibers nicknamed *NETs* for *neutrophil extracellular traps.* Neutrophils synthesize NETs via a unique form of cellular suicide involving the disintegration of their nuclei. As the nuclear envelope breaks down, DNA and histones are released into the cytosol and the mixing of nuclear components with cytoplasmic granule membranes and proteins forms NET fibers. Reactive oxygen species—superoxide and peroxide—kill the neutrophil. The NETs are released from the dying cell as its cytoplasmic membrane ruptures. NETs trap both Gram-positive and Gram-negative bacteria, immobilizing them and sequestering them along with antimicrobial peptides, which kill the bacteria. Thus, even in their dying moments, neutrophils fulfill their role as defensive cells.

Nonspecific Chemical Defenses Against Pathogens

Learning Objectives

✓ Describe the complement system, including its classical and alternative pathways.

✓ Explain the roles of interferons in innate immunity.

Chemical defenses augment phagocytosis in the second line of defense. The chemicals assist phagocytic cells either by directly attacking pathogens or by enhancing other features of innate immunity. Defensive chemicals include lysozyme and defensins (examined previously) as well as complement and interferons.

Complement

The **complement system**—or **complement** for short—is a set of serum proteins designated numerically according to the order of their discovery. These proteins initially act as opsonins and chemotactic factors, and indirectly trigger inflammation and fever. The end result of full complement activation is lysis of foreign cells.

www.microbiologyplace.com **Animations: *Host Defenses: Complement: Overview***

Complement is activated in three ways **(Figure 10)**:

- In the *classical pathway,* antibodies activate complement.
- In the *alternative pathway,* pathogens or pathogenic products (such as bacterial endotoxins and glycoproteins) activate complement.
- In the *lectin pathway,* microbial polysaccharides bind to activating molecules.

As Figure 10 shows, the three pathways merge. Complement proteins react with one another in an amplifying sequence of chemical reactions, in which the product of each reaction becomes an enzyme that catalyzes the next reaction many times over. Such reactions are called *cascades* because they progress in a way that can be likened to a rock avalanche in which one rock dislodges several other rocks, each of which dislodges many others until a whole cascade of rocks is tumbling down the mountain. The products of each step in the complement cascade initiate other reactions, often with wide-ranging effects in the body.

The Classical Pathway Complement got its name from events in the originally discovered "classical" pathway. In this pathway the various proteins act to "complement," or act in conjunction with, the action of antibodies, which we now understand are part of adaptive immunity. As you study the depiction of the classical complement cascade in **Figure 11,** keep the following concepts in mind:

- Complement enzymes in early events cleave other complement molecules to form *fragments.*
- Most fragments have specific and important roles in achieving the functions of the complement system. Some combine together to form new enzymes; some act to increase vascular permeability, which increases diapedesis; others enhance inflammation; still others are involved as chemotactic factors or in opsonization.
- One end product of the cascade is a **membrane attack complex (MAC),** which forms a circular hole in a pathogen's membrane. The production of numerous MACs **(Figure 12)** leads to lysis in a wide variety of bacterial and eukaryotic pathogens. Gram-negative bacteria, such as the bacterium causing gonorrhea, are particularly sensitive to the production of MACs via the complement cascade because their outer membranes are exposed and susceptible. In contrast, a Gram-positive bacterium, which has a thick layer of peptidoglycan overlying its cytoplasmic membrane, is typically resistant to the MAC-induced lytic properties of complement, though it is susceptible to the other effects of the complement cascade.

In addition to its enzymatic roles, fragment C3b acts as an opsonin. Fragments C3a and C5a function as chemotactic factors, attracting phagocytes to the site of infection, and C4b acts as an opsonin. C3a and C5a are also inflammatory agents that trigger increased vascular permeability and dilation. The inflammatory roles of these fragments are discussed in more detail shortly.

The Alternative Pathway The alternative pathway was so named because scientists discovered it second. As previously mentioned, antibodies bound to antigens are necessary for the classical activation of complement, whereas activation of the alternative pathway occurs independently of antibodies. The alternative pathway begins with the cleavage of C3 into C3a and C3b. This naturally occurs at a slow rate in the plasma but proceeds no further because C3b is cleaved into smaller fragments almost immediately. However, when C3b binds to microbial surfaces, it stabilizes long enough for a protein called factor B to adhere. Another plasma protein, factor D, then cleaves factor B, creating an enzyme composed of C3b and Bb. This enzyme, which is stabilized by a third protein—factor P (properdin)—cleaves more molecules of C3 into C3a and C3b, continuing the complement cascade and the formation of MACs.

The alternative pathway is useful in the early stages of an infection, before the adaptive immune response has created the antibodies needed to activate the classical pathway.

The Lectin Pathway Researchers have discovered a third pathway for complement activation that acts through the use of *lectins.* Lectins are chemicals that bind to specific sugar subunits of polysaccharide molecules; in this case, to mannose sugar in mannan polysaccharide on the surfaces of fungi, bacteria, or viruses. Mannose is rare in mammals. Lectins bound to mannose act to trigger a complement cascade by cleaving C2 and C4. The cascade then proceeds like the classical pathway (see steps 3 to 7 in Figure 11).

www.microbiologyplace.com **Animations: *Host Defenses: Complement: Activation and Complement: Results***

CRITICAL THINKING

A patient has a genetic disorder that makes it impossible for her to synthesize complement protein 8 (C8). Is her complement system nonfunctional? What major effects of complement could still be produced?

Inactivation of Complement We have seen that the complement system is nonspecific, and that MACs can form on any cell's exposed membrane. How do the body's own cells withstand the action of complement? Membrane-bound proteins on the body's cells bind with and break down activated complement proteins, which interrupts the complement cascade before damage can occur.

Interferons

So far in this chapter we have focused primarily on how the body defends itself against bacteria and eukaryotes. Now we consider how chemicals in the second line of defense act against viral pathogens.

Viruses use a host's metabolic machinery to produce new viruses. For this reason, it is often difficult to interfere with virus replication without also producing deleterious effects on the host. **Interferons** (in-ter-fēr'onz) are protein molecules released by host cells to nonspecifically inhibit the spread of viral infections. Their lack of

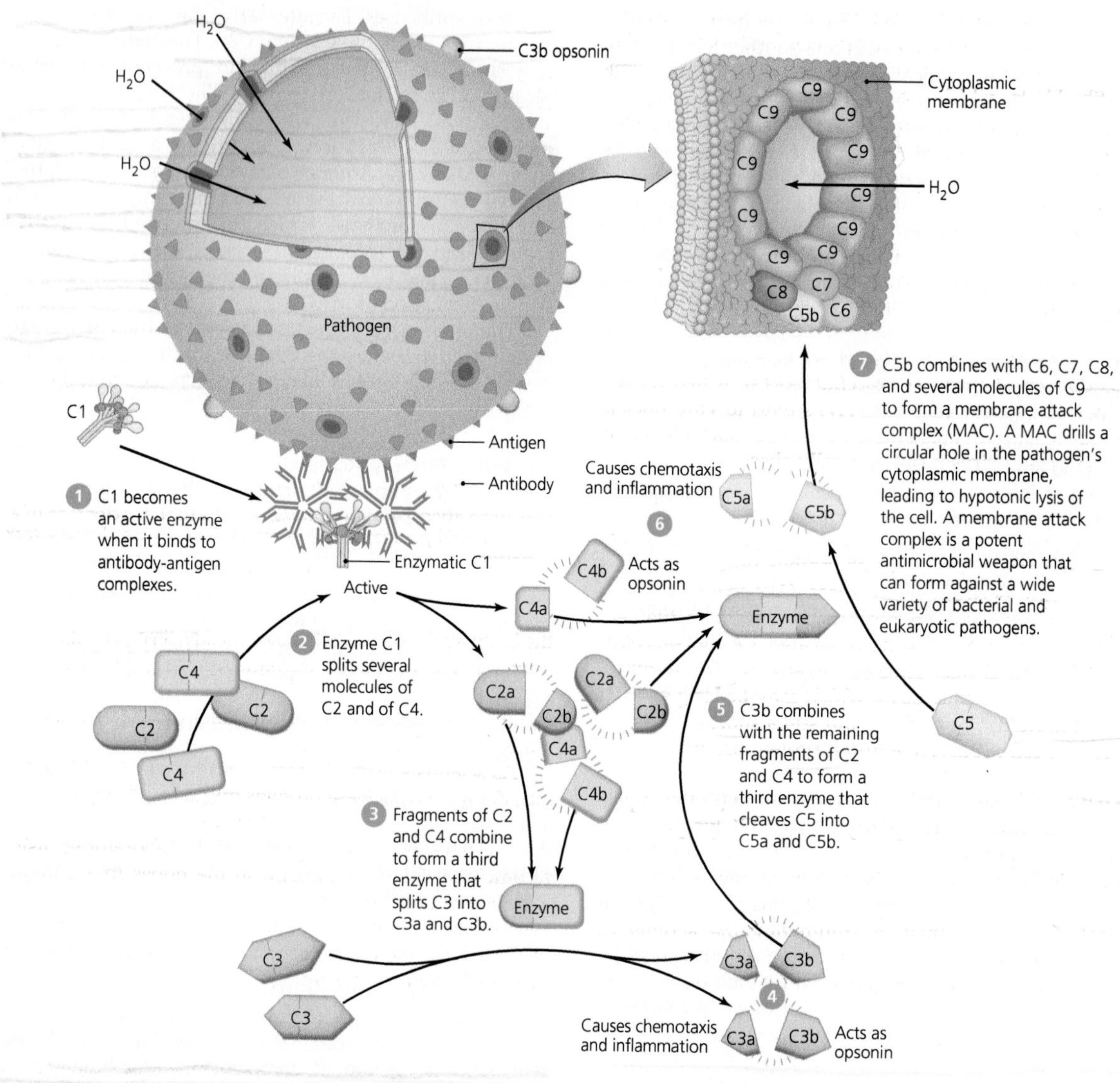

▲ *Figure 11*

The complement cascade. *What proteins would be involved in activating a complement cascade if this were the alternative pathway?*

Figure 11 *Whereas the classical pathway of complement activation involves proteins C1, C2, and C4, the alternative pathway involves factors B, D, and P (properdin).*

specificity means that interferons produced against one viral invader protect somewhat against infection by other types of viruses as well. However, interferons also cause malaise, muscle aches, chills, headache, and fever, which are typically associated with viral infections.

Different cell types produce one of two basic types of interferon when stimulated by viral nucleic acid binding to TLR-3, TLR-7, or TLR-8. Interferons within any given type share certain physical and chemical features, though they are specific to the species that produces them. In general, type I interferons—also known as alpha and beta interferons—are present early in viral infections, whereas type II (gamma) interferon appears somewhat later in the course of infection. Because their actions are identical, we examine alpha and beta interferons together before discussing gamma interferon.

Type I (Alpha and Beta) Interferons Within hours after infection, virally infected monocytes, macrophages, and some lymphocytes secrete small amounts of **alpha interferon (IFN-α)**; similarly, fibroblasts, which are undifferentiated cells in such connective tissues as cartilage, tendon, and bone, secrete small amounts of **beta interferon (IFN-β)** when infected by viruses. The structures of alpha and beta interferons are similar, and their actions are identical.

Interferons do not protect the cells that secrete them—these cells are already infected with viruses. Instead, interferons activate natural killer lymphocytes and trigger protective steps in neighboring uninfected cells. Alpha and beta interferons bind to interferon receptors on the cytoplasmic membranes of neighboring cells. Such binding triggers the production of **antiviral proteins (AVPs),** which remain inactive within these cells until AVPs bind to viral nucleic acids, particularly double-stranded RNA, a molecule that is common among viruses but generally absent in eukaryotic cells **(Figure 13).**

At least two types of AVPs are produced: *oligoadenylate synthetase,* the action of which results in the degradation of mRNA, and *protein kinase,* which inhibits protein synthesis by ribosomes. Between them, these AVP enzymes essentially destroy the protein production system of the cell, preventing viruses from being replicated. Of course, cellular metabolism is also affected negatively. The antiviral state lasts three to four days, which may be long enough for a cell to rid itself of viruses but still a short enough period for the cell to survive without protein production.

Type II (Gamma) Interferon **Gamma interferon (IFN-γ)** is produced by activated T lymphocytes and NK lymphocytes. Because T lymphocytes are usually activated as part of an adaptive immune response days after an infection has occurred, gamma interferon appears later than either alpha or beta interferon. Its action in stimulating the activity of macrophages gives IFN-γ its other name: *macrophage activation factor.* Gamma interferon plays a small role in protecting the body against viral infections; mostly IFN-γ regulates the immune system, as in its activation of phagocytic activity.

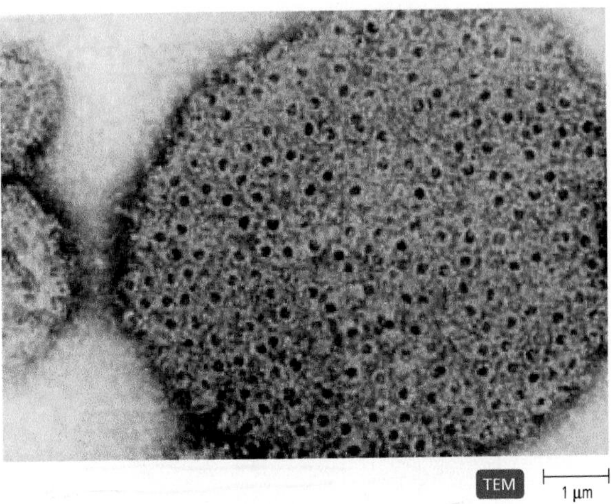

▲ *Figure 12*

Membrane attack complexes. Transmission electron micrograph of a cell damaged by numerous punctures produced by membrane attack complexes.

Table 4 summarizes various properties of interferons in humans.

As scientists learned more about the effects of interferons, many thought these proteins might be a "magic bullet" against viral infections. Many variations of interferons in all three classes have been produced in laboratories using recombinant DNA technology, in the hopes that antiviral therapy can be improved.

Viruses can interfere with the effects of interferon, as discussed in **Applying Molecular Techniques: How Do Viruses Thwart Interferon?**

Table 4 The Characteristics of Human Interferons

	Type I		Type II
Property	Alpha Interferon (IFN-α)	Beta Interferon (IFN-β)	Gamma Interferon (IFN-γ)
Principal source	Epithelium, leukocytes	Fibroblasts	Activated T lymphocytes and NK lymphocytes
Inducing agent	Viruses	Viruses	Adaptive immune responses
Action	Stimulates production of antiviral proteins	Stimulates production of antiviral proteins	Stimulates phagocytic activity of macrophages and neutrophils
Molecular weight (kilodaltons)	16–23	23	20–25
Glycosylated?	No	Yes	Yes
Stable at pH 2?	Yes	Yes	No
Other names	Leukocyte-IFN	Fibroblast-IFN	Immune-IFN, macrophage activation factor

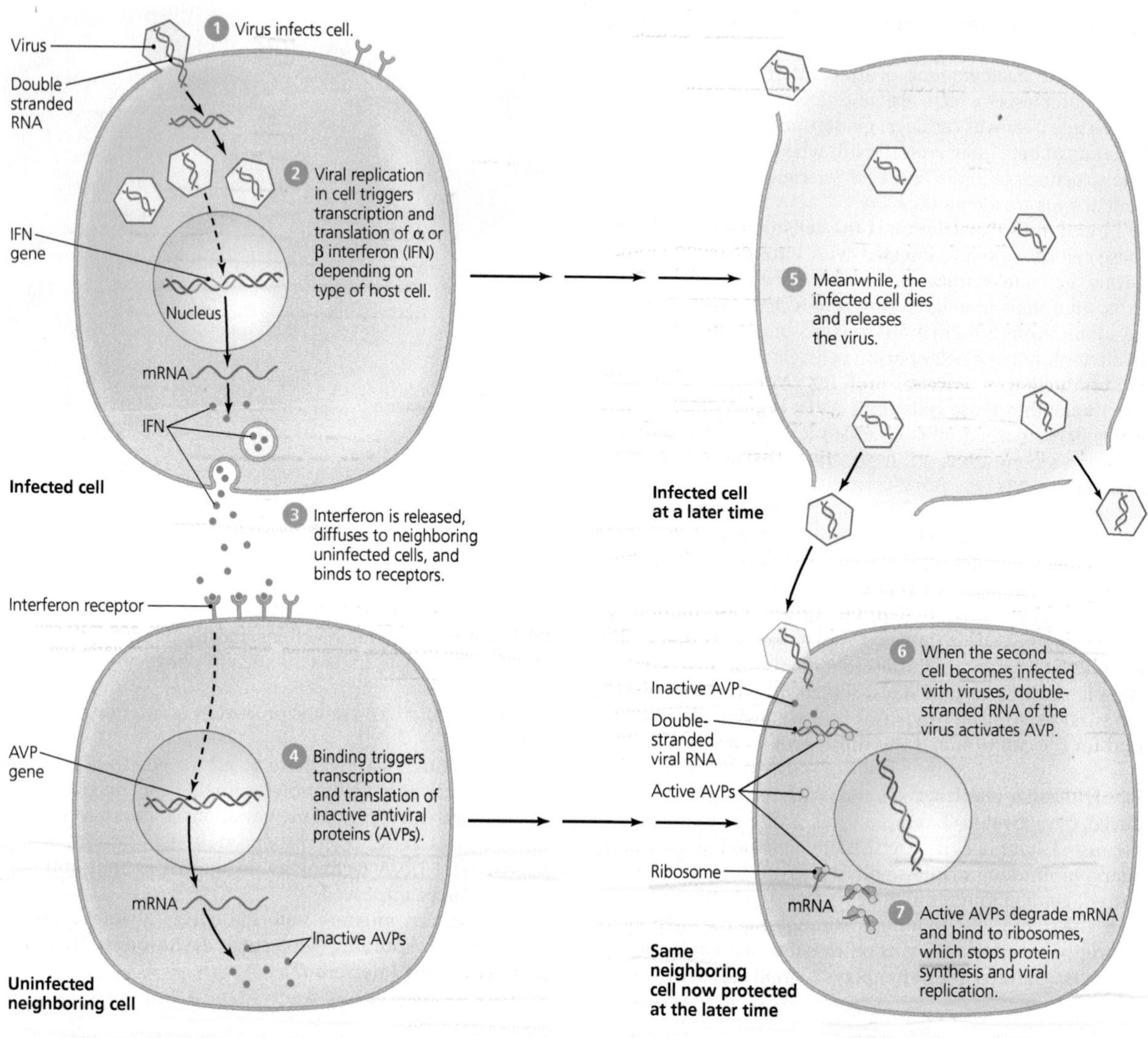

▲ *Figure 13*

The actions of alpha and beta interferons.

Inflammation

Learning Objective

✓ Discuss the process and benefits of inflammation.

Inflammation is a general, nonspecific response to tissue damage resulting from a variety of causes, including heat, chemicals, ultraviolet light (sunburn), abrasions, cuts, and pathogens. **Acute inflammation** develops quickly, is short lived, is typically beneficial, and results in the elimination or resolution of whatever condition precipitated it. Long-lasting (chronic) inflammation cause damage (even death) to tissues, resulting in disease. Both acute and chronic inflammation exhibit similar signs and symptoms, including redness in light-colored skin, (rubor), localized heat (calor), edema (swelling), and pain (dolor).

www.microbiologyplace.com **Animations: *Inflammation: Host Defenses: Overview***

It may not be obvious from this list of signs and symptoms that acute inflammation is beneficial; however, acute inflammation is an important part of the second line of defense because it results in (1) dilation and increased permeability of blood vessels, (2) migration of phagocytes, and (3) tissue repair. Although the chemical details of inflammation are beyond the scope of our study, we now consider these three aspects of acute inflammation.

Dilation and Increased Permeability of Blood Vessels

Part of the body's initial response to an injury or invasion of pathogens is localized dilation (increase in diameter) of blood vessels in the affected region. The process of blood clotting triggers the conversion of a soluble plasma protein into a nine-amino-acid peptide chain called **bradykinin** (brad-e-ki'nin), which is a potent mediator of inflammation. Further, patrolling macrophages, using Toll-like receptors to identify invaders, release other inflammatory chemicals, including **prostaglandins** (pros-tă-glan'dinz) and **leukotrienes** (loo-kō-tri'ēnz). Basophils, platelets, and specialized cells located in connective tissue—called **mast cells**—also release inflammatory mediators, such as **histamine** (his'tă-mēn), when they are exposed to complement fragments C3a and C5a **(Figure 14)**. Recall that these complement peptides were cleaved from larger polypeptides during the complement cascade.

Bradykinin and histamine cause vasodilation of the body's smallest arteries (arterioles) **(Figure 15)**. Vasodilation results in more blood being delivered to the site of infection, which in turn delivers more phagocytes, oxygen, and nutrients to the site. Inflammatory mediators cause cells that line blood vessels to make adhesion molecules, which are receptors for leukocytes. Bradykinin, prostaglandins, leukotrienes, and (to some

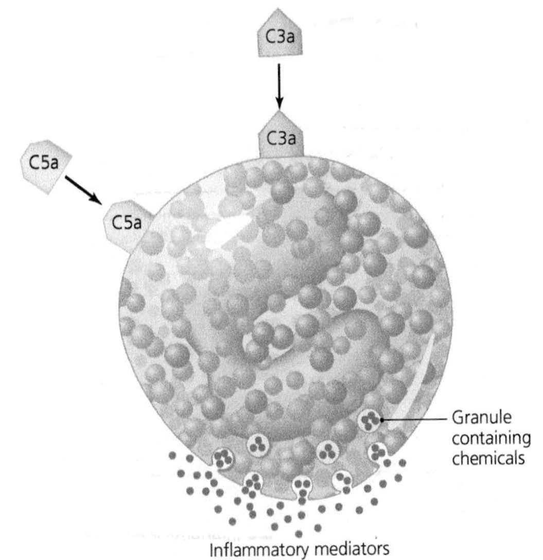

▲ *Figure 14*

The stimulation of inflammation by complement. The complement fragments C3a and C5a bind to platelets, basophils, and mast cells, causing them to release histamine, which in turn stimulates the dilation of arterioles.

Applying Molecular Techniques *How Do Viruses Thwart Interferon?*

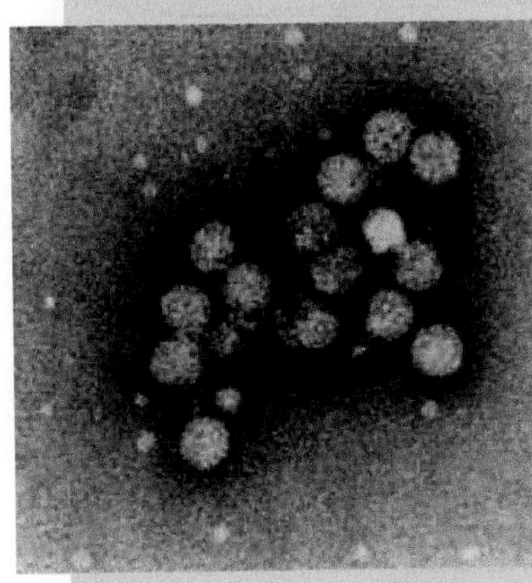

Hepatitis C viruses

Hepatitis C is a viral disease that chronically infects nearly 200 million people worldwide. In an effort to shed light on how viruses thwart the human body's defense mechanisms, researchers at the University of Texas have studied the tactics that the hepatitis C virus uses when infecting a host.

In the human body, interferon is part of the defense against viral infections. When a virus invades a cell, the cell's defense systems produce interferon, which inhibits the spread of the viral infection to neighboring cells. One way that viruses attempt to overcome the body's defenses is by preventing the production of interferon.

Researchers have found that the human body's defense against hepatitis C begins with a gene called *RIG-I*. This gene codes for a protein's shape. The new shape signals other proteins to activate interferon regulatory factor 3 (IRF-3), which turns on the genes that produce interferon.

Hepatitis C virus interrupts this process by producing a protease. Protease chops up the proteins that are needed to carry RIG-I's signal to IRF-3. Since IRF-3 doesn't get the message, no interferon is produced.

Drugs known as protease inhibitors disable the viral protease. Widely used against the human immunodeficiency virus (HIV), protease inhibitors have shown promise in treating patients with hepatitis C. If researchers can identify the exact proteins that are attacked by the hepatitis C protease, they may be able to develop protease inhibitors that are more effective against hepatitis C.

The University of Texas discoveries have far-reaching implications. Tactics used by the hepatitis C virus are likely to be similar to those of the West Nile, influenza, and common cold viruses. Understanding of these mechanisms may lead to the development of treatments against these viruses as well.

Figure 15 ➤

The dilating effect of inflammatory mediators on small blood vessels. The release of mediators from damaged tissue causes nearby arterioles to dilate, which causes capillaries to expand and enables more blood to be delivered to the affected site. The increased blood flow causes the reddening and heat associated with inflammation.

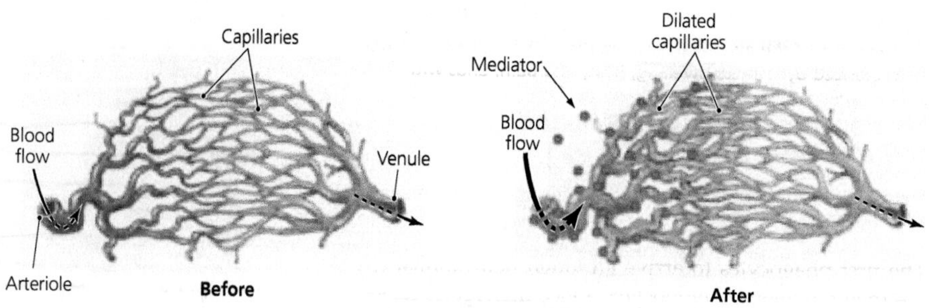

extent) histamine also make small veins more permeable—that is, they cause cells lining the vessels to contract and pull apart, leaving gaps in the walls through which phagocytes can move into the damaged tissue and fight invaders **(Figure 16).** Increased permeability also allows delivery of more blood-borne antimicrobial chemicals to the site.

Dilation of blood vessels in response to inflammatory mediators results in the redness and localized heat associated with inflammation. At the same time, prostaglandins and leukotrienes cause fluid to leak from the more permeable blood vessels and accumulate in the surrounding tissue, resulting in edema, which is responsible for much of the pain of inflammation as pressure is exerted on nerve endings.

Vasodilation and increased permeability also deliver fibrinogen, the blood's clotting protein. Clots forming at the site of injury or infection wall off the area and help prevent pathogens and their toxins from spreading. One result is the formation of *pus,* a fluid containing dead tissue cells, leukocytes, and pathogens in the walled-off area. Pus may push up toward the surface and erupt, or it may remain isolated in the body, where it is slowly absorbed over a period of days. Such an isolated site of infection is called an **abscess.** Pimples, boils, and pustules are examples of abscesses.

The signs and symptoms of inflammation can be treated with antihistamines, which block histamine receptors on blood vessel walls, or with antiprostaglandins. One of the ways aspirin and ibuprofen reduce pain is by acting as antiprostaglandins.

Migration of Phagocytes

Increased blood flow due to vasodilation delivers monocytes and neutrophils to a site of infection. As they arrive, these leukocytes roll along the inside walls of blood vessels until they adhere to the receptors lining the vessels, in a process called **margination.** They then squeeze between the cells of the vessel's wall (diapedesis) and enter the site of infection, usually within an hour of tissue damage. The phagocytes then destroy pathogens via phagocytosis.

As mentioned previously, phagocytes are attracted to the site of infection by chemotactic factors, including C3a, C5a, leukotrienes, and microbial components and toxins.

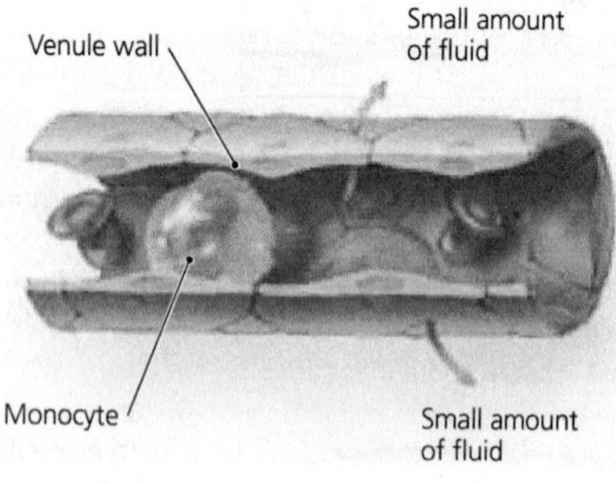

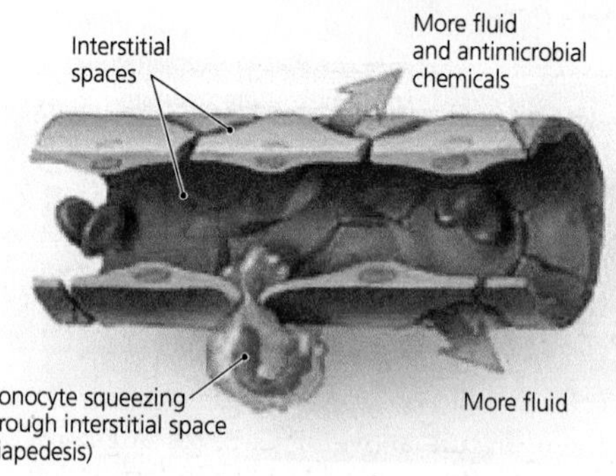

▲ *Figure 16*

Increased vascular permeability during inflammation. The presence of bradykinin, prostaglandins, leukotrienes, or histamine causes cells lining venules to pull apart, allowing phagocytes to leave the bloodstream and more easily reach a site of infection. The leakage of fluid and cells causes the edema and pain associated with inflammation.

Figure 17 ▶

An overview of the events in inflammation. The process, which is characterized by redness, swelling, heat, and pain, ends with tissue repair. *In general, what types of cells are involved in tissue repair?*

Figure 17 Tissue repair is effected by cells that are capable of cytokinesis and differentiation. If fibroblasts are among them, scar tissue is laid down.

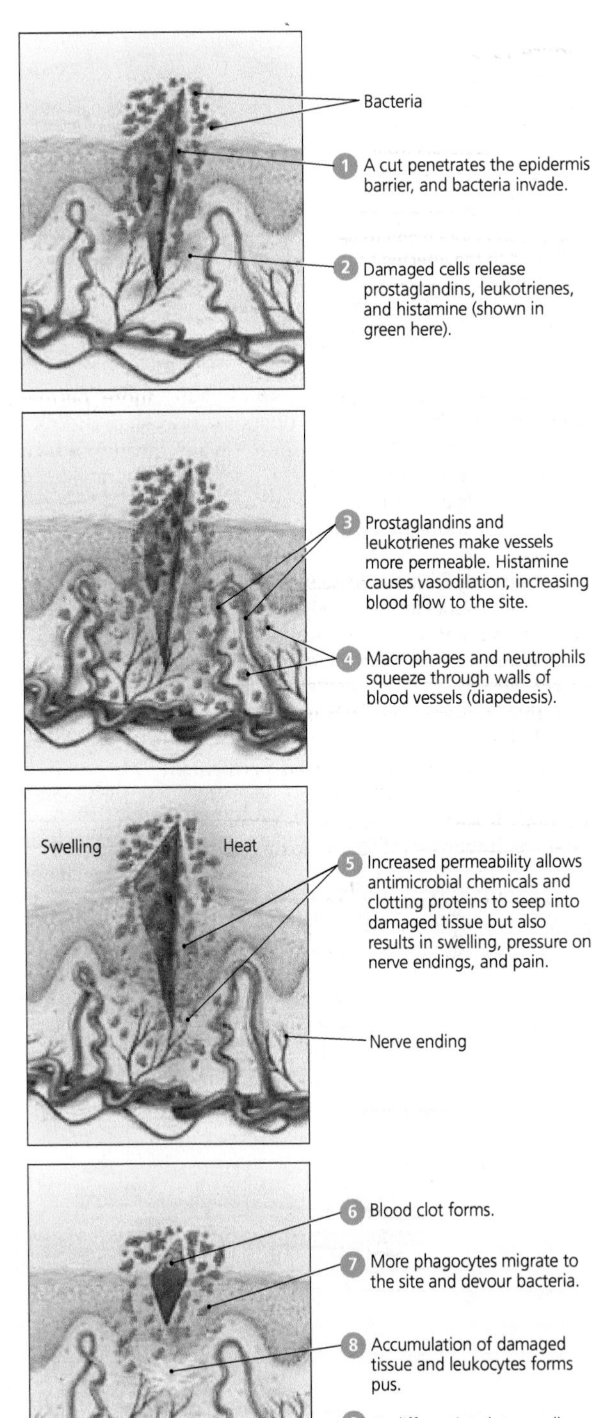
Bacteria
1 A cut penetrates the epidermis barrier, and bacteria invade.
2 Damaged cells release prostaglandins, leukotrienes, and histamine (shown in green here).
3 Prostaglandins and leukotrienes make vessels more permeable. Histamine causes vasodilation, increasing blood flow to the site.
4 Macrophages and neutrophils squeeze through walls of blood vessels (diapedesis).
Swelling
Heat
5 Increased permeability allows antimicrobial chemicals and clotting proteins to seep into damaged tissue but also results in swelling, pressure on nerve endings, and pain.
Nerve ending
6 Blood clot forms.
7 More phagocytes migrate to the site and devour bacteria.
8 Accumulation of damaged tissue and leukocytes forms pus.
9 Undifferentiated stem cells repair the damaged tissue. Blood clot is absorbed or falls off as a scab.

The first phagocytes to arrive are often neutrophils, which are then followed by monocytes. Once monocytes leave the blood, they change and become wandering macrophages, which are especially active phagocytic cells that devour pathogens, damaged tissue cells, and dead neutrophils. Wandering macrophages are a major component of pus.

Tissue Repair

The final stage of inflammation is tissue repair, which in part involves the delivery of extra nutrients and oxygen to the site. Areas of the body where cells regularly undergo cytokinesis, such as the skin and mucous membranes, are repaired rapidly. Some other sites are not fully reparable and form scar tissue.

If the damaged tissue contains undifferentiated stem cells, tissues can be fully restored. For example, a minor skin cut is repaired to such an extent it is no longer visible. However, if cells called *fibroblasts* are involved to a significant extent, scar tissue is formed, inhibiting normal function. Some tissues, such as cardiac muscle and parts of the brain, do not replicate and thus tissue damage cannot be repaired. As a result, these tissues remain damaged following heart attacks and strokes.

Figure 17 gives an overview of the entire inflammatory process. **Table 5** summarizes the chemicals involved in inflammation.

www.microbiologyplace.com **Animations: *Inflammation: Host Defenses: Steps***

CRITICAL THINKING

While using a microscope to examine a sample of pus from a pimple, Maria observed a large number of macrophages. Is the pus from an early or a late stage of infection? How do you know?

Fever

Learning Objective

✓ Explain the benefits of fever in fighting infection.

Fever is a body temperature above 37°C. Fever augments the beneficial effects of inflammation, but like inflammation it also has unpleasant side effects, including malaise, body aches, and tiredness.

The hypothalamus, a portion of the brain just above the brain stem, controls the body's internal (core) temperature. Fever results when the presence of chemicals called

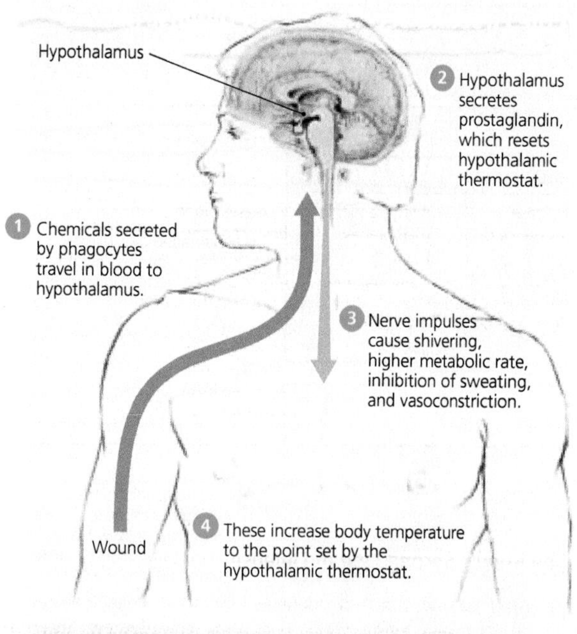
Hypothalamus
2 Hypothalamus secretes prostaglandin, which resets hypothalamic thermostat.
1 Chemicals secreted by phagocytes travel in blood to hypothalamus.
3 Nerve impulses cause shivering, higher metabolic rate, inhibition of sweating, and vasoconstriction.
Wound
4 These increase body temperature to the point set by the hypothalamic thermostat.

▲ *Figure 18*

One theoretical explanation for the production of fever in response to infection.

pyrogens[13] (pī′rō-jenz) trigger the hypothalamic "thermostat" to reset at a higher temperature. Pyrogens include bacterial toxins, cytoplasmic contents of bacteria that are released upon lysis, antibody-antigen complexes formed in adaptive immune responses, and pyrogens released by phagocytes that have phagocytized bacteria. Although the exact mechanism of fever production is not known, the following discussion and **Figure 18** present one possible explanation.

Chemicals produced by phagocytes (1) cause the hypothalamus to secrete prostaglandin, which resets the hypothalamic thermostat by some unknown mechanism (2). The hypothalamus then communicates the new temperature setting to other parts of the brain, which initiate nerve impulses that produce rapid and repetitive muscle contractions (shivering), an increase in metabolic rate, and constriction of blood vessels of the skin (3). These processes combine to raise the body's core temperature until it equals the prescribed temperature setting (4). Because blood vessels in the skin constrict as fever progresses, one effect of inflammation (vasodilation) is undone. The constricted vessels carry less blood to the skin, causing it to feel cold to the touch, even though the body's core temperature is higher. This symptom is the *chill* associated with fever.

Fever continues as long as pyrogens are present. As an infection comes under control and fewer active phagocytes are involved, the level of pyrogens decreases, the thermostat is reset to 37°C, and the body begins to cool by perspiring, lowering the metabolic rate, and dilating blood vessels in the skin. These processes, collectively called the *crisis* of a fever, are a sign that the infection has been overcome and that body temperature is returning to normal.

The increased temperature of fever enhances the effects of interferons, inhibits the growth of some microorganisms, and is thought to enhance the performance of phagocytes, the activity of cells of specific immunity, and the process of tissue repair. However, if fever is too high, critical proteins are denatured; additionally, nerve impulses are inhibited, resulting in hallucinations, coma, and even death.

Because of the potential benefits of fever, many doctors recommend that patients refrain from taking fever-reducing drugs unless the fever is prolonged or extremely high. Other physicians believe that the benefits of fever are too slight to justify enduring the adverse symptoms.

CRITICAL THINKING

How do drugs such as aspirin and ibuprofen act to reduce fever? Should you take fever-reducing drugs or let a fever run its course?

Table 6 summarizes the barriers, cells, chemicals, and processes involved in the body's first two, nonspecific lines of defense.

[13]From Greek *pyr*, meaning fire, and *genein*, meaning to produce.

Table 5 Chemical Mediators of Inflammation

Vasodilating chemicals	Histamine, serotonin, bradykinin, prostaglandins
Chemotactic factors	Fibrin, collagen, mast cell chemotactic factors, bacterial peptides
Substances with both vasodilating and chemotactic effects	Complement fragments C5a and C3a, interferons, interleukins, leukotrienes, platelet secretions

Table 6 A Summary of Some Nonspecific Components of the First and Second Lines of Defense (Innate Immunity)

First Line	Second Line						
Barriers and Associated Chemicals	Phagocytes	Extracellular Killing	Complement	Interferons	Defensins	Inflammation	Fever
Skin and mucous membranes prevent the entrance of pathogens; chemicals (e.g. sweat, acid, lysozyme, mucus) enhance the protection	Macrophages, neutrophils, and eosinophils ingest and destroy pathogens	Eosinophils and NK lymphocytes kill pathogens without phagocytizing them	Components attract phagocytes, stimulate inflammation, and attack a pathogens cytoplasmic membrane	Increase resistance of cells to viral infection, slow the spread of disease	Interfere with membranes, internal signaling, and metabolism; act against pathogens	Increases blood flow, capillary permeability, and migration of leukocytes into infected area; walls off infected region, increases local temperature	Mobilizes defenses, accelerates repairs, inhibits pathogens

CHAPTER SUMMARY

An Overview of the Body's Defenses

1. Humans have **species resistance** to certain pathogens, as well as three overlapping lines of defense. The first two lines of defense compose **innate immunity,** which is generally nonspecific and protects the body against a wide variety of potential pathogens. A third line of defense is **adaptive immunity,** which is a specific response to a particular pathogen. www.microbiologyplace.com **Animations: *Host Defenses: Overview***

The Body's First Line of Defense

1. The first line of defense includes the skin, composed of an outer **epidermis** and a deeper dermis. **Dendritic cells** of the epidermis devour pathogens. Sweat glands of the skin produce salty sweat containing the enzyme called **lysozyme** and **antimicrobial peptides** (defensins), which are small peptide chains that act against a broad range of pathogens. Sebum is an oily substance of the skin that lowers pH, which deters the growth of many pathogens.
2. The mucous membranes, another part of the body's first line of defense, are composed of tightly packed cells often coated with sticky mucus secreted by **goblet cells,** which are produced by **stem cells.**
3. **Microbial antagonism,** the competition between **normal microbiota** and potential pathogens, also contributes to the body's first line of defense.
4. Tears contain antibacterial lysozyme and also flush invaders from the eyes. Saliva similarly protects the teeth. The low pH of the stomach inhibits most microbes that are swallowed.
5. Microbial molecules bind to **Toll-like receptors (TLRs)** on host cells' membranes or to **NOD proteins** inside the cell, triggering innate immune responses.

The Body's Second Line of Defense

1. The second line of defense includes cells (especially **phagocytes**), antimicrobial chemicals (**complement, interferons,** and antimicrobial peptides), and processes (**phagocytosis,** inflammation, and fever).
2. Blood is composed of **formed elements** (cells and parts of cells) within a fluid called **plasma.** Serum is that portion of plasma without clotting factors. The formed elements are **erythrocytes** (red blood cells), **leukocytes** (white blood cells), and **platelets.**
3. Based on their appearance in stained blood smears, leukocytes are grouped as either granulocytes (**basophils, eosinophils,** and **neutrophils**) or agranulocytes (**lymphocytes, monocytes**). When monocytes leave the blood they become macrophages.
4. Basophils function to release histamine during inflammation, whereas eosinophils and neutrophils phagocytize pathogens. They exit capillaries via **diapedesis** (emigration).
5. **Macrophages,** neutrophils, and **dendritic cells** are phagocytic cells of the second line of defense. Many are named for their location in the body: wandering macrophages, alveolar macrophages (the lungs), microglia (the nervous system), and Kupffer cells (the liver).
6. A **differential white blood cell count** is a lab technique that indicates the relative numbers of leukocyte types; it can be helpful in diagnosing disease.
7. **Chemotactic factors,** such as chemicals called **chemokines,** attract phagocytic leukocytes to the site of damage or invasion. Phagocytes attach to pathogens via a process called **adherence.** www.microbiologyplace.com **Animations: *Host Defenses: Phagocytosis: Overview***

8. **Opsonization,** the coating of pathogens by proteins called **opsonins,** makes those pathogens more vulnerable to phagocytes. A phagocyte's pseudopodia then surround the microbe to form a sac called a **phagosome,** which fuses with a lysosome to form a **phagolysosome,** in which the pathogen is killed.
www.microbiologyplace.com **Animations: *Host Defenses: Phagocytosis: Mechanism***
9. Leukocytes can distinguish between the body's normal cells and foreign cells because leukocytes have receptor molecules for foreign cells' components or because the foreign cells are opsonized by complement or antibodies.
10. Eosinophils and **natural killer (NK) lymphocytes** attack non-phagocytically, especially in the case of helminth infections and cancerous cells. **Eosinophilia**—an abnormally high number of eosinophils in the blood—typically indicates such a helminth infection.
11. The **complement system** is a set of proteins that act as chemotactic attractants, trigger inflammation and fever, and ultimately effect the destruction of foreign cells via the formation of **membrane attack complexes (MACs),** which result in multiple, fatal holes in pathogens' membranes. Complement is activated by a classical pathway involving antibodies, by an alternative pathway triggered by bacterial chemicals, or by a lectin pathway triggered by a polysaccharide found on microbial surfaces.
www.microbiologyplace.com **Animations: *Host Defenses: Complement***
12. **Interferons (IFNs)** are protein molecules that inhibit the spread of viral infections. **Alpha interferons** and **beta interferons,** which are released within hours of infection, trigger **antiviral proteins** to prevent viral reproduction in neighboring cells. **Gamma interferons,** produced days after initial infection, activate macrophages and neutrophils.
13. **Acute inflammation** develops quickly and damages pathogens, whereas chronic inflammation develops slowly and can cause bodily damage that can lead to disease. Signs and symptoms of inflammation include redness, heat, swelling, and pain.
www.microbiologyplace.com **Animations: *Host Defenses: Inflammation***
14. The process of blood clotting triggers formation of **bradykinin**—a potent mediator of inflammation.
15. Macrophages with Toll-like receptors release **prostaglandins** and **leukotrienes,** which increase permeability of blood vessels. **Mast cells,** basophils, and platelets release **histamine** when exposed to peptides from the complement system. Blood clots may isolate an infected area to form an **abscess** such as a pimple or boil.
16. When leukocytes rolling along blood vessel walls reach a site of infection, they stick to the wall in a process called **margination** and then undergo diapedesis to arrive at the site of tissue damage. The increased blood flow of inflammation also brings extra nutrients and oxygen to the infection site to aid in repair.
17. **Fever** results when chemicals called **pyrogens,** including substances released by bacteria and phagocytes, affect the hypothalamus in a way that causes it to reset body temperature to a higher level. The exact process of fever and its control are not fully understood.

QUESTIONS FOR REVIEW

Access more review material (including animations and practice tests) online at www.microbiologyplace.com.

Multiple Choice

1. Fixed phagocytes of the epidermis are called
   a. lysozymes.
   b. goblet cells.
   c. Kupffer cells.
   d. dendritic cells.
2. Mucus-secreting membranes are found in the
   a. urinary system.
   b. digestive cavity.
   c. respiratory passages.
   d. all of the above
3. The complement system involves
   a. the production of antigens and antibodies.
   b. serum proteins involved in nonspecific defense.
   c. a set of genes that distinguish foreign cells from body cells.
   d. the elimination of undigested remnants of microorganisms.
4. The alternative pathway
   a. involves factors B, D, and P.
   b. involves the cleavage of C5 to form C9.
   c. is more efficient than the classical pathway.
   d. involves recognition of antigens bound to specific antibodies.
5. Complement must be inactivated because if it were not,
   a. viruses could continue to multiply inside host cells using the host's own metabolic machinery.
   b. necessary interferons would not be produced.
   c. protein synthesis would be inhibited, thus halting important cell processes.
   d. it would make holes in the body's own cells.
6. The type of interferon present late in an infection is
   a. alpha interferon.
   b. beta interferon.
   c. gamma interferon.
   d. delta interferon.

7. Interferons
   a. do not protect the cell that secretes them.
   b. stimulate the activity of neutrophils.
   c. cause muscle aches, chills, and fever.
   d. all of the above

8. In which of the following choices are events in the correct order?
   a. the formation of a MAC, holes in the pathogen's cell membrane, a cascade of reactions, the binding of C1
   b. the binding of C1, a cascade of reactions, the formation of a MAC, holes in the pathogen's cell membrane
   c. a cascade of reactions, the binding of C1, the formation of a MAC, holes in the pathogen's cell membrane
   d. the binding of C1, a cascade of reactions, holes in the pathogen's cell membrane, the formation of a MAC

9. Toll-like receptors (TLRs) act to
   a. bind microbial proteins and polysaccharides.
   b. induce phagocytosis.
   c. cause phagocytic chemotaxis.
   d. destroy microbial cells.

10. Which of the following binds iron?
   a. lactoferrin
   b. siderophores
   c. transferrin
   d. all of the above

Modified True/False

Indicate which statements are true. Correct all false statements by writing in the blank a word that, if substituted for the italicized word, would make the statement true.

____ 1. The surface cells of the epidermis of the skin are *alive.*

____ 2. The surface cells of mucous membranes are *alive.*

____ 3. Wandering macrophages experience *diapedesis.*

____ 4. *Monocytes* are immature macrophages.

____ 5. *Lymphocytes* are large agranulocytes.

____ 6. *Phagocytes* exhibit chemotaxis toward a pathogen.

____ 7. Adherence involves the binding between complementary chemicals on a phagocyte and on the membrane of a *body cell.*

____ 8. *Opsonins* result when a phagocyte's pseudopodia surround a microbe and fuse to form a sac.

____ 9. Lysosomes fuse with phagosomes to form *digestive vesicles.*

____10. A membrane attack complex drills circular holes in a *macrophage.*

____11. Rubor, calor, tumor, and dolor are associated with *fever.*

____12. Acute and chronic inflammation exhibit *similar* signs and symptoms.

____13. The *hypothalamus* of the brain controls body temperature.

____14. Defensins are *phagocytic cells* of the second line of defense.

____15. *NETs* are webs produced by neutrophils to trap microbes.

Matching

In the blank beside each cell, chemical, or process in the left column, write the letter of the line of defense that first applies. Each letter may be used several times.

1. ____ Inflammation
2. ____ Monocytes
3. ____ Lactoferrin
4. ____ Fever
5. ____ Dendritic cells
6. ____ Alpha interferon
7. ____ Mucous membrane of the digestive tract
8. ____ Neutrophils
9. ____ Epidermis
10. ____ Lysozyme
11. ____ Goblet cells
12. ____ Phagocytes
13. ____ Sebum
14. ____ T lymphocytes
15. ____ Antimicrobial peptides

A. First line of defense
B. Second line of defense
C. Third line of defense

Write the letter of the description that applies to each of the following terms.

1. ____ Goblet cell
2. ____ Lysozyme
3. ____ Kupffer cell
4. ____ Dendritic cell
5. ____ Cell from sebaceous gland
6. ____ Bone marrow stem cell
7. ____ Eosinophil
8. ____ Alveolar macrophage
9. ____ Microglia
10. ____ Wandering macrophage

A. Leukocyte that primarily attacks parasitic worms
B. Phagocytic cell in lungs
C. Secretes sebum
D. Devours pathogens in epidermis of skin
E. Breaks bonds in bacterial cell wall
F. Phagocytic cell in central nervous system
G. Phagocytic cell in liver
H. Develops into formed elements of blood
I. Intercellular scavenger
J. Secretes mucus

Short Answer

1. In order for a pathogen to cause disease, what three things must happen?
2. How does a phagocyte "know" it is in contact with a pathogen instead of another body cell?
3. Give three characteristics of the epidermis that make it an intolerable environment for most microorganisms.
4. What is the role of Toll-like receptors in innate immune responses?
5. Describe the classical complement cascade pathway from C1 to the MAC.
6. How do NOD proteins differ from Toll-like receptors?

CRITICAL THINKING

1. John received a chemical burn on his arm and was instructed by his physician to take an over-the-counter, anti-inflammatory medication for the painful, red, swollen lesions. When Charles suffered pain, redness, and swelling from an infected cut on his foot, he decided to take the same anti-inflammatory drug because his symptoms matched John's symptoms. How is Charles's inflammation like that of John? How is it different? Is it appropriate for Charles to medicate his cut with the same medicine John used?
2. What might happen to someone whose body did not produce C3? C5?
3. My-lim, age 65, has had diabetes for 40 years, with resulting damage to the small blood vessels in her feet and toes. Her circulation is impaired. How might this condition affect her vulnerability to infection?
4. A patient's chart shows that eosinophils make up 8% of his white blood cells. What does this lead you to suspect? Would your suspicions change if you learned that the patient had spent the previous three years as an anthropologist living among an African tribe? What is the normal percentage of eosinophils?
5. There are two kinds of agranulocytes in the blood—monocytes and lymphocytes. Janice noted that monocytes are phagocytic and that lymphocytes are not. She wondered why two agranulocytes would be so different. What facts of hematopoiesis can help her answer her question?
6. A patient has a genetic disorder that prevents him from synthesizing C8 and C9. What effect does this have on his ability to resist bloodborne Gram-negative and Gram-positive bacteria? What would happen if C3 and C5 fragments were also inactivated?
7. Sweat glands in the armpits secrete perspiration with a pH close to neutral (7.0). How does this fact help explain body odor in this area as compared to other parts of the skin?
8. Scientists can raise "germ-free" animals in axenic environments. Would such animals be as healthy as their worldly counterparts?
9. Compare and contrast the protective structures and chemicals of the skin and mucous membranes.
10. Scientists are interested in developing antimicrobial drugs that act like the body's normal antimicrobial peptides. What advantage might such a drug have over antibiotics?

ANSWERS TO QUESTIONS FOR REVIEW

Multiple Choice
1. d; 2. d; 3. b; 4. a; 5. d; 6. c; 7. d; 8. b; 9. a; 10. d

Modified True/False
1. dead; 2. true; 3. true; 4. true; 5. monocytes; 6. true; 7. pathogen; 8. phagocytosis; 9. phagolysosomes; 10. pathogen's membrane; 11. inflammation; 12. true; 13. true; 14. protective chemicals; 15. true

Matching
First section: 1. B; 2. B; 3. B; 4. B; 5. A; 6. B; 7. A; 8. B; 9. A; 10. A; 11. A; 12. B; 13. A;14. C; 15. B; Second section: 1. J; 2. E; 3. G; 4. D; 5. C; 6. H; 7. A; 8. B; 9. F; 10. I

CREDITS

Illustration Credits
2–4, 7, 8, 16–18: Kenneth Probst. 10, 11, 13, 14, Case Study 1: Precision Graphics.

Photo Credits
Opener: SPL/Photo Researchers. 1: David Scharf/Peter Arnold. 5a.1,2: Ed Resche/Peter Arnold. 5a.3: Carolina Biological/Phototake. 5b.1,2: J.O. Ballard. 9: Biology Media/Photo Researchers. 12: Sucharit Bhakdi. Applying Microbial Techniques: CDC. Beneficial Microbe 1: Steve Gschmeissner/SPL/Photo Researchers. Highlight 1: Peter Parks /imagequestmarine.com.

Adaptive Immunity

CHAPTER OUTLINE

MicroPrep Pre-Test: Take the pre-test for this chapter on the web. Visit www.microbiologyplace.com.

Imagine that your friend has been bitten on the hand by a dog. The skin is broken, and the wound is deep. Your friend washes the wound with soap and water but does not use any of the more powerful antimicrobial agents. Within 24 hours, his hand and arm are swollen, red, and painful, and he is feeling seriously ill. His body's inflammatory response is in full force as manifested by the swelling and pain, but it isn't strong enough to overcome the virulent invading microorganisms.

Fortunately, infections like this trigger the body's *adaptive immunity* in addition to the innate defense responses. In this chapter we will explore what happens when facets of adaptive immunity—especially lymphocytes—enter the battle against microbial invaders.

White blood cells called lymphocytes are an important component of the specific defense system.

Innate immunity includes two lines of rapid defense against microbial pathogens. The first line includes intact skin and mucous membranes, whereas the second line includes phagocytosis, complement, inflammation, and fever. As is evident in the chapter opening story, innate defenses do not always offer enough protection in defending the body. Although the mechanisms of innate immunity are readily available and fast-acting, they do not adapt to enhance the effectiveness of response to the great variety of pathogens confronting us—a fever is a fever, whether it is triggered by a mild influenzavirus or the deadly Ebola virus. The body augments the mechanisms of innate immunity with a third line of defense that destroys invaders while becoming more effective in the process. This response is called *adaptive immunity*.

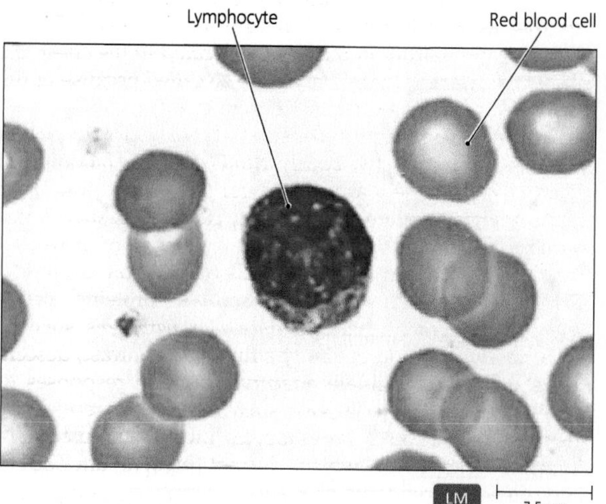

▲ *Figure 1*

Lymphocytes play a central role in adaptive immunity. A resting lymphocyte is the smallest leukocyte—slightly larger than a red blood cell.

Overview of Adaptive Immunity

Learning Objectives

- ✓ Describe five distinctive attributes of adaptive immunity.
- ✓ List the two basic types of white blood cells involved in adaptive immunity.
- ✓ List two basic divisions of adaptive immunity and describe their targets.

Adaptive immunity is the body's ability to recognize and then mount a defense against distinct invaders and their products, whether they are protozoa, fungi, bacteria, viruses, or toxins. *Immunologists*—scientists who study the cells and chemicals involved in immunity—are continually refining and revising our knowledge of adaptive immunity. In this chapter, we will examine some of what they have discovered.

Adaptive immunity has five distinctive attributes:

- *Specificity.* Any particular adaptive immune response acts only against one particular molecular shape and not against others. Adaptive immune responses are precisely tailored reactions against specific attackers, whereas innate immunity involves more generalized responses to molecular shapes common to many microbes.
- *Inducibility.* Cells of adaptive immunity activate only in response to specific pathogens.
- *Clonality.* Once induced, cells of adaptive immunity proliferate to form many generations of nearly identical cells, which are collectively called *clones.*
- *Unresponsiveness to self.* As a rule, adaptive immunity does not act against normal body cells; in other words, adaptive immune responses are self-tolerant. Several mechanisms help ensure that immune responses do not attack the body itself.
- *Memory.* An adaptive immune response has "memory" about specific pathogens; that is, it adapts to respond faster and more effectively in subsequent encounters with a particular type of pathogen or toxin.

These aspects of adaptive immunity involve the activities of **lymphocytes** (lim'fō-sītz), which are a type of leukocyte (white blood cell) that acts against specific pathogens. Lymphocytes in their resting state are the smallest white blood cells, and each is characterized by a large, round, central nucleus surrounded by a thin rim of cytoplasm **(Figure 1).** Initially, lymphocytes of humans form in the *red bone marrow,* located in the ends of long bones in juveniles and in the centers of adult flat bones such as the ribs and hip bones. These sites contain *blood stem cells,* which are cells that give rise to all types of blood cells including lymphocytes.

Although lymphocytes appear identical in the microscope, scientists make distinctions between two main types—*B lymphocytes* and *T lymphocytes*—according to integral surface proteins present in each lymphocyte's cytoplasmic membrane. These proteins allow lymphocytes to recognize specific pathogens and toxins by their molecular shapes and play roles in intercellular communication among immune cells.

Lymphocytes must undergo a maturation process. **B lymphocytes,** which are also called **B cells,** arise and mature in the red bone marrow of adults. However, the designation "B" does not stand for bone marrow, but instead for the *bursa of Fabricius,* which is a unique lymphoid organ located near the end of the intestinal tract in birds. Mammals do not have this bursa, which is where B lymphocytes were originally identified, but the name "B cell" has been retained.

T lymphocytes, also known as **T cells,** begin in bone marrow as well but do not mature there. Instead, T cells travel to and mature in the *thymus,* located in the chest just above the heart. T lymphocytes are so called because of the role the thymus plays in their maturation.

Adaptive immunity consists of two basic types of responses. Historically, bodily fluids such as blood were called *humors* (the Latin word for moisture), and thus immunologists call immune activity centered in such fluids **humoral immune responses.** Descendants of activated B cells are the main defensive cells of humoral immunity. Once induced, they secrete soluble proteins called *antibodies* that act against *extracellular pathogens* such as bacteria and fungi in the body's fluids. In contrast, descendants of T cells regulate adaptive immune responses or attack *intracellular pathogens,* such as viruses replicating inside a cell. Such T lymphocytes mount **cell-mediated immune responses,** which do not involve antibodies. Long-lived descendants of B and T lymphocytes maintain the long-term ability to mount adaptive immunological response against specific pathogens—an ability sometimes called immunological memory.

www.microbiologyplace.com **Animations: *Host Defenses: Humoral Immunity: Overview* and *Cell-Mediated Immunity: Overview***

Both humoral immune responses against extracellular pathogens and cell-mediated immune responses against intracellular pathogens are powerful defensive reactions that have the potential to severely and fatally attack the body's own cells. The body must regulate adaptive immune responses to prevent damage; for example, an immune response requires multiple chemical signals before proceeding, thus reducing the possibility of randomly triggering an immune response against uninfected healthy tissue. Autoimmune disorders, hypersensitivities, or immunodeficiency diseases result when regulation is insufficient or overexcited.

Elements of Adaptive Immunity

Just as the program at a dramatic presentation might present a synopsis of the performance and introduce the actors and their roles, the following sections present elements of adaptive immunity by describing the "stage" and introducing the "cast of characters" involved in adaptive immunity. We will examine the *lymphatic system*—the organs, tissues, and cells of adaptive immunity; then we consider the molecules called *antigens* that trigger adaptive immune responses; next, we take a look at *antibodies;* and finally we examine special *chemical signals* and *mediators* involved in coordinating and controlling a specific immune response.

First, we turn our attention to the lymphatic system, which plays an important role in the production, maturation, and housing of the cells that function in adaptive immunity.

The Tissues and Organs of the Lymphatic System

Learning Objectives

- ✓ Contrast the flow of lymph with the flow of blood.
- ✓ Describe the primary and secondary organs of the lymphatic system.
- ✓ Describe the importance of red bone marrow, the thymus, lymph nodes, and other lymphoid tissues.

The **lymphatic system** is composed of the *lymphatic vessels,* which conduct the flow of a liquid called *lymph;* and lymphatic cells, tissues, and organs, which are directly involved in adaptive immunity **(Figure 2).** Taken together, the components of the lymphatic system constitute a surveillance system that screens the tissues of the body—particularly possible points of entry such as the throat and intestinal tract—for foreign molecules. We begin by examining lymphatic vessels.

The Lymphatic Vessels and the Flow of Lymph

Lymphatic vessels form a one-way system that conducts **lymph** (pronounced limf) from local tissues and returns it to the circulatory system. Lymph is a colorless, watery liquid similar in composition to blood plasma; indeed, lymph arises from fluid that has leaked out of blood vessels into the surrounding intercellular spaces. Unlike blood which supplies nutrients, lymph contains wastes such as degraded proteins and toxins. Lymph is first conducted by remarkably permeable *lymphatic capillaries,* which are located in most parts of the body (exceptions include the bone marrow, brain, and spinal cord). From the lymphatic capillaries, lymph passes into increasingly larger lymphatic vessels until it finally flows via two large *lymphatic ducts* into blood vessels near the heart. One-way valves ensure that lymph flows only toward the heart as skeletal muscular activity squeezes the lymphatic vessels. Unlike the cardiovascular system, the lymphatic system has no unique pump and is not circular; that is, lymph flows in only one direction—toward the heart. Located at various points within the system of lymphatic vessels are about 1000 *lymph nodes,* which house leukocytes that recognize and attack foreigners present in the lymph, allowing for immune system surveillance and interactions.

Lymphoid Organs

Once lymphocytes have arisen and matured in the *primary lymphoid organs* of the red bone marrow and thymus, they migrate to *secondary lymphoid organs* and *tissues,* including lymph nodes, spleen, and other less-organized accumulations of lymphoid tissue, where they in effect lie in wait for foreign microbes. Among these sites are hundreds of **lymph nodes** located throughout the body but concentrated in the cervical (neck), inguinal (groin), axillary (armpit), and abdominal regions (see Figure 2). Each lymph node receives lymph from numerous afferent

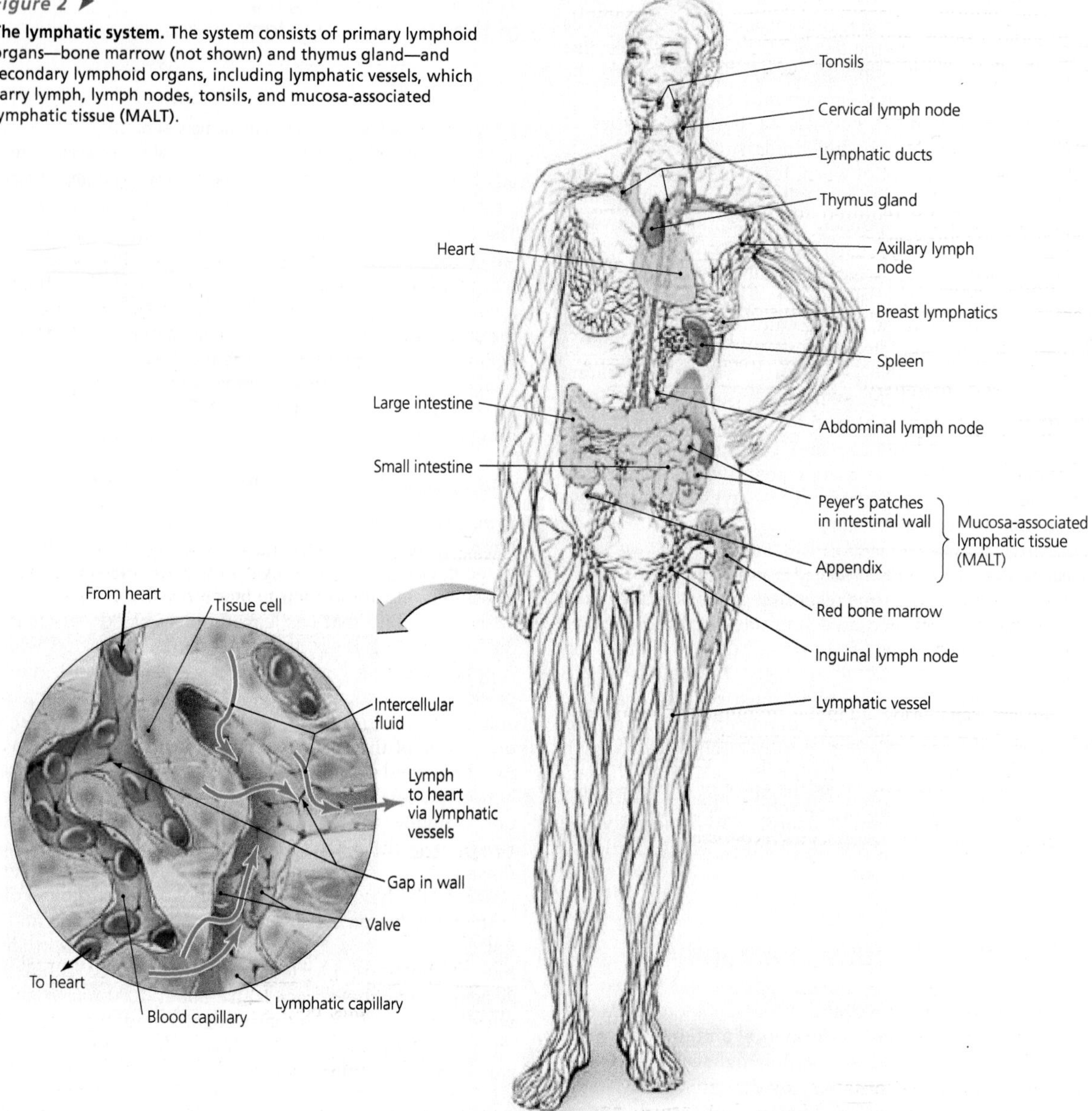

Figure 2 ➤

The lymphatic system. The system consists of primary lymphoid organs—bone marrow (not shown) and thymus gland—and secondary lymphoid organs, including lymphatic vessels, which carry lymph, lymph nodes, tonsils, and mucosa-associated lymphatic tissue (MALT).

(inbound) lymphatic vessels and drains lymph into just one or two efferent (outbound) lymphatic vessels **(Figure 3).** Essentially, lymph nodes are sites to facilitate interactions among immune cells and between immune cells and material draining in the lymph from throughout the body.

A node has a medullary (central) maze of passages, which filter the lymph passing through and house numerous lymphocytes that survey the lymph for foreign molecules and mount specific immune responses against them. The cortex (outer) portion of a lymph node consists of a tough capsule surrounding *germinal centers,* which is where clones of B cells replicate.

CRITICAL THINKING

The cross-sectional area of the afferent lymphatic vessels arriving at a lymph node is greater than the cross-sectional area of the efferent lymphatics exiting the lymph node. The result is that lymph moves slowly through a lymph node. What advantage does this provide the body?

The lymphatic system contains other secondary lymphoid tissues and organs, including the spleen, the tonsils, and *mucosa-associated lymphatic tissue* (*MALT*; see Figure 2). The spleen is similar in structure and function to lymph nodes, except that it filters blood instead of lymph. The spleen removes bacteria, viruses, toxins, and other foreign matter from the blood. It also cleanses the blood of old and damaged blood cells, stores blood platelets (which are required for the proper clotting of blood), and stores blood components such as iron.

The tonsils and MALT lack the tough outer capsules of lymph nodes and the spleen, but they function in somewhat the same way by physically trapping foreign particles and microbes. MALT includes the appendix; lymphoid tissue of the respiratory tract, vagina, urinary bladder, and mammary glands; and discrete bits of lymphoid tissue called *Peyer's patches* in the wall of the small intestine. MALT contains most of the body's lymphocytes.

CRITICAL THINKING

As part of the treatment for some cancers, physicians kill the cancer patients' dividing cells, including the stem cells that produce leukocytes, and then give the patients a bone marrow transplant from a healthy donor. Which cell is the most important cell in such transplanted marrow?

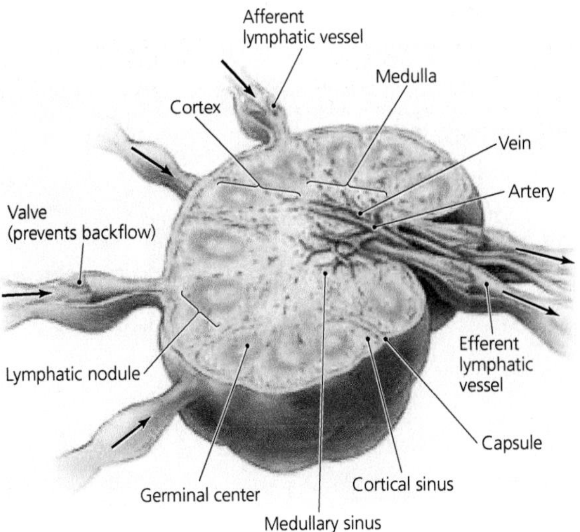

▲ *Figure 3*

A lymph node. Lymph enters the node through afferent lymphatic vessels and exits through one or two efferent lymphatic vessels. The outer cortex contains germinal centers, where B lymphocytes proliferate; the inner medulla contains numerous lymphocytes that encounter foreign antigens. A tough capsule surrounds the entire node. *Why do lymph nodes enlarge during an infection?*

Figure 3 *During an infection, lymphocytes multiply profusely in lymph nodes. This proliferation, and swelling caused by the secretion of inflammatory chemicals, causes lymph nodes to enlarge.*

We are considering adaptive immunity in terms of a "play" taking place on the stage of the lymphatic system with "actors"—the lymphocytes circulating in lymph and lymphoid organs where they await the entry of pathogens and toxins. Now, we turn our attention to another "actor"—the foreign molecules that lymphocytes recognize.

Antigens

Learning Objectives

- ✓ Identify the characteristics of antigens that stimulate effective immune responses.
- ✓ Distinguish among exogenous antigens, endogenous antigens, and autoantigens.

Adaptive immune responses are not directed against whole bacteria, fungi, protozoa, or viruses, but instead against portions of cells, viruses, and even parts of single molecules that the body recognizes as foreign and worthy of attack. Immunologists call these biochemical shapes **antigens**[1] (an'ti-jenz). They bind to lymphocytes and can trigger adaptive immune responses. Antigens from pathogens and toxins are the "villains" of our story.

[1] From *anti*body *gen*erator; antibodies are proteins secreted during a humoral immune response that bind to specific regions of antigens.

Properties of Antigens

Not every molecule is an effective antigen. Among the properties that make certain molecules more effective at provoking adaptive immunity are a molecule's *shape, size,* and *complexity*. The body recognizes antigens by the three-dimensional shapes of regions called **epitopes,** which are also known as *antigenic determinants,* because they are the actual part of an antigen that determines an immune response **(Figure 4a).**

In general, larger molecules with molecular masses (often called molecular weights) between 5000 and 100,000 daltons are better antigens than smaller ones. The most effective antigens are large foreign macromolecules such as proteins and glycoproteins, but carbohydrates and lipids can be antigenic. Small molecules, especially those with a molecular mass under 5000 daltons, make poor antigens by themselves because they evade detection. Such small molecules, called *haptens,* can become antigenic when bound to larger, carrier molecules (often proteins). For example, the fungal product penicillin is too small by itself (molecular mass: 302 daltons) to trigger a specific immune response. However, bound to a carrier protein in the blood, penicillin

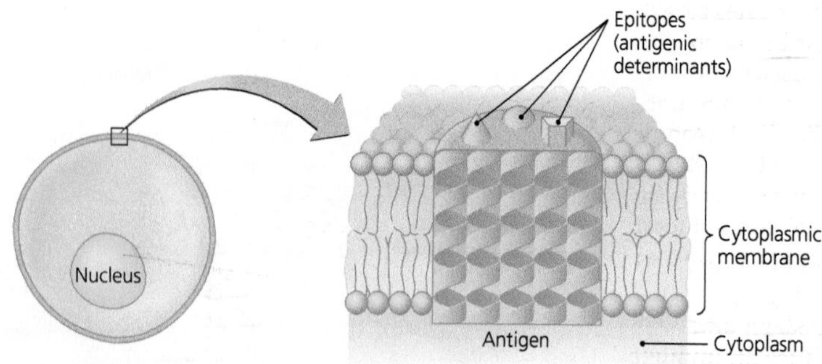

(a) Epitopes (antigenic determinants)

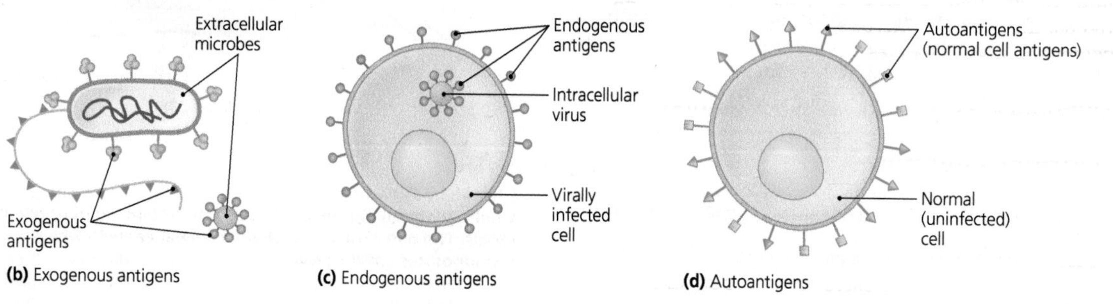

(b) Exogenous antigens (c) Endogenous antigens (d) Autoantigens

▲ *Figure 4*

Antigens, molecules that provoke a specific immune response. (a) Epitopes or antigenic determinants, the three-dimensional regions of antigens whose shapes are recognized by cells of the immune system. **(b–d)** Categories of antigens based on their relationship to the body. Exogenous antigens originate from microbes located outside the body's cells; endogenous antigens are produced by intracellular microbes and are typically incorporated into a host cell's cytoplasmic membrane; autoantigens are components of normal, uninfected body cells that might mistakenly be recognized as foreign.

can become antigenic and trigger an allergic response in some patients.

Complex molecules make better antigens than simple ones because they have more epitopes, like a gemstone with its many facets. For example, starch, which is a very large polymer of repeating glucose subunits, is not a good antigen despite its large size, because it lacks structural complexity. In contrast, complicated molecules, such as glycoproteins and phospholipids, have multiple distinctive shapes and novel combinations of subunits that cells of the immune system recognize as foreign.

Examples of antigens include components of bacterial cell walls, capsules, pili, and flagella, as well as the external and internal proteins of viruses, fungi, and protozoa. Many toxins and some nucleic acid molecules are also antigenic. Invading microorganisms are not the only source of antigens; for example, food may contain antigens called *allergens* that provoke allergic reactions, and inhaled dust contains mite feces, pollen grains, dander (flakes of skin), and other antigenic and allergenic particles.

Types of Antigens

Though immunologists categorize antigens in various ways, one especially important way is to group antigens according to their relationship to the body:

- **Exogenous[2] antigens (Figure 4b).** Exogenous (eks-oj'en-us) antigens include toxins and other secretions and components of microbial cell walls, membranes, flagella, and pili.
- **Endogenous[3] antigens (Figure 4c).** Protozoa, fungi, bacteria, and viruses that reproduce inside a body's cells produce endogenous antigens. The immune system cannot assess the health of the body's cells; it responds to endogenous antigens only if the body's cells incorporate such antigens into their cytoplasmic membranes, leading to their external display.

[2]From Greek *exo,* meaning without, and *genein,* meaning to produce.
[3]From Greek *endon,* meaning within.

- **Autoantigens**[4] **(Figure 4d).** Antigenic molecules found on an individual's normal (uninfected) cells are autoantigens (or *self-antigens*). As we will discuss more fully in a later section, immune cells that treat autoantigens as if they were foreign are normally eliminated during the development of the immune system. This phenomenon, called *self-tolerance*, prevents the body from mounting an immune response against itself.

So far, we have examined two aspects of immune responses in terms of an analogy to a stage play—the lymphoid organs and tissues provide the stage, and antigens of pathogens are the villains that induce an immune response with their epitopes (antigenic determinants). Next, we examine the activities of lymphocytes in more detail. Recall that B and T lymphocytes act against antigens; they are the "heroes" of the action. We begin by considering B lymphocytes.

B Lymphocytes (B cells) and Antibodies

Learning Objectives

- Describe the characteristic of B lymphocytes that furnishes them specificity.
- Describe the basic structure of an immunoglobulin molecule.
- Contrast the structure and function of the five classes of immunoglobulins.

B lymphocytes are found in the spleen, MALT, and primarily in the germinal centers of lymph nodes; only a small percentage of B cells circulate in the blood. The major function of B cells is the secretion of soluble antibodies, which we examine in more detail shortly. As we have established, B cells function in humoral immune responses, each of which is against only a particular epitope. How is such specificity developed and maintained? Specificity comes from membrane proteins called *B cell receptors.*

Specificity of the B Cell Receptor (BCR)

The surface of each B lymphocyte is covered with about 500,000 identical copies of a protein called the **B cell receptor (BCR).** A BCR is a type of *immunoglobulin* (im'yū-nō-glob'yū-lin) *(Ig).* A simple immunoglobulin contains four polypeptide chains—two identical longer chains called *heavy chains,* and two identical shorter *light chains* **(Figure 5).** The terms *heavy* and *light* refer to their relative molecular masses. Disulfide bonds, which are covalent bonds between sulfur atoms in two different amino acids, link the light chains to the heavy chains in such a way that a simple immunoglobulin looks like the letter Y. A BCR has two *arms* and a *transmembrane portion.* Each arm's end is a *variable region,* because terminal ends of each heavy and each light chain vary in amino acid sequence among B cells. The transmembrane portion anchors the BCR in the cytoplasmic membrane and consists of the stem of the Y (composed of the tails of the two heavy chains) and two other polypeptides.

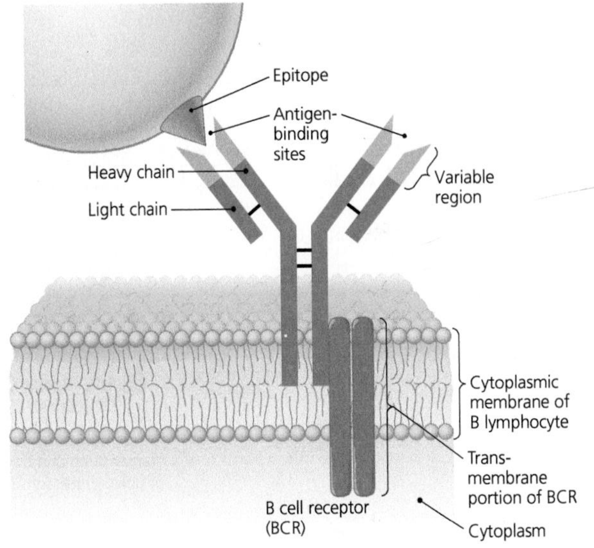

▲ *Figure 5*

B cell receptor (BCR). The B cell receptor is composed of a symmetrical, epitope-binding, Y-shaped protein in association with two transmembrane polypeptides.

Each B cell randomly generates a single BCR gene during its development in the bone marrow. Scientists estimate that there are fewer than 25,000 genes in a human cell, yet there are billions of different BCR proteins in an individual. Obviously, there is not a separate gene for each BCR; instead, a B cell randomly recombines segments from three immunoglobulin regions of DNA and combines these segments to develop novel BCR genes. B cells may also randomly change BCR genes to develop even more diversity. Each newly formed BCR gene codes for a specific and unique BCR. **Highlight: BCR Diversity: The Star of the Show** expands on the genetic explanation for the extensive BCR diversity.

All the BCRs of any particular cell are identical because the variable regions of every BCR on a single cell are identical—the two light chain variable regions are identical and the two heavy chain variable regions are identical. Together the two variable regions form **antigen-binding sites** (see Figure 5). Antigen-binding sites are complementary in shape to the three-dimensional shape of an epitope and bind precisely to it. Exact binding between antigen-binding site and epitope accounts for the specificity of a humoral immune response.

Though all of the BCRs on a single B cell are the same, the BCRs of one cell differ from the BCRs of all other B cells, much like each snowflake is distinct from all others. Scientists estimate that each person forms no less than 10^9 and likely as many as 10^{13} B lymphocytes—each with its

[4]From Greek *autos,* meaning self.

Highlight BCR Diversity: The Star of the Show

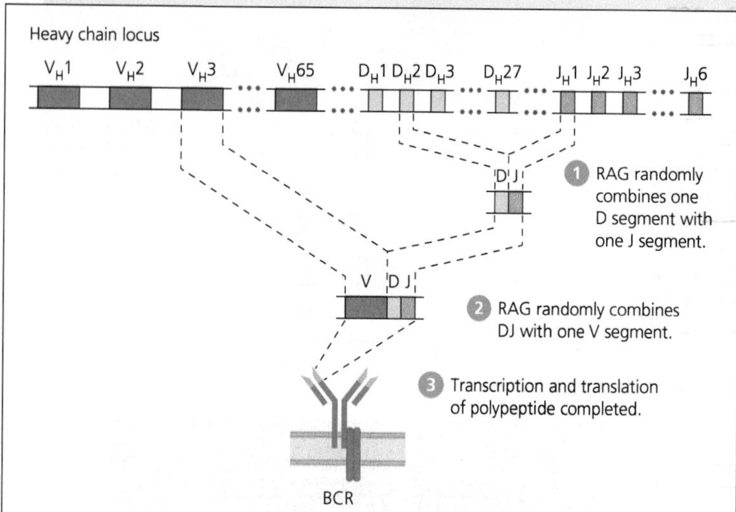
Heavy chain locus
V_H1 V_H2 V_H3 V_H65 D_H1 D_H2 D_H3 D_H27 J_H1 J_H2 J_H3 J_H6
D J
1 RAG randomly combines one D segment with one J segment.
V D J
2 RAG randomly combines DJ with one V segment.
3 Transcription and translation of polypeptide completed.
BCR

How does your body generate billions of unique B cell receptor proteins (BCRs) so as to recognize the thousand of millions of foreign epitopes on pathogens that attack you? There isn't enough DNA in your cells to have individual genes for so many receptors. It would require several thousand times more DNA than you have. The answer to the problem of BCR diversity lies in the fascinatingly ingenious way in which B cells use their relatively small number of diverse BCR genes.

Genes for BCRs occur in discrete stretches of DNA called *loci* (singular: *locus*). Genes for the constant region are located downstream from loci for the variable regions. We will consider the variable region genes first, because it is in the variable region that BCR diversity is greatest.

BCR variable region genes occur in three loci on each of two chromosomes—one locus for the heavy chain variable region and two loci (called *kappa* and *lambda*) for the light chain variable region. Each cell is diploid—having two of each type of chromosome—so there are six loci all together. However, a developing B cell uses only one chromosome's loci for each of its heavy and light chains. Once a locus on a particular chromosome is used, the other chromosome's corresponding locus is inhibited.

Each locus is divided further into distinct genetic segments coding for portions of its respective chain. The heavy chain variable region locus has three segments called *variable (V_H), diversity (D_H),* and *junction (J_H) segments.* In each of your developing B cells there are 65 variable segment genes, 27 diversity segment genes, and 6 junction segment genes. Each light chain variable region locus has an additional *variable segment (V_L)* and a *junction segment (J_L)*. For the kappa locus, there are 40 variable segment genes and 5 junction genes; while the lambda locus is less variable, having only 30 V genes and using a single J gene.

A great variety of BCRs form during B cell maturation as the B cell uses an enzyme called RAG—the *recombination activating gene* protein—to randomly combine one of each kind of the various segments to form its BCR gene. An analogy will help your understanding of this concept. Imagine that you have a wardrobe consisting of 65 different pairs of shoes, 27 different shirts, and 6 different pairs of pants that can be combined to create outfits. You can choose any one shirt, any one pair of pants, and any one pair of shoes each day, so with these 98 pieces of clothing, you will potentially have 10,530 different outfits ($65 \times 27 \times 6$). Your roommate might have the same numbers of items, but in different colors and styles; so between you, you will have twice as many potential outfits—21,600! Similarly, a developing B cell has 10,530 possible combinations of V_H, D_H, and J_H segments on each of its two chromosomes for a total of 21,060 possible heavy chain variable region gene combinations.

The developing B cell also uses RAG to recombine the segments of the light chain variable loci. Since there are 200 (40×5) possible kappa genes and 30 (30×1) possible lambda genes on each chromosome, there are a total of 460 possible light chain genes on the two chromosomes. Therefore, each B cell can make one of a possible 9,687,600 ($21{,}060 \times 460$) different BCRs using only 348 genetic segments in the heavy and light chain loci on its two chromosomes.

Still, these nearly 10 million different BCRs do not account for all the variability seen among BCRs. Each B cell creates additional diversity: RAG randomly removes portions of D and J segments before joining the two together. Another enzyme randomly adds nucleotides to each heavy chain VDJ combination, and B cells in the germinal centers of lymph nodes undergo random point mutations in their V regions. The result of RAG recombinations, random deletions and insertions, and point mutations is tremendous potential variability. Scientists estimate that you have about 10^{23} possible B cell receptor genes. That's one hundred billion trillion—a number ten times greater than all the stars in the universe! Your B cells are indeed stars of the show.

own BCR. Since an antigen, for example a bacterial protein, typically has numerous epitopes of various shapes, many different BCRs will recognize any particular antigen, but each BCR recognizes only one epitope. BCR genes are randomly generated in sufficient numbers that the entire repertoire of BCRs (each carried by a particular B lymphocyte) is capable of recognizing the entire repertoire of thousands of millions of different epitopes. In other words, at least one BCR is fortuitously complementary to any given specific epitope the body may or may not encounter.

An analogy will serve to clarify this point. Imagine a locksmith that has a copy of every possible key to fit every possible lock. If a customer arrives at the shop with a lock needing a key, the locksmith can provide it (though it may take a while to find the correct key). Similarly, you have a BCR complementary to every possible epitope in the environment, though you will not be infected with every epitope. For example, you have lymphocytes with BCRs complementary to epitopes of stingray venom, though it is unlikely you will ever be stabbed by a stingray.

When an antigenic epitope stimulates a specific B cell via the B cell's unique BCR, the B cell responds by undergoing cell division, giving rise to nearly identical offspring that secrete immunoglobulins into the blood or lymph. The immunoglobulins act against the epitope shape that stimulated the B cell. Immunoglobulin-secreting B lymphocytes are called **plasma cells.** They have extensive rough endoplasmic reticulum and many Golgi bodies involved in the synthesis and packaging of the immunoglobulins. Next we consider the structure and functions of the secreted immunoglobulins—called antibodies.

Specificity and Antibody Structure

Antibodies are immunoglobulins and similar to BCRs in shape, though antibodies are secreted and lack the transmembrane portions of BCRs **(Figure 6).** Thus, a basic antibody molecule is Y-shaped with two identical heavy chains and two identical light chains and is nearly identical to the secreting cell's BCR. The antigen-binding sites of antibodies from a given plasma cell are identical to one another and to the antigen-binding sites of that cell's BCR. Antibodies carry the same specificity for an epitope as the BCR of the activated B cell.

Because the arms of an antibody molecule contain antigen-binding sites, they are also known as the F_{ab} *regions* (*fragment, antigen-binding*). The angle between the F_{ab} regions and the stem can change because the point at which they join is hinge-like. An antibody stem, which is formed of the lower portions of the two heavy chains, is also called the F_c *region* (because it forms a *fragment* that is *crystallizable*).

There are five basic types of F_c region, designated by the Greek letters *mu, gamma, alpha, epsilon,* and *delta.* A plasma cell attaches the gene for its heavy chain variable region to one of the five F_c region genes to form one of five classes of antibodies known as IgM, IgG, IgA, IgE, and IgD. Every plasma cell begins by attaching the variable region gene to the gene for the mu F_c region and thus begins by secreting IgM. In a process called **class switching,** a plasma cell then combines the variable region gene to the gene for a different F_c region, say the gamma gene, and begins secreting a new class of antibodies, in this case IgG. A plasma cell may subsequently switch class again to secrete IgA or IgE.

Classes of Antibodies

Threats confronting the immune system can be extremely variable, so it is not surprising that there are several classes of antibody. The class involved in any given humoral immune response depends on the type of invading foreign antigens, the portal of entry involved, and the antibody

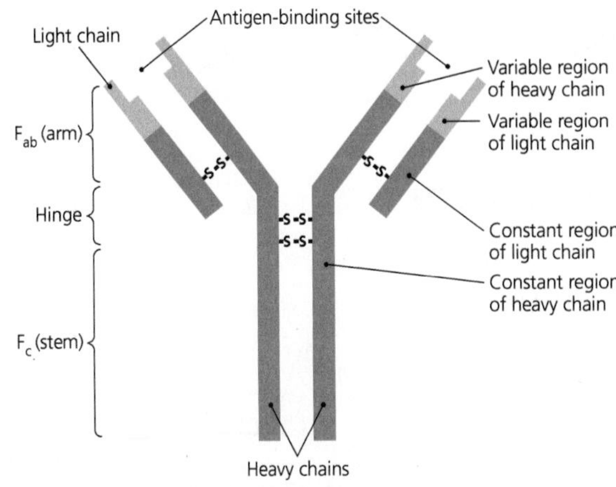

(a)

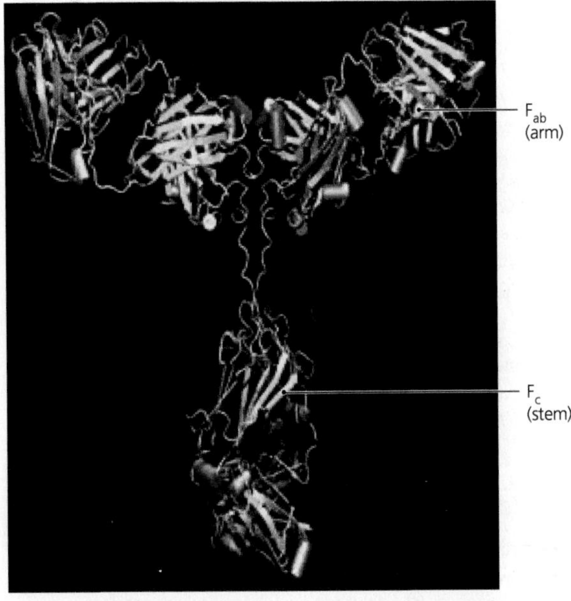

(b)

▲ *Figure 6*

Basic antibody structure. (a) Artist's rendition. Each antibody molecule, which is shaped like the letter Y, consists of two identical heavy chains and two identical light chains held together by disulfide bonds. Five different kinds of heavy chains form an antibody's stem (F_c region). The arms (F_{ab} regions) terminate in variable regions to form two antigen-binding sites. The hinge region is flexible, allowing the arms to bend in almost any direction. **(b)** Three-dimensional shape of an antibody based on X-ray crystallography. *Why are the two antigen-binding sites on a typical antibody molecule identical?*

Figure 6 *The amino acid sequences of the two light chains of an antibody molecule are identical, as are the sequences of the two heavy chains, so the binding sites—each composed of the ends of one light chain and one heavy chain—must be identical.*

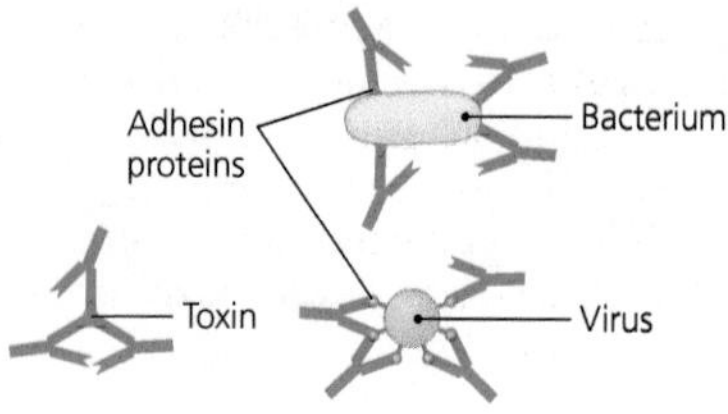

(a) Neutralization

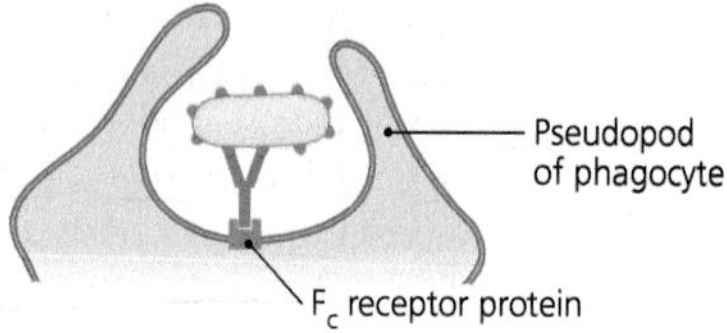

(b) Opsonization

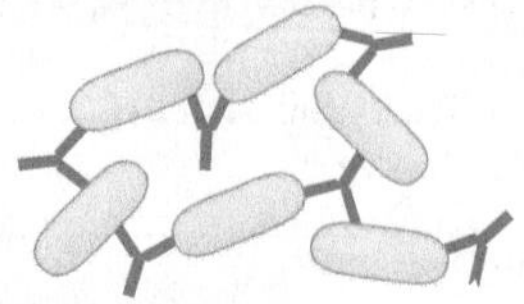

(c) Agglutination

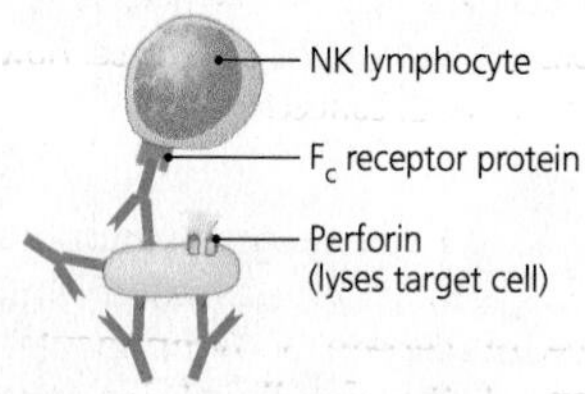

(d) Antibody-dependent cellular cytotoxicity (ADCC)

▲ *Figure 7*

Four functions of antibodies. (a) Neutralization of toxins and microbes. **(b)** Opsonization. **(c)** Agglutination. **(d)** Antibody-dependent cellular cytotoxicity.

function required. Here, we consider the structure and functions of the five classes of antibodies.

As we have seen, plasma cells begin by making class M—**immunoglobulin M (IgM)**—during the initial stages of an immune response. Some simple IgM molecules are put into the cytoplasmic membrane to act as a BCR, but most IgM is secreted. A secreted IgM molecule is more than five times larger than the basic Y-shape because secreted IgM is a pentamer, consisting of five basic units linked together in a circular fashion via disulfide bonds and a short polypeptide *joining (J) chain.* Each IgM subunit has a conventional immunoglobulin structure, consisting of two light chains and two mu heavy chains. IgM is most efficient at complement activation and can be involved in agglutination and neutralization.

After a time of synthesizing IgM, the plasma cell switches antibody class by using a different F_c gene based on mediators near the site of infection. The most common switch is to the gene for heavy chain gamma; the plasma cell switches to synthesizing immunoglobulin G.

Immunoglobulin G (IgG) is the most common and longest-lasting class of antibody in the blood, accounting for about 80% of serum antibodies, possibly because IgG has many functions. Each molecule of IgG has the basic Y-shaped antibody structure.

IgG molecules play a major role in antibody-mediated defense mechanisms, including complement activation, opsonization, neutralization, and antibody-dependent cellular cytotoxicity (ADCC). IgG molecules can leave blood vessels to enter extracellular spaces more easily than can the other immunoglobulins. This is especially important during inflammation, because it enables IgG to bind to invading pathogens before they get into the circulatory systems. IgG molecules are also the only antibodies that cross a placenta to protect a developing child.

Immunoglobulin A (IgA), which has alpha heavy chains, is the immunoglobulin most closely associated with various body mucosal secretions, including tears and breast milk. Some of the body's IgA is a monomer with the basic Y-shape that circulates in the blood, constituting about 12% of total serum antibody. However, plasma cells in the tear ducts, mammary glands, and mucous membranes synthesize IgA dimers linked via a J chain and another short polypeptide (called a *secretory component*) to form **secretory IgA.**

Secretory IgA agglutinates and neutralizes antigens and is of critical importance in protecting the body from infections arising in the gastrointestinal, respiratory, urinary, and reproductive tracts. Plasma cells add secretory component during the transport of secretory IgA across mucous membranes. Secretory component protects secretory IgA from digestion by intestinal enzymes. Secretory IgA provides nursing newborns some protection against foreign antigens because mammary glands secrete IgA into milk. Thus, nursing babies receive antibodies directed against antigens that have infected their mothers and are likely to infect them as well.

Immunoglobulin E (IgE) is a typical Y-shaped immunoglobulin with two epsilon heavy chains. Because it is found in extremely low concentrations in serum (less than 1% of total antibody), it is not critical for most antibody functions. Instead, IgE antibodies act as signal molecules—they attach to receptors on eosinophil cytoplasmic membranes to trigger the release of cell-damaging molecules onto the surface of parasites, particularly parasitic worms. IgE antibodies also trigger mast cells and basophils to release inflammatory chemicals such as histamine. In developed countries, IgE is more likely associated with allergies than with parasitic worms.

Immunoglobulin D (IgD) is characterized by delta heavy chains. IgD molecules are not secreted but are membrane-bound antigen receptors on B cells that are often seen during the initial phases of a humoral immune response. In this regard, IgD antibodies are like BCRs. Not all mammals have IgD, and animals that lack IgD show no observable ill effects; therefore, scientists do not know the exact function or importance of this class of antibody.

Table 1 compares the different classes of immunoglobulins and adds some details of antibody structure.

Antibody Function

As we have seen, antigen-binding sites of antibodies are complementary to epitopes; in fact, the shapes of the two can match so very closely that most water molecules are excluded from the area of contact, producing a strong, noncovalent, hydrophobic interaction. Additionally, hydrogen bonds and other molecular attractions mediate antibody binding to epitope. Antibody binding is the central functional feature of humoral adaptive immune responses. Once bound, antibodies function in several ways. These include activation of complement, neutralization, opsonization, direct killing, agglutination, and antibody-dependent cytoxicity.

Activation of Complement and Inflammation F_c regions of two or more antibodies bind to complement protein 1 (C1), activating it to become enzymatic. This begins the classical complement pathway, which releases inflammatory mediators. Some types of antibodies leave the blood during inflammation.

Neutralization Antibodies can neutralize a toxin by binding to a critical portion of the toxin so that it can no longer function against the body. Similarly, antibodies can block adhesion molecules on the surface of a bacterium or virus, neutralizing the pathogen's virulence because it cannot adhere to its target cell **(Figure 7a).**

Opsonization Antibodies act as **opsonins**[5]—molecules that stimulate phagocytosis. Neutrophils and macrophages have receptors for the F_c regions of IgG molecules; therefore, these leukocytes bind to the stems of antibodies. Once antibodies are so bound, the leukocytes phagocytize them, along with the antigens they carry, at a faster rate compared to antigens lacking bound antibody. Enhanced phagocytosis is called **opsonization** (op'sŏ-nī-zā'shŭn) **(Figure 7b).**

Killing by Oxidation Recently, scientists have shown that some antibodies have catalytic properties that allow them to kill bacteria directly. Specifically, antibodies catalyze the production of hydrogen peroxide and other potent oxidants that kill bacteria.

Agglutination Because each basic antibody has two antigen-binding sites, each can attach to two epitopes at once. Numerous antibodies can aggregate antigens together—a state called **agglutination** (ă-glū-ti-nā'shŭn) **(Figure 7c).** Agglutination of soluble molecules typically causes them to become insoluble and precipitate. Agglutination may hinder the activity of pathogenic organisms and increases the chance that they will be phagocytized or filtered out of the blood by the spleen.

Antibody-Dependent Cellular Cytoxicity (ADCC) Antibodies often coat a target cell by binding to epitopes all over the target's surface. The antibodies' F_c regions can then bind to receptors on special lymphocytes called *natural killer lymphocytes (NK cells)*, which are neither B nor T cells. NK lymphocytes lyse target cells with proteins called **perforin** (per'fōr-in) and **granzyme** (gran'zīm). Perforin molecules form into a tubular structure in the target cell's membrane, forming a channel through which granzyme enters the cell and triggers apoptosis **(Figure 7d).** ADCC is similar to opsonization in that antibodies cover the target cell; however, with ADCC the target dies by apoptosis, whereas with opsonization the target is phagocytized.

www.microbiologyplace.com **Animations: *Host Defenses: Humoral Immunity: Antibody Function***

CRITICAL THINKING

Two students are studying for an exam on the body's defensive systems. One of them insists that complement is part of the nonspecific second line of defense, but the partner insists that complement is part of a humoral immune response in the third line of defense. How would you explain to them that they are both correct?

In most cases, B cells do not mount a humoral immune response directly. Instead, they respond to antigens only with the assistance of certain T lymphocytes. We will continue discussion of the details of humoral immune responses after we consider the various T cells.

T Lymphocytes (T Cells)

Learning Objectives

- ✓ Describe the importance of the thymus to the development of T lymphocytes.
- ✓ Describe the basic characteristics common to T lymphocytes.
- ✓ Compare and contrast three types of T cells.

A human adult's red bone marrow produces T lymphocytes. Sticky, adhesive molecules coupled with the action of chemotactic molecules attract the lymphocytes to the thymus from blood vessels. T cells mature in the thymus under the influence of molecular signals from the thymus. Following maturation, T cells circulate in the lymph and blood and migrate to the lymph nodes, spleen, and Peyer's patches. They account for about 70–85% of all lymphocytes in the blood.

[5]From Greek *opsonein*, meaning to supply food.

Table 1 Characteristics of the Five Classes of Antibodies

	IgG	IgA	IgM	IgE	IgD
	Antigen-binding site; Disulfide bond; γ; Carbohydrate	α; Monomer; Secretory component; J Chain; α; Secretory (dimer)	J Chain; μ	ε	δ
Structure, number of binding sites	Monomer, 2	Monomer, 2 Dimer, 4	Pentamer, 10	Monomer, 2	Monomer, 2
Type of heavy chain	Gamma (γ)	Alpha (α)	Mu (μ)	Epsilon (ε)	Delta (δ)
Functions	Complement activation, neutralization, opsonization, production of hydrogen peroxide, agglutination, and antibody-dependent cellular toxicity (ADCC); crosses placenta to protect fetus	Neutralization and agglutination; dimer is secretory antibody	Monomer can act as BCR; pentamer acts in complement activation, neutralization, agglutination	Triggers release of antiparasitic molecules from eosinophils and of histamines from basophils and mast cells	Unknown, but perhaps acts as BCR
Locations	Serum, mast cell surfaces	Monomer: serum Dimer: mucous membrane secretions; milk	Serum	Serum, mast cell surfaces	B cell surface
Approximate half-life (time it takes for concentration to reduce by half) in blood (days)	20	6	10	2	3
Percentage in serum	80	10–15	5–10	<1	<0.05
Size (mass in kilodaltons)	150	Monomer: 160 Dimer: 385	970	188	184

T lymphocytes are like B cells in their specificity. Each T cell has about half a million copies of a **T cell receptor (TCR)** on its cytoplasmic membrane. Each T cell randomly chooses and combines segments of DNA in TCR gene regions to create a novel gene that codes for that cell's unique and specific TCR. The random production of diverse TCRs accomplished by recombining TCR genes is similar to the way BCRs are produced.

Specificity of the T Cell Receptor (TCR)

In contrast to a BCR, a TCR is composed of only two glycopolypeptide chains; however, like BCRs, the terminal ends of TCRs are composed of variable regions that grant each TCR specific binding properties. The groove between the polypeptides acts as the antigen-binding site (**Figure 8**). Similarly to binding by a BCR, a TCR recognizes and binds to a complementary shape, but TCRs do not recognize epitopes directly. A TCR binds only to an epitope associated with a particular protein called *MHC protein,* which will be discussed shortly. There are at least 10^9 different TCRs—each specific TCR type on a different T cell—which is enough for every epitope–MHC protein.

T lymphocytes act primarily against body cells that harbor intracellular pathogens such as viruses; they also can act against anomalous body cells that produce cell-surface proteins that are abnormal (such as cancer cells). Because

T cells act directly against antigens (they do not secrete immunoglobulins), their immune activities are called cell-mediated immune responses.

Types of T Lymphocytes

Immunologists recognize types of T cells based on surface glycoproteins and characteristic functions. These are *cytotoxic T cells, helper T cells,* and *regulatory T cells.*

Cytotoxic T Lymphocyte Every **cytotoxic T cell (Tc or CD8 cell)** is distinguished by copies of its own unique TCR as well as the presence of CD8 cell-surface glycoprotein. CD (for *cluster of differentiation*) glycoproteins are named with internationally accepted designations consisting of a number following the prefix. These numbers reflect the order in which the glycoproteins were discovered, not the order in which they are produced or function. As the name *cytotoxic T cell* implies, these lymphocytes directly kill other cells—those infected with viruses and other intracellular pathogens, as well as abnormal cells, such as cancer cells. www.microbiologyplace.com **Animations: *Host Defenses: Cell-Mediated Immunity: Cytotoxic T Cells***

Helper T Lymphocyte Immunologists distinguish **helper T cells (Th or CD4 cells)** by the presence of the CD4 glycoproteins. These cells are called "helpers" because their function is to assist in regulating the activity of B cells and cytotoxic T cells during immune responses by providing necessary signals and growth factors. There are two main subpopulations of helper T cells: *type 1 helper T cells (Th1 cells),* which assist cytotoxic T cells and innate macrophages, and *type 2 helper T cells (Th2 cells),* which function in conjunction with B cells. Immunologists distinguish between Th1 and Th2 cells on the basis of their secretions and by characteristic cell-surface proteins.

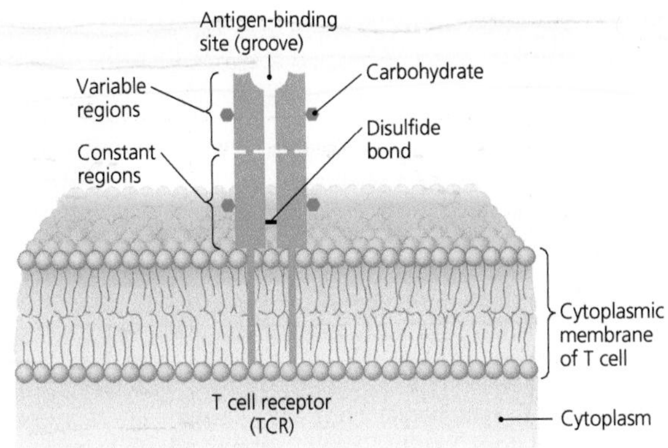

▲ *Figure 8*

A T cell receptor (TCR). A TCR is an asymmetrical surface molecule composed of two polypeptides containing a single antigen-binding site between them.

Helper T cells secrete various soluble protein messengers called *cytokines* that regulate the entire immune system, both adaptive and innate portions. We will consider the types and effects of cytokines shortly. **Highlight: The Loss of Helper T Cells in AIDS Patients** describes some of the effects of the destruction of helper T cells in individuals infected with the human immunodeficiency virus (HIV). www.microbiologyplace.com **Animations: *Host Defenses: Cell-Mediated Immunity: Helper T Cells***

Highlight *The Loss of Helper T Cells in AIDS Patients*

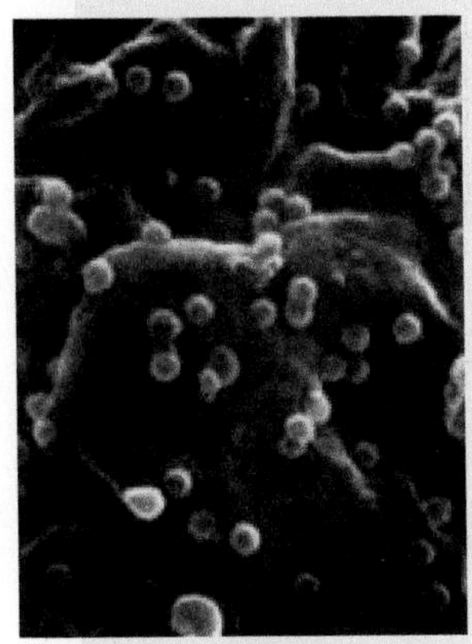

HIV budding from Th cells

Neither B cells nor cytotoxic T cells respond effectively to most antigens without the participation of helper T cells, because signals are passed more effectively among leukocytes when the CD4 molecules of helper T cells bind to certain leukocytes.

We also saw in a previous chapter that in order for viruses to enter cells and replicate, they must first attach to a specific protein on their target cells' surface. In the case of human immunodeficiency virus (HIV), the causative agent of AIDS, the surface protein to which it attaches is CD4, and its target cells are helper T cells. Once HIV enters a helper T cell, it, like other viruses, takes over the cell's protein-synthesizing machinery and directs the cell to produce more viruses.

Because they are essential to mounting an effective immune response, the body normally has a surplus of helper T cells—usually about three times as many as it needs. As a result, individuals infected with HIV can typically lose up to about two-thirds of their helper T cells before signs of immune deficiency appear. Cell-mediated immunity is usually affected first; even though B cells require the assistance of helper T cells to function optimally, they can still be stimulated directly by large quantities of antigen. Normal human blood typically contains about three CD4 helper T cells for every two CD8 cytotoxic T cells—a CD4 to CD8 ratio of 3:2. During the course of HIV infection, however, CD4 helper T cells are lost, reducing the CD4 to CD8 ratio such that individuals with full-blown AIDS may have a ratio lower than 1:7.

Table 2 Characteristics of Selected Lymphocytes

Lymphocyte	Site of Maturation	Representative Cell-Surface Glycoproteins	Selected Secretions
B cell	Red bone marrow	Distinctive BCR and CD40	Antibodies
Helper T cell type 1 (Th1)	Thymus	Distinctive TCR, CD4, and CCR5	Interleukin 2, IFN-γ
Helper T cell type 2 (Th2)	Thymus	Distinctive TCR, CD4, CCR3, and CCR4	Interleukin 4
Cytotoxic T cell (Tc)	Thymus	Distinctive TCR, CD8, and CD95L	Perforin, granzyme
Regulatory T cell (Tr)	Thymus	Distinctive TCR, CD8, and CD25	Cytokines such as interleukin 10

Regulatory T Lymphocyte Formerly known as *suppressor T cells,* **regulatory T cells (Tr cells)** repress adaptive immune responses and prevent autoimmune diseases. Tr cells express CD4 and CD25 glycoproteins. Scientists have not fully characterized the manner in which Tr cells work, but it is known that they secrete immunologically active chemicals called *cytokines,* which we examine in a subsequent section.

Table 2 compares and contrasts the features of various types of lymphocytes. We have considered the primary lymphocytes involved in immune responses. Now, we turn our attention to the way in which the body eliminates T cells and B cells that recognize normal body antigens by means of their BCRs and TCRs, respectively.

Clonal Deletion

Learning Objectives

- ✓ Describe apoptosis and explain its role in lymphocyte editing by clonal deletion.
- ✓ Compare and contrast clonal deletion of T cells and clonal deletion of B cells.

Given that both T and B lymphocytes randomly generate the shapes of their receptors (TCRs and BCRs respectively), every population of maturing lymphocytes includes numerous cells with receptors complementary to normal body components—the autoantigens mentioned earlier. It is vitally important that specific immune responses not be directed against autoantigens; the immune system must be tolerant of "self." When self-tolerance is impaired, the result is an *autoimmune disease.*

The body eliminates self-reactive lymphocytes via **clonal deletion,** so named because elimination of a cell deletes its potential offspring (clones). In this process, lymphocytes are exposed to autoantigens, and those lymphocytes that react to autoantigens undergo *apoptosis*[6] (programmed cell suicide) and are thereby deleted from the repertoire of lymphocytes. Apoptosis is the critical feature of clonal deletion and the development of self-tolerance. The result of clonal deletion is that surviving lymphocytes respond only to foreign antigens.

[6]Greek, meaning falling off.

In humans, clonal deletion occurs in the thymus for T lymphocytes and in the bone marrow for B lymphocytes. Lymphocyte clonal deletion is slightly different in T cells than it is in B cells. We will examine each in turn.

Clonal Deletion of T Cells

As we have seen, T cells recognize epitopes only when the epitopes are bound to MHC protein. Young T lymphocytes spend about a week in the thymus being exposed to all of the body's natural epitopes though a unique feature of thymus cells. As a group, these cells express all of the body's normal proteins, including proteins that have no function in the thymus. For example, some thymus cells synthesize lysozyme, hemoglobin, and muscle cell proteins, though these proteins are not expressed externally to the cells. Rather, thymus cells process these autoantigens so as to express their epitopes in association with MHC I protein. Since the cells collectively synthesize polypeptides from the body's proteins, together they process and present all the body's autoantigens to young T cells.

Immature T cells undergo one of four fates **(Figure 9):**

- Those T cells that do not recognize the body's MHC protein at all undergo apoptosis, in other words, clonal deletion. Since they do not recognize the body's own MHC protein, they will be of no use identifying foreign epitopes carried by MHC protein. T cells that do recognize the body's MHC protein receive a signal to survive.
- Those that subsequently recognize autoantigen in conjunction with MHC protein mostly die by apoptosis, further clonal deletion. A few of these "self-recognizing" T cells remain alive to become regulatory T cells.
- The remaining T cells are those that recognize the body's own MHC protein in conjunction with foreign epitopes and not with autoantigens. These T lymphocytes become the repertoire of protective T cells, which leave the thymus to circulate in the blood and lymph.

Clonal Deletion of B Cells

Clonal deletion of B cells occurs in the bone marrow in a similar fashion **(Figure 10).** Self-reactive B cells may become inactive or change their BCR rather than undergo apoptosis. In any case, self-reactive B cells are removed from the active

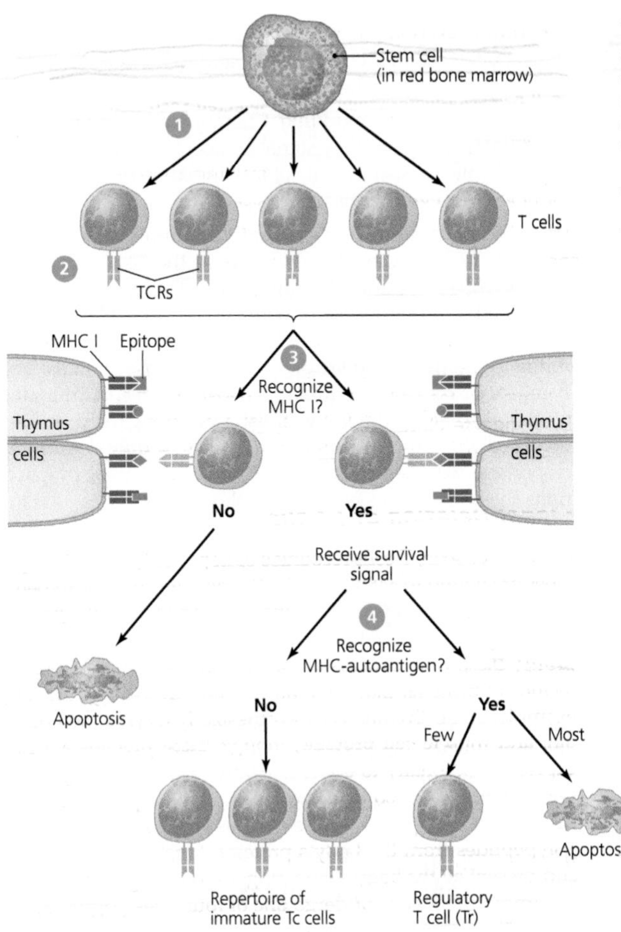

Figure 9

Clonal deletion of T cells. Stem cells in the red bone marrow generate a host of lymphocytes ① that move to the thymus, where each randomly generates a TCR with a particular shape ②. T cells, which are generated in the bone marrow, pass through a series of "decision questions" in the thymus: Are their TCRs complementary to the body's MHC I protein? ③ "No," they undergo apoptosis—*clonal deletion*. "Yes," they survive. Do the surviving cells recognize MHC I protein bound to any autoantigen? ④ "No," they survive and become the repertoire of immature T cells. Yes, then most undergo apoptosis (more clonal deletion); a few survive as regulatory T cells (Tr).

B cell repertoire, so that humoral immunity does not act against autoantigens. Tolerant B cells leave the bone marrow and travel to the spleen where they undergo further maturation before circulating in the blood and lymph.

Surviving B and T lymphocytes move into the blood and lymph where they scan for antigens. They communicate among one another and with other body cells via chemical signals. In terms of our analogy of a stage play, there is a dialogue among the cast of characters, but it is a dialogue consisting of chemical signals called *cytokines*.

Immune System Cytokines

Learning Objective

✓ Describe five types of cytokines.

Cytokines (sī'tō-kīnz) are soluble regulatory proteins that act as intercellular messages when released by certain body cells including those of the kidney, skin, and immunity. Here we are concerned with immune system cytokines, which signal among the various leukocytes. For example, cytotoxic T cells (Tc) do not respond to antigens unless they are first signaled by cytokines.

Immune system cytokines are secreted by various leukocytes and affect diverse cells. Many cytokines are redundant; that is, they have almost identical effects. Such complexity has given rise to the concept of a *cytokine network*—a complex web of signals among all the cell types of the immune system. The nomenclature of cytokines is not based on a systematic relationship among them; instead, scientists named cytokines after their cells of origin, their function, and/or the order in which they were discovered. Cytokines of the immune system include the following substances:

- **Interleukins**[7] (in-ter-lū'kinz) **(ILs).** As their name suggests, ILs signal among leukocytes, though cells other than leukocytes may also use interleukins. Immunologists named interleukins sequentially as they were discovered. Currently, scientists have identified about 33 interleukins.

[7]From Latin *inter,* meaning between, and Greek *leukos,* meaning white.

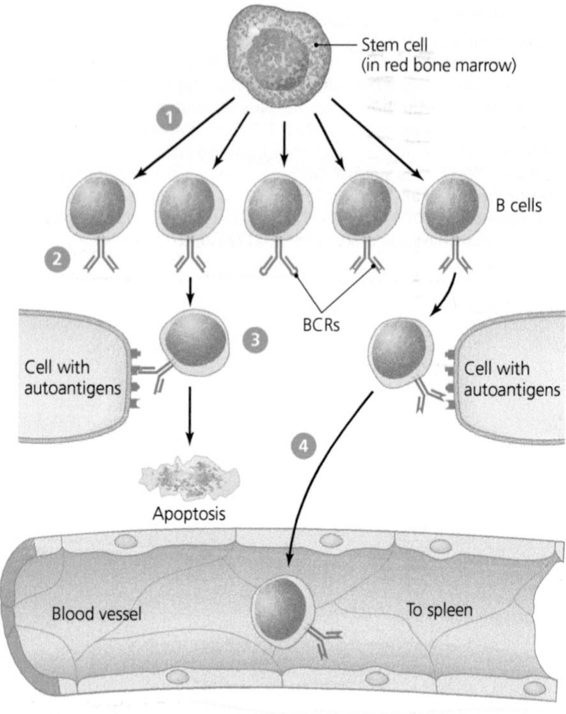

▲ *Figure 10*

Clonal deletion of B cells. Stem cells in the red bone marrow generate a host of B lymphocytes ①. Each newly formed B cell randomly generates a BCR with a particular shape ②. Cells whose BCR is complementary to some autoantigen bind with that autoantigen, stimulating the cell to undergo apoptosis ③. Thus, an entire set of potential daughter B cells (a clone) that are reactive with the body's own cells are eliminated—*clonal deletion.* B cells with a BCR that is not complementary to any autoantigen are released from the bone marrow and into the blood ④. *Of the B cells shown, which is likely to undergo apoptosis?*

Figure 10 The second and third B lymphocytes from the left will undergo apoptosis; their active sites are complementary to the second and fourth autoantigens from the top, respectively.

- **Interferons** (in-ter-fēr′onz) **(IFNs).** These antiviral proteins may also act as cytokines. The most important interferon with such a dual function is gamma interferon (IFN-γ), which is a potent phagocytic activator secreted by Th1 cells.
- **Growth factors.** These proteins stimulate leukocyte stem cells to divide, ensuring that the body is supplied with sufficient white blood cells of all types. The body can control the progression of an adaptive immune response by limiting the production of growth factors.
- **Tumor necrosis[8] factor (TNF).** Macrophages and T cells secrete TNF to kill tumor cells and to regulate immune responses and inflammation.
- **Chemokines** (kē′mō-kīnz). Chemokines are chemotactic cytokines; that is, they signal leukocytes to move; for example, to rush to a site of inflammation or infection, or to move within tissues.

We have been considering adaptive immunity as a stage play. To this point, we have examined the "cast of characters" involved in adaptive immunity. These are: antigens with their epitopes, B cells with their BCRs, plasma cells and their antibodies, T cells with their TCRs, and cytokines. Actors who would disrupt the play—those T cells and B cells that recognize autoantigens—have been eliminated by clonal delation. Before we finish examining the processes involved in humoral immune and cell-mediated immune responses, we need to consider some other initial preparations the body makes before the "play" begins.

Preparation for an Adaptive Immune Response

The body equips itself for specific immune responses by making *major histocompatibility complex proteins* (MHC proteins) and processing antigens so that T lymphocytes can recognize epitopes. We will examine each of these preparations of adaptive immunity, beginning with the roles of the major histocompatibility complex.

The Roles of the Major Histocompatibility Complex

Learning Objective

✓ Describe the two classes of major histocompatibility complex (MHC) proteins with regard to their location and function.

When scientists first began grafting tissue from one animal into another so as to determine a method for treating burn victims, they discovered that if the animals were not closely related, the recipients swiftly rejected the grafts. When they analyzed the reason for such rapid rejection, they found that a graft recipient mounted a very strong immune response against a specific type of antigen found on the cells of unrelated grafts. When the antigen on a graft's cells was sufficiently dissimilar from antigens on the host's cells, as seen with unrelated animals, the grafts were rejected. This is how scientists came to understand how the body is able to distinguish "self" from "nonself."

Immunologists named these types of antigens *major histocompatibility[9] antigens* to indicate their importance in determining the compatibility of tissues in successful grafting. Further research revealed that major histocompatibility antigens are glycoproteins found in the membranes of most cells of vertebrate animals. Major

[8]From Latin *necare,* meaning to kill.
[9]From Greek *histos,* meaning tissue, and Latin *compatibilis,* meaning agreeable.

histocompatibility antigens are coded by a cluster of genes called the **major histocompatibility complex (MHC).** In humans, the MHC is located on each copy of chromosome 6.

Because organ grafting is a modern surgical procedure with no counterpart in nature, scientists reasoned that MHC proteins must have some other "real" function. Indeed, immunologists have determined that MHC proteins in cytoplasmic membranes function to hold and position epitopes for presentation to T cells. Each MHC molecule has an *antigen-binding groove* that lies between two polypeptides; inherited variations in the amino acid sequences of the polypeptides modify the shapes of MHC binding sites and determine which epitopes can be bound and presented. It is important to note that TCRs recognize only epitopes that are bound to MHC molecules.

MHC proteins are of two classes **(Figure 11).** Class I MHC molecules are found on the cytoplasmic membranes of all nucleated cells. Thus red blood cells, which do not have nuclei, do not express MHC proteins, whereas cells such as those of skin and muscles do express MHC class I molecules. In contrast, class II MHC proteins are found only on special cells called **antigen-presenting cells (APCs).** Professional antigen-presenting cells—those that regularly present antigen—are B cells, macrophages, and most importantly **dendritic cells,** which are so named because they have many long, thin cytoplasmic processes called *dendrites*[10] **(Figure 12).** Phagocytic dendritic cells are found under the surface of the skin and mucous membranes and migrate to lymph nodes to interact with B and T lymphocytes. Certain other cells, such as microglia in the brain and Kupffer cells in the liver, may also present antigen under certain conditions. These cells are termed *nonprofessional antigen-presenting cells.*

The cytoplasmic membrane of a professional APC has about 100,000 MHC II molecules, each of which varies in the epitope it can bind. Their diversity is dependent on an individual's genotype. If an antigen fragment cannot be bound to an MHC molecule, it typically does not trigger an immune response. Thus, MHC molecules determine which antigen fragments might trigger immune responses.

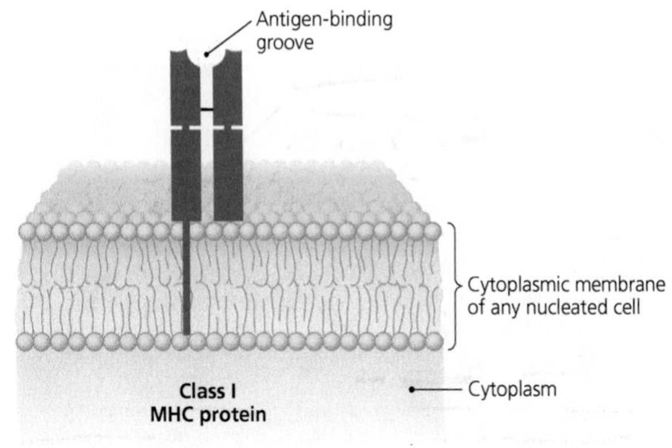

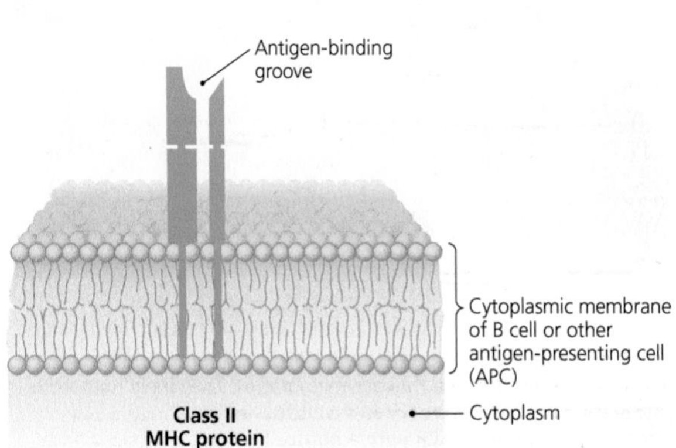

▲ *Figure 11*

The two classes of major histocompatibility complex (MHC) proteins. Each is composed of two polypeptides that form an antigen-binding groove. **(a)** MHC class I glycoproteins, which are found on all cells except red blood cells. **(b)** MHC class II glycoproteins, which are expressed only by B cells and special antigen-presenting cells (APCs).

Antigen Processing

Learning Objectives

- ✓ Explain the roles of antigen-presenting cells (e.g., dendritic cells and macrophages) and MHC molecules in antigen processing and presentation.
- ✓ Contrast endogenous antigen processing with exogenous antigen processing.

Before MHC proteins can display epitopes, antigens must be processed. Antigen processing occurs via somewhat different processes according to whether the antigen is endogenous or exogenous. Recall that endogenous antigens come from the cells' cytoplasm or from pathogens living within the cells, whereas exogenous antigens have extracellular sources, such as lymph.

www.microbiologyplace.com **Animations:** ***Host Defenses: Antigen Processing and Presentation: Overview***

Processing Endogenous Antigens

A few molecules of every new polypeptide produced within nucleated cells—including polypeptides produced by intracellular bacteria or polypeptides coded by viruses—are catabolized into smaller pieces containing

[10]From Greek *dendron*, meaning tree, referring to long cellular extensions that look like branches of a tree.

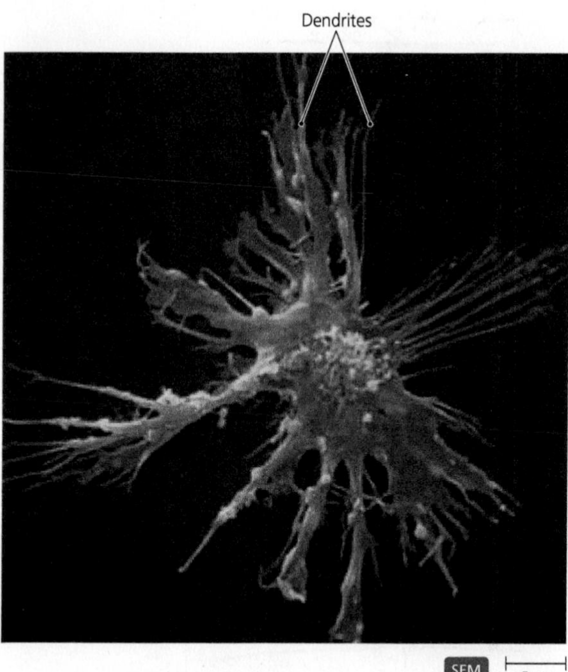

▲ *Figure 12*

Dendritic cell. These important antigen-presenting cells in the body are found in the skin and mucous membranes. They have numerous thin cytoplasmic processes called dendrites.

about 8–12 amino acids. These pieces include the epitopes from the larger polypeptides. Peptides containing epitopes bind onto complementary antigen-binding grooves of MHC class I molecules during biosynthesis in the membrane of the endoplasmic reticulum. This membrane, loaded with MHC class I proteins and epitopes, is then packaged into a vesicle by a Golgi body and inserted into the cytoplasmic membrane. The result is that the cell displays the MHC class I protein–epitope complex on the cell's surface **(Figure 13a).** All nucleated cells express MHC class I molecules and epitopes in this manner.

Processing Exogenous Antigens

For exogenous antigens, a professional antigen-presenting cell (APC), which is usually a dendritic cell, internalizes the invading pathogen and enzymatically catabolizes the pathogen's molecules, producing peptide epitopes, which are contained in a phagolysosome. A vesicle already containing MHC class II molecules in its membrane fuses with the phagolysosome, and each peptide then attempts to bind to an antigen-binding groove of a complementary MHC class II molecule. The fused vesicle inserts successful MHC class II protein–epitope complexes into the cytoplasmic membrane such that the epitopes are presented on the outside **(Figure 13b).** Empty MHC molecules are not stable on a cell's surface and are degraded.

www.microbiologyplace.com **Animations: *Host Defenses: Antigen Processing and Presentation: Steps* and *Antigen Processing and Presentation: MHC***

So far, we have set the stage for the immune system "play" by examining the organs, cells, secretions, and signaling molecules of the immune system, as well as the preparatory steps of antigen processing, antigen presentation, and clonal deletion. We have seen that adaptive immunity is specific, due to the precise and accurate fit of lymphocyte receptors with their complements; that adaptive immunity involves clones of B and T cells, which are unresponsive to self (due to clonal deletion); and that immune responses are inducible against foreign antigens. Now, we can examine cell-mediated and humoral immune responses in more detail. We begin with cell-mediated immunity.

Cell-Mediated Immune Responses

Learning Objectives

✓ Describe a cell-mediated immune response.

✓ Compare and contrast the two pathways of cytotoxic T cell action.

The body uses cell-mediated immune responses to fight intracellular pathogens and abnormal body cells. Recall that inducibility and specificity are two hallmark characteristics of adaptive immunity. The body induces cell-mediated immune responses only against specific endogenous antigens. Given that the many common intracellular invaders are viruses, our examination of cell-mediated immunity will focus on these pathogens. However, cell-mediated immune responses are also mounted against cancer cells, intracellular parasitic protozoa, and intracellular bacteria such as *Mycobacterium tuberculosis* (mī'kō-bak-tēr'ē-ŭm too-ber-kyū-lō'sis), which causes tuberculosis. **Highlight: Attacking Cancer with Lab-Grown T Cells** describes an experimental use of T cells to treat one form of cancer.

Activation of T Cell Clones and Their Functions

The body does not initiate adaptive immune responses at the site of an infection but rather in lymphoid organs, usually lymph nodes, where antigen-presenting cells interact with lymphocytes. The initial event in cell-mediated immunity is the activation of a specific clone of cytotoxic T cells as depicted in **Figure 14:**

1. **Antigen presentation.** A virus-infected antigen-presenting cell (APC), typically a dendritic cell, migrates to a nearby lymph node where it presents virus epitopes

Processing of T-dependent endogenous antigens:

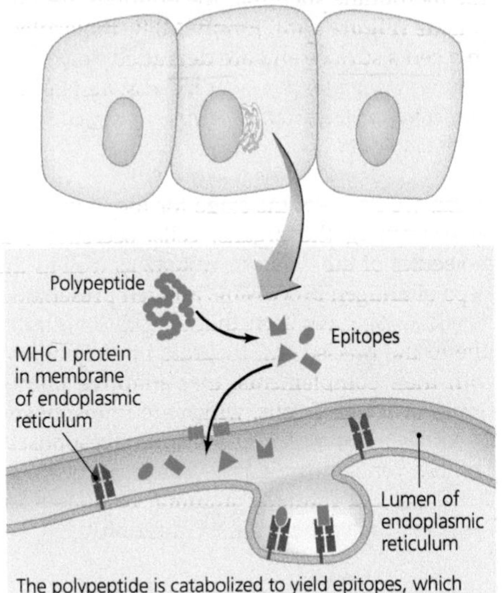

The polypeptide is catabolized to yield epitopes, which are loaded onto complementary MHC I proteins in the ER.

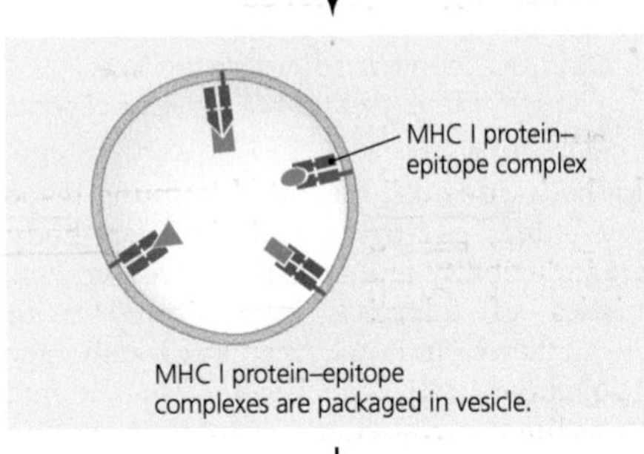

MHC I protein–epitope complexes are packaged in vesicle.

Vesicle fuses with cytoplasmic membrane.

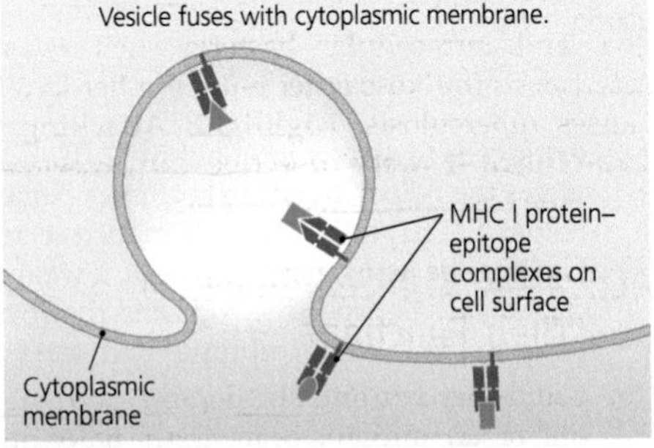

(a) MHC I protein–epitope complexes displayed on cytoplasmic membranes of all nucleated cells

Processing of T-dependent exogenous antigens:

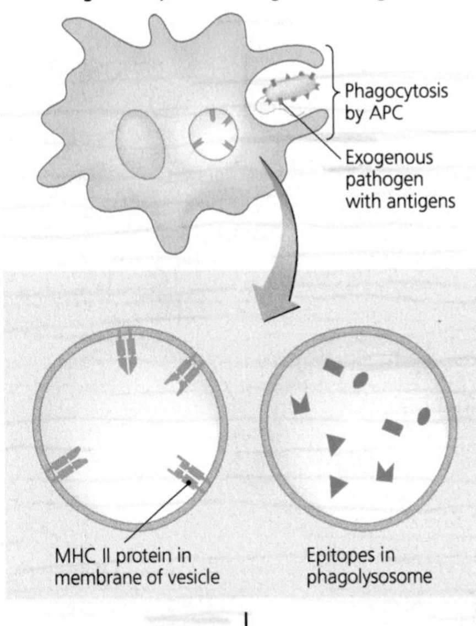

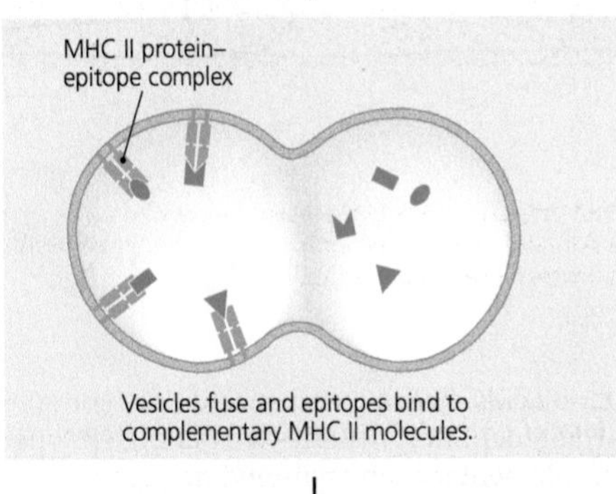

Vesicles fuse and epitopes bind to complementary MHC II molecules.

Vesicle fuses with cytoplasmic membrane.

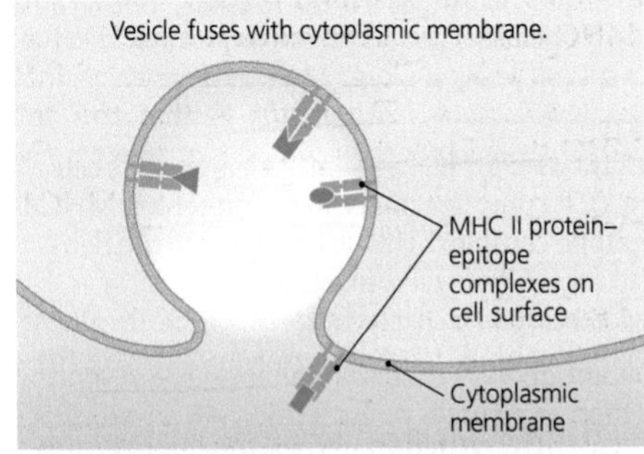

(b) MHC II protein–epitope complexes displayed on cytoplasmic membranes of antigen-presenting cell

▲ *Figure 13*

The processing of endogenous and exogenous antigens. (a) Endogenous antigens. Epitopes from all polypeptides synthesized within a nucleated cell load onto complementary MHC I proteins, which are exported to the cytoplasmic membrane.

(b) Exogenous antigens. Antigens arising outside the body's cells are phagocytized by an APC, which then loads epitopes into complementary antigen-binding grooves of MHC II molecules. The MHC II protein–epitope complexes are then displayed on the outside of the APC's cytoplasmic membrane.

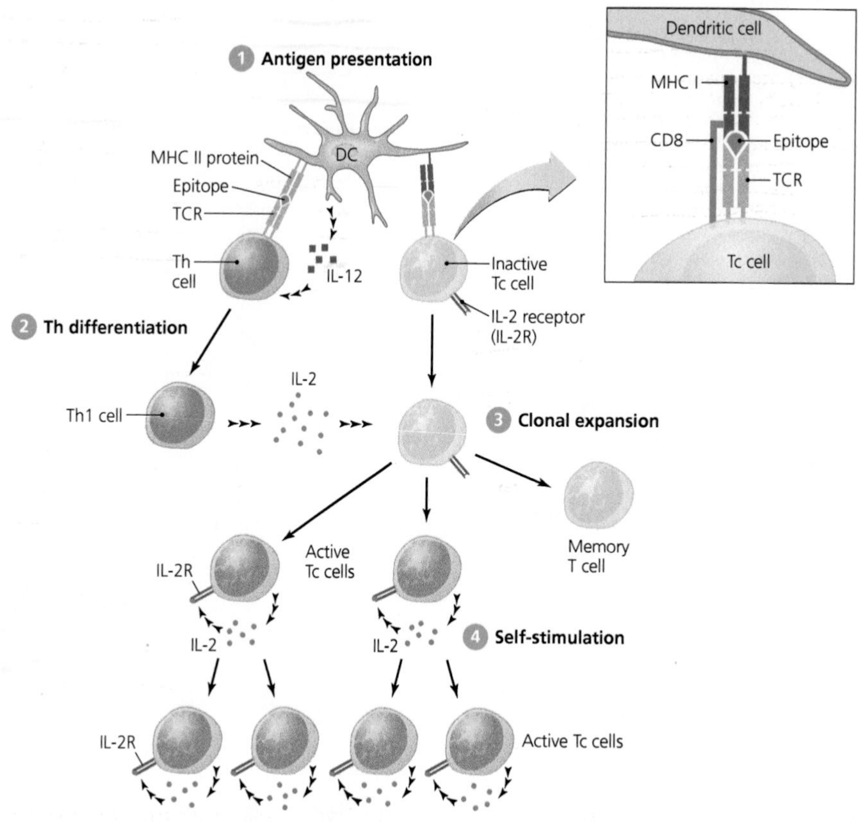

▲ *Figure 14*

Activation of a clone of cytotoxic T (Tc) cells. ① Antigen-presenting cells present epitopes in conjunction with MHC I protein to inactive T cells. ② Infected APCs secrete IL-12, which causes helper T cells to differentiate into Th1 cells. ③ Signaling from the APC and IL-2 from the Th1 cell activate Tc cells that recognize the MHC I protein–epitope complex. IL-2 triggers Tc cell to divide, forming a clone of active Tc cells as well as memory T cells. ④ Active Tc cells secrete IL-2, becoming self-stimulatory.

in conjunction with MHC I protein. At least one Tc cell will have a TCR complementary to the presented MHC I protein–epitope complex. This Tc cell binds to the dendritic cell to form a cell-cell contact site called an *immunological synapse*. CD8 glycoprotein of the Tc cell, which specifically binds to MHC I protein, stabilizes the synapse.

2 **Helper T cell differentiation.** When the interaction between Tc and APC is not particularly strong, a nearby CD4-bearing helper T (Th) lymphocyte helps. The Th cell binds to the APC via the TCR of the helper cell (which is complementary to an MHC II protein–epitope complex presented on the APC) and induces the APC to more vigorously signal the Tc cell. Viruses and some intracellular bacteria induce dendritic cells to secrete interleukin 12 (IL-12), which stimulates the helper T cells to become a clone of type 1 helper T (Th1) cells. Th1 cells in turn secrete IL-2. Lacking the assistance of Th cells, a weak immunological synapse between the APC and the Tc cell fails to progress. This limits improper immune responses.

3 **Clonal expansion.** The dendritic cell imparts a second required signal in the immunological synapse. This signal, in conjunction with any IL-2 from a Th1 cell that may be present, activates the cytotoxic T (Tc) cell to secrete its own IL-2. Interleukin 2 triggers cell division and differentiation in Tc cells. Activated Tc cells reproduce to form memory T cells (discussed shortly) and more Tc progeny—a process known as **clonal expansion.**

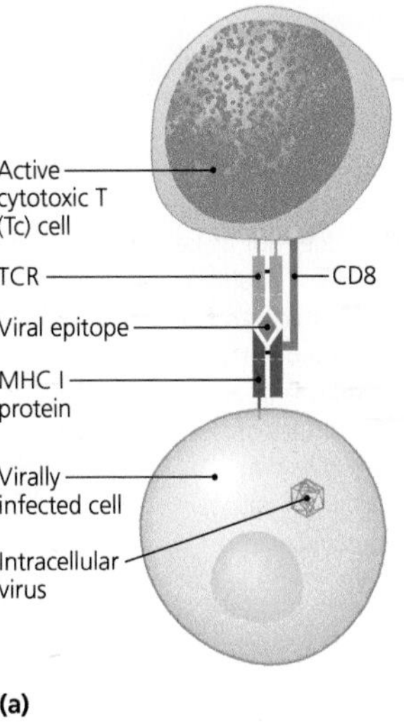

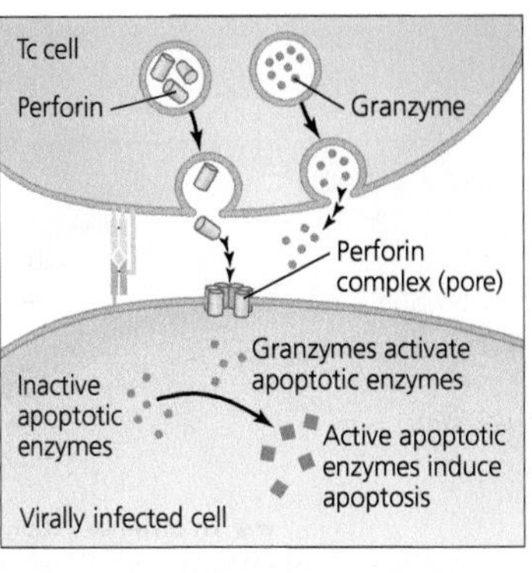

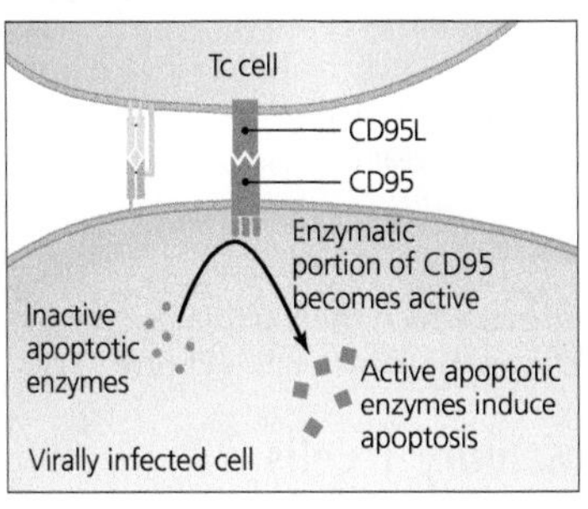

Figure 15 ➤
A cell-mediated immune response. (a) The binding of a virus-infected cell by an active cytotoxic T (Tc) cell. **(b)** The perforin-granzyme cytotoxic pathway. After perforins and granzymes have been released from Tc cell vesicles, granzymes enter the infected cell through the perforin complex pore and activate the enzymes of apoptosis. **(c)** The CD95 cytotoxic pathway. Binding of CD95L on the Tc cell activates the enzymatic portion of the infected cell's CD95 such that apoptosis is induced.

4 **Self-stimulation.** Daughter Tc cells activate and produce both IL-2 receptors (IL-2R) and more IL-2, thereby becoming self-stimulating—they no longer require either an APC or a helper T cell. They leave the lymph node and are now ready to attack virally-infected cells.

As previously discussed, when any nucleated cell synthesizes proteins, it displays epitopes from them in the antigen-binding grooves of MHC class I molecules on its cytoplasmic membrane. Thus, when viruses are replicated inside cells, epitopes of viral proteins are displayed on the host cell's surface. An active Tc cell binds to an infected cell via its TCR, which is complementary to the MHC I protein–epitope complex, and via its CD8 glycoprotein, which is complementary to the MHC class I protein of the infected cell **(Figure 15a)**.

Cytotoxic T cells kill their targets through one of two pathways: the *perforin-granzyme pathway*, which involves the synthesis of special killing proteins, or the *CD95 pathway*, which is mediated through a glycoprotein found on the body's cells.

www.microbiologyplace.com **Animations: *Host Defenses: Cell-Mediated Immunity: Cytotoxic T Cells***

The Perforin-Granzyme Cytotoxic Pathway

The cytoplasm of cytotoxic T cells has vesicles containing two key protein cytotoxins—*perforin* and *granzyme*, which are also used by NK cells in conjunction with antibody-dependent cellular cytotoxicity (discussed previously). When a cytotoxic T cell first attaches to its target, vesicles containing the cytotoxins release their contents. Perforin molecules aggregate into a channel through which granzyme enters, activating apoptosis in the target cell **(Figure 15b)**. Having forced its target to commit suicide, the cytotoxic T cell disengages and moves on to another infected cell.

CRITICAL THINKING

Why did scientists give the name "perforin" to this molecule secreted by Tc cells?

The CD95 Cytotoxic Pathway

The **CD95 pathway** of cell-mediated cytotoxicity involves an integral glycoprotein called *CD95* that is present in the cytoplasmic membranes of many body cells. Activated Tc cells insert *CD95L*—the receptor for CD95—into their cytoplasmic membranes. When an activated Tc cell comes into contact with its target, its CD95L binds to CD95 on the

Highlight *Attacking Cancer with Lab-Grown T Cells*

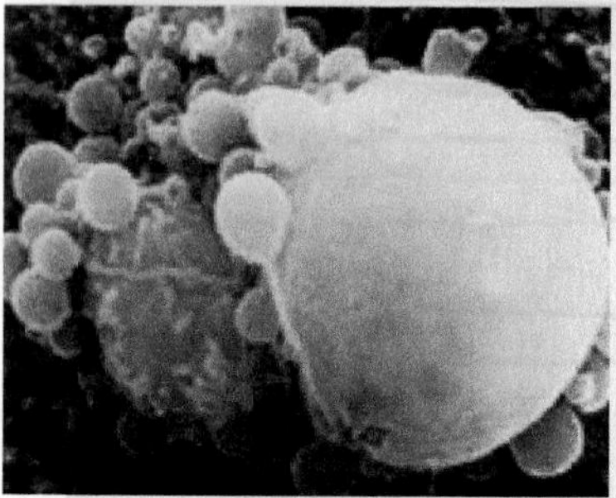

T cells attacking cancer cells

The body naturally manufactures T cells that attack cancer cells, but it sometimes does not make enough of them to shrink tumors and effectively halt the disease's progress. A recent study from the National Institutes of Health, however, shows that cancer-fighting T cells can be mass-produced in a laboratory and injected into patients, where they survive, multiply, and effectively reduce tumors. The study focused on 13 patients with malignant melanoma, an aggressive form of skin cancer. Researchers took samples of the patients' own cancer-fighting T cells and cloned them in a laboratory until they numbered in the billions. These billions of identical T cells were then injected back into the individuals that first produced them. The results were encouraging. Four of the 13 patients became "virtually cancer free," while tumors were substantially reduced in two other patients.

Such T cell therapy remains highly experimental and is still years away from becoming a generally accepted cancer treatment. Scientists do not yet understand why the therapy works in some patients and not others. In addition, because the T cells attack malignant melanoma tumor antigens that are similar to, or the same as, antigens that are present on certain normal body cells, the therapy may cause autoimmune disease in some patients. To date, the therapy has only been tested against malignant melanoma, but planning to test it against other types of cancer is under way, and some scientists believe that a similar therapy may be effective against viral diseases such as hepatitis.

target, which then activates enzymes that trigger apoptosis, killing the target cells **(Figure 15c).**

Memory T Cells

Learning Objective

✓ Describe the establishment of memory T cells.

Some activated T cells become **memory T cells,** which may persist for months or years in lymphoid tissues. If a memory T cell subsequently contacts an epitope–MHC I protein complex matching its TCR, it responds immediately (without a need for interaction with APCs) and produces cytotoxic T cell clones that recognize the offending epitope. These cells need fewer regulatory signals and become functional immediately. Further, since the number of memory T cells is greater than the number of T cells that recognized the antigen during the initial exposure, a subsequent cell-mediated immune response to a previously encountered antigen is much more effective than a primary response. An enhanced cell-mediated immune response upon subsequent exposure to the same antigen is called a **memory response.**[11]

T Cell Regulation

Learning Objective

✓ Explain the process and significance of the regulation of cell-mediated immunity.

The body carefully regulates cell-mediated immune responses so that T cells do not respond to autoantigens. As we have seen, T cells require several signals from an antigen-presenting cell to activate. If the T cells do not receive these signals in a specific sequence—like the sequence of numbers in a combination padlock—they will not respond. Thus, when a T cell and an antigen-presenting cell interact in an immunological synapse, the two cell types have a chemical "conversation" that stimulates the T cell to fully respond to the antigen. If a T cell does not receive the signals required for its activation, it will "shut down" as a precaution against autoimmune responses.

Further, regulatory T (Tr) cells moderate cytotoxic T cells by mechanisms that are beyond the scope of our discussion. Suffice it to say that Tr cells provide one more level of control over potentially dangerous cell-mediated immune responses.

[11]Sometimes also called anamnestic responses, from Greek *ana,* meaning again, and *mimneskein,* meaning to call to mind.

Humoral Immune Responses

As we have discussed, the body induces humoral immune responses against the antigens of exogenous pathogens. Recall that inducibility is one of the main characteristics of adaptive immunity: humoral immunity activates only in response to specific pathogens. The following sections examine the activity of B lymphocytes in humoral immune responses.

Inducement of T-Independent Humoral Immunity

Learning Objectives

✓ Contrast T-dependent and T-independent antigens in terms of size and repetition of subunits.

✓ Describe the inducement and action of a T-independent humoral response.

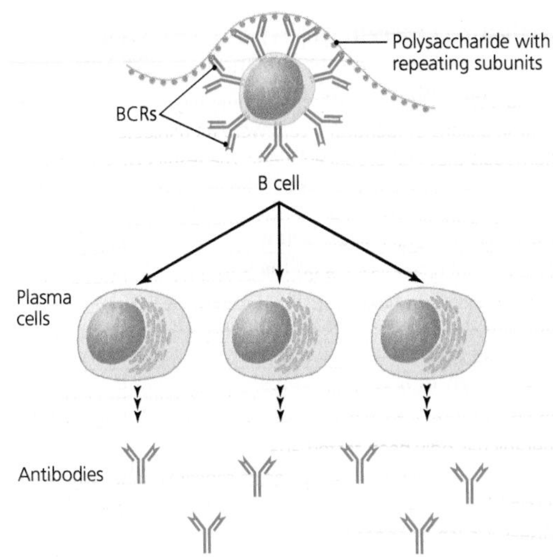

▲ *Figure 16*

The effects of the binding of a T-independent antigen by a B cell. When a molecule with multiple repeating epitopes (such as the polysaccharide shown here) cross-links the BCRs on a B cell, the cell is activated: it proliferates, and its daughter cells become plasma cells that secrete antibodies.

A few large antigens have many identical, repeating epitopes. These antigens can induce a humoral immune response, but not a cell-mediated immune response, without the assistance of a helper T cell (Th cell); therefore, these antigens are called *T-independent antigens,* and they trigger response of **T-independent humoral immunity (Figure 16).**

The repeating subunits of T-independent antigens allow extensive cross-linking between numerous BCRs on a B cell, stimulating the B cell to proliferate. Simultaneous interaction between Toll-like receptors on the B cell, innate mediators, and/or bacterial chemicals may facilitate activation of the B cell. Clones of the activated B cell become plasma cells, which have an extensive cytoplasm rich in rough endoplasmic reticulum and Golgi bodies and which secrete antibodies **(Figure 17).** Though these events occur without the direct involvement of Th cells, cytokines such as tumor necrosis factor (TNF) are required. T-independent humoral immune responses are fast because they do not depend on interactions with Th cells. Their speed is similar to that of innate immunity, but T-independent humoral immunity is relatively weak, disappears quickly, and induces little immunological memory.

T-independent responses are stunted in children, possibly because the repertoire and abundance of B cells is not fully developed in children; therefore, pathogens displaying T-independent antigens can cause childhood diseases, which are rare in adults. An example of such a T-independent antigen and its disease is the capsule of

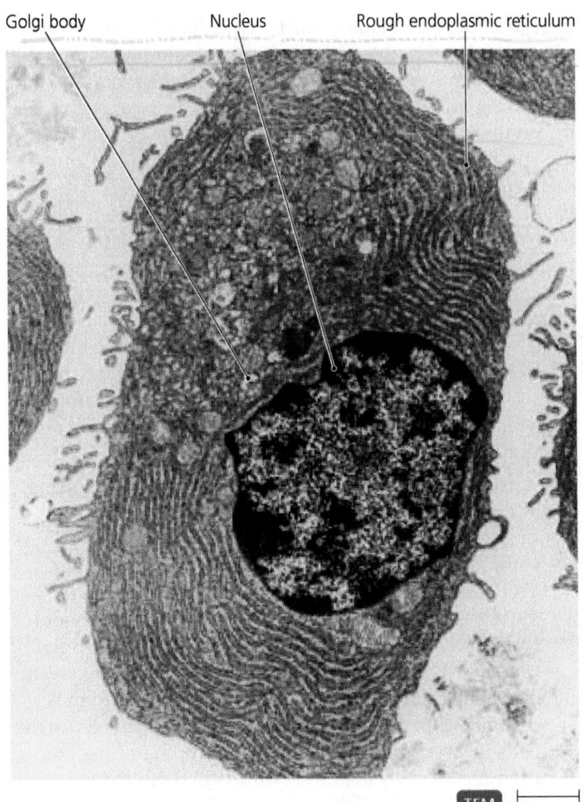

▲ *Figure 17*

A plasma cell. Plasma cells are almost twice as large as inactive B cells and are filled with endoplasmic reticulum and Golgi bodies for the synthesis and secretion of antibodies.

Haemophilus influenzae (hē-mof'i-lŭs in-flu-en'zī) type B that causes most cases of meningitis in unvaccinated children. The capsules of other bacteria, lipopolysaccharide of Gram-negative cell walls, bacterial flagella, and the capsids (outer covering) of some viruses constitute other T-independent antigens.

However most humoral immune responses are of the T-dependent type. We consider them next.

Inducement of T-Dependent Humoral Immunity with Clonal Selection

Learning Objectives

✓ Describe the formation and functions of plasma cells and memory B cells.

✓ Describe the steps and effect of clonal selection.

T-dependent antigens lack the numerous, repetitive, and identical epitopes and the large size of T-independent antigens, and immunity against them requires the assistance of type 2 helper T (Th2) cells. **T-dependent humoral immunity** begins with the action of an antigen-presenting cell (APC), which is usually a dendritic cell. After endocytosis and processing of the antigen, the dendritic cell presents epitopes in conjunction with MHC II proteins. This APC will induce the specific helper T (CD4) lymphocyte with a TCR complementary to the presented MHC II–epitope complex. The activated Th2 cell must in turn induce the equally rare B cell that recognizes the same antigen. Lymph nodes facilitate and cytokines mediate interactions among the antigen-presenting cells and lymphocytes, increasing the chance that the appropriate cells find each other.

Thus, a T-dependent humoral immune response involves a series of interactions among antigen-presenting cell, helper T cells, and B cells, all of which are mediated and enhanced by cytokines. Now we will examine each step in more detail **(Figure 18):**

1. **Antigen presentation for Th activation and cloning.** A dendritic cell, after acquiring antigens in the skin or mucous membrane, moves via the lymph to a local lymph node. The trip takes about a day. As helper T (Th, CD4) cells pass through the lymph node they survey all the resident APCs for complementary epitopes in conjunction with MHC II proteins. Antigen presentation depends on chance encounters between Th cells and the dendritic cells, but immunologists estimate that every lymphocyte browses the dendritic cells in every lymph node every day; therefore, complementary cells eventually find each other. Once they have established an immunological synapse, CD4 molecules in membrane rafts of the Th cell cytoplasmic membrane recognize and bind to MHC II, stabilizing the synapse.

   As we saw in cell-mediated immune responses, helper T cells need further stimulation before they activate. The requirement for a second signal helps prevent accidental inducement of an immune response. As before, the APC imparts the second signal by displaying an integral membrane protein in the immunological synapse. This induces the Th cell to proliferate, producing a clone.
2. **Differentiation of helper T cells into Th2 cells.** In humoral immune responses, the cytokine interleukin 4 (IL-4) acts as a signal to the Th cells to become type 2 helper T cells (Th2 cells). Immunologists do not know the source of IL-4, but it may be secreted initially by innate cells such as mast cells or secreted later in a response by the Th cells themselves.
3. **Clonal selection of B cell.** A B cell attaches to and phagocytizes a complementary antigen, which is a BCR-mediated event. It then displays the pathogen's epitopes in association with MHC II proteins. Antigen binding primes these B cells to participate in humoral immune responses. This is called **clonal selection.**
4. **Activation of B cell.** The repertoire of B cells and newly formed Th2 cells survey one another. A Th2 cell binds to the B cell with an MHC II protein–epitope complex that is complementary to the TCR of the Th2 cell. CD4 glycoprotein again stabilizes the immunological synapse.

   Th2 cells secrete more chemical signal molecules, which induce the selected B cell to move to the cortex of the lymph node. A Th2 cell in contact with an MHC II protein–epitope on a B cell is stimulated, expresses new gene products, and inserts a protein called CD40L into its cytoplasmic membrane. CD40L binds to CD40, which is found on B cells. This provides a second signal in the immunological synapse, triggering B cell activation. The B cells move to a B cell area of the lymph node to form a germinal center.

   The activated B cell proliferates rapidly to produce a population of cells (clone) that make up a germinal center in the lymph node. The clone differentiates into two types of cells—*memory B cells* (discussed shortly) and antibody-secreting *plasma cells.*

www.microbiologyplace.com **Animations: *Host Defenses: Humoral Immunity: Clonal Selection and Expansion***

Most of a clone's progeny become plasma cells. The initial plasma cell descendants of any single activated B cell secrete antibodies with binding sites identical to one another and complementary to the specific antigen recognized by their parent cell. Interestingly, as the plasma cell clones replicate, the cells slightly modify their antigen-binding-site genes such that they secrete antibodies with slightly different variable regions. Plasma cells that secrete antibodies with a higher affinity for the epitope have a selective survival advantage over plasma cells secreting antibodies with a less good fit; that is, active B cells with BCRs that bind the epitope more closely, survive at a higher rate. Thus, as the humoral immune response progresses, there are more and more plasma cells, secreting antibodies whose fitness gets progressively better.

Each plasma cell produces about 2000 molecules of antibody per second. They begin by secreting IgM and then, through class switching, they secrete IgG. Some cells later switch a second time and begin secreting IgA or IgE. As discussed previously, antibodies activate complement, trigger inflammation, agglutinate and neutralize antigen, act as opsonins, directly kill pathogens, and induce antibody-dependent cytoxicity.

Individual plasma cells are short lived, at least in part because of their high metabolic rate; they die within a few days of activation, although their antibodies can remain in body fluids for several weeks. Providentially, their descendants persist for years to maintain long-term adaptive responses.

CRITICAL THINKING

In general, what sorts of pathogens would successfully attack a patient with an inability to synthesize B lymphocytes?

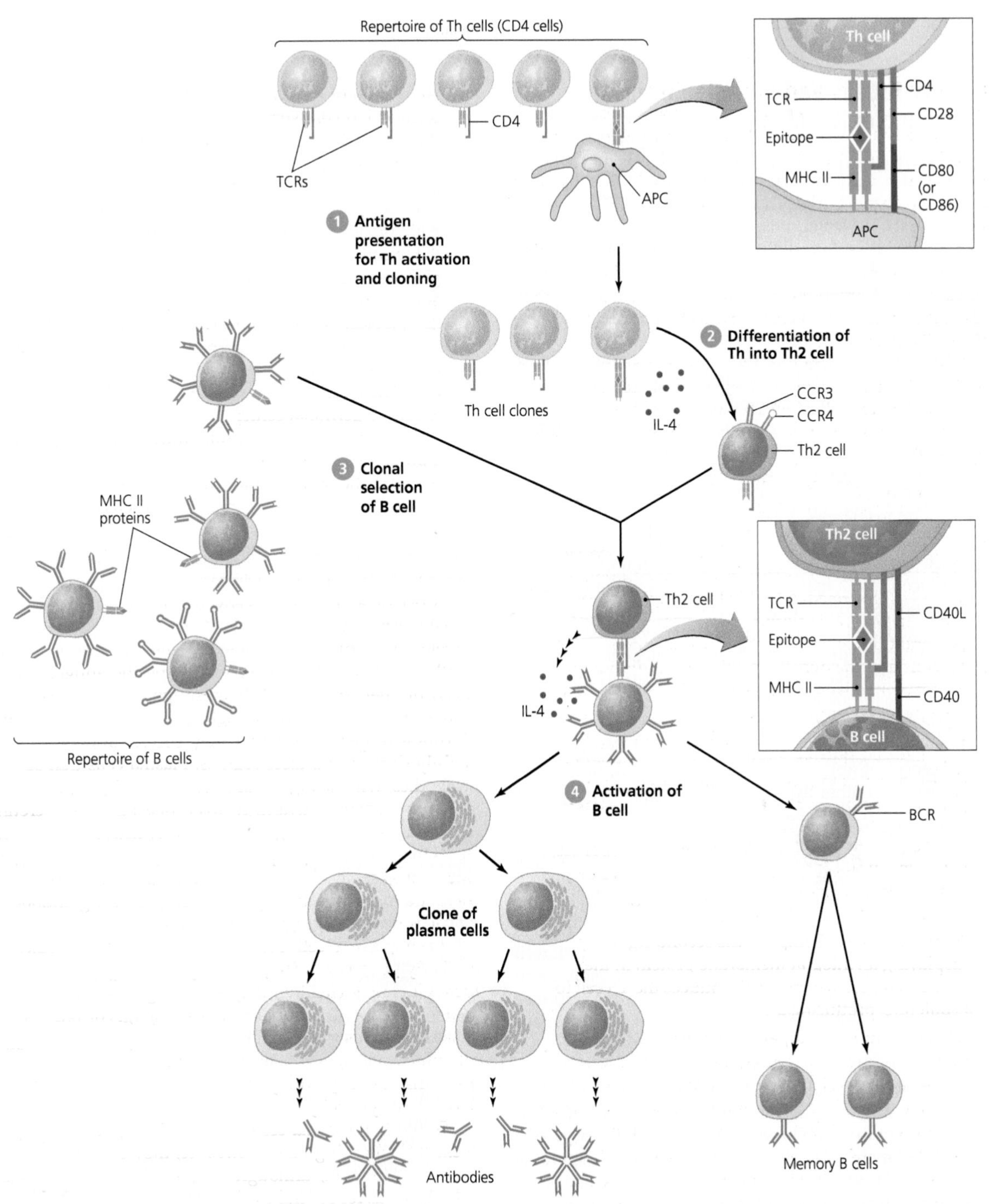

▲ *Figure 18*

A T-dependent humoral immune response. ① Antigen presentation, in which an APC, typically a dendritic cell, presents antigen to a complementary Th cell. ② Differentiation of the Th cell into a Th2 cell. ③ Clonal selection, in which the Th2 cell binds to the B cell clone that recognizes the antigen. ④ Activation of the B cell in response to secretion of IL-4 by the Th2 cell, which causes the B cell to differentiate into antibody-secreting plasma cells and long-lived memory cells.

Memory B Cells and the Establishment of Immunological Memory

Learning Objective

✓ Contrast primary and secondary immune responses.

A small percentage of the cells produced during B cell proliferation do not secrete antibodies but survive as **memory B cells**—that is, long-lived cells with BCRs complementary to the specific epitope that triggered their production. In contrast to plasma cells, memory cells retain their BCRs and persist in lymphoid tissues, surviving for more than 20 years, ready to initiate antibody production if the same epitope is encountered again. Let's examine how memory cells provide the basis for immunization to prevent disease, using tetanus immunization as an example.

Because the body produces an enormous variety of B cells (and therefore BCRs), a few Th cells and B cells bind to and respond to epitopes of *tetanus toxoid* (deactivated tetanus toxin), which is used for tetanus immunization. In a **primary response (Figure 19a),** relatively small amounts of antibodies are produced, and it may take days before sufficient antibodies are made to completely eliminate the toxoid from the body. Though some antibody molecules may persist for three weeks, a primary immune response basically ends when the plasma cells have lived out their normal life spans.

www.microbiologyplace.com **Animations: *Host Defenses: Humoral Immunity: Primary Immune Response***

Memory B cells, surviving in lymphoid tissue, constitute a reserve of antigen-sensitive cells that become active when there is another exposure to the antigen, in this case, toxin from infecting tetanus bacteria. Exposure may be many years later. Thus, tetanus toxin produced during the course of a bacterial infection will restimulate a population of memory cells, which proliferate and differentiate rapidly into plasma cells. The newly differentiated plasma cells produce large amounts of antibody within a few days **(Figure 19b),** and the tetanus toxin is neutralized before it can cause disease. Since many memory cells recognize and respond to the antigen, such a **secondary immune response** is much faster and more effective than the primary response.

www.microbiologyplace.com **Animations: *Host Defenses: Humoral Immunity: Secondary Immune Response***

As you might expect, a third exposure (whether to tetanus toxin or to toxoid in an immunization booster) results in an even more effective response. Enhanced immune responses triggered by subsequent exposure to antigens are memory responses, which are the basis of *immunization.*

CRITICAL THINKING

Plasma cells are vital for protection against infection, but memory B cells are not. Why not?

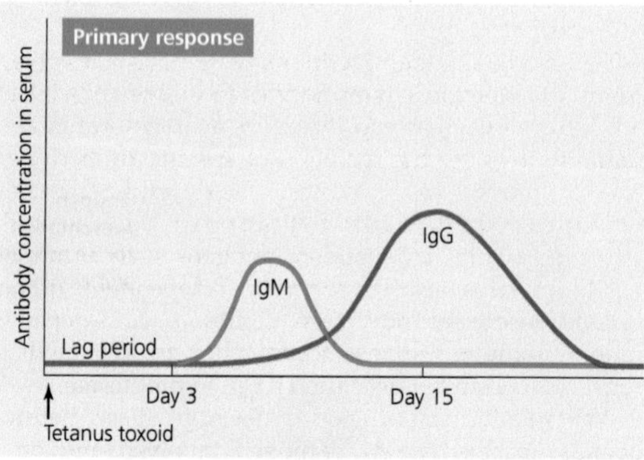

(a)

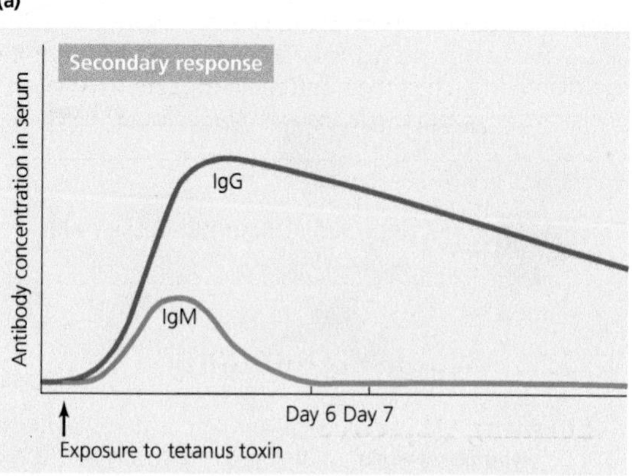

(b)

▲ *Figure 19*

The production of primary and secondary humoral immune responses. This example depicts the events following the administration of a tetanus toxoid in immunization. **(a)** Primary response. After the tetanus toxoid is introduced into the body, the body slowly removes the toxoid while producing memory B cells. **(b)** Secondary response. Upon exposure to active tetanus toxin during the course of an infection, memory B cells immediately differentiate into plasma cells and proliferate, producing a response that is faster and results in greater antibody production than occurs in the primary response.

In summary, the body's response to infectious agents seldom relies on one mechanism alone, because this course of action would be far too risky. Therefore, the body typically uses several different mechanisms to combat infections. In the example from the chapter opener, the body's initial response to intruders was inflammation (a nonspecific, innate response), but a specific immune response against the invading microorganisms was also necessary. APCs phagocytize some of the invaders, process their epitopes, and induce clones of lymphocytes in both humoral and cell-mediated immune responses. Key to enduring protection are the facts that adaptive immunity is unresponsive to self and involves immunological memory brought about by long-lived memory B and T cells.

Cell-mediated adaptive immune responses involve the activity of cytotoxic T lymphocytes in killing cells infected with intracellular bacteria and viruses. Humoral adaptive immunity involves the secretion of specific antibodies that have a variety of functions. T-independent humoral immune responses are rare, but can occur when an adult is challenged with T-independent antigens such as bacterial flagella or capsules. In contrast, T-dependent humoral immune responses are more common. A T-dependent humoral immune response occurs when an APC binds to a specific Th cell and signals the Th cell to proliferate.

The relative importance of each of these pathways depends on the type of pathogen involved and on the mechanisms by which they cause disease. In any case, adaptive immune responses are specific, inducible, involve clones, are unresponsive to self, and give the body long-term memory against their antigenic triggers.

www.microbiologyplace.com **Animations: *Host Defenses: The Big Picture***

CRITICAL THINKING

What sorts of pathogens could successfully attack a patient with an inability to produce T lymphocytes?

Types of Acquired Immunity

Learning Objective

✓ Contrast active versus passive acquired immunity, and naturally acquired versus artificially acquired immunity.

As we have seen, adaptive immunity is acquired during an individual's life. Immunologists categorize immunity as either naturally or artificially acquired. Naturally acquired immunity occurs when the body mounts an immune response against antigens, such as influenzaviruses or food antigens, encountered during the course of daily life. Artificial immunity is the body's response to antigens introduced in vaccines, as occurs with immunization against the flu. Immunologists further distinguish acquired immune responses as either *active* or *passive;* that is, the immune system either responds actively to antigens via humoral or cell-mediated responses, or the body passively receives antibodies from another individual. Next we consider each of four types of acquired immunity.

Naturally Acquired Active Immunity

Naturally acquired active immunity occurs when the body responds to exposure to pathogens and environmental antigens by mounting specific immune responses. The body is naturally and actively engaged in its own protection. As we have seen, once an immune response occurs, immunological memory persists—on subsequent exposure to the same antigen, the immune response will be rapid and powerful and often provides the body complete protection.

Naturally Acquired Passive Immunity

Although newborns possess the cells and tissues needed to mount an immune response, they respond slowly to antigens. If required to protect themselves solely via naturally acquired active immunity, they might die of infectious disease before their immune systems were mature enough to respond adequately. However, they are not on their own; in the womb, IgG molecules cross the placenta from the mother's bloodstream to provide protection, and after birth, babies receive secretory IgA in breast milk. Via these two processes, a mother provides her child with antibodies that protect it during its early months. Because the child is not actively producing its own antibodies, this type of protection is known as **naturally acquired passive immunity.**

Artificially Acquired Active Immunity

Physicians induce immunity in their patients by introducing antigens in the form of vaccines. The patients' own immune systems then mount active responses against the foreign antigens, just as if the antigens were part of a naturally acquired pathogen. Such **artificially acquired active immunity** is the basis of immunization.

Artificially Acquired Passive Immunotherapy

Active immunity usually requires days to weeks to develop fully, and in some cases such a delay can prove detrimental or even fatal. For instance, an active immune response is too slow to protect against infection with rabies or hepatitis A virus. Therefore, medical personnel routinely harvest antibodies specific for toxins and pathogens that are so deadly or so fast-acting that an individual's active immune response is inadequate. They acquire these antibodies from the blood of immune humans or animals, typically a horse. Physicians then inject such *antitoxins* or *antisera* into infected patients to confer **artificially acquired passive immunotherapy.**

Active immune responses, whether naturally or artificially induced, are advantageous because they result in immunological memory and protection against future infections. However, they are slow-acting. Passive process, in which individuals are provided fully formed antibodies, has the advantage of speed but does not confer immunological memory because B and T lymphocytes are not activated. **Table 3** summarizes the four types of acquired immunity.

Table 3 A Comparison of the Types of Acquired Immunity

	Active	Passive
Naturally acquired	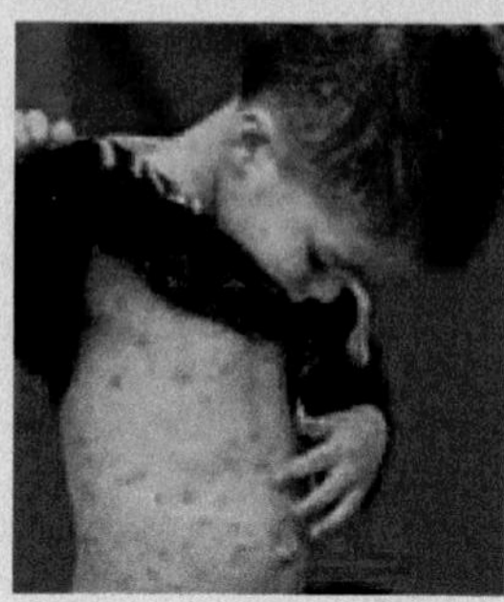 The body responds to antigens that enter naturally, such as during infections.	 Antibodies are transferred from mother to offspring, either across the placenta (IgG) or in breast milk (secretory IgA).
Artificially acquired	 Health care workers introduce antigens in vaccines; the body responds with humoral or cell-mediated immune responses, including the production of memory cells.	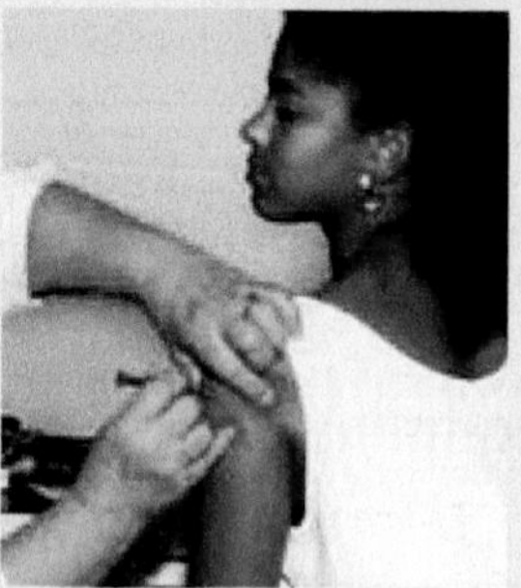 Health care workers give patients antisera or antitoxins, which are preformed antibodies obtained from immune individuals or animals.

CHAPTER SUMMARY

Overview of Adaptive Immunity

1. **Adaptive immunity** is the ability of a vertebrate to recognize and defend against distinct species or strains of invaders. Adaptive immunity is characterized by specificity, inducibility, clonality, unresponsiveness to self, and memory.
2. **B lymphocytes (B cells)** attack extracellular pathogens in **humoral immune responses,** involving soluble proteins called **antibodies. T lymphocytes (T cells)** carry out **cell-mediated immune responses** against intracellular pathogens. www.microbiologyplace.com **Animations: *Host Defenses: Humoral Immunity: Overview*** **and *Cell-Mediated Immunity: Overview*** **and *Host Defenses: The Big Picture***

Elements of Adaptive Immunity

1. The **lymphatic system** is composed of **lymphatic vessels,** which conduct the flow of **lymph,** and lymphoid tissues and organs that are directly involved in specific immunity. The latter include **lymph nodes,** the thymus, the spleen, the tonsils, and mucosa-associated lymphoid tissue (MALT). Lymphocytes originate and mature in the red bone marrow and express characteristic membrane proteins. They migrate to and persist in various lymphoid organs, where they are available to encounter foreign invaders in the blood and lymph.
2. **Antigens** are substances that trigger specific immune responses. Effective antigen molecules are large, usually complex, stable, degradable, and foreign to their host. An **epitope** (or antigenic determinant) is the three-dimensional shape of a region of an antigen that is recognized by the immune system.
3. **Exogenous** antigens are found on microorganisms that multiply outside the cells of the body; **endogenous** antigens are produced by pathogens multiplying inside the body's cells.
4. Ideally, the body does not attack antigens on the surface of its normal cells, called **autoantigens;** this phenomenon is called self-tolerance.

5. B lymphocytes (B cells), which mature in the red bone marrow, make immunoglobulins (Ig), which are **B cell receptors (BCRs)** and **antibodies.** Immunoglobulins are complementary to epitopes and consist of two light chains and two heavy chains joined via disulfide bonds to form Y-shaped molecules. BCRs are inserted into the cytoplasmic membranes of B cells, and antibodies are secreted.

6. Together the variable regions of a heavy and a light chain form an **antigen-binding site,** and the upper portions of antibody molecules are called F_{ab} regions. Each basic antibody molecule has two antigen-binding sites and can potentially bind two epitopes.

7. Antibodies are of five basic classes based upon their stems (F_c regions). Each B cell randomly chooses (once in its life) genes for the upper portion of the "arms" of its immunoglobulin molecules; therefore, the upper portions are called variable regions because they differ from cell to cell.

8. The five types of heavy chains in antibody stems distinguish five different classes of antibodies. **IgM,** a pentamer with 10 antigen-binding sites, is the predominant antibody produced first during a primary humoral response. **IgG** is the predominant antibody found in the bloodstream and is largely responsible for defense against invading bacteria. IgG can cross a placenta to protect the fetus. Two molecules of **IgA** are attached via J chains and a polypeptide secretory component to produce **secretory IgA,** which is found in milk, tears, and mucous membrane secretions. **IgE** triggers inflammation and allergic reactions. It also functions during helminth infections. Immunoglobulin D **(IgD)** is found in cytoplasmic membranes of some animals.

9. Through a process called **class switching,** antibody-producing cells change the class of antibody they secrete, beginning with IgM and then producing IgG and then possibly IgA or IgE.

10. Antibodies function in complement activation, inflammation, **neutralization** (blocking the action of a toxin or attachment of a pathogen), **opsonization** (enhanced phagocytosis), direct killing by oxidation, **agglutination,** and **antibody-dependent cellular cytotoxicity (ADCC).**
www.microbiologyplace.com **Animations: *Host Defenses: Humoral Immunity: Antibody Function***

11. T cells have **T cell receptors (TCRs)** for antigens, mature under influence of signals from the thymus, and attack cells that harbor endogenous pathogens during cell-mediated immune responses.

12. In cell-mediated immunity, **cytotoxic T cells (Tc or CD8 cells)** act against infected or abnormal body cells, including virus-infected cells, bacteria-infected cells, some fungal- or protozoan-infected cells, some cancer cells, and foreign cells that enter the body as a result of organ transplantation.

13. T cells that do not recognize MHC I protein and most T cells that recognize MHC I protein in conjunction with autoantigens are removed by apoptosis. This is **clonal deletion.** A few self-recognizing T cells are retained and become **regulatory T cells (Tr cells).** T cells that recognize MHC I protein but not autoantigens become the repertoire of immature T cells.

14. B cells with B cell receptors that respond to autoantigens are selectively killed via apoptosis— further clonal deletion. Only B cells that respond to foreign antigens survive to defend the body.

15. Two types of **helper T cells—Th1** and **Th2**—are characterized by **CD4.** They direct cell-mediated and humoral immune responses respectively.
www.microbiologyplace.com **Animations: *Host Defenses: Cell-Mediated Immunity: Helper T Cells***

16. **Cytokines** are soluble regulatory proteins that act as intercellular signals to direct activities in immune responses. Cytokines include **interleukin (ILs), interferons (IFNs), growth factors, tumor necrosis factors (TNFs),** and **chemokines.**

Preparation for an Adaptive Immune Response

1. Nucleated cells display epitopes of their own proteins and epitopes from intracellular pathogens such as viruses on **major histocompatibility complex (MHC)** class I proteins.
www.microbiologyplace.com **Animations: *Host Defenses: Antigen Processing and Presentation: Steps*** and ***Antigen Processing and Presentation: MHC***

2. The initial step in mounting an immune response is that antigens are captured, ingested, and degraded into epitopes by **antigen-presenting cells (APCs)** such as B cells, macrophages, and **dendritic cells.** Epitopes are inserted into **major histocompatibility complex (MHC)** class II proteins.

Cell-Mediated Immune Responses

1. Once activated by dendritic cells, cytotoxic T cells (Tc cells) recognize abnormal molecules presented by MHC I protein on the surface of infected, cancerous, or foreign cells. Sometimes cytotoxic T cells require cytokines from Th1 cells.

2. Activated Tc cells reproduce to form memory T cells and more Tc progeny in a process called **clonal expansion.**

3. Cytotoxic T cells destroy their target cells via two pathways: the perforin-granzyme pathway, which kills the affected cells by secreting **perforins** and **granzymes,** or the **CD95 pathway,** in which CD95L binds to CD95 on the target cell, triggering target cell apoptosis. Cytotoxic T cells may also form **memory T cells,** which function in **memory responses.**
www.microbiologyplace.com **Animations: *Host Defenses: Cell-Mediated Immunity: Cytotoxic T Cells***

Humoral Immune Responses

1. T-independent antigens, such as bacterial capsules, trigger **T-independent, humoral immune responses,** which are more common in adults than in children.

2. In **T-dependent humoral immunity,** an APC's MHC II protein–epitope complex activates the helper T cell (Th cell) with a complementary TCR. CD4 stabilizes the connection between the cells, which is called an immunological synapse. Interleukin 4 (IL-4) then induces the Th cell to become a type 2 helper T cell (Th2).

3. In **clonal selection,** an immunological synapse forms between the Th2 cell and the B cell with a complementary MHC II protein–epitope complex. The Th2 cell secretes IL-4, which induces the B cell to divide. Its offspring, collectively called a clone, become plasma cells or **memory B cells.**
www.microbiologyplace.com **Animations: *Host Defenses: Humoral Immunity: Clonal Selection and Expansion***

4. Plasma cells live for only a short time but secrete large amounts of antibodies, beginning with IgM and class switching as they get older. Memory B cells migrate to lymphoid tissues to await a subsequent encounter with the same antigen.
5. The **primary response** to an antigen is slow to develop and of limited effectiveness. When that antigen is encountered a second time, the activation of memory cells ensures that the immune response is rapid and strong. This is a **secondary immune response.** Such enhanced humoral immune responses are memory responses.
www.microbiologyplace.com **Animations: *Host Defenses: Humoral Immunity: Primary Immune Response* and *Humoral Immunity: Secondary Immune Response***

Types of Acquired Immunity

1. When the body mounts a specific immune response against an infectious agent, the result is called **naturally acquired active immunity.**
2. The passing of maternal IgG to the fetus and the transmission of secretory IgA in milk to a baby are examples of **naturally acquired passive immunity.**
3. **Artificially acquired active immunity** is achieved by deliberately injecting someone with antigens in vaccines to provoke an active response, as in the process of immunization.
4. **Artificially acquired passive immunotherapy** involves the administration of preformed antibodies in antitoxins or antisera to a patient.

QUESTIONS FOR REVIEW

Access more review material (including animations and practice tests) online at www.microbiologyplace.com.

Multiple Choice

1. Antibodies function to
   a. directly destroy foreign organ grafts.
   b. mark invading organisms for destruction.
   c. kill intracellular viruses.
   d. promote cytokine synthesis.
   e. stimulate T cell growth.
2. MHC class II molecules bind to ________________ and trigger ____________.
   a. endogenous antigens, cytotoxic T cells
   b. exogenous antigens, cytotoxic T cells
   c. antibodies, B cells
   d. endogenous antigens, helper T cells
   e. exogenous antigens, helper T cells
3. Rejection of a foreign skin graft is an example of
   a. destruction of virus-infected cells.
   b. tolerance.
   c. antibody-mediated immunity.
   d. a secondary immune response.
   e. a cell-mediated immune response.
4. An autoantigen is
   a. an antigen from bacteria.
   b. a normal body component.
   c. an artificial antigen.
   d. any carbohydrate antigen.
   e. a nucleic acid.
5. Among the key molecules that mediate cell-mediated cytotoxicity are
   a. perforin.
   b. immunoglobulins.
   c. complement.
   d. cytokines.
   e. interferons.
6. Which of the following lymphocytes predominates in blood?
   a. cytotoxic T cells
   b. helper T cells
   c. B cells
   d. memory cells
   e. all are about equally prevalent
7. The major class of immunoglobulin found on the surfaces of the walls of the intestines and airways is secretory
   a. IgG.
   b. IgM.
   c. IgA.
   d. IgE.
   e. IgD.
8. Which cells express MHC class I molecules?
   a. red blood cells
   b. antigen-presenting cells only
   c. neutrophils only
   d. all nucleated cells
   e. dendritic cells only
9. In which of the following sites in the body can B cells be found?
   a. lymph nodes
   b. spleen
   c. red bone marrow
   d. intestinal wall
   e. all of the above
10. Tc cells recognize epitopes only when the latter are held by
    a. MHC I proteins.
    b. B cells.
    c. interleukin 2.
    d. granzyme.

Modified True/False

Mark each statement as either true or false. Rewrite false statements to make them true by changing the italicized words.

____ 1. MHC class II molecules are found on *T cells.*

____ 2. *Apoptosis* is the term used to describe cellular suicide.

____ 3. Lymphocytes with CD8 glycoprotein are *helper* T cells.

____ 4. *Cytotoxic T cells* secrete immunoglobulin.

____ 5. Secretion of antibodies by activated B cells is a form of *cell-mediated* immunity.

Matching

1. Match each cell in the left column with its associated protein from the right column.

_____ Plasma cell	A. MHC II molecule
_____ Cytotoxic T cell	B. Interleukin 4
_____ Th2 cell	C. Perforin and granzyme
_____ Dendritic cell	D. Immunoglobulin

2. Match each type of immunity in the left column with its associated example from the right column.

_____ Artificially acquired passive immunotherapy	A. Production of IgE in response to pollen
_____ Naturally acquired active immunity	B. Acquisition of maternal antibodies in breast milk
_____ Naturally acquired passive immunity	C. Administration of tetanus toxoid
_____ Artificially acquired active immunity	D. Administration of antitoxin

Short Answer

1. When is antigen processing an essential prerequisite for an immune response?
2. Why does the body have both humoral and cell-mediated immune responses?

CRITICAL THINKING

1. Why is it advantageous for the lymphatic system to lack a pump?
2. Contrast innate defenses with adaptive immunity.
3. What is the benefit to the body of requiring the immune system to process antigen?
4. Scientists can develop genetically deficient strains of mice. Describe the immunological impairments that would result in mice deficient in each of the following: class I MHC, class II MHC, TCR, BCR, IL-2 receptor, and IFN-γ.
5. Human immunodeficiency virus (HIV) preferentially destroys CD4 cells. Specifically, what effect does this have on humoral and cell-mediated immunity?
6. What would happen to a person who failed to make MHC molecules?
7. Why does the body make five different classes of immunoglobulins?
8. Some materials such as metal bone pins and plastic heart valves can be implanted into the body without fear of rejection by the patient's immune system. Why is this? What are the ideal properties of any material that is to be implanted?
9. What nonmembranous organelle is prevalent in plasma cells? What membranous organelle is prevalent?

ANSWERS TO QUESTIONS FOR REVIEW

Multiple Choice
1. b; 2. e; 3. e; 4. b; 5. a; 6. b; 7. c; 8. d; 9. e; 10. a

Modified True/False
1. antigen-presenting cells; 2. true; 3. cytotoxic; 4. plasma cells; 5. humoral

Matching

1.
D Plasma cell
C Cytotoxic cell
B Th2 cell
A Dendritic cell

2.
D Artificially acquired passive immunity
A Naturally acquired active immunity
B Naturally acquired passive immunity
C Artificially acquired active immunity

CREDITS

Illustration Credits
2, 3: Kenneth Probst. 4–11, 13–18, 19, Highlight 1, Table 1: Precision Graphics.

Photo Credits
Opener: CNRI/Photo Researchers. 1: Michael Ross/Photo Researchers. 6b: Tim Evans/Photo Researchers. 12: David Scharf/Photo Researchers. 17: Dorothea Zucker-Franklin/Phototake. Highlight 2: NIBSC/Photo Researchers. Highlight 3: Andrejs Liepins/SPL/Photo Researchers. Table 3.01: PBWPIX/Alamy. Table 3.02: Diane Macdonald/Stockbyte/Getty Images. Table 3.03: SUPRI/Reuters/Landov. Table 3.04: Barbara Rice, CDC.

Microbial Diseases of the Respiratory System

CHAPTER OUTLINE

MicroPrep Pre-Test: Take the pre-test for this chapter on the web. Visit www.microbiologyplace.com.

A businessman flies from Singapore to Canada sitting next to a sick passenger who coughs throughout the flight. Within a week, the businessman develops a high fever and an aching body. These symptoms soon pass, but three days later, he too begins coughing and laboring for breath. Although the signs and symptoms initially suggest influenza, his doctor discovers that the man is actually a victim of severe acute respiratory syndrome (SARS).

SARS took the world by surprise in November 2002, becoming one of the planet's emerging viral diseases. Originating in China, SARS spread to 26 countries (including Singapore, the United States, and Canada) before the pandemic ended in June 2003, largely because of the imposition of aggressive quarantine procedures. SARS affected almost 9000 patients during the pandemic, and nearly 800 died from this respiratory disease. In this chapter, we examine SARS and other diseases of the respiratory system caused by bacteria, viruses, and fungi.

Ballet students in Hong Kong during the first SARS pandemic

Structures of the Respiratory System

The respiratory system serves the vital function of exchanging gases between the atmosphere and the blood. Anatomists commonly divide its structures into two divisions—the upper respiratory system and the lower respiratory system **(Figure 1a)**. We begin our examination of respiratory anatomy by considering the upper respiratory system and the organs associated with it.

Structures of the Upper Respiratory System, Sinuses, and Ears

Learning Objectives

✓ Describe the structures of the upper respiratory system.

✓ Describe the anatomical relationship between the pharynx and the middle ears and sinuses.

The upper respiratory system collects air; filters dust, pollen, microorganisms, and other contaminants from the air; and delivers it to the lower respiratory organs. The upper respiratory system includes:

- The *nose*, which is the only external part of the respiratory system.
- The *nasal cavity*, which is lined with hairs and a ciliated mucous membrane, receives air from the nose. The hairs filter large dust particles and organisms from the air, while the sticky mucus traps smaller particles and microbes. Ciliary action moves nasal mucus and its contents back and down, into the throat. *Sinuses*, which are air-filled, hollow regions of bones in the skull, often share fluids and—infecting microorganisms—with the nasal cavity.
- The *pharynx*, which is shared with the digestive system, is lined with a ciliated mucous membrane that propels mucus and contaminants into the digestive system. A flap protruding from the roof of the mouth called the *uvula* partially closes the opening between the nasal cavity and the pharynx during swallowing.

Ducts from the eyes carry contaminants into the pharynx. *Auditory* (*eustachian*, yū-stā'shŭn) *tubes* from the ears to the pharynx **(Figure 1b)** allow equalization of air pressure against the inner surfaces of the eardrums. Aggregations of lymphoid tissue called *tonsils* or *adenoids* are located near the junction of the nasal cavity, pharynx, and auditory tubes. The tonsils contain cells and chemicals to combat microbes in this frequent portal of entry.

The mucus of the upper respiratory system contains antimicrobial chemicals, including defensins, lactoferrin, and lysozyme. Defensins are antimicrobial peptides that act against Gram-positive and Gram-negative bacteria, fungi, and some viruses. Lactoferrin sequesters iron, making this important nutrient unavailable to microbial contaminants. Lysozyme breaks down peptidoglycan in the bacterial cell wall.

Structures of the Lower Respiratory System

The lower respiratory system consists of a series of tubes—the *larynx*, *trachea* (windpipe), *bronchi*, *bronchioles*, and smaller respiratory tubes—that lead to hundreds of millions of microscopic air sacs called *alveoli* (al-vē'ō-lī) **(Figure 1c and d)**, which make up the *lungs*. Protective membranes called *pleurae* (plūr'ē) surround the lungs. The major respiratory muscle is the *diaphragm*, located below the lungs.

Because the structures of the lower respiratory system resemble an upside-down tree with branches that gradually decrease in diameter while increasing in number, anatomists refer to it as the *respiratory tree*. In this analogy, the trachea is the trunk, the bronchi and smaller tubes are the branches, and the alveoli represent leaves. When the diaphragm contracts, the lungs inflate, and air flows from the nose through the pharynx and into the respiratory tree.

The larynx contains the vocal cords, which vibrate as air flows over them. A cartilaginous flap called the *epiglottis* folds over the opening of the larynx during swallowing to prevent food and liquids from entering the lower respiratory organs.

Air flows from the larynx through the trachea, through the bronchi and bronchioles, and into the alveoli of the lungs. In the alveoli, oxygen enters the blood by passing through the thin walls of the alveoli and blood capillaries. Carbon dioxide diffuses from the capillaries into the alveoli to be exhaled. Relaxation of the diaphragm, accompanied by contraction of a different set of small muscles attached to ribs, allows the lungs to deflate, and air flows out.

A ciliated mucous membrane lines the trachea, bronchi, and bronchioles. The cilia beat synchronously about 1000 times per minute to carry mucus and trapped contaminants up to the pharynx. Physiologists refer to this action as a *ciliary escalator*. The mucus and its contents pass into the digestive system where digestive juices destroy them. Further protection from pathogens is provided by *alveolar macrophages*, which enter the alveoli from blood capillaries and devour microorganisms. Secretory antibodies (IgA), which are present in tears, saliva, and respiratory mucus, also provide protection from many pathogens.

Normal Microbiota of the Respiratory System

Learning Objective

✓ Describe the normal microbiota of the upper and lower respiratory tracts.

The lower respiratory system is normally devoid of microorganisms because the ciliary escalator, secretory antibodies, and phagocytic cells clear the organs of contaminants. In contrast, many types of microorganisms live in the upper respiratory system. The nose, which is cooler than the rest of the respiratory system, supports the growth of bacteria such as *Haemophilus influenzae* (hē-mof'i-lus in-flū-en'zī, which, contrary to its name, does not cause the flu) and *Moraxella catarrhalis* (mōr'ak-sel'ă ka-tar-hal'is).

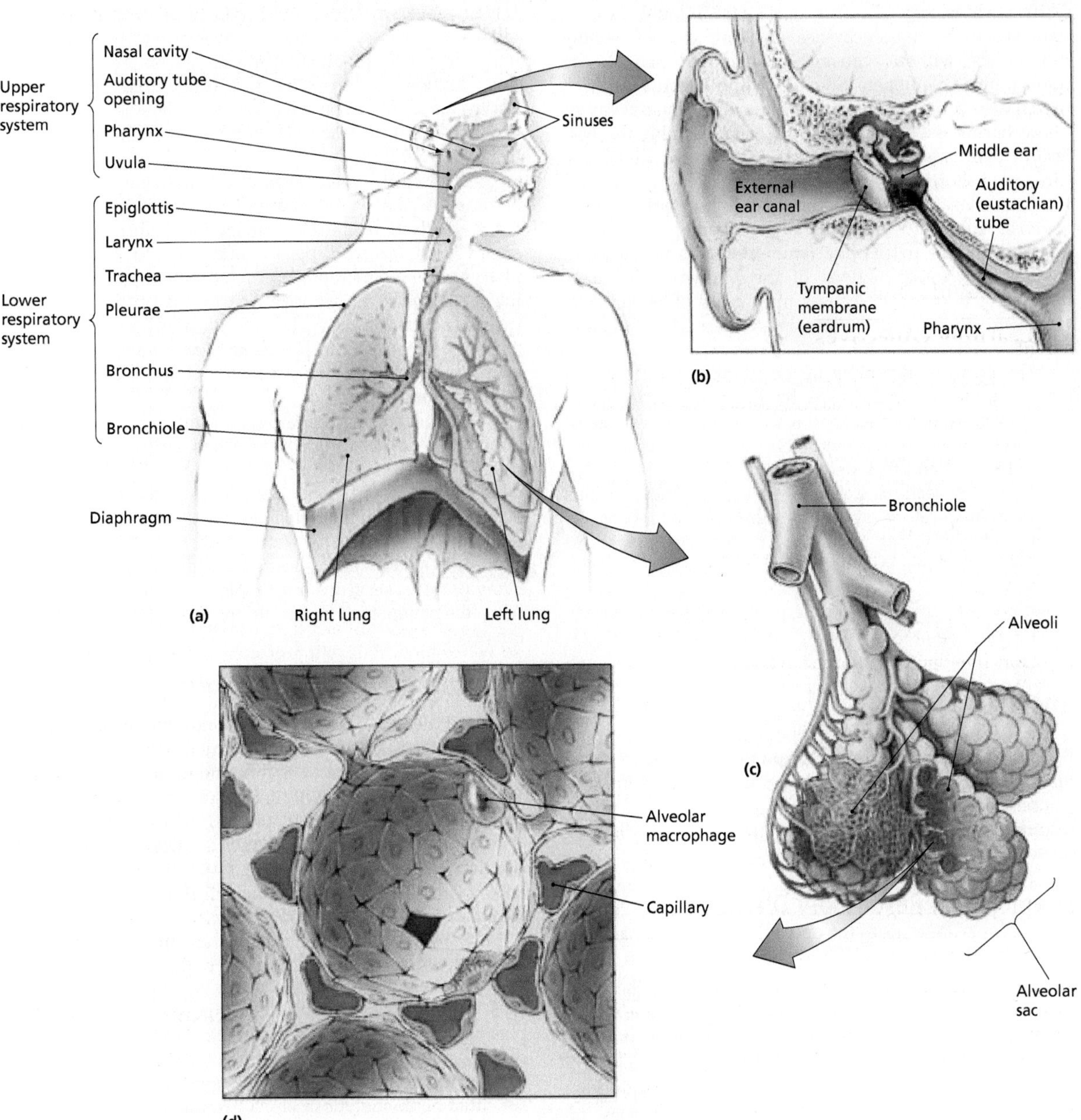

▲ *Figure 1*

Structures of the respiratory system. (a) Section through the body showing the major respiratory organs. **(b)** Enlargement of a portion of the head showing the connection between the middle ear and the pharynx. **(c)** Enlargement of a distal end of the respiratory tree. **(d)** An alveolus.

Gram-positive *Staphylococcus aureus* (staf'i-lō-kok'ŭs o'rē-ŭs) lives in the nasal cavities of about 20% of healthy individuals without causing disease but can be an opportunistic pathogen. So-called **diphtheroids** (dif'thĕ-royds) also commonly colonize the nose and nasal cavity. These harmless Gram-positive bacteria resemble the bacterium that cause a respiratory disease called diphtheria (discussed shortly).

Gram-negative cocci, diphtheroids, opportunistic *Staphylococcus* spp., and alpha-hemolytic streptococci, including *Streptococcus pneumoniae* (strep-tō-kok'ŭs nū-mō'nē-ī), colonize the upper regions of the pharynx. The latter opportunistic pathogen causes most cases of pneumonia. Organisms in the pharynx can infect the middle ears and sinuses.

The normal microbiota of the upper respiratory system limit infection and disease by removing nutrients and releasing substances that inhibit the growth of pathogens. However, some normal microbiota can cause opportunistic diseases when other defensive mechanisms are faulty. The following sections examine some of the more serious microbial respiratory diseases, beginning with bacterial diseases of the upper respiratory system and associated organs.

Bacterial Diseases of the Upper Respiratory System, Sinuses, and Ears

Bacteria can infect the upper respiratory system to cause diseases such as sore throat. They can also spread into the sinuses and auditory tubes. We begin our study of upper respiratory infections by examining a variety of diseases caused by species of *Streptococcus*.

Streptococcal Respiratory Diseases

Learning Objectives

- ✓ Describe four respiratory diseases caused by *Streptococcus*.
- ✓ Identify the structures, enzymes, and toxins of group A *Streptococcus* (*S. pyogenes*) that enable this bacterium to survive against the body's defenses and cause disease.

Physicians recognize a variety of diseases of the respiratory system and associated organs caused by species of *Streptococcus*, depending on the site of infection, the strain of bacteria, and the immune responses of the patient.

Signs and Symptoms

"Strep throat" or **streptococcal pharyngitis** (strep'tō-kok'ăl far-in-jī'tis) is an inflammation of the pharynx caused by streptococci. The back of the pharynx appears red, with swollen lymph nodes and purulent (pus-containing) abscesses covering the tonsils (see Disease at a Glance 1). Usually, fever, malaise,[1] and headache accompany pharyngitis. If bacteria spread into the lower respiratory tract, they may cause inflammation of the larynx or bronchi, conditions known as **laryngitis** and **bronchitis,** respectively. Laryngitis manifests as hoarseness; bronchitis reduces airflow, encourages mucus accumulation in the lungs, and triggers coughing.

The disease **scarlet fever,** also known as *scarlatina,* can accompany pharyngitis caused by a strain of *Streptococcus* carrying a lysogenic bacteriophage that codes for *pyrogenic erythrogenic*[2] *toxins.* Typically, after one to two days of pharyngitis, such streptococci release their toxins, triggering fever and a diffuse rash that begins on the chest and spreads across the body. The tongue usually becomes strawberry red. The rash disappears after about a week, and the skin sloughs off in a manner reminiscent of staphylococcal scalded skin syndrome.

Complications of some cases of untreated streptococcal pharyngitis are *acute glomerulonephritis,* a disease of the kidneys, and **rheumatic fever,** in which inflammation leads to damage of heart valves and muscle. Though the exact cause of such damage is unknown, it appears that this disease is an autoimmune response in which antibodies directed against streptococcal antigens cross-react with heart antigens. In many patients, surgeons must replace damaged heart valves when the patient reaches middle age. Heart failure and death can occur.

Pathogen and Virulence Factors

The bacterial genus *Streptococcus* is a diverse assemblage of Gram-positive, facultatively anaerobic cocci arranged in pairs or chains. Researchers differentiate streptococci using several different, overlapping schemes, including serological classification based on the reactions of antibodies to specific bacterial antigens, type of hemolysis, and physiological properties as revealed by biochemical tests. A serological classification scheme developed in 1938 by Rebecca Lancefield (1895–1981) divides streptococci into serotype groups based on the bacteria's antigens (known as *Lancefield antigens*).

Lancefield group A *Streptococcus* (synonymously known as *S. pyogenes,* pī-oj'en-ēz) is the major cause of bacterial pharyngitis and scarlet and rheumatic fevers. The bacterium shows beta-hemolysis after 24 hours on blood agar plates. In contrast, benign streptococci of the upper respiratory system are either nonhemolytic or alpha-hemolytic.

Strains of group A streptococci have a number of structures, enzymes, and toxins that enable them to survive as pathogens in the body. These include the following:

- *M proteins* destabilize complement component C3b, thereby interfering with opsonization and lysis.

[1]French, meaning discomfort.
[2]From Greek *erythros,* meaning red, and *genein,* meaning to produce.

- The *hyaluronic acid capsule* may "camouflage" the bacterium from phagocytes.
- *Streptokinases* are enzymes that break down blood clots, presumably enabling group A streptococci to spread rapidly through damaged tissues.
- *C5a peptidase* is an enzyme that breaks down complement protein C5a, which is a chemotactic factor. With this enzyme, *S. pyogenes* decreases the movement of leukocytes into the site of infection.
- *Pyrogenic*[3] (also called *erythrogenic*) *toxins* stimulate leukocytes to release cytokines that in turn stimulate fever, rash, and shock.
- *Streptolysins* lyse erythrocytes, leukocytes, and platelets.

One strain of group C *Streptococcus* (also called *S. equisimilis*, ek-wi-si′mi-lis), is also a pathogenic beta-hemolytic bacterium that causes some cases of streptococcal pharyngitis. However, unlike group A strep throat, this kind of group C pharyngitis does not lead to scarlet or rheumatic fevers.

Pathogenesis

Streptococci cause a variety of illnesses depending on the virulence factors present in the various strains. *S. pyogenes* frequently infects the pharynx, but the resulting disease is usually temporary, lasting only until adaptive immune responses against bacterial antigens (particularly M protein and streptolysins) clear the pathogen, usually within a week. Typically, strep throat and streptococcal bronchitis occur only when normal competing microbiota are depleted, when a large inoculum enables the bacterium to gain a rapid foothold before antibodies are formed against it, or when adaptive immunity is impaired. *S. pyogenes* can invade deeper tissues and organs through a break in a mucous membrane to cause *necrotizing fasciitis*.

Epidemiology

People spread *S. pyogenes* via respiratory droplets. Most cases of streptococcal pharyngitis occur during the winter and spring among elementary and middle school children, probably due to crowded conditions such as those in classrooms and day care centers. One person can spread sufficient bacteria to cause disease by coughing or sneezing within a radius of about 1.5 meters of another person.

Group A *Streptococcus* formerly claimed the lives of millions, but because it is sensitive to antimicrobial drugs, its significance as a deadly pathogen has declined. Nevertheless, the bacterium still sickens thousands of Americans annually.

The incidence of rheumatic fever has also declined significantly, from 7491 cases in 1964 to 112 cases in 1994, the last year it was nationally reportable. Epidemiologists do not understand fully the reason for this decline, but the advent of antimicrobial drugs, which limit the growth of the bacterium and thereby the severity of streptococcal pharyngitis, likely played a role. It also appears that there has been a decline in the strains of *Streptococcus* that cause rheumatic fever.

Diagnosis, Treatment, and Prevention

Microbiologists estimate that fewer than 50% of patients diagnosed with strep throat actually have it; the rest have viral pharyngitis. Given that the manifestations of bacterial and viral pharyngitis are nearly identical, a sure diagnosis requires serological testing. Correct diagnosis is essential because bacterial pharyngitis is treatable with antibacterial drugs, whereas viral pharyngitis is not.

Since alpha-hemolytic and nonhemolytic streptococci are normally in the pharynx, the presence of streptococci in a respiratory sample is of little diagnostic value. Physicians should use immunological tests to identify the presence of antigens of beta-hemolytic strains of *Streptococcus*.

Penicillin is very effective against both *S. pyogenes* and *S. equisimilis*. Physicians prescribe erythromycin or cephalosporin to treat penicillin-sensitive patients. Antibodies against M protein provide long-term protection against *S. pyogenes*; however, antibodies directed against the M protein of one strain provide no protection against other strains. For this reason, a person can have strep throat more than once.

Disease at a Glance 1 summarizes the manifestations of streptococcal pharyngitis.

Diphtheria

Learning Objectives

- ✓ Discuss the transmission of *Corynebacterium diphtheriae* and the effect of diphtheria toxin.
- ✓ Describe diphtheria.

Physicians have brought the deadly childhood disease **diphtheria** (dif-thēr′ē-ă) under control in industrialized countries using effective immunization. The disease is still a major threat to children living in less-developed regions of the world.

Signs and Symptoms

Diphtheria manifests as sore throat, localized pain, fever, pharyngitis, and the oozing of a fluid composed of intracellular fluid, blood clotting factors, leukocytes, bacteria, and the remains of dead pharyngeal and laryngeal cells. The fluid thickens into a thick *pseudomembrane* **(Figure 2),** which gives the disease its name: *diphthera* is a Greek word meaning "leather." A pseudomembrane can adhere so tightly to the tonsils, uvula, roof of the mouth, pharynx, and larynx that it cannot be dislodged without ripping the underlying tissue and causing bleeding. In severe cases, the

[3]From Greek *pyr*, meaning fire, and *genein*, meaning to produce.

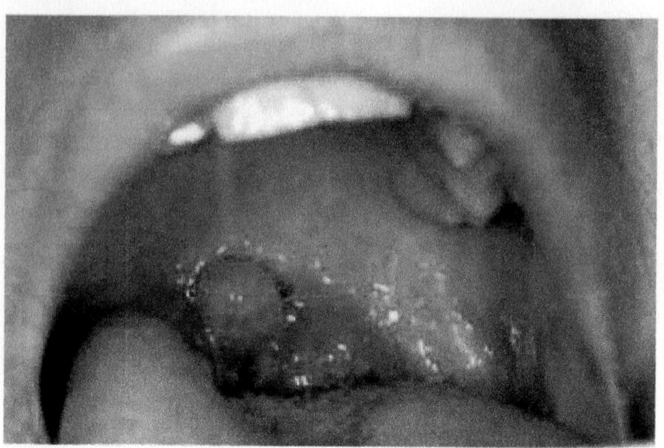

▲ *Figure 2*
A pseudomembrane, characteristic of diphtheria.

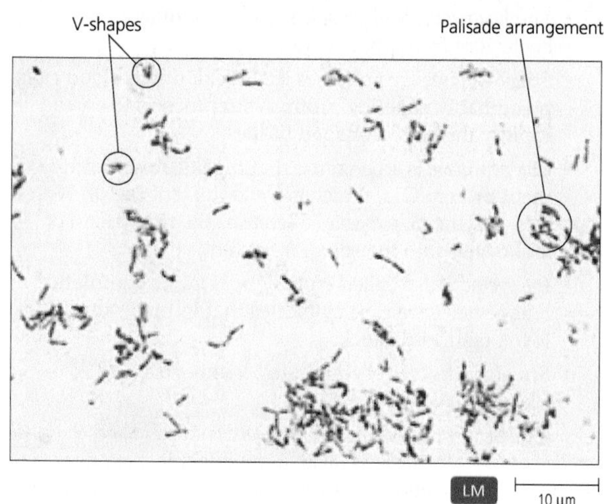

▲ *Figure 3*
Characteristic arrangements of cells of *Corynebacterium diphtheriae*. *What process produces these cellular arrangements?*

Figure 3 "Chinese lettering" and palisade arrangements result from the type of binary fission called snapping division.

pseudomembrane can completely occlude the respiratory passages, resulting in death by suffocation.

Pathogen and Virulence Factors

Corynebacterium diphtheriae (kŏ-rī′nē-bak-tēr′ē-ŭm dif-thi′rē-ī) is a species of high G + C, pleomorphic, non-endospore-forming, Gram-positive bacteria, which is ubiquitous in animals and humans, colonizing the skin and the respiratory, gastrointestinal, urinary, and genital tracts. The bacterium divides via a type of binary fission called snapping division, in which daughter cells remain attached to form characteristic "Chinese lettering" and side-by-side palisade arrangements **(Figure 3).** Although other diphtheroids can be pathogenic, the agent of diphtheria is the most common pathogen of this genus.

Virulent *C. diphtheriae* contains a lysogenic phage that codes for *diphtheria toxin*. The phage and its toxin gene are directly responsible for the signs and symptoms of diphtheria. Like many bacterial toxins, diphtheria toxin consists of two polypeptides. One polypeptide binds to human growth factor receptor on many types of human cells, triggering endocytosis of the bacterium. Once inside a cell, proteolytic enzymes cleave the toxin, releasing the second polypeptide of the toxin into the cytosol. This polypeptide enzymatically destroys a eukaryotic elongation factor—a protein required for translation of polypeptides. Because the action of the toxin is enzymatic, a single molecule of toxin sequentially destroys every molecule of elongation factor in a cell, completely blocking all polypeptide synthesis and resulting in cell death. Diphtheria toxin is thus one of the more potent toxins known.

Pathogenesis and Epidemiology

C. diphtheriae is transmitted from person to person via respiratory droplets or skin contact. Diphtheria is endemic in poorer parts of the world that lack adequate immunization.

Infections with *C. diphtheriae* have different effects depending on a host's immune status and the site of infection. Infections in immune individuals are asymptomatic, whereas infections in immunocompromised individuals result in a mild respiratory disease. Respiratory infections of nonimmune people are most severe, resulting in the sudden and rapid signs and symptoms of diphtheria.

Before immunization, hundreds of thousands of cases of diphtheria occurred in the United States each year. In contrast, health care workers reported only 13 cases total from 1997 to 2007.

Diagnosis, Treatment, and Prevention

Initial diagnosis of diphtheria is based on the presence of a pseudomembrane. Laboratory examination of the membrane or of tissue collected from the site of infection does not always reveal bacterial cells because the effects are due largely to the action of diphtheria toxin and not the cells directly. Culture of specimens on *Loeffler's medium*, which was developed especially for the culture of *C. diphtheriae*, produces three colonial morphologies. Some colonies are large, irregular, and gray; others are small, flat, and gray; and still others are small, round, convex, and black. Even though observations of these distinctive colonies are useful, absolute certainty of diagnosis results only from an immunodiffusion assay, called an *Elek test*, in which antibodies against the toxin react with toxin in a sample of fluid from the patient.

The most important aspect of treatment is the administration of antitoxin (immunoglobulins against the toxin) to neutralize diphtheria toxin before it binds to cells; once the toxin binds to a cell, it enters via endocytosis and kills the cell. Penicillin or erythromycin kills *Corynebacterium*,

DISEASE AT A GLANCE 1

Streptococcal Pharyngitis (Strep Throat)

1. *Streptococcus pyogenes* in respiratory droplets from a nearby cough or sneeze enter the body.
2. Pharyngitis results; the back of the pharynx reddens, lymph nodes swell, and tonsils abscess. Fever, malaise, and headache are typical.
3. If bacteria spread to trachea, laryngitis may result.
4. Infection of the bronchi may cause bronchitis.
5. Erythrogenic toxins trigger scarlet fever, a rash that spreads from the chest, a strawberry-red tongue, headache, chills, and muscle ache.
6. Rheumatic fever may develop with pain in heart and joints.

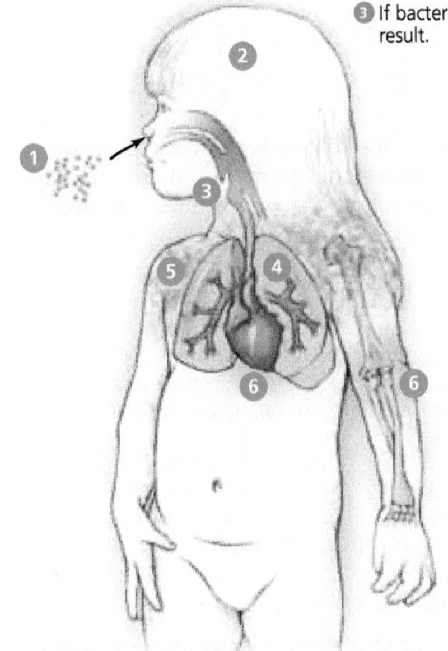

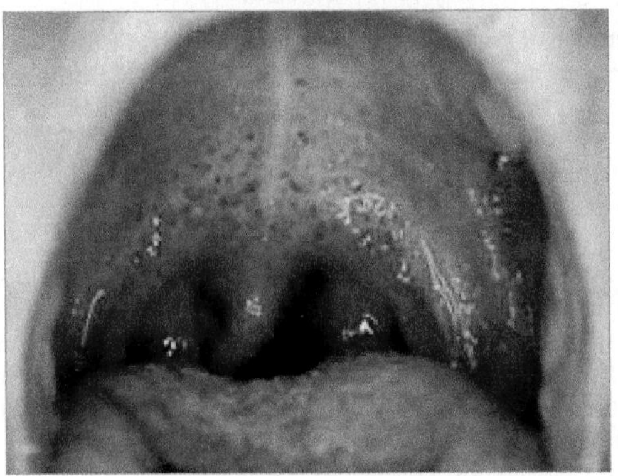

The reddened appearance of a throat with pharyngitis

Cause: Group A streptococci (*Streptococcus pyogenes*)

Portal of entry: Upper respiratory tract.

Signs and symptoms: Sore, red throat; difficulty swallowing; sudden fever; malaise; and loss of appetite. Can develop into scarlet fever, characterized by a "sandpapery" rash that first appears on the neck and chest and spreads all over the body, red "strawberry" tongue, headache, chills, and muscle ache. Rheumatic fever may also develop; symptoms include fever, joint pain (knees, ankles, elbows, and wrists), joint swelling, and possible cardiac problems (chest pain, shortness of breath).

Incubation period: Strep throat: 3–5 days; scarlet fever: 1–2 days following strep symptoms; rheumatic fever: up to 20 days.

Susceptibility: Children are generally the most susceptible. Rheumatic fever is more common in children ages 6–15.

Treatment: A throat culture to diagnose bacterial cause is important. Once streptococcal infection is confirmed, the standard treatment is penicillin or other narrow-spectrum antibiotic. Erythromycin may be given to those sensitive to penicillin. Scarlet fever and rheumatic fever are treated similarly.

Prevention: Sick individuals are contagious for at least two days following antibiotic therapy and should be kept home so as not to infect others. Sore throats in children should be taken seriously and treated so that rheumatic fever does not develop.

preventing the synthesis of more toxin. In severe cases, a blocked airway must be opened surgically or bypassed with a tracheostomy tube.

Because humans are the only known host for *C. diphtheriae,* the most effective way to prevent diphtheria is immunization. Immunization involves the DTaP vaccine, which combines diphtheria and tetanus toxoids (deactivated toxins) with antigens of the pertussis bacterium, at 2, 4, 6, and 15–18 months, and 4–6 years of age, followed by booster immunizations without pertussis antigens (Td vaccine) every 10 years.

CRITICAL THINKING

Why must diphtheria immunization be boosted every 10 years?

Sinusitis and Otitis Media

Learning Objective

✓ Describe the causes, manifestations, diagnosis, treatment, and prevention of sinusitis and otitis media.

Bacteria resident in the pharynx can infect the sinuses or middle ears via their connections with the throat, causing **sinusitis** or **otitis media**[4] (earache).

[4]From Greek *ous,* meaning ear, and *itis,* meaning inflammation.

Signs and Symptoms

Pain and pressure in the region of the affected, inflamed sinus characterize sinusitis. Malaise typically accompanies such headaches.

Otitis media is a common and painful disease of early childhood that manifests with severe pain in the ears, which may end abruptly when the eardrum ruptures, releasing the pressure. Pressure on the eardrums may interfere with hearing and delay speech development in young children. Rarely, fever and vomiting may be present.

Pathogens and Virulence Factors

A number of bacteria that are normally part of the respiratory microbiota cause otitis media. These include *Streptococcus pneumoniae,* an alpha-hemolytic streptococcus that lacks specific Lancefield antigens (about 35% of cases); *Staphylococcus aureus* (1–2% of cases); *Haemophilus influenzae* (20–30% of cases); and *Moraxella catarrhalis* (10–15% of cases). These bacteria also cause most cases of sinusitis. Additionally, *Streptococcus pyogenes* infections of the pharynx can spread into the sinuses and ears. There is some evidence that damage to the mucous membranes of the upper respiratory system and auditory tubes resulting from viral infections, cigarette smoke, and other irritants allows normal microbiota to become opportunistic pathogens.

Pathogenesis and Epidemiology

Infective agents spread from the pharynx into the sinuses via their connections with the throat. Similarly, the middle ears are infected via the auditory tubes. Inflammation, triggered by an infection, is responsible for the signs and symptoms of these diseases.

Sinusitis is more common in adults than in children, presumably because an adult's sinuses are developed more fully. In contrast, otitis media is more common in children, because a child's auditory tubes are more horizontal and have smaller diameters; thus, they are invaded and blocked more easily. More than 85% of children develop otitis media, accounting for almost half of all visits to pediatricians, but as children's heads grow, and they develop specific immunity to the various bacteria, otitis media becomes less common.

Diagnosis, Treatment, and Prevention

In most cases, physicians presume that the signs and symptoms of otitis media indicate bacterial infection, and they treat the condition with antibacterial drugs such as penicillin. Epidemiologists calculate that immunizations against influenzaviruses and *S. pneumoniae* could reduce the number of cases of childhood otitis media by more than 1 million per year.

Physicians may take drastic measures to treat and limit recurrent otitis media. These include lancing the eardrum of the infected ear to relieve pressure, installing plastic tubes through the eardrum to allow drainage of fluid and pus, and removing the tonsils to allow fluid to drain more freely through the auditory tubes. There are no known ways to prevent sinusitis.

We have examined some bacterial diseases of the upper respiratory system. Now we turn our attention to viral infections of these organs.

Viral Diseases of the Upper Respiratory System

Viral respiratory diseases, such as the common cold and influenza, are among the more common human diseases. In the following sections, we examine the primary viral disease of the upper respiratory system—the common cold.

Common Cold

Learning Objective

✓ Describe the manifestations and characteristics of common colds.

The common cold is named well—colds are among the most common of human diseases; an adult averages two colds each year. However, there is not a single common cause of the common cold—numerous viruses cause colds.

Signs and Symptoms

Everyone is familiar with the sneezing, rhinorrhea,[5] congestion, sore throat, malaise, and cough of a cold. Fever does not occur during a cold unless there is secondary bacterial infection. Signs and symptoms usually last a week, though sometimes a mild cough persists for several weeks.

Pathogens and Virulence Factors

Over 200 different *serotypes* (strains) of various viruses cause colds. The most common cold viruses—over 115 serotypes—are small, +ssRNA viruses with naked polyhedral capsids in the genus *Rhinovirus*[6] of the family *Picornaviridae*.[7] Other cold viruses include serotypes of +ssRNA coronaviruses, over 30 different dsDNA adenoviruses, several dsRNA reoviruses, and a few −ssRNA paramyxoviruses.

Rhinoviruses are among the smallest of viruses, about 25 nm in diameter; 500 million rhinoviruses could sit side by side on the head of an ordinary straight pin. Almost all rhinoviruses attach to a human protein named *ICAM-1,* which is found on the cytoplasmic membranes of cells lining the nasal cavities. The complementary binding sites on the viruses lie at the bottom of deep, narrow clefts only 1.3–3 nm wide on the viral capsids. Such deep, narrow sites are

[5]From Greek *rhis,* meaning nose, and *rhoia,* meaning to flow, i.e., a runny nose.
[6]From Greek *rhino,* meaning nose.
[7]From Latin *pico,* meaning small, and RNA virus.

protected from human antibodies and antiviral drugs; thus, prevention of common colds still eludes us.

All cold viruses reproduce most effectively at about 33°C, which is the temperature of the nasal cavity. Cold viruses cannot infect the lower respiratory or gastrointestinal tracts because higher temperatures and low pH inhibit or destroy them.

Pathogenesis

After attaching to cells of the nasal mucous membrane, cold viruses cause the cells to synthesize many more viruses, then kill the cells. The new viruses are released to infect still more cells. When cold symptoms are most severe, there may be over 100,000 virions/ml of nasal mucus. They remain viable for hours outside the body.

Infected cells lose their ciliary action and slough off when they die. These events trigger the release of inflammatory chemicals and stimulate nerve cells, triggering mucus production, sneezing, and localized inflammation of nasal tissue. Inflammation blocks nasal cavities, resulting in congestion.

Epidemiology

Rhinoviruses are extremely infective—a single virus is sufficient to cause a cold in 50% of infected individuals. Symptomatic or not, an infected person can spread viruses in aerosols produced by coughing or sneezing, via *fomites* (fō′mi-tēz, nonliving carriers of pathogens), or via hand-to-hand contact. Epidemiologists do not agree on the most common method for transmitting cold viruses, but it appears that self-inoculation by touching the mucous membranes of the eyes where tears can wash the viruses into the nasal cavity is common. Studies have shown that explosive sneezes rarely transmit colds.

Although people of all ages are susceptible to rhinoviruses, they can acquire some immunity against serotypes that have infected them in the past. For this reason, children typically have six to eight colds per year, younger adults have two to four, and adults over age 60 have one or fewer. An isolated population may acquire a certain amount of *herd immunity* by sharing infections of specific strains of rhinoviruses; however, new serotypes introduced into a population by outsiders or by mutations ensure that no population is free of all colds.

Besides causing colds, adenoviruses can also cause pharyngitis. For some reason, epidemics of respiratory adenoviruses occur on military bases but rarely under the similar conditions found in college dormitories.

Diagnosis, Treatment, and Prevention

The manifestations of a cold are usually diagnostic. Laboratory tests are required only if the actual cause of infection is to be identified.

While many home remedies and over-the-counter medicines exist to treat colds, none prevents the disease or provides a cure. A prescription drug—pleconaril—taken at the onset of symptoms reduces the seriousness and duration of rhinovirus disease. Adenovirus infection can be treated during the early stages with interferon. Antihistamines, decongestants, pain relievers, rest, and drinking fluids relieve cold symptoms and allow the body to mount an effective immune response; they do not reduce the duration of the disease; a cold still lasts about a week.

Because cold viruses do not share any common antigens that are accessible to the immune system, an effective vaccine against all colds is not practical; such a vaccine would have to protect against all the viral serotypes. Nevertheless, a live, attenuated vaccine is available against adenoviruses, though the vaccine is used currently only for military recruits. Because some adenoviruses of animals are known to be oncogenic (cancer causing), there is concern that widespread use of adenovirus vaccine would increase the number of cancer cases.

Hand antisepsis is probably the most important preventive measure against colds, especially if you have touched the hands of an infected person. Disinfection of fomites is somewhat effective in limiting the spread of cold viruses.

CRITICAL THINKING

As you have probably noticed, colds occur more frequently in the fall and winter. One explanation is that more people are crowded together in buildings when school starts and the weather cools. Design an experiment or epidemiological survey to test the hypothesis that crowded conditions explain the prevalence of colds in the fall and winter.

Bacterial Diseases of the Lower Respiratory System

The lower respiratory organs are axenic;[8] that is, they are normally devoid of microorganisms. When bacteria successfully surmount the defenses of the respiratory system or when disease or stress weakens those defenses, life-threatening diseases can result. These include bacterial pneumonias, Legionnaires' disease, pertussis (whooping cough), and tuberculosis.

Bacterial Pneumonias

Learning Objectives

- ✓ Define *pneumonia, empyema,* and *pleurisy.*
- ✓ Describe pneumococcal, primary atypical (mycoplasmal), and *Klebsiella* pneumonias.
- ✓ List five other bacterial species that can cause pneumonia.

---

[8]From Greek *a,* meaning no, and *xenos,* meaning foreigner.

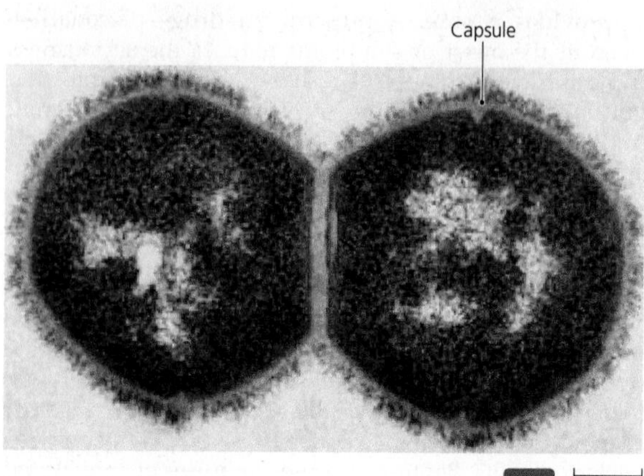

▲ *Figure 4*

***Streptococcus pneumoniae*, the most common cause of bacterial pneumonia.** The cells are commonly paired and covered with a polysaccharide capsule.

The term **pneumonia** (nū-mō′nē-ă) describes an inflammation of the lungs in which the alveoli and bronchioles become filled with fluid. In some patients this fluid is pus—a condition known as *empyema*[9] (em-pī-ē′mă). When the pleurae become inflamed, a painful condition called *pleurisy* results. An estimated 2–5 million cases of pneumonia occur annually.

Physicians describe pneumonias according to the affected region of the lungs or the organism causing the disease; for example, *lobar pneumonia* involves entire lobes of the lungs, and *mycoplasmal pneumonia* is pneumonia caused by the bacterium *Mycoplasma* (mī′kō-plaz-mă). *Nosocomial*[10] *pneumonia,* that is, pneumonia acquired in a health care setting, is a common illness among the elderly and immunosuppressed patients.

A number of bacteria, viruses, and fungi cause pneumonia; bacterial pneumonias are the more serious and in adults the more common. In the following sections, we examine some of the more common bacterial pneumonias, beginning with the most prevalent—pneumococcal pneumonia.

Pneumococcal Pneumonia

Pneumonia caused by *Streptococcus*—also called *pneumococcal pneumonia*—is the most common type of pneumonia, accounting for about 60% of adult cases and most hospitalizations for pneumonia.

Signs and Symptoms Pneumococcal pneumonia is usually lobar, affecting one or more lobes of the lungs. Signs and symptoms include fever, chills, congestion, cough, chest pain, which results in short, rapid breathing, and possibly nausea and vomiting. Blood frequently enters the lungs, causing coughed-up sputum to be rust colored. Neutrophils are present in the patient's sputum smear.

Pathogen and Virulence Factors Louis Pasteur discovered *S. pneumoniae,* and microbiologists have studied the bacterium extensively over the last 125 years, including sequencing the entire genomes of more than 10 strains; nevertheless, scientists still do not fully understand its pathogenicity. The bacterium rarely reaches the lungs because the ciliary escalator sweeps it away.

The bacterium is a Gram-positive coccus that is a normal member of the microbiota of the mouths and pharynges of 75% of humans without causing harm. Commonly known as **pneumococcus,** *S. pneumoniae* forms short chains or, more frequently, pairs. This characteristic explains its former name, "*Diplococcus pneumoniae.*" Pathogenic pneumococci secrete an adhesin, which is a poorly defined protein adhesin that mediates binding of the bacterium to epithelial cells of the pharynx.

Virulent serotypes also have polysaccharide capsules **(Figure 4)** that protect them from lysis by phagocytes. A capsule is required for virulence, as observed by Griffith during his experiments concerning bacterial transformation. Unencapsulated variants are avirulent because alveolar macrophages clear them from the lungs. In addition, *S. pneumoniae* inserts into its cell wall a chemical called *phosphorylcholine,* which by binding to receptors on cells in the lungs stimulates endocytosis of the bacteria.

Pneumococci also secrete a cytotoxin called *pneumolysin,* which binds to cholesterol in the cytoplasmic membranes of ciliated epithelial cells, producing transmembrane pores that result in the lysis of the cells. Pneumolysin also suppresses the digestion of phagocytized bacteria by interfering with the action of lysosomes inside phagocytes.

Pathogenesis and Epidemiology Pneumococci are inhaled occasionally from the pharynx into lungs damaged either by a previous viral disease, such as influenza or measles, or by other conditions, such as alcoholism, congestive heart failure, or diabetes mellitus. Phosphorylcholine triggers endocytosis by lung cells, the capsule protects the bacterium, and thereby pneumococci live in and eventually kill lung cells. From their intracellular "hiding place," *S. pneumoniae* can pass into the blood and brain to cause bacteremia and meningitis.

As the bacteria multiply in the alveoli, they damage the lining of the alveoli, allowing erythrocytes, leukocytes, and blood plasma to enter the lung. This fluid fills the alveoli, reducing the lung's ability to transfer oxygen to the blood and causing the pneumonia. Leukocytes attack the bacteria, in the process secreting inflammatory and pyrogenic chemicals, which add to the manifestations of the disease.

The body acts to limit migration of bacteria throughout the lungs by binding the microbes with the active sites of secretory IgA. The rest of the antibody molecule then binds to mucus, enabling mucus-enveloped bacteria to be swept from the airways by the action of ciliated epithelium.

---

[9]From Greek *en,* meaning in, and *pyon,* meaning pus.
[10]From Greek *nosokomeion,* meaning hospital.

Pneumococcus counteracts this defense by secreting *secretory IgA protease,* which destroys IgA.

Pneumococcal pneumonia constitutes about 85% of all cases of pneumonia. It occurs most frequently in fall and winter in children, the elderly, alcohol and drug abusers, diabetics, and AIDS patients—groups whose immune responses are not fully active.

Diagnosis, Treatment, and Prevention Justifier Medical laboratory technologists can quickly identify diplococci in Gram stains of sputum smears (see Disease at a Glance 2). Because the bacteria are sensitive to most antimicrobial drugs, health care workers must collect samples for smearing before antibacterial therapy has begun. Historically laboratories confirm the presence of pneumococci with anticapsular antibodies that cause pneumococcal capsules to swell—a so-called *quellung reaction.*

Penicillin has long been the drug of choice against *S. pneumoniae,* though about a third of pneumococcal isolates are now penicillin resistant. Cephalosporin, erythromycin, and chloramphenicol are effective alternative treatments.

The Centers for Disease Control and Prevention (CDC) recommends a vaccine against pneumococcus administered at 2, 4, 6, and 12–15 months of age and for all adults over age 65.

Primary Atypical (Mycoplasmal) Pneumonia

Learning Objectives

- ✓ Explain why scientists in different eras have classified mycoplasmas as viruses, Gram-negative bacteria, and Gram-positive bacteria.
- ✓ Describe the features of mycoplasmal pneumonia.

Mycoplasmal pneumonia is the leading type of pneumonia in children and young adults.

Signs and Symptoms Early symptoms of mycoplasmal pneumonia, including fever, malaise, headache, sore throat, and excessive sweating, are not typical of other types of pneumonia; thus mycoplasmal pneumonia is called **primary atypical pneumonia.** The body responds to infection with a persistent, unproductive cough in an attempt to clear the lungs of the pathogen and accumulated mucus. Primary atypical pneumonia may last for several weeks, but it is usually not severe enough to require hospitalization or to cause death. Because symptoms can be mild, the disease is also sometimes called *walking pneumonia.*

Pathogen and Virulence Factors *Mycoplasma pneumoniae* is a strictly aerobic, encapsulated mycoplasma. Mycoplasmas lack cell walls, allowing them to have a variety of shapes—they are *pleomorphic* **(Figure 5).** Further, mycoplasmas have sterols in their cytoplasmic membranes, a feature lacking in other prokaryotes.

Mycoplasmas are the smallest free-living microbes; that is, cells that can grow and reproduce independently of other cells. Their diameters range from 0.1 μm to 0.8 μm. Originally, scientists thought mycoplasmas were viruses because their small size and flexibility enable them to squeeze through the pores of filters that were then commonly used to remove bacteria from solutions; however, mycoplasmas contain both RNA and DNA, and they divide by binary fission—traits that viruses lack.

▲ *Figure 5*

Pleomorphic forms of *Mycoplasma*. *Why do these Gram-positive bacteria appear pink when Gram stained?*

Figure 5 Mycoplasmas lack cell walls; therefore, the decolorizing step of the Gram procedure removes crystal violet from the cells.

Before analysis of mycoplasmal rRNA sequences revealed that they are similar to Gram-positive organisms, mycoplasmas were classified in a separate phylum of Gram-negative bacteria—phylum Mollicutes. Modern taxonomists and the second edition of *Bergey's Manual of Systematic Bacteriology* now categorize mycoplasmas as low G + C, Gram-positive bacteria in the phylum Firmicutes. Despite being Gram-positive, they appear pink when Gram stained, because they lack cell walls.

M. pneumoniae is one of the few mycoplasmas that causes human disease. This is due partly to its production of an adhesive protein that attaches specifically to receptors located at the bases of cilia of epithelial cells lining the respiratory tracts of humans and to its prominent capsule, which provides protection from phagocytosis.

Pathogenesis Attachment of *M. pneumoniae* to the base of cilia causes the cilia to stop beating, and colonization eventually kills the epithelial cells. This interrupts the normal removal of mucus from the respiratory tract by the ciliary escalator, allowing colonization by other bacteria and causing a buildup of mucus that irritates the respiratory tract.

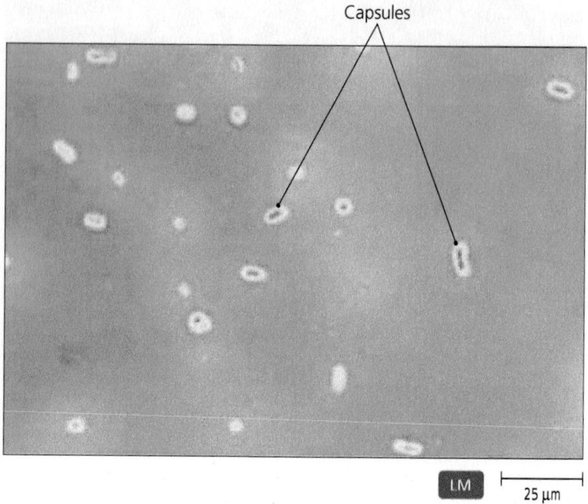

▲ *Figure 6*

The prominent capsule of *Klebsiella pneumoniae*. *How does the capsule function as a virulence factor?*

Figure 6 Capsules inhibit phagocytosis and intracellular digestion by phagocytic cells.

Epidemiology Nasal secretions spread *M. pneumoniae* among people in close contact, such as classmates, family members, and dormitory residents. The disease is uncommon in children under age 5 or in older adults, but it is the most common form of pneumonia seen in high school and college students. However, because primary atypical pneumonia is not a reportable disease and is difficult to diagnose, the actual incidence of infection is unknown.

Primary atypical pneumonia occurs throughout the year. This lack of seasonality is in contrast to pneumococcal pneumonia, which is more commonly seen in the fall and winter.

Diagnosis, Treatment, and Prevention Diagnosis of primary atypical pneumonia is difficult because mycoplasmas are small and difficult to detect in clinical specimens or tissue samples. Further, mycoplasmas grow slowly in culture, requiring two to six weeks before colonies are visible. Colonies of *M. pneumoniae* have a uniform granular appearance when the bacteria grow on solid surfaces, unlike the "fried-egg" appearance of colonies of other species of *Mycoplasma*. Complement fixation, hemagglutination, and immunofluorescent tests confirm a diagnosis, but such tests are nonspecific and are not by themselves diagnostic.

Physicians treat primary atypical pneumonia with antimicrobials such as erythromycin or tetracycline. Prevention is difficult because patients are often infective for long periods without signs or symptoms, and they remain infective even while undergoing antimicrobial treatment. Nevertheless, frequent handwashing, avoidance of contaminated fomites, and reducing aerosol dispersion can limit the spread of the pathogen and reduce the number of cases of disease. No vaccine against *M. pneumonia* is available.

CRITICAL THINKING

Mycoplasma pneumoniae is resistant to penicillin, though *Mycoplasma* does not synthesize β-lactamase. Explain why *Mycoplasma* is resistant to penicillin.

Klebsiella Pneumonia

Gram-negative bacteria are the leading cause of nosocomial infections, and pneumonias caused by Gram-negative bacteria are among the leading causes of nosocomial deaths. *Klebsiella* pneumonia is one type of Gram-negative bacterial pneumonia.

Signs and Symptoms Besides the common signs and symptoms of bacterial pneumonia—coughing, fever, and chest pain—*Klebsiella* pneumonia often involves destruction of alveoli, resulting in the production of thick, bloody sputum. Further, *Klebsiella* pneumonia patients often have recurrent chills. Mortality rates are higher than with pneumococcal or mycoplasmal pneumonias.

Pathogen and Virulence Factors *Klebsiella pneumoniae* (kleb-sē-el'ă nū-mō'nē-ī) is an opportunistic pathogen that infects the respiratory systems of humans and animals following inhalation. It is a nonmotile, Gram-negative rod that produces a prominent capsule **(Figure 6)**, giving *Klebsiella* colonies a mucoid appearance and protecting the bacterium from phagocytosis. Besides causing pneumonia, *K. pneumoniae* may also be involved in meningitis, wound infections, and urinary tract infections.

Pathogenesis and Epidemiology *K. pneumoniae* kills alveolar cells and often invades the blood, resulting in bacteremia. When the bacterial cells die, they release endotoxin, which can trigger shock and disseminated intravascular coagulation, leading to death.

Alcoholics and other patients with compromised immunity such as the elderly, people with AIDS, and very young children are at greater risk of pulmonary disease, including *Klebsiella* pneumonia, because of their poor ability to clear aspirated oral secretions from their respiratory tracts.

Diagnosis, Treatment, and Prevention Physicians diagnose *Klebsiella* pneumonia from its signs and symptoms and by culturing *Klebsiella* from sputum specimens. There is no specific treatment for the disease other than supportive care, rest, and fever-reducing drugs. Antimicrobial drugs, such as cephalosporin and aminoglycosides, may be used against *Klebsiella*, though many strains of the bacterium are resistant. Because of tissue damage and the release of endotoxin,

DISEASE AT A GLANCE 2

Bacterial Pneumonias

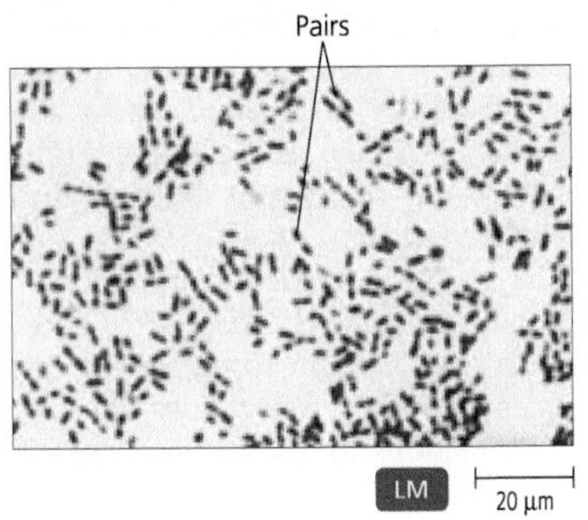

Streptococcus pneumoniae

Causes: *Streptococcus pneumoniae* (Gram-positive diplococcus also known as pneumococcus), *Mycoplasma pneumoniae* (Gram-positive, but pink staining, pleomorphic bacterium), *Klebsiella pneumoniae* (Gram-negative bacillus), *Haemophilus influenzae* (Gram-negative pleomorphic coccobacillus), *Staphylococcus aureus* (Gram-positive coccus), *Yersinia pestis* (Gram-negative rod), and *Chlamydophila psittaci* and *C. pneumoniae* (obligate intracellular pleomorphic bacteria).

Portal of entry: Inhalation, also via blood in case of *Yersinia*.

Signs and symptoms: Dry, unproductive cough, headache, fever, chills, and chest pain. Bloody mucoid sputum with *Klebsiella;* frothy bloody sputum with *Yersinia*.

Incubation period: Pneumococcus: 1–3 days; *M. pneumoniae:* 1–4 weeks; *K. pneumoniae:* 1–3 days; *H. influenzae:* 2–4 days; *S. aureus:* variable, usually days; *Y. pestis:* a few hours to 2 days; *Chlamydophila* spp.: 1–4 weeks.

Susceptibility: Pneumococcus: immunocompromised individuals; *M. pneumoniae:* high school and college students; *K. pneumoniae:* hospitalized individuals; *H. influenzae:* infants and young children; *S. aureus:* very young, patients with respiratory diseases, such as cystic fibrosis patients; *Y. pestis:* people exposed to bubonic plague; *C. pneumoniae:* most common in school-age children; *C. psittaci:* individuals in close contact with birds.

Treatment: Pneumococcus: penicillin G, vancomycin; *Mycoplasma:* tetracycline, erythromycin; *K. pneumoniae* and *H. influenzae:* cephalosporins; *S. aureus:* vancomycin; *Y. pestis:* tetracycline, streptomycin, chloramphenicol; *Chlamydophila* spp.: tetracycline, erythromycin.

Prevention: Use general precautions such as washing hands frequently. Stop smoking and, in the case of *C. psittaci,* avoid infected birds. Vaccines against *S. pneumoniae* and *H. influenzae* are available.

damage to the lungs is often permanent and can be fatal despite treatment. No vaccine is available, and prevention involves good aseptic technique by health care workers.

Other Bacterial Pneumonias

Other species of bacteria also cause pneumonia. Normal respiratory microbiota such as the pleomorphic Gram-negative *Haemophilus influenzae* and Gram-positive *Staphylococcus aureus* cause pneumonia with manifestations and treatment similar to those for pneumococcal pneumonia. *S. aureus* produces empyema in about 3% of patients.

Fever, chills, cough, difficulty breathing, and frothy bloody sputum characterize a form of pneumonia called **pneumonic plague,** which is produced by the bubonic plague bacillus, *Yersinia pestis* (yer-sin'ē-ă pes'tis). This bacterium can enter the lungs in respiratory droplets or via the blood and can cause pneumonia in just a few hours. Rapid shock and death result if a pneumonic plague patient is not treated promptly, but mortality is reduced to about 5% with treatment with antimicrobial drugs.

Chlamydias, which are Gram-negative, obligate intracellular parasites, can also cause respiratory diseases. Chlamydias form extremely small (0.2–0.4 µm diameter), resistant structures called *elementary* bodies that act as infectious agents. Here we examine pneumonia caused by two chlamydias in the genus *Chlamydophila* (formerly known as *Chlamydia*).

Chlamydophila psittaci[11] (kla-mē-dof'ĭ-lă sit'ă-sē) causes **ornithosis**[12] (ōr-ni-thō'sis), which is a disease of birds that can be transmitted to humans, in whom it typically causes flulike symptoms, though in some patients severe pneumonia occurs. Rarely, nonrespiratory conditions such as endocarditis, hepatitis, arthritis, conjunctivitis, and encephalitis are observed. The disease is sometimes called *psittacosis* or *parrot fever* because it was first identified in parrots, but other birds carry the disease as well. The CDC reported only 20 cases of ornithosis in 2006. Physicians treat ornithosis with tetracycline, erythromycin, or rifampin.

Chlamydophila pneumoniae, spread in respiratory droplets, causes bronchitis, pneumonia, and sinusitis. Most infections with this bacterium are mild, producing only malaise and a chronic cough, and do not require specific treatment, though erythromycin, fluoroquinolones, and tetracycline are efficacious. The prevalence of chlamydial pneumonia is unknown because most cases are never diagnosed or reported.

Disease at a Glance 2 summarizes the features of eight types of bacterial pneumonia.

[11]From Greek *psittakos,* meaning parrot.
[12]From Greek *ornith,* meaning bird.

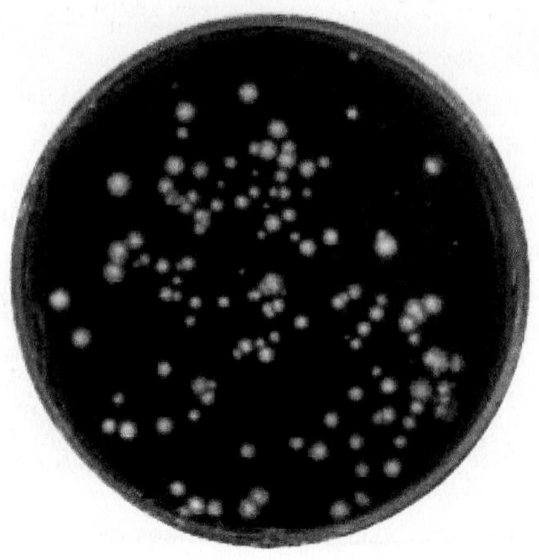

▲ *Figure 7*

***Legionella pneumophila* growing on buffered charcoal yeast extract agar.** This bacterium cannot be grown in culture without such special media.

Another bacterial disease of the lower respiratory system is also a pneumonia, but physicians and clinicians have given it a specific name—legionellosis.

Legionnaires' Disease

Learning Objective

✓ Describe the features of Legionnaires' disease.

In 1976, joyous celebration of the 200th anniversary of the Declaration of Independence was curtailed in Philadelphia when over 200 American Legion members attending a convention were stricken with severe pneumonia; 29 died. After extensive epidemiological research, a new disease was identified and dubbed **Legionnaires' disease** or *legionellosis*. A previously unknown pathogen, *Legionella* (lē-jŭ-nel'lă), causes this disease.

Signs and Symptoms

Legionnaires' disease is characterized by common features of pneumonia—fever, chills, a dry nonproductive cough, and headache; pleurisy—inflammation of the pleurae—may also develop. Complications involving the gastrointestinal tract, central nervous system, liver, and kidneys are common. If Legionnaires' disease is not treated promptly, pulmonary function rapidly decreases, resulting in the death of 20% of patients with normal immunity. Mortality is much higher in immunocompromised individuals, particularly kidney and heart transplant recipients.

Legionella also causes a flulike illness—*Pontiac fever* (after the Michigan city where it was first described). This disease has symptoms similar to those of Legionnaires' disease, but it does not involve pneumonia and is not fatal.

Pathogen and Virulence Factors

To date, scientists have identified over 40 species of *Legionella*. These aerobic, slender, pleomorphic bacteria are Gram-negative and classified in the taxon Gammaproteobacteria. They are extremely fastidious in their nutrient requirements, and laboratory media for culture of *Legionella* must be enhanced with iron salts and the amino acid cysteine. **Figure 7** shows colonies growing on one commonly used medium—buffered charcoal yeast extract agar.

Legionella species are almost universal inhabitants of water, but they had not been isolated before 1976 because they stain poorly and cannot grow on common laboratory media. Nineteen species are known to cause disease in humans, but 85% of all infections in humans are caused by *L. pneumophila*[13] (noo-mō'fi-lă).

Pathogenesis

L. pneumophila presented a conundrum for early investigators: how can such a demanding bacterium be nearly ubiquitous in moist environmental samples? In the original epidemic, for example, *Legionella* was cultured from condensation in hotel air conditioning ducts, an environment that seems unsuitable for such a fastidious microorganism. Investigations revealed that *Legionella* invades freshwater protozoa, typically amoebae, and reproduces inside phagocytic vesicles; thus, the bacterium survives in the environment as an intracellular parasite. Protozoa release *Legionella*-filled vesicles, and humans acquire the disease by inhaling the vesicles.

Within human cells, *L. pneumophila* lives much as it does in the environment—as an intracellular parasite of macrophages and other cells. The bacterium kills human cells, causing tissue destruction and triggering inflammation of the lungs. For unknown reasons, *Legionella* rarely spreads outside the lungs.

Epidemiology

Legionella tolerates heat and chlorination, so it can live in water pipes and other domestic water sources; in fact, legionellosis was not a common disease until modern devices provided a suitable means of transmitting the bacteria to humans: showers, vaporizers, spa whirlpools, hot tubs, air conditioning systems, and cooling towers produce aerosols containing *Legionella*. The Clinical Case Study describes an epidemic triggered by a contaminated grocery store vegetable mister. Epidemiologists have never documented person-to-person spread of legionellosis.

The CDC estimates that about 18,000 people contract Legionnaires' disease each year, but most cases are so mild and isolated that they are never diagnosed or reported. Smokers, the elderly, patients with chronic respiratory diseases, and the immunocompromised are at greatest risk for infection and disease. Most documented

[13]From Greek *pneuma*, meaning breath, and *philos*, meaning love.

cases occur in summer to early fall; the mortality rate is 15–50%, with the higher rates occurring among people with underlying disease.

Diagnosis, Treatment, and Prevention

Physicians diagnose Legionnaires' disease with fluorescent antibody staining or serological testing that reveals the presence of *Legionella* or antibodies against the bacterium in clinical samples. Quinolones or macrolides are the antimicrobial drugs of choice for treating Legionnaires' disease. Pontiac fever is self-limiting and requires no treatment.

Eliminating *Legionella* from water supplies is not feasible, because chlorination and heating are only moderately successful against the microorganism. However, the bacterium is not highly virulent, so reducing its number is typically a successful control measure.

Tuberculosis

Learning Objectives

- ✓ Identify two effects of cord factor of *Mycobacterium tuberculosis*.
- ✓ Describe the transmission and pathogenesis of *M. tuberculosis* and its effects on the body.
- ✓ Discuss the epidemiology, diagnosis, treatment, and prevention of tuberculosis.
- ✓ Define and contrast multi-drug-resistant and extensively drug-resistant tuberculosis.

Many people think that **tuberculosis (TB)** is a disease of the past, one that has little importance to people living in industrialized countries. In part, this attitude results from the success health care workers have had in reducing the number of cases. Nevertheless, epidemiologists warn us that complacency can allow this terrible killer to resurge, as it did during 1985–2002 in the United States after health departments shifted funds from TB eradication programs to other areas.

Signs and Symptoms

Signs and symptoms of TB are not always initially apparent, often being limited to a minor cough and mild fever. Breathing difficulty, fatigue, malaise, weight loss, chest pain, wheezing, and coughing up blood characterize the disease as it progresses.

Pathogen and Virulence Factors

Mycobacterium tuberculosis (mī'kō-bak-tēr'ē-ŭm too-ber-kyū-lō'sis) is a high G + C, non-endospore-forming, Gram-positive rod with cell walls containing an abundance of **mycolic** (mī-kol'ik) **acid,** which is a waxy lipid composed of chains of 60–90 carbon atoms. This lipid is directly responsible for unique characteristics of this pathogen. Specifically, mycobacteria:

- Grow slowly (due in part to the time required to synthesize numerous molecules of mycolic acid). The generation time varies from hours to several days.
- Are protected from lysis once they are phagocytized.
- Are capable of intracellular growth.
- Are resistant to Gram staining, detergents, many common antimicrobial drugs, and desiccation. Because mycobacteria stain only weakly with the Gram procedure (if at all), the acid-fast staining procedure was developed to stain them.

Virulent strains of *M. tuberculosis* produce **cord factor,** a cell wall component that produces strands of daughter cells that remain attached to one another in parallel alignments (see Disease at a Glance 3). Cord factor also inhibits migration of neutrophils and is toxic to mammalian cells. Mutant mycobacteria that are unable to synthesize cord factor do not cause disease.

Pathogenesis

The waxy wall protects the pathogen from desiccation; it can remain viable in dried aerosol droplets for eight months. *Mycobacterium* is not particularly virulent, as only about 5% of people infected with the bacterium develop disease; however, it kills about 50% of untreated patients. Clinicians divide tuberculosis into three types: primary TB, secondary (or reactivated) TB, and disseminated TB.

Primary Tuberculosis Although *M. tuberculosis* can infect any organ, 85% of infections remain in the lungs. Primary TB, which typically occurs in children, involves the formation of small, hard nodules in the lungs called **tubercles** (too'ber-klz), which are characteristic of TB and give it its name. The five stages of a primary infection are as follows **(Figure 8a):**

1. *Mycobacterium* typically infects the respiratory tract via inhalation of respiratory droplets formed when infected individuals talk, sing, cough, or sneeze. A respiratory droplet is about 5 μm in diameter and carries one to three bacilli. The minimum infectious dose is about 10 cells.
2. Macrophages in the alveoli of the lungs phagocytize the pathogens but are unable to digest them in part because the bacterium inhibits fusion of lysosomes to the endocytic vesicle.
3. Instead, the bacteria replicate freely within macrophages, gradually killing them. Bacteria released from dead macrophages are phagocytized by other macrophages, beginning the cycle anew. This stage of infection, which lasts for a few weeks, is typically asymptomatic or associated with a mild fever.
4. Infected macrophages present antigen to T lymphocytes, which produce lymphokines that attract and activate more macrophages and trigger inflammation. Tightly appressed macrophages surround the site of infection, forming a tubercle.
5. Other cells of the body deposit collagen fibers, enclosing infected macrophages and lung cells

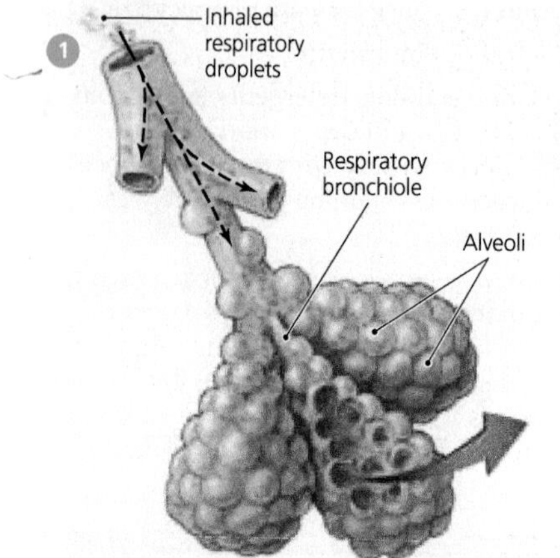

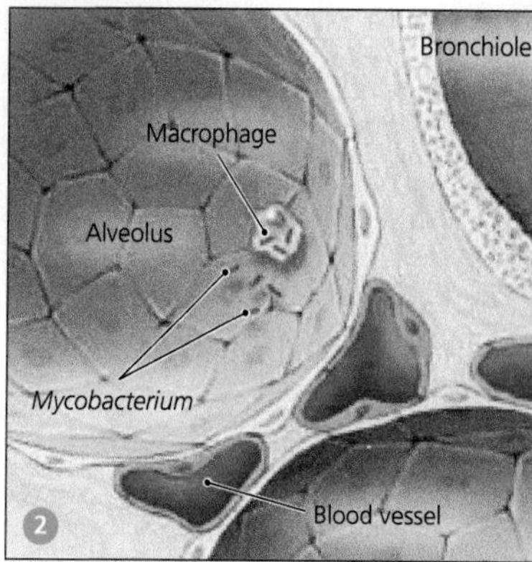

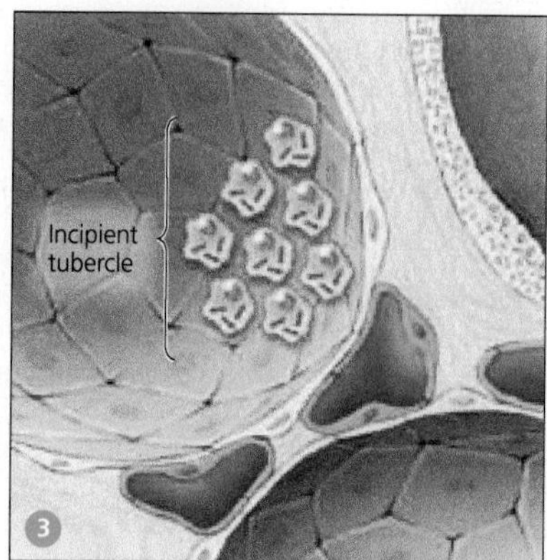

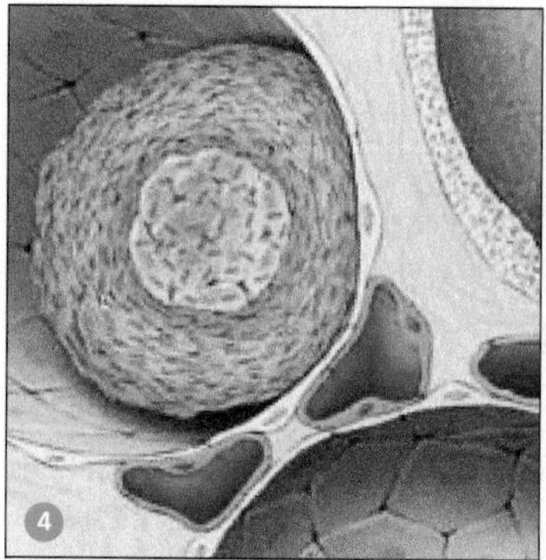

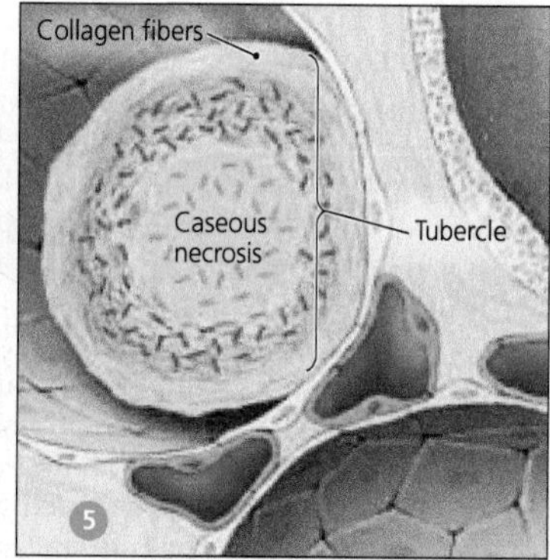

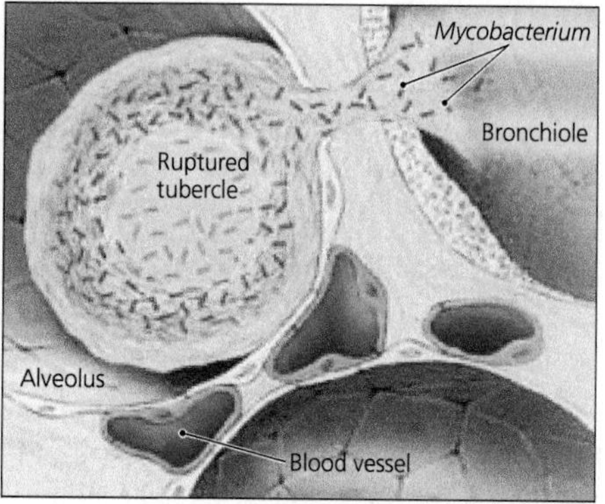

(a) Primary tuberculosis infection

(b) Secondary or reactivated tuberculosis

▲ *Figure 8*

The processes involved in the development of tuberculosis in the lungs. (a) The formation of tubercles in primary tuberculosis. **(b)** Events in secondary (reactivated) tuberculosis.

within the tubercle. Infected cells in the center of the tubercle die, releasing *M. tuberculosis* and producing *caseous*[14] *necrosis*—the death of tissue that takes on a cheese-like consistency due to the presence of protein and fat released from dying cells. Sometimes, for an unknown reason, the center liquefies and subsequently fills with air. Such a tubercle is called a *tuberculous cavity*.

In most patients, the immune system reaches a stalemate with the bacterium at this point: the immune system is able to prevent further spread of the pathogen and stop the progression of the disease, but it is not able to rid the body of all mycobacteria. *M. tuberculosis* may remain dormant for decades within macrophages and in the centers of tubercles. If the immune system breaks the stalemate by killing all the mycobacteria, the body deposits calcium around the tubercles, which are then called *Ghon complexes*.

Secondary or Reactivated Tuberculosis Reactivated tuberculosis results when *M. tuberculosis* breaks the stalemate, ruptures the tubercle, and reestablishes an active infection in which the bacteria spread through the lungs via the bronchioles **(Figure 8b).** Reactivated TB is a common occurrence in TB-infected individuals with suppressed immune systems.

Disseminated Tuberculosis Disseminated TB results when some macrophages carry the pathogen via the blood and lymph to a variety of sites, including the bone marrow, spleen, kidneys, spinal cord, and brain. The signs and symptoms of disseminated TB vary with the sites of infection. The common name for TB in the early 1900s—*consumption*—reflects the wasting away of the body resulting from the involvement of multiple sites.

[14]From Latin *caseus*, meaning cheese.

Epidemiology

Tuberculosis has probably killed more people than any other disease in history, including on average four people every minute today, mostly in Asia and Africa. Tuberculosis is on the decline in the U.S., though the CDC estimates that *M. tuberculosis* still infects more than 9 million Americans. The disease is pandemic in other parts of the world. One-third of the world's population is infected and over 9 million new cases of TB are seen each year, causing 1 to 3 million deaths. Risk factors include diabetes, poor nutrition, stress, crowded living conditions, alcohol consumption, drug abuse, and smoking. Patients with lowered immunity are at the greatest risk of infection. TB is a leading killer of HIV-infected patients.

Diagnosis

A *tuberculin skin test* is used to screen patients for possible exposure to tuberculosis. In this test, a health care worker injects about 0.1 ml of cell wall antigens from *M. tuberculosis* into a patient's skin. The appearance of a hard, red swelling at the test site within 24–72 hours is a positive test **(Figure 9a)**. The reaction is a type IV (cell-mediated) hypersensitivity response, which indicates past infection or immunization but not necessarily current disease; in other words, a positive tuberculin skin test is not sufficient to distinguish among patients with active disease, chronic carriers, and those who have been exposed or immunized but are currently uninfected.

Chest X rays reveal the presence of tubercles in the lungs **(Figure 9b)**. Primary tuberculosis appears as tubercles in the lower and central areas of the lungs, whereas secondary tuberculosis more commonly appears higher in the lungs. The presence of acid-fast cells and cords in sputum confirms an active case of tuberculosis (see Disease at a Glance 3).

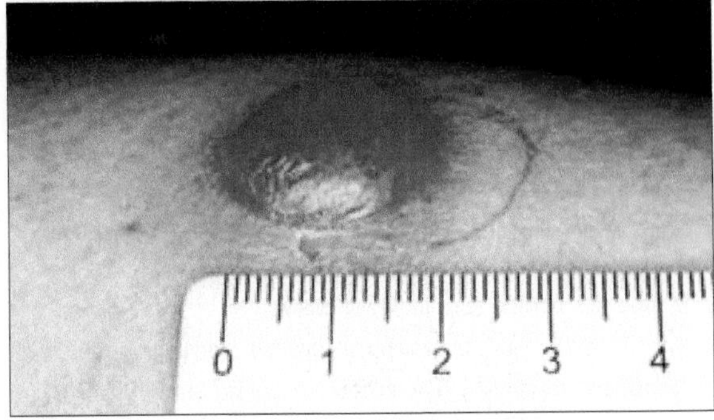

(a)

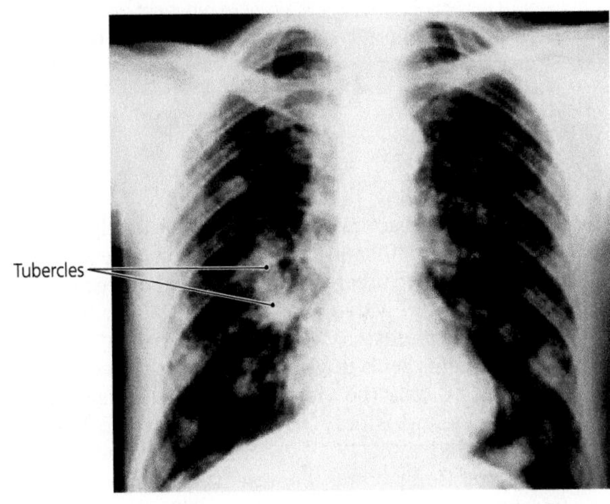

(b)

▲ *Figure 9*

Diagnosis of tuberculosis. (a) The enlarged, reddened, and raised inoculation site of a positive tuberculin skin test. **(b)** An X ray of a tuberculosis patient showing white patches indicative of tubercles.
What does a positive tuberculin test indicate?

Figure 9 *A positive tuberculin skin test indicates that a patient has cell-mediated memory against antigens of M. tuberculosis, as a result of either infection or immunization.*

Treatment

Common antimicrobials such as penicillin and erythromycin have little effect on *M. tuberculosis* because it grows so slowly that the drugs are cleared from the body before they have a significant effect. Further, antimicrobial drugs have little impact on *M. tuberculosis* living within macrophages. Generally, the currently recommended treatment is a combination of isoniazid (INH), rifampin, and one of a number of other drugs (such as ethambutol or streptomycin) for two months, followed by INH and rifampin alone for four months.

Multi-drug-resistant (MDR) strains of *M. tuberculosis*—strains resistant to at least isoniazid and rifampin—have arisen in several countries. Health care officials are even more concerned about the emergence of **extensively drug-resistant (XDR) TB,** which is defined as disease caused by *M. tuberculosis* that is resistant *in vitro* to at least isoniazid, rifampin, and three or more other antitubercular drugs. MDR and XDR strains make it more difficult to rid the world of tuberculosis, so officials encourage strict adherence to antitubercular drug regimens. The World Health Organization (WHO) and the CDC recommend a strategy of drug delivery called *Directly Observed Treatment, Shortcourse (DOTS),* in which health care workers observe patients to ensure they take their medications on schedule. Effective treatment of cases of MDR tuberculosis is quite expensive. Researchers are developing a subcutaneous implant that would gradually deliver drugs directly into the body over a period of months so that direct DOTS is not required.

DISEASE AT A GLANCE 3

Tuberculosis

Cause: *Mycobacterium tuberculosis* (aerobic acid-fast bacillus).

Portal of entry: Inhalation.

Signs and symptoms: Fatigue, malaise, weight loss, cough, chest pain, and sweating.

Incubation period: Four to twelve weeks.

Susceptibility: Individuals living in crowded conditions.

Treatment: Combination antibiotic therapy: isoniazid, rifampin, streptomycin and/or ethambutol.

Prevention: Preventive isoniazid therapy for those exposed to a primary TB patient. BCG vaccine is available but is not widely given in the United States in part because immunization would be more costly than is treatment.

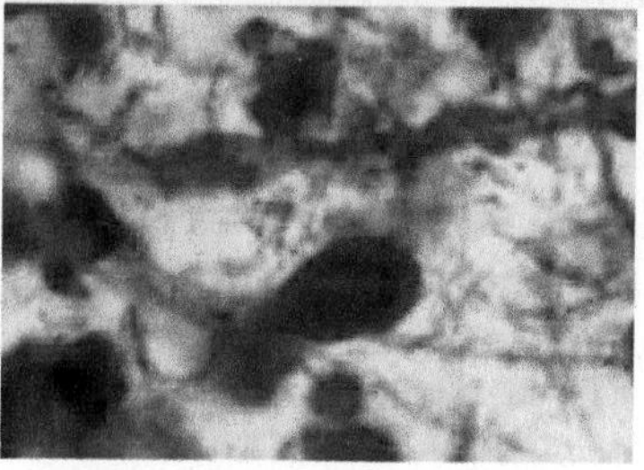

The pink appearance of *Mycobacterium tuberculosis* when prepared with an acid-fast stain. Note the corded growth (parallel alignments).

Prevention

Physicians use antibacterial drugs prophylactically to treat patients who have either shown a recent conversion from a negative to a positive tuberculin test or have undergone significant exposure to active cases of tuberculosis. In countries where tuberculosis is common, health care workers immunize patients with *BCG*[15] *vaccine*, which is composed of attenuated *M. bovis* (bō'vis), a species that causes tuberculosis in cattle and is only rarely transmitted to humans via contaminated milk. BCG vaccine is not used for immunocompromised patients, because it can cause disease.

Immunization induces immunity in 80% of patients and its use significantly reduces the spread of disease. However, in the United States the cost of mass immunization is not warranted because of the relatively low prevalence of tuberculosis. Further, immunized patients have a positive skin reaction for the rest of their lives, even if they have not been infected with *M. tuberculosis*, and such "false positive" results would hinder the work of epidemiologists trying to track the spread of the disease.

Renewed efforts to detect and stop infection and the implementation of DOTS have reduced the number of reported U.S. cases of TB. The CDC predicts that the current downward trend in case number indicates that a TB-free country is attainable in the near future.

Disease at a Glance 3 summarizes the characteristics of tuberculosis.

CRITICAL THINKING

Why don't physicians try to prevent the spread of TB by simply administering prophylactic antimicrobial drugs to everyone living in endemic areas?

[15]French, *bacille Calmette-Guérin*, named for its developers.

Pertussis (Whooping Cough)

Learning Objective

✓ Describe the characteristics of pertussis.

What could be more agonizing to a parent than observing one's child being tortured by persistent, powerful coughing spells that leave the child exhausted, blue, and with ruptured blood vessels in the eyes? **Pertussis,** commonly called **whooping cough,** produces these manifestations.

Signs and Symptoms

The beginning signs and symptoms of pertussis resemble those of a common cold—rhinorrhea, slight cough, and mild fever—if they occur at all. After one to two weeks, the signature symptom of severe coughing occurs. Vomiting, diarrhea, and choking can accompany this stage. Oxygen exchange in the lungs may be so severely limited that *cyanosis* develops (the patient turns blue) and death results.

Pathogen and Virulence Factors

Bordetella pertussis (bōr-dē-tel'ă per-tus'is), a small, aerobic, nonmotile, Gram-negative coccobacillus in the class Betaproteobacteria is responsible for pertussis. Various adhesins and toxins mediate the disease. Two adhesins are *filamentous hemagglutinin* and *pertussis toxin.* Four toxins are:

- *Pertussis toxin,* a portion of which interferes with ciliated epithelial cells' metabolism, resulting in increased mucus production. (Note that pertussis toxin is both an adhesin and a toxin.)
- *Adenylate cyclase toxin,* which triggers increased mucus production and inhibits leukocyte movement, phagocytosis, and killing.

DISEASE AT A GLANCE 4

Pertussis (Whooping Cough)

Cause: *Bordetella pertussis* (Gram-negative coccobacillus).

Portal of entry: Inhalation.

Signs and symptoms: Catarrhal stage begins with signs and symptoms resembling the common cold that last one to two weeks. The following paroxysmal stage lasts two to four weeks and is characterized by persistent, violent coughing spells that consist of three or four coughs without a breath, followed by a high-pitched, wheezing inhalation or "whoop." The convalescent stage lasts several weeks as the cough subsides.

Incubation period: Six to twenty days, with an average of seven to ten days.

Susceptibility: Unimmunized children.

Treatment: Supportive care; erythromycin has only little effect.

Prevention: DTaP vaccine.

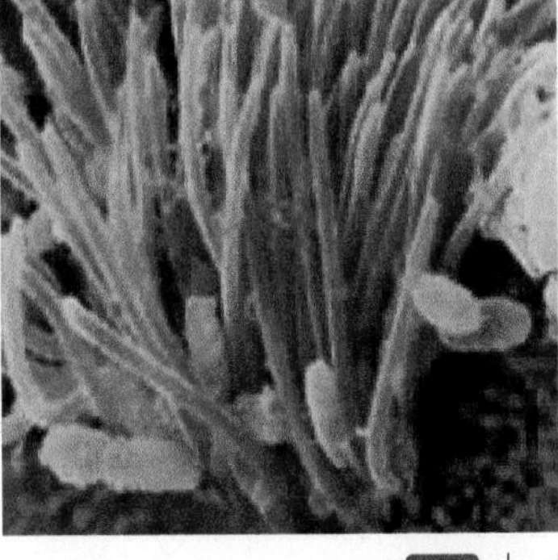

Bordetella pertussis bound to cilia of a tracheal epithelial cell. The bacteria (colored yellow) eventually cause the loss of the cells.

- *Dermonecrotic toxin,* which causes localized constriction and hemorrhage of blood vessels, resulting in cell death and tissue destruction.
- *Tracheal cytotoxin,* which at low concentrations inhibits the movement of cilia on ciliated respiratory cells, and at high concentrations causes the expulsion of these cells from the lining of the trachea.

Pathogenesis

Via its adhesins, inhaled *B. pertussis* binds to cilia in the trachea (see Disease at a Glance 4), interfering with their action and stopping the ciliary escalator. Filamentous hemagglutinin also binds to the cytoplasmic membranes of neutrophils, initiating endocytosis of the bacterium. *B. pertussis* survives within the phagocytes, evading the immune system. Pertussis toxin causes infected cells to produce more receptors for filamentous hemagglutinin, leading to further bacterial attachment and phagocytosis.

Pertussis progresses through four phases: incubation, catarrhal[16] (kă-tah'răl), paroxysmal[17] (par-ok-siz'măl), and convalescent **(Disease at a Glance 4).** The characteristic sign of whooping cough occurs during the two to four weeks of the paroxysmal phase: to clear mucus from the lungs, the patient coughs two or three times without inhalation, followed by the characteristic "whoop" of inhalation through a congested trachea. Each day a patient may experience 40–50 of these coughing spells, which often end with vomiting and exhaustion. Coughing may be so brutal that blood vessels in the eyes burst.

[16]From Greek *katarheo,* meaning to flow down.
[17]From Greek *paroxysmos,* meaning to irritate.

Epidemiology

Pertussis is highly contagious, spreading through the air in respiratory droplets. It is considered a pediatric disease, as life-threatening cases occur in children younger than five years old. More than 60 million people worldwide suffer from pertussis each year, including over 10,000 reported cases in the United States. However, these figures considerably underestimate the actual number of cases, because patients with chronic coughs are not routinely tested for infection with *Bordetella,* and because the disease in older children and adults is typically less severe and is frequently misdiagnosed as a cold or influenza.

Diagnosis, Treatment, and Prevention

The symptoms of pertussis are usually diagnostic. Even though health care workers may isolate *B. pertussis* from respiratory specimens, the bacterium is extremely sensitive to desiccation, so specimens must be inoculated at the patient's bedside onto *Bordet-Genou medium,* which is specially designed to support the growth of this bacterium.

Treatment for pertussis is primarily supportive. By the time the disease is recognized, the immune system has often already "won the battle." Recovery depends on regeneration of the tracheal epithelium, not on the number of bacteria; therefore, antibacterial drugs have little effect on the course of the disease, though they may reduce the patient's infectivity.

Given that *B. pertussis* has no reservoir, and that an effective vaccine (the "P" of DTP vaccine) has been available since 1949, whooping cough could be eradicated. Despite this possibility, the number of cases of pertussis in the U.S. increased from a low of 0.5 cases per 100,000 in

1976 to 9 per 100,000 in 2005—a prevalence not seen since the 1960s. This increase resulted in part from the refusal of parents to immunize their children following publicity concerning adverse reactions to the original attenuated vaccine (DTP), and to the fact that immunity is not lifelong. The CDC now recommends *DTaP vaccine*, which contains an acellular pertussis (aP) component. DTaP has fewer side effects than DTP vaccine but is equally effective in engendering an immune response. Currently, the incidence of pertussis is declining as more parents immunize their children.

Inhalational Anthrax

Learning Objective

✓ Describe inhalational anthrax.

The government classifies the bacillus of **anthrax** as one of a handful of potential biological terror agents. In 2001, terrorists spread the disease via the U.S. postal system by sending letters filled with endospores. Twenty-two people sickened, and five died. There are three forms of anthrax: *cutaneous anthrax* manifests on the skin; *gastrointestinal anthrax* is a rare human disease of the digestive system; and **inhalational anthrax**—the most severe form of anthrax in humans—is a respiratory disease, which is examined here.

Signs and Symptoms

The initial symptoms of inhalational anthrax resemble those of a common cold or flu—sore throat, mild fever, myalgia (muscle aches), mild cough, and malaise. After several days, the symptoms progress to include more severe coughing, nausea, vomiting, fainting, confusion, lethargy, shock, and death.

Pathogen and Virulence Factors

Bacillus anthracis, a Gram-positive, endospore-forming, aerobic, rod-shaped bacterium, causes anthrax. Resistant endospores allow the bacillus to survive in the environment indefinitely. In the body, *B. anthracis* forms a protective capsule of glutamic acid, which inhibits phagocytosis by alveolar macrophages. The bacterium also secretes *anthrax toxin*, which kills human cells and triggers edema (swelling due to fluid accumulation).

Pathogenesis and Epidemiology

An infective dose of *B. anthracis* endospores involves inhalation of at least 8000–50,000 endospores. In the lungs, the endospores germinate, and vegetative cells secrete anthrax toxin, which impairs respiratory function, initiates toxemia, and often results in death.

Anthrax does not spread from person to person; rather, people must acquire *B. anthracis* from infected animals either by contact or via inhalation of endospores in dust or on animal hides or wool. Most inhalational anthrax patients die, even with full supportive care and timely use of antimicrobial drugs.

Diagnosis, Treatment, and Prevention

Clinicians can readily identify the large, Gram-positive cells of *Bacillus* in the sputum of patients, but endospores are seen rarely. Unlike harmless environmental species of *Bacillus*, laboratory-cultured *B. anthracis* colonies are sticky and nonhemolytic when grown on blood agar. Serological, DNA, and biochemical testing confirms the presence of *B. anthracis*.

Many antimicrobials, including penicillin, doxycycline, and ciprofloxacin, are effective against *B. anthracis*; however, damage to the lungs and toxemia can be so severe and rapid that treatment is often ineffectual. During the bioterrorism attack of 2001, physicians learned that early and aggressive treatment of inhalation anthrax with antimicrobial drugs accompanied by persistent drainage of fluid from around the lungs increased the survival rate from less than 1% to almost 50%.

An efficacious vaccine is available to select military personnel, researchers, people who work closely with animals, and health care professionals with anthrax patients.

Viral Diseases of the Lower Respiratory System

We have considered important bacterial and viral diseases of the upper respiratory system and bacterial diseases of the lower respiratory organs. Now we turn our attention to viral diseases of the lower respiratory system, beginning with influenza.

Influenza

Learning Objectives

✓ Describe the general characteristics of influenza.

✓ Describe the roles of hemagglutinin and neuraminidase in the replication cycle of influenzaviruses and in the origin of new influenzaviruses.

Imagine being the only elementary schoolchild of your sex in your midsized Swedish town because all of your peers died six winters ago; or imagine returning to college after a break, only to learn that half of your fraternity brothers had died during the previous two months. These vignettes are not fictional; they happened to relatives of this author during the great flu pandemic in the winter of 1918–19 **(Figure 10)**. During that winter, half the world's population was infected with a new, extremely virulent strain of influenzavirus, and approximately 40 million died during that one flu season. In some U.S. cities, 10,000 people died each week for several months. Could it happen again? In this section we will learn about the characteristics of influenzaviruses that enable flu—a common disease, second in prevalence only to common

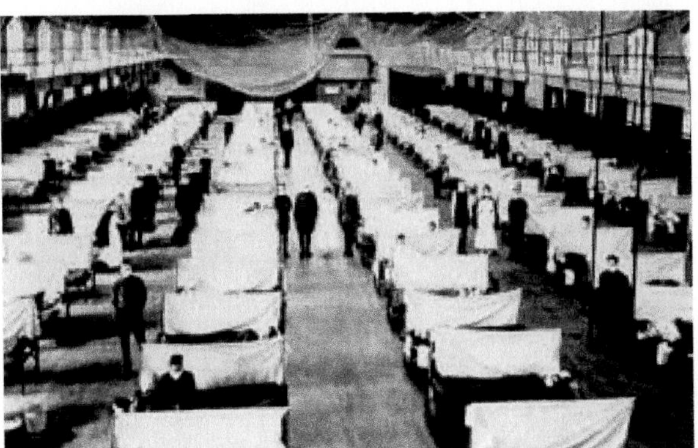

▲ *Figure 10*

A scene from the flu pandemic of 1918–19. Influenza afflicted so many people in the United States that gymnasiums were used as hospital wards.

colds—to produce such devastating epidemics and we will examine some ways to protect ourselves.

Signs and Symptoms

Following infection, influenza has an incubation period of about one day. The signs and symptoms of **influenza**[18] (in-flū-en′ză) or **flu** usually include sudden fever between 39°C and 41°C (102–106°F), pharyngitis, congestion, dry cough, malaise, headache, and myalgia. Most people recover in one to two weeks.

Pathogens and Virulence Factors

Two species of orthomyxoviruses, designated types A and B, cause influenza. A flu virion is segmented, having eight different −ssRNA molecules surrounded by a pleomorphic envelope studded with prominent glycoprotein spikes composed of either **hemagglutinin**[19] (hē-mă-glū′ti-nin; **HA**) or **neuraminidase** (nūr-ă-min′i-dāz; **NA**) **(Figure 11).** Both HA and NA play roles in attachment: NA spikes provide the virus access to cell surfaces by hydrolyzing mucus in the lungs, whereas HA spikes actually bind to pulmonary epithelial cells and trigger endocytosis. Because influenzaviruses rarely attack cells outside the lungs, so-called *stomach flu* is probably caused by other viruses or bacteria.

The genomes of flu viruses are extremely variable, especially with respect to the genes that code for HA and NA. Mutations in the genes coding for these glycoprotein spikes are responsible for the production of new strains of influenzavirus, via processes known as antigenic drift and antigenic shift.

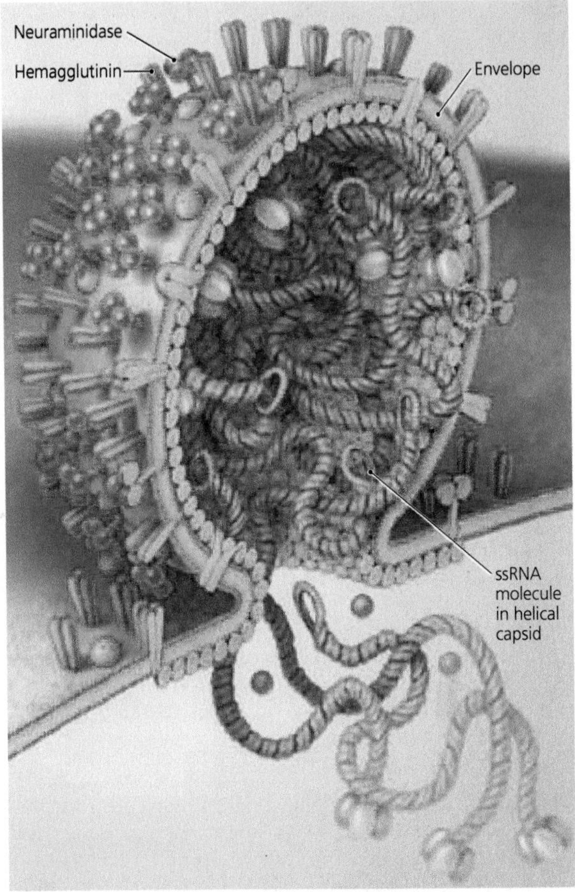

▲ *Figure 11*

Artist's rendition of a cross-sectioned influenzavirus budding from a cell. The viral genome consisting of eight segments of ssRNA, each of which is enclosed in a helical capsid. *What are the types of glycoprotein spikes, and what is their relationship to viral strain?*

Figure 11 *Glycoprotein spikes on influenzavirus are neuraminidase (NA) and hemagglutinin (HA); variations in these glycoproteins determine the strain of the virus.*

Antigenic drift (Figure 12a) refers to the accumulation of hemagglutinin and neuraminidase gene mutations within a single strain of virus in a given geographic area. Because of relatively minor changes in the virus population's antigens, localized increases in the number of flu infections occur about every two years. The slow, gradual change in the viral antigens gives the name drift to the process.

In contrast, **antigenic shift (Figure 12b)** is a major antigenic change that results from the reassortment of genes from different influenza A viruses infecting the same host cell (either human cells or animal cells, including cells of birds and pigs). On average, antigenic shift of influenza A

[18] *Influenza,* which is Italian for "influence," derives from the mistaken idea that the alignment of celestial objects caused or influenced the disease.

[19] The word *hemagglutinin* refers to these spikes' ability to attach to and clump (agglutinate) erythrocytes.

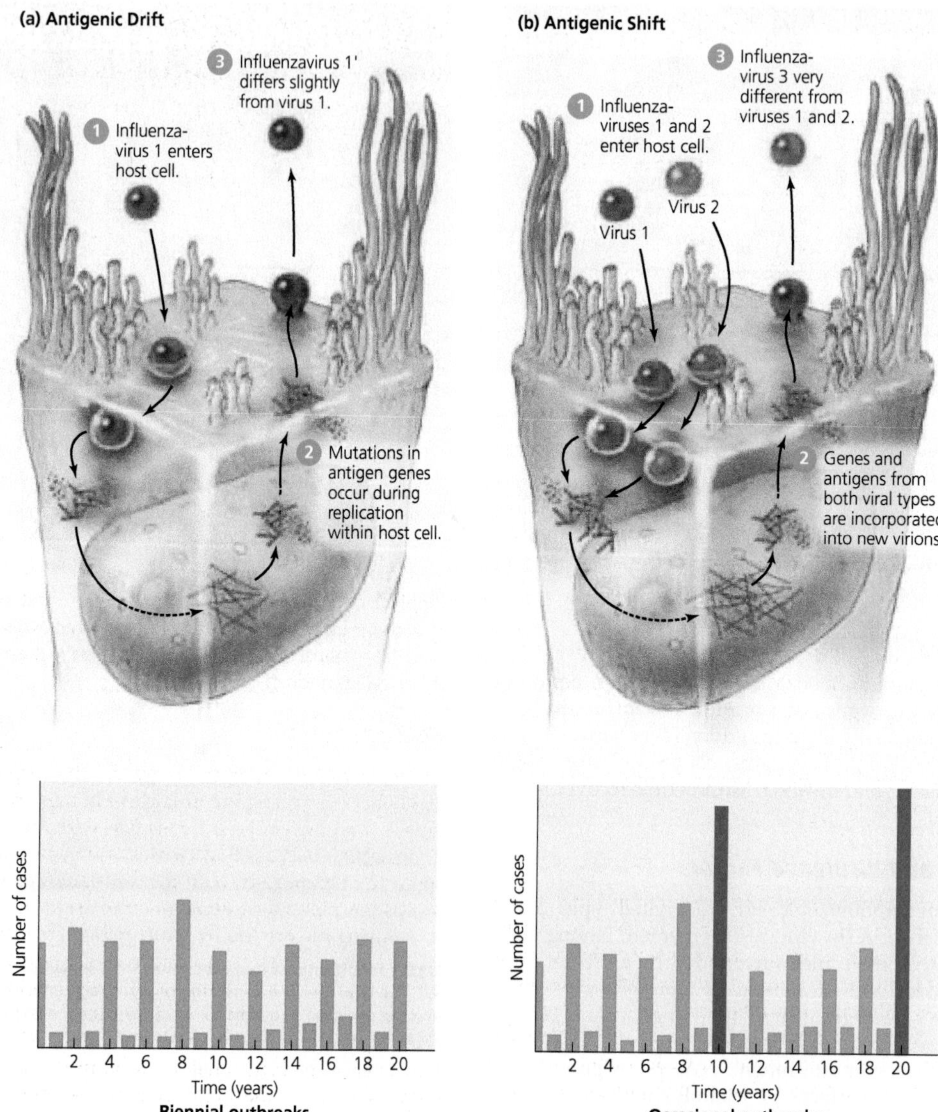
(a) Antigenic Drift
1 Influenza-virus 1 enters host cell.
2 Mutations in antigen genes occur during replication within host cell.
3 Influenzavirus 1' differs slightly from virus 1.
Number of cases
2 4 6 8 10 12 14 16 18 20
Time (years)
Biennial outbreaks of mild influenza
(b) Antigenic Shift
1 Influenza-viruses 1 and 2 enter host cell.
Virus 1
Virus 2
2 Genes and antigens from both viral types are incorporated into new virions.
3 Influenza-virus 3 very different from viruses 1 and 2.
Number of cases
2 4 6 8 10 12 14 16 18 20
Time (years)
Occasional outbreaks of very severe influenza

▲ *Figure 12*

The development of new strains of flu viruses. (a) Antigenic drift, which results from variation in the NA and HA spikes of a single strain of influenzavirus, either A or B. **(b)** Antigenic shift, which occurs when RNA molecules from two or more strain A influenzaviruses infecting a single cell are incorporated into a single virion. Because antigenic shift produces significantly greater antigenic variability than occurs in antigenic drift, antigenic shifts can result in major epidemics.

occurs every 10 years. Influenza B does not undergo antigenic shift.

Strains of influenza are named by type (A or B), location and date of original identification, and type of antigens (HA and NA). For example, A/Singapore/1/80 (H1N2) is influenza type A, isolated in Singapore in January 1980, that contains HA and NA antigens of type 1 and type 2, respectively. If the virus is isolated from an animal, the animal name is appended to the location. From these names, common names such as "Hong Kong flu" or "swine flu" arise.

Clinical Case Study *The Coughing Sister*

Nineteen-year-old Marjorie comes to the family practice office for evaluation of a dry cough that is not getting better over the last seven days. Before she started coughing, she had a mild fever, runny nose, and sneezing for 10 days, but was able to carry out her usual routine. She reports "coughing spells" frequently during the day and recalls one episode where she gagged and vomited after one of the spells. She has a mild coughing episode while in the office, and while it is paroxysmal, there is no "whoop" noted.

Marjorie is a part-time college student attending evening classes and helps her mom with her younger sisters during the day. Her siblings are five years old and six weeks old and also come to the same office for health care. Both sisters appear well, without any symptoms, and a review of their charts reveals they are current for all scheduled vaccines. Marjorie's last vaccine was at age 16.

1. Why should pertussis be something to consider?
2. What are the three clinical stages of pertussis?
3. If this is pertussis, why doesn't Marjorie have the classic "whoop"?
4. What are the CDC recommendations for adults ages 19–64?
5. Which family members are at the highest risk in this situation?
6. What test can her provider do to confirm the suspicion that Marjorie has pertussis?
7. Is treatment recommended at this time?
8. How is pertussis spread, and how could Marjorie prevent the spread of her infection to others?

The number of possible flu strains is almost infinite. Asia is a major site of antigenic shift, and the source of most pandemic strains, because of the continent's very high population densities of humans, ducks, chickens, and pigs—all of which serve as influenzavirus hosts.

Epidemiologists are concerned about influenzavirus H5N1, which is an avian influenzavirus that kills birds swiftly and has spread across Asia and Europe and into Africa and North America. H5N1 influenzavirus has a fatality rate of over 50% in infected humans. Fortunately, the virus very rarely spreads from human to human; rather, humans are infected following close contact with infected birds. The deadly nature of H5N1 influenzavirus, the speed with which it has spread throughout the world, and its mortality rate in humans cause epidemiologists to predict the arrival of a major flu pandemic to rival that of the winter of 1918–19.

H5N1 influenzavirus preferentially infects cells of the lower respiratory tract. For this reason it is seldom found in respiratory droplets, which originate in the upper respiratory tract, and thus is not normally transmitted among humans. However, scientists are concerned that a mutation of H5N1's genome could allow the virus to colonize upper respiratory cells, making it more likely that viruses could spread among humans. If this occurred, this avian virus could pose health care challenges greater than those of any microbe in modern history.

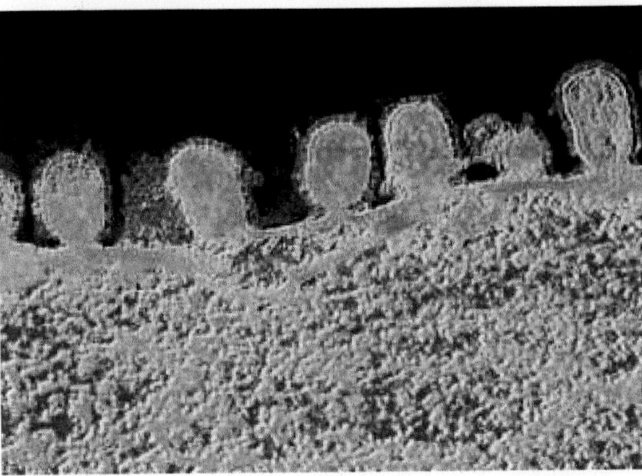

▲ *Figure 13*
Influenzaviruses budding from an infected cell.

Pathogenesis

Influenzaviruses enter the body via the respiratory route. Epithelial cells lining the lungs take in the viruses via endocytosis, and the viral envelopes fuse with the membranes of phagocytic vesicles. Flu viruses multiply using positive-sense RNA molecules both for translation of viral proteins and as templates for transcription of −ssRNA genomes.

During the process by which virions bud from the cytoplasmic membrane of infected cells **(Figure 13),** NA keeps viral proteins from clumping. During budding, genomic segments are enveloped in a random manner, such that each virion ends up with about 11 RNA molecules. However, to be functional, a virion must have at least one copy of each of the eight genomic segments. Numerous defective particles are released for every functional virion formed.

The deaths of epithelial cells infected with influenzaviruses eliminate the lungs' first line of defense against infection, their epithelial linings. As a result, flu patients are more susceptible to secondary bacterial infection. One common infecting bacterium is *H. influenzae,* which was so named because it was found in many flu victims. Cytokines released as part of the immune response induce the typical signs and symptoms of flu.

Epidemiology

The changing antigens of flu viruses guarantee that there will be susceptible people, especially children, each season.

Infection occurs primarily through inhalation of airborne viruses released by coughing or sneezing, but self-inoculation can occur as people transfer viruses on their fingers to their mouths or noses.

Infected people are contagious one day before the disease is manifested and for a week or more after signs and symptoms begin. Some individuals are carriers—infected people who are not sick. About 15–20% of the U.S. population gets the flu each year, usually in the winter. About 200,000 victims are hospitalized, and 36,000 die annually. The elderly (over age 65), the very young (under age 2), pregnant women, and people with chronic diseases whose immune systems are suppressed are most at risk for serious complications, including bacterial pneumonia, bronchitis, otitis media, and heart failure.

Diagnosis, Treatment, and Prevention

Having the signs and symptoms of flu during a community-wide outbreak is sufficient for an initial diagnosis of influenza. Laboratory tests such as immunofluorescence, ELISA, polymerase chain reaction, and commercially available rapid antigen testing can distinguish strains of flu virus. Early and accurate diagnosis is important because antiviral therapy must begin promptly to be effective; further, early diagnosis can forestall the writing of inappropriate prescriptions for antibacterial drugs.

The Centers for Disease Control and Prevention (CDC) recommends the use of either of two drugs to treat influenza: Oseltamivir pills or inhaled zanamivir mist inhibit type A and type B neuraminidase, blocking the release of virions from infected cells. These prescription drugs must be taken during the first 48 hours of infection in order to be effective, because they cannot prevent later manifestations of the disease. As of January 2000, the CDC discouraged using two older antiflu drugs—amantadine and rimantadine—because the viruses are growing resistant to both. The CDC is evaluating the drugs' efficacy to see if this recommendation should remain in effect.

Hundreds of millions of dollars are spent each year in the United States on antihistamines and pain relievers to alleviate the symptoms of the flu. Aspirin and aspirin-like products should not be used to treat the symptoms of flu in children and teenagers because of increased risk of Reye's syndrome, which is a potentially fatal syndrome that sometimes follows viral infections, especially in children who have taken aspirin.

The greatest success in controlling flu epidemics has come from immunization with multivalent vaccines; that is, vaccines that contain several antigens at once. The CDC has personnel in Asia who detect changes in the HA and NA antigens of drifting flu viruses. Antigens of emerging viruses are then used to create a flu vaccine in advance of the next flu season in the United States. Scientists particularly monitor any increase in incidence of avian flu because some virulent strains of avian influenza type A virus also infect people, making antigenic shift possible. Avian recombinants caused the three major pandemics of flu in the 20th century (1918–19, 1957–58, 1968–69).

Flu vaccines are at least 70% effective, but only against the viral antigens they contain. A flu vaccine usually provides protection against the strains included in the vaccine for three years or less. Natural active immunity following infection lasts much longer but is probably not lifelong. In 2003, the U.S. Food and Drug Administration (FDA) approved a flu vaccine administered by means of a nasal spray.

The FDA has also approved the use of zanamivir and oseltamivir for flu prevention in adults. Both drugs prevent development of the flu in individuals who begin treatment with 36 hours of exposure to influenzavirus.

Clinical Case Study: Influenza examines some aspects of influenza infection and immunization.

Severe Acute Respiratory Syndrome (SARS)

Learning Objective

✓ Describe severe acute respiratory syndrome.

In the spring of 2003, **severe acute respiratory syndrome (SARS)** literally changed the face of China (see chapter opening photo) as people donned masks to prevent the spread of this emerging respiratory disease.

Signs and Symptoms

SARS manifests with a high fever (greater than 38.0°C) accompanied by shortness of breath, difficulty in breathing, malaise, and body aches. About 10–20% of patients have diarrhea. After about a week, SARS patients develop a dry cough and pneumonia, and about 10% die.

Pathogen and Virulence Factors

Only four weeks after SARS was recognized as a newly emerging disease, scientists had identified and sequenced the genome of the coronavirus that causes SARS—an unprecedented epidemiological and genomic accomplishment. The virus surface has a molecule that adheres to mammalian heart, lung, and kidney cells. Bats are the natural reservoir host of SARS virus.

Coronaviruses are enveloped, +ssRNA viruses with helical capsids whose envelopes form crown-like (corona-like) halos around the capsids, giving the viruses their name (see Disease at a Glance 5). Because diseases of coronaviruses are usually mild—coronaviruses are the second most common causes of common colds—the fatalities in the 2003 SARS pandemic were particularly alarming.

Pathogenesis and Epidemiology

SARS virus enters the body via respiratory droplets and adheres to lung cells. The virus destroys these cells, triggering the respiratory symptoms of SARS, and then spreads via the bloodstream to the heart and kidneys.

Clinical Case Study *Influenza*

A 26-year-old man reports to his physician in late October, complaining of a sudden onset of fever, a dry cough, headache, and body aches. The man states that he received his flu shot 10 days prior and must have gotten the flu from the immunization. He also states that he had just returned two days before from a weeklong trip to Hong Kong. He mentions that a highlight of his trip was a visit to the farmers' market filled with fresh produce and livestock. A culture confirms the patient is infected with influenza virus.

1. How should the physician counter the patient's assertion that he "got the flu" from the vaccine?
2. Explain the occurrence of this influenza case before the onset of the recognized flu season.
3. Why might the patient have been infected with influenzavirus even after receiving a vaccine?
4. The culture indicates that this is a drastically different flu strain than has been seen in recent years. What phenomenon explains this?
5. Will prescription drugs likely be effective in this patient's case? Why or why not?

Epidemiologists accomplished a praiseworthy task in tracking the spread of SARS in only six months from Guangdong Province, China, to an apartment building in Hong Kong, and from there to more than two dozen nations in Asia, Europe, and the Americas. WHO reported that 8096 people became sick and 774 died from SARS. In the four years following the first pandemic, physicians have reported about a dozen cases of SARS in China, including several cases among workers in SARS laboratories.

Diagnosis, Treatment, and Prevention

Physicians diagnose SARS based upon signs and symptoms, particularly in patients in endemic areas of China, and confirm it by isolating the virus or antibodies against the virus in the patient's blood. These techniques are not rapid; therefore, scientists are developing polymerase chain reaction tests that will allow rapid diagnosis, which is necessary if future epidemics are to be avoided.

Physicians provide supportive care for SARS patients. As of 2007, no antiviral drug has proven universally effective against SARS virus, though scientists are testing a drug that binds to the SARS-receptor protein on human cells in the hope that the drug will prevent attachment of SARS. Scientists have developed a recombinant DNA vaccine against SARS virus and are testing the vaccine for safety and efficacy.

Despite the speed with which researchers identified and characterized the SARS virus using modern genetic and immunological techniques, the pandemic was brought under control using centuries-old methods of isolation and quarantine of SARS patients and their contacts. The combination of historical and modern epidemiological practices rendered the SARS pandemic much less severe than many epidemiologists and health officials first feared.

Disease at a Glance 5 summarizes the characteristics of SARS.

DISEASE AT A GLANCE 5

Severe Acute Respiratory Syndrome (SARS)

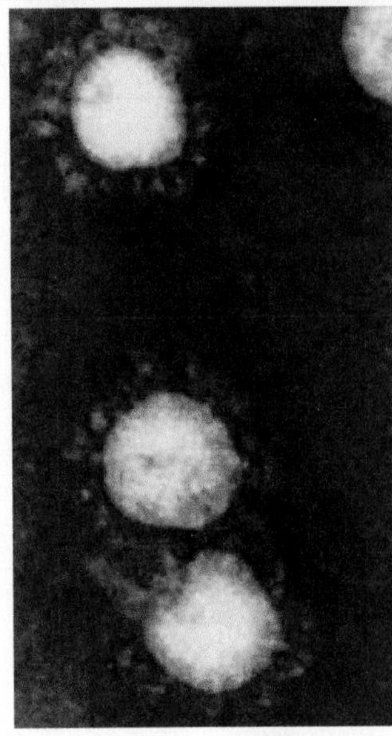

SARS virus, a coronavirus.

Cause: SARS-associated coronavirus (+ssRNA helical virus).

Portal of entry: Respiratory droplets enter through mucous membranes via close person-to-person contact.

Signs and symptoms: High fever, headache and body aches, malaise, dry cough developing into pneumonia.

Incubation period: Generally 2–7 days, up to 10 days in some cases.

Susceptibility: Studies suggest that some people are genetically more susceptible than others are.

Treatment: Treatment is mostly supportive, athough studies show a combination of steroids and antiviral interferon may be effective in treating SARS.

Prevention: Limit travel to endemic areas, use handwashing precautions, quarantine infected persons and their contacts.

Respiratory Syncytial Virus Infection

Learning Objectives

- ✓ Describe the features of respiratory syncytial virus infection.
- ✓ Compare the effects of RSV infection in infants and adults.

Respiratory syncytial virus (RSV) infection is the most common childhood respiratory disease in newborns and young children. Annual community-wide outbreaks lasting four to six months are common during late fall, winter, and early spring.

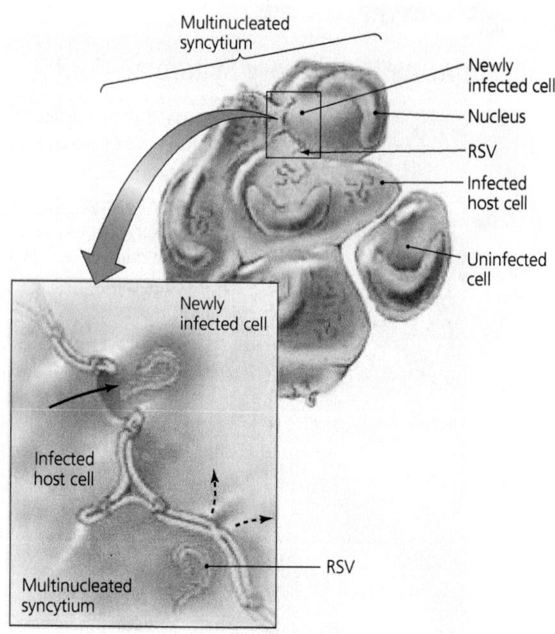

▲ *Figure 14*

A syncytium forms when RSV triggers infected cells to fuse with uninfected cells. Virions moving through these large multinucleated cells can infect new cells, all the while evading the host's immune system.

Signs and Symptoms

About four to six days following infection, RSV triggers fever, rhinorrhea, coughing, and sometimes wheezing in babies and the immunocompromised. RSV is the leading cause of *bronchiolitis* (inflammation of the bronchioles) and pneumonia among children less than one year of age and the leading respiratory killer of infants worldwide. Infections of RSV in older children and adults with normal immune systems results in coldlike symptoms. Some children develop *tracheobronchitis*, known commonly as **croup** (krūp), which is inflammation of the trachea and bronchi, resulting in breathing difficulty accompanied by a barking cough.

Pathogen

RSV (genus *Pneumovirus*, family *Paramyxoviridae*) is an enveloped, helical, −ssRNA virus. It is relatively unstable outside the body, surviving about five hours in the environment or two hours on skin or used facial tissues. Soap and water as well as disinfectants deactivate RSV.

Pathogenesis

As its name indicates, the virus causes **syncytia** to form in the lungs. A syncytium is a giant, multinucleated cell formed from the fusion of virally infected cells to neighboring cells **(Figure 14).** Plugs of mucus, fibrin, and dead cells in the bronchioles make it difficult to breathe. The action of cytotoxic T cells and other specific immune responses to RSV infection further damages the lungs.

Epidemiology

RSV spreads easily during close contact with infected persons, such as through kissing, touching, and shaking hands, and via contact with recently contaminated fomites. Spread via respiratory droplets is less frequent. Immunocompromised older patients and babies, especially those who are premature, immune impaired, exposed to tobacco smoke, who attend day care, or who have older school-aged siblings, are most at risk. RSV is prevalent in the United States; epidemiological studies reveal that about 98% of children in day care centers are infected by age three. Up to 125,000 of these children require hospitalization each year, and 2000 die. Additionally, RSV kills about 9000 elderly patients annually.

Diagnosis, Treatment, and Prevention

Prompt diagnosis is essential if infected infants are to get the care they need. The signs of respiratory distress provide some diagnostic clues, but verification of RSV infection is made by immunoassay. Specimens of respiratory fluid may be tested by immunofluorescence, ELISA, or complementary nucleic acid probes.

Older children and most adults require no treatment because their disease is mild. For younger children, supportive treatment includes administration of oxygen, intravenous fluids, drugs to reduce fever, and antibiotics to reduce secondary bacterial infections. Immunoglobulins against RSV, derived from blood donations, have proven effective for treating severe cases. Ribavirin via inhalation in mist form is used to treat extreme cases in premature and immunocompromised infants.

Control of RSV is limited to attempts to delay infection of susceptible infants through proper aseptic techniques, especially by health care workers and day care employees. Handwashing and the use of gowns, goggles, masks, and gloves are important measures to reduce nosocomial infections. Attempts at developing a vaccine with deactivated RSV have proven difficult because the vaccine enhances the severity of the cellular immune response and lung damage.

Hantavirus Pulmonary Syndrome (HPS)

Learning Objective

✓ Describe *Hantavirus* pulmonary syndrome.

True story: A young Native American scores an impressive 56 points for his tribal team during a basketball game one night. After the game, he is aware of muscle pains, but attributes them to his athletic endeavors; five days

later he is dead, a victim of ***Hantavirus* pulmonary syndrome (HPS).**

Signs and Symptoms

Early symptoms of HPS include fever, fatigue, and muscle aches, particularly in the large muscles of the thighs, hips, and back. Some patients experience headache, chills, and gastrointestinal symptoms, such as nausea, vomiting, diarrhea, and abdominal pain. An elevated leukocyte count and a low or falling platelet count are indicative of HPS.

Four to ten days after the initial manifestations, the patient begins coughing, goes into shock, and has difficulty breathing as the lungs rapidly fill with fluid. Fifty percent of diagnosed patients die, drowning in their own fluids, despite intensive medical care.

Pathogen

Hantavirus (han'tă-vī-rŭs) is a genus of enveloped, segmented, −ssRNA viruses in the family *Bunyaviridae* **(Figure 15)** that infect various species of mice, particularly deer mice (see Disease at a Glance 6), without causing disease. Two American strains of *Hantavirus* are transmitted via inhalation in dried mouse urine, feces, or saliva to infect the lungs of humans and cause HPS.

Pathogenesis

Following inhalation, *Hantavirus* enters the blood via an unknown mechanism and travels throughout the body infecting the cells that make up blood capillary walls, particularly in the lungs. The body responds with inflammation, which causes the capillaries to leak fluid into the surrounding tissue. Blood pressure drops precipitously, and about 50% of patients die from pneumonia and shock.

Epidemiology

Epidemiologists have reported several hundred cases in the United States since HPS was first recognized during an epidemic in the Four Corners[20] area of the United States in May 1993. Nevertheless, the syndrome has probably been around as long as mice and mankind have shared domiciles. The number of infections increases when abundant rainfall stimulates plant growth, providing abundant food material for the host mouse species. As the mouse population increases dramatically, humans are more likely to contact mice and their excrement and saliva. Despite a large number of virions in the blood vessels of infected humans, few viruses pass out of the lungs; therefore, person-to-person spread does not occur.

Diagnosis, Treatment, and Prevention

Physicians diagnose *Hantavirus* pulmonary syndrome based on typical manifestations of the disease—low platelet count, sudden onset of fever, and muscle ache in the major muscles of the legs and trunk—in patients who have contacted mice. Diagnosis is confirmed by detection

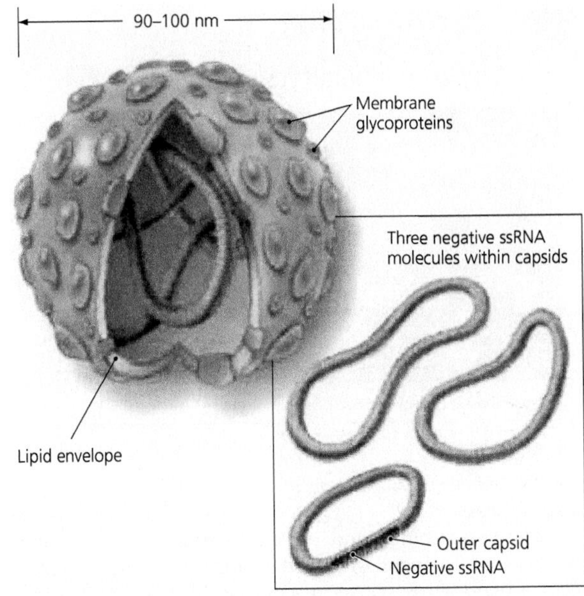

▲ *Figure 15*
***Hantavirus* is an enveloped, segmented, −ssRNA bunyavirus.** *What does the term* segmented *mean in reference to a viral genome?*

Figure 15 A segmented genome has more than one nucleic acid molecule.

of anti-hantavirus IgM, a rising titer of similar IgG, or demonstration of hantaviral RNA in clinical specimens using polymerase chain reaction.

No specific treatment exists for HPS. Supportive care may include pulmonary intubation, fever-reducing drugs, pain medication, and supplemental oxygen. No vaccine against *Hantavirus* exists. Rodent control is necessary to prevent infection. This includes keeping food in sealed containers, blocking openings into homes (deer mice can squeeze through a hole the size of a man's shirt button), sleeping on a ground cover when camping, and removing mouse feces, urine, and nesting material from the home.

Disease at a Glance 6 summarizes the features of *Hantavirus* pulmonary syndrome.

Other Viral Respiratory Diseases

Learning Objective

✓ Describe human *Metapneumovirus* and parainfluenzavirus infections.

Other viruses cause common respiratory illnesses in children, elderly adults, and the immunocompromised. Among these

[20]Four Corners is the geographic area where Arizona, Colorado, Utah, and New Mexico meet.

DISEASE AT A GLANCE 6

Hantavirus Pulmonary Syndrome

The deer mouse, *Peromyscus maniculatus*

Cause: *Hantavirus* (enveloped, segmented, −ssRNA virus).

Portal of entry: Inhalation of infected rodent excrement or saliva.

Signs and symptoms: Sudden onset of fever, fatigue, muscle aches, headache, chills, abdominal pain; followed by coughing and severe difficulty in breathing.

Incubation period: Fourteen to thirty days.

Susceptibility: Those exposed to rodents in endemic areas.

Treatment: Supportive therapy for symptoms must occur under hospital supervision.

Prevention: Avoid rodent droppings, camp on ground sheet, carefully clean out potential rodent nesting sites at home, and keep home clean.

are *Cytomegalovirus, Metapneumovirus* (MPV), and *parainfluenzaviruses.*

Metapneumovirus and parainfluenzaviruses are enveloped, unsegmented, −ssRNA viruses in the family *Paramyxoviridae.* Scientists discovered MPV in 2001 using nucleic acid probes which bound to genetic sequences that did not match the sequences of any known organism or virus. Since then, researchers have found that antibodies against the virus form in all children by age five, and they estimate that MPV is second only to rhinoviruses as a common cause of viral respiratory disease. As with most viral diseases, there is no treatment.

Three strains of parainfluenzaviruses cause croup and viral pneumonia, particularly in young children. There is no specific antiviral treatment beyond support and careful monitoring to ensure that airways do not become completely occluded, requiring intubation. Most patients recover from parainfluenza infections within two days. Frequent handwashing reduces the spread of the virus.

Clinical Case Study *A Blue Baby*

A woman reports to the emergency room in January with her cyanotic (blue-colored) 10-month-old child. The mother reports that the infant has had a runny nose, fever, and slight cough for a day and has had increasing trouble breathing. The child does not have a history of bronchial disease and was not premature. The mother also states that the infant's five-year-old brother is recovering from symptoms that resemble a cold.

1. What is the presumptive diagnosis?
2. How can the doctor confirm the diagnosis?
3. Describe the possible treatment for the child.
4. Were the parents irresponsible for not immunizing their child?
5. Is it likely that the infant caught the disease from his older brother? If so, why did the older child not display signs of respiratory distress?

To this point, we have considered respiratory diseases caused by bacteria and viruses. Next, we turn our attention to respiratory diseases caused by fungi.

Mycoses of the Lower Respiratory System

Learning Objective

✓ Define *systemic mycosis.*

The number of cases of **mycoses** (diseases caused by fungi) has increased over the last two decades, mostly because AIDS patients are susceptible to fungal infections. The following sections examine three *systemic mycoses*—fungal infections that spread throughout the body—seen in North America **(Figure 16)** and a type of fungal pneumonia common to AIDS patients. We begin with a systemic mycosis caused by *Coccidioides.*

Coccidioidomycosis

Learning Objective

✓ Describe coccidioidomycosis.

Coccidioidomycosis (kok-sid'ē-oy'dō-mī-kō'sis), commonly known as *valley fever,* occurs primarily in the San Joaquin Valley of California.

Signs and Symptoms

The major manifestation of coccidioidomycosis is pulmonary, initially resembling pneumonia or tuberculosis, though about 60% of patients experience only mild, unre-

(a) Coccidiomycosis

(b) Blastomycosis

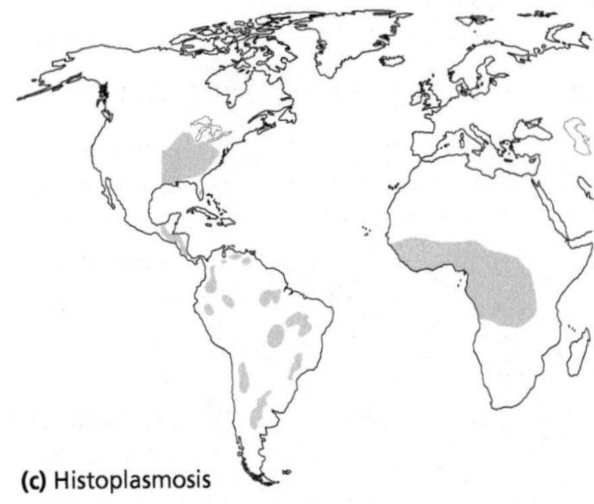
(c) Histoplasmosis

▲ *Figure 16*

The geographic distributions of three systemic fungal diseases endemic to North America.

markable respiratory symptoms that typically resolve on their own. Other patients develop more severe infections characterized by fever, cough, chest pain, difficulty breathing, coughing up or spitting blood, headache, night sweats, weight loss, and pneumonia; in some individuals, a diffuse rash may appear on the trunk.

In less than 1% of cases, generally in patients who are severely immunocompromised, the fungus disseminates from the lungs to various other sites. Invasion of the central nervous system may result in meningitis, headache, nausea, and emotional disturbance. Dissemination can also occur to the bones, joints, and subcutaneous tissues; subcutaneous lesions are inflamed masses of granular material **(Figure 17)**.

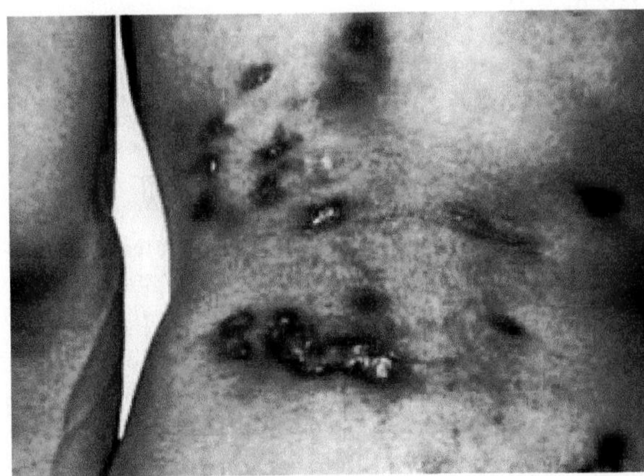

▲ *Figure 17*

Coccidioidomycosis lesions in subcutaneous tissue. Dissemination of *Coccidioides immitis* from the lungs causes the lesions.

Pathogen and Virulence Factors

Coccidioides immitis (kok-sid-ē-oy′dēz im′mi-tis) is a dimorphic soil fungus in the division Ascomycota. In the warm and dry summer and fall months, particularly in drought cycles, *C. immitis* grows as a mycelium and produces sturdy chains of asexual spores called *arthroconidia*. Mature arthroconidia germinate into mycelia. The fungus assumes a pathogenic yeast form at human body temperature.

Pathogenesis

Coccidioides enters the body through inhalation of arthroconidia from the soil. Disease begins as a generalized pulmonary infection that then disseminates to the rest of the body. Arthroconidia germinate in the alveoli into a form called a *spherule* (sfer′ool) **(Figure 18)**. As each spherule matures, it enlarges and generates a large number of spores via multiple cleavages, until it ruptures and releases the spores into the surrounding tissue. Each spore then forms a new spherule to continue the cycle of division and release. This type of spreading growth accounts for the seriousness of coccidioidomycosis.

Epidemiology

Coccidioides is found almost exclusively in the southwestern United States and northern Mexico (see Figure 16a). Small, focally endemic areas also exist in semiarid parts of Central and South America. About 3% of people living in endemic areas develop the disease each year.

Any activity that disrupts the soil can disseminate arthroconidia into the air. Local epidemics have occurred among archeologists, model plane enthusiasts practicing their hobby in the desert, and drivers of off-road vehicles. Windstorms and earthquakes can disturb large tracts of contaminated soil, spreading arthroconidia for miles. In 1978, there were many cases of coccidioidomycosis in Sacramento, California, 500 miles north of the endemic area, following a severe dust storm in southern California.

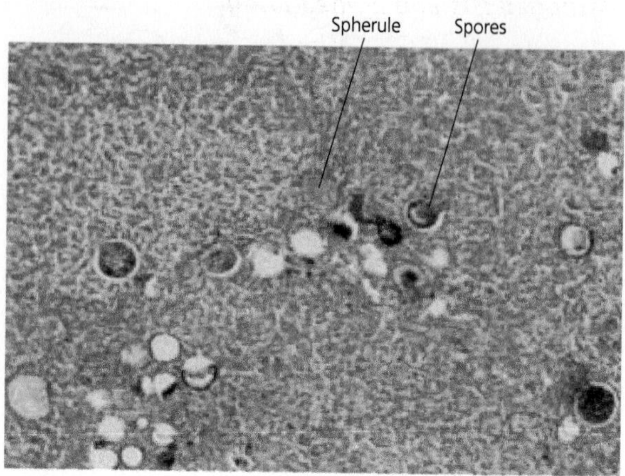

▲ *Figure 18*

Spherules of *Coccidioides immitis*. Note the numerous spores within a spherule.

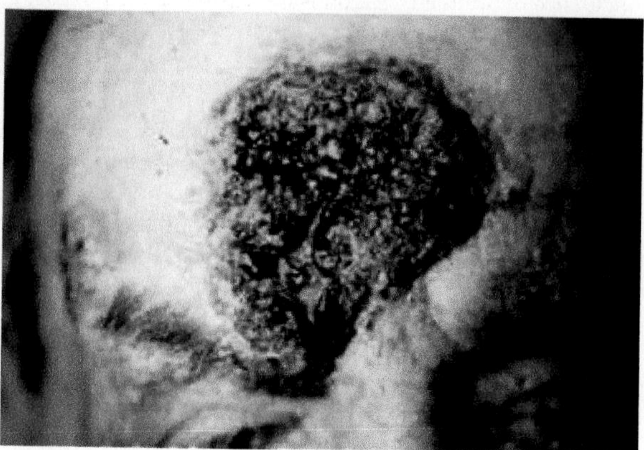

▲ *Figure 19*

Cutaneous blastomycosis. The lesions result from the dissemination of *Blastomyces dermatitidis* from the lungs to the skin.

Diagnosis, Treatment, and Prevention

Diagnosis of coccidioidomycosis is based on the identification of spherules in clinical specimens; diagnosis is confirmed by injecting antigen beneath the skin and observing an inflammatory response.

Although infections in otherwise healthy patients generally resolve on their own, when the fungus spreads to the brain and spinal cord the disease is fatal without treatment. Amphotericin B is the drug of choice; unfortunately, it is one of the more toxic antifungal agents to humans. In AIDS patients, maintenance therapy with other antifungal drugs, such as itraconazole or fluconazole, is recommended to prevent relapse or reinfection. The wearing of protective masks in endemic areas can prevent exposure to arthroconidia, although it may be impractical for daily use for all but those whose occupations put them at clear risk of infection.

CRITICAL THINKING

Could a traveler with coccidioidomycosis establish an endemic region of the disease in northern Russia?

Blastomycosis

Learning Objective

✓ Describe blastomycosis.

Another systemic fungal disease that begins as a respiratory infection is **blastomycosis** (blas′tō-mī-kō′sis), which is endemic across the southeastern United States north to Canada (see Figure 16b).

Signs and Symptoms

Blastomycosis begins with flulike signs and symptoms. The fungus may then spread to cause cutaneous blastomycosis (in 60–70% of cases), which manifests as generally painless lesions on the face or upper body **(Figure 19).** In roughly 30% of cases, purulent (pus-filled) lesions may develop and expand in the bones, prostate, testes, or other organs as the yeast multiplies, resulting in necrosis (death of tissues) and cavity formation.

Pathogen

A dimorphic, pathogenic ascomycete—*Blastomyces dermatitidis* (blas-tō-mī′sēz der-mă-tit′i-dis)—causes blastomycosis. The fungus normally grows in soil rich in organic material such as decaying vegetation and animal wastes, where cool, damp conditions favor growth and sporulation. The fungus assumes a yeast form in the higher temperature of the human body.

Pathogenesis and Epidemiology

Inhalation of dust carrying fungal spores infects the lungs. In the lungs, spores germinate to form yeasts and multiply. Initial pulmonary lesions are asymptomatic in most individuals. In otherwise healthy people, pulmonary blastomycosis and minor skin lesions typically resolve, though the disease may become chronic and fatal. Respiratory failure and death occur at a high frequency among immunocompromised patients.

Epidemiologists have reported blastomycoses in Latin America, Africa, Asia, and Europe. One to two cases occur annually per 100,000 population in endemic areas. The

incidence of human infection is increasing as the number of immunocompromised individuals rises.

Diagnosis, Treatment, and Prevention

Diagnosis relies on identification of *B. dermatitidis* in culture or direct examination of various samples such as sputum, bronchial washings, biopsies, cerebrospinal fluid, or skin scrapings. Observation of dimorphism in laboratory cultures coupled with microscopic examination is diagnostic.

Physicians treat blastomycosis with amphotericin B for 10 weeks, though longer treatment may be necessary. Oral itraconazole may be used as an alternative but must be administered for a minimum of three to six months. Relapse is common in AIDS patients, and suppressive maintenance therapy with itraconazole is recommended.

Scientists have developed a live recombinant DNA vaccine against *Blastomyces* that provides protection in mice.

CRITICAL THINKING

Outbreaks of blastomycosis have occurred in Latin America even though the organism itself is not normally found there. Explain why a few cases of blastomycosis might appear outside of endemic areas.

Histoplasmosis

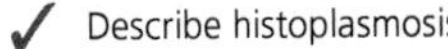

Learning Objective

✓ Describe histoplasmosis.

Histoplasmosis (his'tō-plaz-mō'sis) is the most common fungal systemic disease affecting humans.

Signs and Symptoms

In almost 95% of individuals, histoplasmosis is asymptomatic, subclinical, and resolves without damage. About 5% of patients develop clinical histoplasmosis, which is characterized by severe coughing with blood-tinged sputum or skin lesions. An AIDS patient with histoplasmosis often rapidly develops an enlarged spleen and liver, which can be fatal. Some patients' bodies mount a type I hypersensitivity reaction against the fungus in the eyes, producing inflammation and redness.

Pathogen

Histoplasma capsulatum (his-tō-plaz'mă kap-soo-lā'tŭm), the causative agent of histoplasmosis, is a dimorphic ascomycete that is found in moist soils containing high levels of nitrogen such as from the droppings of bats and birds, especially chickens, starlings, and blackbirds. The fungus becomes a pathogenic yeast at human body temperature.

Pathogenesis and Epidemiology

H. capsulatum is an intracellular parasite that, upon inhalation, first attacks alveolar macrophages in the lungs. Infected macrophages disperse the fungus beyond the lungs via the blood and lymph. Cell-mediated immunity eventually develops, clearing the organism from healthy patients.

Histoplasmosis is particularly prevalent in the eastern United States along the Ohio River Valley (see Figure 16c), but endemic areas also exist in Africa and Central and South America. People inhale spores that have become airborne when soil containing the fungus is disturbed by wind or by human activities.

Diagnosis, Treatment, and Prevention

Diagnosis of histoplasmosis is based on the identification of budding yeast within macrophages or in stained samples of skin scrapings, sputum, cerebrospinal fluid, or various tissues; the diagnosis is confirmed by the observation of dimorphism in cultures grown from such samples. Cultured *H. capsulatum* produces distinctively spiny spores that are also diagnostic (see Disease at a Glance 7). Antibody tests are not useful indicators of *Histoplasma* infection because many people have been exposed without contracting disease. In the endemic regions of the United States, close to 90% of the population have antibodies against *H. capsulatum*.

Infections in immunocompetent individuals typically resolve without treatment. When symptoms do not resolve, physicians can prescribe itraconazole, ketoconazole, or amphotericin B. Maintenance therapy for AIDS patients is recommended.

Disease at a Glance 7 summarizes the features of histoplasmosis.

CRITICAL THINKING

Statistically, men are more likely than women to contract histoplasmosis. What might explain this fact?

Pneumocystis Pneumonia (PCP)

Learning Objective

✓ Describe *Pneumocystis* pneumonia.

Before the AIDS epidemic, ***Pneumocystis*** (nū-mō-sis'tis) **pneumonia** (PCP[21]) was observed only in malnourished, premature infants and debilitated elderly patients; now, the disease is almost diagnostic for AIDS.

[21] Originally stood for the old name of the fungus: *Pneumocystis carinii* pneumonia.

DISEASE AT A GLANCE 7

Histoplasmosis

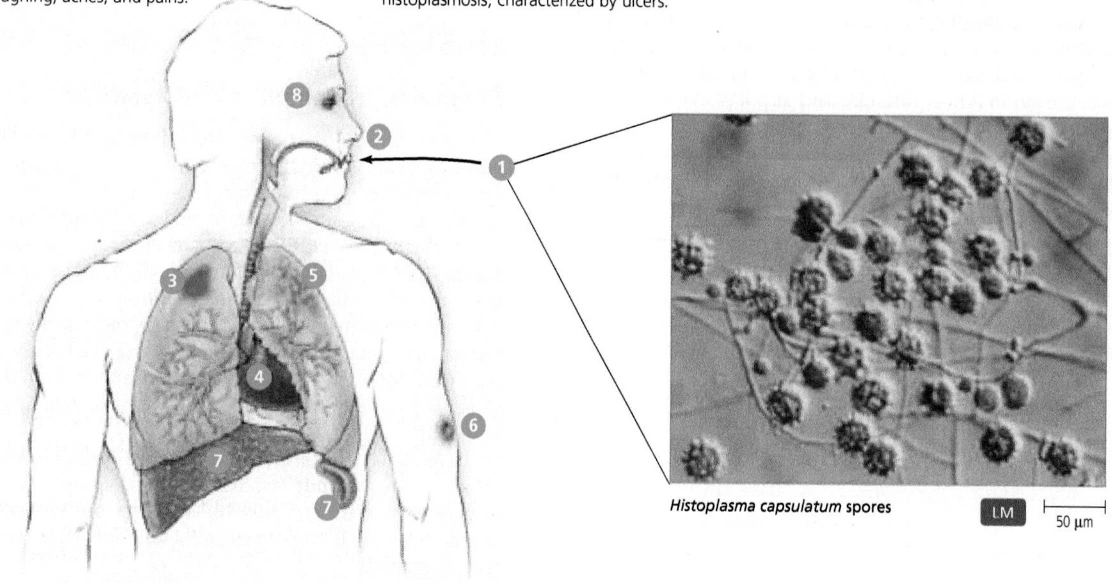

1 Spores of *Histoplasma capsulatum* present in moist, nitrogen-rich soils, especially at sites of bat and bird droppings.
2 Airborne spores are inhaled.
3 Spores attack alveolar macrophages. Symptoms in 95% of infections are mild: coughing, aches, and pains.
4 Infected macrophages carry spores through circulatory and lymphatic systems.
5 Patient may develop chronic pulmonary histoplasmosis with symptoms similar to tuberculosis.
6 Patient may develop chronic cutaneous histoplasmosis, characterized by ulcers.
7 Immunocompromised patients may develop systemic histoplasmosis characterized by enlargement of spleen and liver; death may result.
8 Ocular histoplasmosis may develop. Inflamed, red eyes indicate type I hypersensitivity to the fungus.
LM
50 μm

Histoplasma capsulatum spores

Cause: *Histoplasma capsulatum* (dimorphic ascomycete fungus).
Portal of entry: Inhalation.
Signs and symptoms: Dry, unproductive cough, shortness of breath, chest pain, fever, chills, headache, and malaise.

Incubation period: Approximately 10 days.
Susceptibility: Anyone, but more common in children up to 15 years old and those exposed to the soil in endemic areas.

Treatment: Itraconazole, ketoconazole, or amphotericin B.
Prevention: Minimize exposure to soil, especially near chicken coops or bat caves, or wear a mask.

Signs and Symptoms

Signs and symptoms of PCP include increasing difficulty in breathing, mild anemia, hypoxia (low tissue oxygen), and fever. A nonproductive cough occurs in some cases. Rarely, extrapulmonary lesions develop in the lymph nodes, spleen, liver, and bone marrow. If left untreated, PCP involves more and more lung tissue until death occurs.

Pathogen

Pneumocystis jiroveci (nū-mō-sis′tis jē-rō-vĕt′zē), which is a normal member of the respiratory microbiota, is an obligate parasitic ascomycete formerly known as "*P. carinii.*" Originally it was considered a protozoan due to its morphology and development, but scientists have reclassified it as a fungus based on rRNA nucleotide sequences and biochemistry.

Pathogenesis and Epidemiology

P. jiroveci cannot survive on its own in the environment; therefore, transmission most likely occurs through inhalation of droplet nuclei containing the fungus. In normal people, infection is asymptomatic, and generally clearance of the fungus from the body is followed by lasting immunity. However, some individuals may remain infected indefinitely; in such carriers, the organism remains in the alveoli and can be passed in sputum and presumably in respiratory droplets. Once the fungus enters the lungs of an immunocompromised patient, it multiplies rapidly, extensively colonizing the lungs.

P. jiroveci is distributed worldwide in humans. Based on serological confirmation of antibodies, 75% of healthy children have been exposed to the fungus by the age of five, but disease results only in immunocompromised patients. PCP is one of the more common diseases seen in AIDS patients.

Diagnosis, Treatment, and Prevention

Diagnosis of PCP relies on clinical and microscopic findings. Chest X rays usually reveal abnormal lung features. Stained specimens of fluid from the lungs or from biopsies can reveal distinctive morphological forms of the fungus **(Figure 20).** The use of fluorescent antibody on samples taken from patients is more sensitive and provides a more specific diagnosis.

Both primary treatment and maintenance therapy are with an oral or intravenous combination of trimethoprim and sulfamethoxazole known as TMP-SMX. It is virtually impossible to prevent infection because *P. jiroveci* is ubiquitous in humans; however, the fungus produces disease only in immunocompromised individuals, so steps to ensure a healthy immune system such as cessation of smoking, good nutrition, and prevention of HIV infection can prevent PCP in most people.

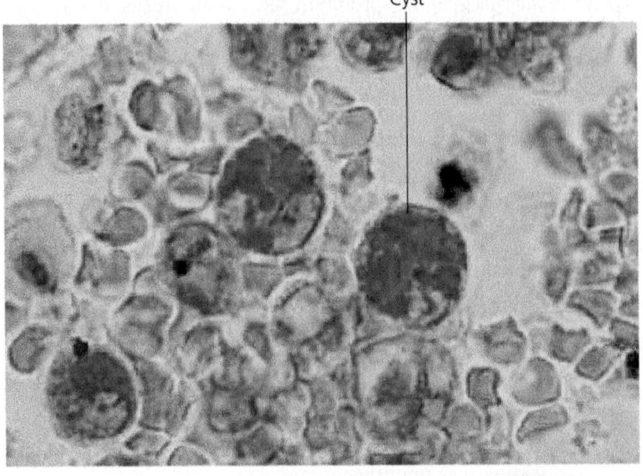

▲ *Figure 20*

Cysts of *Pneumocystis jiroveci* in lung tissue. Such microscopic findings are diagnostic for PCP.

CHAPTER SUMMARY

Structures of the Respiratory System

1. The upper respiratory system—consisting of the nose, nasal cavity, and pharynx—collects and filters air.
2. Cilia move mucus with trapped microorganisms to the pharynx to be swallowed.
3. Chemicals and cells of the tonsils fight microbial contaminants.
4. The lower respiratory system resembles an upside-down tree, composed of the larynx, trachea, bronchi, bronchioles, and alveoli of the lungs. They carry air through progressively smaller tubes to eventually allow exchange of gases with the blood capillaries of the lungs.
5. Pathogens cause inflammation of the respiratory tubes, resulting in restricted air flow.
6. Microbes stuck in mucus are carried by a ciliary escalator up and out of the bronchioles, bronchi, and trachea.
7. Alveolar macrophages and secretory antibodies (IgA) provide protection from many pathogens.
8. Harmless **diphtheroids** and other microbiota are commonly found in the nose and nasal cavity along with many types of opportunistic pathogens.

Bacterial Diseases of the Upper Respiratory System, Sinuses, and Ears

1. **Streptococcal pharyngitis**—caused by streptococcal inflammation of the pharynx—is commonly known as strep throat.
2. Pharyngitis can progress into **scarlet fever** (scarlatina) when *Streptococcus* releases toxins that trigger fever and a bright red skin rash.
3. Untreated streptococcal pharyngitis can spread to cause complications in the kidneys (acute glomerulonephritis) and **rheumatic fever,** which may result in heart damage.
4. Inflammation of the larynx, **laryngitis,** causes hoarseness, and inflammation of the bronchi—**bronchitis**—results in restricted airflow to the lungs.
5. Group A *Streptococcus* (*S. pyogenes*) is the major cause of bacterial pharyngitis, scarlet fever, and rheumatic fever. Its survival in the body is aided by M protein, a hyaluronic acid capsule, pyrogenic toxins, streptolysins, and enzymes that allow the pathogen to spread in a variety of ways.
6. *S. pyogenes* from one individual travels via respiratory droplets to other individuals.
7. *Corynebacterium diphtheriae* produces a toxin that causes **diphtheria,** a disease characterized by the formation of a thick pseudomembrane on the surfaces of the upper respiratory tract.
8. **Sinusitis** (inflammation of the sinuses) and **otitis media** (earache) are usually caused by *S. pneumoniae, Haemophilus influenzae,* or *Moraxella catarrhalis,* which spread from the pharynx to the sinuses or ears.

Viral Diseases of the Upper Respiratory System

1. Of the over 200 different serotypes of viruses that cause colds, the most common are in the genus *Rhinovirus* (family

Picornaviridae). Some coronaviruses, adenoviruses, reoviruses, and paramyxoviruses also cause colds.

2. Cold viruses are sensitive to warm temperatures and low pH, so they do not infect the lower respiratory tract.
3. Rhinoviruses are extremely infective and are transmitted via respiratory droplets, skin contact, and fomites.

Bacterial Diseases of the Lower Respiratory System

1. **Pneumonia** results from pulmonary inflammation and the accumulation of fluid in the alveoli and bronchioles of the lungs. Physicians give different names to pneumonias, which are derived from the affected region of the lungs or from the causative organism.
2. The most common type of pneumonia is pneumococcal pneumonia, which is caused by *Streptococcus pneumoniae* (commonly known as **pneumococcus**).
3. Mycoplasmal pneumonia, caused by *Mycoplasma pneumoniae,* is also called **primary atypical pneumonia** or walking pneumonia.
4. *Klebsiella* pneumonia produces thick, bloody sputum and recurrent chills.
5. **Pneumonic plague** is a form of pneumonia caused by *Yersinia pestis,* the bubonic plague bacterium.
6. *Chlamydophila psittaci* causes **ornithosis** in birds, which is a disease that manifests as severe pneumonia in humans.
7. *Chlamydophila pneumoniae* causes bronchitis, pneumonia, and sinusitis.
8. **Legionnaires' disease** or legionellosis is a pneumonia caused by *Legionella,* a genus of bacteria that are transmitted in aerosols.
9. The cell walls of *Mycobacterium tuberculosis* contain **mycolic acid**, which protects the pathogen when it infects the lungs, where it forms nodules called **tubercles** and the disease **tuberculosis (TB)**. **Multi-drug-resistant (MDR)** and **extensively drug-resistant (XDR)** strains of *Mycobacterium* pose a significant challenge to health care workers.
10. **Cord factor** is another cell wall component of *M. tuberculosis* that inhibits migration of neutrophils and kills cells.
11. A skin test determines if a person has been exposed to *M. tuberculosis* antigens. Chest X rays reveal tubercles in the lungs. Directly Observed Treatment, Shortcourse (DOTS) is a strategy to ensure treatment of TB patients.
12. *Bordetella pertussis* causes **pertussis (whooping cough)** by interfering with ciliated epithelial cells of the trachea via adhesins and toxins.
13. Pertussis progresses in four stages: incubation, catarrhal phase, paroxysmal phase, and convalescent phase.
14. *Bacillus anthracis* causes the most lethal form of anthrax—**inhalational anthrax,** which progresses from the manifestations of a common cold to lethargy and shock.

Viral Diseases of the Lower Respiratory System

1. Orthomyxoviruses are surrounded by lipid envelopes with glycoprotein spikes composed of **hemagglutinin (HA)** or **neuraminidase (NA)** that play roles in the attachment of the viruses to the cells of the lungs to cause **influenza (flu).**
2. The accumulation of HA and NA mutations in a geographic area results in an increase in cases of flu and is called **antigenic drift.**
3. **Antigenic shift** is a major antigenic change resulting from the reassortment of genomes from different influenzavirus A strains. Such shifts may result in pandemics.
4. **Severe acute respiratory syndrome (SARS)** is a newly emerging disease caused by a coronavirus, which destroys lung cells and spreads via the bloodstream to the heart and kidneys.
5. **Respiratory syncytial virus (RSV) infection** is a common childhood respiratory disease. RSV causes giant, multinucleated cells **(syncytia)** to form in the lungs, leading to bronchiolitis or tracheobronchitis, commonly known as **croup.**
6. ***Hantavirus* pulmonary syndrome (HPS)** is a potentially fatal respiratory disease caused by *Hantavirus,* which is transmitted in dried mouse excreta.
7. **Parainfluenzavirus** strains 1, 2, and 3 are associated with croup and viral pneumonia.
8. *Metapneumovirus* (MPV) is the second most common cause of respiratory tract disease in children.

Mycoses of the Lower Respiratory System

1. **Mycoses** are diseases caused by fungi; spread throughout the body they are called systemic mycoses.
2. *Coccidioides immitis* causes **coccidioidomycosis,** also known as valley fever. The initial manifestation resembles pneumonia or tuberculosis. In immunocompromised patients the manifestations include meningitis, headache, nausea, and emotional disturbance.
3. *Blastomyces dermatitidis* causes **blastomycosis,** a systemic fungal disease that begins as a flulike infection. The fungus may spread to cause lesions on the upper body and destroy tissues in bone, prostate, testes, and other organs.
4. *Histoplasma capsulatum* causes **histoplasmosis**—the most common fungal systemic disease affecting humans. About 5% of patients develop chronic pulmonary histoplasmosis, chronic cutaneous histoplasmosis, systemic histoplasmosis, or ocular histoplasmosis.
5. *Pneumocystis jiroveci* causes ***Pneumocystis* pneumonia (PCP)** in malnourished, premature, debilitated elderly, and immunocompromised patients.

QUESTIONS FOR REVIEW

Access more review material (including animations and practice tests) online at www.microbiologyplace.com.

Multiple Choice

1. The movement of mucus from lungs to pharynx is due to
   a. epiglottal flow.
   b. a ciliary escalator.
   c. sneezing.
   d. pharyngeal reflux.
2. Compared to the upper respiratory system, the lower respiratory system
   a. provides an environment conducive to the growth of microorganisms.
   b. is normally devoid of microorganisms.
   c. provides an ideal environment for diphtheroids.
   d. is several degrees cooler.
3. The major cause of bacterial pharyngitis is
   a. group A *Streptococcus*.
   b. group B *Streptococcus*.
   c. influenzavirus.
   d. *Bordetella pertussis*.
4. The glycoprotein spikes on orthomyxoviruses are composed of
   a. cord factor.
   b. hemagglutinin or neuraminidase.
   c. streptokinase and hyaluronic acid.
   d. M proteins.
5. Group A *Streptococcus* is camouflaged from phagocytes by
   a. M protein.
   b. a hyaluronic acid capsule.
   c. pus resulting from the action of streptokinase.
   d. streptolysin.
6. The action of streptolysin results in
   a. breaking the hyaluronic acid capsule around cells.
   b. the inhibition of complement protein and decrease in the number of leukocytes at the site of infection.
   c. breaks in the membranes of erythrocytes, leukocytes, and platelets.
   d. the destruction of streptococcal bacteria.
7. Which pathogenic fungus is found in the droppings of bats, chickens, and blackbirds?
   a. *Histoplasma capsulatum*
   b. *Blastomyces dermatitidis*
   c. *Coccidioides immitis*
   d. *Parainfluenzavirus*
8. Which term associated with tuberculosis refers to calcified nodules in the lungs?
   a. tubercles
   b. caseous necrosis
   c. tuberculous cavities
   d. Ghon complexes
9. The phase of whooping cough in which the characteristic "whoop" is obvious is the
   a. paroxysmal phase.
   b. catarrhal phase.
   c. convalescent phase.
   d. incubation phase.
10. Which of the following is associated with the fusion of neighboring cells?
   a. neuraminidase
   b. respiratory syncytial virus
   c. tuberculin
   d. agglutinin

Fill in the Blanks

1. The medical name for the inflammation of the throat known as strep throat is ______________.
2. A thick leathery membrane in the throat is a sign of ______________.
3. RSV is characterized by the formation of giant multinucleated cells in the lungs called ______________.
4. A drug commonly used to treat systemic fungal diseases is ______________.
5. A condition in adolescents associated with taking aspirin to treat viral infections is ______________ syndrome.

Modified True/False

Modify each false statement to make it true by changing the italicized word(s).

___ 1. A normal cold *produces* fever in most cases.

___ 2. The number of fungal infections has increased over the last 20 years because of *damp climatic conditions*.

___ 3. Antigenic *shift* accounts for an increase in flu infections at a locality every two years.

___ 4. The formation of a hard, red lesion at the site of a tuberculosis skin test is a conclusive indication of *the presence of* the tuberculosis bacterium.

___ 5. Death by pneumonia would be similar to *drowning*.

Short Answer

1. What is the function of adenoids?
2. Explain why the lower respiratory system is called the "respiratory tree."
3. The microorganisms that cause diphtheria and pneumonia are frequently found in the upper pharynx of healthy individuals. Why do relatively few individuals contract these two illnesses?
4. After listening to a lecture on diseases caused by *Streptococcus* spp., a student exclaimed, "Do you mean to say that *Streptococcus* can make a person kill his own heart?" To what was the student referring?
5. Describe the action of diphtheria toxin.

6. Give two reasons why there is no prevention for the common cold.
7. Give two reasons why cold viruses are more prolific in the winter.
8. On what basis is the decision made concerning the antigens selected for the flu vaccine in the U.S. each year?
9. Contrast the way infections of *Chlamydophila psittaci* spread from the way *C. pneumoniae* spreads.

CRITICAL THINKING

1. Explain the following identification label from a laboratory vial of influenza virus: B/Kuwait/6/97/(H1N3).
2. An elderly man is admitted to the hospital with severe pneumonia, from which he eventually dies. What bacterial species is the most likely cause of his demise? What antimicrobial drug is effective against this species? How could the man have been protected from infection? Is the hospital staff at significant risk of infection from the man? Which groups of patients would be at risk if the man had visited their rooms before he died?
3. Compare and contrast viral pneumonia with bacterial pneumonia in terms of cause, prevention, and potential seriousness.
4. Laboratory observation of *Pneumocystis jiroveci* led one researcher to conclude that it was a protozoan. Why has it been classified as a fungus?
5. A patient is admitted to a hospital in Ohio with a respiratory fungal infection. He had returned the previous month from a trip to Arizona where he bought some dusty old blankets and two pots from a roadside vendor. What diseases might he have?
6. Compare and contrast antigenic drift and antigenic shift in influenza A virus.
7. In mid-November, a worried couple brought their 29-day-old newborn to their small-town doctor's office. The weak infant had been coughing severely over the past five days, so much so that she was choking on her formula. During her examination, the infant became blue and breathless. The baby girl tested positive on a DNA amplification test for *Bordetella pertussis*. (Adapted from *MMWR* 54:71–72. 2005.) Why is this disease so dangerous for small infants? Why did this baby become ill when this disease is preventable with vaccination?

ANSWERS TO QUESTIONS FOR REVIEW

Multiple Choice
1. b; 2. b; 3. a; 4. b; 5. b; 6. c; 7. a; 8. d; 9. a; 10. b

Fill in the Blank
1. streptococcal pharyngitis; 2. diphtheria; 3. syncytia; 4. amphotericin B; 5. Reye's

Modified True/False
1. does not produce; 2. the susceptibility of AIDS patients; 3. drift; 4. exposure to; 5. true

CREDITS

Illustration Credits
1, 8, 11, 12, 14, 15: Kenneth Probst. 16, Disease Box 1 and 7: Kenneth Probst/Precision Graphics.

Photo Credits
Opener: Associated Press, AP. 2: Medical-on-Line/Alamy. 3: CDC. 4: Electron micrograph by Vincent A. Fischetti, Rockefeller University, NY. 5: Institut Pasteur/Phototake. 6: Gladden Willis/Visuals Unlimited. 7: Jim Feeley, CDC. 9a: Everett Burke/Visuals Unlimited. 9b: Biophoto Associates/Photo Researchers. 10: Iowa State University Library, University Archives. 13: NIBSC/Photo Researchers. 17: L. Ajello/Doctor Fungus Corporation/Visuals Unlimited. 18: E. C. Chan/Visuals Unlimited. 19: Ken Greer/Visuals Unlimited. 20: *Microbiology: A Photographic Atlas for the Laboratory*, Benjamin Cummings, 2001. Disease Box 1: CDC. Disease Box 2: John Durham/Photo Researchers. Disease Box 3: *Microbiology: A Photographic Atlas for the Laboratory*, Benjamin Cummings, 2001. Disease Box 4: NIBSC/Science Photo Library. Disease Box 5: Kjell-Olof Hedlund/Smittskyddsinstitutet (SMI). Disease Box 6: Rob and Ann Simpson/Visuals Unlimited. Disease Box 7: Arthur Siegelman/Visuals Unlimited.

Microbial Diseases of the Digestive System

CHAPTER OUTLINE

MicroPrep Pre-Test: Take the pre-test for this chapter on the web. Visit www.microbiologyplace.com.

Mary Mallon is one of the most famous cooks in history—but not for the tastiness of her dishes. An asymptomatic carrier of typhoid, Mary caused outbreaks of typhoid fever in at least seven New York families for whom she worked during the early 1900s. She came to attention in 1906 following an outbreak of typhoid fever in a Long Island household. Investigations revealed Mary's history of working in households whose members fell ill. Public health authorities confirmed the presence of *Salmonella,* the cause of typhoid fever, in her stool and gallbladder. Refusing to have her gallbladder removed and deemed a public health hazard, "Typhoid Mary" was quarantined in 1907 and released in 1910, with the provision that she was never to work as a cook again. Within a few years, however, she was working as a food preparer—and spreading typhoid. Officials kept Mary in quarantine until she died from a stroke in 1938.

Salmonella, the cause of typhoid fever

Typhoid is one example of gastrointestinal disorders caused by microbes. Microbial infections of the digestive system range from tooth cavities or mild episodes of diarrhea to life-threatening illnesses such as dysentery and hepatitis. In this chapter, we examine representative bacterial, viral, protozoan, and helminthic diseases of the digestive system.

Structures of the Digestive System

Learning Objectives

- ✓ Describe the structure and function of the major parts of the gastrointestinal tract.
- ✓ List the accessory digestive organs and describe their functions in digestion.

Anatomists often divide the structures of the digestive system into two groups: those of the *gastrointestinal (GI)* (or *digestive*) *tract*—the tubular path from the mouth to the anus—and those of the *accessory digestive organs,* which either grind food or inject digestive secretions. We begin our survey by examining the GI tract.

The Gastrointestinal Tract

The gastrointestinal tract is a long tube lined with mucous membrane and composed of the mouth, esophagus, stomach, small intestine, large intestine, rectum, and anus **(Figure 1a).** The GI tract processes food into nutrients, absorbs nutrients and water into the blood, and eliminates waste. A membranous covering called the *peritoneum* surrounds and protects most organs of the GI tract.

When we eat, we chew and moisten the food in the *mouth* before swallowing. Muscle contractions, called *peristalsis,* move moistened food down the *esophagus,* which is the muscular tube at the back of the throat, to the *stomach.* The stomach secretes hydrochloric acid and a protein-catabolizing enzyme called *pepsin.* These chemicals further the chemical digestion of food as it is held in the stomach. The stomach gradually moves partially digested food into the small intestine.

The *small intestine* is so named because it is only about 3 cm in diameter, though it is about 6 m long. This portion of the GI tract has three subdivisions—the *duodenum* (doo-od'ĕ-nŭm), the *jejunum* (jĕ-joo'nŭm), and the *ileum* (il'ē-ŭm)—which are responsible for most of the digestion and absorption of nutrients. To this end, the internal surface of the small intestine folds into millions of fingerlike projections called *villi,* each of which is lined with cells having convoluted *microvilli,* giving the small intestine an absorptive surface area estimated to be about 2 million cm^2 (about 2150 ft^2)—the size of an average two-story house!

Intestinal peristalsis moves remaining undigested and unabsorbed material into the *large intestine* or *colon,* which is about 7 cm in diameter and 1.5 m long. Anatomists name the regions of the colon for their location or shape—the

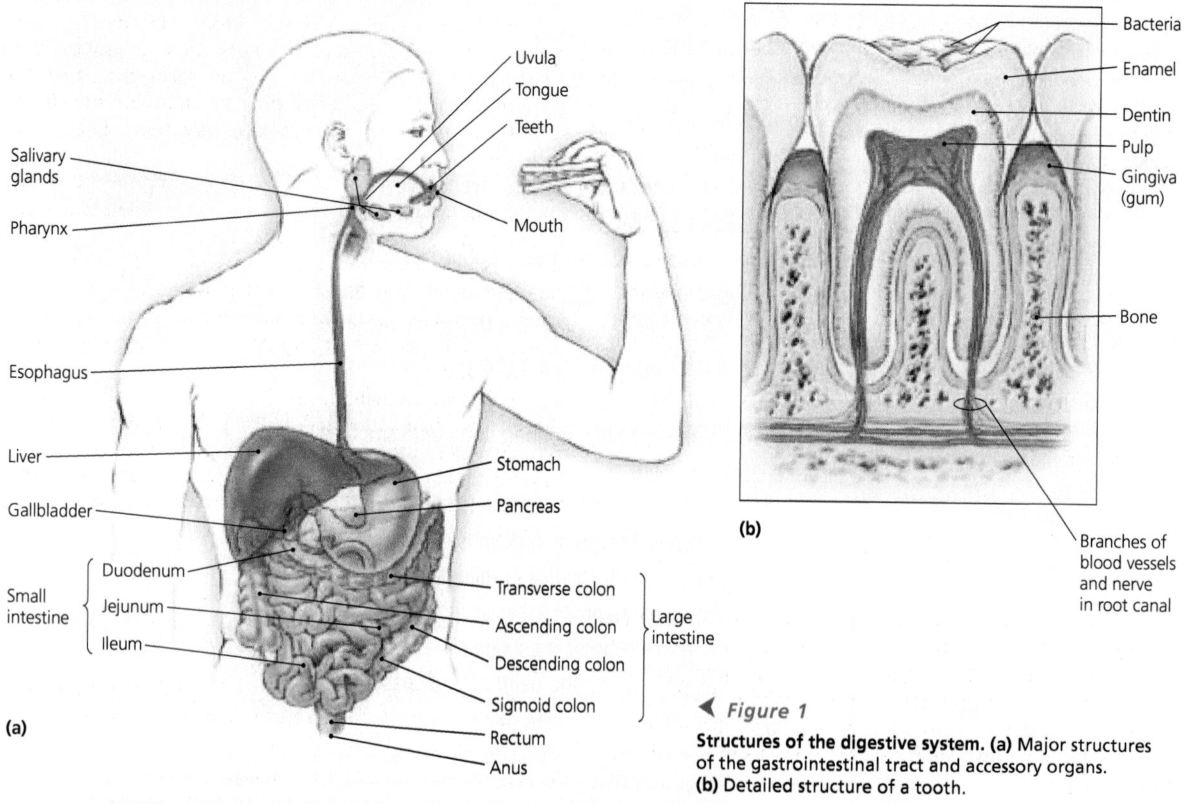

Figure 1

Structures of the digestive system. (a) Major structures of the gastrointestinal tract and accessory organs. **(b)** Detailed structure of a tooth.

ascending colon, the *transverse colon,* the *descending colon,* and the *sigmoid*[1] *colon* (see Figure 1a). The colon completes absorption of nutrients and water.

The remaining undigested materials, called *feces,* are mostly fiber. Feces pass into the *rectum,* which stores them until they are eliminated through the *anus,* a process called *defecation.*

The Accessory Digestive Organs

Accessory digestive organs include the tongue, teeth, liver, gallbladder, and pancreas. The *teeth* and *tongue* are important accessory organs of the mouth that masticate (chew) food into small bits, while the *salivary glands* secrete saliva that lubricates the food for swallowing. Saliva also contains *salivary amylase* that begins the digestion of starch.

Teeth have two functions in mastication. The *incisors* and *canines* at the front of the mouth tear food, and *molars* near the back of the mouth grind it. The surface of a tooth is *enamel*—a hard calcium phosphate mineral **(Figure 1b).** A softer material called *dentin* composes the body of a tooth, which extends as one or more roots into the *gingiva* (jin'ji-vă) (gums) and bone of the jaw. The interior of a tooth contains soft *pulp* with blood vessels and nerves.

The *liver* serves several major functions in the body, including production of *bile* to aid digestion and neutralization or removal of harmful substances from the blood. Bile, a yellow-greenish solution, is concentrated and stored in the *gallbladder.* Bile moves into the duodenum where it emulsifies fat, that is, helps turn large fat globules into millions of smaller ones, making them more accessible to digestive enzymes. The liver breaks down, excretes, or sequesters toxins, including *bilirubin,* a breakdown product of hemoglobin from dead erythrocytes. Liver damage leads to toxin buildup in the blood and jaundice from bilirubin buildup.

The *pancreas* produces *pancreatic juice*—digestive enzymes and bicarbonate buffer—which is released into the duodenum of the small intestine. The buffer neutralizes stomach acid as it enters the intestine and the enzymes are responsible for food digestion.

Normal Microbiota of the Digestive System

Learning Objective

✓ Describe the types and locations of normal microbiota in the mouth and intestines.

The esophagus, stomach, and duodenum are almost free of microbes. Peristalsis helps prevent the accumulation of food particles and microorganisms in the esophagus, and stomach acid (about pH 2.0) is antimicrobial. Further, the relatively rapid transport of food through the stomach and duodenum prevents most microbes from colonizing these regions.

However, microorganisms colonize the tongue, teeth, jejunum, ileum, colon, and rectum. The mouth and pharynx provide numerous microscopic pits and crevices as well as food for bacteria, fungi, and a few protozoa that colonize all oral surfaces. Each milliliter of saliva contains millions of bacteria, and scientists have discovered more than 700 species in oral biofilms. Most prevalent of the oral microbes are species of *Streptococcus* known as **viridans**[2] **streptococci.** Viridans streptococci are alpha-hemolytic, Gram-positive, and lack so-called Lancefield carbohydrates; thus, they do not fall into any of the Lancefield classifications. Each strain of viridans streptococci has an adhesion factor allowing it to attach to specific chemicals on the gingiva, lining of the cheeks, tongue, pharynx, intestine, or teeth. *S. mutans* is the species that grows specifically on teeth.

The lower small intestine and colon are home to an estimated 100 trillion (10^{14}) bacteria, and over 10^{11} bacteria are in every gram of feces, accounting for approximately 40% of total fecal mass. Most of the bacteria are species of Gram-negative anaerobes of the genus *Bacteroides* (bak-ter-oy'dēz), followed in predominance by Gram-positive *Lactobacillus* (lak'tō-bă-sil'ŭs) and facultative enterobacteria such as *Escherichia* (esh-ĕ-rik'ē-ă), *Enterobacter* (en'ter-ō-bak'ter), *Proteus* (prō'tē-ŭs), and *Klebsiella* (kleb-sē-el'ă). Fungi such as the yeast *Candida* (kan'did-ă) and protozoa such as *Entamoeba* (ent-ă-mē'bă) also live in the colon. Normal intestinal microbiota feed on the partially digested and indigestible contents of the colon. The mucous membrane lining the GI tract prevents most microbes from entering the blood, though some microbes can affect the body negatively without invading by changing the chemical nature of ingested chemicals, increasing toxicity, or producing carcinogens.

Generally, intestinal microbiota serve to protect the body by outcompeting pathogens—a situation called **microbial antagonism.** The metabolism of intestinal microorganisms also produces vitamins, including vitamin B_{12}, folic acid, biotin, and vitamin K, in addition to a daily 500 ml of *flatus*—intestinal gas composed of nitrogen gas, carbon dioxide, hydrogen gas, and quite odorous dimethyl sulfide and methane.

Oral antimicrobials, taken for any disorder, can inhibit intestinal microbiota, thus undermining their defensive properties. Their loss during long-term antimicrobial therapy can allow colonization by pathogenic microbes. **The Beneficial Microbe: Microbes to the Rescue** examines potential benefits of changing the makeup of the microbiota.

CRITICAL THINKING

How could infection of the accessory digestive organs affect health?

Not all microbes in the GI tract are helpful or benign members of the protective microbiota, numerous bacteria, fungi,

[1]Named for the Greek letter sigma, which is S-shaped.

[2]From Latin *viridis,* meaning green, for the pigment produced when grown on blood media.

The Beneficial Microbe *Microbes to the Rescue?*

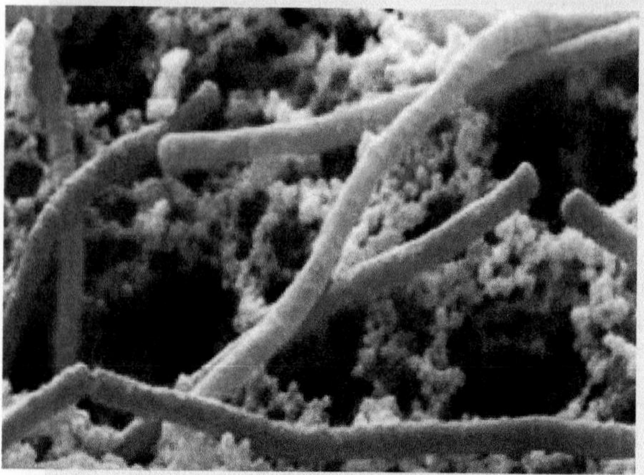

Lactobacillus, a potential probiotic

The digestive tract is home to viruses, bacteria, protozoa, fungi, and parasitic helminths. The normal microbiota helps protect the body by competing with pathogens for nutrients and space. Recent scientific studies indicate that microbes could be added to people's diets to improve and maintain health. Many researchers, nutritionists, and health care professionals are excited about the possibilities.

Some research indicates that consumption of living microbes in food or dietary supplements may be beneficial, presumably by changing the normal microbiota of the digestive tract. Such microbes may help ward off bowel problems such as irritable bowel syndrome, reduce incidence of yeast infection, alleviate symptoms of gastroenteritis, and shorten the duration of colds by 36 hours. Probiotics, as such microbes are called, are often bacteria used to ferment food, particularly species of *Lactobacillus* or the related genus *Bifidobacterium*. Despite favorable anecdotal evidence and partial support in laboratory studies for the benefits of probiotics, most scientists remain skeptical that consumers can successfully change the makeup of their intestinal microbiota or that probiotics are really helpful.

Other research suggests that the makeup of the microbiota mediates whether a person is obese or lean. Obese people have a greater percentage of Gram-positive bacteria in their colons, whereas lean people have a larger proportion of Gram-negative bacteria called bacteroids. Gram-positive bacteria break down indigestible polysaccharides, releasing sugars that can be absorbed and add to weight gain. In lean people with bacteroids, the polysaccharides remain undigested and pass from the body. When scientists changed the gut microbiota of mice, obese mice became thin even though they ate the same amount and kind of food and exercised the same amount.

Could probiotics of the future change the makeup of the microbiota of the digestive tract and alleviate disease and reduce obesity? Researchers continue working to answer these questions.

viruses, and protozoa cause diseases of the digestive system. The following sections examine some of the more common diseases, beginning with diseases caused by bacteria.

Bacterial Diseases of the Digestive System

In the United States and other developed nations, bacterial diseases of the digestive system are generally viewed as an annoyance, but in many areas of the world, these diseases are fatal. We begin by examining bacterial diseases of the mouth.

Dental Caries, Gingivitis, and Periodontal Disease

Learning Objectives

- ✓ Explain the process of dental caries formation.
- ✓ Describe the progression to gingivitis and more severe periodontal disease.
- ✓ Describe the treatment and prevention of cavities and periodontal disease.

Dental **caries**[3] (kār′ēz, *tooth decay* or *cavities*) are second only to common colds in frequency. They occur in people of all age groups, though they usually form during childhood. **Gingivitis**—inflammation of the gums—is a form of **periodontal disease,** which is inflammation and infection of the tissues surrounding and supporting the teeth.

Signs and Symptoms

Caries generally appear as holes or pits in the teeth, particularly in the later stages of disease, and can result in tooth loss. Initially, cavities are painless, but as they continue to develop, toothaches occur, often coinciding with the consumption of sweet, hot, or cold foods or drinks. Fractured teeth or an inability to bite down on a tooth without pain is also a sign of caries.

General symptoms of periodontal disease include swollen and/or bleeding gums, gums that are tender to the touch and appear shiny, or gums that appear bright red or red-purple in color. In the case of advanced periodontal disease, loose teeth and a foul breath odor occur. An extreme and rare type of periodontal diseases is *acute necrotizing ulcerative gingivitis (ANUG),* which was called *trench mouth* during World War I. Patients with ANUG show the manifestations of other periodontal diseases with the addition of craterlike ulcers between

[3]Latin, meaning decay.

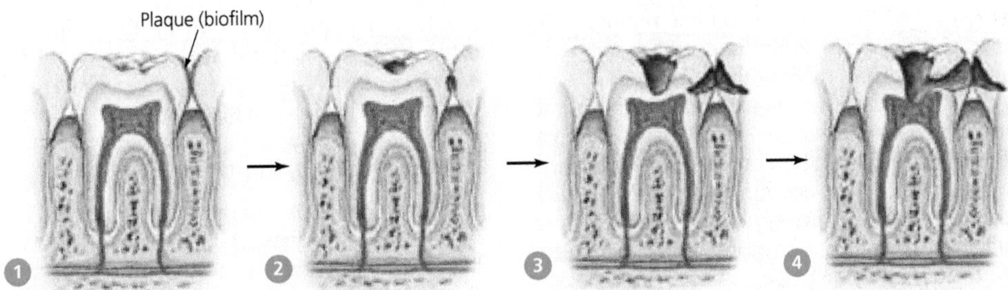

▲ *Figure 2*

The process of tooth decay. *Streptococcus mutans* produces dextran from sucrose, allowing plaque formation in pits and crevices on enamel ①. *Lactobacillus* and other bacteria ferment sugars to acids, which dissolve enamel ②. Decay continues into the dentin ③ and pulp ④.

the teeth, profuse gum bleeding, a foul taste in the mouth, and a grayish biofilm that appears on the gums.

Pathogens, Virulence Factors, and Pathogenesis

Dental caries begins when bacteria, particularly *Streptococcus mutans* (strep-tō-kŏk'ŭs mū'tans; a viridans streptococcus), produce an insoluble, sticky, polysaccharide slime called *dextran* from sucrose (table sugar). Dextran and adhesion factors, such as pili, allow bacteria to form a biofilm known as *dental plaque* on tooth enamel. Dental plaque may be more than 500 bacterial cells thick and contain nearly 10 billion bacteria.

S. mutans and other bacteria in plaque, such as *Lactobacillus*, ferment sugars to acid (about pH 5), which dissolves tooth enamel and allows bacterial invasion of the dentin and pulp inside the tooth **(Figure 2).** The bacteria and their secretions can destroy dentin, pulp, and eventually the nerves and blood vessels of a tooth, possibly leading to loss of the tooth.

Hard deposits called *tartar* or *dental calculus* form when calcium salts mineralize plaque. Tartar trapped at the base of the teeth triggers the initial form of periodontal disease—gingivitis. Swelling of the gums, plaque, and tartar can also form oxygen-free pockets that become colonized by anaerobic bacteria, such as *Porphyromonas gingivalis* (pōr-fir-ō-mōn'ăs jin'ji-val-is), compounding the infection and producing a condition called *periodontitis*. *P. gingivalis* produces five proteases that break down gingival tissue. Further destruction occurs as bacteria invade the bone, causing *osteomyelitis* (abscesses in the bones), and teeth become loose and fall out.

Scientists do not know the exact cause of trench mouth, but they suspect an overabundance of anaerobes and spirochetes, including nonculturable species of *Treponema* (trep-ō-nē'mă).

Epidemiology

About 6% of personal health care expenditures in the United States are for dental services. Of Americans over age 65, 99.5% have experienced dental caries, with 78% of children having at least one cavity by age 17. Diets high in sucrose increase the risk of tooth decay by increasing bacterial dextran and acid production. Continual snacking stimulates continual microbial activity, decreasing the pH further. Foods high in natural acid content, such as citrus fruit, can contribute to the problem.

Plaque buildup, injury or trauma to the gums, misaligned teeth, rough edges to fillings, ill-fitting dental appliances (such as dentures), and cavities contribute to gingivitis. Additional contributory factors to gingivitis include pregnancy, uncontrolled diabetes, general poor health and diet, poor dental hygiene, use of birth control pills, and lead poisoning. Gingivitis occurs frequently in many people and to varying degrees over the course of one's lifetime, though it usually first appears during puberty and early adulthood. If not treated, it leads to recurrent gingivitis or periodontal disease, which occurs in about 70% of the U.S. population, with up to 20% experiencing bone loss.

Diagnosis, Treatment, and Prevention

Dentists diagnose dental caries by visual inspection or physical examination during routine checkups. Probing with sharp dental instruments and X rays can reveal soft spots prior to the formation of observable pits. Dentists diagnose gingivitis by observation of excessive plaque and tartar near the gum line, swollen red to purple gums that are sensitive to touch, receding gums with enlarged pockets around the bases of the teeth, or loose teeth. Dental X rays reveal loss of bone structure that occurs in advanced periodontal disease.

Dentists can treat cavities that are diagnosed early with minimal expense and pain. They fill small cavities by removing softened tissue and filling the resulting hole with silver alloy, gold, porcelain, or composite resin. When cavities have destroyed a significant portion of a tooth, dentists remove soft material and overlay the tooth with a *crown* (cap) of gold, porcelain, or porcelain overlaid on metal. Decay resulting in death of the nerves feeding the tooth necessitates a *root canal,* in which a dentist removes the decayed material, pulp, nerves, and blood vessels from the core of the tooth and replaces them with a sealant.

Dental hygienists and dentists initially treat gingivitis and other periodontal diseases with *scaling*—the physical removal of plaque and tartar from the teeth in order to reduce inflammation. Scaling may result in bleeding, discomfort, or pain, which can be treated with over-the-counter pain relievers. They also repair dental irritants, such as loose-fitting dentures and misaligned teeth, so they no longer rub against the gums. Scaling must be followed by strict and effective daily oral hygiene in conjunction with regular professional cleanings, or the problems will return. Dentists may prescribe antibacterial mouth rinses. In the case of advanced periodontal disease, surgery may be required to expose and clean deep pockets in the gums and remove severely damaged teeth.

Prevention of dental caries, gingivitis, and periodontal disease relies on healthy eating habits and good oral hygiene practices. Avoiding foods containing sucrose, as well as sticky foods, reduces plaque formation and acidification. People should floss daily and brush their teeth at least twice a day with fluoride-containing toothpastes; ideally they should brush after every meal. Brushing and flossing disrupt the biofilm (plaque) on teeth, between teeth, and from the gums. Rinsing the mouth with water after a meal or snack can reduce plaque buildup when brushing is not possible. Additionally, teeth should be cleaned regularly in a dental office as part of routine care.

Fluoridation of water is the single most effective way to prevent dental diseases. Fluoride is incorporated into the developing enamel of new teeth, strengthening them against the effects of acid and protecting them from the inside. The cost to fix a single cavity is greater than the cost of providing fluoridation to an individual for a lifetime. Today, most municipal water systems in the U.S. add fluoride to drinking water.

CRITICAL THINKING

Why is the elimination of sucrose sugar from the diet not enough to prevent the formation of all dental caries?

Peptic Ulcers

Learning Objectives

- ✓ Describe the effect of *Helicobacter pylori* on the lining of the human stomach.
- ✓ Describe the virulence factors of *H. pylori* that allow it to colonize the stomach and to survive phagocytosis.
- ✓ Describe the manifestations, treatment, and prevention of ulcers.

Peptic[4] **ulcers** are erosions of the linings of either the stomach (*gastric ulcer*) or duodenum of the small intestine (*duodenal ulcer*). Ulcers that pierce the stomach or intestine are referred to as *perforations.* At one time, physicians considered peptic ulcers to be the result of drinking too much alcohol, smoking, eating the wrong foods, stress, or worry. We now know that most ulcers are actually due to the invasive activity of a bacterium.

Signs and Symptoms

Abdominal pain is the major symptom of ulcers; shock, in which the cardiovascular system fails to deliver enough blood to vital organs, is usually the major sign of a perforation. Some patients have nausea, vomiting (with or without blood), weight loss, chest pain, or bloody stools. Left untreated, ulcers can lead to a variety of complications including internal bleeding and bowel obstruction—both of which constitute medical emergencies requiring immediate medical intervention.

Pathogen and Virulence Factors

Helicobacter pylori (hel'ī-kō-bak'ter pī'lō-rē)—a Gram-negative, slightly helical, highly motile bacterium—causes most peptic ulcers (see Disease at a Glance 1). *H. pylori* possesses numerous virulence factors that enable it to colonize the human stomach: a protein that inhibits acid production by stomach cells; flagella that enable the bacterium to burrow through the mucus lining the stomach; adhesins that facilitate binding to gastric cells; enzymes that inhibit phagocytic killing; and urease. Urease degrades urea, present in gastric juice, to produce highly alkaline ammonia, which neutralizes stomach acid.

Pathogenesis

Figure 3 illustrates the formation of a peptic ulcer. *H. pylori* (protected by urease) burrows through the stomach's protective mucus layer to reach the underlying epithelial cells ❶, where the bacterium attaches to the cells' cytoplasmic membranes and multiplies. A variety of factors—the triggering of inflammation by bacterial toxins and perhaps the destruction of mucus-producing cells—causes the mucus layer to become thin ❷, allowing acidic gastric juice to digest the stomach lining. Once gastric juice has ulcerated the epithelial layer, *H. pylori* gains access to the underlying muscle tissue and blood vessels ❸. Bacteria that are phagocytized by leukocytes survive through the actions of catalase and superoxide dismutase, enzymes that neutralize part of the phagocytes' killing mechanism.

Epidemiology

H. pylori colonizes people with peptic ulcers, but not all who have *H. pylori* get ulcers. Colonization of the stomach suggests a fecal-oral path of infection and studies have shown that *H. pylori* in human or cat feces on the hands, in well water, or on fomites infects humans.

Risk factors include use of aspirin, ibuprofen, or other nonsteroidal anti-inflammatory medications, excessive alcohol consumption, smoking cigarettes or using other tobacco products, and a family history of ulcers. Emotional stress does

[4]From Greek *pepto,* meaning to digest, referring to the stomach enzyme pepsin.

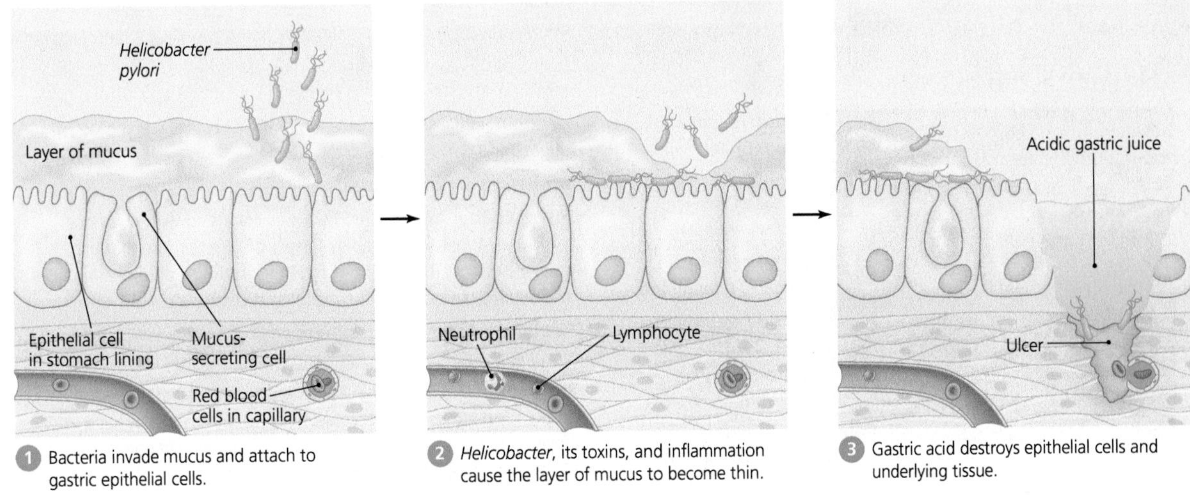
Helicobacter pylori
Layer of mucus
Epithelial cell in stomach lining
Mucus-secreting cell
Red blood cells in capillary
Neutrophil
Lymphocyte
Acidic gastric juice
Ulcer
1 Bacteria invade mucus and attach to gastric epithelial cells.
2 Helicobacter, its toxins, and inflammation cause the layer of mucus to become thin.
3 Gastric acid destroys epithelial cells and underlying tissue.

▲ *Figure 3*
The Role of *Helicobacter pylori* in the formation of ulcers.

not cause ulcers but can exacerbate symptoms and make treatment more difficult.

Diagnosis, Treatment, and Prevention

An upper GI series of X rays following ingestion of barium reveals the presence of ulcers. Laboratory technicians find *H. pylori* in Gram-stained smears of clinical specimens, and a positive urease test indicates the presence of *H. pylori* in specimens from the stomach within one to two hours of culturing.

Treatment with one or more antimicrobial drugs in combination with drugs that inhibit acid production generally resolves most ulcers in six to eight weeks. Recurrence can be curtailed by continuation of acid-blocking medications after antibacterial therapy has been completed. Surgery may be required in cases of excessive ulceration, perforation, or failure of medicinal interventions. Preventing infection involves preventing fecal-oral transmission of bacteria and lifestyle changes to eliminate other risk factors.

Disease at a Glance 1 summarizes the major features of ulcers.

CRITICAL THINKING

How can eating spicy foods further antagonize tissue damaged by *Helicobacter pylori*?

Bacterial Gastroenteritis

Learning Objectives

- ✓ Compare and contrast the virulence factors of five bacteria that cause gastroenteritis.
- ✓ Describe common prevention methods for avoiding gastroenteritis.

Bacterial gastroenteritis is an inflammation of the stomach or intestines caused by the presence of bacteria. Gastroenteritis occurs worldwide (the general incidence of bacterial gastroenteritis is roughly one in every 1000 people) but is most often associated with poorly prepared foods, contaminated washing or drinking water, and communities with poor living conditions. Institutional settings are prone to outbreaks in developed countries. Travel to areas with poor sanitation can lead to infection and export of disease.

General Features

Manifestations of gastroenteritis are usually similar regardless of the causative agent: some cases are asymptomatic or involve only mild diarrhea, but most patients have nausea, vomiting, diarrhea, loss of appetite, abdominal pain, and cramps. Some patients experience malaise and fever. In rare cases, the infection spreads beyond causing the initial gastrointestinal disease, resulting in kidney failure or anemia. In a severe and painful type of gastroenteritis known as **dysentery,** stools are loose, frequent, and contain mucus and blood.

Physicians diagnose most cases of bacterial gastroenteritis based on signs and symptoms, though victims with mild manifestations rarely seek medical treatment. Lab technicians can identify the causative bacterium from stool cultures (usually several are needed to ensure capture of the agent), fecal smears, or analysis of suspect food.

Treatment of gastrointestinal diseases involves replacement of fluids and electrolytes lost to diarrhea and vomiting. In most cases, fluid replacement can be self-administered by drinking water and over-the-counter electrolyte solutions (sports drinks). Some patients need medication to suppress nausea so that fluids can be taken; in rare cases, intravenous fluid is required. Antidiarrheal drugs may prolong symptoms

DISEASE AT A GLANCE 1

Peptic Ulcers

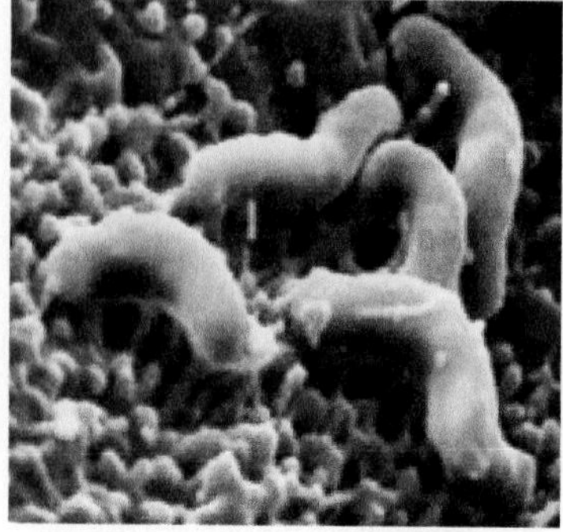

Helicobacter pylori, the cause of peptic ulcers

Cause: *Helicobacter pylori* (Gram-negative, slightly helical motile bacterium).

Portal of entry: Probably through the mouth as a result of fecal contamination.

Signs and symptoms: Abdominal pain several hours after eating or skipping a meal, pain that is relieved with antacids or milk, heartburn, indigestion, nausea, vomiting of blood, weight loss, fatigue, and dark or bloody stools.

Incubation period: Variable.

Susceptibility: Anyone who becomes colonized with *H. pylori*, particularly those with a family history of ulcers, those that use tobacco, aspirin, ibuprofen, or other nonsteroidal anti-inflammatory medications, and those who consume excessive alcohol.

Treatment: Antimicrobial drugs given in conjunction with acid-blocking drugs.

Prevention: Good personal hygiene, adequate sanitation and proper food handling to decrease fecal-oral transmission, and lifestyle changes to reduce risk, including dietary changes to reduce stomach acid imbalances and lowering consumption of alcohol, tobacco, and aspirin-like pain medication.

by allowing the organisms to remain in the intestines. Major symptoms of gastroenteritis generally disappear within hours or days, and recovery from dehydration may take up to a week.

Prevention involves proper handling, storage, and preparation of food. Food should be thoroughly cleaned before consumption or use in cooking. All cooked foods, particularly ground meats, should be thoroughly cooked at a temperature high enough to kill bacteria. Utensils used for food preparation should always be cleaned between foods. Milk and juices should be pasteurized. Good sanitation and good personal hygiene are also essential. Thorough handwashing is probably the best prevention for transmission of these fecal-borne illnesses.

CRITICAL THINKING

A pharmacist in a small town of 4300 observes hundreds of people buying antidiarrheal medicines in one week. Obviously, there is an epidemic of gastroenteritis! What utilities and city services will epidemiologists examine? Explain your reasoning.

A number of pathogens cause particular types of gastroenteritis. The following sections examine five of the more common of these diseases.

Cholera

Epidemiologists have identified seven pandemics of **cholera** since 1817. A current epidemic, centering on India, may spread worldwide to become an eighth pandemic.

Pathogen and Virulence Factors *Vibrio cholerae* (vib'rē-ō kol'er-ī)—a slightly curved, Gram-negative bacillus with polar flagella (see Disease at a Glance 2)—causes cholera. The genus *Vibrio* is composed of species that occur naturally in estuarine and marine environments worldwide, preferring warm, salty, and alkaline water. *V. cholerae* is the only species that can survive in both salt- and freshwater. In saltwater it survives by forming biofilms, which are not infective, but in freshwater the biofilms fall apart and single *Vibrio* cells become motile and infective.

A strain known as O1 El Tor is responsible for the pandemics, but a new strain, *V. cholerae* O139 Bengal, which arose in India in 1992, is spreading across Asia. This strain is the first non-O1 strain capable of causing epidemic disease. Other strains of *V. cholerae* do not produce epidemic cholera, only mild gastroenteritis.

Recent research indicates that the environment within the human body activates some *Vibrio* genes, making a bacterium in the body more virulent than its counterpart in water. Scientists hypothesize that such gene activation may explain the rapid, almost explosive, nature of cholera epidemics. The most important virulence factor of *V. cholerae* is a potent poison called *cholera toxin*, which is coded by a plasmid.

Pathogenesis and Epidemiology Figure 4 illustrates the action of cholera toxin in producing the severe diarrhea that characterizes cholera. Cholera toxin is an A-B toxin composed of one A subunit and five B subunits. One of the B subunits binds to a glycolipid receptor in the cytoplasmic membrane of an intestinal epithelial cell, resulting in cleavage of the A subunit (1). Part of A, an enzyme called A1, enters the cell's cytosol (2) and activates an enzyme—adenylate cyclase (3). This enzyme in turn converts ATP into cyclic AMP (cAMP) (4), which stimulates the active secretion of electrolytes (sodium, chlorine, potassium, and bicarbonate ions) from the cell into the intestinal lumen (5). Water follows the movement of these ions from the cell via osmosis (6). Severe fluid and electrolyte losses result in dehydration, metabolic acidosis (decreased pH of

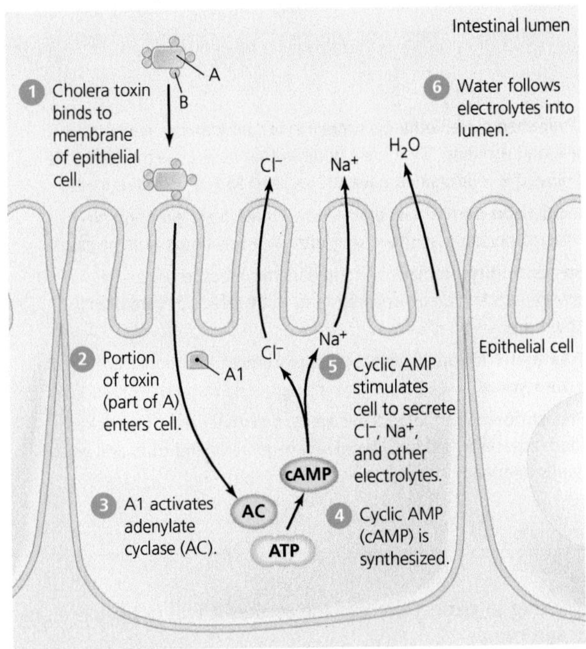

▲ *Figure 4*

The action of cholera toxin in intestinal epithelial cells.

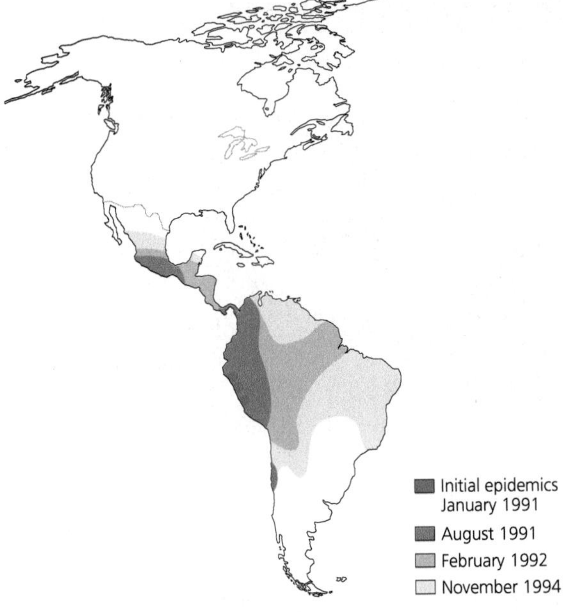

▲ *Figure 5*

Cholera pandemic. Cholera caused by *Vibrio cholerae* O1 El Tor, which started in Indonesia, spread throughout Latin America in the first half of the 1990s. *Why is the cholera pandemic unlikely to establish itself in the United States?*

Figure 5 The United States employs sewage treatment to prevent contamination of drinking water.

body fluids) due to loss of bicarbonate ions, hypokalemia,[5] and hypovolemic shock caused by reduced blood volume in the body. These conditions can produce muscle cramping, heartbeat irregularities, kidney failure, coma, and death.

Epidemiologists documented the spread of the seventh pandemic around the world, beginning in Indonesia in 1961. It reached South America, which had not seen cholera for a century, in 1991. **Figure 5** illustrates the progression of cholera throughout Latin America in the first half of the 1990s. Over a million people reported symptoms, and researchers documented over 6300 deaths, in Latin America alone.

Diagnosis, Treatment, and Prevention Physicians in endemic areas diagnose cholera based on its manifestations, particularly so-called "rice-water stool," which is watery, colorless, odorless, and flecked with mucus, which looks like bits of rice. In addition to supportive care, physicians may prescribe a tetracycline for cholera; the drug reduces the production of cholera toxin.

Researchers have developed a vaccine, available in the United States, against the O1 El Tor strain of *V. cholerae,* but its protective value is unfortunately short lived; there is no vaccine for the O139 strain. Antimicrobial prophylaxis for those who travel to endemic areas has not proven effective.

Fortunately, because the infective dose for *V. cholerae* is high, proper hygiene generally makes immunization and prophylaxis unnecessary.

Disease at a Glance 2 summarizes the major features of cholera.

Shigellosis

Another bacterial gastroenteritis is **shigellosis,** which is characterized primarily by fever, abdominal cramps, diarrhea, and sometimes by a bloody stool.

Pathogens and Virulence Factors *Shigella* (shē-gel'ă) is a Gram-negative, nonmotile bacillus. Four different species of *Shigella* cause shigellosis: *S. dysenteriae* (dis-en-te'rē-ī), *S. flexneri* (fleks'ner-ē), *S. boydii* (boy'dē-ē), and *S. sonnei* (sōn'ne-ē). *S. sonnei* is the most common species isolated in industrialized nations, whereas *S. flexneri* is the predominant species in developing countries. Shigellosis is much more common outside of the United States than in this country.

All four *Shigella* species produce *type III secretion systems* and diarrhea-producing *enterotoxins.* Type III secretion systems are complex structures composed of 20 different poly-

[5]From Greek *hypo,* meaning under; Latin *kalium,* meaning potassium; and Greek *haima,* meaning blood.

DISEASE AT A GLANCE 2

Cholera

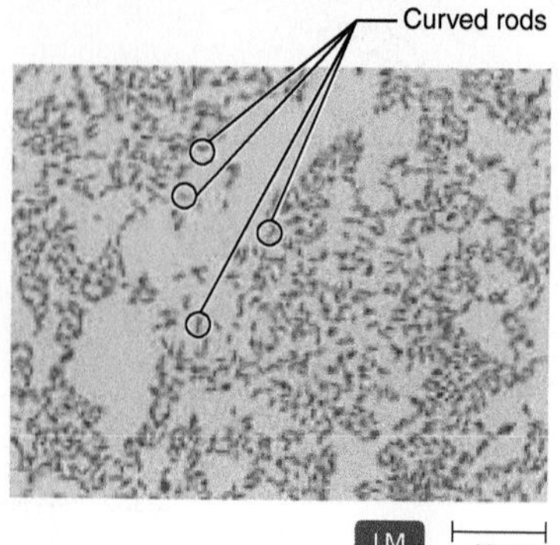

Vibrio cholerae, the causative agent of cholera

Cause: *Vibrio cholerae* (comma-shaped Gram-negative bacillus).

Portal of entry: Ingestion of contaminated water or raw/undercooked seafood.

Signs and symptoms: Sudden onset of "rice-water" diarrhea, dehydration (dry skin, excessive thirst, rapid yet diminished pulse, lethargy, sunken eyes), abdominal cramps, nausea, and vomiting. Death can occur within hours; the mortality rate is 25–50% in untreated patients, reduced to 1% with treatment.

Incubation period: Generally two to three days, although an infected person may show symptoms in a few hours in some cases.

Susceptibility: Humans living in endemic areas, especially in poverty-stricken areas; children tend to be affected more than adults are.

Treatment: Fluid and electrolyte replacement and administration of a tetracycline.

Prevention: When in endemic areas, boil water, eat only cooked food (especially seafood), avoid raw vegetables and fruit, and wash hands frequently.

peptides that span both membranes of the bacterial cell. They insert into a host cell's cytoplasmic membrane, forming a channel through which bacterial proteins are introduced into the host cell. Enterotoxins are so named because they bind to surface proteins on epithelial cells lining the intestines, triggering the loss of electrolytes and water in a manner similar to cholera toxin. *S. dysenteriae* secretes **Shiga toxin,** which is an endotoxin that stops protein synthesis in a host's cells, resulting in a more severe form of shigellosis with a mortality rate as high as 20%.

Pathogenesis and Epidemiology Initially, *Shigella* colonizes cells of the small intestine, causing diarrhea; the main events in shigellosis, however, begin once the bacterium invades cells of the large intestine and end about seven days later. **Figure 6** illustrates the pathogenesis of *Shigella:* The pathogen attaches to epithelial cells in the large intestine (1), stimulating endocytosis of the bacterium (2), which then multiplies within the cell's cytosol (3). *Shigella* polymerizes the host's actin fibers, propelling itself out of the host cell and into adjacent cells (4), in the process evading the host's immune system. As the bacterium kills host cells, abscesses form in the mucosa (5); any bacteria that enter the blood from a ruptured abscess are quickly phagocytized and destroyed, making bacteremia a rare condition in shigellosis (6).

Diagnosis, Treatment, and Prevention Physicians diagnose shigellosis based on symptoms and the presence of *Shigella* in the stool. Treatment involves supportive care and the use of antimicrobial drugs such as ciprofloxacin, azithromycin, or rifaximin. Antimicrobials may shorten the duration of disease and reduce the spread of *Shigella* to close contacts of the patient.

A recently developed, live, attenuated vaccine against *S. flexneri* has been successful in preventing the dysentery caused by this species, although the participants in the study still experienced mild diarrhea and fever. Researchers are working to perfect the vaccine so that it will not cause signs or symptoms.

Traveler's Diarrhea

Escherichia coli (esh-ĕ-rik'ē-ă kō-lē) is the most common and important of the bacteria causing diarrhea in travelers—thus its common name, **traveler's diarrhea.**

Pathogen and Virulence Factors *E. coli* is one of a group of colon-dwelling bacteria called *coliforms* (kŏ'li-formz). These bacteria are aerobic or facultatively anaerobic, Gram-negative bacilli that ferment lactose to form gas within 48 hours of being placed in a lactose broth at 35°C. Besides living in the intestinal tracts of animals and humans, coliforms can survive in soil and on plants and decaying vegetation, but their presence in water is indicative of poor sewage treatment.

Scientists have identified numerous so-called O, H, and K antigens used to describe different strains of *E. coli.* Some antigens, such as O157, O111, H8, and H7, are associated with virulence. Virulent strains have genes (located on transmissible plasmids) for fimbriae, adhesins, and a variety of toxins that enable these strains to colonize human tissue and cause disease.

One of the more dangerous of the toxins is the *Shiga-like toxin* of *E. coli* O157:H7; this toxin inhibits protein synthesis, kills cells, and can cause kidney failure, resulting in death. *E. coli* O157:H7 also produces a type III secretion system. One set of secreted proteins disrupts the host cell's metabolism; another set becomes lodged in the cell's cytoplasmic membrane and forms receptors for the attachment of additional *E. coli* O157:H7 bacteria. Such attachment apparently enables this strain of *E. coli* to displace normal harmless strains.

Pathogenesis and Epidemiology Generally, *E. coli* diarrhea appears 24–72 hours after consumption of the bacterium.

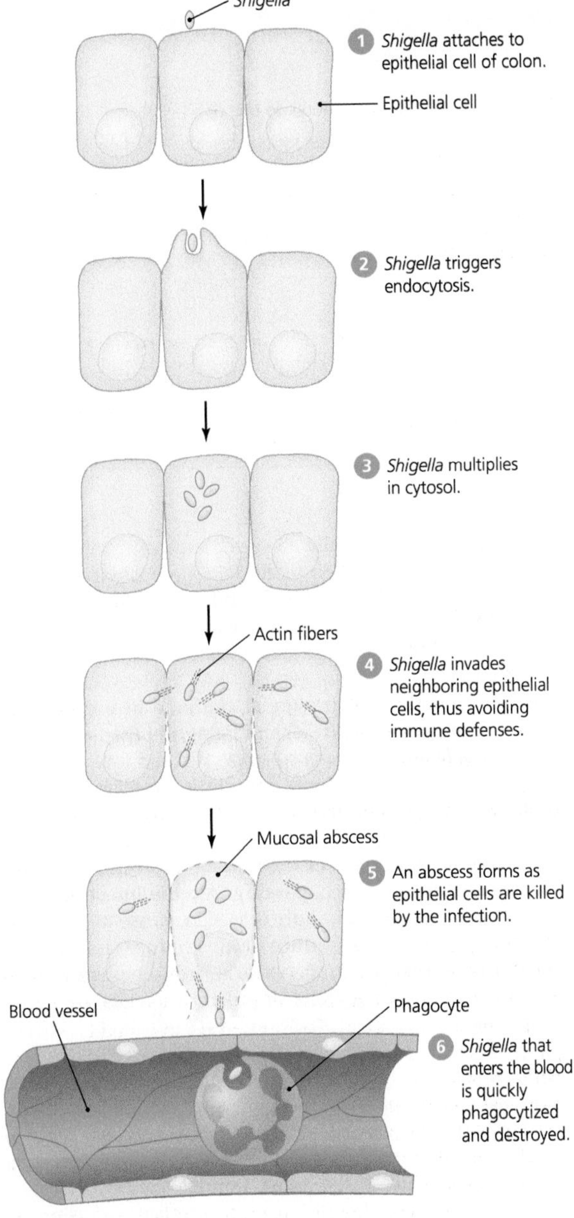
Shigella
1 Shigella attaches to epithelial cell of colon.
Epithelial cell
2 Shigella triggers endocytosis.
3 Shigella multiplies in cytosol.
Actin fibers
4 Shigella invades neighboring epithelial cells, thus avoiding immune defenses.
Mucosal abscess
5 An abscess forms as epithelial cells are killed by the infection.
Blood vessel
Phagocyte
6 Shigella that enters the blood is quickly phagocytized and destroyed.

▲ *Figure 6*

The events in shigellosis.

Diarrhea is mediated by enterotoxins delivered via a type III secretion system. Strains that produce enterotoxins are common in developing countries and are important causes of pediatric diarrhea.

Shiga-like endotoxin attaches to the surfaces of neutrophils and is spread by them throughout the body, causing widespread death of host cells and tissues. Antimicrobial drugs induce *E. coli* O157:H7 to increase its production of Shiga-like toxin, exacerbating disease. Investigators have found *E. coli* O157:H7 in almost 50% of beef carcasses in the U.S. Despite its prevalence, only about 1 in 10 million deaths in the United States is attributed to consuming *E. coli* O157:H7 in ground beef.

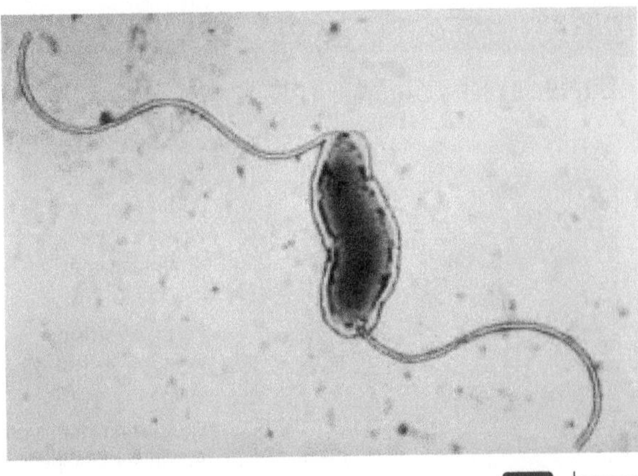
TEM
0.3 µm

▲ *Figure 7*

***Campylobacter jejuni*, the most common cause of bacterial gastroenteritis in the United States.**

Diagnosis, Treatment, and Prevention Physicians diagnose traveler's diarrhea based on signs and symptoms in patients returning from trips, though many cases are so mild, patients do not seek medical care. Treatment involves replacing lost fluid and electrolytes. Antidiarrheal drugs prolong the symptoms by delaying expulsion of the bacterium from the digestive tract. Patients should avoid dairy products until diarrhea is over (generally after two to three days); dairy foods can aggravate the symptoms because of temporary lactose intolerance in cases of *E. coli* gastroenteritis. No vaccine against *Escherichia* is available.

Campylobacter *Diarrhea*

Campylobacter is responsible for more cases of diarrhea that send people to doctors in the United States than any other bacterium.

Pathogen and Virulence Factors *Campylobacter jejuni*[6] (kam' pi-lō-bak'ter jē-jū'nē), the causative agent of *Campylobacter* diarrhea, is a Gram-negative, slightly curved bacterium with polar flagella **(Figure 7)**. Scientists do not fully understand the virulence of *C. jejuni*, but the bacterium possesses

[6]From Greek *kampylos*, meaning curved, and *jejunum*, the middle portion of the small intestine.

DISEASE AT A GLANCE 3

Bacterial Diarrhea

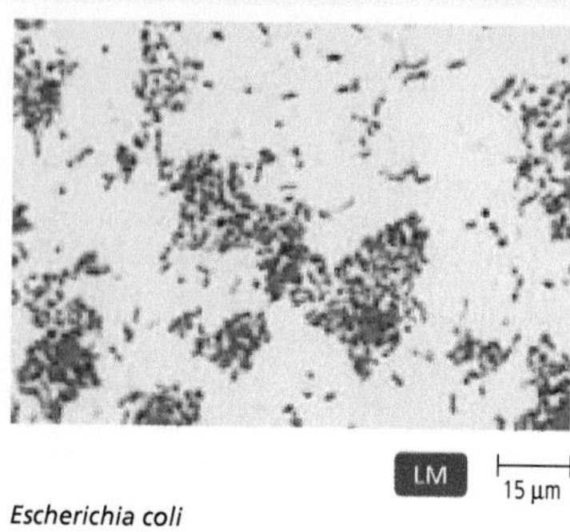

Escherichia coli

Causes: Primarily *Escherichia coli*, *Shigella* spp., and *Campylobacter jejuni* (Gram-negative bacilli).

Portal of entry: Ingestion via fecal-oral route.

Signs and symptoms: Abdominal cramps, bloody stools, nausea, vomiting, and diarrhea.

Incubation period: A few hours to one day.

Susceptibility: All humans are susceptible, but infection is generally worse in children and immunocompromised individuals.

Treatment: Rehydration via fluid and electrolyte replacement.

Prevention: Eat only thoroughly cooked meat products and pasteurized milk and juices, serve food piping hot, and practice good hygiene.

adhesins, cytotoxins, and endotoxin (lipid A). The bacterium survives inside cells after being endocytized. Interestingly, nonmotile mutants of *C. jejuni* are avirulent.

Pathogenesis and Epidemiology One study found *campylobacter* in 81% of supermarket chickens. The virulence factors of *Campylobacter* enable colonization and invasion of the jejunum, ileum, and colon, producing bleeding lesions and triggering inflammation. The U.S. Centers for Disease Control and Prevention (CDC) estimates that more than 1 million people have *Campylobacter* diarrhea each year. Of these, about 100 die.

Diagnosis, Treatment, and Prevention Signs and symptoms combined with demonstration of the bacterium in the stool suffice for diagnosis. Most cases resolve without treatment, though severe cases require supportive therapy and the use of antimicrobial drugs such as ciprofloxacin or azithromycin. A vaccine does not exist for this type of bacterial gastroenteritis.

Washing kitchen surfaces contaminated by raw chicken or turkey, thoroughly cooking food, and similar commonsense culinary hygiene reduces *Campylobacter* infections. Communities should prevent contamination of drinking water with feces from stockyards, feedlots, and slaughterhouses.

Disease at a Glance 3 summarizes the features of diarrhea caused by *Escherichia, Shigella,* and *Campylobacter.*

Salmonellosis and Typhoid Fever

Species of Salmonella cause two disease conditions: **typhoid fever** and a form of gastroenteritis called **salmonellosis.**

Pathogen and Virulence Factors *Salmonella* (sal'mŏ-nel'ă) is a genus of motile, Gram-negative, peritrichous bacilli that live in the intestines of virtually all vertebrates, especially reptiles, and are eliminated in their feces. *Salmonella* is not part of the normal microbiota of humans. Scientists have identified more than 2000 unique serotypes (strains) of *Salmonella,* though analysis of DNA sequences has revealed that all belong to a single species—*S. enterica* (en-ter'i-kă). However, many researchers and medical personnel continue to use historical names. Serotypes Typhi (tī'fē) and Paratyphi (par'a-tī'fē) (formerly *S. typhi* and *S. paratyphi*) cause typhoid fever, a disease unique to humans. Serotypes Enteritidis (en-ter-it'id-iss) and Typhimurium (tī'fē-mur-ē-ŭm) cause most U.S. cases of human salmonellosis.

Virulent serotypes of *Salmonella* tolerate the acidic condition of the stomach, passing into the intestine where they attach via specific adhesins. They use type III secretion systems to introduce toxins into a host's cells. These toxins disrupt mitochondria, inhibit phagocytosis, rearrange the cytoskeletons of eukaryotic cells, or induce apoptosis.

Pathogenesis and Epidemiology Humans acquire typhoid fever via consumption of food or water contaminated with the feces from a carrier of *S. enterica* serotypes Typhi or Paratyphi. The carrier may remain asymptomatic; the chapter opener discusses the most famous carrier, "Typhoid Mary" Mallon. People often acquire serotypes causing salmonellosis by eating or cooking with contaminated eggs. About one-third of chicken eggs carry *Salmonella,* even those laid by asymptomatic chickens. The bacterium in feces covers some eggs when they are laid; additionally, eggs may harbor *Salmonella* internally, having been produced by chickens with infected ovaries. Salmonellae released during the cracking of an egg on a kitchen counter and then inoculated into other foods can reproduce into millions of cells in just a few hours.

An infective dose of serotype Typhi is about 1000–10,000 cells. *Salmonella* passes through the intestinal cells into the bloodstream where it is phagocytized. These defensive cells do not digest the pathogen but carry it to the liver, spleen, bone marrow, and gallbladder. Patients typically experience gradually increasing fever, headache, muscle pains, malaise, and loss of appetite that may persist for a week or more. Bacteria may be released from the gallbladder to reinfect the intestines, producing gastroenteritis and abdominal pain, followed by a recurrence of bacteremia. In some patients, the bacterium ulcerates and perforates the intestinal wall, allowing bacteria from the intestinal tract to enter the abdominal cavity, which causes *peritonitis* (inflammation of the peritoneum). Typhoid fever may last four weeks, and 12–30% of patients die without treatment.

Figure 8 depicts the events of typhoid fever and salmonellosis. After *Salmonella* passes through the stomach, it attaches to cells lining the small intestine 1 and inserts toxins to induce endocytosis 2. The pathogen reproduces within phagocytic vesicles 3 eventually killing the host cells 4 and inducing signs and symptoms of salmonellosis—fever, abdominal cramps, and diarrhea. Cells of some strains, most notably serotype Typhi, can subsequently enter the blood 5. Phagocytic cells then carry *Salmonella* through the blood to the liver, spleen, bone marrow, and gallbladder where, having resisted phagocytic killing, they can establish semipermanent infection, particularly in the gallbladder. Carriers can remain infected for years even with treatment.

Typhoid fever is most common among impoverished people, particularly in the Southern Hemisphere. It is rare in industrialized countries.

Diagnosis, Treatment, and Prevention Diagnosis is made by finding *Salmonella* in the stools of patients. Typhoid fever patients typically have a sustained fever as high as 40°C (104°F) accompanied by weakness, abdominal pain, headache, and loss of appetite.

Salmonellosis is generally self-limiting within a week. Health care providers can replace lost fluids and electrolytes and treat typhoid fever with antimicrobial drugs, such as ampicillin or ciprofloxacin.

Prevention centers on good hygiene, especially in the kitchen. The CDC recommends "Boil it, cook, it, peel it, or forget it"; that is, boil drinking water (though this will not protect from many other types of gastroenteritis) and avoid uncooked foods except fruits or vegetables that can be peeled. Gloves should be worn whenever handling pet reptiles and when cleaning their cages to avoid infection.

Disease at a Glance 4 summarizes the features of typhoid fever and salmonellosis. **Table 1** compares and contrasts the more common forms of bacterial gastroenteritis.

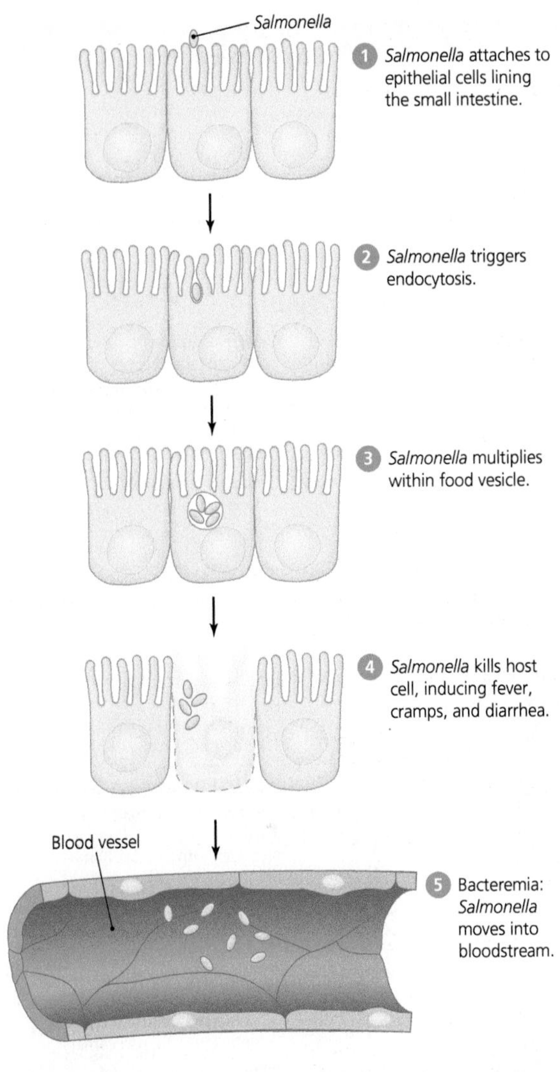
Salmonella
1 *Salmonella* attaches to epithelial cells lining the small intestine.
2 *Salmonella* triggers endocytosis.
3 *Salmonella* multiplies within food vesicle.
4 *Salmonella* kills host cell, inducing fever, cramps, and diarrhea.
Blood vessel
5 Bacteremia: *Salmonella* moves into bloodstream.

▲ *Figure 8*

The events in salmonellosis. *How is the multiplication of* Shigella *within host cells different from multiplication of* Salmonella *in host cells?*

Figure 8 *Shigella multiplies in the cytosol of colon cells, Salmonella in phagocytic vesicles of small intestine cells.*

CRITICAL THINKING

Rank the forms of gastroenteritis discussed in Table 1 in terms of severity, with the least severe first and the most severe last (consider this with regard to the most normal course of infection).

Table 1 Forms of Bacterial Gastroenteritis

Disease	Pathogen (Minimum Infectious Dose)	Source of Infection	Incubation Period	Distinguishing Manifestations	U.S. Annual Incidence	Complications
Cholera	*Vibrio cholerae* (>10^8 cells)	Fecally contaminated food or water	48–72 hours	Rice-water stool (watery, colorless, odorless stools flecked with mucus) lasting 2–3 days; patients may lose up to 1 L of fluid per hour	0–8	Death can occur within 48 hours of symptom onset if untreated (25–50% mortality rate)
Shigellosis	*Shigella dysenteriae*, *S. flexneri*, *S. boydii*, *S. sonnei* (200 cells)	Self-inoculation from fecally contaminated hands, secondarily through consumption of fecally contaminated foods; direct person-to-person spread	1–7 days	Purulent (containing mucus and pus) bloody stools, crampy rectal pain, fever, vomiting, and nausea lasting 2–3 days	>18,000	Severe dehydration; febrile seizures, confusion, and other neurological complications may appear in children
Traveler's diarrhea	*Escherichia coli* (unknown)	Fecally contaminated food or water	24–72 hours	Nausea, vomiting, and diarrheal symptoms lasting 1–3 days	Unknown as diagnosis is difficult, estimated >80,000	Dehydration
***E. coli* O157:H7 infection**	*E. coli* strain O157:H7 (10 cells)	Fecally contaminated milk, fruit juice, or ground beef	24–72 hours	Bloody diarrhea, fatal hemorrhagic colitis, hemolytic uremic syndrome—destruction of erythrocytes and kidney failure	2000–3000	Death
***Campylobacter* diarrhea**	*Campylobacter jejuni* (500 cells)	Zoonotic from domestic poultry, dogs, cats, rabbits, pigs, cattle, and minks through consumption of food, milk, or water contaminated with animal feces; close contact with infected humans	2–5 days	10 or more bowel movements per day lasting 2–5 days; blood may be present in diarrhea	35,000–40,000 confirmed cases but more than 1 million estimated	Sepsis, arthritis, Guillain-Barré syndrome (temporary nerve paralysis)
Salmonellosis	*Salmonella enterica* serotypes Enteritidis and Typhimurium (>10^6 cells)	Zoonotic from domestic poultry through consumption of fecally contaminated meat or eggs, or consumption of inadequately pasteurized contaminated milk; close contact with infected reptiles; contact with human carriers	8–48 hours	Nonbloody diarrhea, nausea, vomiting, fever, headache, and pain lasting 1–2 weeks; rash of tiny rose spots may appear on the skin	45,000	Dehydration
Typhoid fever	*Salmonella enterica* serotypes Typhi and Paratyphi (>10^6 cells)	Primarily contaminated eggs	8–48 hours	High fever (40°C), headache, muscle and stomach pain, malaise, loss of appetite, rose-colored spots	300–400	Intestinal perforation, hemorrhaging, kidney failure, peritonitis, and death

Bacterial Food Poisoning (Intoxication)

Learning Objectives

- ✓ Distinguish between intoxication and gastroenteritis.
- ✓ Describe the virulence factors of *Staphylococcus* that allow it to cause food poisoning.
- ✓ Describe methods to prevent food poisoning.

Food poisoning is a rather broad term used collectively to refer to consuming either pathogens or their toxins. Infections of the gastrointestinal tract are more appropriately referred to as gastroenteritis. In this section, we focus on **bacterial intoxications** (*toxifications*), which are food poisonings caused by toxins—the microbe itself is either not present or not the immediate problem.

Botulism is a form of intoxication that affects the nervous system. Here we examine other forms of bacterial intoxication, using staphylococcal food poisoning as a model.

DISEASE AT A GLANCE 4

Typhoid Fever and Salmonellosis

1. *Salmonella* is ingested in contaminated water or food, particularly chicken eggs.
2. Bacterium passes through the stomach, attaches to cells lining the small intestine, and induces endocytosis.
3. The pathogen eventually kills host cells.
4. This triggers fever, abdominal cramps, and diarrhea.
5. Cells of serotype Typhi can subsequently enter the blood, where they are phagocytized but not digested.
6. Phagocytes carry *Salmonella* serotype Typhi to the liver, spleen, bone marrow, and gallbladder.
7. *Salmonella* serotype Typhi can establish semipermanent infection in the gallbladder. Carriers can remain infected for years even with treatment.
8. *Salmonella* is shed in feces.

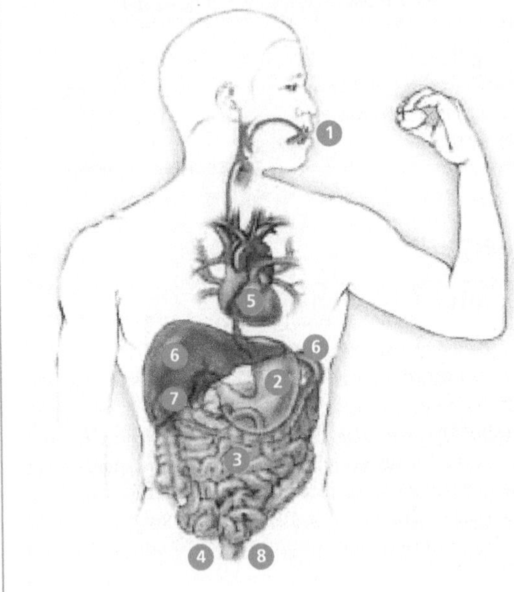

Cause: Serotypes Typhi or Paratyphi of *Salmonella enterica* (Gram-negative, peritrichous bacillus) cause typhoid fever; serotypes Enteritidis and Typhimurium commonly cause salmonellosis.

Portal of entry: Mouth and mucous membranes of the intestine by fecal-oral transmission; this involves ingestion of food or water contaminated with sewage from a carrier or food directly handled by an asymptomatic carrier.

Signs and symptoms: Gradually increasing fever, headache, muscle pains, malaise, and loss of appetite that may persist for a week or more; "rose spot" rash may appear on lower chest and abdomen. Gastrointestinal symptoms common to other forms of bacterial gastroenteritis may occur. With typhoid fever, life-threatening complications are possible, including intestinal hemorrhage, perforation, kidney failure, or peritonitis (inflammation of the peritoneum).

Incubation period: 8 to 48 hours.

Susceptibility: Travel to countries lacking adequate sanitation; contact with asymptomatic carriers.

Treatment: Fluid and electrolyte replacement are indicated for salmonellosis; antimicrobials are used against typhoid fever. Carriers may require removal of the gallbladder to end carrier status.

Prevention: Proper and adequate sanitation and food handling, immunization for travelers to endemic areas, and preventing carriers from working as food handlers.

Signs and Symptoms

General symptoms of bacterial intoxication include nausea, vomiting, diarrhea, abdominal cramping, discomfort, bloating, loss of appetite, and fever. Symptoms may range from mild to severe. Some types of intoxications also produce weakness, headache, and difficulty in breathing. Symptoms differ to some extent depending on the toxins present and can be confused with bacterial or viral gastroenteritis. Dehydration resulting from fluid loss in diarrhea may become significant, but most cases exemplified by staphylococcal food poisoning are self-limiting and last no more than 24 hours.

Pathogens and Virulence Factors

Toxins of *Staphylococcus aureus,* which is a normal member of the microbiota of the skin and upper respiratory system, cause staphylococcal food poisoning. Food preparers frequently introduce *Staphylococcus* from their bodies into foods during cooking. The bacterium grows particularly well in foods at room temperature, where it produces toxins. Foods commonly associated with staphylococcal food poisoning include processed meats, custard pastries, potato salad, and ice cream.

S. aureus has several virulence factors, but important ones in cases of food poisoning are five enterotoxins. These proteins (designated A through E) stimulate intestinal muscle contractions, trigger nausea, and cause intense vomiting. The enterotoxins are heat stable, remaining functional at 100°C for up to 30 minutes, which means they are not inactivated by warming or reheating food.

Pathogenesis and Epidemiology

Bacterial intoxication can affect a single individual or hundreds of people at once. Outbreaks are usually associated with picnics, school cafeterias, or large social functions where food stands unrefrigerated or where food preparation

DISEASE AT A GLANCE 5

Staphylococcal Intoxication (Food Poisoning)

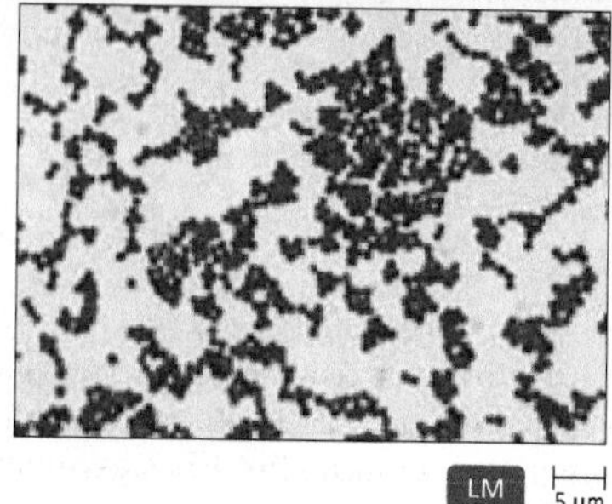

Staphylococcus aureus

Cause: *Staphylococcus aureus* (facultatively anaerobic, Gram-positive cells arranged in clusters).

Portal of entry: Toxin crosses mucous membranes of the intestinal tract following consumption of contaminated food; *Staphylococcus* is not directly involved in the disease.

Signs and symptoms: Nausea, vomiting, diarrhea, cramping, discomfort, bloating, loss of appetite, and fever; all lasting 24 hours or less.

Incubation period: Four to six hours.

Susceptibility: Everyone is susceptible because the organism is a normal member of the microbiota, but intoxication results only when inoculated food is not properly refrigerated or cooked prior to consumption.

Treatment: Self-administered replacement of fluids and electrolytes.

Prevention: Thorough handwashing before and after handling foods, cleaning of utensils between use on different foods, and prompt refrigeration of leftovers all decrease risk of staphylococcal food poisoning.

is less than optimal. It takes several hours at room temperature or higher for *Staphylococcus* to grow and secrete toxins. Food harboring *Staphylococcus* does not appear or taste unusual.

Because most cases of staphylococcal food poisoning are self-limiting and relatively mild, the number of cases is unknown—by the time a patient would see a doctor, the symptoms are gone.

Diagnosis, Treatment, and Prevention

Diagnosis is generally based on signs, symptoms, and patient history. Tests may be done on samples from vomit, blood, stool, or any leftover food deemed suspicious. Stool cultures positive for *S. aureus* are indicative of staphylococcal food poisoning, but other examinations are often inconclusive. Replacement of fluids and electrolytes is the only treatment and can be self-administered. Good hygiene and proper food handling reduce incidence.

Disease at a Glance 5 summarizes features of staphylococcal intoxication.

We have examined bacterial diseases and intoxication of the digestive system. The next section considers viral diseases of this system.

Viral Diseases of the Digestive System

Several viruses cause diseases of the digestive system almost indistinguishable from those caused by bacteria. Among these are various types of gastroenteritis. Viruses also cause far more severe digestive system diseases, including hepatitis.

We begin by considering *oral herpes*—a disease of the oral cavity and thus of the beginning of the digestive system.

Oral Herpes

Learning Objectives

- ✓ Describe the appearance of oral herpes infection.
- ✓ Describe methods of prevention and options for treatment for oral herpes.

The family *Herpesviridae* contains a large group of linear dsDNA viruses with enveloped polyhedral capsids. Many of these herpesviruses infect humans, and their high infection rates make them among the more prevalent DNA viral pathogens. Oral herpes is among the most common of their infections.

Signs and Symptoms

Painful, itchy, creeping skin lesions on the lips, called **fever blisters** or **cold sores,** characterize **oral herpes**[7] **(Figure 9).** Fever blisters appear one to two weeks after exposure to an infected individual. Initial infections may be accompanied by flulike symptoms such as malaise, fever, and muscle pain. The fluid-filled lesions eventually break, crust over, and fall off (within 7–10 days) to reveal pink healing skin. Subsequent lesions are generally less severe.

Severe infections in which the lesions extend into the oral cavity, called *herpetic gingivostomatitis,* are most often seen in young patients and in patients with lowered immune function due to disease, chemotherapy, or radiation treatment. Young adults with sore throats resulting from other viral infections may develop *herpetic pharyngitis,* in which the pharynx becomes infected and inflamed. Immunosuppressed individuals may develop *herpes esophagitis,* characterized by extremely painful and difficult swallowing, fever, and sometimes chills.

[7]From Greek *herpo,* meaning to creep.

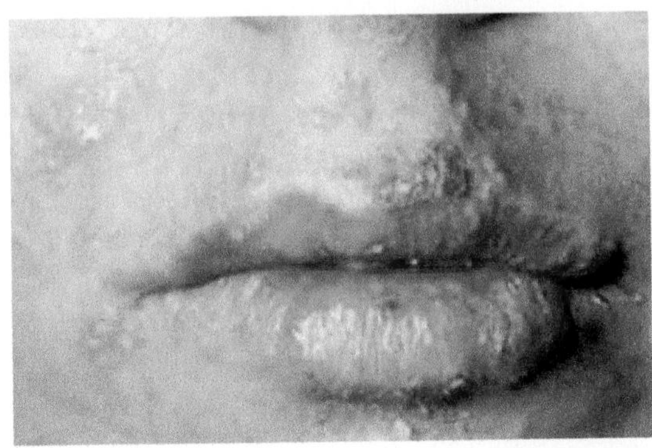

▲ *Figure 9*
Oral herpes lesions.

Pathogen and Pathogenesis

Herpes simplex virus type 1 (HSV-1; sometimes called human herpesvirus 1) causes most cases of oral herpes; HSV-2, which usually infests the genitalia, can also infect the oral cavity. After entering the body through cracks or cuts in mucous membranes, herpesviruses reproduce in epithelial cells near the site of infection, triggering inflammation and cell death and resulting in painful, localized lesions on the skin. By causing infected cells to fuse with uninfected neighboring cells to form a structure called a *syncytium,* herpes virions spread from cell to cell, avoiding the host's immune system.

As illustrated in **Figure 10,** HSV-1 eventually establishes latent infections in the trigeminal nerve ganglion[8] by entering sensory nerve cells and being carried by cytoplasmic flow to the ganglion. Latent viruses may reactivate later in life when the immune system is suppressed by emotional stress, fever, trauma, sunlight, menstruation, or disease. Reactivated viruses travel down the nerve to produce recurrent lesions as often as every two weeks. Recurrent lesions are rarely as severe as the initial lesions because of immunological memory.

Epidemiology

HSV-1 accounts for 90% of all cold sores; HSV-2, the normal cause of genital herpes, causes the other 10% of cold sores. HSV-1 is transmitted by close contact with infected individuals who have active lesions. Primary HSV-1 infections typically occur via casual contact during childhood, and usually produce no signs or symptoms; in fact, HSV-1 has asymptomatically infected about 80% of children by age two.

Diagnosis, Treatment, and Prevention

Diagnosis of oral herpes is generally by observation of the characteristic recurring lesions. Microscopic examination of infected tissue reveals syncytia. Positive diagnosis is achieved by immunoassay that demonstrates the presence of viral antigen. Topical creams containing acyclovir limit the duration of the lesions and reduce viral shedding, but are not a cure and do not eliminate latency in the trigeminal ganglia.

Washing with soap and water may minimize spread of the virus, but prevention depends on avoiding direct contact with infected individuals. Patients with active lesions are more likely to spread the disease, but asymptomatic carriers still shed viruses. Contaminated fomites, such as razor blades, toothbrushes, towels, and dishes, also spread herpesviruses. Oral sex should be avoided to prevent transfer of HSV-1 to the genitalia. Patients should not touch their own lesions lest they spread viruses into their eyes or onto

[8]A ganglion is a collection of nerve cell bodies containing their nuclei.

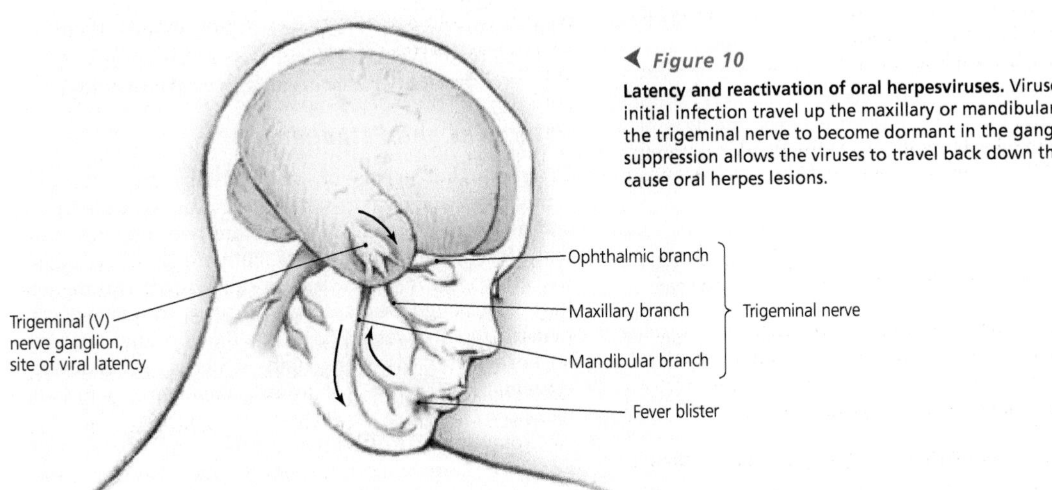

◀ *Figure 10*
Latency and reactivation of oral herpesviruses. Viruses from the initial infection travel up the maxillary or mandibular branches of the trigeminal nerve to become dormant in the ganglion. Immune suppression allows the viruses to travel back down the nerve to cause oral herpes lesions.

DISEASE AT A GLANCE 6

Mumps

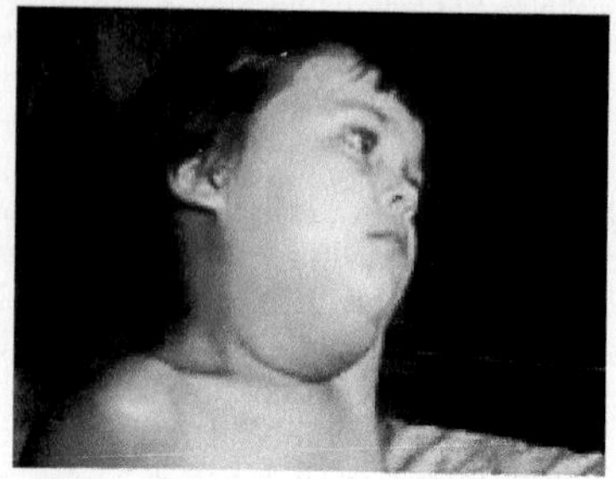
Mumps

Cause: Mumps virus (enveloped, helical, unsegmented, −ssRNA virus of genus *Rubulavirus*).

Portal of entry: Mucous membranes of the upper respiratory tract.

Signs and symptoms: Parotitis (swelling of the parotid salivary glands), face pain, fever, headache, and sore throat are the most common symptoms. Some infections may be asymptomatic.

Incubation period: Twelve to twenty-four days.

Susceptibility: Unimmunized individuals are at risk.

Treatment: Comfort care only, including hot or cold packs, soft foods, fluids, and warm-water gargles.

Prevention: MMR vaccine.

other areas of the skin. Further, broken lesions may provide a portal, leading to secondary bacterial infections.

CRITICAL THINKING

Based on your understanding of the human GI tract, explain why a disease such as herpes esophagitis would be limited to individuals who are immunocompromised or immunosuppressed.

Mumps

Learning Objective

✓ Describe the cause, manifestations, and prevention of mumps.

Mumps, in which viruses infect the largest salivary glands located on each side of the face (see Disease at a Glance 6), was once among the more common of childhood diseases. Today, mumps is nearly nonexistent in developed nations due to effective childhood immunization. Epidemics of mumps in the late winter and early spring still occur in countries that lack immunization programs (or allow them to lapse).

Humans are the only natural host for the mumps virus, which is a −ssRNA virus in the genus *Rubulavirus.* Mumps virus infects unimmunized children between the ages of 2 and 12 who are exposed to an infected person or to fomites carrying contaminated saliva. The virus enters via the respiratory tract, multiplies, invades the blood, and can infect many organs in addition to the salivary glands. Some patients suffer inflammation of the testes, meninges, or pancreas, and rarely mumps virus causes deafness in one ear.

There is no specific treatment for mumps. A recovered patient has effective, lifelong immunity. **Disease at a Glance 6** summarizes the features of mumps.

CRITICAL THINKING

Why and when should parents have their children immunized against mumps?

Viral Gastroenteritis

Learning Objectives

✓ List the three viral causes of gastroenteritis.

✓ Describe the diagnosis, treatment, and prevention of viral gastroenteritis.

Bacteria are not the only microbes that infect the digestive tract to produce gastroenteritis—many viruses can too. Viral gastroenteritis, however, is generally less severe than bacterial forms of the disease.

Signs and Symptoms

The general manifestations of **viral gastroenteritis** are the same as for bacterial gastroenteritis—abdominal pain and cramping, diarrhea, nausea, and vomiting. Additional signs and symptoms may include fever, chills, clammy skin, weight loss, or lack of appetite. Dehydration is the most common complication. Symptoms generally appear within 24 hours of consuming contaminated food and resolve within 12 to 60 hours. Vomiting, bloody stool, life-threatening diarrhea, and dysentery rarely occur with viral gastroenteritis.

Pathogens and Pathogenesis

Common viral agents of gastroenteritis are caliciviruses, astroviruses, and rotaviruses. Caliciviruses (kal'i-sē-vī'rŭs-ez) and astroviruses (as'trō-vī-rŭs-ez) are two +ssRNA viruses that cause acute gastroenteritis. Both are small, naked, star-shaped, and have polyhedral capsids **(Figure 11a)** that enter the body through the digestive tract by consumption of contaminated food or water. The most studied of the caliciviruses are **noroviruses,** discovered in the stools of victims during an epidemic of diarrhea in Norwalk, Ohio, from which their name comes.

Rotaviruses (rō'ta-vī-rŭs-ez), members of the dsRNA *Reoviridae,* are almost spherical and have prominent glycoprotein spikes **(Figure 11b)** that act as attachment

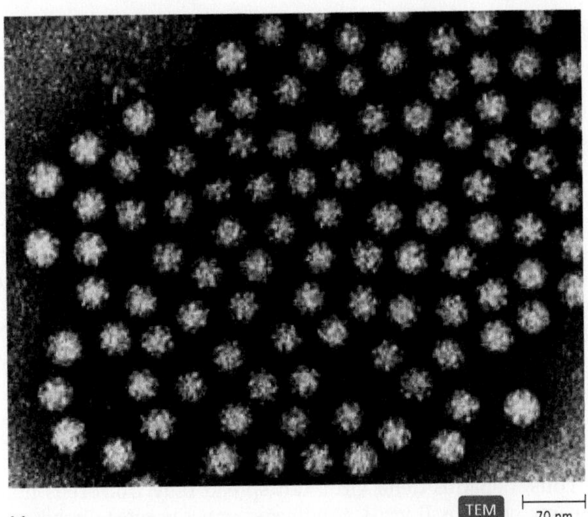

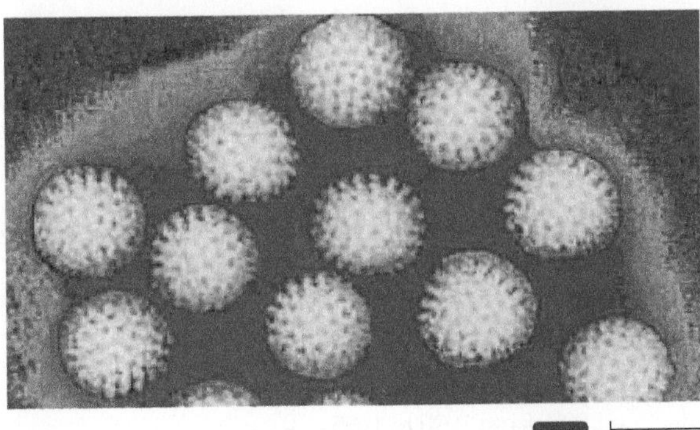

▲ *Figure 11*

Some viruses causing gastroenteritis. (a) Caliciviruses, such as noroviruses, and astroviruses have naked "star-shaped" capsids. **(b)** The wheel-like appearance of rotaviruses, from which they get their name.

molecules and trigger endocytosis. Rotaviruses are naked, though during replication they acquire and then lose envelopes. Their transmission is via the fecal-oral route from contaminated food or water. Infected children may pass as many as 100 trillion virions per gram of stool.

All three of these viruses—caliciviruses, astroviruses, and rotaviruses—infect cells lining the intestinal tract where they undergo lytic replication. As epithelial cells die, the normal function of the intestinal tract is lost. Infections are generally self-limiting—after the virus has destroyed the epithelial layer, replacement epithelial cells grow and function is restored.

Epidemiology

Cases of viral gastroenteritis are more frequent in winter, being facilitated by close living conditions. Noroviruses cause 90% of nonbacterial gastrointestinal infections (about 10% of all cases of gastroenteritis) worldwide and have caused outbreaks of gastroenteritis in day care centers, schools, hospitals, nursing homes, and restaurants. Epidemics of noroviral gastroenteritis have increased in recent years on cruise ships. Generally, these viruses infect adults and school-age children.

Rotaviruses cause infantile gastroenteritis and account for approximately 50% of all cases of diarrhea in children requiring hospitalization because of fluid and electrolyte loss (up to 70,000 hospitalizations and 60 deaths per year in the United States). In developing countries, rotaviruses annually kill 600,000 children—about 5% of all childhood deaths **(Figure 12).**

Diagnosis, Treatment, and Prevention

Serological tests performed on stool samples can distinguish between surface antigens of caliciviruses, astroviruses, and rotaviruses. There is no specific treatment for any of these infections except support and replacement of lost fluid and electrolytes. Antidiarrheal medications may only prolong symptoms, because diarrhea tends to clear the viruses from the system.

Prevention involves adequate sewage treatment, purification of water supplies, frequent handwashing, good personal hygiene, and disinfection of contaminated surfaces and fomites.

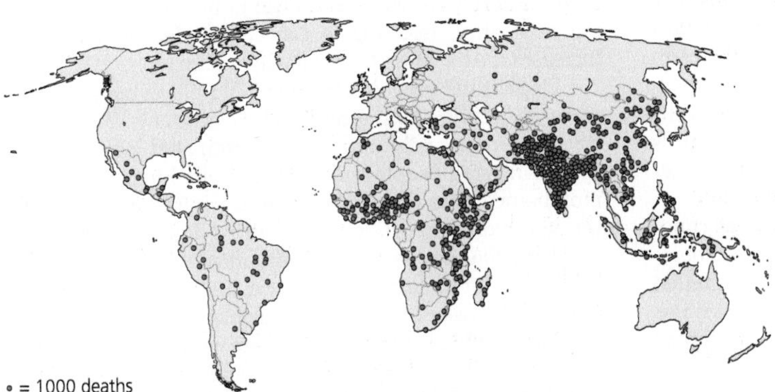

◀ *Figure 12*

Deaths from rotaviral diarrhea are most common in developing countries. (Data from 2005.)

Attenuated oral vaccines against rotaviruses exist and safely protect against up to 98% of severe rotaviral diarrhea requiring hospitalization. Some pediatricians recommend three doses of vaccine at two, four, and six months.

CRITICAL THINKING

What social and environmental conditions contribute to the much higher rate of rotavirus infections outside of the United States?

Viral Hepatitis

Learning Objectives

- ✓ Describe the three primary forms of viral hepatitis, the agents that cause them, and ways to prevent infection by each.
- ✓ List the common risk factors for hepatitis.

Hepatitis (hep-ă-tī′tis) is inflammation of the liver produced by autoimmune disease, alcohol or drug abuse, genetic disorders, or microbial infection. Three viruses are responsible for most virally caused forms of the disease.

Signs and Symptoms

The liver has many functions, including synthesis of blood clotting factors, storing glucose and other nutrients, assisting in the digestion of lipids, and removing wastes from the blood. When a viral infection damages the liver, all of these functions are disturbed, though signs and symptoms may not occur until years after initial infection. Manifestations may include yellowing of the skin and eyes called *jaundice* (jawn′dis) (see Disease at a Glance 7), abdominal pain and distention, dark urine, light- or clay-colored stools, loss of appetite, nausea, vomiting, fatigue, fever, and weight loss. Patients may become stuporous and eventually go into a coma because of the accumulation of wastes in the blood. Complications from chronic (long-term) infection are serious and life threatening, including permanent liver damage (cirrhosis), liver failure, or liver cancer.

Pathogens and Pathogenesis

Five viruses cause hepatitis; they are *Hepatovirus Hepatitis A virus* (HAV), *Orthohepadnavirus Hepatitis B virus* (HBV), *Hepacivirus Hepatitis C virus* (HCV), *Deltavirus Hepatitis delta virus* (HDV, also called delta agent), and *Hepevirus Hepatitis E virus* (HEV). The specific epithet is the same as the common name for each of these viruses.

Host cellular immune responses that kill infected cells cause most of the liver damage. Hepatitis A and hepatitis E viruses are usually cleared in the process, but the other viruses typically remain, resulting in chronic infection.

Hepatitis A virus can survive on surfaces such as countertops and cutting boards for days, resists common household disinfectants such as chlorine bleach, and is transmitted in fecally contaminated food or water. Patients release virions in their feces and are infective even without developing symptoms. Hepatitis A, also called *infectious hepatitis,* is typically a mild condition with 99% of patients recovering fully.

HBV replicates in liver cells and is released by exocytosis, rather than cell lysis, so infected cells serve as a source for the continual release of virions, resulting in billions of virions per milliliter of blood, which gives the disease its common name—*serum hepatitis.* Virions in the blood are shed into saliva, semen, and vaginal secretions, such that sexual transmission, particularly via anal intercourse, is the most common mode of transmission. The virus is also transmitted via contaminated needles. HBV results in serious liver damage in less than 10% of cases, but simultaneous infection (*coinfection*) with hepatitis delta virus increases the risk of permanent liver damage and liver cancer. Babies of infected mothers can become infected during childbirth. The carrier state is age related—newborns are much more likely to remain chronically infected than are individuals infected as adults.

Hepatitis delta virus is unique in that it does not carry genes for a capsid; instead, it utilizes hepatitis B capsomeres. Thus, hepatitis delta virus can spread only from cells that carry hepatitis B virus. Coinfected patients typically have a more severe acute disease than chronic HBV patients who are subsequently infected with delta agent—a condition called a *superinfection.*

Table 2 compares and contrasts the features of hepatitis viruses.

Epidemiology

One-third of Americans have antibodies against hepatitis A virus, and 1.25 million are chronically infected with HBV. Immunizations against the viruses have reduced the number of cases significantly—from an estimated 125 annual cases of hepatitis A per 100,000 population during 1980–1994 to 1.5 cases per 100,000 population in 1995. Cases of hepatitis B declined 80% from 1990 to 1995.

An association between HBV and hepatic (liver) cancer is indicated by strong medical evidence. Hepatic cancer is common in geographic areas with a high prevalence of HBV infection, and chronic carriers of HBV are 200 times more likely to develop hepatic cancer than noncarriers are. Furthermore, the HBV genome has been found integrated into hepatic cancer cells, and these same cells typically express HBV antigens. It is possible that integration of the virus activates oncogenes or suppresses oncogene repressor genes. Another theory is that repair and cell growth in response to liver damage proceeds out of control, resulting in cancer. Coinfection with HDV increases the likelihood of severe liver damage.

Hepatitis C virus infects over 170 million people worldwide, including about 4 million U.S. residents. The virus is transmitted sexually and via contaminated needles. Over 80% of infected people remain chronically infected (the common name of the disease is *chronic hepatitis*), and 70% suffer serious liver damage, many requiring liver transplants. In the past, blood transfusions accounted for many cases of hepatitis C, but testing blood for HCV has considerably reduced the risk of infection by this means.

Most outbreaks of hepatitis E are associated with fecally contaminated drinking water, so the common name of the disease is *enteric hepatitis.* Cases of enteric hepatitis in the U.S.

Table 2 Comparison of Hepatitis Viruses

Feature	*Hepatovirus* Hepatitis A virus (HAV)	*Orthohepadnavirus* Hepatitis B virus (HBV)	*Hepacivirus* Hepatitis C virus (HCV)	*Deltavirus* Hepatitis delta virus (HDV)	*Hepevirus* Hepatitis E virus (HEV)
Virus family	*Picornaviridae*	*Hepadnaviridae*	*Flaviviridae*	*Arenaviridae*	*Hepeviridae*
Genome	+ssRNA	Partly ssDNA, partly dsDNA	+ssRNA	−ssRNA	+ssRNA
Envelope present?	No	Yes	Yes	Yes	No
Transmission	Fecal-oral	Needles; sex	Needles; sex	Needles; sex	Fecal-oral
Incubation period	15–45 days	70–100 days	42–49 days	7–24 days	15–60 days
Severity (mortality rate)	Mild (<0.5%)	Occasionally severe (15–25%)	Usually subclinical (0.5–4%)	Requires simultaneous hepatitis B infection to replicate; together severity may be very high (10–20%)	Mild (1–3%; pregnant women 15–25%)
Chronic carrier state?	No	Yes	Yes	No	No
Common name of disease	Infectious hepatitis	Serum hepatitis	Non-A, non-B hepatitis; chronic hepatitis	Hepatitis delta	Enteric hepatitis
Other disease associations	—	Hepatic cancer	Hepatic cancer	Cirrhosis	—

usually involve people infected in an endemic region, such as Mexico, northern Africa, or the developing nations of Asia.

Diagnosis, Treatment, and Prevention

Initial diagnosis of hepatitis may involve observation of the presence of jaundice, an enlarged liver, or fluid in the abdomen. Laboratory tests include serological studies of body fluids to detect viral antigens or antibodies against hepatitis viruses, liver function tests, or liver biopsy to determine the extent of liver damage.

Microscopists can observe specific HBV proteins in body fluids: so-called Dane particles, spherical particles, and filamentous particles **(Figure 13)**. Dane particles are complete, infectious virions, whereas spherical and filamentous

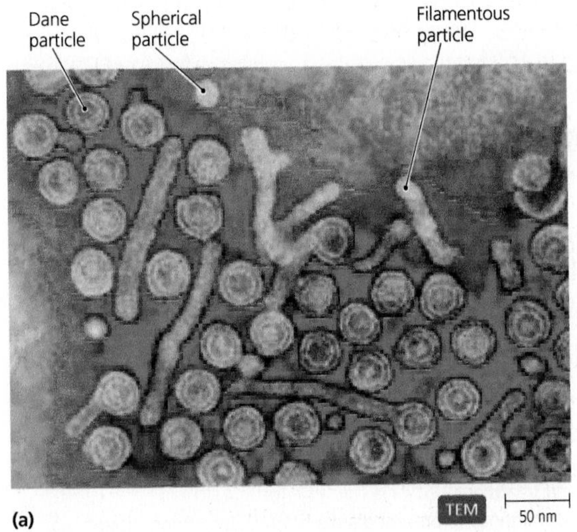

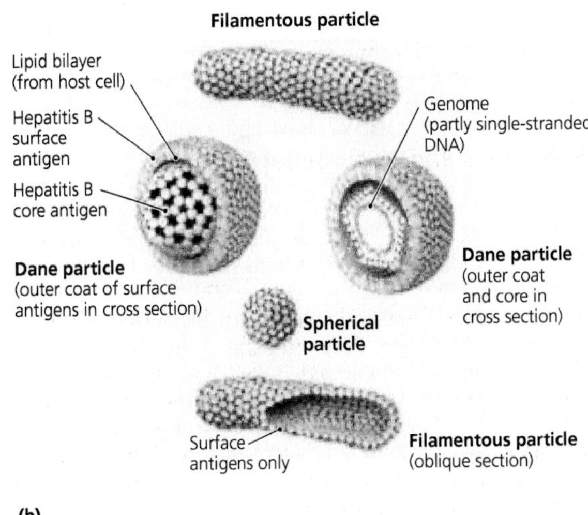

▲ *Figure 13*
Three types of viral protein particles produced by hepatitis B viruses. Dane particles are complete virions, whereas filamentous particles and spherical particles are capsomeres that have assembled without genomes. **(a)** Micrograph. **(b)** Artist's rendition.

DISEASE AT A GLANCE 7

Hepatitis

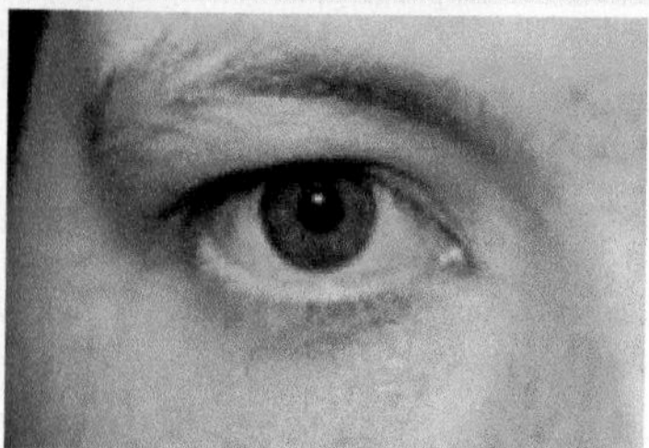

Yellow skin and eyes characterize jaundice.

Cause: Hepatitis A virus (naked, +ssRNA virus), hepatitis B virus (enveloped, partly dsDNA virus), hepatitis C virus (enveloped, +ssRNA virus), hepatitis delta virus (delta agent) (incomplete −ssRNA virus), hepatitis E virus (naked, +ssRNA virus).

Portal of entry: A and E—ingestion via fecal-oral route; B, C, delta—parenteral (blood- and fluid-borne) transmission.

Signs and symptoms: Jaundice, fatigue, abdominal pain, loss of appetite, nausea, and diarrhea. Additional symptoms: A—fever; B—vomiting and joint pain; C—dark urine; D—vomiting and dark urine, E—vomiting and dark urine.

Incubation period: A—15 to 45 days; B—70 to 100 days; C—42 to 49 days; delta—7 to 24 days; E—15 to 60 days.

Susceptibility: Adults generally display more symptoms than children do and are at greater risk due to behavioral activities, though children are more at risk for chronic infections and complications thereof.

Treatment: For all—supportive therapy and rest; A—anti-HAV immunoglobulin; B—alpha interferon, adefovir dipivoxil, and lamivudine; C—alpha interferon and ribavirin; delta—control of HBV co-infection.

Prevention: Practice good hygiene and drink sterilized water, especially when traveling in areas endemic for hepatitis A and E. Limit activities where body fluids may be acquired (such as sexual intercourse, sharing needles) to help prevent transmission of hepatitis B, C, and delta. Vaccines are available for hepatitis A and hepatitis B.

particles are "empty" viral surface antigens that serve as a decoy in the host—the binding of antibody to empty capsids reduces antibody response against Dane particles.

Treatment of hepatitis involves rest and reducing inflammation; there are no cures. Immunoglobulin against the viruses given immediately after exposure offers some protection. Alpha interferon or nucleotide analogs, such as adefovir dipivoxil or lamivudine, help in 40% of cases of HBV infection. Alpha interferon and ribavirin provide some relief for hepatitis C infection.

Prevention generally involves avoiding exposure. To reduce infections by HAV and HEV, wash hands often and avoid undercooked foods or contaminated water in endemic areas. For HBV, HCV, and HDV, avoid sharing needles for drugs, tattooing, or piercing. Heath care workers should be cautious with needles and other sharp instruments. All blood and blood products should be screened before use. Abstinence is the only sure way to prevent sexually transmitted infection; condoms can reduce risk but not eliminate it.

Two vaccines are available against hepatitis A; both are administered in two doses separated by 6–12 months. Immunization is recommended for children between the ages of one and two years, adults who travel to high-risk areas (South America, Africa, and Asia other than Japan), men who have sex with men, and intravenous drug users.

The vaccine against HBV is given over a six-month period, resulting in protection against the virus in 95% of individuals. Immunity against HBV lasts for at least 15 years, and probably for life. Immunization is recommended for everyone.

There are no vaccines against hepatitis C, delta, or E viruses, though scientists have identified a protease enzyme required for HCV viability and are working to develop a protease inhibitor.

Disease at a Glance 7 summarizes the features of viral hepatitis.

CRITICAL THINKING

In areas of poor sanitation, which form of hepatitis would you expect to be most common—infectious hepatitis, serum hepatitis, or chronic hepatitis? Why?

Protozoan Diseases of the Intestinal Tract

Protozoa as a whole are the most significant human pathogens worldwide, but relatively few of them cause infections of the gastrointestinal tract. Here we examine three of them.

Giardiasis

Learning Objectives

- ✓ Describe the disease giardiasis, including its cause, epidemiology, and treatment.
- ✓ List methods to prevent giardiasis infections during recreational activities and in places such as day care centers.

Giardiasis (jē-ar-dī'ă-sis) is one of the more common waterborne gastrointestinal diseases in the United States.

Signs and Symptoms

Giardiasis is often asymptomatic but can cause one to two weeks of significant gastrointestinal distress, including severe greasy, frothy, fatty diarrhea, abdominal pain, flatus, nausea, vomiting, loss of appetite, ineffective absorption of nutrients, and low-grade fever. Patients' stools are foul smelling, usually with the "rotten-egg" smell of hydrogen sulfide. In extreme cases, the attachment of parasites to the intestinal mucosa can cause superficial tissue damage, and fluid loss can be life threatening. Acute disease generally lasts one to four weeks following an incubation period of about two weeks. Chronic giardiasis can occur, often in animals.

Pathogen and Pathogenesis

A diplomonad (two-nuclei) flagellate named *Giardia intestinalis* (jē-ar'dē-ă) (formerly called G. *lamblia,* lăm'lē-a) causes giardiasis. The protozoan has two forms—a motile feeding *trophozoite* and a dormant *cyst,* which has a tough shell composed of the polysaccharide chitin. The cyst is resistant to environmental conditions such as chlorine, heat, desiccation, and stomach acid.

The *Giardia* life cycle is simple: An ingested cyst excysts to release trophozoites in the small intestine. Trophozoites multiply via binary fission and either remain free or attach to the intestinal lining via a ventral adhesive disk **(Figure 14).** They interfere with intestinal absorption, resulting in a large quantity of undigested food, which is then broken down by bacteria, producing flatus. *Giardia* does not invade the intestinal wall. As trophozoites pass into the colon, encystment occurs. Cysts are immediately infective upon release.

Epidemiology

Cases of giardiasis occur in both developed and developing countries; recent trends have shown increases in the number of cases worldwide. Infection usually results from ingestion of cysts in contaminated drinking water, but infections can also occur from the accidental ingestion of water during swimming or other water activities, eating unwashed raw fruits or vegetables contaminated by feces, or contact with feces during sex. Outbreaks of giardiasis in day care facilities are usually the result of children putting contaminated toys or eating utensils into their mouths.

Hikers, campers, and their pets are at particular risk because wild animals shed *Giardia* cysts into mountain streams; in one study, scientists found cysts in every stream tested in the Rocky Mountains. Because beavers are common zoonotic sources of *Giardia,* giardiasis is sometimes referred to as "beaver fever." Even if humans avoid drinking stream water, they usually do not think twice about letting their dogs drink it. The dogs in turn pass the infection on to their owners. Domesticated animals, such as sheep, can also carry *Giardia.* The organism is hardy in the environment, and can survive for months due to the protective outer shell of its cyst.

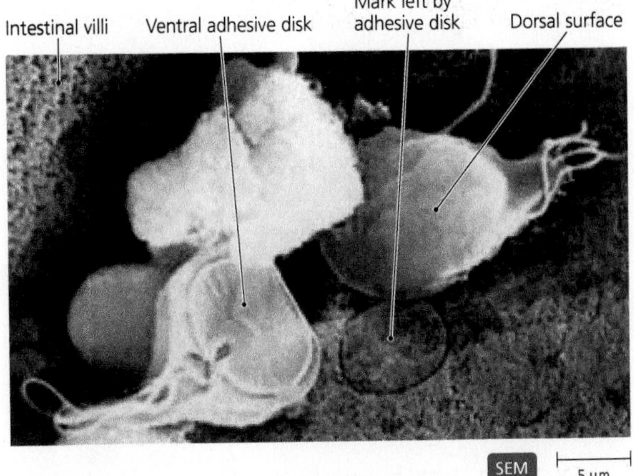

▲ *Figure 14*

Trophozoites of *Giardia intestinalis.* This flagellated protozoan attaches to the intestinal lining.

Diagnosis, Treatment, and Prevention

Diagnosis of *Giardia* relies on direct microscopic examination of stool specimens to reveal the flat, pear-shaped trophozoites or cysts.

Some infections resolve spontaneously without treatment, but physicians usually prescribe metronidazole for adults and furazolidone for children when diarrhea is present. Health care workers provide supportive care to replace lost fluids, especially with young children. Cure rates are generally high (80%), but sometimes drug resistance or long-term infections can lead to difficulties in resolution.

Water must be filtered to prevent infection in regions where *Giardia* is endemic. When hiking, neither humans nor their pets should drink unfiltered stream or river water. Most stores that sell camping and hiking equipment sell portable water filtration kits, making it unnecessary to carry bottled water. Boiling or treating water with iodine may also work. Eating utensils should be cleaned with filtered water. In day care facilities, scrupulous hygiene practices and the separation of feeding and diaper-changing areas are essential to preventing transmission. Individuals recovering from infection should also be extremely vigilant with their personal hygiene to avoid transmitting *Giardia* to family members, and they should avoid swimming in public or natural waterways for several weeks after recovery to ensure they do not shed parasites into the water.

Disease at a Glance 8 ummarizes the features of giardiasis.

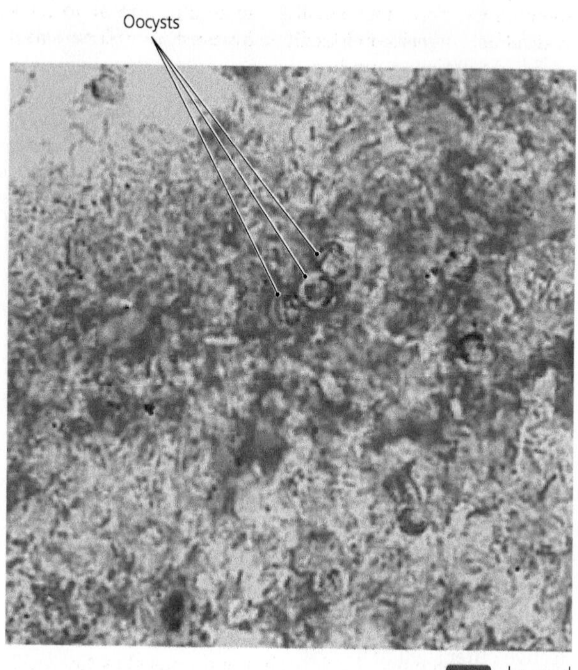

▲ *Figure 15*

Oocysts of *Cryptosporidium parvum* embedded in the wall of the intestine.

DISEASE AT A GLANCE 8

Giardiasis

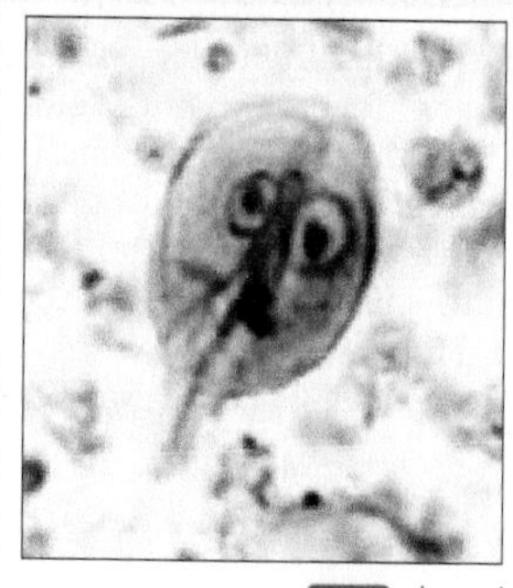

Trophozoite of *Giardia intestinalis* in a fecal smear

Cause: *Giardia intestinalis* (formerly *G. lamblia*) (diplomonad protozoan).

Portal of entry: Ingestion of infectious cyst.

Signs and symptoms: Greasy, frothy, fatty diarrhea with horrific odor, and abdominal distension and cramps.

Incubation period: One to two weeks.

Susceptibility: Everyone is susceptible, especially hikers and campers who drink out of contaminated streams.

Treatment: Metronidazole for adults; furazolidone for children.

Prevention: Practice good hygiene and avoid drinking untreated water from streams, lakes, or ponds.

CRITICAL THINKING

A child in a day care center is diagnosed with giardiasis. What steps should be taken to keep other children from becoming sick?

Cryptosporidiosis

Learning Objectives

- ✓ Describe the cause and symptoms of cryptosporidiosis.
- ✓ Describe methods to prevent the transmission of cryptosporidiosis.

In 1993, a water plant in Milwaukee, Wisconsin, malfunctioned for two weeks. Within days, over 403,000 people developed **cryptosporidiosis** (krip'tō-spō-rid-ĕ-ō'sis)—a zoonotic disease once thought to be limited to animals—and 100 died.

Signs and Symptoms

Severe watery diarrhea several times a day lasting about two weeks is a common manifestation of cryptosporidiosis. Headache, muscular pain, cramping, nausea, fatigue, and severe fluid and weight loss accompany the diarrhea. Life-threatening malabsorption, hepatitis, and pancreatitis can complicate the disease.

Pathogen and Pathogenesis

The protozoan *Cryptosporidium parvum* (krip'tō-spō-rid'ē-ŭm par'vŭm) causes cryptosporidiosis. The infectious form of this parasite is a banana-shaped, motile *sporozoite* that has an apical complex of organelles specialized for penetrating host cells; thus, it is an *apicomplexan.* Sporozoites form thick-shelled *oocysts,* which are the infective stage, inside cells **(Figure 15).** With a complex series of cell divisions and stages, oocysts eventually develop four internal sporozoites, which escape to continue the life cycle.

Infection most commonly results from drinking water contaminated with oocysts, but direct fecal-oral transmission resulting from poor hygienic practices also occurs, particularly in day care facilities. Scientists do not understand the pathogenicity of *Cryptosporidium,* but some think that destruction of intestinal cells and the subsequent inflammatory response trigger loss of electrolytes and water and decrease absorption of nutrients. In healthy adults, the infection clears spontaneously with time, often up to a month.

Epidemiology

About 30% of people living in developing nations carry *Cryptosporidium* asymptomatically. It is estimated that most natural waterways in the United States are contaminated with oocysts introduced in livestock wastes. People with AIDS, transplant patients, and other immunocompromised individuals are at higher risk for severe disease. In HIV-positive individuals, chronic cryptosporidiosis is one of the life-threatening indicator diseases that reveals the clinical stage of AIDS.

Diagnosis, Treatment, and Prevention

The presence of oocysts in feces is diagnostic of the disease. Health care workers provide supportive care, primarily in the form of fluid and electrolyte replacement. There is no other effective treatment. Prevention involves good hygiene, not consuming contaminated water or food, and avoiding fecal exposure during sex.

Amebiasis

Learning Objectives

- ✓ Describe the three forms of amebiasis seen in humans.
- ✓ Describe methods for preventing amebiasis.

Amoebae (ă-mē′bē) are protozoa with no truly defined shape that use pseudopodia to move and acquire food. They are abundant throughout the world in water and moist soil.

Signs and Symptoms

Depending on the health of the host and the virulence of the particular infecting strain, three types of **amebiasis** (ă-mē-bī′-ă-sis) occur. The least severe form, *luminal amebiasis,* occurs in otherwise healthy individuals and is asymptomatic. Invasive *amebic dysentery* is a more serious form of infection characterized by severe diarrhea, colitis (inflammation of the colon), appendicitis, ulceration of the intestinal mucosa, bloody mucus-containing stools, and pain. In the most serious disease—*invasive extraintestinal amebiasis*—potentially fatal necrotic lesions form in the liver, lungs, spleen, kidneys, or brain.

Pathogen, Virulence Factors, and Pathogenesis

Entamoeba histolytica (ent-ă-mĕ′bă his-tō-li′ti-kă) causes all forms of amebiasis. A motile trophozoite (see Disease at a Glance 9) develops into an infective, resistant, chitin-shelled cyst. Virulent strains of *Entamoeba* produce adhesion proteins, proteases, proteins that create ion channels in host membranes, and other small proteins that appear to have toxic effects on cells and facilitate invasion. Avirulent strains of *Entamoeba* do not produce these four types of proteins and so remain in the lumen of the intestine.

Infection begins with ingestion of thick-shelled cysts, which pass successfully through the acid of the stomach and excyst in the small intestine to release trophozoites. These migrate to the large intestine and multiply by binary fission, producing any signs and symptoms in one to four weeks. Trophozoites use pseudopodia to attach to specific receptors on the intestinal lining, where they feed. Both trophozoites and cysts are shed into the environment in feces, but trophozoites die.

Trophozoites in the lumen of the intestine do little damage and typically produce no symptoms, but when trophozoites invade the peritoneal cavity and bloodstream, amebic dysentery or invasive extraintestinal amebiasis occur. The difference in severity is due to the production of virulence factors.

Epidemiology

E. histolytica is carried asymptomatically in the digestive tracts of roughly 10% of the world's human population. Infection arises following consumption of contaminated water or food, ingestion from contaminated hands, or during oral-anal intercourse. Cockroaches and houseflies can facilitate the spread of cysts under conditions of overcrowding. Travelers, immigrants, institutionalized populations, and male homosexuals are at greatest risk within industrialized nations. No animal reservoirs exist, but human carriers are sufficiently numerous to ensure continued transmission.

Approximately 90% of people with amebiasis develop the luminal form. Dysentery and invasive disease occur in less than 10% of cases but can be fatal, causing a worldwide mortality of over 100,000 people annually. Carriers predominate in the populations of less developed countries, especially in rural areas, where human feces are used to fertilize food crops and where water purification is

Clinical Case Study *The Case of the Lactovegetarians*

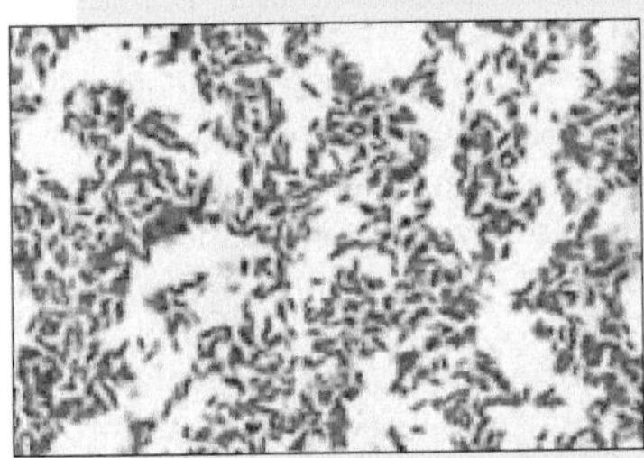

Two patients—a woman and her husband, ages 23 and 22, respectively—arrive at the health clinic one morning. They report having had severe abdominal cramps, grossly bloody diarrhea, nausea, and fever for 48 hours. Cultures of stool samples grown under microaerophilic, capneic conditions contain comma-shaped, Gram-negative bacilli (see the photo). Both the patients are lactovegetarians and report being part of a "cow leasing" program at a local dairy in which patrons lease part of a cow's milk production so they can drink natural, whole, raw milk. The couple devised the program so that they and several neighbors could circumvent state regulations prohibiting the sale of unpasteurized milk. Investigators obtained and cultured a milk sample from the dairy's bulk milk tank: the cultures contained the bacterium pictured.

1. What is the pathogen?
2. How did the couple become infected?
3. Are the couple's colleagues at work at risk of acquiring an infection from the couple?
4. What other foods that are common sources of this bacterium can be ruled out in this case?

Reference: *MMWR* 51:548–549. 2002.

DISEASE AT A GLANCE 9

Amebiasis

1. Consumption of cysts of *Entamoeba histolytica*, usually in contaminated water.
2. Excystment in small intestine releases trophozoites.
3. Trophozoites multiply in large intestine and attach to intestinal lining, causing luminal amebiasis.
4. They may invade the peritoneum to cause amebic dysentery.
5. They may invade the bloodstream to be carried throughout the body.
6. They cause invasive extraintestinal amebiasis when they infect the liver, lungs, spleen, kidneys, or brain, and may cause death.
7. Cysts are shed in stool.

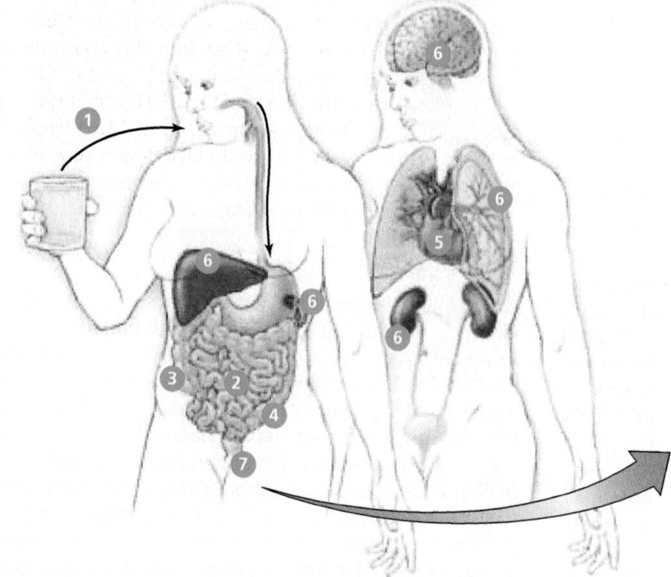

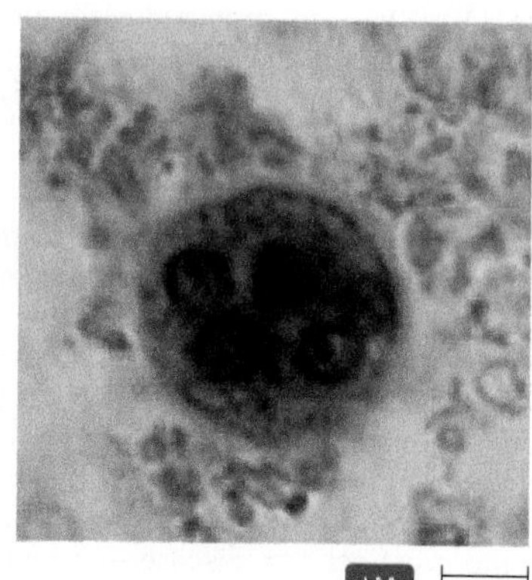

Cyst of *Entamoeba histolytica*

Cause: *Entamoeba histolytica.*
Portal of entry: Oral.
Signs and symptoms: Luminal amebiasis is asymptomatic. Invasive amebic dysentery involves severe diarrhea, colitis, appendicitis, ulceration of the intestinal mucosa, bloody and mucus-containing stools, and pain. In invasive extraintestinal amebiasis, potentially fatal necrotic lesions form in the liver, lungs, spleen, kidneys, or brain.

Incubation period: Six to twenty days.
Susceptibility: People who live in developing nations that have poor sanitation; travelers, immigrants, institutionalized populations, and male homosexuals are at greatest risk within industrialized nations.

Treatment: Oral rehydration; iodoquinol or paromomycin for asymptomatic infections; metronidazole followed by iodoquinol for symptomatic amebiasis.
Prevention: Avoid drinking contaminated water or eating foods washed or irrigated with contaminated water; do not use human feces as fertilizer; avoid oral-fecal contact during sex.

inadequate. Malnutrition, immune deficiency, old age, cancer, pregnancy, alcoholism, and the use of certain drugs, such as steroids, are risk factors for more severe forms of amebiasis.

Diagnosis, Treatment, and Prevention

Diagnosis is based on the identification of microscopic cysts or trophozoites recovered from either fresh stool specimens or intestinal biopsies. Microscopic analysis is necessary to distinguish amebic dysentery from bacterial dysentery. Serological identification of antigens may be used to distinguish *E. histolytica* from nonpathogenic amoebae.

Treatment involves oral rehydration therapy (vital in severe cases) and antiamebic drugs. Iodoquinol and paromomycin are effective for asymptomatic infections. Physicians may prescribe metronidazole followed by iodoquinol for symptomatic amebiasis. Antibacterial agents may also be prescribed to prevent secondary bacterial infections. Antidiarrheal medications should be avoided as they may worsen the condition by retaining the organism in the intestinal tract as a result of limiting diarrhea.

Several preventive measures interrupt the transmission cycle of *Entamoeba.* In areas where amebiasis is common, people should avoid eating uncooked vegetables or unpeeled fruit and should drink bottled water. Human feces should not be used as fertilizer. Effective processing of water requires chemical treatment, filtration, or extensive boiling. Good personal hygiene and safer sexual practices can reduce transmission during intimate contact.

Disease at a Glance 9 summarizes the features of amebiasis.

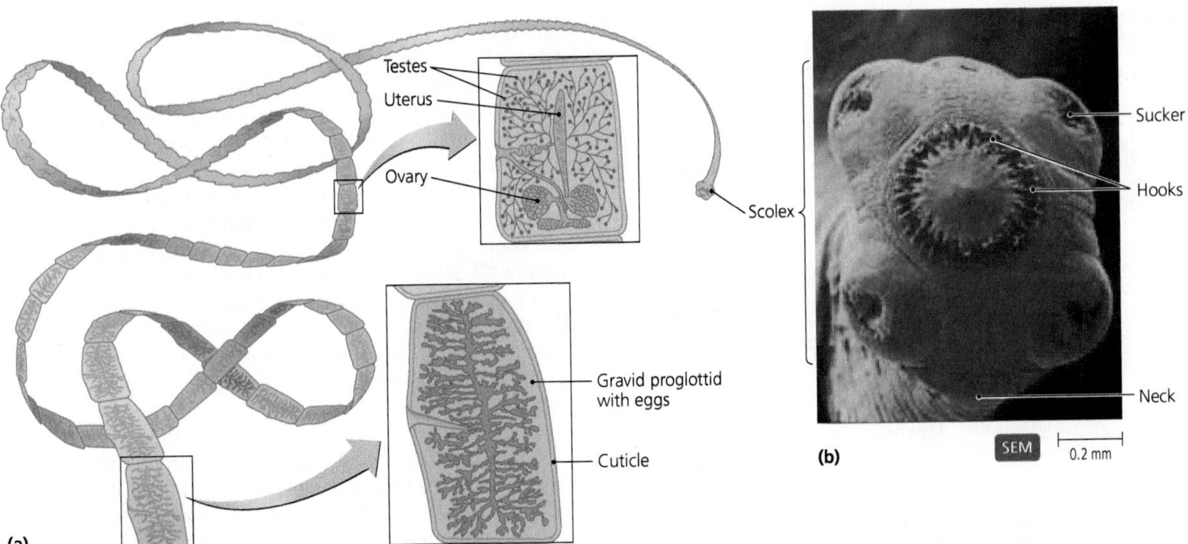

▲ *Figure 16*

Features of tapeworm morphology. Each tapeworm consists of an organ of attachment called a scolex (which in this case bears hooks in addition to suckers), a neck, and a long chain of segments called proglottids. **(a)** Artist's rendition. **(b)** Micrograph. *How does a tapeworm acquire food?*

Figure 16 Tapeworms absorb food through their cuticles.

CRITICAL THINKING

How does the visually distinctive appearance of *Giardia* trophozoites improve the success of medical treatment of giardiasis as compared to that for amebic infections?

Helminthic Infestations of the Intestinal Tract

Helminths—macroscopic, multicellular, eukaryotic worms—generally do not cause specific diseases in humans, but they can infest the GI tract as non-disease-causing parasites.

Tapeworm Infestations

Learning Objectives

- ✓ Describe the common features of the life cycles of tapeworms that infect humans.
- ✓ List the predominant modes of infestation for *Taenia* and suggest measures to prevent infestation.

Tapeworm is the common name for a **cestode** (ses'tōd), which is a flat, segmented, parasitic helminth. All tapeworms are intestinal parasites and completely lack their own digestive systems.

Signs and Symptoms

Tapeworm infestations are usually asymptomatic; in most cases, people do not know they are infected unless they begin to pass segments of the worms. Rarely, nausea, abdominal pain, weight loss, and diarrhea may accompany infestation or long worms may physically block the intestine, causing pain and preventing normal bowel function.

Pathogens

The common human tapeworms are *Taenia saginata* (te'ne-a sa-ji-na'ta), called the beef tapeworm, and *Taenia solium* (so'lī-um), called the pork tapeworm; the common names come from the fact that the worms develop during part of their lives in cattle and swine, respectively. **Figure 16a** illustrates a tapeworm body plan. The outer surface of the tapeworm is a *cuticle* ("skin"), through which a tapeworm steals nutrients from its host by absorption. The **scolex** (skō'leks) is a small attachment organ that possesses suckers and/or hooks to attach the worm to host tissue to prevent dislodgment **(Figure 16b).** Behind the scolex is the neck region from which body segments called **proglottids** (prō-glot'idz) originate. New proglottids grow continuously from the neck, displacing

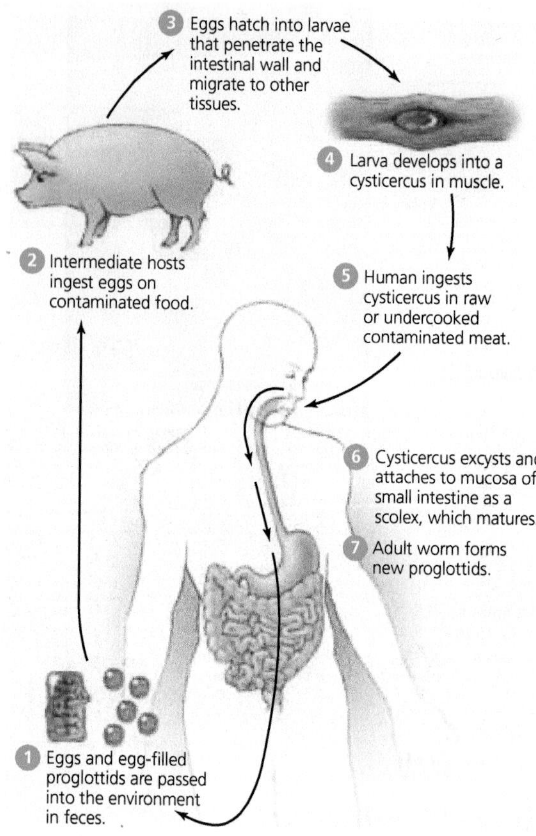
3 Eggs hatch into larvae that penetrate the intestinal wall and migrate to other tissues.
4 Larva develops into a cysticercus in muscle.
2 Intermediate hosts ingest eggs on contaminated food.
5 Human ingests cysticercus in raw or undercooked contaminated meat.
6 Cysticercus excysts and attaches to mucosa of small intestine as a scolex, which matures.
7 Adult worm forms new proglottids.
1 Eggs and egg-filled proglottids are passed into the environment in feces.

▲ *Figure 17*

Life cycle of *Taenia solium*.

older ones, which move farther from the neck to form a chain, or *strobila*. Tapeworms can attain lengths greater than 4 meters.

Proglottids mature as they are pushed away from the neck, producing both male and female internal reproductive organs. Each proglottid is monoecious[9] and may fertilize other proglottids of the same or different tapeworm. After fertilization, proglottids furthest from the neck become *gravid*[10] (full of fertilized eggs), break off the chain, and pass out of the intestine with feces. In a few cases, proglottids rupture within the intestine, releasing eggs directly into the feces. Some tapeworms produce proglottids large enough to be obviously visible in stools. Additionally, proglottids from the beef tapeworm are motile, providing a memorable experience for the person who passes them!

Each tapeworm spends part of its life in a *definitive* or *primary host,* in which the sexual stage of the helminth develops, and part of its life in an *intermediate* or *secondary host.* **Figure 17** illustrates the life cycle of *Taenia solium* in its hosts—a human and a pig. Gravid proglottids and eggs enter the environment in feces from an infected human 1 and are consumed by a pig 2. The eggs hatch into larvae in the pig's intestines and penetrate through the intestinal wall 3. Larvae migrate to other tissues 4, often muscle, where they develop into harmless immature forms called **cysticerci** (sis'ti-ser-sī). Humans become infected by consuming raw or undercooked meat containing cysticerci 5. Cysticerci excyst in the human intestine 6, attach to the intestinal wall, and mature into new adult tapeworms 7, which eventually shed gravid proglottids, thus completing the cycle. Infested human hosts pass approximately six proglottids per day. *T. solium* adults average 1000 proglottids in length. Each proglottid contains about 50,000 eggs.

In rare cases, humans become intermediate hosts of *T. solium* when they ingest eggs or gravid proglottids. Larvae released from the eggs invade human muscle or brain tissue and encyst. Encystment in muscle tissue generally results in no symptoms, but if cysticerci form in the brain, seizures and other neurological problems can occur.

The life cycle of *T. saginata* is nearly identical, except the intermediate host is a bovine, adult worms have 1000–2000 proglottids (each of which can contain 100,000 eggs), and cysticerci of *T. saginata* do not develop in humans, who consume the eggs.

Epidemiology

Taenia species live worldwide in areas where beef and pork are food. The highest incidences of human infestation are in poor rural areas with inadequate sewage treatment and regions where humans and livestock live in close proximity. Infestations are rare in the United States.

Diagnosis, Treatment, and Prevention

Clinicians can observe proglottids (or sometimes eggs) in fecal samples at least three months after infestation, which is the basis of diagnosis. Examination of the scolex is required to differentiate between *T. solium* and *T. saginata.*

Treatment with a single oral dose of niclosamide or praziquantel generally eliminates intestinal infestation. Rarely, surgery may be necessary to remove the tapeworms from the intestinal tract and to open blockages.

Thoroughly cooking or freezing meat is the easiest method of prevention. Because cysticerci are readily visible in meat, giving it a "mealy" look, inspecting meat either before shipment to market or before purchase can reduce the rate of infestation. Good sewage treatment to prevent human feces from entering the intermediate hosts' food also breaks a human tapeworm's life cycle.

CRITICAL THINKING

Infestation of an intermediate host requires consumption of eggs in fecally contaminated food. How might humans become accidental intermediate hosts for *T. solium*?

[9]From Greek *mono,* meaning one, and *oikos,* meaning house; monoecious means that an organism contains both types of sex organs.
[10]From Latin *gravidus,* meaning heavy, that is, pregnant.

Pinworm Infestations

Learning Objectives

✓ Describe the common characteristics of nematodes.
✓ Describe methods for preventing pinworm infestations.

Pinworm, *Enterobius vermicularis* (en-ter'ō'bī-ŭs ver-mi-kū-lar'is), commonly infests the intestines of children.

Signs and Symptoms

One-third of all pinworm infestations are asymptomatic. Symptomatic infestations involve intense perianal itching, irritability and sleep disturbance due to itching, decreased appetite, and possibly weight loss.

Pathogen and Infestation

Enterobius is a **nematode** (nem'ă-tōd)—a long, thin, unsegmented cylindrical helminth tapering to points at each end **(Figure 18a).** All nematodes possess complete digestive tracts, have a protective cuticle, and are dioecious,[11] with females being larger than males. Nematodes as a group have variable reproductive strategies that make them highly successful parasites of almost all vertebrate animals, including humans. Humans are the only known host for pinworms.

After mating in the colon, female pinworms migrate at night to the anus, where they deposit eggs perianally before returning to the colon. Scratching dislodges eggs onto clothes or bedding, where they dry, become aerosolized, and settle in water or on food, which is consumed. Alternatively, scratching leaves eggs on the skin and under the fingernails, such that infected individuals can continually reinfect themselves by ingesting the eggs on their hands. Adult worms mature in several weeks and live in the intestinal tract for approximately two months.

[11]From Greek *di,* meaning two, and *oikos,* meaning house; dioecious worms have separate sexes.

Clinical Case Study *Painful Dysentery*

A 43-year-old immigrant from Bangladesh reports to a clinic with his 9-year-old son who has had bloody diarrhea with mucus, stomach pain, and a fever for the past 24 hours. He reports that his son was healthy when they arrived in the United Sates a week prior to the start of his symptoms. Trophozoites are subsequently microscopically identified in the boy's stool.

1. What is the diagnosis and causative agent?
2. What other diseases are caused by this organism?
3. Describe the other diseases caused by this organism.
4. How did the patient likely acquire this disease?
5. What is the best course of treatment?

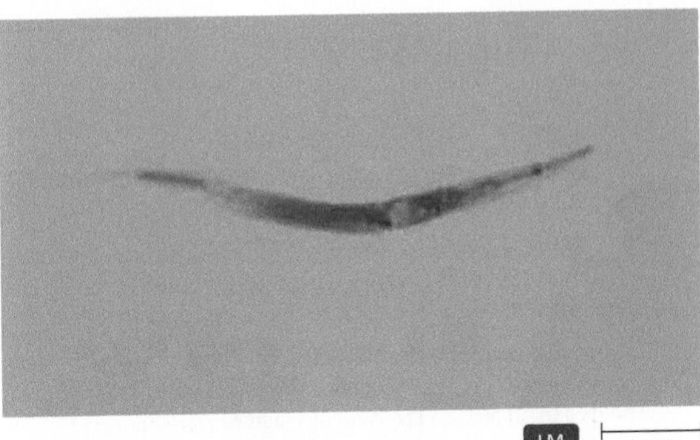

(a)

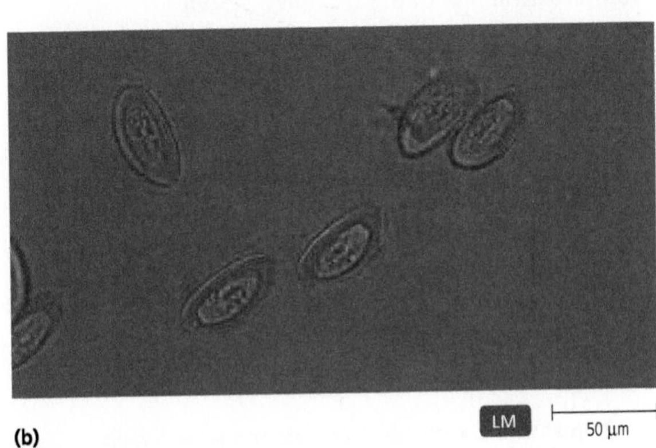

(b)

▲ *Figure 18*

Nematodes. (a) Shown here is an adult female pinworm, *Enterobius vermicularis.* **(b)** Pinworm eggs.

Epidemiology

E. vermicularis infests about 500 million people worldwide, particularly in temperate climates, in school-age children, and in conditions of overcrowding. *Enterobius* is the most common parasitic worm found in the United States, affecting 40 million Americans.

Diagnosis, Treatment, and Prevention

Microscopy is used for diagnosis: in the morning, before bathing or defecation, transparent sticky tape is applied to the perianal area to collect the readily identifiable microscopic eggs **(Figure 18b).** Adult worms, if recovered, are also diagnostic. Treatment with albendazole or mebendazole followed by a second treatment two weeks later to kill any newly acquired worms is usually successful. In some cases, an entire household must be treated.

Strict personal hygiene prevents reinfestation. Thorough laundering of all clothes and bedding of infested individuals and other members of the household, thorough handwashing, and prevention of scratching reduce the chance of reinfestation and spread of the worms to others.

CHAPTER SUMMARY

Structures of the Digestive System

1. The digestive system is composed of the gastrointestinal (GI) tract and the accessory digestive organs.
2. The GI tract is composed of the mouth with its teeth, the esophagus, stomach, small intestine, large intestine, and anus. The primary function of the GI tract is to digest and absorb nutrients.
3. Digestive enzymes enter the GI tract from accessory digestive organs—the liver, gallbladder, salivary glands, and pancreas. The liver also aids in removal of wastes.

Normal Microbiota of the Digestive System

1. Normal microbiota colonize the digestive system except for some accessory organs and the esophagus, stomach, and duodenum.
2. **Viridans streptococci** are the most common normal microbiota of the mouth. *Bacteroides, Lactobacillus, Escherichia* and other enterobacteria, and *Candida* predominate in the lower small intestine and colon.
3. Intestinal normal microbiota provide some vitamins to the host. They also produce flatus and convert some substances to toxins and carcinogens. Their primary benefit is to inhibit pathogens by **microbial antagonism.**

Bacterial Diseases of the Digestive System

1. Dental **caries,** or tooth decay, are the second most common infection of humans. Plaque and acid produced by mouth bacteria, usually *Streptococcus mutans* (a viridans streptococcus) and *Lactobacillus,* destroy the enamel of teeth to create cavities, which can lead to tooth loss.
2. Caries, plaque, and tartar when untreated can lead to a **periodontal disease** called **gingivitis,** which is inflammation of the gums. Severe periodontal disease manifests as increased inflammation, loss of bone, and tooth loss.
3. *Helicobacter pylori* causes **peptic ulcers.** The bacterium burrows through the mucus lining of the stomach, allowing entry to stomach acid, which can dissolve a hole and cause pain.
4. **Bacterial gastroenteritis,** caused by many types of bacteria, is characterized by nausea, vomiting, diarrhea, cramping, and often fever. **Cholera, traveler's diarrhea, shigellosis,** *Campylobacter* gastroenteritis, and salmonellosis are examples.
5. *Vibrio cholerae* produces cholera toxin, which stimulates the secretion of excess amounts of electrolytes and water from an infected cell, leading to severe dehydration.
6. *E. coli* O157:H7 produces Shiga-like toxin as well as other enterotoxins to cause sometimes fatal gastroenteritis. Shiga-like toxin is related to the **Shiga toxin** of *Shigella,* several species of which produce gastroenteritis called shigellosis.
7. Infections with *Salmonella* can result in **salmonellosis** or **typhoid fever,** a more severe form of infection that can be fatal. *Salmonella* produce many virulence factors that aid in colonization of the host.
8. Bacterial food poisoning includes infection (more properly called bacterial gastroenteritis) and **bacterial intoxication,** in which a toxin is present and active, while the bacteria are not.
9. Staphylococcal food poisoning is a common intoxication produced by enterotoxins of *Staphylococcus aureus*—a normal member of the microbiota.

Viral Diseases of the Digestive System

1. **Fever blisters** and **cold sores** are alternative names for **oral herpes** infections. These recurrent lesions on and around the lips are usually caused by lifelong infection with herpes simplex virus 1.
2. **Mumps** is a relatively benign infection with mumps virus of the parotid salivary glands of children. MMR vaccine has almost eliminated mumps from the U.S.
3. **Viral gastroenteritis** displays symptoms similar to bacterial gastroenteritis except that in all cases the viral form is milder. Caliciviruses (especially **noroviruses**), astroviruses, and rotaviruses are the leading causes of viral gastroenteritis.
4. Many things can cause **hepatitis**—inflammation of the liver—including five viruses: hepatitis A, B, C, D (delta), and E viruses. Hepatitis A and E spread via the fecal-oral route, whereas hepatitis B, C, and delta are spread sexually and via contaminated needles.

Protozoan Diseases of the Intestinal Tract

1. **Giardiasis** is a severe, foul-smelling, watery diarrhea caused by *Giardia intestinalis,* a common resident of waterways throughout the United States.
2. **Cryptosporidiosis**—caused by *Cryptosporidium parvum*—is another intestinal disease with signs and symptoms that include diarrhea, cramping, and nausea.
3. Infection with *Entamoeba histolytica* can result in one of three forms of **amebiasis:** luminal amebiasis, which is generally asymptomatic; amebic dysentery, a significant diarrheal disease; and invasive extraintestinal amebiasis, a potentially fatal disease in which the amoebae invade the body and form necrotic lesions in various organs.

Helminthic Infestations of the Intestinal Tract

1. **Tapeworm (cestode)** infestations are relatively rare in the United States due to inspection of meats, good sewage treatment, and freezing. Beef tapeworm (*Taenia saginata*) and pork tapeworm (*T. solium*) are acquired by eating meat containing tapeworm cysts; the worms then mature in the human intestine.
2. The tapeworm body plan includes an attaching **scolex,** a neck region, and a strobila (chain) of **proglottids** (body segments). Monoecious proglottids are fertilized to become gravid with eggs and shed into the environment where they are consumed by intermediate hosts. Eggs hatch in these animals and eventually form **cysticerci** (cysts) in muscle tissue.
3. **Pinworm** (*Enterobius vermicularis*), a type of **nematode,** is a common helminthic parasite in the United States. Male and female worms mate in the human intestinal tract, and the female crawls out the anus to lay eggs. This leads to the intense itching characteristic of this type of infestation.

QUESTIONS FOR REVIEW

Access more review material (including animations and practice tests) online at www.microbiologyplace.com.

Multiple Choice

1. Which of the following is not part of the gastrointestinal tract?
   a. stomach
   b. colon
   c. liver
   d. mouth
2. The major portion of food digestion occurs in the
   a. mouth.
   b. stomach.
   c. small intestine.
   d. large intestine.
3. The majority of microbes composing the normal microbiota of the GI tract are in the genus
   a. *Bacteroides.*
   b. *Escherichia.*
   c. *Clostridium.*
   d. *Staphylococcus.*
4. Diets high in sugars and starches increase the risk of tooth decay because they
   a. are acidic and destroy tooth enamel.
   b. are acidic and destroy the gingiva.
   c. are converted to acids by bacteria; the acid then destroys tooth enamel.
   d. are converted to acids by bacteria; the acid then destroys the gingiva.
5. Which of the following is a virulence factor important to *Helicobacter pylori* during the formation of ulcers?
   a. type III secretion system
   b. capsule formation
   c. flagella
   d. spore formation
6. Urease helps in the production of ulcers by *H. pylori* by
   a. increasing acid production by cells lining the stomach.
   b. neutralizing acid produced by cells lining the stomach.
   c. degrading mucus-producing cells.
   d. preventing destruction of *H. pylori* following phagocytosis.
7. Which causative agent of bacterial gastroenteritis is the most common in the U.S.?
   a. *Campylobacter jejuni*
   b. *Vibrio cholerae*
   c. *Salmonella* serotype Typhi
   d. *Shigella* spp.
8. Fever blisters are most often caused by
   a. HBV.
   b. HCV.
   c. HSV-1.
   d. HSV-2.
9. Most of the symptoms associated with hepatitis are due to
   a. destruction of liver cells by virus.
   b. cellular immune reactions against virus and infected liver cells.
   c. exotoxin production.
   d. endotoxin production.
10. One of the more common waterborne gastrointestinal diseases seen in the United States is
    a. amebiasis.
    b. *E. coli* O157:H7.
    c. giardiasis.
    d. salmonellosis.
11. Which one of the following diseases is an indicator disease signaling that an HIV-positive individual has progressed to AIDS?
    a. amebiasis
    b. cryptosporidiosis
    c. pinworm
    d. shigellosis
12. *Taenia saginata* is a
    a. bacterium.
    b. protozoan.
    c. cestode.
    d. nematode.
13. Which microbial group contributes the greater number of causative agents to overall digestive tract diseases in the United States?
    a. bacteria
    b. helminths
    c. protozoa
    d. viruses
14. Typhoid fever is caused by a genus of bacteria that also causes
    a. cholera.
    b. cryptosporidiosis.
    c. mumps.
    d. salmonellosis.
15. Frothy, greasy diarrhea is caused by
    a. *Escherichia.*
    b. *Salmonella.*
    c. *Giardia.*
    d. *Helicobacter.*

Modified True/False

Indicate whether each statement is true or false. If the statement is false, change the italicized nontaxonomic word or phrase to make the statement true.

_____ 1. Plaque leads to the formation of dental caries *but does not* contribute to periodontal disease.

_____ 2. *Stress* contributes to the formation of peptic ulcers.

_____ 3. *Campylobacter jejuni* and *E. coli* are both causative agents of gastroenteritis, but only *E. coli* is an example of a *coliform.*

_____ 4. Proper treatment of most forms of gastroenteritis *does not require* firm laboratory confirmation and identification of the causative agent.

_____ 5. Viral gastroenteritis is generally *more severe* than bacterial gastroenteritis.

_____ 6. Hepatic cancer is associated strongly with *HBV infection.*

_____ 7. Giardiasis is a common *bacterial* infection of the digestive tract.

_____ 8. Cryptosporidiosis *has been proven* to affect humans as well as livestock.

_____ 9. Vaccines are available against hepatitis B and *hepatitis C.*

_____ 10. *Vibrio cholerae* forms biofilms in *seawater* but not in *freshwater.*

Fill in the Blanks

1. Teeth are composed of three main layers, a hard layer called ________ overlying the softer ________ and the inner ________.
2. The most common bacterium involved in cavity formation is ________.
3. Peptic ulcers collectively include ________ ulcers of the stomach and ________ ulcers of the intestine.
4. ________ toxin, produce by *Shigella dysenteriae,* is similar to the ________ toxin produced by *E. coli* O157:H7.
5. "Cold sores" are alternate names for ________.
6. Swelling of the parotid glands is the major symptom of ________.
7. One of the primary symptoms of hepatitis is ________, a yellowing of the skin and eyes.
8. Beaver fever is another name for ________.
9. The B subunit of cholera toxin binds to an intestinal ________ cell, and a portion of the A subunit acts as an enzyme that activates ________.
10. The attachment organ of a cestode is its ________.

Matching

Match the disease on the left with the causative pathogen on the right. Each answer is used only once.

_____ 1. Viral gastroenteritis	A. *Shigella sonnei*
_____ 2. Cholera	B. *Enterobius vermicularis*
_____ 3. Typhoid fever	C. *Helicobacter pylori*
_____ 4. Pinworm	D. *Entamoeba histolytica*
_____ 5. Ulcers	E. *Vibrio* sp.
_____ 6. Tapeworm	F. *Staphylococcus aureus*
_____ 7. Bacterial gastroenteritis	G. Viridans streptococci
_____ 8. Periodontal disease	H. *Taenia solium*
_____ 9. Amebiasis	I. Rotaviruses
_____ 10. Food intoxication	J. *Salmonella enterica* serotype Typhi

Short Answer

1. What role do normal microbiota play in protecting the GI tract from colonization by pathogens?
2. Describe how gingivitis arises from untreated dental cavities.
3. How do antacids help alleviate the symptoms of peptic ulcers?
4. Describe the process by which cholera toxin leads to severe fluid and electrolyte loss during diarrhea.
5. Why is poor sanitation such a big factor in the continued occurrence of gastrointestinal disease?
6. What is the difference between gastroenteritis and intoxication?
7. How does hepatitis B decoy the immune system?
8. Explain why it is unlikely *Giardia intestinalis* will be eradicated from the environment.
9. What is the genetic difference between virulent and avirulent strains of *Entamoeba*?
10. Tapeworms do little obvious damage to their human hosts and yet they should not be allowed to remain in the GI tract. Why not?

CRITICAL THINKING

1. Prescription antacids are useful for treating peptic ulcers and allowing the stomach lining time to heal. Antacids, however, can actually increase the risk of contracting other bacterial and viral gastrointestinal diseases. How?
2. Why is it necessary to establish childhood immunization for hepatitis B virus in order to attempt to eliminate hepatic cancer? Why would it not be enough to vaccinate only those who have been exposed to HBV?
3. Most gastrointestinal tract diseases are ultimately self-limiting and nonfatal, so long as fluids can be replaced. How do these two general observations help explain why such diseases so commonly affect humans?
4. Infections with HBV and HCV usually take years, even decades, before visible signs of hepatitis manifest themselves. Epidemiologically, how does this influence our ability to track such diseases in a population and prevent transmission?
5. Why did soldiers living in battlefield trenches in Europe during World War I frequently suffer from acute necrotizing ulcerative gingivitis (trench mouth)?
6. A respiratory therapy student is puzzled about mumps. Her textbook covers the disease in the chapter on the digestive system, but her teacher insists the mumps virus is respiratory. Explain why both sources are accurate.
7. No vaccine against hepatitis delta virus exists, and researchers are not seeking one—there would be no market for it. Why?

ANSWERS TO QUESTIONS FOR REVIEW

Multiple Choice

1. c; 2. c; 3. a; 4. c; 5. c; 6. b; 7. a; 8. c; 9. a; 10. c; 11. b; 12. c; 13. a; 14. d; 15. c

Modified True/False

1. and does; 2. *H. pylori*; 3. true; 4. true; 5. less severe; 6. true; 7. protozoan; 8. true; 9. hepatitis A; 10. true

Fill in the Blank

1. enamel, dentin, pulp; 2. *Streptococcus mutans* (viridans streptococcus); 3. gastric, duodenal; 4. Shiga, Shiga-like; 5. oral herpes; 6. mumps; 7. jaundice; 8. giardiasis; 9. epithelial, adenylate cyclase; 10. scolex

Matching

1. I; 2. E; 3. J; 4. B; 5. C; 6. H; 7. A; 8. G; 9. D; 10. F

CREDITS

Illustration Credits

1, 10, 13, 17: Kenneth Probst. 2–6, 8, 12, 16: Precision Graphics. Disease Box 4 and 9: Kenneth Probst/Precision Graphics.

Photo Credits

Chapter 23 Opener: David Scharf/Peter Arnold. 7: Barry Dowsett/Photo Researchers. 9: Medical-On-Line Ltd. 11a: Moredun Animal Health Ltd./Photo Researchers. 11b: Linda Stanard/Photo Researchers. 13a: Linda Stanard/UCT/Photo Researchers. 14: From "Ultrastructural Observations of Giardiasis in a Murin Model," by Robert Owen, Paulina Nemanio, and David P. Stevens. *Gastroenterology*, 76:757–769, © 1979, American Gastroenterology Association. 15: *Microbiology: A Photographic Atlas for the Laboratory*, Benjamin Cummings, 2001. 16b: Stanley Flegler. 18: *Microbiology: A Photographic Atlas for the Laboratory*, Benjamin Cummings, 2001. Beneficial Microbe 1: Andrew Syred/Photo Researchers. Case Study 2: Marc Lontie, Medisch Centrum voor Huisartsen, Leuven, Belgium. Disease Box 1: Eye of Science/Photo Researchers. Disease Box 2: *Microbiology: A Photographic Atlas for the Laboratory*, Benjamin Cummings, 2001. Disease Box 3: M. Peres/Custom Medical Stock Photo. Disease Box 5: Eye of Science/Photo Researchers. Disease Box 6: Barbara Rice, NIP, CDC. Disease Box 7: Garry Watsib/Photo Researchers. Disease Box 8: Steve J. Upton, Parasitology Research, Division of Biology, Kansas State University. Disease Box 9: ASCP.

Epidemiology

Epidemiology

I PRINCIPLES OF EPIDEMIOLOGY

II CURRENT EPIDEMICS

III EPIDEMIOLOGY AND PUBLIC HEALTH

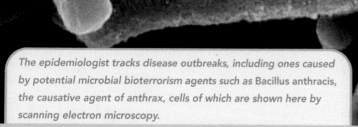

The epidemiologist tracks disease outbreaks, including ones caused by potential microbial bioterrorism agents such as Bacillus anthracis, the causative agent of anthrax, cells of which are shown here by scanning electron microscopy.

Dennis Kunkel/Dennis Kunkel Microscopy

I PRINCIPLES OF EPIDEMIOLOGY

Individuals may acquire pathogens through infected *vectors* (living carriers) and *vehicles* (non-living carriers) and spread the pathogens to other members of a population. Here we consider how pathogens spread to individuals through populations. **Epidemiology** is the study of the occurrence, distribution, and determinants of health and disease in a population. It thus deals with public health. Here we examine the principles of epidemiology and their application to the control of infectious diseases.

Many infectious diseases are adequately controlled in developed countries. In most developed countries, infectious diseases cause far fewer deaths than noninfectious diseases. Worldwide, however, infectious diseases remain serious public health problems, accounting for nearly 30% of the 56 million annual deaths. Even in developed countries, new infectious diseases such as West Nile fever are emerging, and previously controlled diseases such as tuberculosis are reemerging. In the United States, deaths due to infectious diseases are increasing (Figure 1). Effective control of infectious diseases remains a worldwide challenge that requires scientific, medical, economic, sociological, political, and educational solutions.

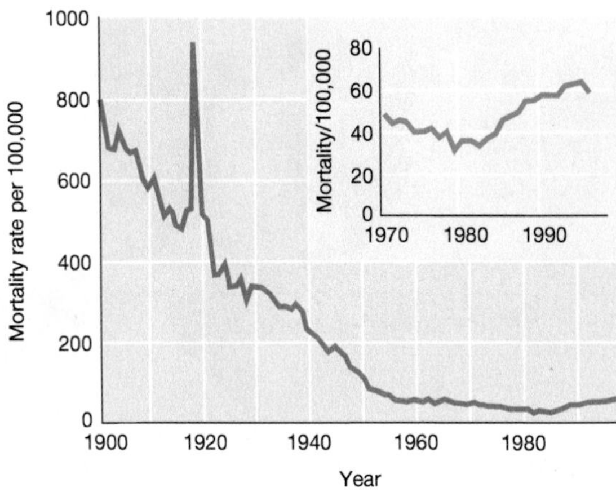

Figure 1 **Deaths due to infectious disease in the United States.** Although infectious disease death rates steadily declined throughout most of the twentieth century (except for the large numbers of deaths in 1918–1919 due to the influenza pandemic), the death rate has increased significantly since 1980. Adapted from Hughes, J. M. 2001. Emerging Infectious Diseases: A CDC Perspective. *Emerg. Infect. Dis.* 17: 494–496.

1 The Science of Epidemiology

To cause disease, a pathogen must grow and reproduce in the host. For this reason, epidemiologists track the natural history of pathogens. In many cases, an individual pathogen cannot grow outside the host; if the host dies, the pathogen also dies. Pathogens that kill the host before they move to a new host will become extinct. Most host-dependent pathogens must therefore adapt to coexist with the host.

A well-adapted pathogen lives in balance with its host, taking what it needs for existence and causing only a minimum of harm. Such pathogens may cause **chronic infections** (long-term infections) in the host. When equilibrium between host and pathogen exists, both host and pathogen survive. On the other hand, the host can be damaged when resistance of the host is low because of factors such as poor diet, age, and other stressors. In addition, new natural pathogens sometimes emerge for which the individual host, and sometimes the entire species, has not developed resistance. Such emerging pathogens often cause **acute infections**, characterized by rapid and dramatic onset. In these cases, pathogens can be selective forces in the evolution of the host, just as hosts, as they develop resistance, can be selective forces in the evolution of pathogens.

In cases where the pathogen is not dependent on the host for survival, the pathogen can cause devastating acute disease. Organisms in the genus *Clostridium*, for example, ubiquitous inhabitants of the soil, are occasional accidental human pathogens, causing life-threatening diseases such as tetanus, botulism, gangrene, and certain gastrointestinal diseases.

The epidemiologist traces the spread of a disease to identify its origin and mode of transmission. Epidemiologic data are obtained by collecting disease information in a population. With the goal of defining common factors for an illness, data are gathered from disease-reporting surveillance networks, clinical records, and patient interviews. This is in contrast to individual patient treatment and diagnosis in the clinic or laboratory. Knowledge of both the population dynamics and clinical problems associated with a given disease are important if public health measures to control diseases are to be effective.

1 MiniReview

Epidemiology is the study of the occurrence, distribution, and determinants of health and disease in a population. To understand infectious disease, effects on both populations and individuals must be studied. The interactions of pathogens with hosts are dynamic, affecting the long-term evolution and survival of all species involved.

- How does an epidemiologist differ from a microbiologist?
- Why do epidemiologists acquire population-based data for infectious diseases?

2 The Vocabulary of Epidemiology

A number of terms have specific meaning to the epidemiologist. A disease is an **epidemic** when it occurs in an unusually high number of individuals in a population at the same time;

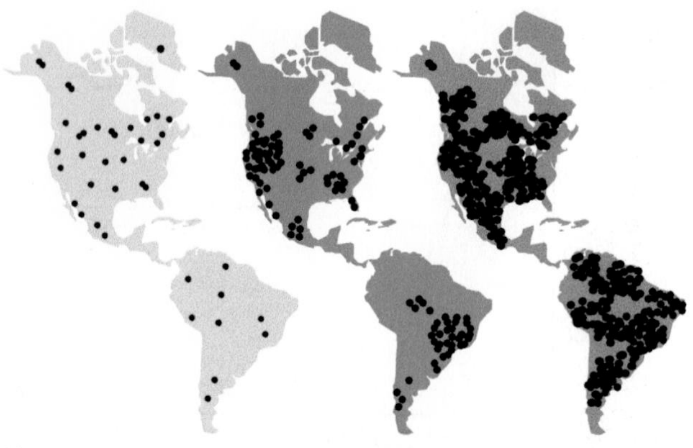

(a) Endemic disease (b) Epidemic disease (c) Pandemic disease

Figure 2 **Endemic, epidemic, and pandemic disease.** Each dot represents several cases of a particular disease. *(a)* Endemic diseases are always present in a population in a given geographical area. *(b)* Epidemic diseases show high incidence in a wider area, usually developing from an endemic focus. *(c)* Pandemic diseases are distributed worldwide. Diseases such as influenza are endemic in certain areas and develop into annual epidemics under appropriate circumstances, such as crowding. Epidemics may develop into pandemics.

a **pandemic** is a widespread, usually worldwide, epidemic (Figure 2). By contrast, an **endemic disease** is one that is constantly present, usually at low incidence, in a population. An endemic disease implies that the pathogen may not be highly virulent, or the majority of individuals in the selected population may be immune, resulting in low disease incidence. However, as long as an endemic situation exists, the infected individuals are reservoirs of infection, providing a source of viable infectious agents from which other individuals may be infected.

The **incidence** of a particular disease is the number of new cases of an individual disease in a population in a given time period. For example, in 2005 there were 41,953 new cases of AIDS in the United States, for an incidence of 14 new cases per 100,000 people per year. The **prevalence** of a given disease is the total number of new and existing disease cases reported in a population in a given time period. For example, there were 425,910 persons living with AIDS at the end of 2005 within the United States. Expressed another way, the prevalence of AIDS in this population was 176.2 per 100,000 in 2005. Thus, *incidence* provides a record of new cases of a disease, whereas *prevalence* indicates the total disease burden in a population.

Sporadic cases of disease may occur when individual cases are recorded in geographically separated areas, implying that the incidents are not related. A disease **outbreak**, on the other hand, occurs when a number of cases are observed, usually in a relatively short period of time, in an area previously experiencing only sporadic cases of the disease. Finally, diseased individuals who show no symptoms or only mild symptoms have what are called *subclinical infections*. Subclinically infected individuals are frequently **carriers** of a particular disease, because even though they themselves show few (or perhaps no) symptoms, they may be actively carrying and shedding the pathogen.

Mortality and Morbidity

The incidence and prevalence of disease, as determined from statistical analyses of illness and death records, is an indicator of the public health of a selected group such as the total global population or the population of a localized region, such as a city, state, or country. Public health conditions and concerns vary with location and time, and the assessment of public health at a given moment provides only a snapshot of a dynamic situation. Public health policies are designed to reduce incidence and prevalence of disease and can be adequately assessed only by examining public health statistics over longer time periods.

Mortality is the incidence of *death* in the population. Infectious diseases were the major causes of death in 1900 in developed countries, but they are now much less significant. Noninfectious "lifestyle" diseases such as heart disease and cancer are now much more prevalent and cause higher mortality than do infectious diseases. However, the current situation could change rapidly if a breakdown in public health measures were to occur. In developing countries, infectious diseases are still major causes of mortality (Table 1 and Section 10).

Morbidity refers to the incidence of *disease* in populations and includes both fatal and nonfatal diseases. Morbidity statistics define the public health of a population more precisely than mortality statistics because many diseases have relatively low mortality. The major causes of illness are quite different from the major causes of death. High morbidity diseases include acute respiratory diseases such as the common cold and acute digestive disorders. Both can be due to infectious agents but seldom directly cause death in the population of developed countries.

Disease Progression

In terms of clinical symptoms, the course of a typical acute infectious disease can be divided into stages:

1. *Infection:* The organism invades, colonizes, and grows in the host.
2. *Incubation period:* A period of time elapses between infection and the appearance of disease symptoms. Some diseases, like influenza, have very short incubation periods, measured in days; others, like AIDS, have longer ones, sometimes extending for years. The incubation period for a given disease is determined by inoculum size, virulence, and life cycle of the pathogen, resistance of the host, and distance of the site of entrance from the focus of infection. At the end of incubation, the first symptoms, such as headache and a feeling of illness, appear.
3. *Acute period:* The disease is at its height, with overt symptoms such as fever and chills.

Table 1 Worldwide deaths due to infectious diseases, 2002

Disease	*Deaths*	*Causative agent(s)*
Acute respiratory infections[a, b]	3,963,000	Bacteria, viruses, fungi
Acquired immunodeficiency syndrome (AIDS)	2,777,000	Virus
Diarrheal diseases	1,798,000	Bacteria, viruses
Tuberculosis[a]	1,566,000	Bacterium
Malaria	1,272,000	Protist
Measles[a]	611,000	Virus
Pertussis (whooping cough)[a]	294,000	Bacterium
Tetanus[a]	214,000	Bacterium
Meningitis, bacterial[a]	173,000	Bacterium
Hepatitis (all types)[a, c]	157,000	Viruses
Syphilis	153,000	Bacterium
Leishmaniasis	51,000	Protist
Trypanosomiasis (sleeping sickness)	48,000	Protist
Chlamydia	16,000	Bacterium
Schistosomiasis	15,000	Helminth
Chagas disease	14,000	Helminth
Japanese encephalitis	14,000	Virus
Dengue	13,000	Virus
Intestinal nematode infections	12,000	Helminth
Other communicable diseases	1,700,000	Various agents

Globally, there were about 57 million deaths from all causes in 2002. About 14.9 million deaths were from communicable infectious diseases, nearly all in developing countries. Data show the 20 leading causes of death due to infectious diseases. The world population in 2002 was estimated at 6.2 billion.

Data are from the World Health Organization (WHO), Geneva, Switzerland.

[a]Diseases for which effective vaccines are available.

[b]For some acute respiratory agents such as influenza and *Streptococcus pneumoniae* there are effective vaccines; for others, such as colds, there are no vaccines.

[c]Vaccines are available for hepatitis A virus and hepatitis B virus. There are no vaccines for other hepatitis agents.

4. *Decline period:* Disease symptoms are subsiding, any fever subsides, usually following a period of intense sweating, and a feeling of well-being develops. The decline period may be rapid (within 1 day), in which case it is said to occur by *crisis,* or it may be slower, extending over several days, in which case it is said to be by *lysis*.
5. *Convalescent period:* The patient regains strength and returns to normal.

During the later stages of the infection cycle, the immune mechanisms of the host become increasingly important, and in most cases complete recovery from the disease requires (and results in) active immunity.

2 MiniReview

An endemic disease is constantly present at low incidence in a specific population. An epidemic disease occurs in unusually high incidence in a specific population. Incidence is a record of new cases of a disease, whereas prevalence is a record of total cases of a disease in a population. Infectious diseases cause morbidity (illness) and may cause mortality (death). An infectious disease follows a predictable clinical pattern in the host.

- Distinguish between an endemic disease, an epidemic disease, and a pandemic disease.
- Distinguish between morbidity and mortality. Is host mortality advantageous for the pathogen?

3 Disease Reservoirs and Epidemics

Reservoirs are sites in which infectious agents remain viable and from which infection of individuals may occur. Reservoirs may be either animate or inanimate. Table 2 lists some human infectious diseases with epidemic potential and their reservoirs. Some pathogens are primarily saprophytic (living on dead matter) and only incidentally infect humans and cause disease. For example, *Clostridium tetani* (the causal agent of tetanus) normally inhabits the soil. Infection of animals by this organism is an accidental event. That is, infection of a host is not essential for its continued existence, and in the absence of susceptible hosts, *C. tetani* would still survive in nature.

For many other pathogens, however, living organisms are the only reservoirs. In these cases, the reservoir host is essential for the life cycle of the infectious agent. A number of

Table 2 Epidemic diseases: Agents, sources, reservoirs, and control

Disease	*Causative agent*[a]	*Infection sources*	*Reservoirs*	*Control measures*
Common-source epidemics[b]				
Anthrax	*Bacillus anthracis* (B)	Milk or meat from infected animals	Cattle, swine, goats, sheep, horses	Destruction of infected animals
Bacillary dysentery	*Shigella dysenteriae* (B)	Fecal contamination of food and water	Humans	Detection and control of carriers; oversight of food handlers; decontamination of water supplies
Botulism	*Clostridium botulinum* (B)	Soil-contaminated food	Soil	Proper preservation of food
Brucellosis	*Brucella melitensis* (B)	Milk or meat from infected animals	Cattle, swine, goats, sheep, horses	Pasteurization of milk; control of infection in animals
Cholera	*Vibrio cholerae* (B)	Fecal contamination of food and water	Humans	Decontamination of public water sources; immunization
E. coli O157:H7 food infection	*Escherichia coli* O157:H7 (B)	Fecal contamination of food and water	Humans, cattle	Decontamination of public water sources; oversight of food handlers; pasteurization of beverages
Giardiasis	*Giardia* spp. (P)	Fecal contamination of water	Wild mammals	Decontamination of public water sources
Hepatitis	Hepatitis A, B, C, D, E (V)	Infected humans	Humans	Decontamination of contaminated fluids and fomites; immunization if available (A and B)
Legionnaire's disease	*Legionella pneumophila* (B)	Contaminated water	High-moisture environments	Decontamination of air conditioning cooling towers, etc.
Paratyphoid	*Salmonella paratyphi* (B)	Fecal contamination of food and water	Humans	Decontamination of public water sources; oversight of food handlers; immunization
Typhoid fever	*Salmonella typhi* (B)	Fecal contamination of food and water	Humans	Decontamination of public water sources; oversight of food handlers; pasteurization of milk; immunization
Host-to-host epidemics				
Respiratory diseases				
Diphtheria	*Corynebacterium diphtheriae* (B)	Human cases and carriers; infected food and fomites	Humans	Immunization; quarantine of infected individuals
Hantavirus pulmonary syndrome	Hantavirus (V)	Inhalation of contaminated fecal material; contact	Rodents	Control of rodent population and exposure
Hemorrhagic fever	Ebola virus (V)	Infected body fluids	Unknown	Quarantine of active cases
Meningococcal meningitis	*Neisseria meningitidis* (B)	Human cases and carriers	Humans	Exposure treated with sulfadiazine for susceptible strains; immunization
Pneumococcal pneumonia	*Streptococcus pneumoniae* (B)	Human carriers	Humans	Antibiotic treatment; isolation of cases for period of communicability
Tuberculosis	*Mycobacterium tuberculosis* (B)	Sputum from human cases; infected milk	Humans, cattle	Treatment with isoniazid; pasteurization of milk
Whooping cough	*Bordetella pertussis* (B)	Human cases	Humans	Immunization; case isolation
German measles	Rubella virus (V)	Human cases	Humans	Immunization; avoid contact between infected individuals and pregnant women

pathogens live only in humans, and maintenance of the pathogen requires person-to-person transmission. This is common for viral and bacterial respiratory pathogens and sexually transmitted pathogens. The staphylococci and streptococci are examples of human-restricted pathogens, as are the agents that cause diphtheria, gonorrhea, and mumps. As we shall see, pathogens that live their entire life cycle dependent on a single host species, especially humans, can be eradicated and many are controlled.

Zoonosis

A number of infectious diseases are caused by pathogens that propagate in both humans and animals. A disease that primarily infects animals but is occasionally transmitted to humans is called a **zoonosis**. Because public health measures for animal populations are much less developed than for humans, the infection rate for veterinary diseases may be higher when animal-to-animal transmission is the rule. Occasionally, transmission is from animal to human; person-to-person transfer of these pathogens is rare, but does occur. Factors leading to the emergence of zoonotic disease include the existence of the infectious agent, the proper environment for propagation and transfer of the agent, and the presence of the new susceptible host species. When there is animal-to-human transmission, a new infectious disease may suddenly emerge in the exposed human population. For examples, see the

Table 2 (continued)

Disease	*Causative agent*[a]	*Infection sources*	*Reservoirs*	*Control measures*
Respiratory diseases				
Influenza	Influenza virus (V)	Human cases	Humans, animals	Immunization
Measles	Measles virus (V)	Human cases	Humans	Immunization
Sexually transmitted diseases[c]				
Acquired immunodeficiency syndrome (AIDS)	Human immunodeficiency virus (HIV)	Infected body fluids, especially blood and semen	Humans	Treatment with metabolic inhibitors (not curative)
Chlamydia	*Chlamydia trachomatis* (B)	Urethral, vaginal, and anal secretions	Humans	Testing for organism during routine pelvic examinations; chemotherapy of carriers and potential contacts; case tracing and treatment
Genital warts, cervical cancer	Human papilloma-virus (HPV)	Urethral and vaginal secretions	Humans	Immunization
Gonorrhea	*Neisseria gonorrhoeae* (B)	Urethral and vaginal secretions	Humans	Chemotherapy of carriers and potential contacts; case tracing and treatment
Syphilis	*Treponema pallidum* (B)	Infected exudate or blood	Humans	Identification by serological tests; antibiotic treatment of seropositive individuals
Trichomoniasis	*Trichomonas vaginalis* (P)	Urethral, vaginal, and prostate secretions	Humans	Chemotherapy of infected individuals and contacts
Vectorborne diseases				
Epidemic typhus	*Rickettsia prowazekii* (B)	Bite from infected louse	Humans, lice	Control louse population
Lyme disease	*Borrelia burgdorferi* (B)	Bite from infected tick	Rodents, deer, ticks	Avoid tick exposure; treat infected individuals with antibiotics
Malaria	*Plasmodium* spp. (P)	Bite from *Anopheles* mosquito	Humans, mosquito	Control mosquito population; treat infected humans with antimalarial drugs
Plague	*Yersinia pestis* (B)	Bite from flea	Wild rodents	Control rodent populations; immunization
Rocky Mountain spotted fever	*Rickettsia rickettsii* (B)	Bite from infected tick	Ticks, rabbits, mice	Avoid tick exposure; treat infected individuals with antibiotics
Direct-contact diseases				
Psittacosis	*Chlamydia psittaci* (B)	Contact with birds or bird excrement	Wild and domestic birds	Avoid contact with birds; treat infected individuals with antibiotics
Rabies	Rabies virus (V)	Bite by carnivores, contact with infected neural tissue	Wild and domestic carnivores	Avoid animal bites; immunization of animal handlers and exposed individuals
Tularemia	*Francisella tularensis* (B)	Contact with rabbits	Rabbits	Avoid contact with rabbits; treat infected individuals with antibiotics

[a]B, Bacteria; V, virus; P, protist.
[b]Some common-source diseases can also be spread from host to host.
[c]Sexually transmitted diseases can also be controlled by effective use of condoms and by sexual abstinence.

Microbial Sidebar, "SARS as a Model of Epidemiological Success" for a discussion of severe acute respiratory syndrome (SARS) and other zoonotic epidemics.

In many cases, control of a zoonotic disease in the human population does not eliminate the disease as a potential public health problem. Eradication of the human form of a zoonotic disease can generally be achieved only through elimination of the disease in the animal reservoir. This is because maintenance of the pathogen in nature depends on animal-to-animal transfer, and humans are incidental, nonessential hosts. For example, plague is primarily a disease of rodents. Effective control of plague is achieved by control of the infected rodent population and the insect (flea) vector. These methods are more effective in preventing plague transmission than interventions such as vaccines in the incidental human host. Zoonotic bovine tuberculosis is indistinguishable from human tuberculosis. Often spread from infected cattle to humans, control was achieved primarily by identifying and destroying infected animals. Pasteurization of milk was also of considerable importance because milk was the main vehicle of bovine tuberculosis transmission to humans.

Certain infectious diseases, particularly those caused by organisms such as protists, have more complex life cycles, involving an obligate transfer from a nonhuman host to humans, followed by transfer back to the nonhuman host (for example, malaria). In such cases, the disease may potentially be controlled in either humans or the alternate animal host.

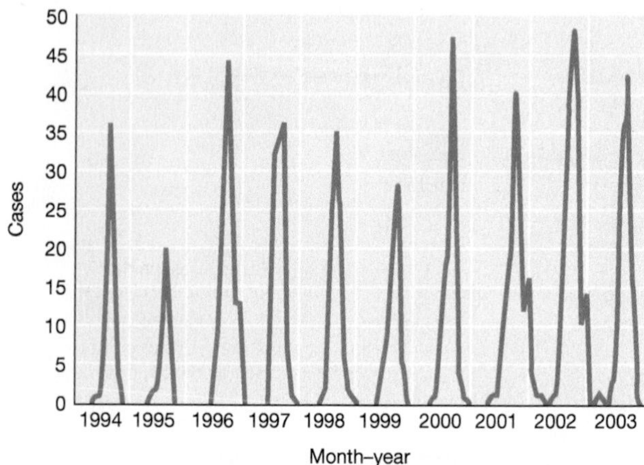

Figure 3 The incidence of California encephalitis in the United States by year and month of onset. Note the sharp rise in late summer, followed by a complete decline in winter. The disease cycle follows the yearly cycle of the mosquito vector prevalence. In 2003 there were 108 cases in 12 states. Data are from the Centers for Disease Control and Prevention, Atlanta, GA, USA.

Carriers

A *carrier* is a pathogen-infected individual showing no signs of clinical disease. Carriers are potential sources of infection for others. Carriers may be individuals in the incubation period of the disease, in which case the carrier state precedes the development of actual symptoms. Respiratory infections such as colds and influenza, for example, are often spread via carriers because they are unaware of their infection and so are not taking any precautions against infecting others. For such acute carriers, the carrier state lasts for only a short time. On the other hand, chronic carriers may spread disease for extended periods of time. Chronic carriers usually appear perfectly healthy. They may be individuals who have recovered from a clinical disease, but still harbor viable pathogens, or they may be individuals with inapparent infections.

Carriers can be identified in populations using diagnostic techniques such as culture or immunoassay surveys. For example, skin testing with *Mycobacterium tuberculosis* antigens tests for delayed hypersensitivity. This reaction, easily detected in the skin test, reveals exposure and previous or current infection with *M. tuberculosis* and is widely used to identify previous infection and carriers of tuberculosis. Other diseases in which carriers are important for the spread of infection include hepatitis, typhoid fever, and AIDS. Culture or immunoassay surveys of food handlers and health-care workers are sometimes used to identify individuals who are carriers and pose a risk as common sources of infection.

A classic example of a chronic carrier was the woman known as Typhoid Mary, a cook in New York City in the early part of the twentieth century. Typhoid Mary (her real name was Mary Mallon) was employed as a cook during a typhoid fever epidemic in 1906. Investigations revealed that Mary was associated with a number of the typhoid outbreaks. She was the likely source of infection because her feces contained large numbers of the typhoid bacterium, *Salmonella typhi*. She remained a carrier throughout her life, probably because her gallbladder was infected and continuously secreted organisms into her intestine. She refused to have her gallbladder removed and was imprisoned. Released on the pledge that she would not cook or handle food for others, Mary disappeared, changed her name, and continued to cook in restaurants and public institutions, leaving behind epidemic outbreaks of typhoid fever. After several years, she was again arrested and imprisoned and remained in custody until her death in 1938.

3 MiniReview

Many pathogens exist only in humans and are maintained only by transmission from person to person. Some human pathogens, however, live mostly in soil, water, or animals. An understanding of disease reservoirs, carriers, and pathogen life cycles is critical for controlling disease.

- What is a disease reservoir?
- Distinguish between acute and chronic carriers. Provide an example of each.

4 Infectious Disease Transmission

Epidemiologists follow the transmission of a disease by correlating geographic, climatic, social, and demographic data with disease incidence. These correlations are used to identify possible modes of transmission. A disease limited to a restricted geographic location, for example, may suggest a particular vector; malaria, a disease of tropical regions, is transmitted only by mosquito species restricted to tropical regions. A marked seasonality or periodicity of a disease is often indicative of certain modes of transmission. Such is the case for influenza, where disease incidence increases dramatically when children enter school and come in close contact, increasing opportunities for person-to-person viral transmission.

Finally, pathogen survival depends on efficient host-to-host transmission. Pathogens often have modes of transmission that are related to the preferred habitat of the pathogen in the body. Respiratory pathogens are typically airborne, for example, whereas intestinal pathogens are spread through contaminated food or water. In some cases, environmental factors such as weather patterns may influence the survival of the pathogen. For example, California encephalitis, caused by single-stranded RNA bunyaviruses, occurs primarily during the summer and fall months and disappears every winter in a predictable cyclical pattern (Figure 3). The virus is transmitted from mosquito hosts that die during the winter months, causing the disease to disappear until the insect host reappears and retransmits the virus in the summer months. Virtually all mosquito-transmitted encephalitis viruses follow the same seasonal pattern.

Pathogens can be classified by their mechanism of transmission, but all mechanisms have these stages in common: (1) escape from the host, (2) travel, and (3) entry into a new host. Pathogen transmission can be by direct or indirect mechanisms.

Direct Host-to-Host Transmission

Host-to-host transmission often occurs when an infected host transmits a disease directly to a susceptible host without the assistance of an intermediate host or inanimate object. Upper respiratory infections such as the common cold and influenza are most often transmitted directly by droplets resulting from sneezing or coughing. Many of these droplets, however, do not remain airborne for long. Transmission, therefore, requires close, although not necessarily intimate, person-to-person contact.

Some pathogens are extremely sensitive to environmental factors such as drying and heat and are unable to survive for significant periods of time away from the host. These pathogens, transmitted only by intimate person-to-person contact such as exchange of body fluids in sexual intercourse, include those responsible for sexually transmitted diseases such as syphilis (*Treponema pallidum*) and gonorrhea (*Neisseria gonorrhoeae*).

Direct contact also transmits skin pathogens such as staphylococci (boils and pimples) and fungi (ringworm). These pathogens, however, are relatively resistant to environmental conditions such as drying, and they often spread by indirect means as well.

Indirect Host-to-Host Transmission

Indirect transmission of an infectious agent can be facilitated by either living or inanimate agents. Living agents transmitting pathogens are called **vectors**. Commonly, arthropod insects (mites, ticks, or fleas) or vertebrates (dogs, cats, or rodents) act as vectors. Arthropod vectors may not be hosts for the pathogen, but may carry the agent from one host to another. Many arthropods obtain their nourishment by biting and sucking blood, and if the pathogen is present in the blood, the arthropod vector may ingest the pathogen and transmit it when biting another individual. In some cases viral pathogens replicate in the arthropod vector, which is then considered an alternate host. Such is the case for West Nile virus. Such replication leads to an increase in pathogen numbers, increasing the probability that a subsequent bite will lead to infection.

Inanimate agents such as bedding, toys, books, and surgical instruments can also transmit disease. These inanimate objects are collectively called **fomites**. Food and water are potential disease **vehicles**. Fomites can also be disease vehicles, but major epidemics originating from a single-vehicle source are typically traced to food or water because these are consumed in large amounts by many individuals in a population.

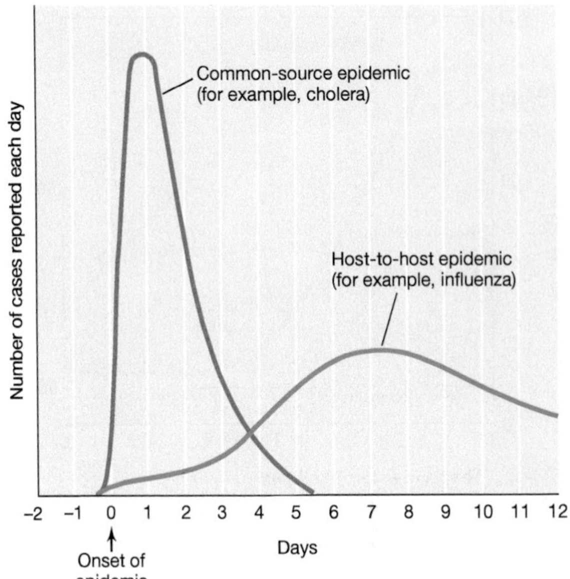

Figure 4 Origins of epidemics. The shape of the epidemic curve identifies the likely origin. In a common-source epidemic, such as from contaminated food or water, the curve is characterized by a sharp rise to a peak, with a rapid decline, which is less abrupt than the rise. Cases continue to be reported for a period approximately equal to the duration of one incubation period of the disease. In a host-to-host epidemic, the curve is characterized by a relatively slow, progressive rise, and cases continue to be reported over a period equivalent to several incubation periods of the disease.

Epidemics

Major epidemics are usually classified as *common-source* or *host-to-host* epidemics. These two types of epidemics are contrasted in Figure 4. Table 2 summarizes the key epidemiological features of major epidemic diseases.

A **common-source epidemic** arises as the result of infection (or intoxication) of a large number of people from a contaminated common source such as food or water. Such epidemics are often caused by a breakdown in the sanitation of a central food or water distribution system. Foodborne and waterborne common-source epidemics are primarily intestinal diseases; the pathogen leaves the body in fecal material, contaminates food or water supplies due to improper sanitary procedures, and then enters the intestinal tract of the recipient during ingestion. Waterborne and foodborne diseases are generally controlled by public health measures. A classic example of a common-source epidemic is that of cholera. In 1855 the British physician John Snow showed that cholera spreads through drinking water. His classic studies of water distribution systems in London clearly demonstrated that cholera is spread by fecal contamination of a water supply. In the case of cholera, the infectious agent, the bacterium *Vibrio cholerae*, was transmitted through consumption of the contaminated common-source vehicle, water.

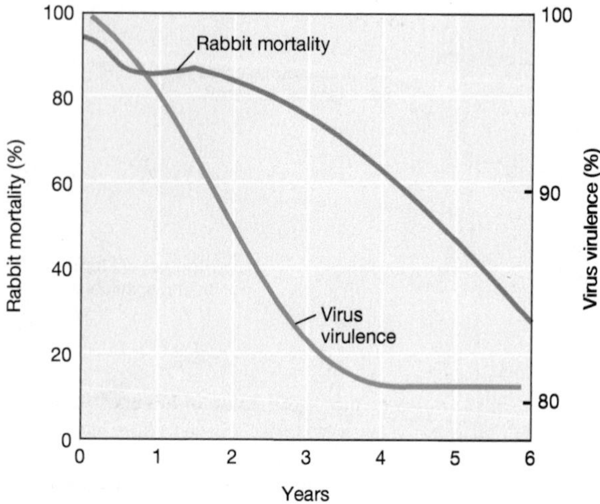

Figure 5 Myxoma virus, virulence, and Australian rabbit susceptibility. Data were collected after myxoma virus was introduced into Australia in 1950. Virus virulence is given as the average mortality in standard laboratory rabbits for virus recovered from the field each year. Rabbit susceptibility was determined by removing young feral rabbits from dens and infecting them with a virus strain of moderately high virulence. The test strains killed 90–95% of normal laboratory rabbits.

The disease incidence for a common-source outbreak is characterized by a rapid rise to a peak because a large number of individuals become ill within a relatively brief period of time (Table 4). Assuming that the pathogen-contaminated common source is discovered and sanitized, the incidence of a common-source illness also declines rapidly, although the decline is less rapid than the rise. Cases continue to be reported for a period of time approximately equal to the duration of one incubation-period of the disease.

In a **host-to-host epidemic**, the disease incidence shows a relatively slow, progressive rise (Table 4) and a gradual decline. Cases continue to be reported over a period of time equivalent to several incubation periods of the disease. A host-to-host epidemic can be initiated by the introduction of a single infected individual into a susceptible population, with this individual infecting one or more people. The pathogen then replicates in susceptible individuals, reaches a communicable stage, and is transferred to other susceptible individuals, where it again replicates and becomes communicable. Influenza and chickenpox are examples of diseases that are typically spread in host-to-host epidemics.

4 MiniReview

Infectious diseases can be transmitted directly from one host to another, or indirectly by living vectors or inanimate objects (fomites) and common vehicles such as food and water. Epidemics may be of common-source or host-to-host origin.

- Distinguish between direct and indirect transmission of disease. Cite at least one example of each.
- Distinguish between a common-source epidemic and a host-to-host epidemic. Cite at least one example of each.

5 The Host Community

The colonization of a susceptible, unimmunized host by a pathogen may first lead to explosive infections, transmission to uninfected hosts, and an epidemic. As the host population develops resistance, however, the spread of the pathogen is checked, and eventually a balance is reached in which host and pathogen are in equilibrium. In an extreme case, failure to reach equilibrium could result in death and eventual extinction of the host species. If the pathogen has no other host, then the extinction of the host also results in extinction of the pathogen. Thus, the evolutionary success of a pathogen may depend on its ability to establish a balanced equilibrium with the host, rather than its ability to destroy the host. In most cases, the evolution of the host and the pathogen affect one another; that is, the host and parasite *coevolve*.

Coevolution of a Host and a Parasite

A classic example of host and pathogen coevolution occurred when a virus was intentionally introduced for purposes of controlling feral rabbits in Australia. Rabbits introduced into Australia from Europe in 1859 spread until they were overrunning large parts of the continent and causing massive crop and vegetation damage.

Myxoma virus was introduced into Australia in 1950 to control the rabbit population. The virus is extremely virulent and usually causes a fatal infection. It spreads rapidly through mosquitoes and other biting insects. Within several months, the virus spread over a large area, rising to a peak in the summer when the mosquito vectors were present and declining in the winter. During the first year of the epidemic, over 95% of the infected rabbits died. However, when virus isolated from infected rabbits was characterized for virulence in newborn feral and laboratory rabbits, the viral isolates from the field had decreased virulence and the resistance of the feral rabbits had increased dramatically. Within 6 years, rabbit mortality dropped to about 84% (Figure 5). In time, all of the surviving feral rabbits acquired the resistance factors. By the 1980s the rabbit population in Australia was nearing the premyxomatosis levels, with widespread environmental destruction and pressure on native plants and animals.

In 1995, Australian authorities began controlled releases of another highly virulent rabbit pathogen, the rabbit hemorrhagic disease virus (RHDV), a single-stranded, positive-sense RNA virus. Because RHDV is spread by direct contact and kills animals within days of initial infection, authorities believed the infections would kill all rabbits in a local population, preventing the emergence of resistance. Thus, they reasoned, the virus–host relationship could be maintained in favor of the pathogen more reliably than the arthropod-borne myxomatosis virus. Initial reports indicated that RHDV was very effective at reducing local rabbit populations. However, natural infection of some rabbits by an indigenous hemorrhagic fever virus conferred immune cross-resistance to the introduced RHDV. This unpredictable immune response limited the effectiveness of the control program in certain areas of Australia. Again, the host developed resistance to the control agent, moving the host–pathogen balance toward equilibrium.

Although coevolution of host and pathogen may be common in diseases that rely on host-to-host transmission, for pathogens that do not rely on host-to-host transmission, as we mentioned for *Clostridium*, there is no selection for decreased virulence to support mutual coexistence. Vector-borne pathogens normally transmitted by the bite of arthropods or ticks are also under no evolutionary pressure to spare the human host. As long as the vector can obtain its blood meal before the host dies, the pathogen can maintain a high level of virulence, decimating the human host in the process of infection. For example, the malaria parasites *Plasmodium* spp. show antigenic variations in their coat proteins that aid in avoiding the immune response of the host. This genetic ability to avoid the host responses increases pathogen virulence without regard to the susceptibility of the host. However, as we shall see for the disease malaria, the host may develop disease-specific resistance under the constant evolutionary pressure exerted by a highly virulent pathogen.

Other evidence for the phenomenon of continually increasing pathogen virulence comes from studies of supervirulent diarrheal diseases in newborns. In hospital situations, *Escherichia coli* can cause severe diarrheal illness and even death, and virulence seems to increase with each passage of the pathogen through a hospital patient. The *E. coli* organisms replicate in one host and are then transferred to another patient through carriers such as healthcare providers or on fomites such as soiled bedding and furniture. Even if the host dies or cannot contact others to transfer the disease, the virulent *E. coli* strain infects others through transmission by means other than the person-to-person route. Extraordinary efforts such as completely washing the nursery and furniture with disinfectant and transferring staff are sometimes necessary to interrupt the cycle of these highly virulent infections.

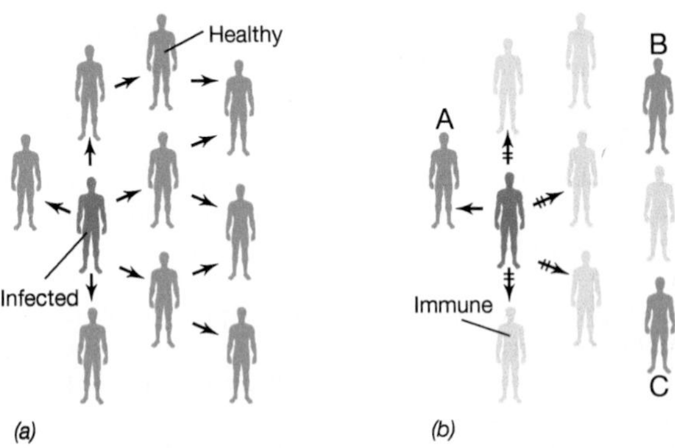

Figure 6 **Herd immunity and transmission of infection.** Immunity in some individuals protects nonimmune individuals from infection. *(a)* In an unprotected population, an infected individual can successfully infect (arrows) all of the healthy individuals. Newly infected individuals will in turn transfer the pathogen directly to other healthy individuals. *(b)* For a moderately transmissible pathogen such as *Corynebacterium diphtheriae* (diphtheria) in a population of moderate density, the infected individual cannot transfer the organism to all susceptible individuals because resistant individuals, immune by virtue of previous exposure or immunization, break the cycle of pathogen transmission. Even if healthy individual A becomes infected, other healthy individuals, B and C, are protected. For a moderately transmissible pathogen such as *C. diphtheriae*, 70% immunity confers resistance to the entire population. For highly transmissible pathogens such as chickenpox (varicella), higher levels of herd immunity, on the order of 90%, are needed to stop transmission.

Herd Immunity

Herd immunity is the resistance of a group to infection due to immunity of a high proportion of the members of the group. Assessment of herd immunity is important for understanding the development of epidemics. In general, if a high proportion of individuals in a group are immune to an infectious agent, then the whole population will be protected. A higher proportion of individuals must be immune to prevent an epidemic by a highly virulent agent or one with a long period of infectivity and a lower proportion for a less virulent agent or one with a brief period of infectivity. In the absence of immunity, even poorly infective agents can be transmitted person-to-person if susceptible hosts have repeated or constant contact with an infected individual. Such appears to be the case for the transmission of H5N1 avian influenza between and among humans.

The proportion of the population that must be immune to prevent infection in the rest of the population can be estimated from data derived from immunization programs. For example, for poliovirus immunization in the United States, studies of polio incidence in large populations indicate that if a population is 70% immunized, polio will be essentially absent from the population. The immunized individuals protect the rest of the population because they cannot acquire and pass on the pathogen, thus breaking the cycle of infection (Figure 6). For highly infectious diseases such as influenza and measles, up to 90–95% of the population must be immune to confer herd immunity.

A value of about 70% of the population immunized has also been estimated to confer herd immunity for diphtheria, but studies of several small diphtheria outbreaks indicate that in densely populated areas a much higher proportion of susceptible individuals must be immunized to prevent an epidemic. With diphtheria, an additional complication arises because immunized persons can still harbor the pathogen and can thus be chronic carriers. This is because immunization protects against the effects of the diphtheria toxin, but not necessarily against infection by *Corynebacterium diphtheriae*, the bacterium that causes diphtheria.

Cycles of Disease

Certain diseases occur in cycles. For example, influenza occurs in an annual cyclic pattern, causing epidemics propagated in school children and other populations. Influenza infectivity is high in crowded situations such as schools because the virus is transmitted by the respiratory route. Major epidemic strains of influenza virus change virtually every year, and as a result most children are highly susceptible to infection. On the introduction of virus into a school, an explosive, propagated epidemic results. Virtually every individual becomes infected and then becomes immune. As the immune population increases, the epidemic subsides.

5 MiniReview

For most epidemic diseases, hosts and pathogens coevolve to reach a steady state that favors the continued survival of both host and pathogen. When a large proportion of a population is immune to a given disease, disease spread is inhibited. Disease cycles occur when a large, recurring, nonimmune population is exposed to a pathogen.

- Explain coevolution of host and pathogen. Cite a specific example.
- How does herd immunity prevent a nonimmune individual from acquiring a disease? Give an example.

II CURRENT EPIDEMICS

Here we examine data collected by national and worldwide disease-surveillance programs that provide a picture of emerging disease patterns for AIDS and healthcare-associated infections.

6 The AIDS Pandemic

Acquired immunodeficiency syndrome (AIDS) is a viral disease that attacks the immune system. The first reported cases of AIDS were diagnosed in the United States in 1981. Through 2005, in the United States 956,666 cases have been reported, with 550,394 deaths. A total of 44,198 new AIDS cases were reported in United States in 2005, and 38,000 or more new cases have been reported every year since 1989 (Figure 7).

Worldwide, from 1981 through 2003, at least 70 million individuals have been infected with human immunodeficiency virus (HIV), the virus that causes AIDS. A total of more than 25 million people have already died from AIDS, and 40 million are currently living with the disease. Globally, another 5 million individuals are infected each year. North America has about 1 million HIV-infected individuals, and over 476,000 individuals are now living with HIV/AIDS in the United States. Sub-Saharan Africa has 26.6 million infected people (Table 3). In the African countries of Botswana and

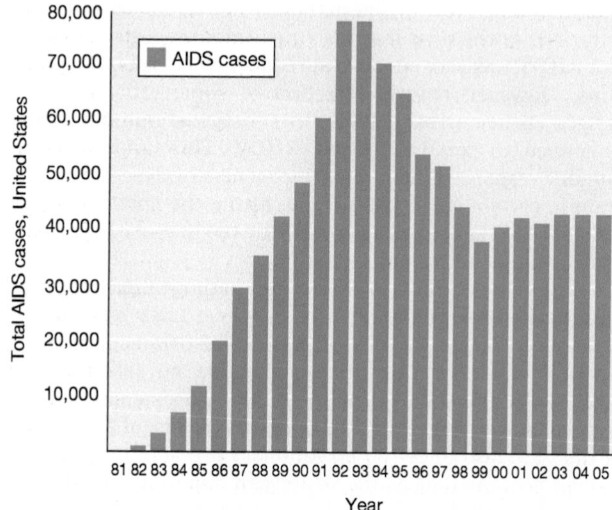

Figure 7 **Annual diagnosed cases of acquired immunodeficiency syndrome (AIDS) since 1981 in the United States.** Cumulatively, there have been 956,666 cases of AIDS through 2005. Data are from the HIV/AIDS Surveillance Report, Centers for Disease Control and Prevention, Division of HIV/AIDS Prevention-Surveillance and Epidemiology.

Swaziland, about 40% of the adult population is infected with HIV. AIDS caused about 3 million deaths in 2003, with 2.3 million of those deaths in sub-Saharan Africa.

Tracking the Epidemic

Initial case studies in the United States suggested an unusually high AIDS prevalence among homosexual men and intravenous drug abusers. This indicated a transmissible agent, presumably transferred during sexual activity or by blood-contaminated needles. Individuals receiving blood or

Table 3 HIV/AIDS infections, worldwide, 2003

Location	*HIV/AIDS Infections*
North America	1 million
Caribbean	460,000
Latin America	1.6 million
Western Europe	600,000
Eastern Europe and Central Asia	1.5 million
North Africa and Middle East	600,000
Sub-Saharan Africa	26.6 million
East Asia and Pacific	1 million
South and Southeast Asia	6.4 million
Australia and New Zealand	15,000

The total number of individuals infected with HIV/AIDS is estimated to be 40 million. Data are from the World Health Organization and the Joint United Nations Programme on HIV/AIDS.

blood products were also at high risk: Hemophiliacs who required infusions of blood products and a small number of individuals who received blood transfusions or tissue transplants before 1982 (when blood-screening procedures were implemented) acquired AIDS. Today, fewer than 1% of the total current AIDS cases can be attributed to these modes of transmission.

Soon after the discovery of HIV, laboratory ELISA and Western blot tests were developed to detect antibodies to the virus in serum. Extensive surveys of HIV incidence and prevalence defined the spread of HIV and ensured that new cases would not be transmitted by blood transfusions. The pattern illustrated in Figure 8 is typical of an agent transmissible by sexual activity or by blood. The identification of well-defined high-risk groups implied that HIV was not transmitted from person to person by casual contact, such as the respiratory route, or by contaminated food or water. Instead, body fluids, primarily blood and semen, were identified as the vehicles for transmission of HIV.

Figure 8 shows that the number of AIDS cases is disproportionately high in homosexual men in the United States, but the patterns in women and in certain racial and ethnic groups indicate that homosexuality is not a prerequisite for acquiring AIDS. Among women, for example, heterosexual women are the largest risk group, whereas in African-American and Hispanic men, intravenous drug use is linked to HIV infection nearly as often as homosexual activity. In fact, if we consider all risk groups, heterosexual activity is the fastest growing risk factor for new AIDS cases among adults.

This cohort of individuals who are at high risk for acquiring AIDS indicates that virtually all who acquire HIV today share two specific behavior patterns. First, they engage in activities (sex or drug use) that involve transfer of body fluids, usually semen or blood. Second, they exchange body fluids with multiple partners, either through sexual activity or through needle-sharing drug activity (or both). Thus, with each encounter they increase the probability of exchanging body fluids with an HIV-infected individual and therefore their chance of acquiring HIV infection.

The incidence of AIDS in hemophiliacs and blood transfusion recipients has been virtually eliminated. This is due to rigorous screening of the blood supply and also because many blood clotting factors needed by hemophiliacs can withstand a heat treatment sufficient to inactivate HIV or are available as genetically engineered products. In 2005, there were 111 cases of pediatric AIDS in the United States. HIV can be transmitted to the fetus by infected mothers and probably also in mothers' milk. Infants born to HIV-infected mothers have maternally derived antibodies to HIV in their blood. However, a positive diagnosis of HIV infection in infants must wait a year or more after birth because about 70% of infants showing maternal HIV antibodies at birth are later found not to be infected with HIV.

Epidemiological studies of AIDS in Africa indicate that transmission of HIV by heterosexual transmission of HIV is the norm. In some regions, fewer men than women are infected with HIV. The identification of high-risk groups such as prostitutes has led to the development of health education campaigns. These campaigns inform the public of HIV transmission methods and define high-risk behaviors. Because no cure or effective immunization for AIDS is available, public health education remains the most effective approach to the control of AIDS and spread of HIV infection.

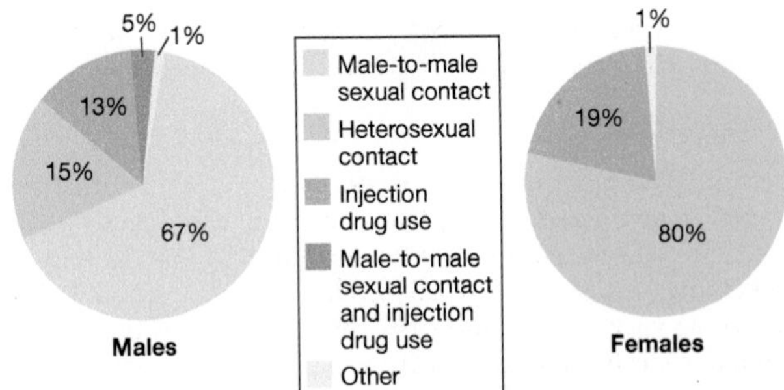

Figure 8 Distribution of AIDS cases by risk group and sex in adolescents and adults in the United States, 2005. Data were collected from 28,037 males and 9893 females diagnosed with HIV/AIDS in 2005.

Source: Centers for Disease Control and Prevention.

6 MiniReview

HIV/AIDS will continue to be a major worldwide public health problem. There is no effective cure or immunization to prevent AIDS. HIV/AIDS transmission control depends on public health surveillance and education.

- Describe the major risk factors for acquiring HIV infection. Tailor your answer to your country of origin.
- Estimate the total number of individuals in the United States who now have AIDS and predict how many will be living with AIDS in the next 2 years.

7 Healthcare-Associated Infections

A healthcare-associated infection (HAI) is a local or systemic condition resulting from an infectious agent or its products that occurs during admission to a healthcare facility and that was not present on admission. HAIs cause significant morbidity and mortality. About 5% of patients admitted to healthcare facilities acquire HAIs, also called **nosocomial infections** (*nosocomium* is the Latin word for "hospital"). In all, there are about 1.7 million nosocomial infections each year in the United States, leading directly or indirectly to about 99,000 deaths.

Some nosocomial infections are acquired from patients with communicable diseases, but others are caused by pathogens that are selected and maintained within the hospital environment. Cross-infection from patient to patient or

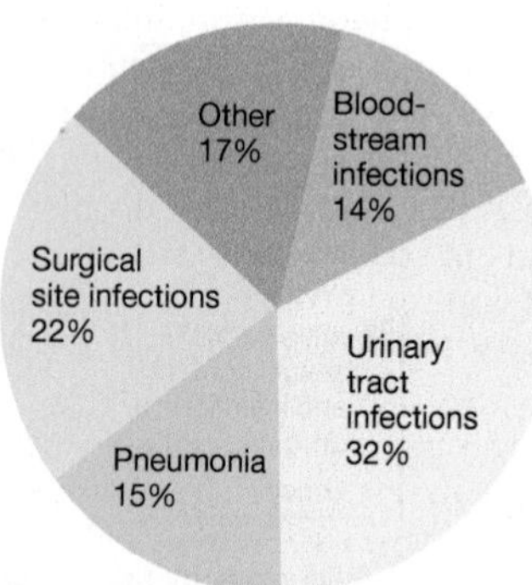

Figure 9 **Healthcare-associated infections, by site.** About 1.7 million healthcare-associated infections occur annually in the United States.

Source: Klevens et al., Estimated Health Care-Associated Infections and Deaths in U.S. Hospitals, 2002. *Public Health Reports* 122: 160–166, 2007.

from healthcare personnel to patient presents a constant hazard. Nosocomial pathogens are often found as normal flora in either patients or healthcare staff.

The Hospital Environment

Infectious diseases are spread easily and rapidly in hospitals for several reasons. (1) Many patients have low resistance to infectious disease because of their illness. For example, intensive care units provide care for the most acute illnesses and account for 24.5% of total HAIs. (2) Healthcare facilities treat infectious disease patients, and these patients may be pathogen reservoirs. (3) Multiple patients in rooms and wards increase the chance of cross-infection. (4) Healthcare personnel move from patient to patient, increasing the probability of transfer of pathogens. (5) Healthcare procedures such as hypodermic injection, spinal puncture, and removal of tissue samples (biopsy) or fluids (drawing blood), breach the skin barrier and may introduce pathogens into the patient. (6) In maternity wards of hospitals, newborn infants are unusually susceptible to certain infections because they lack well-developed defense mechanisms. (7) Surgical procedures expose internal organs to sources of contamination, and the stress of surgery often diminishes the resistance of the patient to infection. (8) Certain therapeutic drugs, such as steroids used for controlling inflammation, increase the susceptibility to infection. (9) Use of antibiotics to control infections selects for antibiotic-resistant organisms.

Infection Sites

The most common sites of HAIs are shown in Figure 9. Of the 99,000 estimated deaths caused by HAIs in 2002, 36,000 were from pneumonia, 31,000 from bloodstream infections, 13,000 from urinary tract infections, 8,000 from surgical site infections, and 11,000 for all other sites. This distribution and the numbers of people infected are similar to annual patterns.

Table 4 **Number of intensive care unit nosocomial infections in the United States, by site and organism**

	Bloodstream	***Pneumonia***	***Urinary Tract***
Pathogen	***Number***	***Number***	***Number***
Enterobacter spp.	1,083	4,444	1,560
Escherichia coli	514	1,725	5,393
Klebsiella pneumoniae	735	2,865	1,891
Haemophilus influenzae		1,738	
Pseudomonas aeruginosa	841	6,752	3,365
Staphylococcus aureus	2,758	7,205	497
Staphylococcus spp.	8,181		838
Enterococcus spp.	2,967	682	4,226
Candida albicans	1,090	1,862	4,856
Other pathogens	3,774	12,537	8,075
Total number[a]	**21,943**	**39,810**	**30,701**
Total %	**23.7**	**43.1**	**33.2**

[a]The total number of nosocomial infections in intensive care units during a recent 8-year time period was 92,454.

Source: National Nosocomial Infections Surveillance System Report, Centers for Disease Control and Prevention, Atlanta, Georgia, USA.

Healthcare-associated Pathogens

Healthcare-associated pathogens preferentially infect several sites in the body, notably the urinary tract, blood, and the respiratory tract. A relatively small number of pathogens cause the majority of nosocomial infections at these sites (Table 4).

One of the most important and widespread hospital pathogens is *Staphylococcus aureus*. It is the most common cause of pneumonia and the third most common cause of blood infections. *S. aureus* is also particularly problematic in nurseries. Many hospital strains of *S. aureus* are unusually virulent and are resistant to common antibiotics, making treatment very difficult. *S. aureus* and other staphylococci together constitute the largest cause of nosocomial blood infections and are also very prevalent in wound infections. Most staphylococci are found in the upper respiratory tract or on the skin, where they are a part of the normal flora in many individuals, including hospital patients and personnel.

Escherichia coli is the most common cause of urinary tract infections in hospitals, but *Enterococcus* species, *Pseudomonas aeruginosa, Candida albicans,* and *Klebsiella pneumoniae* infections are also very common. *Enterococcus, E. coli,* and *K. pneumoniae* are normally found only in the human body. But *Candida* and *Pseudomonas* are opportunistic pathogens; they are commonly found in the environment but cause disease only in individuals with compromised defenses. Isolates of *P. aeruginosa* from healthcare-associated infections are often resistant to many different antibiotics, complicating treatment. *E. coli*, *Staphylococcus*, and *Enterococcus* also have potential for multiple drug resistance.

7 MiniReview

Patients in healthcare facilities are unusually susceptible to infectious disease and are exposed to various infectious agents. Treatment of nosocomial infections is complicated by reduced host resistance; this leads to opportunistic infections, as well as the presence of antibiotic-resistant pathogens.

- Why are patients in healthcare facilities more susceptible than normal individuals to pathogens?
- What is the source of HAI pathogens?

III EPIDEMIOLOGY AND PUBLIC HEALTH

Here we identify some of the methods used to identify, track, contain, and eradicate infectious diseases within populations. We also identify some important current and future threats from infectious diseases.

8 Public Health Measures for the Control of Disease

Public health refers to the health of the general population and to the activities of public health authorities in the control of disease. The incidence and prevalence of many infectious diseases has dropped dramatically over the past century, especially in developed countries, because of universal improvements in basic living conditions. Better nutrition, access to clean potable water, improved public sewage treatment, less crowded living conditions, and lighter workloads have contributed immeasurably to disease control, primarily by reducing risk factors. Several diseases, including smallpox, typhoid fever, diphtheria, brucellosis, and poliomyelitis, have been controlled by active, disease-specific public health measures such as quarantine and vaccination.

Controls Directed against the Reservoir

When the disease reservoir is primarily in domestic animals, the infection of humans can be prevented if the disease is eliminated from the infected animal population. Immunization or destruction of infected animals may eliminate the disease in animals and, consequently, in humans. These procedures have nearly eliminated brucellosis and bovine tuberculosis in humans. These procedures have also been used to control bovine spongiform encephalitis (mad cow disease) in cattle in the United Kingdom, Canada, and the United States. In the process, the health of the domestic animal population is also improved.

When the disease reservoir is a wild animal, eradication is much more difficult. Rabies, for example, is a disease that occurs in both wild and domestic animals but is transmitted to domestic animals primarily by wild animals. Thus, control of rabies in domestic animals and in humans can be achieved by immunization of domestic animals. However, because the majority of rabies cases occur in wild rather than domestic animals, at least in the United States, eradication of rabies would require the immunization or destruction of all wild animal reservoirs, including such diverse species as raccoons, bats, skunks, and foxes. Although oral rabies immunization is practical and recommended for rabies control in restricted wild animal populations, its efficacy is untested in large, diverse animal populations such as the wild animal reservoir in the United States.

If insects such as the mosquito vectors that transmit malaria and West Nile fever are the disease reservoir, effective control of the disease can be accomplished by eliminating the reservoir with insecticides or other agents. The use of toxic or carcinogenic chemicals, however, must be balanced with environmental concerns. In some cases the elimination of one public health problem only creates another. For example, the insecticide dichlorodiphenyltrichloroethane (DDT) is very effective against mosquitoes and is credited with eradicating yellow fever and malaria in North America. However, its use is currently banned in the United States because of environmental concerns. DDT is still used in many developing countries to control mosquito-borne diseases, but its use is declining worldwide.

When humans are the disease reservoir (for example, AIDS), control and eradication can be difficult, especially if there are asymptomatic carriers. On the other hand, certain diseases that are limited to humans have no asymptomatic phase. If these can be prevented through immunization or treatment with antimicrobial drugs, the disease can be eradicated if those who have contracted the disease and all possible contacts are strictly quarantined, immunized, and treated. Such a strategy was successfully employed by the World Health Organization to eradicate smallpox and is currently being used to eradicate polio (discussed below).

Controls Directed against Transmission of the Pathogen

The transmission of pathogens in food or water can be eliminated by preventing contamination of these sources. Water purification methods have dramatically reduced the incidence of typhoid fever. Food protection laws have greatly decreased the probability of transmission of pathogens to humans. For example, the pasteurization of milk has largely controlled bovine tuberculosis in humans.

Transmission of respiratory pathogens is difficult to prevent. Attempts at chemical disinfection of air have been unsuccessful. Air filtration is a viable method but is limited to small, enclosed areas. In Japan, many individuals wear facemasks when they have upper respiratory infections to prevent transmission to others, but such methods, although effective, are voluntary and are difficult to institute as public health measures.

Immunization

Smallpox, diphtheria, tetanus, pertussis (whooping cough), measles, mumps, rubella, and poliomyelitis have been controlled primarily by means of immunization. Effective vaccines are available for a number of other infectious diseases. As we discussed in Section 5, 100% immunization is not necessary for disease control in a population, although the percentage needed to ensure disease control varies with the infectivity and virulence of the pathogen and with the living conditions of the population (for example, crowding).

Measles epidemics offer an example of the effects of herd immunity. The occasional resurgence of the highly contagious measles virus emphasizes the importance of maintaining appropriate immunization levels for a given pathogen. Until 1963, the year an effective measles vaccine was licensed, nearly every child in the United States acquired measles through natural infections, resulting in over 400,000 annual cases. After introduction of the vaccine, the number of annual measles infections dropped precipitously. Case numbers reached a low of 1,497 by 1983. However, by 1990, the percentage of children immunized against measles fell to 70%, and the number of new cases rose to 27,786. Within 3 years, a concerted effort to increase measles immunization levels to above 90% virtually eliminated indigenous measles transmission in the United States, and a total of only 312 measles cases were reported in 1993. Currently, about 100 cases of measles are reported each year in the United States, over half due to infections imported by visitors from other countries.

In the United States, virtually all children are now adequately immunized, but up to 80% of adults lack effective immunity to important infectious diseases because immunity from childhood vaccinations declines with time. When childhood diseases occur in adults, they can have devastating effects. For example, if a woman contracts rubella (a vaccine-preventable viral disease) during pregnancy, the fetus may develop serious developmental and neurological disorders. Measles, mumps, and chickenpox are also more serious diseases in adults than in children.

All adults are advised to review their immunization status and check their medical records (if available) to ascertain dates of immunizations. Tetanus immunizations, for example, must be renewed at least every 10 years to provide effective immunity. Surveys of adult populations have shown that more than 10% of adults under the age of 40 and over 50% of those over 60 are not adequately immunized. Measles immunity in adults should also be reviewed. People born before 1957 probably had measles as children and are immune. Those born after 1956 may have been immunized, but the effectiveness of early vaccines was variable and effective immunity may not be present, especially if the immunization was given before 1 year of age. Reimmunization for polio is not recommended for adults unless they are traveling to countries in western Africa and Asia, where polio may still be endemic or where recent outbreaks of polio have occurred.

Table 5 Reportable infectious agents and diseases in the United States

Diseases caused by *Bacteria*
- Anthrax
- Botulism
- Brucellosis
- Chancroid
- *Chlamydia trachomatis*
- Cholera
- Diphtheria
- Ehrlichiosis
- Enterohemorrhagic *Escherichia coli*
- *Escherichia coli* O157:H7
- Gonorrhea
- *Haemophilus influenzae*, invasive disease
- Hansen's disease (leprosy)
- Hemolytic uremic syndrome
- Legionellosis
- Listeriosis
- Lyme disease
- Meningococcal disease
- Pertussis
- Plague
- Psittacosis
- Q fever
- Rocky Mountain spotted fever
- Salmonellosis
- Shigellosis
- Streptococcal diseases, invasive, Group A
- Streptococcal toxic shock syndrome
- *Streptococcus pneumoniae*, drug-resistant and invasive disease
- Syphilis
- Tetanus
- Toxic shock syndrome
- Tuberculosis
- Tularemia
- Typhoid fever
- Vancomycin Intermediate *Staphylococcus aureus* (VISA)
- Vancomycin Resistant *Staphylococcus aureus* (VRSA)

Diseases caused by fungi (molds, yeast)
- Coccidiomycosis
- Cryptosporidiosis

Diseases caused by viruses
- Acquired immunodeficiency syndrome (AIDS) and pediatric HIV infection
- Encephalitis/meningitis (mosquito-borne)
  - California serogroup
  - Eastern equine
  - Powassan
  - St. Louis
  - Western equine
  - West Nile
- Hantavirus pulmonary syndrome
- Hepatitis A, B, C
- HIV infection
  - Adult
  - Pediatric (<13 yrs)
- Measles
- Mumps
- Poliomyelitis, paralytic
- Rabies, animal, human
- Rubella, acute and congenital syndrome
- Severe acute respiratory syndrome (SARS)
- Smallpox
- Varicella
- Yellow fever

Diseases caused by protists
- Cyclosporiasis
- Malaria
- Giardiasis

Disease caused by a helminth
- Trichinosis

Quarantine

Quarantine restricts the movement of a person with active infection to prevent spread of the pathogen to other people. The length of quarantine for a given disease is the longest period of communicability for that disease. To be effective, quarantine measures must prevent the infected individual from contacting unexposed individuals. Quarantine is not as severe a measure as strict isolation, which is used in hospitals for unusually infectious and dangerous diseases.

By international agreement, six diseases require quarantine: smallpox, cholera, plague, yellow fever, typhoid fever,

Table 6 National Center for Infectious Diseases (NCID) surveillance systems for infectious disease notification and tracking in the United States

Surveillance System (acronym)	*Disease Surveillance Responsibility*
121 Cities Mortality Reporting System	Influenza, pneumonia, all deaths
Active Bacterial Core Surveillance	Invasive bacterial diseases
BaCon Study	Bacterial contamination associated with blood transfusion
Border Infectious Disease Surveillance Project (BIDS)	Infectious disease along the U.S.-Mexican border
Dialysis Survey Network (DSN)	Vascular access infections and bacterial resistance in hemodialysis patients
Electronic Foodborne Outbreak Investigation and Reporting System (EFORS)	Foodborne outbreaks
EMERGEncy ID NET	Emerging infectious diseases
Foodborne Diseases Active Surveillance Network (FOODNET)	Foodborne disease
Global Emerging Infections Sentinel Network (GeoSentinel)	Global emerging diseases
Gonococcal Isolate Surveillance Project (GISP)	Antimicrobial resistance in *Neisseria gonorrhoeae*
Health Alert Network (HAN)	Health threat notification network, especially for bioterrorism
Integrated Disease Surveillance and Response (IDSR)	World Health Organization (WHO/AFRO) initiative for infectious diseases in Africa
Intensive Care Antimicrobial Resistance Epidemiology (ICARE)	Antimicrobial resistance and antimicrobial use in healthcare settings
International Network for the Study and Prevention of Emerging Antimicrobial Resistance (INSPEAR)	Global emergence of drug-resistant organisms
Laboratory Response Network (LRN)	Bioterrorism, chemical terrorism, and public health emergencies
Measles Laboratory Network	Measles in the Americas and the Caribbean
National Antimicrobial Resistance Monitoring System: Enteric Bacteria (NARMS)	Antimicrobial resistance in human nontyphoid *Salmonella*, *Escherichia coli* O157:H7, and *Campylobacter* isolates from agricultural and food sources
National Malaria Surveillance	Malaria in the United States
National Molecular Subtyping Network for Foodborne Disease Surveillance (PulseNet)	Molecular fingerprinting of foodborne bacteria
National Nosocomial Infections Surveillance System (NNIS)	Healthcare-associated infections
National Notifiable Diseases Surveillance System (NNDSS)	Reportable infectious diseases (see Table 4)
National Respiratory and Enteric Virus Surveillance System (NREVSS)	Respiratory syncytial virus (RSV), human parainfluenza viruses, respiratory and enteric adenoviruses, and rotavirus
National Surveillance System for Health Care Workers (NaSH)	Healthcare worker occupational infections
National Tuberculosis Genotyping and Surveillance Network	Tuberculosis genotyping repository
National West Nile Virus Surveillance System	West Nile virus
Public Health Laboratory Information System (PHLIS)	Notifiable diseases
Select Agent Program (SAP)	Regulate potential bioterrorism agents
Surveillance for Emerging Antimicrobial Resistance Connected to Healthcare (SEARCH)	Emerging antimicrobial resistance in healthcare settings
Unexplained Deaths and Critical Illnesses Surveillance System	Emerging infectious diseases worldwide
United States Influenza Sentinel Physicians Surveillance Network	260 clinical sites that report incidence and prevalence of influenza infections
Viral Hepatitis Surveillance Program (VHSP)	Viral hepatitis
Waterborne-Disease Outbreak Surveillance System	Waterborne diseases

and relapsing fever. Each is a very serious, particularly communicable disease. Spread of certain other highly contagious diseases such as Ebola hemorrhagic fever and meningitis may also be controlled by quarantine as outbreaks occur.

Surveillance

Surveillance is the observation, recognition, and reporting of diseases as they occur. Table 5 lists the diseases currently under surveillance in the United States. Several of the epidemic diseases listed in Table 2 and Table 8 are not on the surveillance list. However, many other diseases are surveyed through regional laboratories that identify index cases—those cases of disease that exhibit new syndromes or characteristics or are linked to new pathogens, indicating high potential for new epidemics.

The **Centers for Disease Control and Prevention (CDC)** in the United States, through the National Center for Infectious Diseases (NCID), operates a number of surveillance programs, as shown in Table 6. Many diseases are reportable to more than one surveillance program. Although redundant reporting may at first seem unnecessary, a disease may fall into several categories that affect health-care plans and policies. For example, reporting of vancomycin-resistant staphylococci to the National Nosocomial Infections

Surveillance System (NNIS) and to CDC as a notifiable disease (Table 5) provides a national database. Using this information, a hospital infection team can formulate and implement plans for isolation, diagnosis, and drug-susceptibility testing of staphylococcal infections to identify antibiotic resistant strains, to stop their spread, and to begin appropriate treatment.

Pathogen Eradication

A concerted disease eradication program was responsible for the eradication of naturally occurring smallpox. Smallpox was a disease with a reservoir consisting solely of the individuals with acute smallpox infections, and transmission was exclusively person to person. Infected individuals transmitted the disease through direct contact with previously unexposed individuals. Although smallpox, a viral disease, cannot be treated once acquired, immunization practices were very effective; vaccination with the related vaccinia virus conferred virtually complete immunity. The World Health Organization (WHO) implemented the smallpox eradication plan in 1967. Because of the success of vaccination programs worldwide, endemic smallpox was then confined to Africa, the Middle East, and the Indian subcontinent. WHO workers then vaccinated everyone in remaining endemic areas. Each subsequent outbreak or suspected outbreak was targeted by WHO teams who traveled to the outbreak site, quarantined individuals with active disease, and vaccinated all contacts. To break the chain of possible infection, they then immunized everyone who had contact with the contacts. This aggressive policy eliminated the active natural disease within a decade, and in 1980, WHO proclaimed the eradication of smallpox.

Polio, another viral disease that is largely preventable with an effective vaccine, is also targeted for eradication (endemic polio has been eradicated from the Western Hemisphere). Using much the same strategy to target polio as was used for smallpox, WHO undertook a massive immunization program in the 1990s, concentrating efforts in remaining endemic areas. By 2006, known endemic polio was restricted to Nigeria, India, Pakistan, and Afghanistan. Of 1,500 polio cases reported in 2006, 1,393 were in these countries. The remaining cases were spread among 11 countries in Africa, the Middle East, the Indian subcontinent, and Indonesia. Individual outbreaks are treated with massive regional immunization.

Hansen's disease (leprosy), another disease restricted to humans, is also targeted for eradication. Active cases of Hansen's disease can now be effectively treated with a multidrug therapy that cures the patient and also prevents spread of *Mycobacterium leprae,* the causal agent.

Other communicable diseases are candidates for eradication. These include Chagas' disease (treat active cases and destroy the insect vector of the *Trypanosoma cruzi* parasite in the American tropics) and dracunculiasis (treat drinking water to prevent transmission of *Dracunculus medinensis,* the Guinea helminth parasite in Africa, Saudi Arabia, Pakistan, and other places in Asia). Eradication of syphilis may be possible because the disease is found only in humans and is treatable. Rabies might be eradicated with oral baits that provide immunization of wild carnivores that constitute the reservoir.

8 MiniReview

Food and water purity regulations, vector control, immunization, quarantine, disease surveillance, and pathogen eradication are public health measures that reduce the incidence of communicable diseases.

- Compare public measures for controlling infectious disease caused by insect reservoirs and by human carriers.
- Identify public health methods used to halt the spread of an epidemic disease.
- Outline the steps taken to eradicate smallpox and polio.

9 Global Health Considerations

The World Health Organization has divided the world into six geographic regions for the purpose of collecting and reporting health information such as causes of morbidity and mortality. These geographic regions are Africa, the Americas (North America, the Caribbean, Central America, and South America), the eastern Mediterranean, Europe, Southeast Asia, and the Western Pacific. Here we compare mortality data from a relatively developed region, the Americas, to that from a developing region, Africa.

Infectious Disease in the Americas and Africa: A Comparison

The current worldwide population is now about 6,225,000,000. In 2002, about 57,029,000 individuals died, for an overall mortality rate of 9.2 deaths per 1,000 inhabitants per year. About 14.9 million, or 26%, of these deaths were attributable to infectious diseases. About 853 million people live in the Americas. Each year there are about 6 million deaths, or about 7 deaths per 1,000 inhabitants per year. In Africa, there are about 672 million people and about 10.7 million annual deaths, or about 15.9 deaths per 1,000 inhabitants per year. Although these statistics alone are cause for concern, examination of the causes of mortality in these regions is even more disturbing.

Figure 10 indicates that most African deaths are due to infectious diseases, whereas in the Americas, cancer and cardiovascular diseases are the leading causes of mortality. In Africa, there are about 6.7 million annual deaths due to infectious diseases, over ten times as many as in the Americas. The African death toll due to infectious diseases is 12% of the total deaths in the world and 45% of all worldwide deaths due to infectious diseases. In developed countries, the dramatic reduction in death rates from infection observed over the last century is undoubtedly due to a number of advances in public health. Lack of resources in developing countries limits access to adequate sanitation, safe food and water, immunizations, health care, and medicines.

Travel to Endemic Areas

The high incidence of disease in many parts of the world is a concern for people traveling to such areas. However, travelers can be immunized against many of the diseases that are endemic in foreign countries. Recommendations for immunization for those traveling abroad are shown in Table 7. By international agreement, immunization certificates for yellow fever are required for travel to or from areas with endemic yellow fever. These areas include much of equatorial South America and Africa. Most other nonstandard immunizations are recommended only for people who are expected to be at high risk. In many parts of the world, travelers may be exposed to diseases for which there are no effective immunizations (for example, AIDS, Ebola hemorrhagic fever, dengue fever, amebiasis, encephalitis, malaria, and typhus). Travelers should take precautions such as avoiding unprotected sex, avoiding insect and animal bites, drinking only water that has been properly treated to kill all microorganisms, eating properly stored and prepared food, and undergoing antibiotic and chemotherapeutic programs for prophylaxis or for suspected exposure.

9 MiniReview

Infectious diseases account for 26% of all mortality worldwide. Most infectious diseases occur in developing countries. Infection control can be accomplished by application of public health measures.

- Contrast mortality due to infectious diseases in Africa and the Americas.
- List a series of infectious diseases for which you have not been immunized and with which you could come into contact next year.

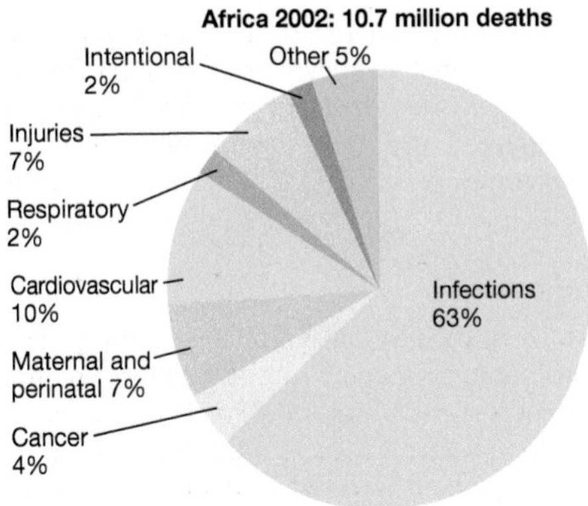

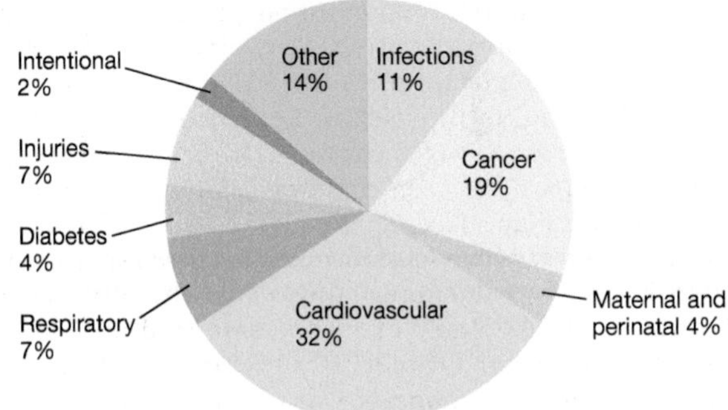

Figure 10 Causes of death in Africa and the Americas, 2002, by percentage of cause. There were 10.7 million deaths in Africa, 6.7 million due to infectious diseases. There were 6 million deaths in the Americas, 623,000 due to infectious diseases. Intentional deaths include murder, suicide, and war.

10 Emerging and Reemerging Infectious Diseases

Infectious diseases are global, dynamic health problems. Here we examine some recent patterns of infectious disease, some reasons for the changing patterns, and the methods used by epidemiologists to identify and deal with new threats to public health.

Emerging and Reemerging Diseases

The worldwide distribution of diseases can change dramatically and rapidly. Alterations in the pathogen, the environment, or the host population contribute to the spread of new diseases, with potential for high morbidity and mortality. Diseases that

Table 7 Immunizations required or recommended for international travel[a]

Disease	*Destination*	*Recommendation*[b]
Yellow fever	Tropical and subtropical countries, especially in sub-Saharan Africa and South America	*Immunization required* for entry and exit from endemic regions
Rabies	Rural, mountainous, and upland areas	*Immunization recommended* if direct contact with wild carnivores is anticipated
Typhoid fever	Many African, Asian, Central, and South American countries	*Immunization recommended* in areas endemic for typhoid fever

[a]*National Center for Infectious Diseases Travelers' Health*, U.S. Department of Health and Human Services, http://www.cdc.gov/travel/

[b]Vaccinations are generally recommended for diphtheria, pertussis, hepatitis A, hepatitis B, tetanus, polio, measles, mumps, rubella, and influenza as appropriate for the age of the traveler as well as the destination. Many U.S. citizens are immunized against these diseases through normal immunization practices. Requirements for specific vaccinations for each country are found at the website. Recommendations are also made for other appropriate infectious disease prevention measures, such as prophylactic drug therapy for malaria and plague prevention when visiting endemic areas. Yellow fever immunizations are required for travel to or from endemic areas.

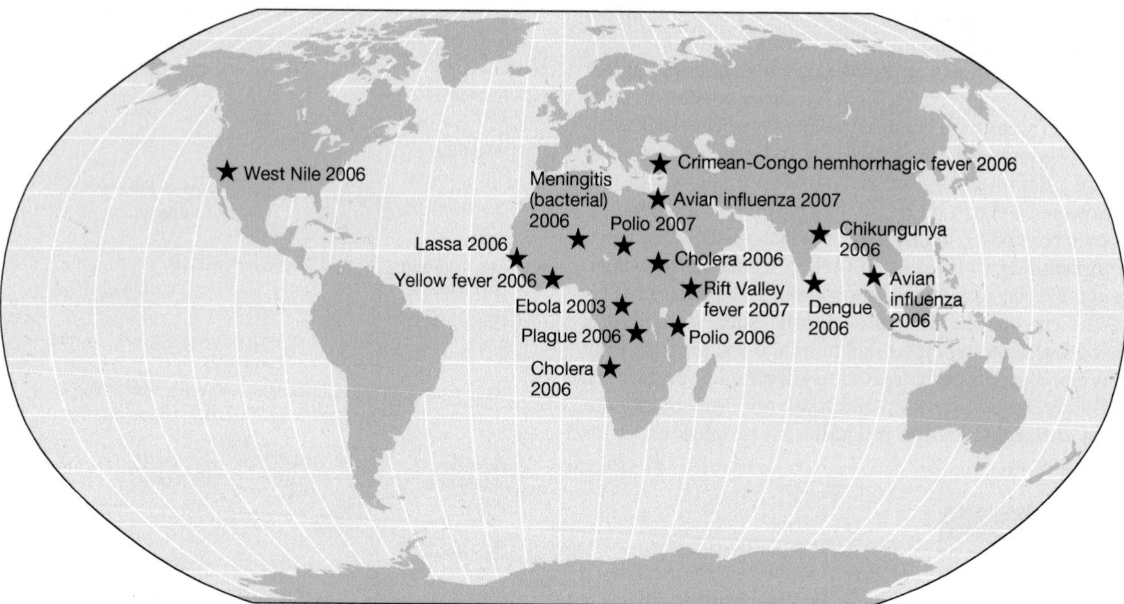

Figure 11 **Recent outbreaks of emerging and reemerging infectious diseases.** Emerging and reemerging diseases are first recognized as local epidemics. Recent human outbreaks of significant but rare diseases are recorded here. All of these diseases are capable of producing widespread epidemics and pandemics. Established pandemic diseases such HIV/AIDS and predictable annual epidemic diseases such as human influenza are not shown.

suddenly become prevalent are **emerging** diseases. Emerging infections are not limited to "new" diseases but also include **reemerging** diseases that were previously under control; reemerging diseases are especially a problem when antibiotics become less effective and public health systems fail. Recent dramatic examples of global emerging and reemerging disease are shown in Figure 11. Diseases with potential for emergence or reemergence are described in Table 8. In addition, the epidemic diseases listed in Table 2 have the potential to emerge or reemerge as widespread epidemics and pandemics.

Emerging epidemic diseases are not a new phenomenon. Some of the diseases that rapidly and sometimes catastrophically emerged in the past were syphilis (caused by *Treponema pallidum*) and plague (caused by *Yersinia pestis*). In the Middle Ages, up to one-third of all humans were killed by the plague epidemics that swept Europe, Asia, and Africa. Influenza caused a devastating worldwide pandemic in 1918–1919, claiming up to 230 million lives. In the 1980s, legionellosis (caused by *Legionella pneumophila*), acquired immunodeficiency syndrome (AIDS), and Lyme disease emerged as major new diseases. Current emerging pathogens in the United States include West Nile virus. Health officials worldwide are concerned about the potential for rapid emergence of pandemic influenza developing from avian influenza.

Emergence Factors

Some factors responsible for emergence of new pathogens are (1) human demographics and behavior; (2) technology and industry; (3) economic development and land use; (4) international travel and commerce; (5) microbial adaptation and change; (6) breakdown of public health measures; and (7) abnormal natural occurrences that upset the usual host–pathogen balance.

The demographics of human populations have changed dramatically in the last two centuries. In 1800, less than 2% of the world's population lived in urban areas. By contrast, today nearly one-half of the world's population lives in cities. The numbers, sizes, and population density in modern urban centers make disease transmission much easier. For example, dengue fever (Table 8) is now recognized as a serious hemorrhagic disease in tropical cities, largely due to the spread of dengue virus in the mosquito *Aedes aegypti*. The disease now spreads as an epidemic in tropical urban areas. Prior to 1950, dengue fever was rare, presumably because the virus was not easily spread among a more dispersed, smaller population.

Human behavior, especially in large population centers, also contributes to disease spread. For example, sexually promiscuous practices in population centers have been a major contributing factor to the spread of hepatitis and AIDS.

Technological advances and industrial development have a generally positive impact on living standards worldwide, but in some cases these advances have contributed to the spread of diseases. For example, although tremendous technological advances have been made in healthcare during the twentieth century, there has been a dramatic increase in nosocomial infections (Section 7). Antibiotic resistance in microorganisms

Table 8 Emerging and reemerging epidemic infectious diseases

Agent	*Disease and symptoms*	*Mode of transmission*	*Cause(s) of emergence*
Bacteria, Rickettsias, and Chlamydias			
Bacillus anthracis	Anthrax: respiratory distress, hemorrhage	Inhalation or contact with endospores	Bioterrorism
Borrelia burgdorferi	Lyme disease: rash, fever, neurological and cardiac abnormalities, arthritis	Bite of infective *Ixodes* tick	Increase in deer and human populations in wooded areas
Campylobacter jejuni	Campylobacter enteritis: abdominal pain, diarrhea, fever	Ingestion of contaminated food, water, or milk; fecal-oral spread from infected person or animal	Increased recognition; consumption of undercooked poultry
Chlamydia trachomatis	Trachoma, genital infections, conjunctivitis, infant pneumonia	Sexual intercourse	Increased sexual activity; changes in sanitation
Escherichia coli O157:H7	Hemorrhagic colitis; thrombocytopenia; haemolytic uremic syndrome	Ingestion of contaminated food, especially undercooked beef and raw milk	Development of a new pathogen
Haemophilus influenzae biogroup aegyptus	Brazilian purpuric fever; purulent conjunctivitis, fever, vomiting	Discharges of infected persons; flies are suspected vectors	Possible increase in virulence due to mutation
Helicobacter pylori	Gastritis, peptic ulcers, possibly stomach cancer	Contaminated food or water, especially unpasteurized milk; contact with infected pets	Increased recognition
Legionella pneumophila	Legionnaires' disease: malaise, myalgia, fever, headache, respiratory illness	Air-cooling systems, water supplies	Recognition in an epidemic situation
Mycobacterium tuberculosis	Tuberculosis: cough, weight loss, lung lesions; infection can spread to other organ systems	Sputum droplets (exhaled through a cough or sneeze) of a person with active disease	Immunosuppression, immunodeficiency
Neisseria meningitidis	Bacterial meningitis	Person-to-person contact	Urbanization, breakdown or lack of local public health surveillance
Staphylococcus aureus	Abscesses, pneumonia, endocarditis, toxic shock	Contact with the organism in a purulent lesion or on the hands	Recognition in an epidemic situation; possibly mutation
Streptococcus pyogenes	Scarlet fever, rheumatic fever, toxic shock	Direct contact with infected persons or carriers; ingestion of contaminated foods	Change in virulence of the bacteria; possibly mutation
Vibrio cholerae	Cholera: severe diarrhea, rapid dehydration	Water contaminated with the feces of infected persons; food exposed to contaminated water	Poor sanitation and hygiene; possibly introduced via bilge water from cargo ships
Viruses			
Chikungunya virus (CHIKV)	Debilitating fever, nausea, muscle pain, chronic fatigue	Bite of an infected mosquito (*Aedes* spp. in Africa and Asia)	Poor mosquito control; outdoor exposure; rapid spread to nonimmune populations
Dengue	Hemorrhagic fever	Bite of an infected mosquito (primarily *Aedes aegypti*)	Poor mosquito control; increased urbanization in tropics; increased air travel
Filoviruses (Marburg, Ebola)	Fulminant, high mortality, hemorrhagic fever	Direct contact with infected blood, organs, secretions, and semen	Unknown; in Europe and the United States, virus-infected monkeys shipped from developing countries via air
Hendravirus	Respiratory and neurological disease in horses and humans	Contact with infected bats, horses	Human intrusion into natural environment
Hantaviruses	Abdominal pain, vomiting, hemorrhagic fever	Inhalation of aerosolized rodent urine and feces	Human intrusion into virus or rodent ecological niche
Hepatitis B	Nausea, vomiting, jaundice; chronic infection leads to hepatocellular carcinoma and cirrhosis	Contact with saliva, semen, blood, or vaginal fluids of an infected person; mode of transmission to children not known	Probably increased sexual activity and intravenous drug abuse; transfusion (before 1978)
Hepatitis C	Nausea, vomiting, jaundice; chronic infection leads to hepatocellular carcinoma and cirrhosis	Exposure (percutaneous) to contaminated blood or plasma; sexual transmission	Recognition through molecular virology applications; blood transfusion practices, especially in Japan
Hepatitis E	Fever, abdominal pain, jaundice	Contaminated water	Newly recognized

Table 8 Emerging and reemerging epidemic infectious diseases (continued)

Agent	*Disease and symptoms*	*Mode of transmission*	*Cause(s) of emergence*
Viruses			
Human immunodeficiency viruses: HIV-1 and HIV-2	HIV disease, including AIDS: severe immune system dysfunction, opportunistic infections	Sexual contact with or exposure to blood or tissues of an infected person; vertical transmission	Urbanization; changes in lifestyle or mores; increased intravenous drug use; international travel; medical technology (transfusions and transplants)
Human papillomavirus	Skin and mucous membrane lesions (genital warts); strongly linked to cancer of the cervix and penis	Direct contact (sexual contact or contact with contaminated surfaces)	Increased surveillance and reporting
Human T cell lymphotrophic viruses (HTLV-I and HTLV-II)	Leukemias and lymphomas	Vertical transmission through blood or breast milk; exposure to contaminated blood products; sexual transmission	Increased intravenous drug abuse; medical technology (transfusion and transplantation)
Influenza	Fever, headache, cough, pneumonia	Airborne; especially in crowded, enclosed spaces	Animal-human virus reassortment; antigenic shift
Lassa	Fever, headache, sore throat, nausea	Contact with urine or feces of infected rodents	Urbanization and conditions favoring infestation by rodents
Measles	Fever, conjunctivitis, cough, red blotchy rash	Airborne; direct contact with respiratory secretions of infected persons	Deterioration of public health infrastructure supporting immunization
Monkeypox	Rash, lymphadenopathy, pulmonary distress	Direct contact with infected primates and other hosts	Travel to endemic areas, consumption and handling of infected primates and other hosts
Nipah virus	Hemorrhagic fever	Close contact with bats and pigs in Malaysia	Exposure to infected animals
Norwalk and Norwalk-like agents	Gastroenteritis; epidemic diarrhea	Most likely fecal-oral; vehicles may include drinking and swimming water, and uncooked foods	Increased recognition
Rabies	Acute viral encephalomyelitis	Bite of a rabid animal; contact with infected neural tissue	Introduction of infected host reservoir to new areas
Rift Valley	Febrile illness	Bite of an infective mosquito	Importation of infected mosquitoes and/or animals; development (dams, irrigation)
Rotavirus	Enteritis: diarrhea, vomiting, dehydration, and low-grade fever	Primarily fecal-oral; fecal-respiratory transmission can also occur	Increased recognition
Venezuelan equine encephalitis	Encephalitis	Bite of an infective mosquito	Movement of mosquitoes and hosts (horses)
West Nile virus	Meningitis, encephalitis	*Culex pipiens* mosquito and avian hosts	Agricultural development, increase in mosquito breeding areas, rapid spread to nonimmune populations
Yellow fever	Fever, headache, muscle pain, nausea, vomiting	Bite of an infective mosquito (*Aedes aegypti*)	Lack of effective mosquito control and widespread vaccination; urbanization in tropics; increased air travel
Protists and Fungi			
Candida	Candidiasis: fungal infections of the gastrointestinal tract, vagina, and oral cavity	Endogenous flora; contact with secretions or excretions from infected persons	Immunosuppression; medical devices (catheters); antibiotic use
Cryptococcus	Meningitis; sometimes infections of the lungs, kidneys, prostate, liver	Inhalation	Immunosuppression
Cryptosporidium	Cryptosporidiosis: infection of epithelial cells in the gastrointestinal and respiratory tracts	Fecal-oral, person to person, waterborne	Development near watershed areas; immunosuppression
Giardia lamblia	Giardiasis; infection of the upper small intestine, diarrhea, bloating	Ingestion of fecally contaminated food or water	Inadequate control in some water supply systems; immunosuppression; international travel
Microsporidia	Gastrointestinal illness, diarrhea; wasting in immunosuppressed persons	Unknown; probably ingestion of fecally contaminated food or water	Immunosuppression; recognition

Table 8 (continued)

Agent	Disease and symptoms	Mode of transmission	Cause(s) of emergence
Protists and Fungi			
Plasmodium	Malaria	Bite of an infective *Anopheles* mosquito	Urbanization; changing protist biology; environmental changes; drug resistance; air travel
Pneumocystis carinii	Acute pneumonia	Unknown; possibly reactivation of latent infection	Immunosuppression
Toxoplasma gondii	Toxoplasmosis; fever, lymphadenopathy, lymphocytosis	Exposure to feces of cats carrying the protists; sometimes foodborne	Immunosuppression; increase in cats as pets
Other Agents			
Bovine prions	Bovine spongiform encephalitis (BSE, animal) and variant Creutzfeld-Jacob disease (vCJD, human)	Foodborne	Consumption of contaminated beef

is another negative outcome of modern healthcare practices. For example, vancomycin-resistant enterococci and staphylococci and multiple drug-resistant *Streptococcus pneumoniae* are important emerging pathogens in developed countries.

Transportation, bulk processing, and central distribution methods have become increasingly important for quality assurance and economy in the food industry. However, these same factors can increase the potential for common-source epidemics when sanitation measures fail. For example, a single meat-processing plant spread *Escherichia coli* O157:H7 (Table 8) to at least 500 individuals in four states in the United States. The contaminated food source, ground beef, was recalled and the epidemic was eventually stopped, but not before several people died. There was a similar incident with spinach contaminated by *Escherichia coli* O157:H7 in runoff from a dairy farm in 2006. The *E. coli*-contaminated spinach was distributed nationally by a single packing plant and caused illness, kidney failure, and a few deaths; this prompted a United States Food and Drug Administration recommendation that fresh spinach not be consumed for a time.

Economic development and changes in land use can also promote disease spread. For example, Rift Valley fever, a mosquito-borne viral infection, has been on the increase since the completion of the Aswan High Dam in Egypt in 1970. The dam flooded 2 million acres, and the enlarged shoreline increased breeding grounds for mosquitoes at the edge of the new reservoir. The first major epidemic of Rift Valley fever developed in Egypt in 1977, when an estimated 200,000 people became ill and 598 died. There have been several epidemic outbreaks in the area since then, and the disease has become endemic near the reservoir.

Lyme disease, the most common vectorborne disease in the United States, is on the rise largely due to changes in land use patterns. Reforestation and the resulting increase in populations of deer and mice (the natural reservoirs for the disease-producing *Borrelia burgdorferi*) have resulted in greater numbers of infected ticks, the arthropod vector. In addition, larger numbers of homes and recreational areas in and near forests increase contact between the infected ticks and humans, consequently increasing disease incidence.

International travel and commerce also affect the spread of pathogens. For example, filoviruses (*Filoviridae*), a group of RNA viruses, cause fevers culminating in hemorrhagic disease in infected hosts. These untreatable viral diseases typically have a mortality rate above 20%. Most outbreaks have been restricted to equatorial central Africa, where the natural primate hosts and other vectors live. Travel of potential hosts to or from endemic areas is usually implicated in disease transmission. For example, one of the filoviruses was imported into Marburg, Germany, with a shipment of African green monkeys used for laboratory work. The virus quickly spread from the primate host to some of the human handlers. Twenty-five people were initially infected, and six more developed disease as a result of contact with the human cases. Seven people died in this outbreak of what became known as the *Marburg virus*. Another shipment of laboratory monkeys brought a different filovirus to Reston, Virginia, in the United States. Fortunately, the virus was not pathogenic for humans, but due to its respiratory transmission mode, the Reston virus infected and killed most of the monkeys at the Reston facility within days. These two filoviruses are closely related to the Ebola virus (Table 8).

Sporadic Ebola outbreaks in central Africa, often characterized by mortality rates greater than 50%, highlight a group of viral hemorrhagic fever pathogens for which there is no immunity or therapy. These pathogens could potentially be spread via air travel throughout the world in a matter of days. A highly contagious respiratory agent such as the Reston virus that also has the high mortality potential of the Ebola virus could devastate population centers worldwide in a matter of weeks.

Table 9 Virulence factors encoded by bacteriophages, plasmids, and transposons

Genetic element	*Organism*	*Virulence factors*
Bacteriophage	*Streptococcus pyogenes*	Erythrogenic toxin
	Escherichia coli	Shiga-like toxin
	Staphylococcus aureus	Enterotoxins A, D, E, staphylokinase, toxic shock syndrome toxin-1 (TSST-1)
	Clostridium botulinum	Neurotoxins C, D, E
	Corynebacterium diphtheriae	Diphtheria toxin
Plasmid	*Escherichia coli*	Enterotoxins, pili colonization factor, hemolysin, urease, serum resistance factor, adherence factors, cell invasion factors
	Bacillus anthracis	Edema factor, lethal factor, protective antigen, poly-D-glutamic acid capsule
	Yersinia pestis	Coagulase, fibrinolysin, murine toxin
Transposon	*Escherichia coli*	Heat-stable enterotoxins, aerobactin siderophores, hemolysin and pili operons
	Shigella dysenteriae	Shiga toxin
	Vibrio cholerae	Cholera toxin

Pathogen adaptation and change can contribute to pathogen emergence. For example, nearly all RNA viruses, including influenza, HIV, and the hemorrhagic fever viruses, undergo rapid, unpredictable genetic mutations. Because RNA viruses lack correction mechanisms for errors made during RNA replication, they incorporate genome mutations at an extremely high rate compared with most DNA viruses. The RNA viruses can present major epidemiological problems because of their easily changeable genomes.

Bacterial genetic mechanisms are capable of enhancing virulence and promoting emergence of new epidemics. Virulence-enhancing factors are often carried on mobile genetic elements such as bacteriophages, plasmids, and transposons. Table 9 lists some virulence factors carried on these mobile genetic elements that contribute to pathogen emergence.

Drug resistance is another factor in the reemergence of some bacterial and viral pathogens. Although several drugs are effective against certain viral diseases, resistance to these drugs is very common, especially among the RNA viruses. For example, many strains of HIV develop resistance to azidothymidine (AZT) unless it is used in combination with other drugs.

A breakdown of public health measures is sometimes responsible for the emergence or reemergence of diseases. For instance, cholera (caused by *Vibrio cholerae*) can be adequately controlled, even in endemic areas, by providing proper sewage disposal and water treatment. However, in 1991 an outbreak of cholera due to contaminated municipal water supplies in Peru was one of the first indications that the current cholera pandemic had reached the Americas. In 1993, the municipal water supply of Milwaukee, Wisconsin, was contaminated with the chlorine-resistant protist *Cryptosporidium*, resulting in over 400,000 cases of intestinal disease, 4,000 of which required hospitalization. Enhanced filtration systems rid the water supply of the pathogen.

Inadequate public vaccination programs can lead to the resurgence of previously controlled diseases. For example, recent outbreaks of diphtheria in the former Soviet Union resulted from inadequate immunization of susceptible children due to the breakdown in public health infrastructures. Pertussis, another vaccine-preventable childhood respiratory disease, has increased recently in Eastern Europe and in the United States due to inadequate immunization among adults.

Finally, abnormal natural occurrences sometimes upset the usual host–pathogen balance. For example, hantavirus is a well-known human pathogen that occurs naturally in rodent populations, including some laboratory animals. A number of fatal cases of hantavirus infection and disease were reported in 1993 in the American Southwest and were linked to exposure to wild animal droppings. The likelihood of exposure to mice and droppings was increased due to a larger than normal wild mouse population resulting from near-record rainfall, a long growing season, and a mild winter. The pathogen density was increased by favorable environmental conditions. These factors enhanced exposure probability for susceptible human hosts.

Addressing Emerging Diseases

Many of the emerging diseases we consider here are absent from the official notifiable disease list for the United States (Table 5). How then do public health officials define emerging diseases and prevent major epidemics? The keys for addressing emerging diseases are recognition of the disease and intervention to prevent pathogen transmission.

The first step in disease recognition is surveillance. Epidemic diseases that exhibit particular clinical syndromes warrant intensive public health surveillance. These syndromes are (1) acute respiratory diseases, (2) encephalitis and aseptic meningitis, (3) hemorrhagic fever, (4) acute diarrhea, (5) clusterings of high fever cases, (6) unusual clusterings of any disease or deaths, and (7) resistance to common drugs or treatment. Thus, new diseases are primarily recognized because of their epidemic incidence, clusterings, and syndromes. As the prevalence and pathology of an emerging disease are recognized, the disease is added to the notifiable disease list.

Table 10 Bioterrorism agents and diseases

Bacteria and rickettsias
Bacillus anthracis (anthrax)
Brucella sp. (brucellosis)
Burkholderia mallei (glanders)
Burkholderia pseudomallei (melioidosis)
Chlamydia psittaci (psittacosis)
Vibrio cholerae (cholera)
Clostridium botulinum toxin (botulism[a])
Clostridium perfringens (Epsilon toxin[a])
Coxiella burnetii (Q fever)
Escherichia coli O157:H7 (gastrointestinal disease)
Francisella tularensis (tularemia)
Yersinia pestis (plague)
Staphylococcus aureus enterotoxin B[a]
Salmonella Typhi (typhoid fever)
Salmonella sp. (salmonellosis)
Shigella (shigellosis)
Rickettsia prowazekii (typhus)
Viral agents
Variola major (smallpox)
Alphaviruses (viral encephalitis)
Venezuelan equine encephalitis virus
Eastern equine encephalitis virus
Western equine encephalitis virus
Nipah virus
Viral hemorrhagic fevers viruses
filoviruses; Ebola, Marburg
arenaviruses; Lassa, Machupo
hantaviruses
Protists
Cryptosporidium parvum (waterborne gastroenteritis)
Plants
Ricinus communis (ricin toxin from castor bean[a])

[a]Preformed toxin; all other agents require infection.

Source: Information is from the Centers for Disease Control and Prevention, Atlanta, GA, USA.

For example, AIDS was recognized as a disease in 1981 and became a reportable disease in 1984. Likewise, outbreaks of gastrointestinal disease due to enteropathogenic *Escherichia coli* O157:H7 have increased in recent years, and the strain became a reportable disease in 1995 (Table 5).

Intervention to prevent spread of emerging infections must be a public health response employing various methods. Disease-specific intervention is the key to controlling individual outbreaks. Methods such as quarantine, immunization, and drug treatment must be applied to contain and isolate outbreaks of specific diseases. Finally, for vectorborne and zoonotic diseases, the nonhuman host or vector must be identified to allow intervention in the life cycle of the pathogen and interrupt transfer to humans. International public health surveillance and intervention programs were instrumental in controlling the emergence of severe acute respiratory syndrome (SARS), a disease that emerged rapidly, explosively, and unpredictably from a zoonotic source (see the Microbial Sidebar, "SARS as a Model of Epidemiological Success").

10 MiniReview

Changes in host, vector, or pathogen conditions, whether natural or artificial, can result in conditions that encourage the explosive emergence or reemergence of infectious diseases. Global surveillance and intervention programs must be in place to prevent new epidemics and pandemics.

- What factors are important in the emergence or reemergence of potential pathogens?
- Indicate general and specific methods that would be useful for dealing with emerging infectious diseases.

11 Biological Warfare and Biological Weapons

Biological warfare is the use of biological agents to incapacitate or kill a military or civilian population in an act of war or terrorism. Biological weapons have been used against targets in the United States, and biological weapon-making facilities are suspected to be in the hands of several governments as well as extremist groups.

Characteristics of Biological Weapons

Biological weapons are organisms or toxins that are (1) easy to produce and deliver, (2) safe for use by the offensive soldiers, and (3) able to incapacitate or kill individuals under attack in a reproducible and consistent manner. Many organisms or biological toxins fit these rather general criteria, and we discuss several of these below.

Although biological weapons are potentially useful in the hands of conventional military forces, the greatest likelihood of biological weapons use is probably by terrorist groups. This is in part due to the availibility and low cost of producing and propagating many of the organisms useful for biological warfare. Biological weapons are accessible to nearly every government and well-financed private organization.

Candidate Biological Weapons

Virtually all pathogenic bacteria or viruses are potentially useful for biological warfare, and several of the most likely candidate organisms are relatively simple to grow and disseminate. Commonly considered biological weapons agents are listed in Table 10. The most commonly mentioned candidate as a biological weapon is *Bacillus anthracis,* the causal agent of anthrax. We discuss anthrax in the next section.

Other important candidates as bacterial biological weapons include *Yersinia pestis,* the organism responsible for plague, *Brucella abortus* (fever and bacteremia; brucellosis),

Microbial Sidebar

SARS as a Model of Epidemiological Success

Handling of the Severe Acute Respiratory Disease (SARS) epidemic early in this decade is an excellent example of epidemiological success. Like many other rapidly emerging diseases, SARS was viral and zoonotic in origin. Such characteristics have the potential to trigger explosive disease in humans when the infectious agents cross host species barriers. In many cases, the original viruses have been traced back to an animal host, but in others, the original host is unknown or is so ubiquitous that adequate vector control is nearly impossible, and thus disease persists. For example, West Nile virus is transmitted through mosquitoes that feed on infected birds. Although public health officials knew from the outset that West Nile disease would be seasonal and related to mosquitoes and infected birds, they could not prevent its spread. Thus human West Nile cases spread quickly across the United States over a 5-year period, starting in Florida in 2001, and are still with us today.

In contrast to West Nile disease, a different scenario surrounds the SARS epidemic. The SARS epidemic originated in late 2002 in Guandong Province, China. By the following February, the virus had spread to 32 countries. Global travel provided the major vehicle for SARS dissemination. The etiology of SARS was quickly traced to a coronavirus derived from an animal source. The coronavirus entered the human food chain through exotic food animals such as civet cats. The SARS coronavirus (SARS-CoV), shown in Figure 1, originated in bats. Civet cats consumed fruit contaminated by the bats and acquired the virus in this way. SARS-CoV likely evolved over an extended period of time in bats and developed, quite by accident, the ability to infect civet cats and then humans.

Much like common cold viruses, SARS-CoV is a relatively hardy, easily spread RNA virus that is difficult to contain. Once in humans, SARS-CoV is very contagious because it can be spread in several ways, including person to person by sneezing and coughing and by contact with contaminated fomites or feces. Ordinarily, a new coldlike virus would be of little concern, but SARS-CoV causes infections with significant morbidity and mortality. There have been about 8,500 known SARS-CoV infections and over 800 deaths, for an overall mortality rate of nearly 10%. In persons over 65 years of age, the mortality rate approached 50%, attesting to SARS-CoV virulence as a human pathogen. About 20% of all SARS cases were in healthcare workers, demonstrating the high infectivity of the virus. Standard containment and infection control methods practiced by healthcare personnel were not effective in controlling spread of the disease. When this was realized, SARS patients were confined for the course of the disease in strict isolation in negative-pressure rooms. To prevent infection, healthcare workers wore respirators when working with SARS patients or when handling fomites (bed linens, eating utensils, and so on) contaminated with SARS-CoV.

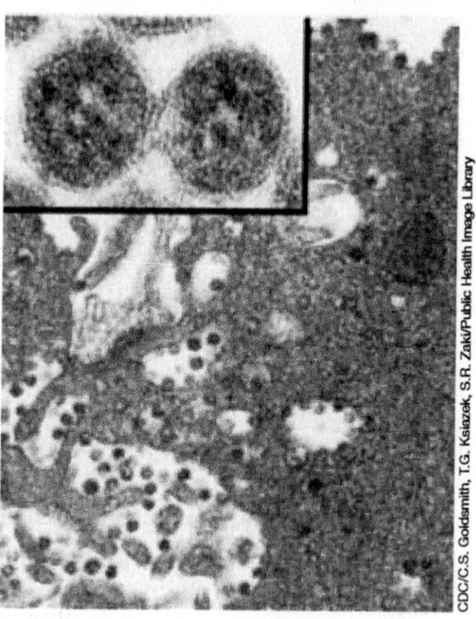

Figure 1 **Severe acute respiratory virus syndrome corona virus (SARS-CoV).** *The upper left panel shows isolated SARS-CoV virions. An individual virion is 133 nm in diameter. The large panel shows coronaviruses within the cytoplasmic membrane-bound vacuoles and in the rough endoplasmic reticulum of host cells. The virus replicates in the cytoplasm and exits the cell through the cytoplasmic vacuoles.*

The recognition and containment of the clinical disease was the start of an international response involving clinicians, scientists, and public officials. Almost immediately, travel to and from the endemic area was restricted, limiting further outbreaks. SARS-CoV isolation was achieved rapidly, and this information was used to develop the PCR tests used to track the disease. As laboratory work progressed, epidemiologists traced the virus back to the civet food source in China and stopped further transmission to humans by restricting the sale of civets and other foods from wild sources. These actions collectively stopped the outbreak.

SARS is an example of a serious infection that emerged very rapidly from a unique source. However, rapid isolation and characterization of the SARS pathogen, nearly instant development of worldwide notification procedures and diagnostic tests, and a concerted effort to understand the biology and genetics of this novel pathogen quickly controlled the disease; there has not been another case of SARS since early 2004. The rapid emergence of SARS, and the equally rapid and successful international effort to identify and control the outbreak, provide a model for the control of emerging epidemics.

As international travel and trade expand, the chances for propagation and rapid dissemination of new exotic diseases will continue to increase. We should therefore anticipate the emergence of other serious infectious zoonotic diseases, including pandemic influenza. We hope that the lessons learned from the SARS epidemic will pay dividends when other emerging diseases appear.

Francisella tularensis ("rabbit fever"), and *Salmonella* (foodborne and waterborne illnesses). Viral pathogens with biological weapons potential include smallpox, hemorrhagic fever viruses, and encephalitis viruses. These agents cause diseases associated with significant morbidity, and some have very high mortality rates.

Bacterial toxins such as botulinum toxin from *Clostridium botulinum* are also potential biological weapons. Large amounts of the preformed toxin delivered to a population through a common vehicle such as drinking water could have devastating consequences: The lethal dose of botulinum toxin for a human is 2 μg or less.

Smallpox

Smallpox virus has intimidating potential as a biological warfare agent because it can be easily spread by contact or aerosol spray and it has a mortality rate of 30% or more. However, its potential for use as a biological weapon is considered low, partly because the only known stocks of smallpox virus are in guarded repositories in the United States and Russia, but a finite possibility remains for terrorist groups or military forces to gain access to smallpox virus. Because of this, the United States government has made provisions to immunize frontline healthcare and public safety personnel for smallpox. Although an extremely effective smallpox vaccine exists using the closely related vaccinia virus as the immunogen, this vaccine has not been in general use for almost 30 years because wild smallpox was eradicated worldwide by 1977. In addition, the vaccine can have serious side effects. As a result, over 90% of the current worldwide population is now inadequately vaccinated and susceptible to the disease. Preparations for a potential smallpox attack in the United States have included recommendations for immunization of select individuals: persons having close contact with smallpox patients; workers evaluating, caring for, or transporting smallpox patients; laboratory personnel handling clinical specimens from smallpox patients; and other persons such as housekeeping personnel who might contact infectious materials from smallpox patients.

Although vaccinia immunization is very effective, it carries significant risk. Normal vaccine reactions include formation of a pustule, with a scab that falls off in 2 to 3 weeks, leaving a small scar. Many people have mild adverse reactions such as fevers and rashes. Vaccination is not currently recommended for persons with eczema or other chronic or acute skin conditions, heart disease, pregnant women, and those with reduced immune competence, such as individuals using anti-inflammatory steroid medications and those with HIV/AIDS.

About 1 in 1,000 vaccinated individuals develop serious complications from the vaccine. These include myocarditis and erythema multiforme, a toxic or allergic response to the vaccine. Generalized vaccinia (systemic vaccinia infection) occasionally occurs in individuals with skin conditions such as eczema. Life-threatening progressive vaccinia sometimes occurs in vaccinated individuals, usually in those who are immunosuppressed due to therapy or disease. On average, one to two people per million who receive the vaccine will die from a vaccinia virus complication.

Delivery of Biological Weapons

Most organisms suitable for biological weapons use can be spread as an aerosol, providing simple, rapid, widespread dissemination leading to infection. Examples of several aerosol exposures are instructive.

In 1962, one of the last outbreaks of smallpox in a developed country occurred in Germany. A German worker developed smallpox after returning from Pakistan, a country with endemic smallpox. The individual was immediately hospitalized and quarantined, but the patient had a cough, and the aerosolized virus caused illness in 19 vaccinated individuals; at least one individual died from the resulting infection.

There have been planned bioterrorist attacks in the United States and other countries even before the anthrax attacks of 2001 (Section 12). In 1984 in The Dalles, Oregon (United States), cultists inoculated a salad bar with a *Salmonella typhimurium* culture in aerosol form at ten local restaurants, causing 751 cases of foodborne salmonellosis in a region that usually has less than 10 cases per year. In 1995, a radical political group released Saran nerve gas into a Tokyo subway, killing several people and injuring scores of others. Although this was a chemical weapon, this group also possessed anthrax cultures, bacteriological media, drone airplanes, and spray tanks.

Delivery of preformed bacterial toxins such as botulinum toxin or staphylococcal enterotoxin to large populations is somewhat impractical because most potent exotoxins are proteins that would lose effectiveness as they are diluted or are destroyed in common sources such as drinking water. However, delivery of toxins could be aimed at selected individuals and small groups, or delivered randomly to instigate panic.

Prevention and Response to Biological Weapons

Proactive measures against the deployment of biological weapons have already begun with periodic planned efforts to update the international agreements of the 1972 Biological and Toxic Weapons Convention. The fifth and most recent update was in 2002. At the practical level, governments are now supporting the large-scale production and distribution of vaccines along with the development of strategic and tactical plans to prevent and contain biological weapons.

The United States government, through the Centers for Disease Control and Prevention, has devised and enhanced the Select Agent Program surveillance systems to monitor possession and use of potential bioterrorism agents. The CDC Laboratory Response Network and the Health Alert Network have been upgraded to enhance their diagnostic capabilities and increase the reporting abilities of local and regional healthcare centers to rapidly identify bioterrorism events as well as emerging diseases.

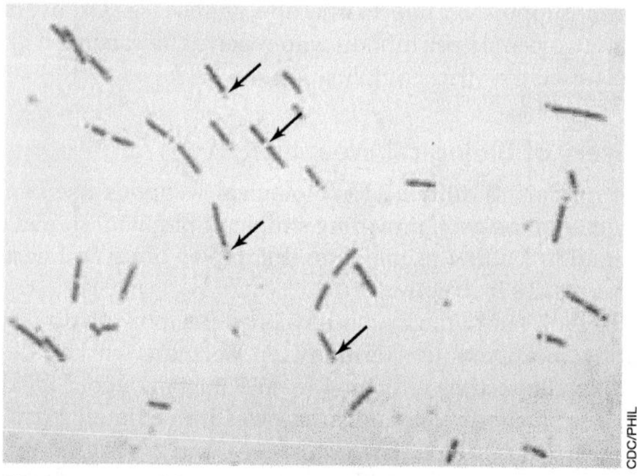

(a)

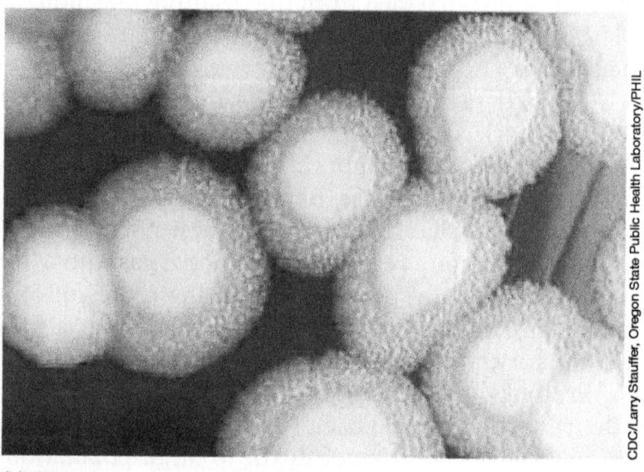

(b)

Figure 12 **Bacillus anthracis.** *(a) B. anthracis* is a gram-positive endospore-forming rod approximately 1 μm in diameter and 3–4 μm in length. Note the developing endospores (arrows). *(b) B. anthracis* colonies on blood agar. The nonhemolytic colonies take on a characteristic "ground glass" appearance.

11 MiniReview

Bioterrorism is a threat in a world of rapid international travel and easily accessible technical information. Biological agents can be used as weapons by military forces or by terrorist groups. Aerosols or common sources such as food and water are the most likely modes of inoculation. Prevention and containment measures rely on a well-prepared public health infrastructure.

- What characteristics make a pathogen or its products particularly useful as a biological weapon?
- Identify two infectious agents that could be effective biological weapons. How could the agents be disseminated?

12 Anthrax as a Biological Weapon

Bacillus anthracis is a preferred agent for biowarfare and bioterrorism. Here we discuss its unique properties, the diseases it causes, and methods for prevention, diagnosis, and treatment.

Biology and Growth

Bacillus anthracis is a ubiquitous saprophytic soil inhabitant. It grows as an aerobic gram-positive rod, 1 μm in diameter and 3–4 μm in length. As with other species of the genus *Bacillus, B. anthracis* produces endospores resistant to heat and drying (Figure 12a). Endospore formation enhances the ability to disseminate *B. anthracis* in aerosols. Viable endospores are sometimes recovered from contaminated animal products such as hides and fur. Growth on blood agar results in large colonies with a characteristic "ground glass" appearance (Table 12*b*). Strains having a poly-D-glutamic acid capsule are resistant to phagocytosis.

Infection and Pathogenesis

Bacillus anthracis endospores are the standard means of acquiring anthrax. The disease usually affects domestic animals, especially ungulates—cows, sheep, and goats. The number of infections in animals, although considerable, is not known. The animals acquire the disease from plants or soil in pastures. In humans and animals, there are three forms of the disease. *Cutaneous anthrax* is contracted when abraded skin is contaminated by *B. anthracis* endospores (Figure 13a). *Gastrointestinal anthrax* is contracted from consumption of endospore-contaminated plants or anthrax-infected carcasses. Cutaneous anthrax cases are rare in the United States. Human gastrointestinal anthrax is rarely seen. *Pulmonary anthrax* is contracted when the endospores are inhaled. Inhalation of the endospores or the live bacteria results in pulmonary infections characterized by pulmonary and cerebral hemorrhage (Figure 13*b*). Untreated pulmonary anthrax infections have a mortality rate of nearly 100%. Pulmonary anthrax cases, even in agricultural workers, are extremely rare. The last naturally acquired pulmonary anthrax case in the United States occurred in 1976. However, several cases of pulmonary anthrax were identified in 2001 due to bioterrorism events.

Pathogenesis results from inhalation of 8000–50,000 endospores of an encapsulated toxigenic strain. Pathogenic *B. anthracis* produces three proteins—*protective antigen* (PA), *lethal factor* (LF), and *edema factor* (EF). PA and LF form *lethal toxin*. PA and EF form *edema toxin*. PA is the cell-binding B component of these AB-type toxins. EF cause edema, and LF causes cell death. Growth of *B. anthracis* in the lymph nodes and lymphatic tissues draining the lungs leads to edema and cell death, culminating in tissue destruction, shock, and death.

Clinical symptoms can start with sore throat, fever, and muscle aches. After several days, symptoms include difficulty in breathing, followed by systemic shock. Fatality rates can approach 90% even when exposure is recognized and treatment is started, and can be nearly 100% in cases for which treatment is not started until after the onset of symptoms.

Weaponized Anthrax

The term *weaponized* is applied to strains and preparations of *B. anthracis,* usually in endospore form, that exhibit properties that enhance dissemination and use as biological weapons. Such strains and preparations were developed in several countries in the post-World War II era, but overt development of new biological weapons was halted by international treaty in 1972. The physical characteristics of the weaponized anthrax preparations typically include a small particle size, usually interspersed with a very fine particulate agent such as talc. This small-particle, powdery form ensures that the endospores will spread easily by air currents. Thus, opening an envelope containing endospores or releasing the powder–endospore mixture into a ventilation system or other air current has the potential to contaminate surrounding areas and personnel.

A weaponized form of anthrax was used in a series of bioterrorism attacks in the United States in 2001. These incidents were carried out by mailing envelopes or packages containing weaponized anthrax endospores. The attacks were apparently directed at the news media (Florida) and the government (Washington, DC area). A third focus of attack, the Pennsylvania-New Jersey-New York area, had no defined single target, but disrupted mail service in the Northeast; some anthrax-contaminated mail facilities were still not in use 2 years later. In all, there were 22 anthrax infections. Eleven were cutaneous anthrax. Of 11 cases of inhalation anthrax, 5 cases resulted in death. The bioterrorists were never identified.

The incidents in the United States were not the first or the most serious anthrax biological weapons infections. In a previous incident, *B. anthracis* spores were inadvertently released into the atmosphere from a biological weapons facility in Sverdlovsk, Russia, in 1979. Less than 1 g of endospores was released, and everyone in the area surrounding the facility was immunized and given prophylactic antibiotic therapy as soon as the first anthrax case was diagnosed. However, 77 individuals outside the facility contracted pulmonary anthrax and 66 died.

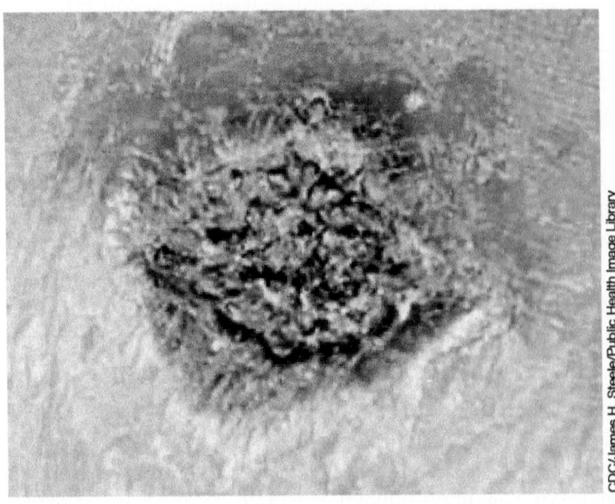

CDC/James H. Steele/Public Health Image Library

(a)

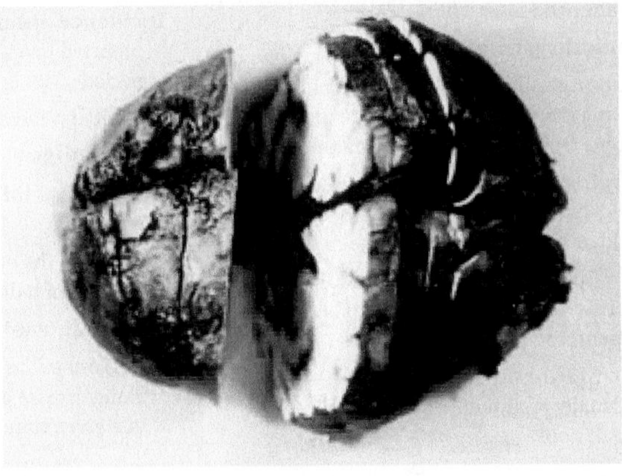

CDC/Public Health Image Library

(b)

Figure 13 Anthrax. *(a)* Cutaneous anthrax. The blackened lesion on the forearm of a patient, about 2 cm in diameter, results from tissue necrosis. Cutaneous anthrax, even when untreated, usually is a localized, nonlethal infection. *(b)* Inhalation anthrax. The fixed and sectioned human brain shows hemorrhagic meningitis (dark coloration) due to a fatal case of inhalation anthrax.

Vaccination, Prophylaxis, Treatment, and Diagnosis

Vaccination for anthrax has thus far been restricted to individuals who are considered at risk. This includes agricultural animal workers and military personnel. The current vaccine, called *anthrax vaccine adsorbed* (AVA), is prepared from a cell-free *B. anthracis* culture filtrate.

Treatment of *B. anthracis* infection, which seems to have a minimum incubation time of about 8 days, is usually done with antibiotics. Ciprofloxacin, a broad-spectrum quinolone antibiotic, is used against strains that are penicillin-resistant, including many laboratory and biological weapons strains. Ciprofloxacin is also used as a prophylactic measure to treat potentially exposed individuals.

Rapid diagnostic tests are available to detect microbial endospores. However, positive identification of *B. anthracis* relies on culture techniques and direct observation of either infected tissues or cultured organisms. The characteristic ground-glass appearance on blood agar, coupled with the isolation of gram-positive endospore-forming rods growing in extended chains, is presumptive evidence for *B. anthracis* (Table 12).

12 MiniReview

Bacillus anthracis has emerged as an important pathogen because of its use as a biological weapon. Highly infective weaponized endospore preparations have been used as bioterror agents. Inhalation anthrax has a fatality rate of over 90% in untreated individuals. Effective treatment relies on timely observation and diagnosis of symptoms. Treatment for inhalation anthrax does not guarantee survival.

- What factors contribute to the preferred use of *B. anthracis* as a biological weapon?
- Indicate the steps you would use to identify the use of *B. anthracis* in a bioterror attack. Indicate treatment steps for potential victims.

Review of Key Terms

Acute infection short-term infection usually characterized by dramatic onset

Biological warfare the use of biological agents to incapacitate or kill humans

Carrier subclinically infected individual who may spread a disease

Centers for Disease Control and Prevention (CDC) an agency of the United States Public Health Service that tracks disease trends, provides disease information to the public and to healthcare professionals, and forms public policy regarding disease prevention and intervention

Chronic long-term infection

Common-source epidemic an epidemic resulting from infection of a large number of people from a single contaminated source

Emerging infection infectious disease whose incidence has increased recently or whose incidence threatens to increase in the near future

Endemic disease a disease that is constantly present, usually in low numbers

Epidemic the occurrence of a disease in unusually high numbers in a localized population

Epidemiology the study of the occurrence, distribution, and determinants of health and disease in a population

Fomite an inanimate object that, when contaminated with a viable pathogen, can transfer the pathogen to a host

Herd immunity resistance of a population to a pathogen as a result of the immunity of a large portion of the population

Host-to-host epidemic an epidemic resulting from person-to-person contact, characterized by a gradual rise and fall in number of cases

Incidence the number of new disease cases reported in a population in a given time period

Morbidity incidence of illness in a population

Mortality incidence of death in a population

Nosocomial infection healthcare-associated infection

Outbreak the occurrence of a large number of cases of a disease in a short period of time

Pandemic a worldwide epidemic

Prevalence the total number of new and existing disease cases reported in a population in a given time period

Public health the health of the population as a whole

Quarantine the practice of restricting the movement of individuals with highly contagious serious infections to prevent spread of the disease

Reemerging infection infectious disease, thought to be under control, that produces a new epidemic

Reservoir a source of viable infectious agents from which individuals may be infected

Surveillance observation, recognition, and reporting of diseases as they occur

Vector a living agent that transfers a pathogen

Vehicle nonliving source of pathogens that infect large numbers of individuals; common vehicles are food and water

Zoonosis a disease that occurs primarily in animals but can be transmitted to humans

Review Questions

1. List the five most common causes of mortality due to infectious diseases throughout the world. Are any of these diseases preventable by immunization (Section 1)?
2. Distinguish between mortality and morbidity, prevalence and incidence, and epidemic and pandemic, as these terms relate to infectious disease (Section 2).
3. Explain the difference between a chronic carrier and an acute carrier of an infectious disease (Section 3).
4. Give examples of host-to-host transmission of disease via direct contact. Also give examples of indirect host-to-host transmission of disease via vector agents and fomites (Section 4).
5. How can immunity to a pathogen by a large proportion of the population protect the nonimmune members of the population from acquiring a disease? Will this herd immunity work for diseases that have a common source, such as water? Why or why not (Section 5)?
6. Identify the major risk factors for acquiring human immunodeficiency virus (HIV) infection in the United States. Does this pattern hold for all geographic regions (Section 6)?
7. Healthcare environments are conducive to the spread of infectious diseases. Review the reasons for the enhanced spread of infection in healthcare facilities. What are the sources of most healthcare-associated infections (Section 7)?
8. Describe the major medical and public health measures developed in the twentieth century that were instrumental for controlling the spread of infectious diseases in developed countries (Section 8).
9. Compare the role of infectious diseases on mortality in developed and developing countries (Section 9).
10. Review the major reasons for the emergence of new infectious diseases. What methods are available for identifying and controlling the emergence of new infectious diseases (Section 10)?
11. Describe the general properties of an effective biological warfare agent. How does smallpox meet these criteria? Identify other organisms that meet the basic requirements for a bioweapon (Section 11).
12. Describe the use of *Bacillus anthracis* as a biological weapon. Devise a plan to protect yourself against a *B. anthracis* attack (Section 12).

Application Questions

1. Smallpox, a disease that was limited to humans, was eradicated. Plague, a disease with a zoonotic reservoir in rodents (Table 2) can never be eradicated. Explain this statement and why you agree or disagree with the possibility of eradicating plague on a global scale. Devise a plan to eradicate plague in a limited environment such as a town or city. Be sure to use methods that involve the reservoir, the pathogen, and the host.
2. Acquired immunodeficiency syndrome (AIDS) is a disease that can be eliminated because it is propagated by person-to-person contact and there are no known animal reservoirs. Do you agree or disagree with this statement? Explain your answer. Design a program for eliminating AIDS in a developed country and in a developing country. How would these programs differ? What factors would work against the success of your program, both in terms of human behavior and in terms of the AIDS disease itself? Why are the numbers of HIV-infected and AIDS patients continuing to grow, especially in developing countries? HIV/AIDS incidence (new cases) in developed countries has been virtually unchanged in this century (Figure 7). The numbers of individuals living with AIDS, however, is increasing. Explain this contradiction.
3. Travel to developing countries involves some exposure to infectious diseases. What general precautions should you take before, during, and after visits to developing countries? Where can you obtain information concerning infectious diseases in a specific foreign country? When you return from a foreign country, are you a disease risk to your family or your associates? Explain.
4. Identify a specific pathogen that would be a suitable agent for effective biological warfare. Describe the properties of the pathogen in the context of its use as a biological weapon. Describe equipment and other resources necessary for growing large amounts of the pathogen. Identify a suitable delivery method. Since you will propagate and deliver the pathogen, describe the precautions you will take to protect yourself. Now reverse your role. As a public health official at your university, describe how you would recognize and diagnose the disease caused by the agent. Indicate the measures you would take to treat the illnesses caused by the agent. How could you best limit the damage? Would quarantine and isolation methods be useful? What about immunization and antibiotics?

Energy Calculations in Microbial Bioenergetics

The information in this appendix 1 is intended to help calculate changes in free energy accompanying chemical reactions carried out by microorganisms. It begins with definitions of the terms required to make such calculations and proceeds to show how knowledge of redox state, atomic and charge balance, and other factors are necessary to calculate free-energy problems successfully.

I. DEFINITIONS

1. ΔG^0 = standard free-energy change of the reaction at 1 atm pressure and 1 *M* concentrations; ΔG = free-energy change under the conditions specified; $\Delta G^{0\prime}$ = free-energy change under standard conditions at pH 7.
2. Calculation of ΔG^0 for a chemical reaction from the free energy of formation, $G_f{}^0$, of products and reactants:

$$\Delta G^0 = \sum \Delta G_f{}^0 \text{ (products)} - \sum \Delta G_f{}^0 \text{ (reactants)}$$

   That is, sum the $\Delta G_f{}^0$ of products, sum the $\Delta G_f{}^0$ of reactants, and subtract the latter from the former.
3. For energy-yielding reactions involving H^+, converting from standard conditions (pH 0) to cellular conditions (pH 7):

$$\Delta G^{0\prime} = \Delta G^0 + m\Delta G_f{}^0(H^+)$$

   where *m* is the net number of protons in the reaction (*m* is negative when more protons are consumed than formed) and $\Delta G_f{}^0$ (H^+) is the free energy of formation of a proton at pH 7 (−39.83 kJ) at 25°C.
4. Effect of concentrations on ΔG: With soluble substrates, the concentration ratios of products formed to exogenous substrates used are generally equal to or greater than 10^{-2} at the beginning of growth and equal to or less than 10^{-2} at the end of growth. From the relation between ΔG and the equilibrium constant (see item 8), it can be calculated that ΔG for the free-energy yield in practical situations differs from the free-energy yield under standard conditions by at most 11.7 kJ, a rather small amount, and so for a first approximation, standard free-energy yields can be used in most situations. However, with H_2 as a product, H_2-consuming bacteria present may keep the concentration of H_2 so low that the free-energy yield is significantly affected. Thus, in the fermentation of ethanol to acetate and H_2 by syntrophic bacteria ($C_2H_5OH + H_2O \longrightarrow C_2H_3O_2^- + 2\ H_2 + H^+$), the $\Delta G^{0\prime}$ at 1 atm H_2 is +9.68 kJ, but at 10^{-4} atm H_2 it is −36.03 kJ. With H_2-consuming bacteria present, therefore, the ethanol fermentation becomes exergonic. (See also item 9.)
5. Reduction potentials: by convention, electrode equations are written in the direction, oxidant + $ne^- \longrightarrow$ reductant (that is, as reductions), where *n* is the number of electrons transferred. The standard potential (E_0) of the hydrogen electrode, $2\ H^+ + 2\ e^- \longrightarrow H_2$, is set by definition at 0.0 V at 1 atm pressure of H_2 gas and 1.0 *M* H^+ at 25°C. E_0' is the standard reduction potential at pH 7. See also Table 2.
6. Relation of free energy to reduction potential:

$$\Delta G^{0\prime} = -nF\Delta E_0'$$

   where *n* is the number of electrons transferred, *F* is the Faraday constant (96.48 kJ/V), and $\Delta E_0'$ is the E_0' of the electron-*accepting* couple minus the E_0' of the electron-*donating* couple.
7. Equilibrium constant, *K*. For the generalized reaction $aA + bB \rightleftharpoons cC + dD$,

$$K = \frac{[C]^c[D]^d}{[A]^a[B]^b}$$

   where A, B, C, and D represent reactants and products; *a, b, c,* and *d* represent number of molecules of each; and brackets indicate concentrations. This is true only when the chemical system is in equilibrium.
8. Relation of equilibrium constant, *K*, to free-energy change. At constant temperature, pressure, and pH,

$$\Delta G = \Delta G^{0\prime} + RT \ln K$$

   where *R* is a constant (8.29 J/mol/°K) and *T* is the absolute temperature (in °K).
9. Two substances can react in a redox reaction even if the standard potentials are unfavorable, provided that the concentrations are appropriate.

Assume that normally the reduced form of A would donate electrons to the oxidized form of B. However, if the concentration of the reduced form of A was low and the concentration of the reduced form of B was high, it would be possible for the reduced form of B to donate electrons to the oxidized form of A. Thus, the reaction would proceed in the direction opposite that predicted from standard potentials. A practical example of this is the utilization of H^+ as an electron acceptor to produce H_2. Normally, H_2 production in fermentative bacteria is not extensive because H^+ is a poor electron acceptor; the E_0' of the $2\ H^+/H_2$ pair is −0.41 V. However, if the concentration of H_2 is kept low by continually removing it (a process done by methanogenic *Archaea*, which use $H_2 + CO_2$ to produce methane, CH_4, or by many other anaerobes capable of consuming H_2 anaerobically), the potential will be more positive and then H^+ will be a suitable electron acceptor.

II. OXIDATION STATE OR NUMBER

1. The oxidation state of an element in an elementary substance (for example, H_2, O_2) is zero.
2. The oxidation state of the ion of an element is equal to its charge (for example, $Na^+ = +1$, $Fe^{3+} = +3$, $O^{2-} = -2$).
3. The sum of oxidation numbers of all atoms in a neutral molecule is zero. Thus, H_2O is neutral because it has two H at +1 each and one O at −2.
4. In an ion, the sum of oxidation numbers of all atoms is equal to the charge on that ion. Thus, in the OH^- ion, O(−2) + H(+1) = −1.
5. In compounds, the oxidation state of O is virtually always −2 and that of H is +1.
6. In simple carbon compounds, the oxidation state of C can be calculated by adding up the H and O atoms present and using

the oxidation states of these elements as given in item 5, because in a neutral compound the sum of all oxidation numbers must be zero. Thus, the oxidation state of carbon in methane, CH_4, is −4 (4 H at +1 each = +4); in carbon dioxide, CO_2, the oxidation state of carbon is +4 (2 O at −2 each = −4).

7. In organic compounds with more than one C atom, it may not be possible to assign a specific oxidation number to each C atom, but it is still useful to calculate the oxidation state of the compound as a whole. The same conventions are used. Thus, the oxidation state of carbon in glucose, $C_6H_{12}O_6$, is zero (12 H at +1 = 12; 6 O at −2 = −12) and the oxidation state of carbon in ethanol, C_2H_6O, is −2 each (6 H at +1 = +6; one O at −2).
8. In all oxidation-reduction reactions there is a balance between the oxidized and reduced products. To calculate an oxidation-reduction balance, the number of molecules of each product is multiplied by its oxidation state. For instance, in calculating the oxidation-reduction balance for the alcoholic fermentation, there are two molecules of ethanol at −4 = −8 and two molecules of CO_2 at +4 = +8 so the net balance is zero. When constructing model reactions, it is useful to first calculate redox balances to be certain that the reaction is possible.

III. CALCULATING FREE-ENERGY YIELDS FOR HYPOTHETICAL REACTIONS

Energy yields can be calculated either from free energies of formation of the reactants and products or from differences in reduction potentials of electron-donating and electron-accepting partial reactions.

Calculations from Free Energy

Free energies of formation are given in Table 1. The procedure to use for calculating energy yields of reactions follows.

1. *Balancing reactions.* In all cases, it is essential to ascertain that the coupled oxidation-reduction reaction is balanced. Balancing involves three things: (a) the *total number of each kind of atom* must be identical on both sides of the equation; (b) there must be an *ionic balance* so that when positive and negative ions are added up on the right side of the equation, the total ionic charge (whether positive, negative, or neutral) exactly balances the ionic charge on the left side of the equation; and (c) there must be an *oxidation-reduction balance* so that all the electrons removed from one substance are transferred to another substance. In general, when constructing balanced reactions, one proceeds in the reverse of the three steps just listed. Usually, if steps (c) and (b) have been properly handled, step (a) becomes correct automatically.
2. *Examples:* (a) What is the balanced reaction for the oxidation of H_2S to SO_4^{2-} with O_2? First, decide how many electrons are involved in the oxidation of H_2S to SO_4^{2-}. This can be most easily calculated from the oxidation states of the compounds, using the rules given previously. Because H has an oxidation state of +1, the oxidation state of S in H_2S is −2. Because O has an oxidation state of −2, the oxidation state of S in SO_4^{2-} is +6 (because it is an ion, using the rules given in items 4 and 5 of the previous section). Thus, the oxidation of H_2S to SO_4^{2-} involves an *eight-electron transfer* (from −2 to +6). Because each O atom can accept two electrons (the oxidation state of O in O_2 is zero, but in H_2O is −2), this means that two molecules of molecular oxygen, O_2, are required to provide sufficient electron-accepting capacity. Thus, at this point, we know that the reaction requires 1 H_2S and 2 O_2 on the left side of the equation, and 1 SO_4^{2-} on the right side. To achieve an ionic balance, we must have two positive charges on the right side of the equation to balance the two negative charges of SO_4^{2-}. Thus, 2 H^+ must be added to the right side of the equation, making the overall reaction.

$$H_2S + 2\,O_2 \longrightarrow SO_4^{2-} + 2\,H^+$$

By inspection, it can be seen that this equation is also balanced in terms of the total number of atoms of each kind on each side of the equation.
(b) What is the balanced reaction for the oxidation of H_2S to SO_4^{2-} with Fe^{3+}as electron acceptor? We have just ascertained that the oxidation of H_2S to SO_4^{2-} is an eight-electron transfer. Because the reduction of Fe^{3+} to Fe^{2+} is only a one-electron transfer, 8 Fe^{3+} will be required. At this point, the reaction looks like

$$H_2S + 8\,Fe^{3+} \longrightarrow 8\,Fe^{2+} + SO_4^{2-} \text{ (not balanced)}$$

We note that the ionic balance is incorrect. We have 24 positive charges on the left and 14 positive charges on the right (16+ from Fe, 2− from sulfate). To equalize the charges, we add 10 H^+on the right. Now our equation looks like:

$$H_2S + 8\,Fe^{3+} \longrightarrow 8\,Fe^{2+} + 10\,H^+ + SO_4^{2-} \text{ (not balanced)}$$

To provide the necessary hydrogen for the H^+ and oxygen for the sulfate, we add 4 H_2O to the left and find that the equation is now balanced:

$$H_2S + 4\,H_2O + 8\,Fe^{3+} \longrightarrow 8\,Fe^{2+} + 10\,H^+ + SO_4^{2-} \text{ (balanced)}$$

In general, in microbiological reactions, ionic balance can be achieved by adding H^+ or OH^- to the left or right side of the equation, and because all reactions take place in an aqueous medium, H_2O molecules can be added where needed. Whether H^+ or OH^- is added generally depends on whether the reaction is taking place under acidic or alkaline conditions.
3. *Calculation of energy yield for balanced equations from free energies of formation.*Once an equation has been balanced, the free-energy yield can be calculated by inserting the values for the free energy of formation of each reactant and product from Table 1 and using the formula in item 2 of the first section of this appendix.

For instance, for the equation

$$H_2S + 2\,O_2 \longrightarrow SO_4^{2-} + 2\,H^+$$

$$G_f^0 \text{ values} \longrightarrow (-27.87) + (0)(-744.6) + 2\,(-39.83) \text{ (assuming pH 7)}$$

$$\Delta G^{0\prime} = -796.39 \text{ kJ}$$

The G_f^0 values for the products (right side of equation) are summed and subtracted from the G_f^0 values for the reactants (left side of equation), taking care to ensure that the arithmetic signs are correct. From the data in Table 1, a wide variety of free-energy yields for reactions of microbiological interest can be calculated.

Calculation of Free-Energy Yield from Reduction Potential

Reduction potentials of some important redox pairs are given in Table 2. The amount of energy that can be released from two half reactions can be calculated from the *differences* in reduction potentials of the two reactions and from the number of electrons transferred. The farther apart the two half reactions are, and the greater the number of electrons transferred, the more energy released.

The conversion of potential difference to free energy is given by the formula $\Delta G^{0\prime} = -nF\Delta E_0{}'$, where n is the number of electrons, F is the Faraday constant (96.48 kJ/V), and $\Delta E_0{}'$ is the difference in potentials. Thus, the 2 H^+/H_2 couple has a potential of −0.41 V and the $\frac{1}{2}O_2/H_2O$ pair has a potential of +0.82 V, and so the potential difference is 1.23 V, which (because two electrons are involved) is equivalent to a free-energy yield (ΔG^0) of −237.34 kJ. On the other hand, the potential difference between the $2H^+/H_2$ and the NO_3^-/NO_2^- reactions is less, 0.84 V, which is equivalent to a free-energy yield of −162.08 kJ.

Because many biochemical reactions are two-electron transfers, it is often useful to give energy yields for two-electron reactions, even if more electrons are involved. Thus, the SO_4^{2-}/H_2 redox pair involves eight electrons, and complete reduction of SO_4^{2-} with H_2 requires 4 H_2 (equivalent to eight electrons). From the reduction potential difference between 2 H^+/H_2 and SO_4^{2-}/H_2S (0.19 V), a free-energy yield of −146.64 kJ is calculated, or −36.66 kJ per two electrons. By convention, reduction potentials are given for conditions in which equal concentrations of oxidized and reduced forms are present. In actual practice, the concentrations of these two forms may be quite different. As discussed earlier in this appendix (Section I, item 9), it is possible to couple half reactions even if the potential difference is unfavorable, providing the concentrations of the reacting species are appropriate.

Table 1 Free energies of formation (G_f^0) for some substances (kJ/mol)[a]

Carbon compound	*Carbon compound*	*Metal*	*Nonmetal*	*Nitrogen compound*
CO, −137.34	Glutamine, −529.7	Cu^+, +50.28	H_2, 0	N_2, 0
CO_2, −394.4	Glyceraldehyde, −437.65	Cu^{2+}, +64.94	H^+, 0 at pH 0;	NO, +86.57
CH_4, −50.75	Glycerate, −658.1	CuS, −49.02	−39.83 at pH 7	NO_2, +51.95
H_2CO_3, −623.16	Glycerol, −488.52	Fe^{2+}, −78.87	(−5.69 per pH unit)	NO_2^-, −37.2
HCO_3^-, −586.85	Glycine, −314.96	Fe^{3+}, −4.6	O_2, 0	NO_3^-, −111.34
CO_3^{2-}, −527.90	Glycolate, −530.95	$FeCO_3$, −673.23	OH^-, −157.3 at pH 14;	NH_3, −26.57
Acetaldehyde, −139.9	Glyoxalate, −468.6	FeS_2, −150.84	−198.76 at pH 7;	NH_4^+, −79.37
Acetate, −369.41	Guanine, +46.99	$FeSO_4$, −829.62	−237.57 at pH 0	N_2O, +104.18
Acetone, −161.17	α-Ketoglutarate, −797.55	PbS, −92.59	H_2O, −237.17	
Alanine, −371.54	Lactate, −517.81	Mn^{2+}, −227.93	H_2O_2, −134.1	
Arginine, −240.2	Lactose, −1515.24	Mn^{3+}, −82.12	PO_4^{3-}, −1026.55	
Aspartate, −700.4	Malate, −845.08	MnO_4^-, −506.57	Se^0, 0	
Benzene, +124.5	Mannitol, −942.61	MnO_2 −456.71	H_2Se, −77.09	
Benzoic acid, −245.6	Methanol, −175.39	$MnSO_4$, −955.32	SeO_4^{2-}, −439.95	
n-Butanol, −171.84	Methionine, −502.92	HgS, −49.02	S^0, 0	
Butyrate, −352.63	Methylamine, −40.0	MoS_2, −225.42	SO_3^{2-}, −486.6	
Caproate, −335.96	Oxalate, −674.04	ZnS, −198.60	SO_4^{2-}, −744.6	
Citrate, −1168.34	Palmitic acid, −305		$S_2O_3^{2-}$, −513.4	
o-Cresol, −37.1	Phenol, −47.6		H_2S, −27.87	
Crotonate, −277.4	*n*-Propanol, −175.81		HS^-, +12.05	
Cysteine, −339.8	Propionate, −361.08		S^{2-}, +85.8	
Dimethylamine, −3.3	Pyruvate, −474.63			
Ethanol, −181.75	Ribose, −757.3			
Formaldehyde, −130.54	Succinate, −690.23			
Formate, −351.04	Sucrose, −370.90			
Fructose, −951.38	Toluene, +114.22			
Fumarate, −604.21	Trimethylamine, −37.2			
Gluconate, −1128.3	Tryptophan, −112.6			
Glucose, −917.22	Urea, −203.76			
Glutamate, −699.6	Valerate, −344.34			

[a]Values for free energy of formation of various compounds can be found in Dean, J. A. 1973. *Lange's Handbook of Chemistry*, 11th edition. McGraw-Hill, New York; Garrels, R. M., and C. L. Christ. 1965. *Solutions, Minerals, and Equilibria*. Harper and Row, New York; Burton, K. 1957. In Krebs, H. A., and H. L. Komberg. Energy transformation in living matter, *Ergebnisse der Physiologie* (appendix): Springer-Verlag, Berlin; and Thauer, R. K., K. Jungermann, and H. Decker. 1977. Energy conservation in anaerobic chemotrophic bacteria. *Bacteriol Rev* 41:100–180.

Table 2 Microbiologically important reduction potentials[a]

Redox pair	E_0' (V)
SO_4^{2-}/HSO_3^-	−0.52
CO_2/formate	−0.43
$2H^+/H_2$	−0.41
$S_2O_3^{2-}/HS^- + HSO_3^-$	−0.40
Ferredoxin ox/red	−0.39
Flavodoxin ox/red[b]	−0.37
NAD^+/NADH	−0.32
Cytochrome c_3 ox/red	−0.29
CO_2/acetate$^-$	−0.29
S^0/HS^-	−0.27
CO_2/CH_4	−0.24
FAD/FADH	−0.22
SO_4^{2-}/HS^-	−0.217
Acetaldehyde/ethanol	−0.197
Pyruvate$^-$/lactate$^-$	−0.19
FMN/FMNH	−0.19
Dihydroxyacetone phosphate/glycerolphosphate	−0.19
$HSO_3^-/S_3O_6^{2-}$	−0.17
Flavodoxin ox/red[b]	−0.12
HSO_3^-/HS^-	−0.116
Menaquinone ox/red	−0.075
APS/AMP + HSO_3^-	−0.060
Rubredoxin ox/red	−0.057
Acrylyl-CoA/propionyl-CoA	−0.015
Glycine/acetate$^-$ + NH_4^+	−0.010
$S_4O_6^{2-}/S_2O_3^{2-}$	+0.024
Fumarate^{2-}/succinate^{2-}	+0.033
Cytochrome *b* ox/red	+0.035
Ubiquinone ox/red	+0.113
AsO_4^{3-}/AsO_3^{3-}	+0.139
Dimethyl sulfoxide (DMSO)/dimethylsulfide (DMS)	+0.16
$Fe(OH)_3 + HCO_3^-/FeCO_3$ (Fe^{3+}/Fe^{2+}, pH 7)	+0.20
$S_3O_6^{2-}/S_2O_3^{2-} + HSO_3^-$	+0.225
Cytochrome c_1 ox/red	+0.23
NO_2^-/NO	+0.36
Cytochrome a_3 ox/red	+0.385
Chlorobenzoate$^-$ /benzoate$^-$ + HCl	+0.297
NO_3^-/NO_2^-	+0.43
SeO_4^{2-}/SeO_3^{2-}	+0.475
Fe^{3+}/Fe^{2+} (pH 2)	+0.77
Mn^{4+}/Mn^{2+}	+0.798
O_2/H_2O	+0.82
ClO_3^-/Cl^-	+1.03
NO/N_2O	+1.18
N_2O/N_2	+1.36

[a]Data from Thauer, R. K., K. Jungermann, and K. Decker, 1977. Energy conservation in anaerobic chemotrophic bacteria. *Bacteriol. Rev.* 41:100–180.

[b]Separate potentials are given for each electron transfer in this potentially two-electron transfer.

Index

Page references followed by "f" indicate illustrated figures or photographs; followed by "t" indicates a table.

B

C

E

J

K

L

Q

R

S

T

U